EARTH'S HABITABLE ZONE

					5 Boron B	6 Carbon C	7 Nitrogen N	8 Oxygen O	9 Fluorine F	10 Neon Ne
					13 Aluminum Al	14 Silicon Si	15 Phosphorus P	16 Sulfur S	17 Chlorine Cl	18 Argon Ar
26 Iron Fe	27 Cobalt Co	28 Nickel Ni	29 Copper Cu	30 Zinc Zn	31 Gallium Ga	32 Germanium Ge	33 Arsenic As	34 Selenium Se	35 Bromine Br	36 Krypton Kr
44 Ruthenium Ru	45 Rhodium Rh	46 Palladium Pd	47 Silver Ag	48 Cadmium Cd	49 Indium In	50 Tin Sn	51 Antimony Sb	52 Tellurium Te	53 Iodine I	54 Xenon Xe
76 Osmium Os	77 Iridium Ir	78 Platinum Pt	79 Gold Au	80 Mercury Hg	81 Thallium Tl	82 Lead Pb	83 Bismuth Bi	84 Polonium Po*	85 Astatine At*	86 Radon Rn*

Radioactive isotopes are indicated by (*).

LIVING ORGANISM: MAN

					5 Boron B	6 Carbon C	7 Nitrogen N	8 Oxygen O	9 Fluorine F	10 Neon Ne
					13 Aluminum Al	14 Silicon Si	15 Phosphorus P	16 Sulfur S	17 Chlorine Cl	18 Argon Ar
26 Iron Fe	27 Cobalt Co	28 Nickel Ni	29 Copper Cu	30 Zinc Zn	31 Gallium Ga	32 Germanium Ge	33 Arsenic As	34 Selenium Se	35 Bromine Br	36 Krypton Kr
44 Ruthenium Ru	45 Rhodium Rh	46 Palladium Pd	47 Silver Ag	48 Cadmium Cd	49 Indium In	50 Tin Sn	51 Antimony Sb	52 Tellurium Te	53 Iodine I	54 Xenon Xe
76 Osmium Os	77 Iridium Ir	78 Platinum Pt	79 Gold Au	80 Mercury Hg	81 Thallium Tl	82 Lead Pb	83 Bismuth Bi	84 Polonium Po*	85 Astatine At*	86 Radon Rn*

Radioactive isotopes are indicated by (*).

CHEMISTRY, MATTER, AND THE UNIVERSE

An Integrated Approach to General Chemistry

CHEMISTRY, MATTER, AND THE UNIVERSE

An Integrated Approach to General Chemistry

RICHARD E. DICKERSON   IRVING GEIS

BENJAMIN/CUMMINGS

Menlo Park, California • Reading, Massachusetts • London • Amsterdam • Don Mills, Ontario • Sydney

The source of all energy on Earth is the sun,
which is symbolized on the front cover
by the Zia Indian sign. The sun, which
dominates our planet, actually is only one
star in an immense universe (back cover).

Second printing, June 1978

ISBN 0-8053-2369-4
DEFGHIJ-HA-798

Preface

In his *Voices of Silence*, André Malraux characterizes modern books of art reproductions as "Museums without Walls," lifting the observer out of the confines of any one museum and showing him the entire world of art. In the same spirit, this book attempts to combine text and illustrations to remove chemistry from the laboratory and present "Chemistry without Walls." The proper setting for the study of chemistry is the entire material universe, living and nonliving, and this is the motivation behind the writing of this book.

Chemistry sometimes is taught as a laboratory-oriented science, in which a practitioner at the bench adds one substance to another, and precipitates a third substance that subsequently is analyzed or used. Chemistry then becomes narrowed down to an intellectual exercise carried out by human beings. This is one aspect of the subject, it is true, but it bears the same relationship to the chemistry of this book as an exercise machine does to bicycle touring. Everything is chemistry. There is no change that occurs in our material universe that does not involve chemical processes. At one extreme, nuclear reactions can be described in chemical terms if proper account is taken of the conversion of mass to energy. At the other extreme, the activities of living organisms have their foundations in chemical processes. One of the most exciting future areas for study will be that of discovering in more detail how chemical reactions lead to the observed behavior of living organisms, and how these complex, living chemical systems evolved on our planet (and perhaps others).

Modern chemistry is essentially pictorial. Most of our success in explaining how chemical reactions take place has come from a knowledge of the structures of molecules in three dimensions, and the arrangements of electrons in molecules. Although the calculations of modern theoretical chemistry can be complicated, they are based firmly on models of molecules and reactions. The chemist combines information from many sources, and uses his imagination to "see" molecules that are below the resolving power of the finest microscope.

A one-line chemical equation can conjure up images of moving and colliding molecules in the mind of an experienced chemist, but to a beginner it can conceal as much as it reveals. An introductory chemistry textbook should illustrate in clear detail exactly what these shorthand equations really symbolize. At the beginning level, the guiding principle should be, "When in doubt, draw it out." An ideal combination of authors would be a chemist who understands the art of graphic presentation, and an illustrator who understands chemistry. This is the combination that we have tried to put together in this book.

The format of *Chemistry, Matter, and the Universe* is unusual. Every important chemical concept is illustrated, with an average of more than a figure per page, yet the book is not "illustrated" at all in the traditional sense. The writer and artist planned this book together as coauthors from the very first stages, discussing each two-page layout extensively from a chapter outline before either text or drawings existed. What were the key ideas of each chapter, and how could they be expressed pictorially? Every illustration performs some pedagogical function, even the outrageous cartoons. Drawings and narrative were planned together to form an organic whole, which is why no figure numbers are used. When the words describe an idea, the graphic realization of that idea is in front of the reader as reinforcement. This has made the book more laborious to produce, but has made the finished product a better teaching device.

Chemistry, Matter, and the Universe is intended primarily for a two-semester course, although it has been designed so it can be used for several shorter courses if desired. Each chapter in this book builds on what has come before. Although it is not easy to skip from one chapter to another, it is easy to progress steadily through the book but to stop at any one of several points. The first ten chapters are devoted to a qualitative and descriptive look at the chemical elements, the periodic table, molecular structure and bonding, and the chemical nature of our world. These chapters provide suitable material for a ten- or twelve-week course in chemistry for liberal arts or humanities students, and should leave the reader with at least an appreciation of the chemical nature of our universe. Chapters 11 through 17 introduce chemistry as a quantitative science, with discussions of mass, energy, entropy, chemical equilibrium, and the rates and mechanisms of reaction. Together, these seventeen chapters can be used in a half-year or two-term chemistry course for nonmajors.

After a shift in perspective in Chapter 18, the final eight chapters lead the reader into the world of carbon compounds, macromolecules, and living organisms. Blaise Pascal described the universe as extending between two infinities, the infinitely large and the infinitely small; or in the language of science, from galaxies to nuclei. To these limits Teilhard de Chardin added a third: the infinitely complex. Life would be impossible without complex networks of reactions involving macromolecules, and of all the elements known, only carbon appears to be capable of building such molecules. Chemical systems complicated enough to show the properties of life must be organized both in space and in time; they must possess both a structure and a metabolism. The study of carbon-based life, and the question of whether it is the only possible form of life, are subjects that our recent advances in space exploration have transformed from philosophy into experimental chemistry. *Chemistry, Matter, and the Universe* ends with what the authors believe to be the most exciting great challenge facing chemistry: the problem of *life*.

In the traditional nomenclature, Chapters 1–10 would be described as inorganic chemistry, Chapters 11–17 as physical chemistry, Chapters 18–21 as organic chemistry, and Chapters 22–26 as biochemistry. Although this is true in principle, we try to show that these categories overlap, and are more pedagogical than real. Chemistry should be thought of as a unified whole, and in the most general terms as a framework for explaining the world in which we live, and from which we have evolved.

January 1976   Richard E. Dickerson
                                                   Irving Geis

Contents

CHAPTER 1

The View From a Distant Universe

Many reasons can be given for studying chemistry, ranging from, "It is an intellectual adventure," to "I can make a good living at it," or even "It is required for graduation." But the most valid response is simple. Chemistry is the study of how matter behaves. We have only one world in which to live. If we want to know how we can change it and what we cannot alter, or even simply to appreciate what we already have, then we must know how it works. Chemistry is the subject that tells us this. Physics may teach us fundamental facts about elementary particles, matter, and energy, but it stops short of drawing conclusions about how the different kinds of matter around us change and react. Biology describes the large-scale behavior of organisms, which at their core are elaborate chemical systems. Some of the most fruitful advances in biology in the past two decades have come from a thoroughly chemical approach. If we can expand the concept of chemistry beyond our present limited and inadequate knowledge, then biology fundamentally is the highest form of applied chemistry. If chemistry is the study of how matter behaves, we must not forget that we, ourselves, are an integral part of this material world.

If we look at the world around us with a beginner's eye, it seems terrifyingly complex. Everything material is chemical, and everything is reacting, on one time scale or another. How can we possibly keep track of what is going on around us, let alone understand the principles involved? The chemical reactions that go on in our world are more tightly interlocked than was realized only a few years ago. How can we manipulate these reactions to our own advantage, and how can we be sure that if we change things at one place, this will not create unforeseen troubles somewhere else? These are real problems, and as the population of this planet has increased and the resources available recognized as finite, a great many people have come to ponder such problems. Chemistry, considered as a technique for managing a small planet,

Edge view of our own galaxy, the Milky Way, which has approximately 200 billion stars. One of these stars, 30,000 light years from the center, is our Sun.

Out of 1000 atoms in the universe, 999 are either hydrogen (light dots) or helium (color dots). Only one atom out of a thousand is one of the heavier elements (white dot).

seems much more formidable now than a few years ago when it was regarded only as a method of making new plastics and fuels. If you want to learn something about chemistry today, where do you begin?

The easiest way to begin is to step back a few million light years, and take a more detached view of the material universe. Some of the complexities then smooth out and the scene becomes simpler. What we see are many glowing bodies—stars—organized into star clusters, galaxies, and clusters of galaxies, extending to the outermost reaches of the universe. In our field of view, 999 out of 1000 atoms are either of the two lightest chemical elements—hydrogen or helium—with only a lone one-in-a-thousand being a heavier atom (left). All of the elements, compounds, and substances that loom so large on our planet are nothing more than "minor impurities" in the universe as a whole. The dust clouds between stars are predominately hydrogen, although careful examination will show a few other simple molecules. The heavier elements are found scattered in these dust clouds, in the centers of stars, and in the cold satellites such as Earth, which travel virtually undetected around some of the stars. On this scale, the material universe mainly is a world of hydrogen and helium.

A SIMPLE WORLD

Things are simpler in such a world. The same pieces that make up all atoms—protons, neutrons, and electrons—also make up hydrogen and helium, but in an especially simple way. In the following chapter, we will begin the study of atomic structure with a detailed discussion of hydrogen and helium. The reactions that these elements by themselves can undergo are simple and few. Four hydrogen atoms can fuse to make a helium atom, and the stars are fueled by the energy from this reaction. If the temperature at the center of a star is high enough, hydrogen fusion can be followed by helium fusion, and successive reactions, to produce the heavier elements. The heaviest of these elements have a tendency to break down again spontaneously, in the process of atomic fission.

These examples all are *nuclear reactions*, in which one element is changed into another element by altering the structure of its nucleus. Nuclear reactions ordinarily are considered as part of the realm of physics, not chemistry. At far lower temperatures, closer to those of our own planet, the first true chemical reactions can take place, in which atoms come together, separate, and associate with other atoms, without altering their nuclear structures and their own identities. If two hydrogen atoms are brought together at a moderate temperature, they will bind to one another to form an H—H or H_2 molecule. Helium atoms do not behave in this way. When they collide, they bounce away unchanged and show little tendency to associate. The concept of the *chemical bond* that holds H atoms together, but not those of He, is the most important single idea in chemistry. When do bonds form between atoms, and why, and in what directions? How do these bonds determine how the resulting chemical substances behave?

THE STATES OF MATTER

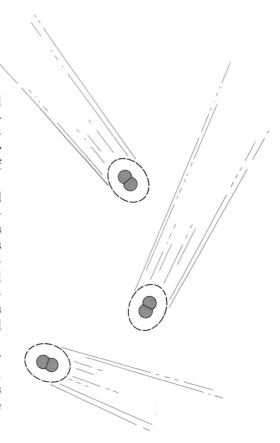

At temperatures similar to those on our planet, helium atoms (He) and hydrogen molecules (H_2) move about individually. Each atom or molecule in a *gas* moves independently with a speed that depends on its energy of motion. The higher the temperature, the faster the atoms or molecules of a gas move; and temperature in fact is a direct measure of the average energy of the molecules of a gas.

Gases are not the only form of matter in the universe. Liquids and solids also exist, especially with larger molecules and at lower temperatures. Every atom or molecule has a weak attraction for other atoms and molecules, or a "stickiness" on contact, known as van der Waals attraction. If the temperature is low and the energy of motion of a collection of molecules is small enough, this van der Waals attraction will hold the molecules together in a *liquid*. The molecules remain in contact but are free to slide past one another. At even lower temperatures and molecular energies, this freedom of motion is reduced further, and the molecules become locked into the frozen geometry of a *solid*.

Tiny particles such as He and H_2 must be cooled to extremely low temperatures before they condense to a liquid or freeze to a solid. Larger molecules with more surface area have greater van der Waals "stickiness," and occur as liquids or solids at room temperature. Some

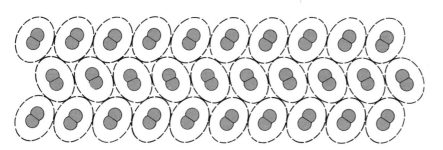

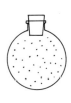

GAS: In a gas the individual molecules move freely through space, and do not touch except at the moments of collision, from which they rebound. A gas has neither a fixed shape nor a fixed volume; it adapts to the shape of its container and can be expanded or compressed.

LIQUID: The molecules of a liquid are in contact with one another, but have enough energy to slip past one another and change their positions. Therefore, a liquid has a relatively fixed volume, but no definite shape.

SOLID: In a crystalline solid the molecules are packed against one another in a regular pattern, and do not have enough energy to break that pattern and slide from one place to another. Crystals have a definite volume and shape, and work must be done to deform or break them.

atoms can gain or lose electrons to become electrically charged *ions*. These ions are held together in solids known as salts by the electrostatic forces between ions of opposite charge. After the study of bond-making-and-breaking reactions that molecules can undergo, one of the most important areas of chemistry is to explain the behavior and properties of substances in terms of the interactions between the molecules of which they are made.

THE BIOGRAPHY OF A UNIVERSE

The universe is very far from being chemically uniform, which is a result of the way the universe developed. The earliest stars, perhaps thirteen billion years ago, condensed from a thin gas of hydrogen. As a star condensed, the heat generated in its center triggered the hydrogen fusion process, in which four hydrogen nuclei coalesce to a helium nucleus with the release of a large amount of energy. The star "switched on." In big stars with sufficient ability to retain heat, higher temperatures in the center led to the successive triggering of helium fusion and then to reactions producing the heavier elements. The stars were the "crucibles" in which the heavier elements were formed. Supernova explosions scattered these elements through the cosmos as debris from which, in time, the second-generation suns such as our own formed.

Our solar system thus was enriched in heavy elements from its very beginning. As the sun coalesced at the center of a cloud of diffused matter, so did the various planets farther out. The large planets with enough gravitational pull to retain all of their original material, such as Jupiter and Saturn, remained sunlike in overall composition. The Earth and the other small inner planets had their volatile elements driven away by the heat of the sun and by the weakness of their own attraction for them. The only substances left were the nonvolatiles; thus Earth became a denuded ball of rock. This is why our planet is so rich in silicon–oxygen minerals today; these were the substances that would not boil away.

Our Earth has an atmosphere today only because of outgassing of the planetary interior, mainly through volcanic action after surface temperatures had fallen. The gases that were emitted were not those that were most common in the original material of the solar system, but those that could be trapped in chemical combination with minerals: water vapor, ammonia, hydrogen sulfide, carbon dioxide, and other small carbon and nitrogen molecules. The helium that was present initially was lost because it did not react chemically and could not be retained in a nonvolatile form.

Our present atmosphere, which essentially is 80% nitrogen and 20% oxygen, is quite different even from the original outgassed atmosphere. That primal atmosphere contained many components that would combine readily with oxygen, but did not contain free oxygen itself. Today's oxygen-rich atmosphere is the result of the slow action by one of the most remarkable phenomena to arise in the universe: Life. Out of this pool of carbon, oxygen, nitrogen, and hydrogen compounds, on the surface of a ball of silicate rock, there evolved the most complex and most subtle chemical systems that the universe has known: living

THE CONE NEBULA: The dark cone is a cloud of gas, mainly hydrogen, which obscures the light of the more luminous stars behind. New stars condense from such dark gas clouds. Courtesy of The Hale Observatories.

4

organisms. The story of how living organisms evolved and how they have transformed our planet is a fascinating one, but one that will have to wait until we have laid a chemical basis for understanding it. In the last chapters of this book we will return to this subject, as an attempt to tie everything together. Life was the final stage of the selection of certain elements from among many, the last of a series of fractionations of chemical elements from a universal pool made up of hydrogen and helium, plus a few trace impurities. We are the result of these impurities, and one central theme of this book is devoted to explaining, to the best of our ability, how this came about.

QUESTIONS

1. Why do liquids and solids have a relatively fixed volume (subject to small expansions and contractions due to temperature), whereas the volume of a gas is much more variable?

2. Why do crystalline solids have a fixed shape, whereas liquids and gases adapt to the shape of their containers?

3. What is different about the way that liquids and gases adapt to their containers?

4. What holds the molecules of a molecular liquid or solid together? Why doesn't this same factor hold for gases?

5. What were the earliest two chemical elements?

6. Why are these two elements so much rarer on Earth than they are in the universe as a whole?

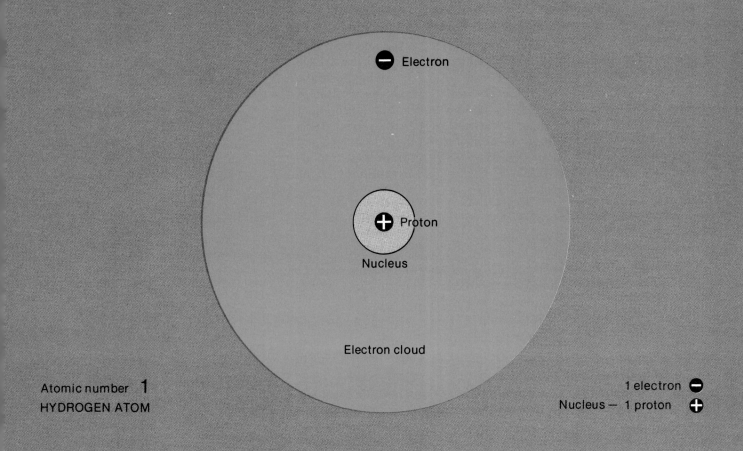

Electron

Proton
Nucleus

Electron cloud

Atomic number 1
HYDROGEN ATOM

1 electron ⊖
Nucleus — 1 proton ⊕

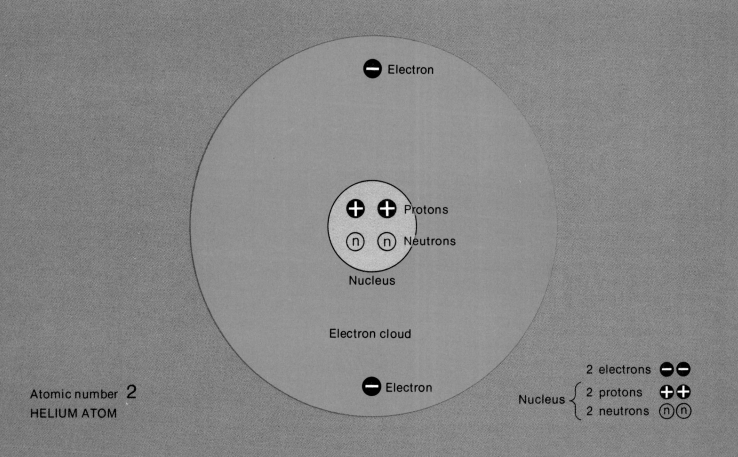

Electron

Protons
Neutrons
Nucleus

Electron cloud

Electron

Atomic number 2
HELIUM ATOM

2 electrons ⊖⊖
Nucleus { 2 protons ⊕⊕
         2 neutrons ⓝⓝ

CHAPTER 2

Atoms, Molecules, and Moles

Hydrogen and helium occupy a special place in the chemical world because they are the elements from which all other elements were made. They have another aspect that makes them useful to us now: They are the simplest of all atoms. All of the ideas about simple atomic structure that can be illustrated with hydrogen and helium will carry directly over to the study of the heavier atoms.

ELECTRONS, NUCLEI, AND ATOMIC NUMBER

An atom is made up of a very small but heavy central nucleus with a positive charge, surrounded by a negatively charged cloud of electrons. Because atoms are so small, the familiar units of feet or centimeters are useless in measuring them. A more common unit of length is the angstrom, symbolized Å. There are 100,000,000 or 10^8 Å in one centimeter, or to express matters the other way around,

$$1 \text{ Å} = \frac{1}{10^8} \text{ cm} = 10^{-8} \text{ cm} = 0.00000001 \text{ cm}$$

Most atoms are of the order of 1.0 Å to 2.4 Å in diameter, which is why angstroms are so convenient.

The nucleus of an atom is much smaller yet, typically with a diameter of 10^{-13} cm or 10^{-5} Å. If an atom were as large as a football stadium, the nucleus would be the size of a small ladybug crawling across the 50-yard line. In spite of this size difference, virtually all of the mass of an atom is concentrated in its nucleus. One electron, which has a negative charge, weighs only 1/1836 as much as the lightest of all nuclei, that of the hydrogen atom (proton).

An atomic nucleus is built from two major kinds of particles: protons and neutrons. A proton carries one unit of positive charge, which

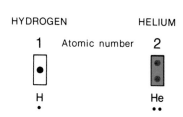

The electron shells of hydrogen and helium atoms will be symbolized by rectangles. When the shell is filled (as in helium), the rectangle will be colored.

Fundamental particles of matter

Particle	Charge	Mass (amu)
Proton	+1	1.00728
Neutron	0	1.00867
Electron	−1	0.000549

balances the negative charge on an electron. The neutron is uncharged. The standard unit for measuring masses of atoms is the *atomic mass unit* (amu) defined such that the most common kind of carbon atom weighs exactly 12 amu. On this scale, a proton has a mass of 1.00728 amu and is slightly lighter than a neutron, which has a mass of 1.00867 amu. Protons and neutrons usually are thought of as having unit masses (1 amu) unless exact calculations are called for. On this scale, an electron weighs only 0.00055 amu. The charge and mass relationships between these three fundamental particles are summarized in the table to the left.

The two simplest kinds of atoms are hydrogen (H) and helium (He), diagramed on Page 6. Hydrogen has one proton in its nucleus and one electron around it. Helium has two protons and hence must have two electrons, since the number of positive and negative charges in a neutral atom must be the same. Because electrons surround an atom, and the nucleus is small and deeply buried, the outer part of the electron cloud is all that another atom "sees." It is the electron cloud that gives each atom its chemical character. Reactions leading to the making of chemical bonds involve the gain, loss, or sharing of electrons between atoms, as we shall see in subsequent chapters. Since the number of electrons in a neutral atom must equal the number of protons in its nucleus, the number of protons indirectly decides the chemical behavior of the atom. All atoms with the same number of protons are defined as the same *chemical element*, and the number of protons is its *atomic number*. The atomic number sometimes is written as a subscript in front of the symbol of the element, such as $_1$H and $_2$He. This is convenient but unnecessary, since, for example, every atom with atomic number 2 by definition is called helium and given the symbol He.

Every addition of a proton to a nucleus leads to a new chemical element. The elements following He in sequence are

$_3$Li = lithium, a soft, reactive metal

$_4$Be = beryllium, a harder metal

$_5$B = boron, a borderline nonmetal

$_6$C = carbon, a nonmetal and the fundamental atom in living organisms

$_7$N = nitrogen, a nonmetal common in living organisms and the major component of the Earth's present atmosphere

$_8$O = oxygen, a nonmetal and the other main component of the atmosphere, and the essential element in the combustion of materials

$_9$F = fluorine, a relatively scarce nonmetallic element, but one that combines with other substances even more vigorously than oxygen does

$_{10}$Ne = neon, an inert gas closely resembling helium

$_{11}$Na = sodium, a soft, reactive metal similar to lithium

The way in which electrons are arranged around a nucleus and the effect that this has on chemical behavior are the subject of the next chapter. At the moment, notice only the trend from metals, to nonmetals, to an inert gas, and the beginning of a repetition of properties with the inert gas neon and the soft metal sodium. Chemical properties are *periodic* functions of the atomic number—in a listing of elements by increasing atomic number, similar properties are encountered again and again at regular intervals. This is one of the most important generalizations in chemistry.

ISOTOPES OF HYDROGEN

So far we have said nothing about neutrons. The most common type of hydrogen has none in its nucleus. Other kinds of hydrogen atoms, as depicted at the right, have either one or two neutrons, in addition to the proton that defines their chemical character. Atoms such as these three, with the same atomic number but with different numbers of neutrons in their nuclei, are called *isotopes* of the same chemical element. The sum of the number of protons and neutrons is the *mass number*, and is written as a superscript before the symbol of the element: $_1^1H$, $_1^2H$, $_1^3H$.

The three isotopes of hydrogen have quite different masses: approximately 1, 2, and 3 amu. But because the number of protons is the same, they have the same number of electrons around the nucleus. To an approaching atom, all hydrogen atoms look much the same, and exhibit virtually the same chemical behavior. The differences are important only in properties such as rates of reaction or rates of diffusion of molecules, for which the mass of an atom and its speed are important. For heavier elements, the addition of one or two neutrons has a less important effect on properties; thus isotopes are not given special names. Only for hydrogen, in which additional neutrons double or triple the atomic mass, have special names and symbols been developed:

$_1^1H$ = H = light hydrogen or "ordinary" hydrogen, with one proton and no neutrons in the nucleus

$_1^2H$ = D = deuterium (from "deutero-" or two), with one proton and one neutron in the nucleus

$_1^3H$ = T = tritium (from "tri-" or three), with one proton and two neutrons in the nucleus

Ordinary water has the chemical formula H_2O. Heavy water, D_2O, has become familiar because of its use as a moderator or neutron absorber in certain types of nuclear reactors. About 150 hydrogen atoms per million on our planet are D atoms. Tritium is radioactive and must be produced artificially.

If protons and neutrons each weighed exactly 1 amu, and there was no change in mass when the nucleus was formed, then the mass number of an isotope would equal the sum of the masses of the protons and neutrons in amu, or its *atomic weight*. This is not strictly true. Not only are protons and neutrons slightly heavier than 1 amu, there is a small loss in mass when they combine to form a nucleus. This missing mass is converted to energy during the nucleus-forming process and is lost by the atom. The nucleus cannot be taken apart again unless the lost energy is resupplied to make up the full mass, that is, the mass of the initial protons and neutrons. This missing energy represents the *binding energy* of the nucleus, or the energy that holds the nucleus together. Nevertheless, for approximate calculations we can think of the atomic weight of an isotope as being approximately equal to the sum of its protons and neutrons, or to its mass number.

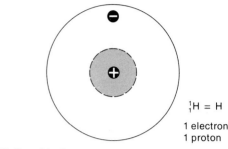

$_1^1H$ = H
1 electron
1 proton

"Ordinary" hydrogen

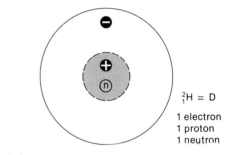

$_1^2H$ = D
1 electron
1 proton
1 neutron

Deuterium

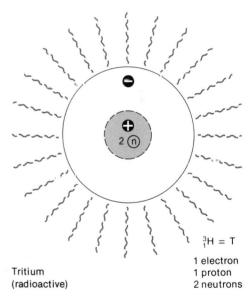

$_1^3H$ = T

Tritium
(radioactive)

1 electron
1 proton
2 neutrons

The three isotopes of hydrogen, ordinary hydrogen, deuterium, and tritium, differ only in the number of neutrons in their nuclei. Tritium atoms are unstable and radioactive because they have too many neutrons for the number of protons present. 99.98% of all hydrogen found on Earth is the ordinary variety, 0.02% is deuterium, and tritium does not occur naturally.

9

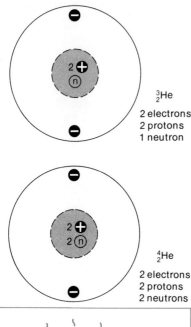

$_2^3$He

2 electrons
2 protons
1 neutron

$_2^4$He

2 electrons
2 protons
2 neutrons

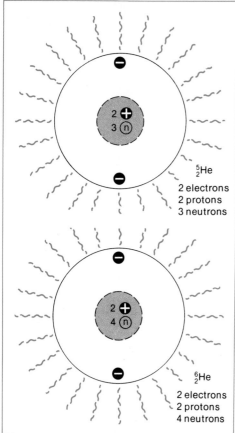

$_2^5$He

2 electrons
2 protons
3 neutrons

$_2^6$He

2 electrons
2 protons
4 neutrons

Helium has four isotopes, each with two protons, but with one to four neutrons. Only 0.00013% of natural helium is helium-3 with one neutron, and the rest is helium-4 with two neutrons. Helium-5 and helium-6 (which are radioactive) do not occur naturally.

ISOTOPES OF HELIUM

Helium also has isotopes, and these are shown at the left. The difference between superscript and subscript gives the number of neutrons in the nucleus, and this can be 1, 2, 3, or 4. An atom $_n^m$He has m nuclear particles, n protons, and $m - n$ neutrons. Instead of special names, the isotopes of helium and heavier elements are distinguished by giving their name and mass number, for example, helium-3 for $_2^3$He. All but a minute fraction of helium atoms found on Earth are helium-4. Only one atom per million is helium-3, and helium-5 and -6 do not exist naturally.

Some isotopes of an element are stable and show no tendency to break down; others decompose spontaneously and therefore are *radioactive*. Light hydrogen and deuterium are stable, but tritium is radioactive. The $_1^3$H or T nucleus apparently has an overbalance of neutrons to protons. In time it decays spontaneously, effectively converting one of the neutrons into a proton and an electron:

$$_0^1\text{n} \rightarrow \, _1^1\text{p} + \, _{-1}^0\text{e}$$

This reaction is written using the $_n^m$He notation introduced previously, with the subscript now representing the charge on a particle (rather than the number of protons in the nucleus), and the superscript giving the mass number, or approximate mass in amu. A proton, which has a +1 charge and unit mass number, is written $_1^1$p; a neutron, which has no charge and unit mass, is $_0^1$n; and an electron, which has a −1 charge and negligible mass on this rough-counting scale, is $_{-1}^0$e. When a nuclear reaction such as this one is written and balanced properly, the total charge (subscripts) and the total mass number (superscripts) on the left must equal the total charge and mass on the right.

When one of the two neutrons in the tritium nucleus breaks down into a proton and an electron, then a one-proton, two-neutron nucleus of hydrogen is converted into a two-proton, one-neutron nucleus of *helium:*

$$_1^3\text{H} \rightarrow \, _2^3\text{He} + \, _{-1}^0\text{e}$$

This reaction is illustrated below. One element is changed into another, and the electron is released from the nucleus as beta radiation. We shall not be concerned with radioactive decay and unstable isotopes, but it is worth noting at least that atomic nuclei are stable when their ratios of neutrons to protons lie within a certain range, namely, 1:1 or with a slight excess of neutrons. With too many neutrons or too many pro-

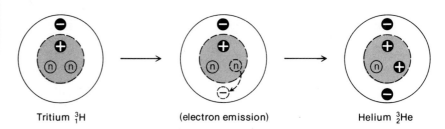

Tritium $_1^3$H   (electron emission)   Helium $_2^3$He

Tritium is a radioactive isotope of hydrogen, and decays by emitting an electron from the nucleus to become helium-3.

tons, a nucleus becomes unstable and decays spontaneously into a more stable isotope of an element with an atomic number close to that of the original element.

ISOTOPES AND OBSERVED ATOMIC WEIGHTS

Most of the naturally occurring elements are mixtures of several isotopes. Of the carbon found on this planet, 98.9% is carbon-12, or ^{12}C, which has six protons and six neutrons. (The atomic mass scale is defined so that an atom of carbon-12 weighs exactly 12 amu.) 1.1% is carbon-13, with one additional neutron. Both of these isotopes are stable, but carbon-14 is radioactive, and is present in minute amounts only because it is being produced constantly by cosmic-ray bombardment of nitrogen in the upper atmosphere. Carbon-14 is the basis of radiocarbon dating. As long as a tree or other organism is alive, it constantly takes in more carbon from its surroundings, and the ratio of ^{14}C to ^{12}C equals that in the atmosphere as a whole. Radioactive decay and replenishment from the atmosphere are in balance. When the tree dies, this intake stops and what little carbon-14 it has begins to disappear. By measuring the ratio of ^{14}C to ^{12}C in a wood or other carbon-containing relic from an archaeological site, scientists can calculate how long in the past the specimen ceased to be alive and thus ceased to exchange ^{14}C with its surroundings. We will see examples of this in Chapter 11.

The atomic weight of an element in nature is the weighted average, in terms of natural abundance, of the atomic weights of its naturally occurring isotopes. Boron is a good example since it has appreciable amounts of two stable isotopes.

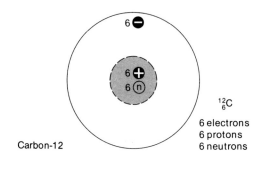

Carbon-12

$^{12}_{6}C$

6 electrons
6 protons
6 neutrons

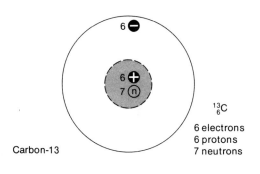

Carbon-13

$^{13}_{6}C$

6 electrons
6 protons
7 neutrons

Isotope	Atomic weight	Abundance
$^{10}_{5}B$	10.013 amu	19.8%
$^{11}_{5}B$	11.009 amu	80.2%

The weighted average of these two isotopes is

Boron-10: 19.8% × 10.013 amu = 1.983 amu
Boron-11: 80.2% × 11.009 amu = 8.829 amu
Average atomic weight = 10.812 amu

This is the value that is tabulated in the back end papers. Naturally occurring boron has an atomic weight of 10.8 because it is an 8-to-2 mixture of isotopes 11 and 10, respectively.

Because isotopes of the same element have such similar chemical properties, the ratio of isotopes ordinarily is unchanged during chemical reactions. If individual isotopes are wanted, they must be separated by some technique, such as diffusion or mass spectrometry, that is sensitive to small mass differences. To the chemist, all isotopes of an element react in much the same way. What is important to chemical behavior is not the number of neutrons in an atom, but the number of protons because this determines the number of electrons, and electrons give rise to all of the important chemical properties of the elements.

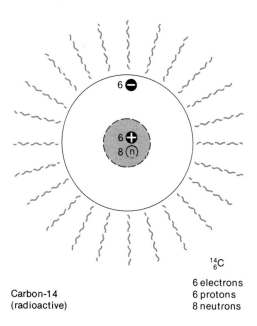

Carbon-14
(radioactive)

$^{14}_{6}C$

6 electrons
6 protons
8 neutrons

Carbon has three isotopes, two stable (carbon-12 and carbon-13) and one radioactive (carbon-14). Radioactive carbon-14 is useful in archaeological dating of wood or wood products up to 20,000 years old.

11

HYDROGEN AND HELIUM GASES

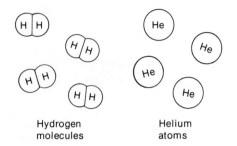

Hydrogen
molecules

Helium
atoms

Hydrogen gas is made up of two-atom
molecules, H_2, whereas helium gas is made up
of isolated He atoms.

HYDROGEN MOLECULE

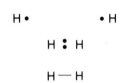

Each hydrogen atom has one electron. The
pair of electrons is shared in the bond between
atoms in H_2. This bond also can be represented
by a line between atoms.

BONDING FORCES

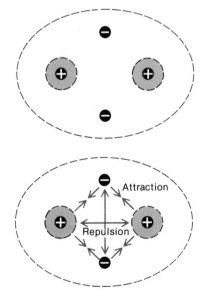

Bonding forces in the H_2 molecule represent a
balance between nucleus–nucleus and
electron–electron repulsions arising from
charges of the same sign, and the four possible
electron–nucleus attractions between opposite
charges.

BONDS BETWEEN ATOMS

At ordinary temperatures and pressures, both hydrogen and helium are gases (upper left). Individual particles move freely, are far apart on the average, and are independent of one another except when they collide. Their energy of motion is sufficiently greater than the van der Waals attractions that when they do collide, they rebound rather than stick together. Hydrogen and helium gases both are made up of essentially free particles. There is one important difference, however, illustrated in the drawings at the left. In helium gas the particles are single helium atoms, but the particles in hydrogen gas are two atoms stuck together in an H_2 hydrogen *molecule*. Why the difference?

Atoms combine into molecules because by doing so they achieve a state of lower energy. Making molecules from atoms is a "downhill" process, and tearing molecules apart again into atoms always requires energy to go back up the energy hill. We usually can think of molecules as being held together by bonds between pairs of atoms within them. A key question in chemistry is: Which atoms will combine with one another, in what way, and why? At the beginning of this century chemical bonding was still a mystery. One of the triumphs of quantum mechanics, a shatteringly unorthodox theory developed between 1900 and 1926, was the successful explanation not only of atomic structure, but of bonding between atoms in molecules. We can take some of the pictorial conclusions from quantum mechanics and use them to predict the behavior of atoms in molecules, without becoming involved in the mathematics. This is done in Chapters 7–9.

A simple explanation of a chemical bond was given by G. N. Lewis in 1914: A bond is formed between two atoms when a pair of electrons is shared between them. This is the electron-pair, or *covalent* bond, which is the subject of Chapter 4. Two hydrogen atoms, each with a single electron, can share their electrons and form a covalent bond, as shown at center left. If you were to perform a quantum-mechanical calculation to see how the electrons in an H—H bond were distributed, you would find that most of the time they are *between* the two H nuclei. One positive nucleus is attracted to the two electrons, which simultaneously attract the other nucleus. At the same time, the two electrons shield or screen the nuclei from one another and decrease the repulsion between their positive charges. The negatively charged electrons are the "glue" that holds the positive nuclei together.

The energy of two hydrogen atoms can be represented in a diagram such as that on Page 13. The horizontal axis indicates the distance between atoms in angstrom units, and the vertical axis indicates the energy, with lower energy and greater stability represented downward. The zero point of energy has been chosen to be that of two infinitely separated, noninteracting atoms.

Two hydrogen atoms infinitely far apart obviously do not interact, and thus have no bond between them (Point 1 in the diagram at the right). As the atoms come closer together, little happens until their interatomic distance decreases to a few angstroms (Point 2). Then the electron of one atom begins to be "seen" by the nucleus of the other. Each electron is attracted by the other nucleus, the electrons become concentrated between the nuclei, and a bond begins to form. The en-

12

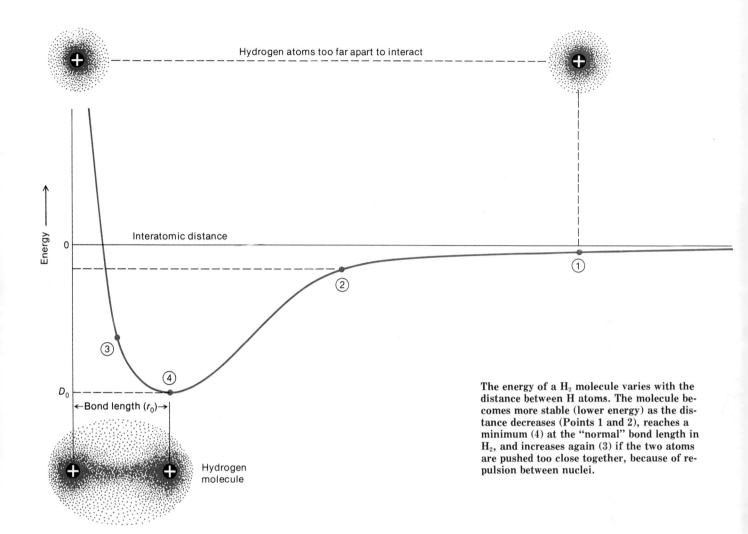

The energy of a H_2 molecule varies with the distance between H atoms. The molecule becomes more stable (lower energy) as the distance decreases (Points 1 and 2), reaches a minimum (4) at the "normal" bond length in H_2, and increases again (3) if the two atoms are pushed too close together, because of repulsion between nuclei.

ergy of the two atoms decreases as the attraction of each nucleus for the other electron becomes significant. Energy continues to decrease as the atoms come closer and the screening of nuclear charges by electrons increases. If the process is carried too far, however, the electrons are "squeezed out" from between the nuclei, which have come so close together that the repulsion between their positive charges becomes quite strong. The molecule is made *less* stable (Point 3).

At some intermediate point between 2 and 3, screening by electrons and repulsion of nuclei will balance: The H—H molecule will have the lowest energy and will be most stable (Point 4). If the nuclei are pushed any closer, nuclear repulsion pushes them back again; if they are pulled apart, electron-pair screening is lost. This lowest-energy separation, r_0, is the *bond length* of the H—H bond, and the energy required to pull the molecule apart into isolated atoms again, D_0, is the bond dissociation energy or *bond energy*. The atoms in a molecule oscillate about this minimum-energy position; thus r_0 is the *average* bond length. In the H—H or H_2 molecule this distance is 0.74 Å.

G. N. Lewis symbolized an electron-pair bond by two dots for the electrons. It is more common today to represent the bond by a single line connecting the bonded atoms, but you should remember that each such bond consists of a pair of electrons.

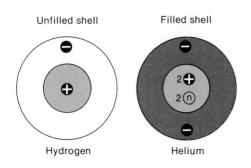

Unfilled shell   Filled shell

Hydrogen   Helium

BONDING AND ANTIBONDING ELECTRONS

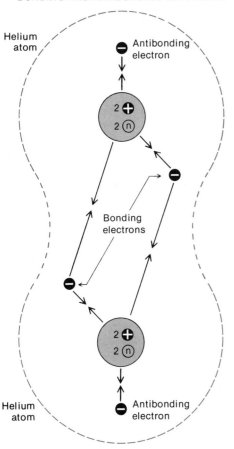

Helium atom

Antibonding electron

Bonding electrons

Helium atom

Antibonding electron

ELECTRON SHELLS

We still have not answered the question as to why hydrogen atoms form molecules but helium atoms do not. From what has been said so far, you might expect that helium atoms would share two electron pairs to make two bonds per He_2 molecule, or perhaps to make long —He—He—He—He— chains or rings of atoms. Why doesn't this happen? To answer this question we must introduce another idea from quantum mechanics, that of *electron shells*. Electrons in atoms behave as though they were grouped into levels or shells, with all electrons in one shell having approximately the same energies, but with large energy differences between shells. Each shell can hold only a certain maximum number of electrons. If one shell is filled, then an additional electron will be forced to go into a higher-energy, less-stable shell, and this electron will be lost easily during chemical reactions. Conversely, if an atom lacks only one or two electrons to complete a shell, the atom will have a strong attraction for electrons, and can take them away from the type of atom mentioned previously. A completely filled electron shell, with no vacancies and no extra electrons outside it, is a particularly stable situation for an atom. Not only can atoms gain and lose electrons, they can share them in covalent bonds. When they do, all the shared electrons contribute toward filling vacancies in the outer electron shell of each atom.

The innermost shell in any atom can hold a maximum of only two electrons, and the second shell can hold eight. We will defer the reasons for this to Chapter 8, but can use the conclusions now. Each hydrogen atom lacks one electron of having a closed inner shell, so when the two atoms combine to form an H_2 molecule, each atom gains an electron and satisfies its deficiency. Helium atoms do not combine because they already have their shells filled with two electrons. If two helium atoms were forced together, they would have four electrons in the vicinity of the nuclei (left). Two would be located between the nuclei and would hold the atoms together as in H_2. The other two would be forced to the outside of the He_2 molecule, away from the first two. Not only would these contribute no screening and bonding, they would attract the nuclei and pull them away from one another. With two electrons pulling together and two pulling apart, there would be no net bonding, and the two He atoms would separate. The two electrons that would tend

Two electrons in the H_2 molecule are found mainly between the nuclei, where they help to hold the molecule together. If the He_2 molecule existed, two electrons also would be found between the nuclei. The other two electrons in He_2 would have to remain on the outside of the molecule, where they would pull the two He nuclei apart. H_2 with two electrons is stable, but He_2 with four electrons does not exist.

to hold the molecule together are called *bonding* electrons, and the two that would tend to pull the nuclei apart and rupture the molecule are *antibonding* electrons.

MOLECULES, MOLECULAR WEIGHT, AND MOLES

A molecule is a collection of atoms held together by covalent bonds. In our simple universe of hydrogen and helium, the only possible molecule is H_2; but the one-in-a-thousand heavier atoms are the basis for a vast array of more complex molecules. The champion of molecule-forming atoms is carbon, for reasons that will become clear as we learn more about atomic structure. The chemistry of carbon compounds is so varied that it is given a special name, organic chemistry. The term "organic" is a reminder that carbon compounds are the basis for the most complex chemical phenomenon of all, life.

The *molecular weight* of any molecule is the sum of the atomic weights of all its atoms. Since the atomic weight of a hydrogen atom is 1.008 amu (relative to carbon-12 as exactly 12 amu), the molecular weight of the H_2 molecule is twice this value, or 2.016 amu. The average atomic weight of the naturally occurring mixture of ^{12}C, ^{13}C, and ^{14}C is 12.011 amu, so the molecular weight of methane gas, CH_4, is

C: 1×12.011 amu $= 12.011$ amu
H: 4×1.008 amu $= \underline{4.032}$ amu
Molecular weight $= \overline{16.043}$ amu

The molecular weight of water, H_2O, is

H: 2×1.008 amu $= 2.016$ amu
O: 1×15.999 amu $= \underline{15.999}$ amu
Molecular weight $- \overline{18.015}$ amu

Large biological molecules can have molecular weights of several millions.

Chemists talk about reactions between molecules, yet except for certain extraordinary experimental conditions, no one can see a molecule. There is no easy way to count out equal numbers of various kinds

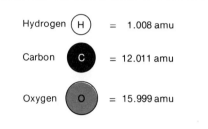
MOLECULAR WEIGHT

The sum of the atomic weights of the atoms in a molecule is the molecular weight.

Hydrogen molecule (H_2) $= 2 \times 1.008$
$= 2.016$ amu

Methane molecule (CH_4) $= 12.011 + 4(1.008)$
$= 16.043$ amu

Water molecule (H_2O) $= 15.999 + 2(1.008)$
$= 18.015$ amu

MOLES

Molecular weights in atomic mass units scaled up to grams (below) becomes *moles*—of hydrogen, methane, and water.

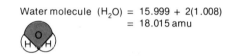

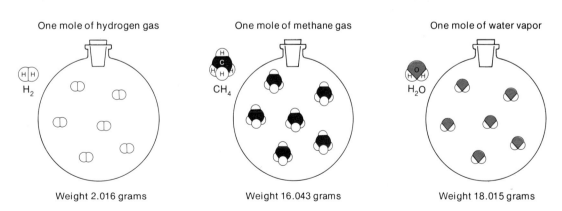

One mole of hydrogen gas   One mole of methane gas   One mole of water vapor

H_2 CH_4 H_2O

Weight 2.016 grams   Weight 16.043 grams   Weight 18.015 grams

Equal volumes of gas have the *same* number of molecules, but *different* weights.

AVOGADRO'S NUMBER (*N*)

$N = 6.022 \times 10^{23}$ molecules per mole

Equal volumes of a gas contain an equal number of molecules.
1 gram = 6.022×10^{23} amu.

Hydrogen gas (H_2)

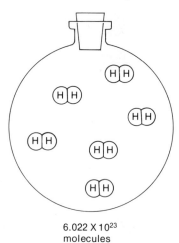

6.022×10^{23}
molecules

One molecule of hydrogen gas weighs 2.016 amu. One *mole* of hydrogen gas contains 6.022×10^{23} molecules and therefore weighs 2.016 grams.

Oxygen gas (O_2)

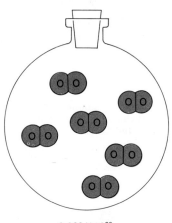

6.022×10^{23}
molecules

One molecule of oxygen gas (O_2) weighs 32.000 amu. One *mole* of oxygen gas contains 6.022×10^{23} molecules and therefore weighs 32.000 grams.

Avogadro's number of molecules at standard temperature and pressure or STP (1 atm pressure, 0°C) occupies a volume of 22.4 liters, and would fill a sphere approximately 14 inches in diameter.

of molecules in preparation for a chemical reaction. There is a simple way, however, to *weigh* different amounts of various molecules and to be sure that the resulting amounts *each contain the same number of molecules.* Since the molecular weights of hydrogen gas, methane, and water are 2.016 amu, 16.043 amu, and 18.015 amu, respectively, we can be sure that 2.016 tons of hydrogen gas, 16.043 tons of methane, and 18.015 tons of water each contain the *same number* of molecules, although we may have no idea what that number is. By the same principle, if we know that walnuts weigh twice as much as peanuts, we can be sure that two pounds of walnuts and one pound of peanuts contain the same number of nuts, without counting them or knowing exactly how many there are. If our only goal is to pair off walnuts with peanuts, or to pair off molecules in chemical reactions, then this limited information is good enough.

Example. A hardware store clerk is told to weigh one pound of machine bolts for a customer, and also to weigh approximately enough hexagonal nuts to go with them. He finds that a hex nut weighs 0.40 as much as a machine bolt of the type requested. How many nuts should he include with the order?

Answer. He should include

$$0.40 \times 1 \text{ pound} = 0.40 \text{ pound of hex nuts}$$

Such a procedure would be good enough for most real situations, and a lot easier and faster than sitting down and counting individual pieces. This is exactly what the chemist does with molecules.

Example. A chemist wants to make as much methane, CH_4, as he can from 100 g of carbon. How much hydrogen will be required?

Solution. The atomic weight of hydrogen is 1.008 amu, and that of carbon is 12.011 amu. Four hydrogen atoms are required for each carbon atom, so 4×1.008 amu $= 4.032$ amu of hydrogen will be needed for each 12.011 amu of carbon. The relative weights of hydrogen and carbon will be 4.032 units of hydrogen to 12.011 units of carbon, whatever the weighing units chosen. The problem was expressed in grams. Thus

$$100 \text{ g carbon} \times \frac{4.032 \text{ g hydrogen}}{12.011 \text{ g carbon}} = 33.6 \text{ g hydrogen}$$

will be required. Like the hardware store clerk, the chemist can weigh 100 g of carbon and 33.6 g of hydrogen and assume that he has the right *relative* number of atoms without counting them.

Most chemical measurements are made in grams. An amount of any substance in grams that is numerically equal to its atomic or molecular weight in amu has been defined as *one mole* of that substance.[1] By

---

[1] From the Latin "moles," meaning a mass or pile of material. A "molecule" is therefore a "little pile" of matter. The International Union of Pure and Applied Chemistry (IUPAC) now defines 1 mole as the amount of a substance that contains as many elementary entities (about 6.022×10^{23}) as there are in 0.012 kg (exactly 12 g) of carbon-12. This is a pragmatic working definition of a mole, but it is important to realize that this strange number was chosen because it leads to a quantity of material in grams that is numerically equal to the atomic or molecular weight in amu.

16

this definition, one mole of hydrogen is 2.016 grams, one mole of methane is 16.043 grams, and one mole of water is 18.015 grams. We can convert any gram quantity of a chemical substance to moles by dividing by its molecular weight. Once we have done this, we know that equal numbers of moles of all kinds of substances must have equal numbers of molecules. The same number of molecules is present in a mole of hydrogen, water, methane, or any other substance. This is very useful, because then we can measure the right amounts of starting material for chemical reactions, and can tell from the results how many molecules of product were formed per molecule of reactants.

Example. How many moles of carbon are present in the 100 g of the preceding example? How many moles of hydrogen atoms would be needed to combine with these? How many grams of hydrogen would be needed?

Solution. The number of moles of carbon is

$$\frac{100 \text{ g carbon}}{12.011 \text{ g mole}^{-1}} = 8.33 \text{ moles of carbon}^2$$

Four times as many hydrogen atoms are needed as carbon atoms to make methane, CH_4, so four times as many moles will be required also:

$$\frac{4 \text{ moles hydrogen}}{1 \text{ mole carbon}} \times 8.33 \text{ moles carbon} = 33.3 \text{ moles of hydrogen}$$

Since the atomic weight of hydrogen is 1.008, this corresponds to

$$33.3 \text{ moles hydrogen} \times 1.008 \text{ g mole}^{-1} = 33.6 \text{ g of hydrogen}$$

This is the same answer as we obtained previously, but this time we used moles instead of merely the ratio of atomic weights.

The mole represents a scale-up from atomic mass units to grams. Instead of counting molecules, an impossible task, we can count moles. How many molecules are there in one mole of a substance? We really do not need to know this to use moles in solving chemical problems, any more than the hardware store clerk needed to know how many bolts there were in a pound. But there are situations when this knowledge is useful. The number of molecules of a substance per mole is called *Avogadro's number* and given the symbol N. (By the way in which a mole was defined as an amount of a substance in grams, equal in numerical value to its molecular weight in amu, Avogadro's number also is the number of amu per gram.) This number can be measured experimentally by several independent methods, using gases, liquids, and crystals, and has been found to have the value

$$N = 602,209,430,000,000,000,000,000$$
$$\simeq 6.022 \times 10^{23} \text{ molecules mole}^{-1}$$

As an illustration of how many molecules there are in one mole, if each molecule were represented by an ordinary glass marble, and these marbles were packed as closely together as possible, one mole of marbles

One mole, or 602,209,430,000,000,000,000,000 molecules of H_2, H_2O, and NaCl (table salt) occupy the real space shown below.

One mole of H_2

One mole of H_2O

One mole of NaCl

If each molecule were the size of a marble, then one mole of a substance would cover the U.S.A. to a height of seventy miles.

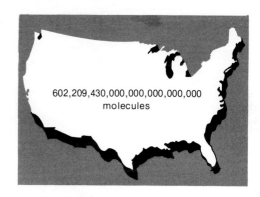

602,209,430,000,000,000,000,000 molecules

---

² We shall use the negative exponent for a unit in the denominator of an equation. The units g mole⁻¹ also could be written g/mole, and are read as "grams per mole." Similarly, speed could be expressed as m sec⁻¹, read as "meters per second," and pressure as lb in.⁻² or "pounds per square inch."

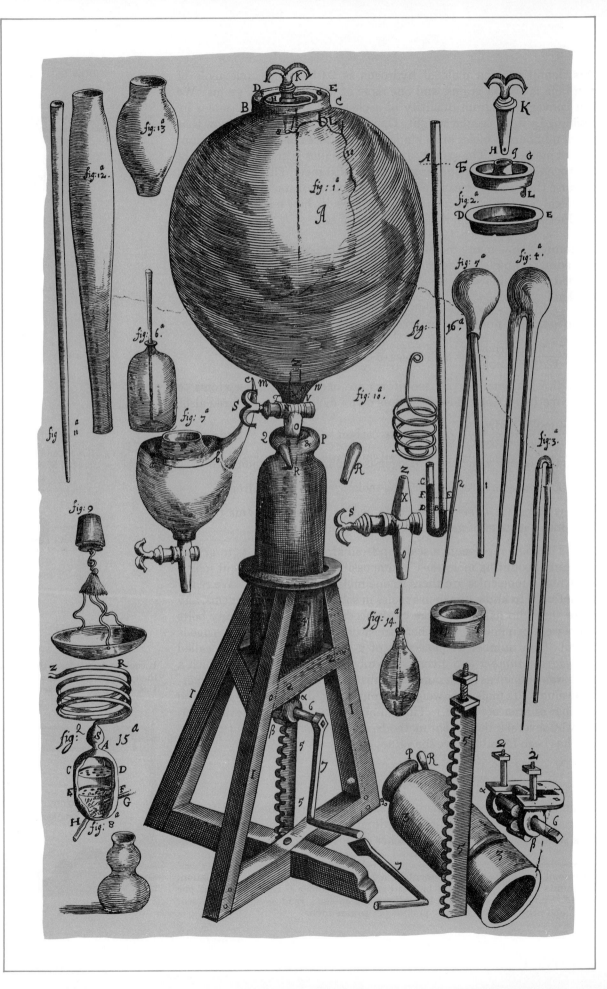

would cover the entire United States with a layer seventy miles deep! All these molecules are contained in only 2.016 grams of hydrogen gas (a balloon 35 cm in diameter), 18.015 grams of water (half of a one-ounce shot glass), or a cube of rock salt 3 cm on a side.

MEASURING MOLES; THE GAS LAWS

There is an easier way of measuring moles when one is dealing with gases. To a very good first approximation, the molecules of any gas are independently moving particles, having mass but negligible volume, and with negligible interactions except at the instant of collision. To the extent that this is so, all gas molecules are alike except for mass. *At the same pressure and temperature, equal volumes of any gases will contain equal numbers of moles and of molecules.* This is known as *Avogadro's principle*, after the man who first proposed it in 1811. It means that we do not have to weigh gases that are to enter into a reaction, we only have to bring them to a common temperature and pressure and measure volumes. If two molecules of hydrogen gas are to react with one molecule of oxygen gas,

$$2H_2 + O_2 \rightarrow 2H_2O$$

then we obtain the correct ratio of reactants by starting with two volumes of hydrogen and one of oxygen (right). Since the reaction produces two molecules of water, we can predict that if the product obtained is water vapor, there will be two volumes of vapor. The reaction by which ammonia, NH_3, is prepared from nitrogen and hydrogen gases is

$$N_2 + 3H_2 \rightarrow 2NH_3$$

Avogadro's principle tells us that if we want to carry out this reaction without waste, we should begin with three times as much hydrogen as nitrogen *by volume* at the same pressure and temperature. The product, ammonia, will have twice the volume of the starting N_2, or half the volume of the entire starting gas mixture. For gases, equal volumes at the same temperature and pressure contain equal numbers of moles.

We can do even better than this. Given the pressure and temperature, we can calculate the volume that a mole of gas should occupy, and can find out how the volume changes as a gas is expanded or compressed, and heated or cooled. The relationship between pressure (P), volume (V), temperature (T), and number of moles (n), is given by the *ideal gas law*,

$$PV = nRT$$

in which R is a constant. But to understand what this gas law means and how to use it, we must back up a step or two.

◄ Apparatus for "New experiments touching the spring of the air; made for the most part in a new pneumatical engine." From a book by Robert Boyle, published at Oxford in 1660. Courtesy Burndy Library, Norwalk, Connecticut.

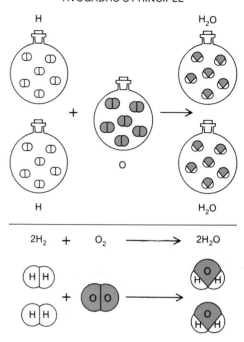

Two molecules of hydrogen gas combine with one molecule of oxygen to yield two molecules of water. Avogadro's principle tells us that equal volumes of different gases contain equal numbers of molecules, at a specified temperature and pressure. Hence two volumes of H_2 gas will combine with one volume of O_2, to produce two volumes of water vapor.

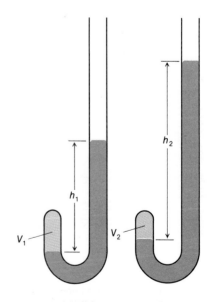

Boyle's device for studying the relationship between pressure and the volume of a gas. An increase in the height of a column of mercury (h) causes a proportional decrease in the volume of the air (V).

Pressure, P (atm)	Volume, V (liters)	$P \times V$ (liter atm)
1	20	20
2	10	20
4	5	20
10	2	20
0.5	40	20

Pressure, volume, and *PV* product for a typical experimental test of Boyle's law. The numerical data in the table above are plotted in the graph at the right. The product of pressure times volume is constant for all points along this curve.

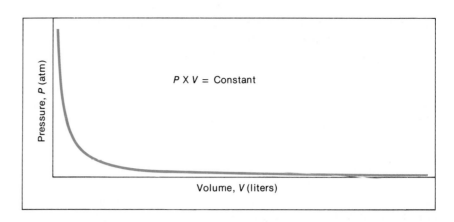

$P \times V$ = Constant

Pressure, P (atm)

Volume, V (liters)

In 1660, Robert Boyle published a book entitled "New Experiments Physico-Mechanical, Touching [concerning] the Spring of the Air." In it he gave the evidence for what is known today as *Boyle's law*. Air does have "spring." If you compress it, it pushes back. Poke an air-filled plastic balloon chair with your fingertip, and you will easily make a large dent, which vanishes when you take your finger away. Yet if you sit down on the chair, the air inside pushes back with enough force to hold up your weight.

If you compress an enclosed body of gas until it is half its original volume, and keep the temperature constant, the pressure will be doubled. If you continue to squeeze until the volume is a quarter of the starting volume, the pressure will be four times as great. Conversely, if you release the constraints on a gas and allow it to expand to twice its initial volume, the pressure of the gas will be halved, if the temperature is kept constant. This behavior is illustrated in the table and *PV* plot above, which describe a hypothetical experiment beginning with 20 liters of a gas at 1 atmosphere pressure. (Pressure usually is measured in atmospheres or millimeters of mercury; 1 atm = 760 mm of Hg.) As you can see, throughout the experiment the volume is inversely proportional to pressure; or to express matters another way, the product of pressure and volume is unchanged. This can be written as

$PV = k$ Boyle's law

in which k is a constant that can be evaluated for a particular temperature from one particular set of pressure–volume conditions. In the table at the top of the page, this constant k is equal to 20 liter atmospheres.

If we want to compare two sets of experimental conditions at constant temperature, designated by subscripts 1 and 2, then Boyle's law can be written

$P_1V_1 = P_2V_2$

Either form of Boyle's law can be used in an actual problem.

Example. An eight-foot diameter weather balloon is filled with 7600 liters of hydrogen gas at sea level where the pressure is 1 atm. By the time the balloon has ascended to an altitude at which the pressure is 0.70 atm, what is the volume of the balloon?

Common units for measuring pressure include pounds per square inch and atmospheres, with 1 atm = 14.7 psi. The hydrogen gas stored at 1600 psi (109 atm) in a 100-liter tank would be enough to fill one and a half eight-foot-diameter weather balloons at atmospheric pressure. (Can you verify this using Boyle's law?)

Solution 1. Use Boyle's law in the form $PV = k$ and evaluate k. At sea level, $P = 1$ atm, and $V = 7600$ liters; thus

$$k = PV = (1 \text{ atm})(7600 \text{ liters}) = 7600 \text{ liter atm}$$

This constant is equally valid for any other P and V, *as long as the temperature is unchanged.* (This is a flaw in our example. The temperature actually would change with altitude.) We can then write

$$(0.70 \text{ atm})V = 7600 \text{ liter atm}$$

$$V = \frac{7600 \text{ liter atm}}{0.70 \text{ atm}} \simeq 10{,}900 \text{ liters}$$

Solution 2. Use Boyle's law in the form $P_1V_1 = P_2V_2$, where conditions (1) are at sea level and (2) are at the higher altitude:

$$(1 \text{ atm})(7600 \text{ liters}) = (0.70 \text{ atm})V_2$$

$$V_2 = \frac{(1 \text{ atm})(7600 \text{ liters})}{(0.70 \text{ atm})} \simeq 10{,}900 \text{ liters}$$

A drop in pressure to 0.70 atm has permitted the gas in the balloon to expand.

The molecular explanation of Boyle's law is simple. The pressure exerted by a gas on the walls of its container arises because the gas molecules strike the walls and rebound (below). How great the pressure is depends on how fast the molecules are moving, and how often they rebound from the container walls. The speed of the molecules depends on the temperature and does not affect Boyle's law, which applies only at a constant temperature. But if we squeeze the gas into half its initial volume, then each cubic centimeter of gas has twice as many molecules (below right). Impacts with the walls occur twice as often, so the pressure is twice as great. Boyle's law is simply a reflection of how often the gas molecules bounce off the walls of the container.

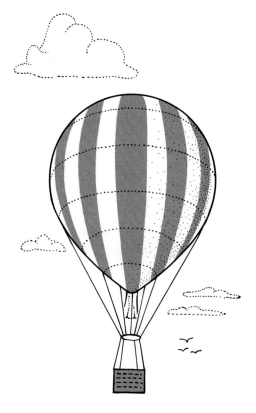

As the balloon rises to higher altitudes and the atmospheric pressure decreases, the gas in the balloon will expand as Boyle's law predicts. It will not expand quite as much as expected, however, because the temperature also decreases at high altitude. The effect of temperature is explained by Charles' law (next page).

BOYLE'S LAW

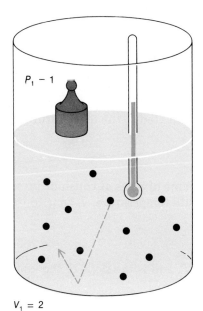

$P_1 - 1$

$V_1 = 2$

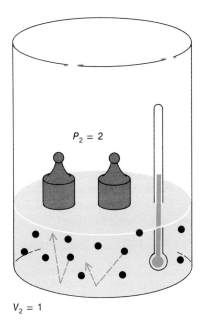

$P_2 = 2$

$V_2 = 1$

Pressure is the result of collisions of molecules with the container walls. If the volume is halved, the molecules strike the walls twice as often because they have less room in which to move, so the pressure is doubled.
Left: $P_1 = 1$, $V_1 = 2$, and $P_1V_1 = 1 \times 2 = 2$
Right: $P_2 = 2$, $V_2 = 1$, and $P_2V_2 = 2 \times 1 = 2$

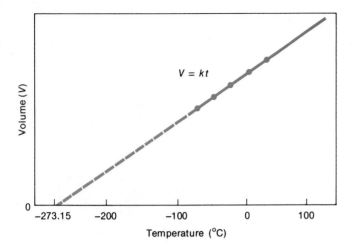
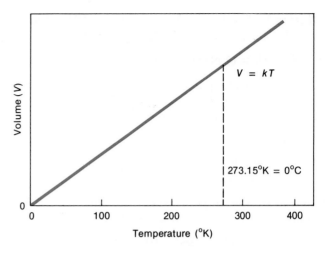

The volume–temperature curve, extrapolated from the experimentally observed points to zero volume, crosses the temperature axis at −273.15°C (left), which can be chosen as zero degrees in an absolute temperature scale (right).

GAS MOLECULES AND ABSOLUTE ZERO

Boyle's experiments all were carried out at constant temperature. A century later, Jacques Charles, in France, studied what happens to the volume of a gas when the temperature is changed and the external pressure is kept constant. This is the problem of heating or cooling a balloon full of air, with a fixed outside pressure exerted by the surroundings. In every gas he studied, Charles observed a steady increase in volume with an increase in temperature. Translating his data into modern units, he found that for every degree Celsius, or centigrade, rise in temperature, the gas volume increased by 1/273 of its volume at 0°C. This is easier to understand from the graph of volume versus temperature shown above. Within the observed range of temperatures, the plot is a straight line. If we extend this straight line back to zero volume, it crosses the temperature axis at −273.15°C. (For simplicity in the discussion that follows, we often shall use −273°C.)

Charles' data suggest that, if a gas continued to behave at lower temperatures in the way that it does at room temperature, its volume would shrink to nothing at −273°C. This is the point at which, in principle, all molecules would come to rest and gases would cease to exert pressure or occupy volume. This theoretically possible but experimentally unattainable temperature is known as *absolute zero*. We can define an absolute temperature scale (also known as the Kelvin scale after the British thermodynamicist Lord Kelvin), in which the temperature (T) in degrees absolute or Kelvin (°K) is related to the temperature in degrees centigrade (t) by the expression

$$T(°K) = t(°C) + 273.15°C$$

The work of Charles tells us that the volume of a gas at constant pressure is directly proportional to its absolute temperature, T (*not* to its centigrade temperature):

$$V = k'T \qquad \text{Charles' law}$$

Here k' is a constant that relates V and T, and is the slope of the lines in the plots at the top of the page.

22

We also can write Charles' law as

$$\frac{V}{T} = \text{constant}$$

If two sets of experimental conditions at the same pressure are being compared, 1 and 2, then Charles' law can be written as

$$\frac{V_1}{T_1} = \frac{V_2}{T_2}$$

It is important to remember that this equality holds *only at constant pressure.*

Example. A hot-air balloon heated by a propane burner has a volume of 500,000 liters when the air inside is heated to 75°C. What will the volume be after the air has cooled to 25°C, if the pressure remains constant?

Solution. The first step is to convert temperature from centigrade to absolute:

$$T_1 = 75°C + 273°C = 348°K$$
$$T_2 = 25°C + 273°C = 298°K$$

Then we can use Charles' law:

$$\frac{500,000 \text{ liters}}{348°K} = \frac{V_2}{298°K}$$

$$V_2 = \frac{298}{348} \times 500,000 \text{ liters} = 428,000 \text{ liters}$$

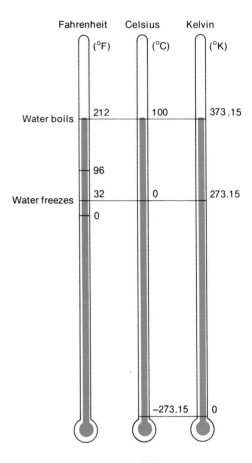

Three temperature scales are in common use. Gabriel Fahrenheit proposed, in 1714, that the range between the coldest temperature obtainable with an ice–salt bath and the temperature of the human body be divided into 96 equal degrees, and this became the Fahrenheit or °F scale (left). In the centigrade or Celsius scale in °C (center), the span between the freezing and boiling points of water is divided into 100 degrees. The absolute or Kelvin scale in °K (right) results from a readjustment of the zero of the centigrade scale.

CHARLES' LAW

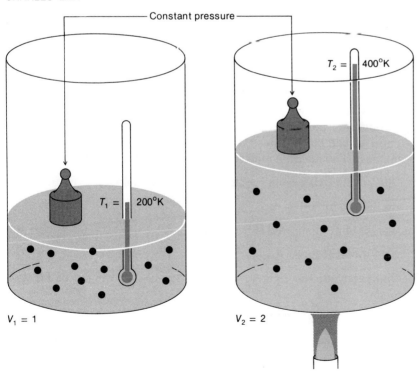

As the gas molecules are heated and move faster, they collide with the walls more often and raise the pressure. The rapidly moving molecules must be given more room to decrease the pressure to its original value.
Left: $T_1 = 200°K$, $V_1 = 1$, and $V_1/T_1 = 1/200$
Right: $T_2 = 400°K$, $V_2 = 2$, and $V_2/T_2 = 2/400$
          $= 1/200$

23

THE IDEAL GAS LAW

Boyle's law describes the relationship between pressure and volume when temperature is fixed; Charles' law relates volume and temperature when the pressure is constant. We can combine these two laws into the *ideal gas law*—ideal because it is obeyed strictly by no real gases, but is followed more and more closely as the pressure decreases and temperature increases. For n moles of an ideal gas

$$PV = nRT$$

The *gas constant*, R, is a fixed quantity, independent of pressure, volume, temperature, or amount of gas. If pressure is measured in atmospheres, volume in liters, and temperature in degrees Kelvin, then R has the numerical value

$$R = 0.0821 \text{ liter atm deg}^{-1} \text{ mole}^{-1}$$

The ideal gas law is much more powerful than either Boyle's or Charles' laws alone. We now can calculate how many moles of hydrogen gas there were in the weather-balloon example, assuming a temperature of 25°C.

Example. An eight-foot diameter weather balloon is filled with 7600 liters of H_2 at 1 atm pressure and 25°C. How many moles of hydrogen gas are present?

Solution. $P = 1$ atm, $V = 7600$ liters, $T = 25°C = 298°K$.

$$n = \frac{PV}{RT} = \frac{(1 \text{ atm})(7600 \text{ liters})}{(0.0821 \text{ liter atm deg}^{-1} \text{ mole}^{-1})(298°K)}$$

$$= 311 \text{ moles}$$

As an interesting sidelight, we can calculate the lifting power of the balloon.

Solution. The 311 moles of H_2 gas weigh 311 moles $\times$ 2.016 g mole^{-1} = 627 g. The lifting power of the balloon is the difference between this and the weight of the air that the balloon displaces. The same volume of air also would contain 311 moles (Avogadro's principle), and air can be considered a mixture of 80% nitrogen gas and 20% oxygen gas. The *average* molecular weight of the air mixture then is

$$80\% \times 28.013 \text{ g mole}^{-1} + 20\% \times 32.000 \text{ g mole}^{-1}$$

$$= 28.81 \text{ g mole}^{-1}$$

The weight of air displaced is

$$311 \text{ moles} \times 28.81 \text{ g mole}^{-1} = 8960 \text{ g}$$

The buoyancy of the balloon is the difference in weight of air and hydrogen:

$$8960 \text{ g} - 627 \text{ g} = 8333 \text{ g}$$

The balloon therefore can lift slightly more than 8 kilograms, or 18 pounds, of payload.

We now can take into account the simultaneous change of pressure and temperature, and correct the flaw in the weather balloon example first used to illustrate Boyle's law.

Example. An eight-foot diameter weather balloon is filled with 7600 liters of H_2 gas at 1 atm pressure and 25°C. As the balloon rises to an altitude where the pressure is only 0.70 atm, the temperature drops to −20°C. What then is the volume of the balloon?

Solution. Let sea-level conditions be denoted by subscript 1, and high altitude conditions, by 2. The number of moles of gas does not change, so we can use the ideal gas law in the form

$$\frac{PV}{T} = nR = \text{constant}$$

or

$$\frac{P_1 V_1}{T_1} = \frac{P_2 V_2}{T_2}$$

$$\frac{(1\ \text{atm})\ (7600\ \text{liters})}{(298°\text{K})} = \frac{(0.70\ \text{atm})\,V_2}{(253°\text{K})}$$

$$V_2 = \frac{253}{298} \times \frac{1.00}{0.70} \times 7600\ \text{liters} = 9218\ \text{liters}$$

The decrease in pressure to 0.70 atm causes an increase in volume by a factor of 1.00/0.70, but the simultaneous drop in temperature causes a shrinkage by a factor of 253/298. The balloon does not expand as much as it would have if the temperature had remained constant.

At the beginning of the section on gas laws, we said that all gases have the same volume per mole at constant pressure and temperature. We now can calculate what this *molar volume* is. Scientists refer to 1 atm pressure and 0°C (273.15°K) as "standard temperature and pressure," or STP. At STP, the volume per mole of a gas is

$$\frac{V}{n} = \frac{RT}{P} = \frac{(0.0821\ \text{liter atm deg}^{-1}\ \text{mole}^{-1})\ (273°\text{K})}{(1\ \text{atm})}$$

$$= 22.4\ \text{liters} = 22{,}400\ \text{cm}^3$$

A 22.4-liter sphere has a diameter of 35 cm, and this was the calculation that produced the figure quoted previously in this chapter. One mole of any gas at STP fills a flask fourteen inches in diameter (right).

The ideal gas law describes the behavior of a fictional gas. Real gases act at room temperature *as if* they would shrink to nothing at absolute zero, when in fact they condense first. Before reaching absolute zero, all real gases liquefy or solidify, behavior for which the ideal gas law cannot account. No gas obeys the conditions $PV = nRT$ perfectly, but all gases come close at room temperatures and low pressures. This is the reason that we can apply the gas law to any gas, including an atmospheric mixture of N_2 and O_2, without worrying about the composition of the mixture. One molecule is the same as any other in an ideal gas. The ideal gas law assumes that attractions between molecules are negligible when compared with their energies of motion, and that the actual volumes of gas molecules are negligible in comparison with the total volume occupied by the gas. This is close to being true at room

At standard temperature and pressure, 273°K and 1 atm, Avogadro's number of molecules (6.022×10^{23}) occupy a sphere approximately 14 inches in diameter.

H_2 at 273°K

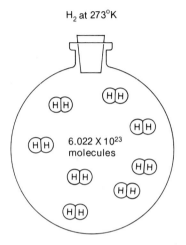

Volume = 22.4 liters at 273°K

H_2 at 20°K

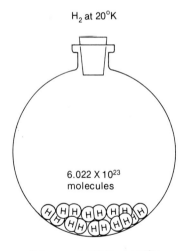

Volume = 0.065 liter at 20°K

At 20°K, the same number of hydrogen molecules stick together as a liquid and occupy only 0.065 liter instead of 22.4 liters.

A CHEMICAL WORLD IN MINIATURE

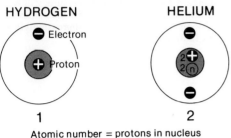

HYDROGEN — Electron, Proton — 1

HELIUM — 2

Atomic number = protons in nucleus

Isotopes of hydrogen

"Ordinary" hydrogen

Deuterium

Tritium

Electron shells

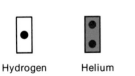

Hydrogen   Helium

Covalent bond

H•   •H

Hydrogen atoms

H⦂H

or

H——H

Hydrogen molecule

---

temperature and 1 atm pressure. At lower temperatures and slower speeds, the attractive forces between molecules no longer can be ignored. At higher pressures, at which molecules are closer together, the volume occupied by the molecules themselves becomes an appreciable part of the volume filled by the gas. The ideal gas law begins to fail badly. Nevertheless, under ordinary conditions the expression $PV = nRT$ is a surprisingly good description of real gas behavior.

A CHEMICAL WORLD IN MINIATURE: A SUMMARY

We began these first two chapters with the statement that ours was a universe mainly of hydrogen and helium, which at the same time are the simplest and the oldest two elements. These two elements illustrate in miniature most of the chemical principles that we will encounter with the heavier elements.

The other elements, like hydrogen and helium, are built from positively charged nuclei containing protons and neutrons, surrounded by enough negatively charged electrons to neutralize the positive charge of the protons. The number of protons, or the *atomic number*, determines the chemical behavior of an atom because it determines the number of electrons that surround a neutral atom; and the gain, loss, and sharing of electrons is responsible for an atom's chemical properties. The number of neutrons usually is equal to or slightly greater than the number of protons. Neutrons have little effect on chemical properties of an atom, except for those that are influenced by mass. Atoms with the same atomic number but different numbers of neutrons are called *isotopes*. The total number of neutrons and protons in the nucleus is the *mass number* of the atom, and the actual mass in amu is the *atomic weight* relative to that of carbon-12 as exactly 12 amu. Observed atomic weights usually are averages of the weights of several naturally occurring isotopes.

Electrons in atoms surround the nucleus in a series of shells, with similar energies within one shell and different energies from one shell to the next. The innermost shell can hold two electrons and the next, eight. A completely filled shell is a particularly stable arrangement for an atom. Helium atoms will not combine with one another, for each already has the two electrons necessary to fill its inner electron shell. Hydrogen atoms lack one electron of having a completely filled shell, and two H atoms can share a pair of electrons to form an H_2 molecule. In this way each of the atoms in the molecule has two electrons in its immediate vicinity, and thereby attains a full-shell structure. The bond in the H—H molecule can be thought of as the prototype of the electron-pair or *covalent bond* in larger molecules.

An amount of any compound in grams, numerically equal to its atomic or molecular weight in amu, is one *mole* of that substance. The mole concept allows one to measure equal numbers of atoms or molecules of various material, even without a knowledge of how many molecules there are. The actual number of molecules in one mole, *Avogadro's number*, has been measured as $N = 6.022 \times 10^{23}$. From the way in which the mole is defined, this value is also the conversion factor between amu and grams as units of mass: $1 \text{ g} = 6.022 \times 10^{23}$ amu. One

26

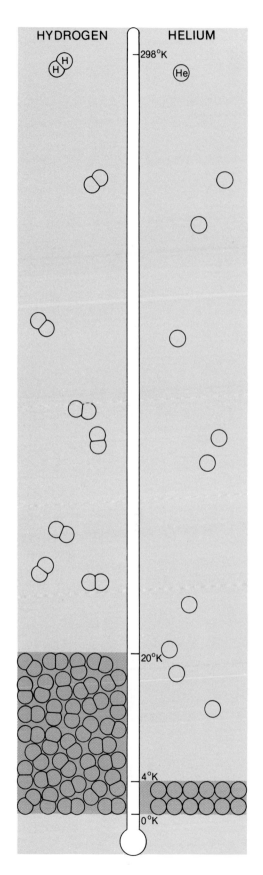

mole of H_2 molecules weighs 2.016 grams, and one mole of He atoms, 4.003 g.

All atoms and molecules have a very weak, short-range attraction for one another known as *van der Waals attraction*. They also have finite though tiny molecular volumes. At ordinary temperatures, where the molecules of a gas are moving rapidly, and at moderate pressures, where on the average they are far apart, both van der Waals attractions and molecular volumes can be neglected, and molecules can be treated as freely moving, nonattracting point particles. Under these conditions the behavior of all gases is described by the *ideal gas law, PV = nRT*, in which T is the absolute temperature, obtained by adding 273.15° to the centigrade temperature. The speed with which molecules move in a gas depends on its temperature; and in principle, if ideal gas behavior were followed all the way to absolute zero, all molecular motion would stop at that point and both pressure and volume would fall to zero.

In practice, before this point is reached, van der Waals attractions and molecular volumes become too important to be ignored, and gases deviate from ideal behavior. The most striking deviation occurs when slowly moving molecules "stick" to one another, and a gas condenses into a liquid. At still lower temperatures, the liquid freezes into a crystalline solid. The boiling point of a liquid is a useful measure of the strength of van der Waals forces between molecules, because the smaller the molecules and the weaker these forces are, the lower the temperature can be before the gas molecules stick together and condense as a liquid. Of the two elements in our simple universe, H_2 molecules must be cooled to −253°C, or 20°K, before they condense. This is the boiling point of liquid hydrogen at a pressure of 1 atm. The single atoms of helium gas are smaller, with less surface area. They must be cooled to 4°K before their attractive forces cause them to condense.

Hydrogen and helium illustrate many chemical properties, but by themselves they are a dead end. They are not capable of the great variation seen in the chemistry of the heavier elements. If stellar syntheses had gone no farther than hydrogen fusion, the universe would have been stillborn. To continue, we must turn to the elements heavier than helium, and this is the subject of the next chapters.

QUESTIONS

1. A common model-building kit has a scale of 2 cm to the angstrom unit. What magnification factor would this be over the actual atomic sizes? Roughly how big would atoms be in these models? If nuclei were shown, how big would they be on the same scale?

2. Which are heavier, neutrons or electrons? Which are more highly charged? What counterbalances the charge on the protons in a neutral atom? Where is the proton charge located in the atom, and where is the counterbalancing charge?

3. What is the difference between the nuclei of hydrogen and helium atoms? How does this affect the number of electrons in each atom?

4. What is the difference between the various kinds of hydrogen atoms? What are such variations in the same type of atom called?

5. If you know that an atom is a carbon atom, what can you tell about the number of electrons, neutrons, and protons? What new information do you have if you know that it is carbon-13?

6. Which is more important in determining the chemical behavior of an atom, the number of neutrons or the number of protons? Why?

7. What holds two hydrogen atoms together in a molecule? Why do two helium atoms not form a stable molecule?

8. Why do two hydrogen atoms become more stable if they are brought together, but then become less stable again if they are brought too close?

9. How is the molecular weight of a molecule related to the atomic weights of the atoms from which it is made?

10. What is a mole of a chemical substance? How is the mole concept useful in chemistry?

11. How many molecules are present in one mole of water vapor? Of liquid water? Of ethyl alcohol?

12. What is the molecular explanation for the phenomenon of pressure?

PROBLEMS

1. Natural lithium is 92.58% lithium-7, with atomic weight 7.016, and 7.42% lithium-6, with atomic weight 6.015. What is the observed atomic weight of lithium as it occurs in nature?

2. The observed atomic weight of chlorine in nature is 35.453, and 75.53% of this is chlorine-35, with an atomic weight of 34.97. If there is only one other chlorine isotope, what is its approximate atomic weight?

3. The formula for methyl alcohol is CH_3OH. What is its molecular weight?

4. At 120°C, which weighs more, a mole of water vapor or a mole of methyl alcohol (also a gas at this temperature)? Which occupies more volume? Calculate the weight and volume of each. How many molecules are in each?

5. How many oxygen atoms are present in one mole of O_2 molecules? How many moles of oxygen atoms are present in a mole of O_2 molecules?

6. How many grams of oxygen are involved with 50 grams of carbon in methyl alcohol? How many moles of oxygen *atoms* does this correspond to?

7. What is the molecular weight of ethyl alcohol (ethanol), C_2H_5OH? In an equimolar mixture of ethanol and water, what is the percent ethanol by weight?

8. In the old definition, 100-proof alcohol was the weakest alcohol–water mixture that could be set afire by a match after being poured over gunpowder. In a more recent definition, 100-proof spirit is 49.28% ethanol by weight. What is the ratio of relative numbers of moles of ethanol and water in 100-proof gin? (Ignore minor components.)

9. The Hindenberg and the Graf Zeppelin II, Germany's last two great lighter-than-air craft, originally were designed to use helium for lift rather than hydrogen, and only the American embargo on export of helium from the Texas oil fields forced the Hindenberg to use hydrogen. The result was the tragic crash and fire in New Jersey in 1936, which marked the effective end of commercial dirigible travel. The total volume of the Hindenberg's gas bags was 200,000 cubic meters. At 25°C and 1 atm pressure, how many moles of hydrogen gas would be required to fill them? How much would this hydrogen weigh?

10. How much would an equivalent volume of air weigh (see Problem 9)? How much weight could the Hindenberg lift (including the weight of the airship itself)?

11. If the U. S. government had allowed helium to be exported, how many moles of helium would have been needed to fill the Hindenberg? How much weight could the ship then have lifted, using He instead of H_2?

12. Why are H_2 and He the only two gases that can be used in lighter-than-air craft?

13. If the gas bags were filled on a hot day, at 30°C, by what percent would they have shrunk if the temperature fell to 15°C?

14. If H_2, N_2, and O_2 all behave as ideal gases, would the lifting ratio of a balloon (the number of times the weight of gas it can lift) change as the temperature changed? Why, or why not?

15. When 1 g of unknown liquid is vaporized at 80°C and 1.01 atm pressure, it occupies a volume of 0.622 liter. How many moles of the liquid are present?

16. What is the molecular weight of the liquid of Problem 15?

17. If the molecules of the liquid in Problem 15 are 34.7% oxygen by weight, and contain only carbon, hydrogen, and oxygen, what might the liquid be? (We have encountered it previously in this problem set.)

THE NEUTRAL ATOM

The number of positive charges from protons (⊕) in the nucleus is balanced exactly by the number of negatively charged electrons (⊖) surrounding the nucleus.

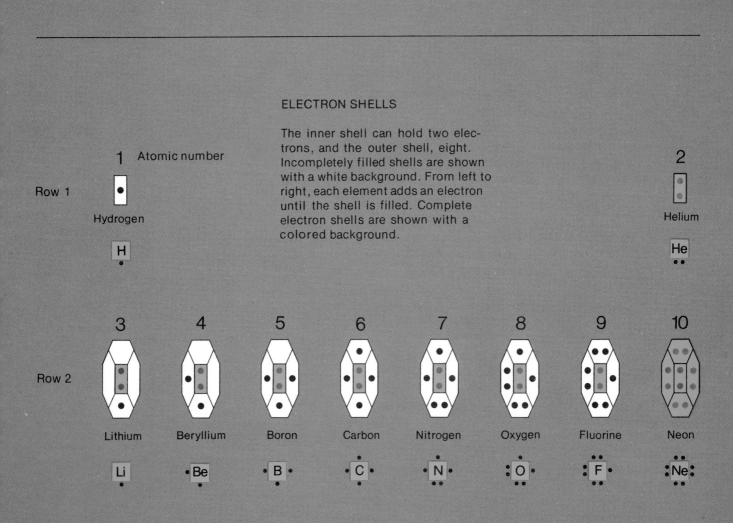

ELECTRON SHELLS

The inner shell can hold two electrons, and the outer shell, eight. Incompletely filled shells are shown with a white background. From left to right, each element adds an electron until the shell is filled. Complete electron shells are shown with a colored background.

CHAPTER 3

Eight-Electron Chemistry: Lithium Through Neon

We have only to look around us to recognize that our world is not a world of hydrogen and helium. The chemistry in the first two chapters is quite inadequate for dealing with our corner of the universe. For this, we need to understand the heavier elements, which have more protons in their nuclei and more electrons around them. As was mentioned in Chapter 2, the innermost shell of any atom can hold a maximum of two electrons, and the second shell can hold eight electrons. We can build up a series of ten atoms with increasing numbers of electrons, before we run out of room in the first two electron shells. The next three chapters are devoted to these simplest ten atoms. With them, we can outline the chemistry of our world, although the heavier elements will be necessary to fill in the details. These ten elements are the atoms of life, for they make up 99.35% of the material in any living organism.

THE BUILDUP OF THE ELEMENTS

A heliumlike arrangement with two electrons filling the first shell around the nucleus is a particularly favorable situation, as we saw previously. Now let us imagine constructing a series of atoms by adding electrons to helium one at a time in the *second* electron shell, making the corresponding addition of protons in the nucleus to keep the atoms electrically neutral. The atomic structures of the first ten atoms are diagramed at the top of the facing page. The number of protons is shown within each nucleus (gray) and the number of electrons is indicated outside. The lower diagrams at the left focus attention on the inner two electron shells, showing how they are gradually filled from hydrogen to neon. Electrons are represented by dots, with a maximum of two in the inner shell and eight in the second shell. Partially filled shells are white and filled shells are colored.

Helium

Neon

Helium and neon, with completely filled outer shells, exhibit similar properties. Both are inert, unreactive, monatomic gases at room temperature. Other elements tend to gain or lose outer electrons to achieve this stable filled-shell arrangement.

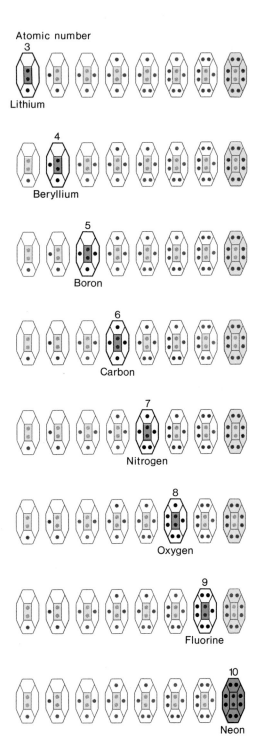

Atomic number
3
Lithium

4
Beryllium

5
Boron

6
Carbon

7
Nitrogen

8
Oxygen

9
Fluorine

10
Neon

Electron shells of the second-row elements.
The row is repeated eight times to accent the
relationship between each element and its
neighbors to either side in the row.

Lithium (symbol Li) has one electron outside the two-electron "helium core" and three protons in its nucleus, giving an electronic arrangement that can be represented by Li 2,1. In the electron diagrams at the beginning of the chapter and in the left margin, Li has one dot in the white region that represents the incomplete second shell. The man who invented the idea of electron-pair bonds, University of California chemist G. N. Lewis, represented the outer-shell electrons of atoms as dots around the atomic symbol, as shown at the far right on Page 33. Lithium is a soft, silvery metal that enters into chemical reactions with other substances extremely readily, losing its outer electron in the process.

Beryllium (Be) has two electrons in its second shell, and is symbolized by Be 2,2 or by the Lewis dot structure at the right. It is a harder and less reactive metal than lithium. *Boron*, with three outer electrons (B 2,3), is gray, brittle, and only slightly metallic.

Carbon (C 2,4) and the elements that follow all are nonmetals. Pure carbon occurs both as the slightly metallic black graphite, and the clear and extremely hard nonmetallic diamond. But carbon is much more familiar in the myriad compounds that it forms with other elements. Carbon compounds are the basis of all life. We cannot open our eyes on this planet without seeing carbon compounds, from the most distant treeline to the tip of our own nose.

Nitrogen (N 2,5) has five outer electrons. It combines readily with carbon to form compounds in living organisms. Nitrogen is found as two-atom or diatomic molecules, N_2 (recall the H_2 molecules of hydrogen). N_2 gas makes up nearly 80% of the Earth's atmosphere. The electron-shell diagram for nitrogen at the left, and the Lewis dot structure at the far right, both suggest that two of the five outer electrons are paired in some way. This is true. The pairing of electrons around an atom is as important in determining its chemical properties as is the pairing of electrons in a bond between atoms. A lone nitrogen atom has one pair of electrons and three unpaired electrons in its outer shell available for making chemical bonds. The outer electronic shell, when full, has its eight electrons arranged in four electron pairs.

Oxygen (O 2,6) has six outer electrons, and as the electron diagrams suggest, they occur as two electron pairs and two unpaired electrons. Diatomic O_2 gas makes up the other 20% of the atmosphere of our planet, with other gases being present only in small amounts. Oxygen combines readily with carbon compounds and releases large amounts of heat when it does so. This is why oxygen was selected during the evolutionary process as the main energy source for living organisms. It is wrong to think of oxygen chiefly as an atmospheric gas involved in respiration, however. Nearly half the atoms in our planet are oxygen atoms, locked with metals and silicon atoms in the silicate minerals beneath our feet.

Fluorine (F 2,7) has seven outer electrons, arranged in three electron pairs and one lone electron. F_2 is a yellow-green gas, and is even more reactive and heat-emitting when it combines with carbon compounds than oxygen is. But the evolutionary process still chose O and not F for its energy-yielding chemistry, probably because F is scarce on this planet and not obtained easily. *Neon*, with eight outer electrons

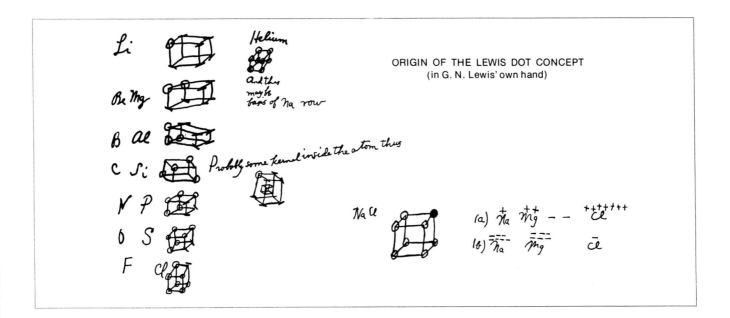

ORIGIN OF THE LEWIS DOT CONCEPT
(in G. N. Lewis' own hand)

(Ne 2,8) in four electron pairs, closes the series with a noble[1] gas resembling helium. Neon, like helium, does not combine chemically with anything; thus pure neon, like pure helium, exists as a monatomic gas.

This is as far as we can go with the first two electron shells. Any additional electrons would have to begin a third shell (which also can hold eight electrons). We will return to this in Chapter 6, after we have looked more closely at the behavior of the second-shell elements.

Why should atoms contain outermost electron shells that have room for a maximum of eight electrons? G. N. Lewis first proposed this "rule of eight" at the turn of the century, and initially pictured the electrons as occupying the corners of a cube around the atom. Some of his sketches from a notebook page of 1902 are shown above. Lewis soon realized that the eight electrons were arranged in four electron pairs, like the electron pairs involved in chemical bonding. No good explanation for these four electron pairs per shell was forthcoming until physicists began applying quantum mechanics to chemistry in the 1920's. We will use their results in Chapters 7 and 8, but will avoid the mathematics that led to the results. For the moment we will say only that in the second electron shell there are four different "orbitals" or ways of locating electrons in space around the nucleus, with each of these orbitals capable of holding two electrons. In Chapter 9 we shall see that the calculated arrangement of these orbitals in space leads to a correct prediction of the observed *shapes* of molecules, a powerful indication that the quantum-mechanical treatment is correct.

Above is a page from a 1902 notebook of G. N. Lewis, showing how he was moving gradually toward the idea of eight electrons being important in chemical bonding. From *Valence* by G. N. Lewis, a Dover reprint.

Li •Be •B• •C• •N• :O• :F• :Ne:

Lewis dot structures for the second-shell atoms (above), with dots representing the outer-shell electrons.

[1] The unreactive gases with filled outer shells such as helium, neon, argon, and xenon have been called the "inert," "noble," and "rare" gases. All of these terms are misleading. Helium today is not overly rare, xenon forms compounds and hence is not inert, and nobility is in the eye of the beholder. We shall use the term "noble gas" as being the least wrong choice.

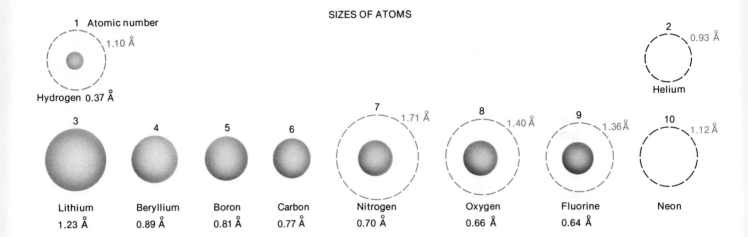

Bonding and packing dimensions of the first ten elements. Gray spheres represent the effective radii of atoms when involved in metallic or covalent (electron-pair) single bonds. Colored dashed circles represent the packing radii for nonbonded atoms.

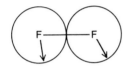

The covalent radius of fluorine in the F_2 molecule is half the distance between centers of two bonded atoms.

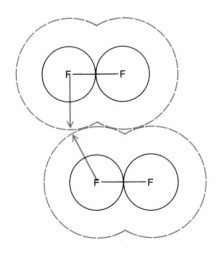

The packing radius of fluorine in the F_2 molecule is half the distance of closest approach between centers of two nonbonded atoms in different molecules. It is approximately twice the covalent bonding radius, because two atoms can come closer together by sharing electrons in a chemical bond.

HOW BIG IS AN ATOM?

Democritus, Newton, and Dalton all used atoms as philosophical ideas without worrying about the actual size of one such particle of matter. They would not have known how to begin to calculate the size of an atom. We can find out roughly how big a typical atom is with only a short scratch-paper calculation. The density of lithium metal is measured to be 0.534 g cm^{-3}, but for this rough calculation two figures are good enough. Since 1 cm = 10^8 Å, we can write the density of lithium (ρ) in grams per cubic angstrom as

$$\rho = 0.53 \times 10^{-24} \text{ g Å}^{-3}$$

We can convert this to moles per cubic angstrom by dividing by the atomic weight of Li, 7.0 g mole^{-1}, and then to atoms per cubic angstrom by multiplying by Avogadro's number, 6.0×10^{23} atoms mole^{-1}:

$$\rho = 0.53 \times 10^{-24}\frac{\text{g}}{\text{Å}^3} \times \frac{1 \text{ mole}}{7.0 \text{ g}} \times \frac{6.0 \times 10^{23} \text{ atoms}}{1 \text{ mole}}$$

$$\rho = \frac{0.53 \times 0.60}{7.0} \text{ atoms Å}^{-3} = 0.045 \text{ atoms Å}^{-3}$$

The inverse of this is the volume per atom: $v = 22$ Å^3 atom^{-1}. Each atom in a block of lithium metal occupies a volume of approximately 22 cubic angstroms. Without worrying about the geometry of the way spheres pack together, we can take the cube root of this volume and say that lithium atoms should have a diameter of approximately 2.8 Å, or a radius of 1.4 Å.

The true radius of a spherical atom can be defined as half the distance from its center to the center of a like atom when they are touching. As shown at the left, two atoms that share an electron pair in a bond can come closer than two atoms that merely pack against one another but are not bonded. Hence we must define two measures of atomic size: bonding radii and packing radii, with the latter usually about twice as large as the former. Bonding and packing radii for the first- and second-shell atoms are shown above. The values of 0.37 Å and 1.10 Å for hydrogen tell us that the centers of two bonded atoms in a H_2 molecule are separated by 2×0.37 Å $= 0.74$ Å, but that the centers of hydrogen atoms in different H_2 molecules in closely packed solid hydrogen (at very low temperatures) are 2×1.10 Å $= 2.20$ Å apart. No bonding radii are given for the noble gases helium and neon because they do not make chemical bonds.

A helium atom is smaller than a hydrogen atom. Although helium has one more electron, it also has an additional positive charge on the nucleus that pulls both electrons closer to the nucleus. Atoms of the second-shell elements Li through Ne are larger than either hydrogen or helium because the second electron shell is farther from the nucleus. Also, there is a gradual *decrease* in atomic size from Li to Ne. The inner two electrons shield the nucleus, so the outer electrons experience the pull from a "helium core" with a net positive charge that is *two less* than the actual atomic number. The lone outer electron in Li feels a net central charge of $+3 - 2 = +1$. The four outer electrons in C experience a central attraction of $+6 - 2 = +4$, and the seven electrons around F experience a charge attraction of $+7$. As the central charge increases with atomic number from Li to Ne, the outer electrons are drawn more tightly toward the nucleus by electrostatic attraction, thereby causing the atoms to be successively smaller. This has an important effect on their chemical behavior.

GAIN AND LOSS OF ELECTRONS; IONIZATION ENERGY

Atoms interact with one another to form bonds in molecules by gaining, losing, or sharing electrons. A key idea in chemistry is the great stability of filled electron shells around an atom. Since lithium has only one electron outside a filled helium core, it can lose that electron easily and become a positively charged *ion:*

$$\underset{\text{lithium atom}}{\text{Li}} \rightarrow \underset{\text{lithium ion}}{\text{Li}^+} + e^-$$

This *ionization* is shown schematically at the upper right. Much more energy would be needed to remove electrons from the first or inner shell, and this ordinarily does not happen in chemical reactions. A beryllium atom, with two electrons outside the closed helium shell, can lose both electrons to become a doubly charged ion, as shown at the right:

$$\underset{\text{beryllium atom}}{\text{Be}} \rightarrow \underset{\text{beryllium ion}}{\text{Be}^{2+}} + 2e^-$$

At the other end of the second-shell elements, neon is stable and unreactive because it already has a filled outer shell of eight electrons. Fluorine, with seven outer electrons, can achieve the neon configuration by picking up an electron from another atom to become a negative ion:

$$\underset{\text{fluorine atom}}{\text{F}} + e^- \rightarrow \underset{\text{fluoride ion}}{\text{F}^-}$$

The filled-shell structure of a fluoride ion is shown at the lower right.

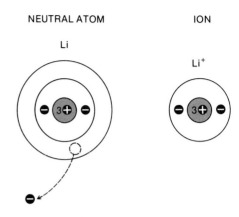

NEUTRAL ATOM   ION

Lithium loses its lone outer electron to become a lithium ion, Li^+.

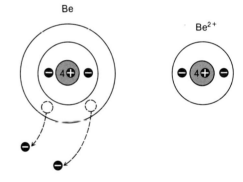

Beryllium loses both outer electrons to become a beryllium ion, Be^{2+}.

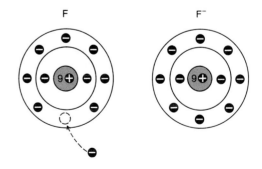

Fluorine gains an electron to complete its outer shell and become a fluoride ion, F^-.

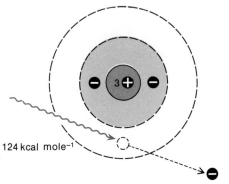

FIRST IONIZATION ENERGY FOR LITHIUM

124 kcal mole^{-1}

First electron

Outer electron removed

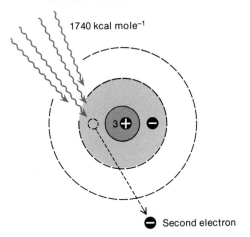

SECOND IONIZATION ENERGY

1740 kcal mole^{-1}

Second electron

One inner-shell electron removed

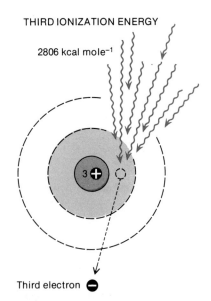

THIRD IONIZATION ENERGY

2806 kcal mole^{-1}

Third electron

Final inner-shell electron removed

Carbon, in the center of the list, has four of the eight electrons needed to complete the second shell. One could imagine that it acquires four more electrons to become a quadruply charged negative ion:

$$C + 4e^- \overset{?}{\rightarrow} C^{4-}$$

with the neon arrangement, or alternatively that it loses four electrons to acquire the helium arrangement:

$$C \overset{?}{\rightarrow} C^{4+} + 4e^-$$

Neither process takes place in chemical reactions. Too much energy is required to pile up four positive or four negative charges on a tiny carbon atom. Instead, carbon *shares* its four outer electrons with other atoms in electron-pair bonds, thereby gaining eight electrons around its inner helium core.

The energy required to remove *one* electron from a gaseous neutral atom and convert it into a positive ion is its *first ionization energy* (abbreviated IE). Subsequent energies needed to take away more electrons from the positive ion are called the second, third, etc., ionization energies. Ionization energies, like other energies dealing with molecules in chemistry, usually are measured in *kilocalories* per mole of molecules or atoms.[2]

The ionization energies of a lithium atom give us information about its electron-shell structure. It is relatively easy to take away the lone outer electron in the second shell (left), because this electron is far from the nucleus and sees only a net nuclear charge of +1 because of shielding by the inner electrons:

$$Li \rightarrow Li^+ + e^- \qquad \text{first IE} = 124 \text{ kcal mole}^{-1}$$

The second ionization energy is much higher, and beyond what can be accomplished in chemical reactions:

$$Li^+ \rightarrow Li^{2+} + e^- \qquad \text{second IE} = 1740 \text{ kcal mole}^{-1}$$

More energy is required to remove this electron because a negative charge is being removed from an object that is already positively charged. Even more importantly, this electron comes from the inner electron shell, which is not shielded by an intervening pair of electrons and therefore feels the full +3 attraction of the nucleus. The even larger third IE,

$$Li^{2+} \rightarrow Li^{3+} + e^- \qquad \text{third IE} = 2806 \text{ kcal mole}^{-1}$$

---

[2] The calorie is a convenient unit for measuring heat, work, and energy. One calorie of heat is the amount required to raise the temperature of one gram of water by 1°C, from 14.5°C to 15.5°C, and a kilocalorie, or kcal, is 1000 calories. When a 150-pound man walks up one flight of stairs, he does approximately ½ kcal of work against the pull of gravity. The Calorie (capitalized) used by nutritionists in calculating daily energy needs is actually our kilocalorie. An average human being needs from 1500 to 2500 Calories (kcal) of energy per day from food intake. Breaking a typical chemical bond in a molecule requires 80 to 150 kcal per mole of bonds.

arises because one now must pull a negative charge away from a highly charged +3 nucleus. There can be no fourth IE for lithium, because it only has three electrons.

If you looked at the four successive ionization energies of the beryllium atom, you would find that the first two are relatively small, but the third and fourth, representing removal of inner-shell electrons, are far higher. In general, much more energy is needed to remove electrons from a closed inner shell than to take electrons away from a partly filled outer electron shell.

First ionization energies are a good index of how tightly different atoms hold their electrons in the outermost shell. Values for the elements H through Ne are shown in the graph at the bottom of the page. First IE's for H and He are especially high because the electrons are close to the nucleus in the inner shell, and the value for He is double that of H because the charge on the nucleus is doubled. First IE's for the second-shell atoms are lower because the electrons are farther from the nucleus and are shielded by the inner electron pair. They generally increase with atomic number because the nuclear charge increases. For elements at the far right of the graph, it is nearly as hard to take an electron away from a neon atom with a closed eight-electron shell as it is to remove one electron from helium with its closed two-electron shell.

What does ionization energy have to do with chemical behavior? The low IE of lithium is characteristic of a *metal*, and causes it to form salts and other compounds in which lithium exists as a positively charged Li^+ ion. Lithium loses its outer electron readily:

$$\underset{\text{lithium atom}}{Li} \quad \rightarrow \quad \underset{\text{lithium ion}}{Li^+} \quad + \quad e^-$$

If lithium ions are brought near negatively charged fluoride ions (F^-), the opposite electrostatic charges attract. The ions can pack into a three-dimensional lattice, as shown at the right, to form a solid known as a *salt*. Common table salt is sodium chloride, in which sodium ions (Na^+) and chloride ions (Cl^-) are arranged in the same way as the Li^+ and F^- ions.

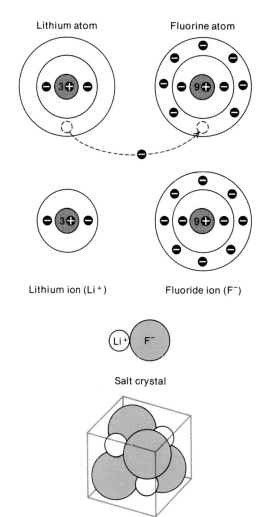

FORMATION OF LiF SALT

Lithium atom

Fluorine atom

Lithium ion (Li⁺)

Fluoride ion (F⁻)

Salt crystal

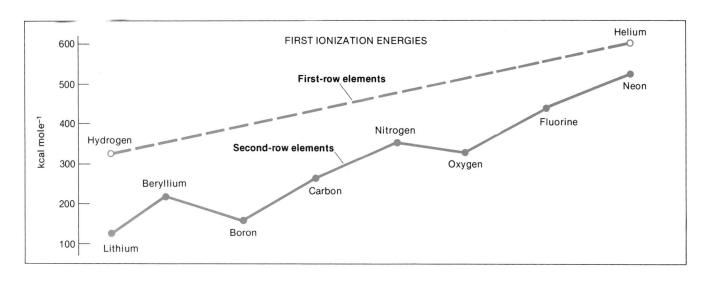

FIRST IONIZATION ENERGIES

First-row elements

Second-row elements

kcal mole⁻¹

Hydrogen

Lithium

Beryllium

Boron

Carbon

Nitrogen

Oxygen

Fluorine

Neon

Helium

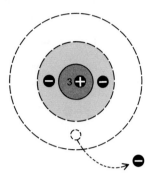

FORMATION OF A METAL

Lithium loses an electron and becomes a positive Li⁺ ion.

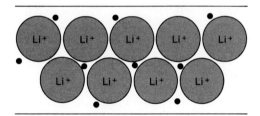

Lithium metal consists of packed Li⁺ ions held together by a "glue" of mobile electrons.

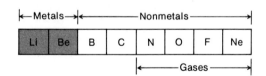

If many lithium atoms are brought together into a solid, their loosely held outer electrons are free to wander through the entire metal block under the influence of external electrostatic forces. One can think of a metal as a closely packed collection of positive ions held together by a "glue" of mobile electrons (see left). These mobile electrons are responsible for the physical properties that we associate with a metal: conduction of electricity and heat, metallic luster or sheen, and mechanical deformability. We will look at metals in more detail in Chapter 5.

Lithium is a relatively soft metal because it has only one electron per positive ion to serve as "glue" in holding the metal together. In contrast, beryllium has two electrons outside the inner helium core. Beryllium metal has twice as many electrons per ion, and therefore is harder than lithium. For boron, the energy required to remove its three outer electrons is too great. Boron atoms do not lose three electrons and form boron ions (B^{3+}). Instead, they share electrons with neighbor atoms in covalent, or electron-pair, bonds. Lithium and beryllium are metals; boron lies on the borderline between these metallic elements and the nonmetals carbon, nitrogen, oxygen, and fluorine.

ELECTRON AFFINITY

Each of the seven outer electrons in a fluorine atom experiences an effective nuclear charge of $+9 - 2 = +7$. There is room for one more electron in the second shell, and if an electron is brought near the F atom, it too will feel the pull from a $+7$ charge. Energy is given off when the F atom and an electron combine to form the more stable F^- ion:

$$\underset{\text{fluorine atom}}{F} \quad + \quad e^- \quad \rightarrow \quad \underset{\text{fluoride ion}}{F^-} \quad \text{(energy is released)}$$

This same amount of energy must be resupplied to pull the electron away again:

$$\underset{\text{fluoride ion}}{F^-} \quad \rightarrow \quad \underset{\text{fluorine atom}}{F} \quad + \quad e^- \quad \text{(energy must be supplied)}$$

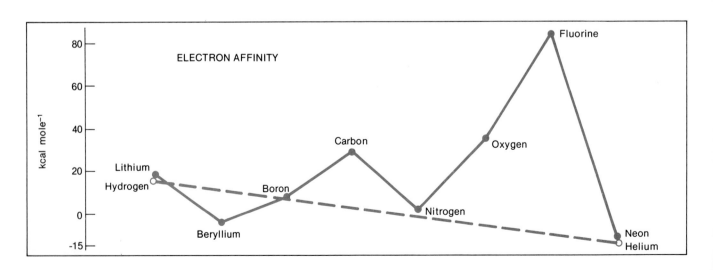

The energy given off when one electron is added to a neutral atom is called the *electron affinity* of the atom.

Electron affinities for the simplest ten elements are shown at the bottom of the opposite page. (Electron affinities are harder to measure than ionization energies, and these values are only approximate.) Neon has no electron affinity, because it already has its full complement of eight outer electrons. Fluorine has the largest electron affinity, 83.5 kilocalories per mole; thus the F⁻ ion is formed easily. Oxygen has a smaller electron affinity because the net charge pulling on the outer electrons is +6 rather than +7. The affinities of other neutral atoms of the second-shell elements for extra electrons are weaker yet.

ELECTRONEGATIVITY

Ionization energies describe how unwilling an atom is to lose an electron, and electron affinities measure how eager a neutral atom is to add one more electron. Both of these quantities describe the attraction of an atom for an electron under special conditions. *Electronegativity* is a more general measure of the attraction of an atom for an electron in bond-forming situations. Electronegativities could be calculated from ionization energies and electron affinities, but in practice they are obtained by measuring the strengths of different types of bonds in molecules.

Linus Pauling and Robert Mulliken independently devised the electronegativity concept. In the Pauling electronegativity scale, the electron-losing lithium atom is assigned an electronegativity (or EN) of 1.0, the electron-grabbing fluorine is given an EN of 4.0, and the other atoms are assigned intermediate values, as shown below. In a bond between two atoms, the electrons will be attracted more strongly to the atom with the greater electroncgativity. The EN's of carbon and hydrogen are similar: 2.5 and 2.1. Thus in a molecule containing carbon and hydrogen the electron pair will be shared almost equally between them in an electron-pair, or covalent, bond. In contrast, Li and F have radically different electronegativities: 1.0 and 4.0. In the com-

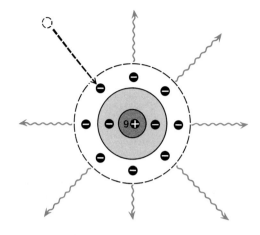

Electron affinity is the energy given off when an electron is added to a neutral atom.

Electronegativities for the first ten elements are represented by color tints, with the Pauling values superimposed. Electronegativity values are not assigned to helium and neon because they neither gain nor lose electrons in interactions with other atoms.

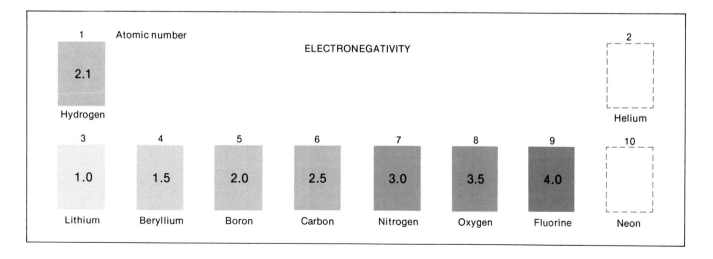

ELECTRONEGATIVITY

Atomic number							
1							2
2.1							
Hydrogen							Helium
3	4	5	6	7	8	9	10
1.0	1.5	2.0	2.5	3.0	3.5	4.0	
Lithium	Beryllium	Boron	Carbon	Nitrogen	Oxygen	Fluorine	Neon

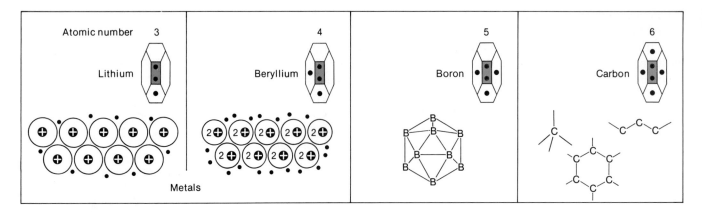

Atomic number 3	4	5	6
Lithium	Beryllium	Boron	Carbon

Metals

Lithium and beryllium share their outer electrons with many other atoms in a metal, boron and carbon make single electron-pair bonds with several other atoms in solids, and nitrogen, oxygen, and fluorine share electrons with a single neighbor in diatomic gas molecules. Neon stands alone as a monatomic gas.

pound LiF, the electrons will be seized almost entirely by the F atoms, forming Li$^+$ and F$^-$ ions in a salt, as described previously. LiF is said to be held together by *ionic* bonds. Pure ionic and pure covalent bonds are extreme types of bonds; most real bonds are somewhere in between. The type of bond that will be formed between atoms depends entirely on their relative electronegativities, or electron-pulling power, as in the HF bond at the left. For this reason, electronegativity is the most important single concept in predicting the nature of chemical bonds.

FILLED SHELLS AND THE RULE OF EIGHT: A SUMMARY

The theme of this chapter has been the special stability of a closed inner shell of two electrons, and of a filled second shell of eight electrons. Atoms such as lithium, which have only a few electrons outside the inner shell, will lose them easily and show a low electronegativity. In contrast, O and F, which lack only one or two electrons of completing the second shell, will attract electrons and show a high electronegativity. Electronegativity describes in relative terms how bonded atoms will compete for electrons.

Covalent and ionic bonds are extreme types, with most actual bonds being intermediate in character. Whether a bond is described as mainly covalent or mainly ionic depends on whether the electron pair of the bond is shared more or less equally between atoms, or is pulled sharply toward one of them. When like atoms are bonded, whether the bond is unlocalized and metallic (as in Li, as discussed previously), or localized as an electron pair shared between two particular atoms, depends on how tightly the atoms normally hold electrons. The bonding in the pure second-row elements is shown in the table across the top of these two pages. The next chapter will be con-

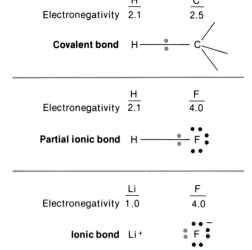

Hydrogen and carbon have similar electronegativities and form a shared electron-pair bond. In hydrogen fluoride the electronegativities are more different, and the electron pair of the bond is drawn to the more electronegative fluorine atom. The bond is said to be *polar*. Electronegativities of lithium and fluorine are so different that an electron is taken from a lithium atom by a fluorine atom to form Li$^+$ and F$^-$ ions.

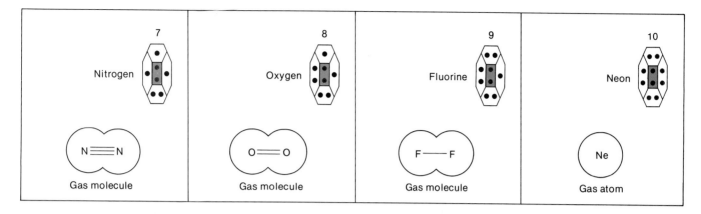

Nitrogen 7	Oxygen 8	Fluorine 9	Neon 10
N≡N	O=O	F—F	Ne
Gas molecule	Gas molecule	Gas molecule	Gas atom

cerned with covalent bonds between atoms of similar electronegativities. Chapter 5 will be devoted to ionic bonds between atoms of quite different electronegativities.

The second electron shell is not the end of the road for atom building. In Chapter 6 we will see a third electron shell, again capable of holding eight outer electrons. Elements of atomic number 11 through 18 show chemical properties very similar to elements 3 through 10 that have corresponding numbers of outer electrons, because it is these outer electrons that react with other atoms, and thus give each atom its distinctive chemical properties. This recurrence of chemical properties whenever the same outer electron-shell arrangement is encountered is called periodicity of behavior, and is most easily understood with the help of a *periodic table*. The beginning of such a table is shown below, with each electron shell represented by a horizontal row of elements.

Finally, in Chapters 7 and 8 we shall see the theoretical reasons for shell structure, the periodic repetition of chemical properties, and the structure of the periodic table. Although the full story will turn out to be more complicated, eight is a "magic number" for these simple atoms because of their electronic structures.

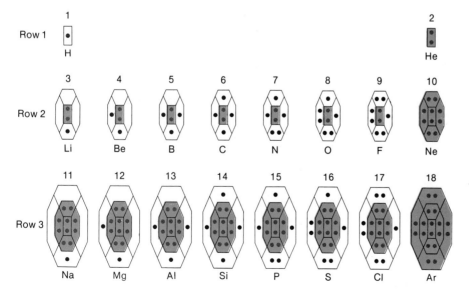

PERIODICITY OF BEHAVIOR. The two elements, H and He, with electrons only in the inner shell, make up the first row of the *periodic table* of the elements. The eight second-shell elements form a second row, and eight third-shell elements, to be discussed in Chapter 6, make up yet a third row of the table. Elements in the same vertical column have the same number of electrons in their outermost shell, and thus have similar chemical properties. Outer electron shells being filled are uncolored. The filled inner shells of Rows 1, 2, and 3 are in color.

QUESTIONS

1. How are the second-shell atoms "built up" one after the other from lithium to neon?

2. Why are the second-shell atoms larger than hydrogen and helium?

3. Why do the second-shell atoms decrease in size from lithium to neon?

4. Which of the second-shell elements are metals, and which are non-metals? Do the metals have a nearly empty second shell, or a nearly full second shell?

5. How many electrons can be accommodated in the second shell? What element has this shell completely filled? Which first-shell element does it resemble in chemical behavior? What chemical behavior is characteristic of these two elements?

6. Which of the pure elements in the second-shell series are solids at room temperature, which are liquids, and which are gases?

7. Which of the gases among the second-shell elements are diatomic like H_2, and which are monatomic like He?

8. What is the difference between the covalent radius and the non-bonded or packing radius of an atom?

9. What is "ionization" of an atom? How many electrons will an atom of lithium give up easily? How many will beryllium give up when it ionizes? How many will boron give up? What do these numbers tell us about electron-shell structure?

10. Why does carbon not ionize in its ordinary chemical reactions? If it did, what would be the charge on the ion, following the principle implied in the preceding question? What do carbon atoms do instead of ionizing?

11. Does a fluorine atom gain, or lose, electrons when it ionizes? Why? How many electrons are gained or lost when an oxygen atom forms an oxide ion? What neutral atom has the same number of electrons as these ions?

12. What is the difference between ionization energy and electron affinity? Could you think of the first ionization energy of the lithium atom as the electron affinity of the Li^+ ion? Is energy absorbed, or given off, when Li^0 adds an electron? When Li^+ adds an electron?

13. What is a calorie, and what does it measure? What is a kilocalorie?

14. A reasonable intake of food for an average human being per day is 2000 kilocalories. A 176-pound man weighs approximately 80 kilograms. If we consider the man to be essentially water (not a bad first approximation), and he used his entire food intake as a source of heat, by how much would his temperature be raised?

15. Why is the first ionization energy higher for first-shell elements (H and He) than for the second-shell elements?

16. Why does the first ionization energy generally increase from lithium to neon?

17. Why would you expect a sudden and dramatic increase between the fourth and fifth ionization energies of carbon? What does this tell you about the reality of the shell model of the atom?

18. How does bonding in a metal differ from that between atoms in the water molecule?

19. Why do carbon atoms neither attain a He-shell configuration by losing their four outer electrons, nor achieve a Ne configuration by gaining four more electrons? How are electrons in carbon usually involved in chemical bonding?

20. Why is lithium a softer metal than beryllium?

21. Why should electronegativity increase from Li to F? Why is Ne assigned no electronegativity?

22. How do electronegativities affect the nature of chemical bonds? What kind of bond would you expect between carbon and nitrogen? Between lithium and oxygen?

PROBLEMS

1. If covalent bond radii are additive, what should the distance between centers of carbon and hydrogen atoms be in methane, CH_4? This distance is called the carbon–hydrogen single bond length.

2. What should the carbon–oxygen and oxygen–hydrogen bond lengths be in methanol, or methyl alcohol, which has the bonding structure

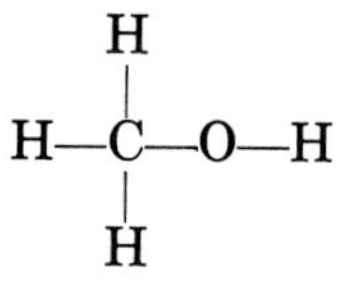

$$
\begin{array}{c}
\text{H} \\
| \\
\text{H---C---O---H} \\
| \\
\text{H}
\end{array}
$$

3. Lithium atoms in the metal are packed together in such a way that they take up 68% of the available volume, with the rest being empty space between atoms. Therefore an atom of actual volume $V = 4/3\ \pi r^3$, in which r is the atomic radius, would account for $V' = V/0.68$ of crystal volume per atom. From the crystal volume per atom calculated for lithium in the text, calculate the actual radius of a lithium atom in the metal. How does this compare with the rough figure arrived at in the text, and with the tabulated metallic radius for lithium seen previously in the chapter?

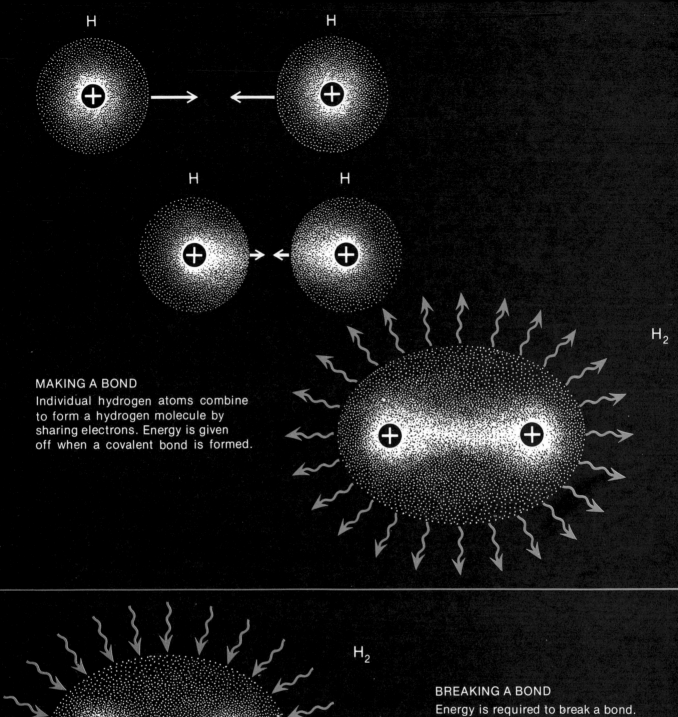

MAKING A BOND
Individual hydrogen atoms combine to form a hydrogen molecule by sharing electrons. Energy is given off when a covalent bond is formed.

H₂

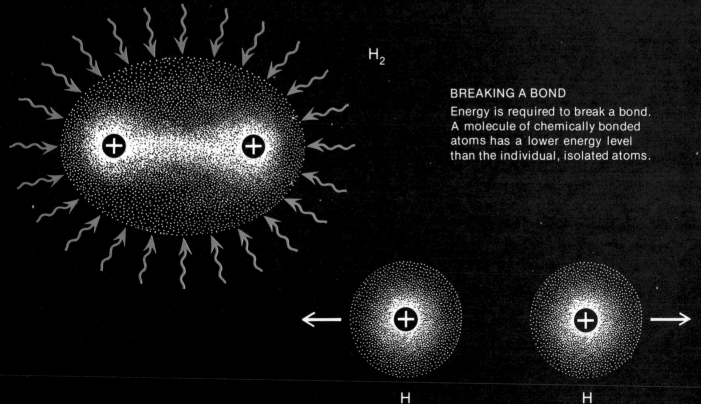

H₂

BREAKING A BOND
Energy is required to break a bond. A molecule of chemically bonded atoms has a lower energy level than the individual, isolated atoms.

CHAPTER 4

Electron Sharing and Covalent Bonds

What is a covalent chemical bond? In a simple wooden model, two balls representing atoms are connected by a stick symbolizing the bond. What is the "stick" that holds the atoms together in a real molecule? How does a pair of electrons keep two atoms from flying apart? Just as important, how many bonds can a particular type of atom form with other atoms, and in what directions in space? Only when we can answer these questions can we understand how molecules are constructed and how they behave.

As we saw with the H_2 molecule in Chapter 2, a bond between two atoms is formed by the sharing of a pair of electrons between the atoms. This is illustrated on the facing page. The bonding pair of electrons spends most of its time between the two atomic nuclei, thereby screening the positive charges from one another and enabling the nuclei to come closer together than if the bonding electrons were absent. The negative charge on the electron pair attracts both nuclei and holds them together in a bond.

Just as the hydrogen atom is represented by a Lewis diagram consisting of the atomic symbol plus a dot for the electron, $H \cdot$, the H_2 molecule can be written as two atomic symbols separated by a pair of dots for the bonding electrons, $H:H$ (right). A more common practice is to replace the dots by a straight line connecting the bonded atoms, $H—H$, but you should remember that this straight line represents a bonding pair of electrons.

From an energy standpoint, when we say two atoms are chemically bonded we mean that the two atoms close together have less energy and therefore are more stable than when separated. Energy is given off when atoms form a bond, and energy must be supplied to pull them apart:

$$\underset{\text{hydrogen atoms}}{H + H} \quad \rightarrow \quad \underset{\text{hydrogen molecule}}{H_2} \qquad \text{(energy is given off)}$$

$$H_2 \rightarrow H + H \qquad \text{(energy must be added)}$$

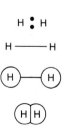

Four representations of the covalent bond in the hydrogen molecule

45

To tear apart one mole of H_2 molecules into two moles of H atoms requires 103.24 kcal of energy; thus we say that the bond energy of the H—H bond is 103.24 kcal mole^{-1}. We can represent H_2 molecules and H atoms on an energy-level diagram as at the bottom of the page, where the vertical direction symbolizes increasing energy (and less stability). When we tear H_2 molecules apart, we store energy in the atoms in the same way that we store potential energy in a boulder when we roll it uphill. This energy is released when the atoms form a bond, or when the boulder rolls downhill.

HOW MANY BONDS PER ATOM?

In general, the second-shell nonmetal atoms, C, N, O, and F, make covalent bonds by sharing electrons in pairs with other atoms of similar electronegativity. As you would expect from electronegativity values, C—H bonds are almost purely covalent, or electron-sharing, whereas at the opposite extreme, H—F bonds have a large ionic character, with the electrons drawn toward the F atom. If each of two atoms contributes one electron to a covalent bond, then because the bonded atoms are held close to one another, both electrons help to fill the outer shell of each atom. An atom may form several covalent bonds, in which case it acquires one new outer electron for every bond it makes.

In the most common bonding behavior, an atom makes as many covalent bonds as are needed to fill its outer shell with eight electrons.

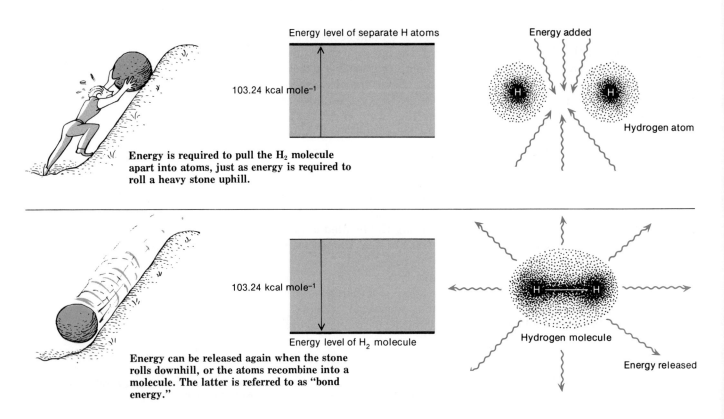

Energy level of separate H atoms

103.24 kcal mole^{-1}

Energy is required to pull the H_2 molecule apart into atoms, just as energy is required to roll a heavy stone uphill.

Energy added

Hydrogen atom

103.24 kcal mole^{-1}

Energy level of H_2 molecule

Energy can be released again when the stone rolls downhill, or the atoms recombine into a molecule. The latter is referred to as "bond energy."

Hydrogen molecule

Energy released

For atoms of C, N, O, and F, this means 4, 3, 2, and 1 electrons, respectively. If these elements are bonded to hydrogen, we find the expected CH_4 methane molecule, NH_3 for ammonia, H_2O for water, and HF for the hydrogen fluoride molecule. Another way of looking at the bonding behavior is to say that each of the *unpaired* electrons in C, N, O, and F is available for pairing in a covalent bond. The pair of electrons in the N atom, the two electron pairs in O, and the three pairs in the F atom do not need to find outside electrons to interact with because they already *are* paired. They are called *lone pairs* to distinguish them from the electron pairs of a chemical bond, which are called *bonding pairs*. These lone pairs and bonding pairs for the simple molecules mentioned previously are illustrated in the table below.

It is sometimes possible to unpair all of the electrons in the outer shell of a second-shell atom and to use them all in bonding. For example, in the nitric acid molecule, which we shall discuss in the following chapter, we must assume that nitrogen shares five electrons with oxygen atoms, not just three. This unpairing of electrons is easier to accomplish with the third-shell atoms, where the electrons are farther from the nucleus and thus more weakly held, and where the atoms are larger so that more atoms can crowd around for bonding. For the moment, however, we need only consider nitrogen, which has one lone pair and three unpaired bonding electrons.

To illustrate these ideas of electron-pair bonding, and to introduce the ideas of molecular shape and of double and triple bonds, let us look at the simplest covalent molecules of C, N, O, and F.

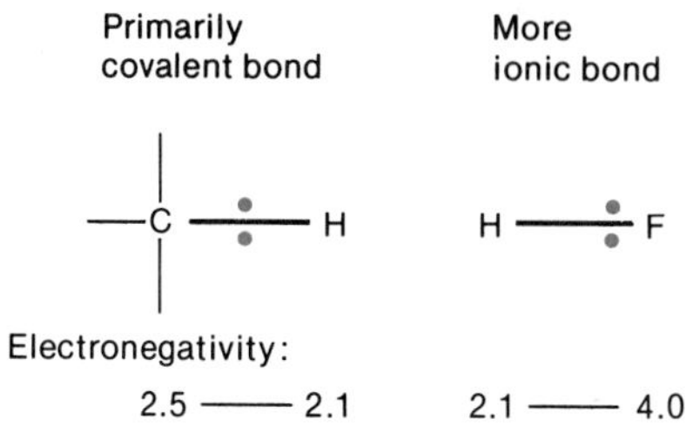

The larger the difference in electronegativities between two bonded atoms, the more of an ionic character the bond between them will have.

The second-row nonmetals make enough covalent bonds with hydrogen atoms to complete their outer shell with eight electrons.

	Carbon	Nitrogen	Oxygen	Fluorine	Neon
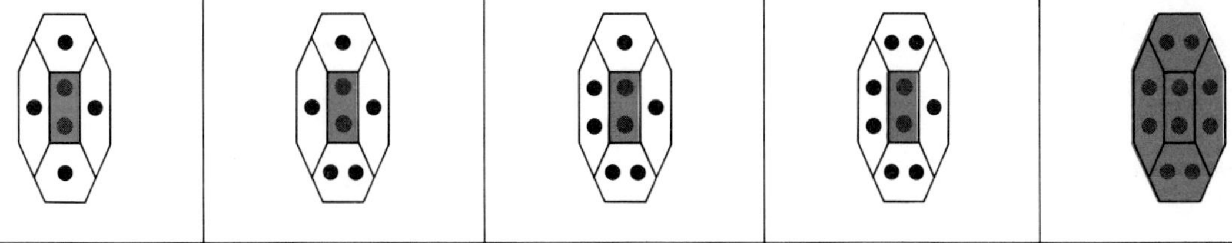					
Outer-shell electrons	• C •	• N •	• O •	• F •	• Ne •
Unpaired electrons (color)	• C • (4)	• N • (3)	• O • (2)	• F • (1)	• Ne • (0)
Bonds	H—C—H with H top and bottom	H—N—H with H top	O—H with H top	H—F	No bonding
Molecule	Methane CH_4	Ammonia NH_3	Water H_2O	Hydrogen fluoride HF	No molecule

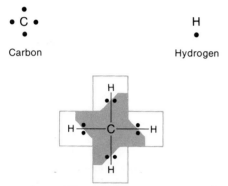

BONDING IN METHANE

Carbon

Hydrogen

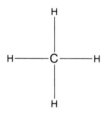

Methane, CH₄, with electrons represented as Lewis dots

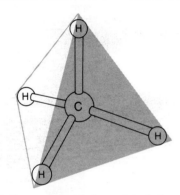

Methane represented with stick bonds

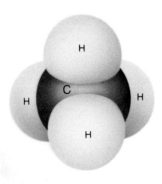

Methane represented as a tetrahedron in three dimensions

Methane represented as four space-filling hydrogen atoms bonded to a central carbon atom. If we could actually see a methane molecule, this is probably how it would look.

CARBON COMPOUNDS

Carbon has four outer electrons, and thus can complete its eight-electron "neon" shell by sharing electrons in four covalent bonds. The simplest carbon compound is methane, CH_4. The methane molecule is diagramed at the left, first with Lewis electron pairs, then with stick bonds, and finally in a representation of the actual tetrahedral shape of the molecule.

The four hydrogen atoms in methane are at the four corners of a tetrahedron with the carbon atom at the center. All of the atoms are as far from one another as they can be, given a fixed C—H distance. This is a general principle: The four electron pairs around a central atom such as a carbon atom repel one another as all negative charges do, and the lowest energy state is that with the four bonds directed tetrahedrally away from the central atom. Any other arrangement of C—H bonds in methane would bring two bonding pairs closer together, and electrostatic repulsion would push them apart again. This very simple but useful way of predicting molecular shapes has been given the grandiose name of the *valence-shell electron-pair repulsion* theory, or VSEPR theory, but essentially it is nothing more than common sense. We shall develop simple VSEPR theory as it is needed, and will find that this theory accounts for almost all of the observed geometries of molecules.

The electronegativities of carbon and hydrogen are almost the same, 2.5 and 2.1, respectively. Electrons in the C—H bonds are shared

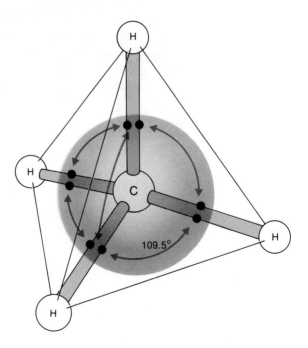

The valence-shell electron-pair repulsion (VSEPR) theory states that the four pairs of electrons in methane repel each other equally, placing the hydrogen atoms at the four corners of a tetrahedron.

48

almost equally by the two atoms, with little tendency to shift toward either C or H. The bonds are said to be *nonpolar*, because there is no accumulation of positive charge at one end and negative charge at the other caused by the movement of the bonding electron pair toward one atom. In contrast, the bond in H—F is quite polar because the high electronegativity of F pulls the bonding electron pair toward F, leaving the molecule with a positive charge on the H atom and a negative charge on the F atom.

Most of the forces between molecules are electrostatic, caused by attractions between the positive and negative charges on different parts of the molecule. Methane has no such charges, and hence has little tendency for two molecules to stick together. The only attractions between molecules are the weak van der Waals forces mentioned previously for H_2 and He. These attractions arise because, although an atom in a molecule may be electrically nonpolar on the average over a finite period of time, at any given instant the electrons may not be distributed symmetrically around the nucleus. This is illustrated for three atoms at the right. The first drawing shows the time average, with a symmetrical distribution of electrons around each nucleus. The following three drawings show "snapshots" of the atoms at three instants in time when the random motion of electrons has brought about short-lived attractions between atoms A and B, B and C, and A and C. These attractions may seem small, but they are not insignificant. They are the forces between atoms in neighboring methane molecules that make methane gas finally condense to a liquid at $-164°C$. The strengths of van der Waals forces depend mainly on surface areas of molecules. Hence gaseous H_2 molecules, which are smaller than CH_4 molecules, must be cooled to $-253°C$ before they move slowly enough that van der Waals attractions can make them stick to one another in a liquid.

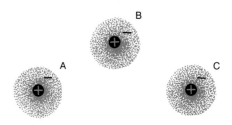

Three nonbonded atoms, A, B, and C. The concentration of negative charge at any instant in time is indicated by the density of stippling.

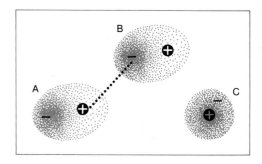

Instant 1: A and B are attracted momentarily to each other because of fluctuations in the electron distribution around them. (Note the off-center electron-density stippling.)

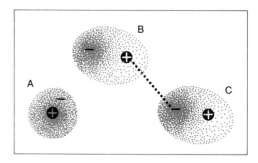

Instant 2: B and C are attracted momentarily to each other.

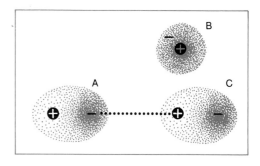

Instant 3: A and C are attracted momentarily to each other.

These fluctuating attractive forces add up to a physical reality shown at the left.

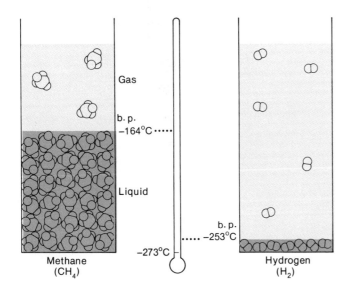

The boiling points of methane and hydrogen are related to the sizes of the molecules. Methane, with a larger surface area than hydrogen, is "stickier" and condenses to a liquid at a higher temperature.

HYDROCARBONS

Hydrocarbons are straight and branched chain polymers of C and H. The lighter molecules are gases at room temperature; the heavier gasolines and oils are liquids, and the paraffin waxes are solids. The attractions between hydrocarbon molecules are van der Waals forces.

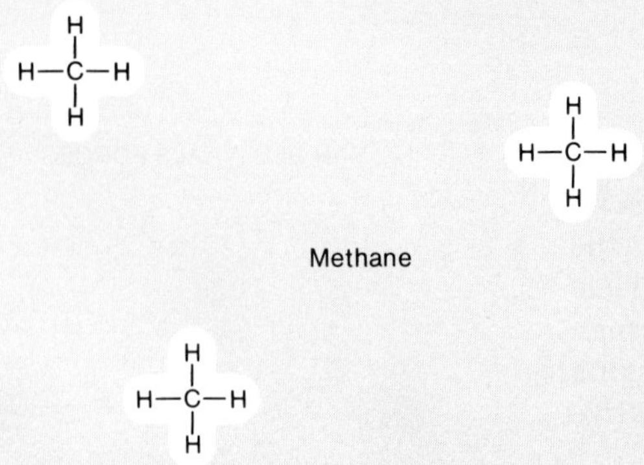

Methane

GASES

Methane, ethane, propane, butane, and pentane, with from one to five carbons.

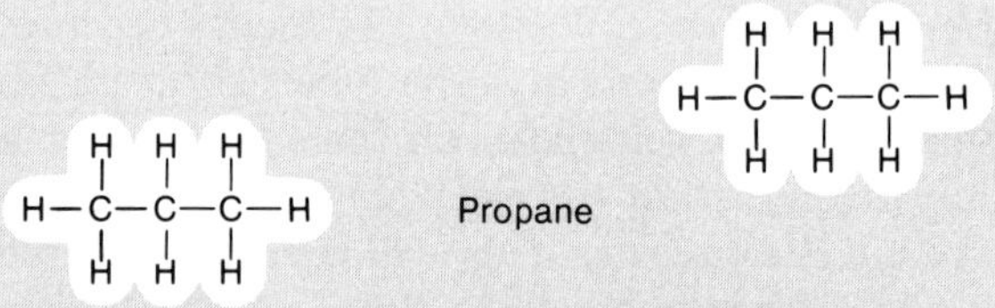

Propane

LIQUIDS

Gasolines are hydrocarbons with six to nine carbon atoms; kerosenes have ten to sixteen carbons, and lubricating oils have up to nineteen or twenty.

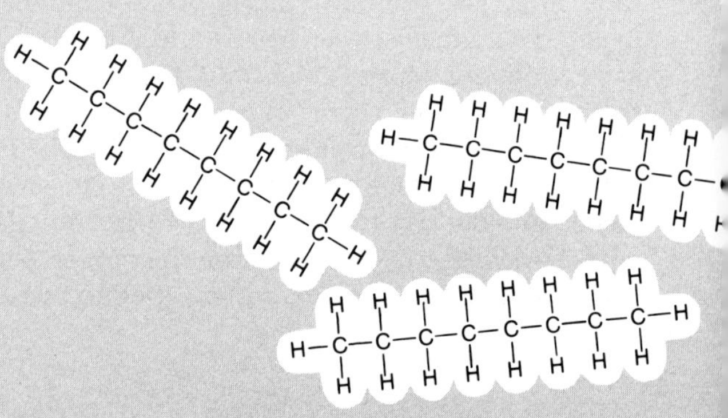

Octane gasoline

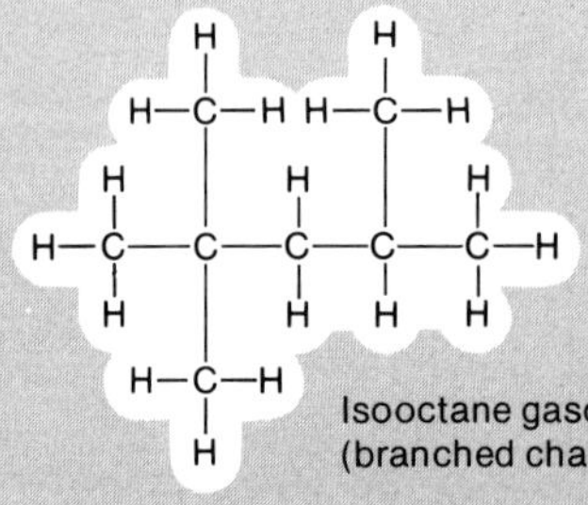

Isooctane gasoline
(branched chain)

SOLIDS

Chains with twenty or more carbon atoms are paraffin waxes.

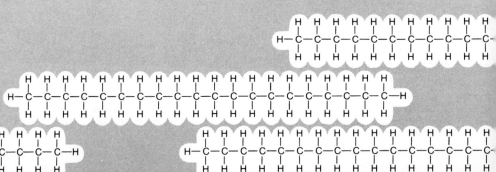

One of the most important properties of carbon is that it can make strong electron-pair bonds with other carbon atoms. A C—C bond is nearly as strong as a C—H bond (83 kcal mole^{-1} versus 99 kcal mole^{-1}). Virtually endless carbon chains thus are possible, as well as branched chains of the type shown at the left. Straight- and branched-chain compounds of C and H are called *hydrocarbons*, of which propane gas, gasoline, motor oil, paraffin wax, and polyethylene plastic are familiar examples. Chapters 19 through 21 will be devoted entirely to carbon compounds, and will be the bridge into the chemistry of living organisms. These simple hydrocarbons are built from chains of linked carbon tetrahedra, with the general formula CH_3—CH_2—CH_2—···—CH_2—CH_3. The smaller hydrocarbons such as propane, CH_3—CH_2—CH_3, have such weak van der Waals forces between molecules that they are gases at room temperature. Gasolines, with six to nine carbon atoms in a chain, have sufficiently large surface areas and strong enough van der Waals attractions that they are liquids. Paraffin waxes with 20 or more carbons per chain are solids, and at the extreme limit of several thousand carbon atoms per chain we find the tough and chemically unreactive polyethylene plastic, familiar to us in lightweight water bottles for hikers and acid-resistant laboratory beakers.

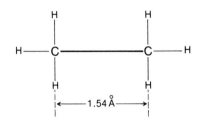

Ethane has a single bond between carbon atoms, with a bond length of 1.54 angstroms (Å).

DOUBLE AND TRIPLE BONDS

Carbon and the other second-shell nonmetals, except fluorine, have another very special property: they can share more than one electron pair with the same neighbor atom, thereby creating double and triple bonds. Ethane (top right) is a two-carbon compound with only single electron-pair bonds: H_3C—CH_3. Ethylene, H_2C=CH_2, is a two-carbon compound with a double bond between the carbon atoms (middle right). Each carbon atom still shares four electron pairs, but with only three neighbors in ethylene instead of four as in ethane. In acetylene, H—C≡C—H, the carbon atoms are bound together by three electron pairs in a triple bond (bottom right). For reasons that will become apparent in Chapter 9, two carbon atoms cannot share four electron pairs in a quadruple bond.

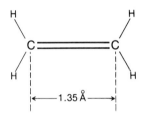

Ethylene has a double bond between carbons, of length 1.35 Å.

Two atoms must come closer together to share the second electron pair than they do to share the first. Singly bonded carbon atoms are 1.54 Å apart no matter where they are found, but carbon atoms in a double bond are only 1.35 Å apart. The limit of sharing is a triple bond with three electron pairs shared between carbon atoms only 1.21 Å apart. This ability to make multiple bonds also is found in the second-shell nonmetals N and O, and as we shall see in the latter chapters of this book, double bonding is important in determining the geometry and energy-trapping properties of key biological molecules. Except for special circumstances, the larger third-shell atoms, which we shall discuss in Chapter 6, cannot get close enough to one another to make multiple bonds. This flaw, alone, would be enough to rule them out as candidates for a chemistry of life.

A special kind of multiple bonding, which we will learn later is vital in energy-trapping molecules such as chlorophyll, is illustrated by

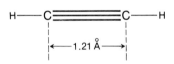

Acetylene has a triple bond between carbons, 1.21 Å in length. The bond length shortens as the strength of the bond increases.

BENZENE

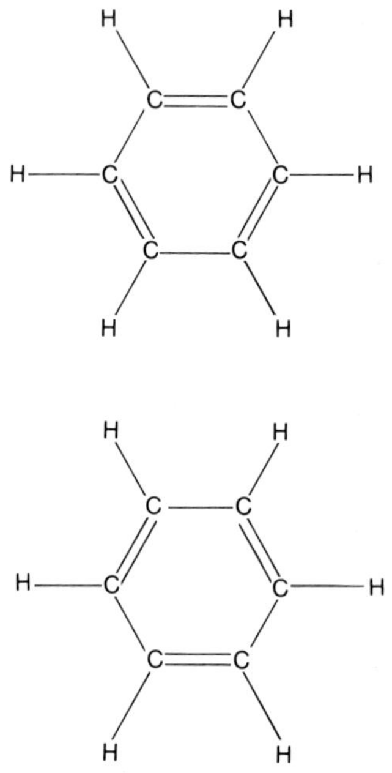

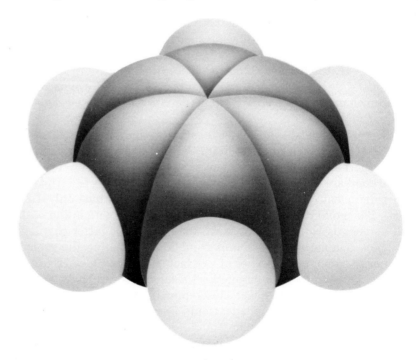

Two possible arrangements of alternating single and double bonds around the benzene ring. These are called Kekulé structures, after the man who first suggested them in 1865.

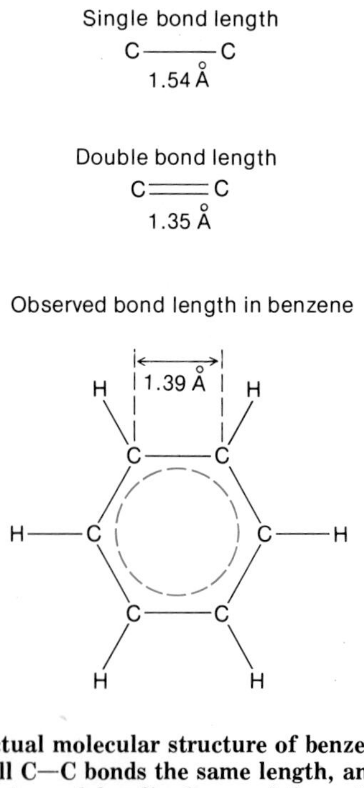

Single bond length
C————C
1.54 Å

Double bond length
C=C
1.35 Å

Observed bond length in benzene

H |← 1.39 Å →| H
C———C
H——C   C——H
C———C
H   H

The actual molecular structure of benzene, with all C—C bonds the same length, and with six electrons delocalized around the entire ring

benzene, C_6H_6. As indicated below, the six carbon atoms in benzene are linked into a hexagon, with each carbon atom bonded to two other carbon atoms and one hydrogen atom. This leaves each of the six carbon atoms with one additional electron, and these six electrons are the raw materials for three more electron-pair bonds. One way of picturing these bonds would be an alternation of single bonds and double bonds around the hexagon, as shown in the left margin. This would imply an alternation of long and short C—C bonds around the ring, yet every physical measurement that we can carry out on benzene suggests that all of the C—C bonds are alike.

The six leftover carbon electrons in benzene are not tied up in three double bonds. Instead, all six electrons are completely spread out or *delocalized* around the carbon ring. Every C—C bond is approximately a "one-and-a-half bond," as is suggested by the observed bond length of 1.39 Å, which is intermediate between a single bond, 1.54 Å, and a double bond, 1.35 Å. One consequence of this delocalization or "spreading out" of the six leftover electrons is that the benzene molecule is 40 kcal mole^{-1} lower in energy, or more stable, than would be calculated from the alternating bond models at the upper left and from known C—C and C=C bond energies. This is an important general principle: Whenever electrons are delocalized in a molecule, the molecule becomes more stable. Delocalization is possible whenever single and double bonds alternate along a chain:

$$—C=C—C=C—C=C—\quad C=C—C=C—C=C—$$

whether the chain is linear or is bent into a closed ring as in benzene. Such alternating-bond molecules are called *conjugated* molecules, and some rings with alternating single and double bonds, such as benzene,

Space-filling model of the benzene molecule, as it would appear if we could actually see it

52

are *aromatic* molecules. (The name originally referred to their odor, but now denotes their electronic behavior.) Conjugated molecules such as chlorophyll and carotene, as we shall see in Chapter 19, are used in trapping light energy in plants, and as photoreceptors in the eye. In a sense we even can think of the stability of the H—H bond in a H_2 molecule as arising from delocalization: Two electrons, each of which were confined to the vicinity of one H nucleus in the atoms, become delocalized and spread over two nuclei in the H_2 molecule, although the electrons are concentrated between the nuclei. The extra stability brought about by this delocalization is part of the strength of the H—H bond.

DIAMOND AND GRAPHITE

In the simple, single-bonded hydrocarbons discussed previously, some of the four tetrahedrally arranged atoms around each carbon are hydrogen atoms and some are carbon atoms. One can imagine a three-dimensional tetrahedral framework in which all of the atoms are carbons and no hydrogens are present. The result would be the tetrahedral structure shown below, with each carbon atom connected to four other carbon atoms by single electron-pair bonds. This is the structure of *diamond*. Diamond is very hard and rigid because any breaking off or deforming of part of the diamond structure requires a breaking or stretching of strong electron-pair bonds. In contrast, paraffin wax has linear chains of carbon atoms, but only weak van der Waals forces to hold the molecules together. If subjected to external stress, the molecules slip past one another to new positions. Wax is soft because the van der Waals forces are weak; diamond is hard because the electron-pair bonds in its three-dimensional network are strong.

Diamond can be made from carbon atoms only under special conditions of high temperature and pressure. Artificial diamond-making

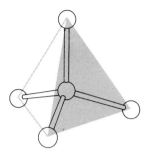

DIAMOND STRUCTURE

In diamond each carbon atom is covalently bonded to four others, making a tetrahedron.

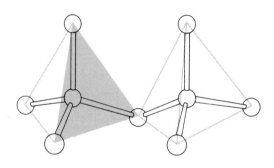

These tetrahedra are linked together by sharing carbon atoms at the corners · · ·

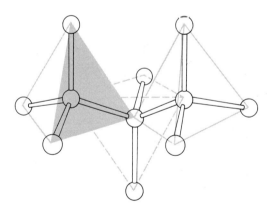

· · · and interlocked to form the hard, pure carbon crystals known as diamond.

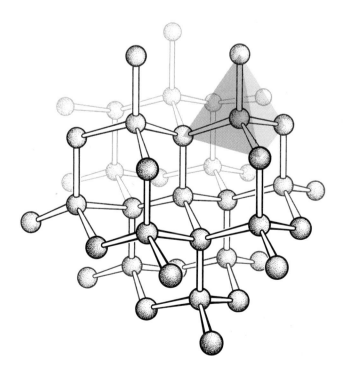

In a sense, a diamond crystal is really one large, nearly infinite molecule of carbon, with the structure at the left. The tetrahedral unit is shown in color.

CARBON   GRAPHITE

In graphite, each carbon atom makes three single bonds to other carbon atoms, leaving one electron free as in the benzene ring (below).

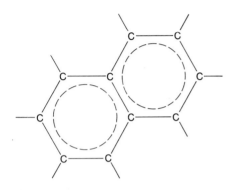

These extra electrons are then free to move about over the entire plane of hexagons. Graphite is an extended form of planar benzene (below) in the same sense that diamond is an extended form of tetrahedral methane or ethane. The individual planes of graphite are held together only by van der Waals forces and are free to slip past one another easily. This makes graphite a good lubricant.

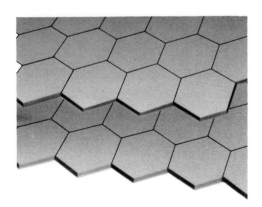

in the laboratory is a recent art, and still inferior to the natural subterranean processes. An easier form of pure carbon to obtain is *graphite*, which has the structure shown at the left. In graphite the carbon atoms are arranged in layers of hexagons, with each atom bonded to three others. Each carbon atom has one leftover electron, as in benzene. These electrons are delocalized and are free to move about within one layer of atoms. This helps to make graphite more stable. It also allows graphite to conduct electricity, but only along the separate planes of hexagons. The electrons cannot jump from one layer to another. In effect, graphite is a "two-dimensional metal." The layers themselves are held together only by van der Waals forces, and are relatively free to slip past one another. It is this slippage of layers that makes powdered graphite a good lubricant.

NITROGEN AND AMMONIA

Nitrogen has five electrons in its outer shell: one lone electron pair and three unpaired electrons that are available for bonding. Its Lewis diagram is shown below. In the simplest nitrogen compound, ammonia (NH_3), these three bonding electrons each are paired with one electron from a hydrogen atom. As in methane, the central atom in the ammonia molecule is surrounded by four electron pairs in approximately tetrahedral orientation. There is one critical difference, however, which will lead us to an improvement in the VSEPR theory. The three bonding pairs each are shared between two atoms and hence are attracted by H as well as N. In contrast, the nitrogen lone pair is held only by the N atom. The lone pair is closer to N than the bonding pairs are, and therefore repels the bonding pairs more strongly than would a fourth bonding pair. This extra repulsion by the lone pair pushes the three N—H bonds closer together. In a perfect tetrahedron the H—N—H angles all would be 109.5°, as in methane. In the ammonia molecule the three H—N—H angles are only 107°. The ammonia molecule has the shape of a pyramid with the lone pair at the apex; and the pyramid is slightly steeper than it would have been if the lone pair had not been closer to the N atom.

The electronegativities of H and N are appreciably different: 2.1 and 3.0, respectively. The three H—N bonds therefore are partly ionic,

NITROGEN

 Lone pair

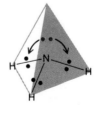

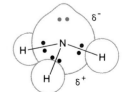

AMMONIA MOLECULE

Nitrogen has three bonding electrons and one lone pair. In the ammonia molecule the lone pair (center) pushes the three N—H bonds closer together than in idealized tetrahedral bonding. Ammonia is a dipolar molecule, with a slight excess of negative charge (δ^-) at the lone pair and of positive charge (δ^+) at the hydrogens (right).

Dipoles

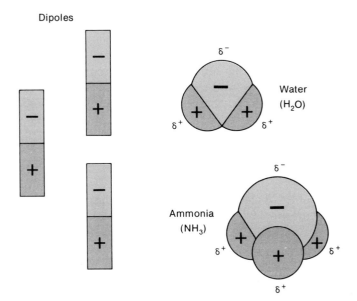

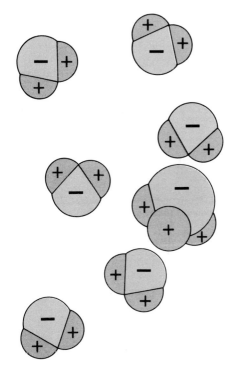

Water and ammonia both are dipolar
molecules, and are attracted to one another.

or polar, with the electrons held more tightly by N than by H. The
charge in the molecule also is asymmetrical, because of the extra electron pair at the apex of the pyramid and three H atoms with an electron
deficiency at the base. This means that there actually exists a small
separation of charge on the molecule: The apex is slightly negative and
the base is slightly positive. Thus the molecule is said to have a tiny
dipole.

A dipole is any object with a separation of electrostatic charge,
positive at one end and negative at the other (bottom right). It is the
electrostatic equivalent of a magnet; and as with magnets, opposite
ends of dipoles attract one another. Water is a liquid at room temperature, and ammonia gas is easily liquefied at $-33°C$, because their molecules are dipoles and are attracted to one another. Methane lacks these
dipole attractions and therefore must be cooled to $-164°C$ before van
der Waals forces cause it to liquefy. Water is a good solvent for other
molecules with dipoles, and for ionic salts, because the charges at the
ends of the water molecules can interact with opposite charges on the
molecules or ions being dissolved.

The force of attraction of a dipolar molecule for another molecule
or ion depends on how much charge is separated and how great the
separation is. The strength of a dipole is measured by its *dipole moment*, μ. If two equal and opposite charges, $+q$ and $-q$, are separated
by a distance r, then the dipole moment is defined as

$$\mu = qr$$

Either doubling the charges, or doubling the separation between them,
has the effect of doubling the strength with which the molecule will attract its neighboring molecules. The dipole moment of a molecule is an
easy quantity to measure and is a useful indication of a molecule's
chemical and physical behavior.

The unit of measure for dipole moments is the debye (abbreviated
D). A proton and an electron held 1 Å apart would constitute a dipole

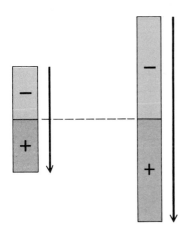

Doubling the charges or doubling the distance
between charges in a dipole doubles its attractive power for other charged or polar objects.

55

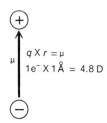

DIPOLE MOMENTS

$$q \times r = \mu$$
$$1e^- \times 1\text{Å} = 4.8\,D$$

A +1 and a −1 charge, one angstrom apart, have a dipole moment of 4.8 debye (D). The dipole moment increases with the size of the separated charges and the distance between them.

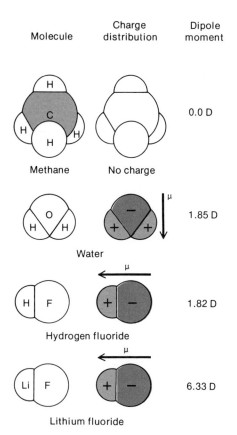

Molecule	Charge distribution	Dipole moment
Methane	No charge	0.0 D
Water		1.85 D
Hydrogen fluoride		1.82 D
Lithium fluoride		6.33 D

The measured dipole moment of a molecule can be converted into percent ionic character of the bonds within the molecule (right). The percent ionic character increases from N—H to O—H to H—F to Li—F because the difference in electronegativities of the atoms bonded also increases, thereby pulling the electron pair more toward one atom than the other.

moment of 4.8 debye. (The 4.8 factor has no deep significance, but merely comes from the size of the charge on an electron.) Methane has no dipole moment, and ammonia has a dipole moment of 1.47 D. Water is slightly more polar, with a dipole moment of 1.85 D. If lithium fluoride salt is vaporized at temperatures above 1676°C, the gaseous LiF molecules have the quite large dipole moment of 6.33 D. In the preceding chapter we said that most real bonds were intermediates between the extremes of completely covalent and totally ionic. Measured dipole moments allow us to calculate the percent of ionic and covalent character of a bond. Since two charges of +1 and −1, located 1.0 Å apart, yield a dipole moment of $\mu = 4.8$ D, we can write

$$\mu = 4.8\ qr$$

with q in units of electron charge and r in angstroms. The atoms in an HF molecule are 0.92 Å apart, and the measured dipole moment is 1.82 D. Hence,

$$1.82 = 4.8 \times 0.92\ q$$

$$q = 0.41 \text{ of the charge on an electron}$$

The measured dipole moment of the HF molecule is what would be found if 41% of a full electron charge were shifted toward the F atom and away from the H by a distance corresponding to the actual H—F distance of 0.92 Å (see below). A purely covalent bond has equal sharing and no dipole moment; and in a purely ionic bond the electron is entirely shifted from one atom to the other. Hence we can say that the HF bond in this example has 41% ionic character and 59% covalent, or electron-sharing, character.

The same calculation tells a different story for gaseous LiF molecules, which are obtained from LiF salt at high temperatures. The dis-

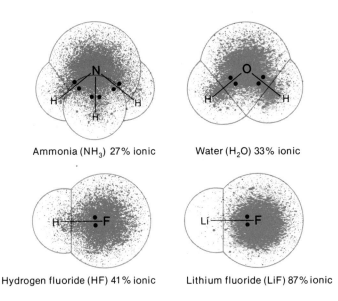

Ammonia (NH₃) 27% ionic   Water (H₂O) 33% ionic

Hydrogen fluoride (HF) 41% ionic   Lithium fluoride (LiF) 87% ionic

The bond in gaseous lithium fluoride, above 1676°C, is 87% ionic and 13% covalent. In the salt at room temperature, transfer of the electron is complete, and the salt is 100% ionic.

56

tance between Li and F atoms is 1.52 Å, and the measured dipole moment is $\mu = 6.33$ D. The magnitude of the charge can be calculated:

$$6.33 = 4.8 \times 1.52\, q$$

$$q = 0.87 \text{ of the charge on an electron}$$

The bond in LiF is 87% ionic and only 13% covalent.

Similar calculations can be carried out for H_2O and NH_3, but they are complicated by the fact that two or three individually polar bonds are pointing in different directions. What is measured for the whole molecule is their vector sum. In calculating the dipole moment of an entire molecule, one can add the individual dipole moments of the polar bonds as if they were small vectors, of length proportional to the dipole moments, and pointing from the negative ends of the bonds to the positive ends, as shown at the right. When the geometry of the molecule is taken into account correctly, the conclusion is that the H—F bond in HF is 41% ionic, the O—H bond in water is 33% ionic, and the N—H bond in ammonia is 27% ionic. This agrees with what one would expect from the decrease in electronegativities found in going from F to O to N. We can obtain no information from dipole moments about the polarity of the C—H bond in a methane molecule, because the four tetrahedrally arranged C—H bonds would add up to a net molecular dipole moment of zero, even if the individual bonds had a large dipole moment.

Nitrogen cannot make long chains in the way that carbon can, for two reasons. The lone electron pairs on adjacent nitrogen atoms in a —N—N—N—N— chain repel one another more strongly than bonding pairs in the C—H bonds of hydrocarbons do. This weakens the N—N bond and makes it only half as strong as a C—C bond. The second factor is the great stability of the pieces of the ruptured chain, N_2 molecules. Nitrogen has three unpaired electrons for bonding, and it can share all three with a neighboring atom to produce the N≡N molecule shown at the lower right. Pure nitrogen therefore is a diatomic gas, N_2, similar to H_2. Because the triple bond is quite strong, N_2 is a stable and relatively unreactive molecule. If "quadruple bonds" were possible, with four electron pairs shared between two atoms, then perhaps carbon also would be a diatomic gas, C_2. But this is not possible, so carbon bonds to more than one neighbor and forms the three-dimensional structures of graphite and diamond. The sudden change in properties between solid diamond and gaseous nitrogen is one of the most dramatic among the chemical elements. The weakness of long —N—N—N—N— chains and the stability of the triple-bonded N_2 molecules both make long-chain nitrogen compounds explosively unstable. A few of the shorter ones have been synthesized. Hydrazine, H_2N—NH_2, is a good rocket fuel, but the longer chain compounds are too dangerous to handle.

If nitrogen atoms are separated by carbon atoms in chains, then the nitrogen lone pairs do not repel significantly, and the chain is stable. Many important organic and biological molecules are built from mixed chains of carbon and nitrogen. Proteins, for example, have a backbone of

$$—C—C—N—C—C—N—C—C—N—C—C—N—$$

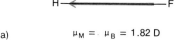
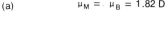

(a) $\mu_M = \mu_B = 1.82$ D

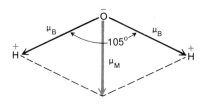

(b) $\mu_M = 2\mu_B \cos\left(\dfrac{105°}{2}\right)$

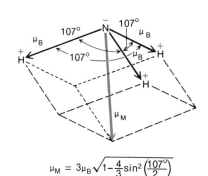

(c) $\mu_M = 3\mu_B \sqrt{1 - \dfrac{4}{3}\sin^2\left(\dfrac{107°}{2}\right)}$

The molecular dipole moment is the sum of the individual bond dipole moments, added together with regard for their direction as well as their magnitude—that is, as vectors. (a) HF, (b) H_2O, and (c) NH_3. The bond moment, μ_B, and molecular moment, μ_M, are identical for HF, and the relationship between them is easy for H_2O. Can you use geometry to verify the relationship between μ_B and μ_M for NH_3?

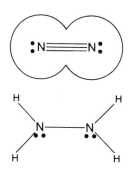

The N_2 molecule is exceptionally stable because of the triple bond between atoms. Chains of nitrogen atoms such as in hydrazine, H_2N—NH_2, are quite unstable, making them useful as rocket fuels.

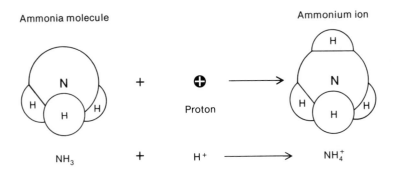

Ammonia molecule

+

Proton

→

Ammonium ion

NH₃ + H⁺ ⟶ NH₄⁺

The lone pair of the ammonia molecule can furnish both electrons for a covalent bond with a proton, which has no electrons. The result is the ammonium ion, NH₄⁺. All four N—H bonds in the ammonium ion are identical.

Nitrogen atoms also make double bonds with carbon and oxygen quite readily.

The lone electron pair on nitrogen also is available for making a covalent bond in which it supplies both of the electrons. An ammonia molecule can bind another proton (H⁺) and become an ammonium ion, NH₄⁺, by the reaction shown above. The positively charged H⁺ ion, or proton, is attracted to the lone pair at the negative end of the ammonia dipole. The covalent bond formed is then completely indistinguishable from the other three N—H bonds. The ammonium ion is a regular tetrahedron with 109.5° H—N—H angles all around. Thus it has the same arrangement of atom centers and electrons as the methane molecule. If by some magic one could reach into the nitrogen nucleus in an NH₄⁺ ion and turn off the charge on one proton, the result would be a methane molecule. The sole but crucial difference is that the ammonium ion has one more proton in the nucleus of the central atom and hence an overall charge of +1. We will come back to the chemical significance of this after we have discussed oxygen and its hydrogen compound, water.

The methane molecule and the ammonium ion are identical except for the charges on their nuclei. They have the same number and arrangement of electrons holding together atoms in the same tetrahedral geometry. The methane molecule is electrostatically neutral, but the ammonium ion has a +1 charge; therein lies their great difference in chemical properties.

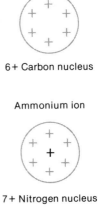

Methane

6+ Carbon nucleus

Ammonium ion

7+ Nitrogen nucleus

ISOELECTRONIC MOLECULES

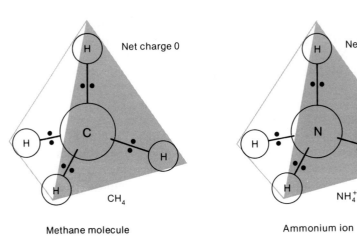

Net charge 0

CH₄

Methane molecule

Net charge +1

NH₄⁺

Ammonium ion

OXYGEN AND WATER

The crust of the Earth is 60% oxygen (atomic percent), in combination with silicon and various third-shell and heavier metals. This is an enormous local enrichment, since the universe as a whole is only 0.05% oxygen. Living organisms are 26% oxygen, mainly in combination with H, C, and N.

Oxygen has six outer electrons, two lone pairs and two unpaired electrons that are easily available for bonding. When oxygen makes two covalent bonds as in water, H_2O, it is surrounded by four electron pairs, two bonding pairs and two lone pairs, in roughly tetrahedral arrangement (see right). This restriction to four electron pairs around the atom, which we have seen for nitrogen and carbon, is mainly a consequence of the small size of the atoms. An oxygen atom does not share more of its outer-shell electrons because there is no room around it for more than four neighbor atoms. In larger atoms with the same six-electron outer-shell structure of oxygen, such as sulfur (third shell), selenium, and tellurium, all six of the electrons can be shared, thereby bringing six electron pairs around the central atom. But with the small second-row elements, four pairs is the maximum, and an eight-electron shell is full.

One oxygen atom can satisfy all of its electron-sharing needs by using both unpaired electrons in a double bond to another oxygen atom, as shown in the lower figure. Oxygen therefore occurs as a diatomic gas, O=O or O_2, similar to N_2 gas but totally unlike the infinite solid structures of carbon in diamond or graphite. Solid boron and solid carbon are held together by covalent bonds in a three-dimensional network, and melt only at very high temperatures: 2037°C for boron and 3500°C for graphite. Molecules of solid N_2 and O_2 are held together only by van der Waals forces, and therefore melt at a low −210°C and −219°C, respectively.

The formation of a water molecule, H—O—H or H_2O, is shown at right. The two lone pairs repel one another, and each repels the bonding pairs more than the bonding pairs themselves repel one another. The H—O—H angle therefore is squeezed down from an ideal tetrahedral angle of 109.5° to 105°. Oxygen is more electronegative than nitrogen, so each O—H bond has 33% ionic character, whereas the N—H bond in ammonia has only 27% ionic character. This plus the presence of two lone electron pairs on O increase the dipole moment of the molecule as a whole to 1.85 D, to be compared with 1.47 D for ammonia. Each

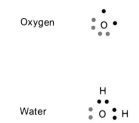

Lewis dot models for the oxygen atom and the water molecule

GEOMETRY OF THE WATER MOLECULE

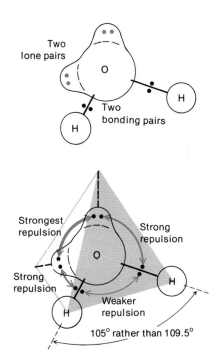

Stronger electrostatic repulsion by the lone electron pairs, which are closer to the O than are the bonding pairs, forces the two O—H bonds closer together than the tetrahedral angle of 109.5°.

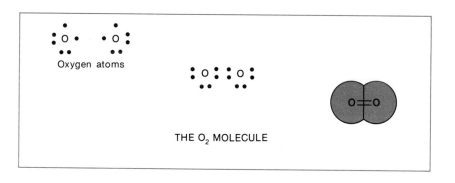

THE O_2 MOLECULE

Two oxygen atoms contribute two electrons each to form a double bond, which holds the atoms together in an O_2 molecule.

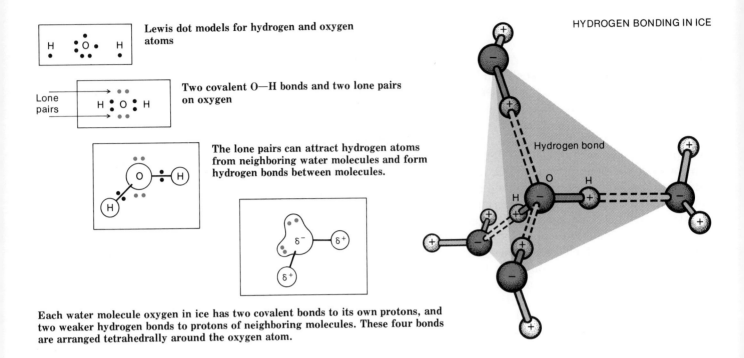

Lewis dot models for hydrogen and oxygen atoms

Two covalent O—H bonds and two lone pairs on oxygen

Lone pairs

The lone pairs can attract hydrogen atoms from neighboring water molecules and form hydrogen bonds between molecules.

Hydrogen bond

Each water molecule oxygen in ice has two covalent bonds to its own protons, and two weaker hydrogen bonds to protons of neighboring molecules. These four bonds are arranged tetrahedrally around the oxygen atom.

hydrogen atom in water has a partial positive charge, and the oxygen atom has a partial negative charge. An H_2O molecule is a miniature dipole.

The attractions between water molecules are more than just the attractions of one tiny dipole for another. Each hydrogen atom with its partial positive charge is attracted to one of the lone pairs on an oxygen of a neighbor molecule, by a weak ionic attraction known as a *hydrogen bond* (above). Hydrogen bonds can be formed whenever a hydrogen atom with a partial positive charge is near a small N, O, or F atom carrying an excess of negative charge. Such bonds, although weak, are important in holding molecules such as proteins together because there are so many of them. We will discuss the occurrence of hydrogen bonds in living organisms in Chapter 22. For example, the most central process in all living organisms, the coding of genetic information in molecules of DNA, also depends on hydrogen bonds for the preservation of the message.

The structure of solid water, or ice, is shown at the top of these two pages. Each oxygen atom is surrounded tetrahedrally by oxygens of neighboring molecules. An oxygen atom has two O—H bonds extended toward two of these neighbors, and is hydrogen bonded to them. In turn, this oxygen atom receives two hydrogen bonds from two other neighbors. In one form of ice the oxygen atoms are arranged like the carbon atoms in diamond. The more common ice structure shown here represents another way of connecting atoms by tetrahedral bonds. If the ice structure is thought of as stacked layers of tetrahedra connected by hydrogen bonds, then the structure shown at the upper right and the diamondlike structure merely represent different ways of stacking the layers.

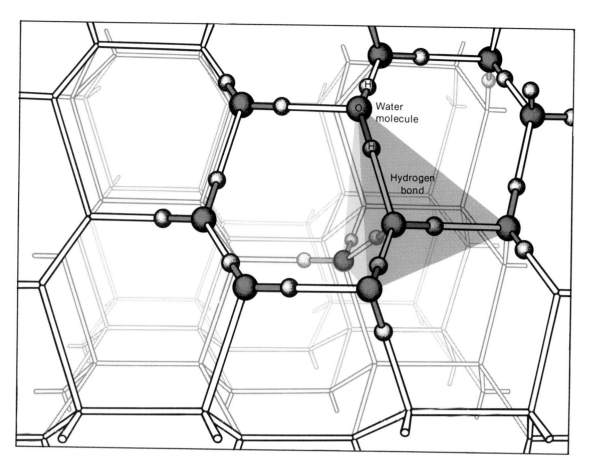

The common form of ice shown above has open, cagelike channels running through the structure. Ice indeed is an open framework structure, and the water molecules can get closer together if they break the framework and pack together in a more random manner in a liquid. This is the reason why ice is less dense than liquid water, and floats at the surface of a lake. With the exception of a few bismuth–cadmium alloys used in making printer's type, no other liquid expands upon freezing, and no other solid floats on its own liquid. This is an important property of water for life on Earth, for if ice sank to the bottom as it froze, then the bottom of the world's oceans would be perpetually frozen, with the melting boundary rising in winter and falling again in summer. The ocean floor would be covered with a permanent layer of ice. With the coldest water at the bottom next to the ice surface, there would be no convection currents and no mixing of materials in the ocean. One can pursue this line of thought and predict that in such a world, life probably never would have evolved. It is tempting to speculate that, on this basis alone, life wherever it is to be found in the universe probably will be associated with water-bearing planets.

When ice melts, all of the hydrogen bonds do not collapse at once. The cagelike framework disintegrates piecemeal, and even in liquid water at room temperature there are clusters of several hundred water molecules hydrogen-bonded together in ways similar to that of ice. As the temperature is raised, these icelike domains break up more and

Ice is an open-cage structure of oxygen atoms connected by O—H···O hydrogen bonds (above). With only 90% of the density of liquid water, in which the cage structure has partially collapsed, ice floats on the surface of the oceans and lakes.

Water is a polar molecule. The partial charges on H and O atoms will be represented by + and − signs in space-filling sketches of the H₂O molecule.

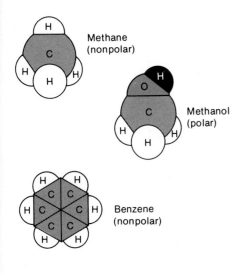

Methane (nonpolar)

Methanol (polar)

Benzene (nonpolar)

Lithium fluoride (ionic salt)

Types of interactions between water and a nonpolar liquid, benzene (below left); a polar liquid, methanol (center); and an ionic salt, LiF (right). Water and benzene separate into layers; water and methanol intermix, attracted by dipolar forces; and water molecules surround and hydrate the Li⁺ and F⁻ ions. Water is a good solvent for methanol and LiF, but not for benzene.

more, and the same quantity of water takes up less room. At the same time, the bulk solution is expanding as the temperature rises. These two effects are in competition. When ice first melts, the breaking up of the cage structure predominates, and water contracts. It continues to contract as the temperature increases from 0°C to 4°C, and more of the icelike structures are broken up. Not until the temperature rises above 4°C does the normal thermal expansion become more important than the breakup of the hydrogen-bonded cages. Water has its minimum volume and maximum density at 4°C, and only above this temperature does it begin to expand as it is heated, as does any other liquid.

THE INTERACTION OF AMMONIA AND WATER; BASES

Polar molecules such as water or ammonia attract one another in the same way that they attract other molecules of their own kind. The positive region of one molecule is attracted to the negative region of a neighbor, as shown below. Molecules of methane, CH₄, are nonpolar. If one of the —H groups in methane is replaced by an —OH, the molecule is methyl alcohol, CH₃—OH. This is a polar molecule, with a slight negative charge on the O and a slight positive charge on the H. Methyl alcohol and water molecules interact with one another, and hence mix well in solution. Each is a good solvent for the other.

In contrast, benzene molecules (C₆H₆) are nonpolar and do not interact with the dipoles of the water molecules. Even worse, they get in the way of the mutual interaction of water molecules. A mixture of benzene and water is more stable if it separates into a benzene layer held together by van der Waals forces, and an aqueous (water) layer with dipole interactions and hydrogen bonds.

A salt is composed of positive and negative ions. When a salt dissolves in water, each positive ion is surrounded by water molecules with their negative oxygen atoms pointing toward it. Each negative ion also is surrounded by other water molecules, with their positive hydrogens oriented toward it. The ions are said to be *hydrated*, and we shall see in the next chapter that hydration is an important property of ions.

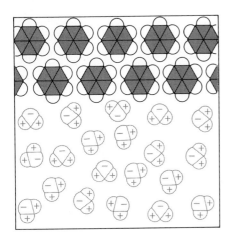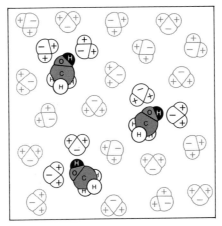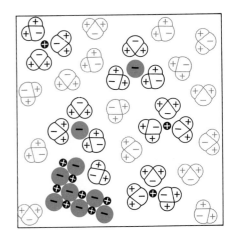

Proton

Hydroxide ion

Water helps to break up the solid salt crystal by making strong polar interactions with its ions.

The attraction between ammonia and water is even more striking. Water molecules dissociate spontaneously to a certain extent into protons and hydroxide ions:

$$\underset{\text{water molecule}}{H_2O} \rightarrow \underset{\text{proton}}{H^+} + \underset{\text{hydroxide ion}}{OH^-}$$

When ammonia gas is dissolved in water, it competes with water for one of the water molecule's own hydrogen ions, and some of the protons released by dissociation of water are picked up by ammonia molecules:

$$\underset{\text{ammonia molecule}}{NH_3} + \underset{\text{proton}}{H^+} \rightarrow \underset{\text{ammonium ion}}{NH_4^+}$$

The overall reaction, diagrammed at the right, represents a competition between an ammonia molecule and a hydroxide ion for the proton:

$$NH_3 + H_2O \rightleftharpoons NH_4^+ + OH^-$$

The double arrow indicates that the actual process is not all-or-nothing, but is a competition or balance between the forward and reverse steps.

A substance that produces hydroxide ions in water solution is called a *base*. Lithium hydroxide, LiOH, is a base because it dissociates in water into lithium ions and hydroxide ions:

$$LiOH \rightarrow Li^+ + OH^-$$

Ammonia is a base by this same criterion, even though the hydroxide ions come from the solvent water molecules and not from the ammonia. Hydroxide ions are reactive, and will attack other polar molecules at positions where they carry a local positive charge. (For this reason, many chemical reactions that take place very slowly in a neutral water solution will proceed quite rapidly in the presence of a base.) Bases have a slippery feel because the hydroxide ions attack the oils of the skin and convert them to soap. Ammonia does the same thing to fats and greases, which is why a weak ammonia solution is a useful household cleaner. Bases turn red litmus paper (a common acid–base indicator) blue.

Pure water dissociates to a small extent into protons (H^+) and hydroxide ions (OH^-).

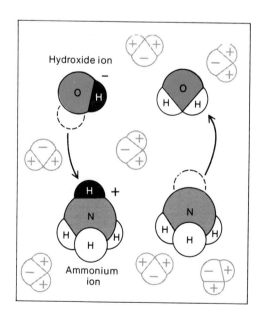

Hydroxide ion

Ammonium ion

The ammonia molecule (NH_3) and the hydroxide ion (OH^-) compete for protons. For every ammonia molecule that captures a proton and becomes an ammonium ion (NH_4^+), a water molecule must dissociate to leave a hydroxide ion. This makes an ammonia solution basic.

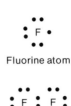

Fluorine atom

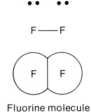

F——F

Fluorine molecule

F F

Fluorine molecule

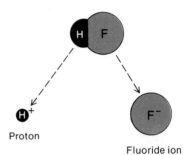

Hydrogen fluoride

H⁺

Proton

F⁻

Fluoride ion

Hydrogen fluoride dissociates partially in water to yield a proton (H⁺) and a fluoride ion (F⁻). The protons and fluoride ions are hydrated by being surrounded by water molecules (right) just as Li⁺ and F⁻ ions are hydrated when lithium fluoride salt dissolves. Unlike LiF, not every HF molecule dissociates.

FLUORINE AND HYDROFLUORIC ACID

Fluorine is the only element that is more electronegative than oxygen. It is the only substance which, when combined with oxygen, pulls the bonding electron pair away from oxygen and toward itself. It has seven electrons in its outer shell and needs only one more to complete the stable octet. Fluorine gas consists of F_2 molecules with a single F—F bond between atoms. Its hydrogen compound is hydrogen fluoride, HF, in which the F atom is surrounded by three lone pairs and one bonding pair (see left). The H—F bond is more polar than the H—O bond, being 41% ionic compared with 33%. But because HF has only one polar bond, whereas H_2O has two, the overall dipole moment is smaller, 1.82 D compared to 1.85 D for water. With only one proton, HF can make only one hydrogen bond to another molecule, so the liquid is not as tightly "stitched" together as water is. Therefore HF boils at 19°C, whereas water boils at 100°C (both values at 1 atm pressure). Neither ammonia nor HF can form the elaborate open-cage structures found in ice. Ammonia can't because it has only one lone pair available for receiving a hydrogen bond, and HF can't because it has only one proton with which to make a hydrogen bond. Water has the fortunate combination of two protons for hydrogen bonding and two lone pairs to receive such bonds from neighbors. The result is the three-dimensional framework structure of ice.

The electrons in the HF molecules are pulled strongly toward the fluorine atom. When HF is dissolved in water, the polar water molecules help to complete the process, and pull many of the HF molecules apart into ions:

$$\text{HF} \rightarrow \text{H}^+ + \text{F}^-$$
hydrogen fluoride   proton   fluoride ion

Just as when a salt crystal dissolves, each ion is thoroughly hydrated by being surrounded by three or four water molecules. Each proton is

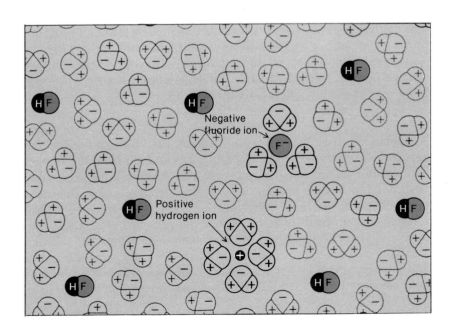

64

surrounded by water molecules with their negatively charged oxygens pointed toward it, and each fluoride ion is surrounded by other water molecules with hydrogens pointed at it (see left page, below). Since water molecules are involved in the pulling apart or dissociation of HF, the preceding reaction really should be written

$$HF + (n + m) \ H_2O \rightarrow H^+ (H_2O)_n + F^- (H_2O)_m$$

The subscripts n and m represent the number of water molecules that can be accommodated around each ion. This is 3 or 4 for these small ions, but for larger ions, n and m can be 6 or even greater. This is another example of how a polar liquid such as water is a good solvent for other polar substances or for salts with charged ions. A more general term for hydration when the solvent is a liquid other than water, such as liquid ammonia, is *solvation*.

When hydrogen fluoride is dissolved in water, the amount of hydrogen ion in the solution increases. Any substance that increases the H^+ content of an aqueous solution is called an *acid*. An aqueous solution of HF molecules is known as hydrofluoric acid. Just as hydroxide ions can assist in chemical reactions by attacking molecules where they have a slight excess of positive charge, so hydrogen ions can attack local negative regions of molecules. Acids and bases both can speed up reactions that would take place very slowly or not at all in a neutral solution. Acids have a sharp taste, familiar in the acetic acid of vinegar and citric acid of lemons. It is *not* advisable ever to taste laboratory acids such as hydrofluoric, hydrochloric, or sulfuric acids, for they are so strong as to be dangerous. The most common laboratory acid–base indicator, litmus paper, is turned red by acids.

ELECTRON SHARING: A SUMMARY

This chapter has been devoted to the chemical bonds produced by electron sharing. We have seen that, unless the bonded atoms have exactly the same electronegativity, sharing between atoms is never equal. Most bonds have a certain element of electron donation, or a certain ionic character, which can be calculated from dipole moments of molecules. The series of bonds of C, N, O, and F with H shows the kind of changes in percent ionic character that we would expect from their electronegativities. (See table below.)

In this chapter we have seen ions as arising from large differences in electronegativities in bonded atoms. The next chapter will be devoted to the behavior of ions, as they are found in salts, solutions, and metals.

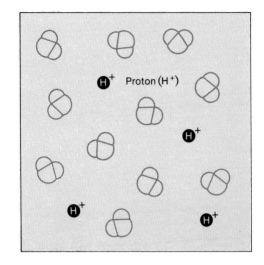

An acid (above) is any substance that increases the number of protons (concentration) of an aqueous solution to which it is added. The acidic solution is symbolized by a color tint.

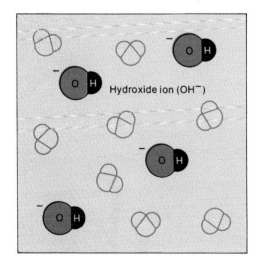

A base (above) is any substance that decreases the hydrogen-ion concentration and increases the hydroxide-ion concentration of an aqueous solution to which it is added. The basic solution is symbolized by a gray tint.

Bond	H—C	H—N	H—O	H—F	Li—F
Difference in electronegativities	0.4	0.9	1.4	1.9	3.0
Percent ionic character	Low	27%	33%	41%	87%

QUESTIONS

1. In which state do two F atoms have lower energy, when they are isolated atoms at a great distance from one another, or close to one another in a F_2 molecule? Is energy absorbed, or given off, when two F atoms join to form a F_2 molecule?

2. How does VSEPR theory explain the observed geometry of molecules of methane, ammonia, and water?

3. If the central atom is represented by X, why does the H—X—H bond angle decrease from $109.5°$ in methane, to $107°$ in ammonia, to $105°$ in water?

4. What kind of force or attraction makes methane condense from a gas to a liquid at low temperatures? Why need the temperature not be reduced as low for condensation to occur for methane as for hydrogen?

5. What second-row atoms can make double and triple electron-pair bonds? How do the bond lengths of single, double, and triple bonds between the same kinds of atoms compare? How might you expect the bond energies to vary?

6. What kinds of bonds are found between carbon atoms in benzene?

7. In what way is the benzene molecular structure like that of graphite?

8. What holds benzene molecules together in liquid benzene? What holds the carbon sheets together in a stack in graphite? How does this explain graphite's usefulness as a lubricant? In what way is this like the reason for the lubricant properties of hydrocarbons with 15 to 20 carbon atoms?

9. In what way is the structure of straight- and branched-chain hydrocarbons like that of diamond?

10. Why is diamond so hard, whereas graphite is soft, if both are only pure carbon?

11. Why does the percent ionic character of the bonds to the central atom increase in the series of molecules: methane, ammonia, water? What effect does this have on the measured dipole moment of each molecule?

12. Why would the methane molecule not have a measurable dipole moment, even if the individual C—H bonds were strongly polar?

13. How are conjugated molecules different from other molecules with double bonds? What is the term for conjugated ring compounds such as benzene?

14. Why does graphite conduct electricity, whereas diamond does not?

15. Why is the N_2 molecule much more stable than F_2?

16. What forces hold the H_2O molecules together in ice?

17. Why does ice float on water, when practically no other solid floats on its own liquid? Why do solid ammonia and solid hydrogen fluoride not float on their own liquids, like solid water does?

18. What type of attractive forces exist between water and benzene? Water and methanol? Water and LiF?

19. Why is water a good solvent for ethanol, or ethyl alcohol, but not for ethane? Would you expect water to be a better, or worse, solvent for octanol, CH_3—CH_2—CH_2—CH_2—CH_2—CH_2—CH_2—CH_2—OH, than for ethanol?

20. What is meant by hydration of a molecule or ion?

21. Why does ammonia increase the concentration of hydroxide ions when it is dissolved in water? What is a substance that behaves in this way called?

22. Why does hydrogen fluoride increase the concentration of hydrogen ions when dissolved in water? What is such a substance called?

23. How does the behavior of HF and LiF differ when each is dissolved in water?

24. Why is some OH⁻ present in water even without an added base? How does this compare with the amount of H⁺ present in pure water?

25. What is the effect of acids and bases on litmus paper? What is such a substance called?

PROBLEMS

1. If the HF molecule had its real bond length of 0.92 Å, but the bond were 75% ionic (instead of 41%), what would be the observed dipole moment of HF?

2. The observed dipole moment of the HCl molecule is 1.07 D, and the distance between atoms is 1.27Å. What is the percent ionic character of the H—Cl bond? Is this more, or less, ionic than the H—F bond? Chlorine is the element analogous to fluorine in the third row of the periodic table (see the end of Chapter 3). What does your calculation tell you about the relative electronegativities of F and Cl?

3. If each of the O—H bonds in water is 33% ionic, as was stated previously in the chapter, what is the *bond* dipole moment for each of the O—H bonds? (The O—H bond length is 0.96 Å.)

4. Using the results of Problem 3, verify that the dipole moment of the entire water molecule is 1.85 D, as was claimed before in the chapter. That is, if the bond moment of the preceding problem is represented by μ_B, what is the vector sum of two vectors of length μ_B that make an angle of 105° to one another?

5. If the N—H bond in ammonia is 27% ionic, and the bond length is 1.01 Å, what is the bond moment of each N—H bond?

6. With the value calculated in Problem 5, show that the observed dipole moment of ammonia should be 1.47 D. That is, what is the vector sum of three vectors of length μ_B that make angles of 107° with one another? (There is more geometry than chemistry in this problem.)

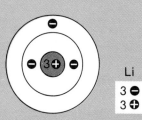

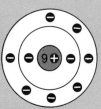

Neutral atoms of lithium (Li) and
fluorine (F). The charges on protons
(+) and electrons (−) exactly balance.

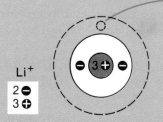

A lithium atom loses an electron and
a fluorine atom gains an electron.
Li now has 2 electrons and F has 10.

With 3 protons and only 2 electrons,
Li⁺ is a positive ion. With 9 protons
and 10 electrons, F⁻ is a negative ion.
Note that lithium shrinks and fluoride
expands as one outer shell is emptied
and the other is filled.

Li⁺ and F⁻ ions attract and neutralize
each other in the salt structure below.

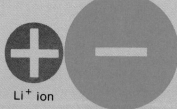

CHAPTER 5

Gain and Loss of Electrons; Ions and Metals

In Chapter 4 we saw examples of equal sharing of electrons in a bond (methane), unequal sharing (ammonia, water, HF), and partial or complete transfer of electrons to form ions (HF and LiF in water). Ions and salts were introduced primarily as a contrast to electron-sharing. Now we turn to the behavior of ions as they are encountered in salts, solutions, and metals. Acids and bases were introduced in Chapter 4 with examples of each: the acid HF and the bases NH_3 and LiOH. Some of the most common and useful acids and bases are oxygen compounds. In this chapter we shall look at oxygen compounds of the second-shell elements and see why electronegativity differences make some of them acids and others bases. Why, for example, does lithium hydroxide (LiOH) behave so differently from nitric acid (HNO_3)? Finally, although the brittle salts and flexible metals both are made from ions, they are as different in properties as two solids can be. The drawings on the opposite page show the essence of salt structure: positive and negative ions, attracted toward one another, and packed in a regular, geometric array into a three-dimensional solid with an alternation of positive and negative charges. By contrast, in a metal all of the ions are positive ions, and these are held together by a sea of mobile electrons. We shall see how the arrangement of ions and electrons in these two kinds of solids makes each behave in its own way.

The ideas of periodicity of chemical behavior and of a periodic table with horizontal rows corresponding to electron shells were introduced at the end of Chapter 3. These second-shell (or second-row) elements, Li to Ne, are a microcosm of the entire periodic table, for the trends and behavior that we will see in this chapter will be encountered again with the heavier elements. We are learning not only about the second-shell elements, but about the basic principles of chemical behavior that are applicable to all atoms. These principles appear in a particularly simple way for the second-shell atoms.

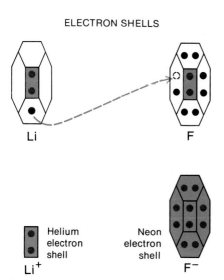

ELECTRON SHELLS

Li   F

Li⁺   F⁻

Helium electron shell   Neon electron shell

When lithium loses an electron, it returns to the electron-shell configuration of helium. When fluorine gains an electron, its electron-shell arrangement becomes that of neon. Both ions have completed outer electron shells.

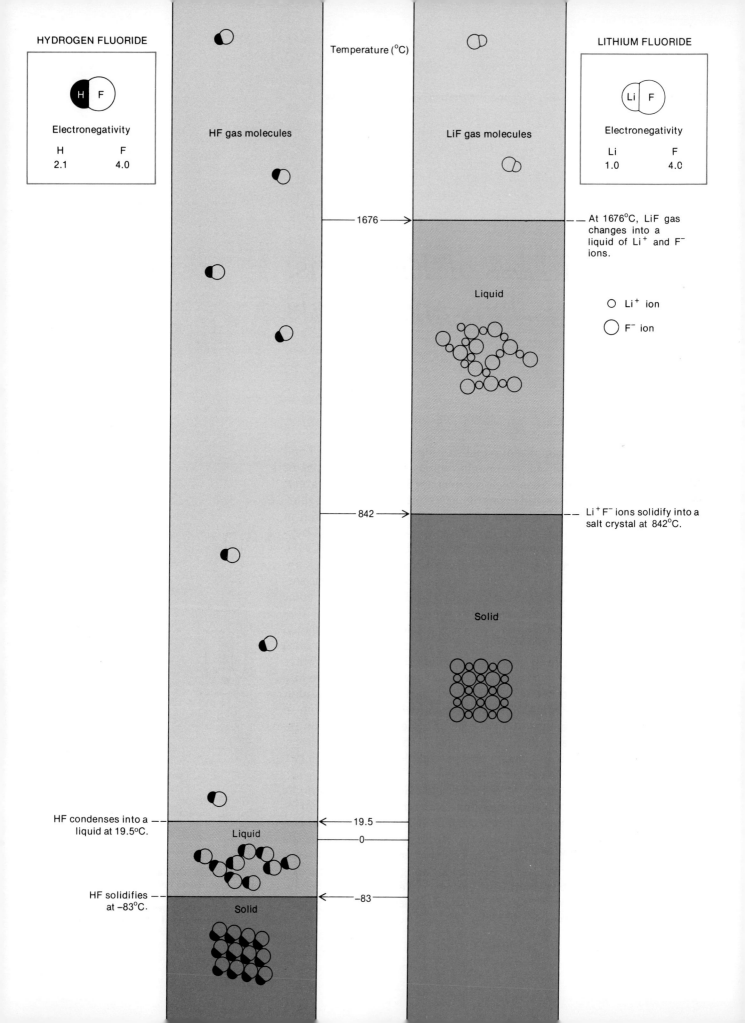

HYDROGEN FLUORIDE

Electronegativity

H	F
2.1	4.0

HF gas molecules

Temperature (°C)

LiF gas molecules

LITHIUM FLUORIDE

Electronegativity

Li	F
1.0	4.0

⟶ 1676 ⟶   At 1676°C, LiF gas changes into a liquid of Li⁺ and F⁻ ions.

○ Li⁺ ion

◯ F⁻ ion

Liquid

⟶ 842 ⟶   Li⁺F⁻ ions solidify into a salt crystal at 842°C.

Solid

HF condenses into a liquid at 19.5°C.   ⟵ 19.5 ⟵

⟵ 0 ⟵

Liquid

HF solidifies at −83°C.   ⟵ −83 ⟵

Solid

IONS AND SALTS

At very high temperatures, around 1700°C, both hydrogen fluoride and lithium fluoride are two-atom molecular compounds in the gas phase (left page). The electronegativities of Li and F are more different (1.0 and 4.0) than those of H and F (2.1 and 4.0), so the LiF molecule is more polar than HF. Measured dipole moments reflect this difference: 6.33 D for LiF versus only 1.82 D for HF. From these values and the observed bond lengths, one can calculate that the Li—F bond in the gaseous diatomic molecule is 87% ionic, whereas the bond in H—F is only 41% ionic. Li has a far greater tendency to lose its outer electron to F and to become a +1 ion than H does.

We can see this electronegativity difference as we begin to cool the gaseous HF and LiF molecules. Nothing happens to HF until the temperature decreases to 19.5°C, at which point the gas molecules are moving so slowly that they can be trapped by forces between molecules and condensed into a liquid. The individual molecules remain intact in the liquid, with the forces between them being a combination of van der Waals interactions and hydrogen bonds from one H to the F on a neighboring molecule. At −83°C, molecular motion becomes so slow that these forces freeze the HF molecules into a crystalline solid. Even in the solid, individual HF molecules remain, held together by the forces between molecules.

LiF behaves entirely differently. The difference in electronegativity between the two atoms is so great that a diatomic LiF molecule is in a highly unfavorable state. There is a strong tendency for the electron pair to be given over completely to the F atom, thereby turning the molecule into two ions:

$$\text{Li}\overset{..}{\underset{..}{\text{—F}}}: \quad \rightarrow \quad \text{Li}^+ \quad + \overset{..}{\underset{..}{:\text{F}}}:^-$$

diatomic molecule   lithium ion   fluoride ion

(The dots represent outer-shell electrons, and the bond line between atoms represents an electron pair.) When this occurs, each Li$^+$ ion attracts all the F$^-$ ions present, and each F$^-$ attracts every Li$^+$. The gas of separate Li—F molecules condenses into a liquid of Li$^+$ and F$^-$ ions (left page) when the temperature decreases below 1676°C. Only above this temperature does LiF have enough energy to force the electron pair back toward the Li$^+$ ion and turn the separate ions into gaseous Li—F molecules.

Molten LiF is a rather unusual liquid compared to benzene or water. The interactions between particles are not the weak van der Waals forces of benzene, or the moderately strong dipole attractions and hydrogen bonds of water, but are the extremely strong electrostatic attractions between ions of opposite charge and the equally strong repulsions between ions of the same charge. Ions can move past one another in the fluid, but there is a tendency for each kind of ion to surround itself with ions of the opposite charge.

If we cool molten LiF to 842°C, the ions move so slowly that they lock into a regular array, with positive and negative charges alternating so that ions of the same charge are shielded from one another. This is the structure of LiF salt crystals, introduced in Chapter 4 and shown

Li$^+$F$^-$ SALT CRYSTALS

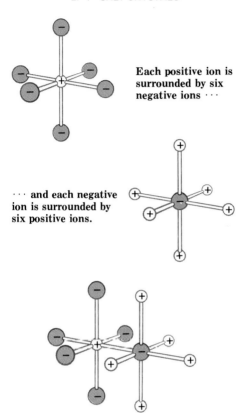

Each positive ion is surrounded by six negative ions · · ·

· · · **and each negative ion is surrounded by six positive ions.**

Taken together they form the framework · · ·

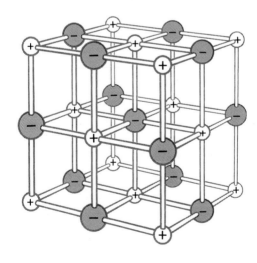

· · · **of a crystal lattice. This is a cubic crystal of a salt.**

Water molecule (H₂O)

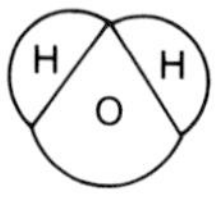

Distribution of charges
on the polar water molecule

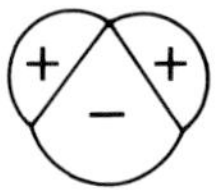

Lithium ion (Li⁺)

Fluoride ion (F⁻)

Lithium fluoride crystal (Li⁺ F⁻)

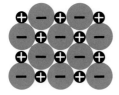

in the margin of the preceding page. The individual Li⁺ and F⁻ ions remain even in the solid, in marked contrast to the behavior of HF. The key to this new behavior is the difference in electronegativities of the atoms.

Atoms or ions in any solid do not sit rigidly in place. Their thermal energy causes them to vibrate about fixed positions in the crystal structure. The higher the temperature, the more energy the atoms in a solid have, and the more they vibrate. The melting point of LiF salt crystals, 842°C, is the temperature at which the ions have enough vibrational energy to shake loose from the crystal structure and circulate past one another in a liquid. The boiling point of molten LiF, 1676°C, is the temperature at which the particles in the melt can break loose and enter the gas phase. To do so they must pair off into Li—F molecules again. An isolated ion of one charge is tolerable when it is surrounded by ions of the opposite charge in a crystal, but isolated gaseous ions of Li⁺ and F⁻ would require much greater energies. This charge separation is avoided by the formation of LiF diatomic molecules.

To produce such a LiF molecule, even though the bond is quite polar, the F⁻ must give some of the borrowed electron pair back to Li⁺. The high boiling point of the salt demonstrates that this is a hard thing to do. The Li⁺ ion does not really want the electron, and accepts it only at high temperatures (high energies). In contrast to liquid LiF (a molten, ionic salt), liquid HF already exists as molecules, so all that is involved in its vaporization from liquid to gas is overcoming van der Waals forces and hydrogen bonds. This can be done at temperatures as low as 19.5°C.

LiF is soluble in water because the polar water molecules attack and hydrate the ions as shown below. It is not soluble in nonpolar liquids because nonpolar molecules show no attraction for the ions and are of no help in pulling the crystal structure apart. Many salts are soluble in water but almost none are soluble in nonpolar liquids such as benzene, gasoline, or carbon tetrachloride, CCl₄. You can drop a small amount of table salt, NaCl, into a glass of water and see the crystals dissolve and disappear quickly. But crush the salt crystals as fine as you like, and after being mixed with olive oil (nonpolar) they will remain as a white, insoluble powder.

1. A salt crystal is dropped into water.

2. Water molecules attack the crystal and liberate ions.

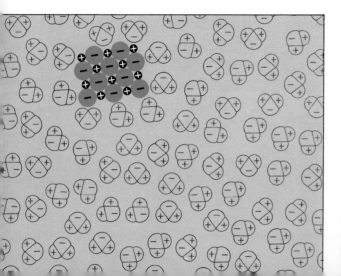

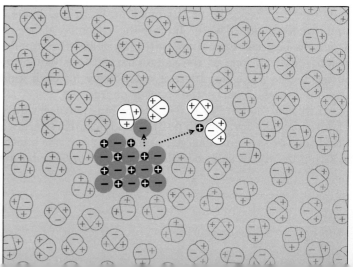

Metals conduct electricity because the outer electrons of their atoms are mobile. If a piece of metal is connected to the terminals of a battery, electrons will flow into one end of the metal block, through the metal, out the other end, and back to the battery (upper right). Only the electrons move; the metal ions remain in place.

Molten salts and salt solutions also conduct electricity, but in a different way. If two electrodes are dipped into molten LiF and then connected to a battery, electrons will flow into the melt at one electrode, and out of the melt and back to the battery at the other (middle right). Within the liquid, electric current is not carried by electrons, but by moving ions. The positive Li^+ ions move toward the electrode (called the *cathode*) where electrons flow into the melt, and the negative F^- ions move to the electrode (called the *anode*) where electrons return to the battery. At each electrode a chemical reaction takes place when the carrier of electric current changes from ions in the melt to electrons in the connecting wires. At the cathode, Li^+ ions accept electrons from the external circuit and become lithium atoms, which plate out as a metal on the surface of the electrode:

$$\underset{\text{lithium ion}}{Li^+} \quad + \quad e^- \quad \rightarrow \quad \underset{\text{lithium atom}}{Li}$$

At the anode, F^- ions give up electrons to the external circuit and combine into neutral F_2 molecules, which bubble away as a gas:

$$\underset{\text{fluoride ions}}{2F^-} \quad \rightarrow \quad \underset{\text{fluorine molecule}}{F_2} \quad + \quad 2e^-$$

Such an arrangement for passing current through a molten salt is called an *electrolysis cell* ("electro-lysis" meaning "breaking down with electricity"). Electrolysis is one of the best ways of preparing pure metals such as aluminum, which is electrolyzed commercially from a melt of aluminum oxide ore. In the context of the present discussion, electrolysis cells themselves are not as important as is the essential idea that current in a molten salt is carried by the migration of positive and negative ions. Current is carried in the same way in a solution of LiF or any other salt in water: The hydrated positive and negative ions move in opposite directions. Salt crystals do not conduct electricity, because the ions are locked in a crystalline lattice and cannot move.

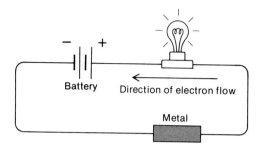

Conduction of electricity through a metal (above). Conduction of electricity through a molten salt (below).

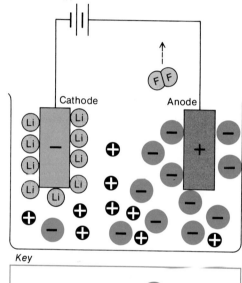

Key

⊕	Li^+ ion	⊖	F^- ion
Li	Lithium metal	F F	Fluorine gas

3. The free ions are hydrated and dispersed in solution.

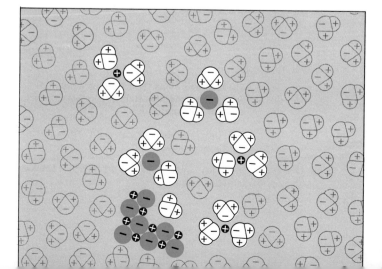

4. The crystal is dissolved, with H_2O molecules surrounding the ions.

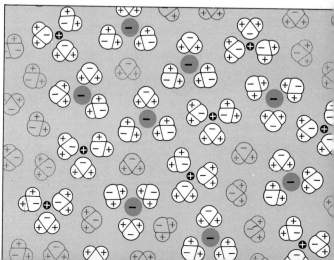

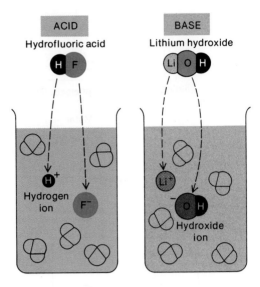

ACID
Hydrofluoric acid

BASE
Lithium hydroxide

Hydrogen ion

F⁻

Li⁺

Hydroxide ion

Hydrofluoric acid (HF) dissolved in water releases hydrogen ions (H⁺) to make an acidic solution. Lithium hydroxide (LiOH) dissolved in water produces hydroxide ions to form a basic solution.

ACID–BASE NEUTRALIZATION AND SALTS

We can regard a salt as the result of the neutralization of an acid and a base. An acid dissolved in water releases hydrogen ions:

$$HF \rightarrow H^+ + F^-$$

and a base dissolved in water produces hydroxide ions:

$$NH_3 + H_2O \rightarrow NH_4^+ + OH^-$$

$$LiOH \rightarrow Li^+ + OH^-$$

(Remember that all ions in aqueous solution are hydrated, or surrounded by water molecules, even though this usually is not written explicitly.) If we mix an acid and a base, a reaction occurs by the combination of H^+ and OH^- ions into water molecules:

$$H^+ + F^- + Li^+ + OH^- \rightarrow H_2O + Li^+ + F^-$$

(Only a small percentage of the H—F molecules in solution will be dissociated into H^+ and F^- ions initially, therefore HF is called a weak acid. As the above reaction occurs, however, more HF will dissociate.) The real reaction is the combination of hydrogen and hydroxide ions; the other ions only go along for the ride:

$$H^+ + OH^- \rightarrow H_2O$$

If the number of H^+ and OH^- ions is the same, the final solution is neutral. The reaction of an acid with a base in general is called *neutralization*, and represents the "canceling out" of the acidic and basic properties of the original solutions by the elimination of H^+ and OH^- ions.

The neutralized solution below is nothing but an aqueous solution of equal quantities of Li^+ and F^- ions. If the solution is evaporated to dryness, salt crystals of LiF are left behind. The result of acid–base neutralization is a salt and water. In principle, a fanatic chemist could season his beefsteak by pouring over it equal quantities of lye or sodium hydroxide, NaOH, and hydrochloric acid, HCl. The result after neutralization would be common table salt, NaCl. *If* the chemist were very precise about quantities, and very thorough about mixing, then he might get away with such a procedure, but it is not recommended.

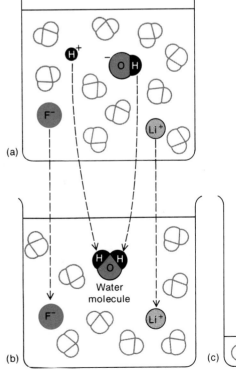

ACID   plus   BASE

H⁺

O H

F⁻

Li⁺

(a)

H H
O
Water molecule

F⁻

Li⁺

(b)

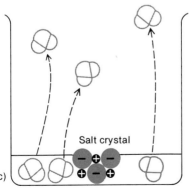

Salt crystal

(c)

(a) Hydrogen ions (H⁺) from acid combine with hydroxide ions (OH⁻) from base to form neutral H_2O molecules.

(b) Equal numbers of Li^+ and F^- ions remain in the neutral solution.

(c) When water is driven off only the LiF salt crystals remain.

OXYGEN COMPOUNDS: ACIDS OR BASES?

About 60% of the Earth's crust, 20% of the air we breathe, and 26% of all living matter are made up of oxygen atoms. How the different elements react when brought close to oxygen is an important part of their chemical behavior. Water, the medium in which life evolved, can be thought of as a medium for bringing oxygen atoms close to other substances. All of the elements that we have discussed so far, with the exception of helium and neon, form compounds with oxygen, called *oxides*. Oxides of metals are bases, and oxides of nonmetals are acids. The reason for this difference in behavior lies in the electronegativities of the atoms bound to oxygen.

The second-shell elements run the gamut of electronegativity from 1.0 (Li) to 4.0 (F). When oxides of these elements are dissolved in water, bonds are formed of the general type

$$X-\overset{..}{\underset{..}{O}}-H$$

in which X is a second-shell element. (Outer-shell electron pairs on oxygen atoms will be shown explicitly in the following discussion. Remember that a chemical bond line as in X—O also represents an electron pair.) Whether a compound containing such an X—O—H group is an acid or a base depends on which bond is stronger, X—O or O—H, as illustrated at the right. If X represents an atom of low electronegativity such as lithium, then oxygen pulls the electrons in the X—O bond toward itself, and in aqueous solutions the substance dissociates in the following way:

$$X-\overset{..}{\underset{..}{O}}-H \quad \rightarrow \quad X^+ \quad + \quad -:\overset{..}{\underset{..}{O}}-H$$
$$\text{positive ion} \quad \text{hydroxide ion}$$

Because hydroxide ions are produced, the substance is a base. Lithium hydroxide, LiOH, is an example.

If, on the contrary, X is an atom of higher electronegativity, such as nitrogen, the electrons are shared between X and O. The electronegativity of O then weakens the O—H bond by pulling the electrons of that bond toward O. In aqueous solution, water molecules cause the substance to dissociate in a different way:

$$X-\overset{..}{\underset{..}{O}}-H \quad \rightarrow \quad X-\overset{..}{\underset{..}{O}}:^- \quad + \quad H^+$$
$$\text{negative ion} \quad \text{hydrogen ion}$$

(Both ions are hydrated, of course.) The solution is acidic because hydrogen ions are produced. As we shall see shortly, this is the behavior of nitric acid, in which the ionization is

$$\underset{:\overset{..}{O}:}{\overset{:\overset{..}{O}}{N}}-\overset{..}{\underset{..}{O}}-H \quad \rightarrow \quad \underset{:\overset{..}{O}:}{\overset{:\overset{..}{O}}{N}}-\overset{..}{\underset{..}{O}}:^- \quad + \quad H^+$$
$$\text{nitric acid molecule} \quad\quad \text{nitrate ion} \quad \text{hydrogen ion}$$

One can explain the behavior of the oxygen compounds of second-shell atoms by imagining what would happen if the positive ions, Li^+, Be^{2+}, through F^{7+}, were dropped into water. This is only an imaginary experiment, because B^{3+}, C^{4+}, N^{5+}, and F^{7+} ions, with their entire

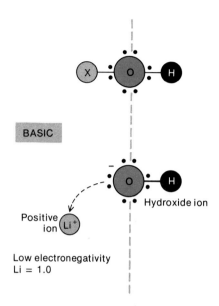

BASIC

Positive ion Li^+

Hydroxide ion

Low electronegativity
Li = 1.0

When X is an atom of low electronegativity such as Li, the Li—O bond breaks and hydroxide ions are produced.

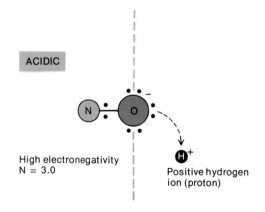

ACIDIC

High electronegativity
N = 3.0

H^+
Positive hydrogen ion (proton)

When X is an atom of high electronegativity such as N, the O—H bond breaks and positive hydrogen ions (protons) are produced.

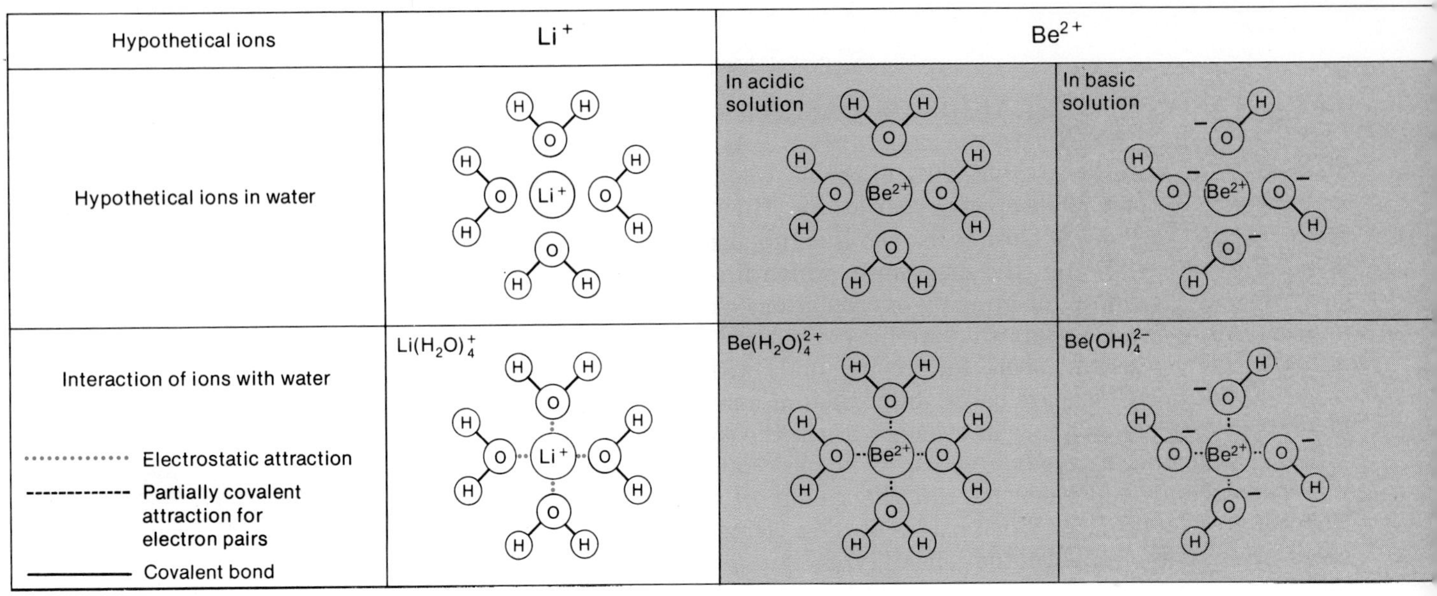

Hypothetical ions	Li$^+$	Be^{2+}	
Hypothetical ions in water		In acidic solution	In basic solution
Interaction of ions with water	Li$(H_2O)_4^+$	Be$(H_2O)_4^{2+}$	Be$(OH)_4^{2-}$
⋯⋯⋯ Electrostatic attraction			
– – – Partially covalent attraction for electron pairs			
—— Covalent bond			

With Li$^+$ the attraction for the oxygen atoms is electrostatic, and with Be^{2+} it is partly electrostatic and partly covalent.

second electron shell stripped off, are too reactive to exist in solution. Nevertheless, the products that these ions would form with water are what actually are observed in solution when the oxides of these elements are dissolved in water.

A Li$^+$ ion in aqueous solution surrounds itself with four water molecules and exists peaceably as a Li$(H_2O)_4^+$ ion, as shown above left. In an acid solution (excess of protons), beryllium also occurs as a hydrated Be$(H_2O)_4^{2+}$ ion (above). Beryllium is more electronegative than lithium, and the beryllium ion is more highly charged. It therefore pulls on the lone electron pairs of water oxygens more than Li$^+$ does. The bond between Li$^+$ and a water oxygen is mainly electrostatic, but the bond between Be^{2+} and water is partially covalent. As Be^{2+} pulls on the water lone pairs, it weakens the O—H bonds of the water molecules. In acidic solution (color background above) Be^{2+} merely holds on tightly to its four hydrating molecules. In basic solutions (gray background), where protons are scarce, the weakened water molecules around Be^{2+} each can release one proton, so the hydrated ion in basic solution is Be$(OH)_4^{2-}$ instead of Be$(H_2O)_4^{2+}$. Each Be^{2+} ion then is surrounded, not by four neutral water molecules, but by four negative hydroxide ions. The cluster, or complex ion, has a negative charge. At intermediate acidities, less than four of the H_2O molecules can lose protons.

A boron ion, B^{3+}, would pull even more strongly on the lone pairs of the water molecules around it, as shown at the top left of the following page. The attraction would be so great that covalent, electron-pair bonds would form between B and O, thereby weakening one O—H bond on each water molecule and allowing a proton to fall away. The result would be borate ions, B$(OH)_4^-$. What can be accomplished only in basic solution for Be, happens even in neutral solution for B. A B^{3+} ion is only a hypothetical entity in solution because its conversion to borate ions would be instantaneous.

A C^{4+} ion would be even more intolerable in water solution. It would pull so strongly on lone pairs of the water molecules around it that *both* of the protons from the water molecules would be released. Because of the gradual shrinkage of atomic radii from Li to F, there is

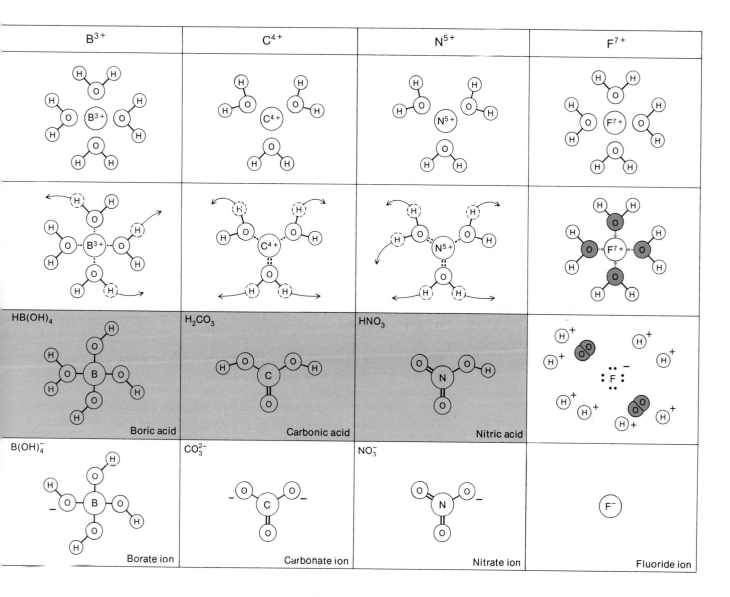

B^{3+}	C^{4+}	N^{5+}	F^{7+}
$HB(OH)_4$	H_2CO_3	HNO_3	
Boric acid	Carbonic acid	Nitric acid	
$B(OH)_4^-$	CO_3^{2-}	NO_3^-	
Borate ion	Carbonate ion	Nitrate ion	Fluoride ion

only room for three water molecules or oxygen atoms around a carbon atom, so after carbon had taken oxygens from three water molecules, it would exist as a carbonate ion, CO_3^{2-} (see above). We will come back to the nature of the bonds between C and O later.

The same story holds for nitrogen. If a N^{5+} ion were introduced into water, it would instantly pull the lone electron pairs on the oxygen atoms of water molecules toward itself so strongly that the water protons would be released, leaving nitrate ions, NO_3^-. These ions are shown above.

A F^{7+} ion would not be satisfied merely with *sharing* lone pairs from water oxygens in covalent bonds. Fluorine is so electronegative that it would strip the lone pairs completely off the water molecules, picking up four such electron pairs to yield F^- ions (above right). The wreckage of the water molecules would remain as O_2 molecules and H^+ ions:

$$F^{7+} + 4H_2O \rightarrow F^- + 2O_2 + 8H^+$$

Although F^{7+} is an imaginary ion, something like this reaction actually occurs when OF_2 is added to water, as we will see later in this chapter.

In B^{3+}, C^{4+}, and N^{5+} (only hypothetical ions in solution), the central ion pulls the oxygen electrons into covalent bonds with itself. In F^{7+} the central atom pulls the electrons completely away from the oxygens and becomes a F^- ion.

LITHIUM OXIDE IN WATER

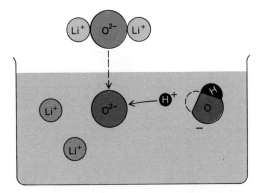

Lithium oxide consists of two lithium ions (Li^+) and one oxide ion (O^{2-}). Dissolved in water, the oxide ion pulls a proton (H^+) from a water molecule...

Basic solution

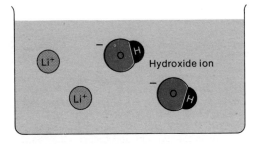

...resulting in two hydroxide ions (OH^-), and causing the solution to become basic.

These all have been hypothetical experiments (except for Li^+ and Be^{2+}), but the products are real. The most stable forms of the common oxides of second-shell elements in water solution are the following ions:

$$Li(H_2O)_4^+ \quad Be(H_2O)_4^{2+} \text{ (in acid)} \quad B(OH)_3(H_2O) \quad HCO_3^-$$

$$\text{or} \qquad\qquad\qquad \text{or} \qquad\quad \text{or}$$

$$Be(OH)_4^{2-} \text{ (in base)} \qquad B(OH)_4^- \qquad CO_3^{2-} \quad NO_3^- \quad F^-$$

The purpose of these imaginary experiments has been to show, in terms of electronegativities and electron-pulling power, why each of the ions above is the prevalent species in solution. With these in mind, we now can turn to the acid–base behavior of the oxides.

BASIC OXIDES: Li_2O

When lithium metal is burned in dry air, the product is a fine white powder of lithium oxide, Li_2O. The 2:1 ratio of atoms is inevitable because each oxygen atom must acquire two electrons to complete its neon shell, but each lithium atom has only one outer electron to give. The powder actually is made of microcrystals of Li^+ and O^{2-} ions in a salt. Li_2O dissolves in water to produce hydrated Li^+ ions and hydroxide ions, so Li_2O is a basic oxide:

$$Li_2O + H_2O \rightarrow 2Li^+ + 2OH^-$$

The important factor in this reaction is the oxide ion, O^{2-} (left). It has such a strong attraction for protons that it can take one away from a water molecule, thereby creating two hydroxide ions:

$$\underset{\text{oxide ion}}{O^{2-}} + \underset{\text{water molecule}}{H-O-H} \rightarrow \underset{\text{hydroxide ions}}{OH^- + OH^-}$$

This reaction should remind you of the way that ammonia molecules produce hydroxide ions by pulling water molecules apart:

$$\underset{\text{ammonia molecule}}{NH_3} + \underset{\text{water molecule}}{H-O-H} \rightarrow \underset{\text{ammonium ion}}{NH_4^+} + \underset{\text{hydroxide ion}}{OH^-}$$

The lithium ions in Li_2O play a passive role, doing nothing more than counter-balancing the negative charges of the O^{2-} ions in the crystal, or the OH^- ions in the basic solution (bottom left). Li^+ ions are hydrated by four water molecules, as mentioned previously. If we evaporate the basic solution obtained from Li_2O to dryness, crystals of lithium hydroxide (LiOH) are obtained, which are made up of Li^+ and OH^- ions. Extra heating in a dry environment is required to drive water molecules off and to reconvert the lithium hydroxide crystals to lithium oxide:

$$2LiOH \rightarrow Li_2O + H_2O$$

The behavior of lithium and its basic oxide that we have just seen is typical of metals in general. Although lithium stands alone in its basic behavior among the second-shell elements, metals and metal hydroxides are very important among the heavier elements.

BOTH ACIDIC AND BASIC: BeO

Burning beryllium metal in dry air produces beryllium oxide, BeO. This is a salt with Be^{2+} and O^{2-} ions in a crystal lattice, although the attractions between Be^{2+} and O^{2-} have an appreciable covalent character. Since each Be atom can give up two electrons, and each oxygen atom needs two electrons, the atoms combine in a 1:1 ratio. There is an important difference between BeO and Li_2O. Because beryllium is more electronegative than lithium, the Be—O bond is not entirely ionic, but has a considerable electron-sharing character. The electrons that surround an O^{2-} ion to complete its neon shell actually are shared to a degree with the beryllium atoms. BeO is not a completely covalent solid like diamond, but it does have a partial covalent character that makes it more difficult to pull apart than Li_2O.

Beryllium oxide cannot be dissolved by pure water; the H_2O molecules are not polar enough to overcome the covalent contribution and pull the crystal apart into Be^{2+} and O^{2-} ions. BeO can be dissolved in acid, however (top right). The protons of the acid attack the O^{2-} ions and help break up the crystal lattice:

$$BeO + 2H^+ \rightarrow Be^{2+} + H_2O$$

or more simply:

$$O^{2-} \text{ (from the crystal)} + 2H^+ \rightarrow H_2O$$

The beryllium ion is hydrated in acid solution with four water molecules, as mentioned previously.

BeO also is soluble in basic solution (bottom right). The hydroxide ions tear the BeO crystal apart by attacking Be^{2+} ions more strongly than water molecules can:

$$Be^{2+} + 4OH^- \rightarrow Be(OH)_4^{2-}$$

The oxide ions then are freed to interact with water molecules:

$$O^{2-} + H_2O \rightarrow 2OH^-$$

The overall reaction is the sum of the two:

$$BeO + 2OH^- + H_2O \rightarrow Be(OH)_4^{2-}$$

This is the species that was mentioned previously as being most stable in basic solution, where a shortage of H^+ ions exists.

The dissolving of BeO is an example of the usefulness of acids and bases in promoting reactions that do not proceed easily or at all in neutral water solution. Because BeO is insoluble in pure water but reacts with either an acid (like a base would) or a base (like an acid would), we say that it is *amphoteric*, from a Greek word meaning "both behaviors." BeO is on the borderline between bases and acids, and the explanation for its amphoteric behavior is to be found in the greater electronegativity of Be than Li, and the partial covalent character of the Be—O bond. Other, heavier metals, such as aluminum, which also are on the borderline between metallic and nonmetallic behavior, have amphoteric oxides, with both basic and acidic properties.

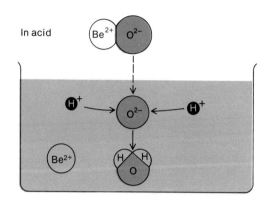

AMPHOTERIC BERYLLIUM OXIDE

Beryllium oxide can be dissolved in acid but not in water. Protons in the acid attack the O^{2-} ions to form water molecules.

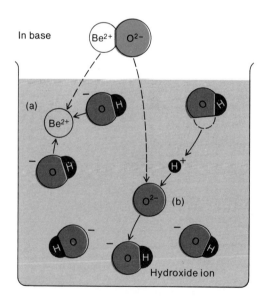

In a basic solution, hydroxide ions attack the Be^{2+} ions of the crystal (a). The oxide ions then are freed to react with water molecules (b), and form more hydroxide ions.

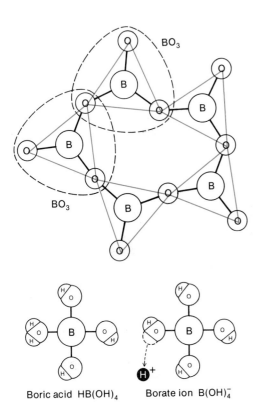

Boric acid HB(OH)$_4$ Borate ion B(OH)$_4^-$

BORIC ACID SOLUTION

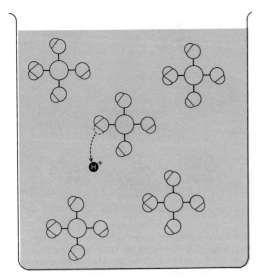

Because few protons dissociate from the boric acid molecule, boric acid is a weak acid.

THE FIRST ENTIRELY ACIDIC OXIDE: B$_2$O$_3$

The bonds in the oxide of boron are covalent, with electron-pair bonds between B and O. Because each boron atom has three outer-shell electrons for sharing, whereas each oxygen atom needs two electrons to share in pair bonds, the ratio of B to O atoms must be 2:3, just as if the interacting species were B^{3+} and O^{2-} ions. Although the overall composition is B$_2$O$_3$, there are no isolated B$_2$O$_3$ molecules. Instead, each boron atom is surrounded by three oxygen atoms 120° apart, and these BO$_3$ triangles are linked by sharing corner oxygens, as shown at the upper left. The structure is not a regular crystal lattice, but is disordered. An orderly, solid array is a crystal, and a disordered array is known as a *glass*. Borate glasses are useful, but not as common as silicate glasses, in which SiO$_4^{4-}$ tetrahedra are linked at corners and arranged in a disordered manner similar to the BO$_3$ triangles. Ordinary window glass is silicate glass, made from sand and metal oxides. Because glasses are made up of disorderly snarls of chains of atoms instead of regular rows in a crystalline lattice, they do not have a definite melting point. As the temperature is increased, more of the glass structure is loosened, and a glass softens and begins to flow; it continues to flow throughout an appreciable temperature range. We will discuss silicate glasses in more detail in Chapter 6.

Boric oxide dissolves in water to form boric acid. In the process, it makes four strong covalent bonds to oxygen atoms to produce borate ions, as described previously:

$$\underset{\text{boric oxide}}{B_2O_3} + 5H_2O \rightarrow \underset{\text{borate ions}}{2B(OH)_4^-} + 2H^+$$

Because hydrogen ions are produced, B$_2$O$_3$ is an acidic oxide. Boric acid might better be written HB(OH)$_4$, to emphasize the proton that dissociates in water (center left).

$$\underset{\text{boric acid}}{HB(OH)_4} \rightarrow H^+ + \underset{\text{borate ion}}{B(OH)_4^-}$$

Unfortunately, the usual practice is to leave out one water molecule and write boric acid as B(OH)$_3$, creating the erroneous impression that it is a hydroxide compound and a base. Boric acid is a very weak acid (bottom left). In aqueous solution, most of the substance is found as undissociated boric acid molecules and very little as borate ions, so the hydrogen ion contribution by boric acid is small. Dilute boric acid solution is mild enough to be used in eyewashes. (Don't try making your own. The results could be dangerous.)

CARBON AND CARBONIC ACID

Beginning with boron, all of the oxides of second-shell elements are acids. In Chapter 4 we noticed a dramatic change in the properties of the elements between carbon and nitrogen. Carbon is a hard solid with four single bonds from each atom to four neighboring atoms in the diamond lattice; nitrogen is a diatomic gas with a triple bond between two atoms. A similar abrupt change in properties of the oxides is found between boron and carbon. Lithium and beryllium oxides are orderly crystals, and boron oxide is a disordered glass. Carbon has two oxides, and both are small, gaseous molecules.

When carbon or its compounds are burned with an excess of oxygen, one of the products is carbon dioxide, CO_2. In this molecule, carbon makes a double bond to each of two oxygen atoms, as shown at the top right. Each oxygen atom also has two lone pairs, so each of the three atoms has eight electrons in its outer shell. The CO_2 molecule is linear; that is, the $O=C=O$ atoms all lie along a straight line. This is explained easily by electron repulsion or VSEPR theory. The carbon atom has two clusters of four bonding electrons around itself, each cluster pointing toward one of the two oxygen atoms. The most stable arrangement of two repelling groups around a spherical atom is at opposite poles of the sphere.

The other oxide of carbon is carbon monoxide, CO. It results from incomplete combustion of carbon or its compounds, when insufficient oxygen is present. It is isoelectronic with the N_2 molecule; if by some magic we could pluck a proton out of the oxygen nucleus in CO and give it to the carbon, N_2 would be the result. Like N_2, CO has a triple bond between atoms and one lone pair on each atom:

$$:N≡N: \qquad :C≡O:$$

The electron pair for the third bond in CO must be provided entirely by the O atom, since it has six electrons in its outer shell, whereas C has only four.

Because CO_2 and CO are small molecules with weak van der Waals forces, they remain gases at ordinary temperatures, like N_2 and O_2. Although one can smother in CO_2 because of the absence of oxygen, carbon dioxide is not intrinsically poisonous. Carbon monoxide is a different story. Oxygen is picked up at the lungs and carried to where it is needed in the tissues by hemoglobin, a protein molecule in the bloodstream. A hemoglobin molecule normally binds O_2, but can be fooled by carbon monoxide, which binds to hemoglobin even more strongly than oxygen does. Unfortunately for the person who breathes CO, once this happens, that particular hemoglobin molecule is permanently out of action and useless thereafter in carrying its proper cargo of O_2. Carbon monoxide thus is poisonous in a sense that carbon dioxide is not.

Carbon monoxide, like the isoelectronic N_2 molecule, is barely soluble in water. Carbon dioxide dissolves easily in water to form carbonic acid:

$$CO_2 + H_2O \rightarrow H_2CO_3$$
carbon dioxide carbonic acid

This is a weak acid with a sharp taste, familiar from carbonated soft drinks. The bubbles in a carbonated drink are incompletely dissolved CO_2 gas. When CO_2 dissolves in water, the carbon atom attracts a lone pair from the oxygen of a water molecule and forms carbonic acid, which has the structure shown on the next page. The carbon atom is double-bonded to one oxygen atom, and single-bonded to each of two —OH groups.

CARBON DIOXIDE (CO_2)

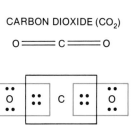

Electron sharing in the CO_2 molecule

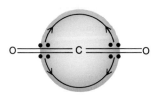

Electron repulsion keeps the two groups of four electrons at opposite poles of a sphere, so $O=C=O$ is a linear molecule.

CARBON MONOXIDE (CO)

Carbon monoxide molecule, with a triple bond as in N_2

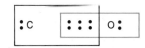

Electron sharing in the CO molecule

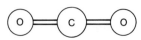

Carbon dioxide combines with H₂O to form carbonic acid.

CARBONIC ACID (H₂CO₃)

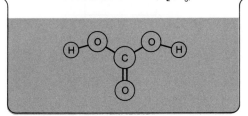

The carbonic acid molecule in water loses its protons in two stages:

BICARBONATE ION (HCO₃⁻)

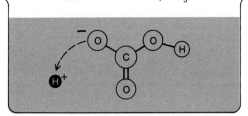

(1) Carbonic acid is stronger than boric acid, but still only about half the carbonic acid molecules dissociate in water.

CARBONATE ION (CO₃²⁻)

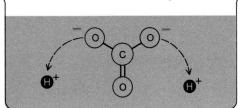

(2) Only a very small percentage of the carbonic acid molecules lose both protons in water solution.

Since carbon is moderately electronegative and the C—O bond in C—O—H is stronger than the O—H bond, the carbonic acid molecule dissociates in water by losing protons, and therefore is an acid. Dissociation takes place in two steps:

$$\underset{\text{carbonic acid}}{H_2CO_3} \rightarrow H^+ + \underset{\text{bicarbonate ion}}{HCO_3^-} \rightarrow 2H^+ + \underset{\text{carbonate ion}}{CO_3^{2-}}$$

The carbonate ion is as hard to represent by a simple Lewis electron-dot model as the benzene molecule is. One can draw many possible structures, and several of these are shown at the far right. Three of these would suggest that carbon is double-bonded to one oxygen, and single-bonded to the two oxygens from which the protons split away. These structures differ only in the choice of the oxygen atom to receive the double bond. None of these structures are correct, because x-ray studies of crystals of carbonate compounds show that all three C—O bonds in the carbonate ion are identical, and that the oxygens lie at the corners of an equilateral triangle around the carbon atom. We can draw such a symmetrical model for the carbonate ion, but it is not very satisfactory because it places a negative charge on each oxygen atom and a positive charge on the carbon (see fourth structure at far right).

We are back at the same dilemma encountered in Chapter 4 with the benzene molecule. The real carbonate ion cannot be described by simple single and double electron-pair bonds. The two negative charges that are left behind when carbonic acid dissociates actually are *delocalized*, or spread over the entire carbonate ion. Each C—O bond is intermediate between a single and a double bond. The true ion can be thought of as a combination of all of the trial structures drawn at the far right, but corresponds to no one of them. We can show the ion either with partial double bonds, or with a cloud of delocalized electrons, as at the bottom of the following page.

X-ray crystal structure analyses of carbonate compounds reveal that each C—O bond is 1.36 Å long. Single C—O bonds in other compounds are 1.43 Å long, and double C=O bonds are 1.23 Å. From these values alone, one would estimate that each carbonate bond has approximately one third of a double-bond character, as if the actual ion were the average of the three models with two single bonds and one double bond shown on the next page.

Delocalization of electrons helps to make carbonic acid a stronger acid than boric acid. For benzene, we found that delocalizing the six ring electrons made the molecule 40 kcal mole⁻¹ more stable than it would be otherwise. The carbonate ion with its two delocalized electrons also is more stable than it would be if the electrons were confined to the two oxygens that released protons during dissociation. Dissociation and association are reversible processes, and both are going on simultaneously:

$$H_2CO_3 \underset{\text{association}}{\overset{\text{dissociation}}{\rightleftarrows}} 2H^+ + CO_3^{2-}$$

The actual amounts of carbonic acid and carbonate ion that exist in solution are the result of a balance, or equilibrium, between the forward and reverse processes. Delocalization, by making the carbonate ion more stable, favors dissociation and discourages association, because the delocalization is destroyed and the electrons are trapped in O—H bonds when the protons rejoin the carbonate ion. This shifts the balance or equilibrium point to the right, thereby producing more H^+ ions, and making carbonic acid a stronger acid than it would be without delocalization.

Another way to look at this behavior is to recognize that the two negative charges on a carbonate ion would have the strongest attraction for protons if they were tied down on specific oxygens on the outside of the ion. If the negative charges are spread over the entire ion, the attraction of the ion for protons is blurred. This discourages association, and ensures that more protons remain loose than would be the case if delocalization did not exist.

When several atoms are covalently bonded into an ion such as CO_3^{2-}, the ion goes through many chemical reactions as a unit, behaving like a single-atom ion of the same charge. Carbonate ions can form salts with Li^+ or other positive ions just as fluoride ions can. Li_2CO_3 is lithium carbonate and, like Li_2O, the crystal structure of this salt has two $+1$ ions (Li^+) for every -2 ion (CO_3^{2-}). $LiHCO_3$, with one positive Li^+ and one positive H^+ ion, is known as lithium hydrogen carbonate (or in an older nomenclature, lithium *bicarbonate* since it contains twice as much carbonate per lithium atom as Li_2CO_3 does). Many negative ions, or *anions*, are built from several covalently bonded atoms; the carbonate ion is an example. Positive ions, or *cations*, with several atoms are less common, in comparison with single-atom metal ions such as Li^+ or Be^{2+}. One exception that we have seen already is the ammonium ion, NH_4^+, in which four H atoms are covalently bonded around a central nitrogen.

CARBONATE ION STRUCTURES

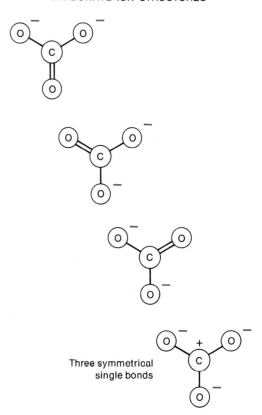

Three symmetrical single bonds

Four possible—but incorrect—structures for the carbonate ion. The correct structure is shown at the bottom left.

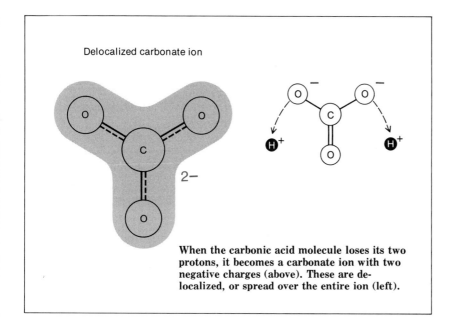

Delocalized carbonate ion

2−

When the carbonic acid molecule loses its two protons, it becomes a carbonate ion with two negative charges (above). These are delocalized, or spread over the entire ion (left).

Carbonic acid would be intrinsically stronger than boric acid because of the greater electronegativity of carbon over boron, but delocalization adds an extra bit of acid strength. There is no delocalization in the borate ion, $B(OH)_4^-$, since every electron is either tied up in a specific electron-pair bond between atoms or occupied as an oxygen lone pair. Even with extra help from delocalization, carbonic acid is weak enough to be drunk in carbonated beverages. Delocalization really becomes important in increasing acidity in the next molecule to be discussed, nitric acid.

NITROGEN AND NITRIC ACID

Nitrogen has many oxides, with varying degrees of electron sharing. These oxides range from colorless gases (N_2O and NO), to a brown gas (NO_2), to an explosive white solid (N_2O_5). If these all were ionic compounds rather than covalent molecules, and if each oxygen atom took two electrons from a nitrogen atom to complete its neon shell, then the formulas of the oxides given above would suggest that nitrogen gave up one electron in N_2O (recall Li_2O), two electrons in NO, four in NO_2, and all five in N_2O_5. This is not what really happens; electrons in these molecules are shared rather than given up. But this formal accounting scheme leads to a useful quantity, the *oxidation number* of nitrogen, which ranges from $+1$ through $+5$ in these oxides. The oxidation number is the charge that the nitrogen atom would have if both electrons in each covalent bond were given to the more electronegative oxygen atom. We will return to the important concepts of oxidation and oxidation numbers in Chapter 6.

The most interesting oxide to us at the moment is the one with the highest oxidation number, N_2O_5. When this compound is added to water, it forms nitric acid, one of the standard reagents of the chemical laboratory:

$$\underset{\substack{\text{nitrogen}\\\text{pentoxide}}}{N_2O_5} + H_2O \rightarrow \underset{\substack{\text{nitric}\\\text{acid}}}{2HNO_3}$$

(There are safer ways of making nitric acid for commercial purposes.) Nitric acid is much stronger than carbonic acid. It is dissociated completely into protons and nitrate ions in water:

$$\underset{\substack{\text{nitric}\\\text{acid}}}{HNO_3} \rightarrow H^+ + \underset{\substack{\text{nitrate}\\\text{ion}}}{NO_3^-}$$

whereas carbonic acid is only partially dissociated, and boric acid is hardly dissociated at all.

It is difficult to draw a Lewis-dot model or simple bond structure for nitric acid. Three such structures, neither of which is correct by itself, are shown in the top right margin of the next page. Four possible structures for the nitrate ion appear beneath them, and others can be drawn. As with the carbonate ion, all three N—O bonds in NO_3^- actu-

NITRIC ACID MOLECULE (HNO₃)

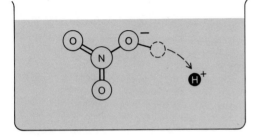

The nitric acid molecule loses its lone proton in water.

NITRIC ACID SOLUTION

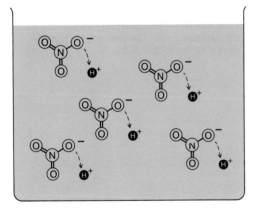

All of the nitric acid molecules lose their protons in water, making HNO_3 a strong acid. Compare this behavior with that of carbonic and boric acids.

ally are the same length. The negative charge that is left behind on the oxygen by the departing proton is delocalized over the entire ion (see structure at bottom right). Delocalization makes the nitrate ion more stable, favors the dissociation of HNO_3, and therefore makes nitric acid stronger than it would be otherwise.

The nitrate ion is isoelectronic with the carbonate ion. If one could reach into the nitrogen nucleus in the NO_3^- ion and "turn off" one proton, then CO_3^{2-} would result, with the same arrangement of atom centers and electrons. The extra nuclear charge on nitrogen causes it to hold the delocalized electron more tightly, and discourages its binding a proton and making the undissociated acid molecule. The nitrate ion has a weaker attraction for protons than the carbonate ion, so nitric acid is stronger than carbonic acid.

The lunar excursion module from the Apollo moon landings used another oxide of nitrogen as part of its propellant. Its fuel was hydrazine (H_2N—NH_2) and methyl hydrazine (CH_3NH—NH_2), and the oxidizer was dinitrogen tetroxide (N_2O_4), a liquefied dimer of gaseous NO_2. Combustion produced mainly nitrogen and water, with a few other oxides of nitrogen:

$$2N_2H_4 + N_2O_4 \rightarrow 3N_2 + 4H_2O + \text{energy}$$

A big advantage for rocket design is that these two liquids are *hypergolic*. This means that they ignite spontaneously when mixed in the combustion chamber, making an ignition system for the rocket motor unnecessary.

FLUORINE, THE ELECTRON GRABBER

With fluorine, the roles of atoms in oxygen compounds are reversed. All of the atoms through nitrogen were less electronegative than oxygen, with the result that electron pairs were shifted toward O or donated to O outright. In contrast, fluorine is more electronegative and pulls electrons toward itself, even in bonds with oxygen. Fluorine has several oxygen compounds, which are chain molecules of the type F—O—F, F—O—O—F, F—O—O—O—F, and so on. These are rare and unimportant, and do not produce oxyacids, such as boric, carbonic, and nitric acids, when added to water. Fluorine is so electronegative that it does not make covalent bonds with coordinating oxygen atoms in water, but steals electrons from them instead to make fluoride ions. OF_2 breaks up water molecules and releases O_2 in the process of producing fluoride ions:

$$\underset{\substack{\text{oxygen} \\ \text{difluoride}}}{OF_2} + H_2O \rightarrow \underset{\substack{\text{fluoride} \\ \text{ions}}}{2F^-} + 2H^+ + O_2$$

In writing formulas of binary compounds, the more electronegative element is written second. Thus writing OF_2 instead of F_2O and naming the compound oxygen difluoride, rather than difluorine oxide, is a reminder that in this compound fluorine is the more electronegative of the two elements.

NITRIC ACID STRUCTURES

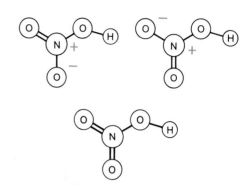

Possible bond models for nitric acid, HNO_3. With simple electron pair bonds, one is forced to assume either charge separation or too many bonds to nitrogen.

NITRATE ION STRUCTURES

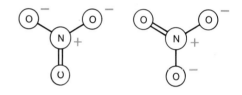

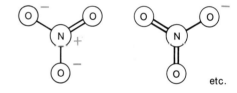

etc.

Four possible bond models for the nitrate ion, NO_3^-. Again, one is faced with the dilemma of excessive charge separation or too many bonds to nitrogen.

Delocalized nitrate ion

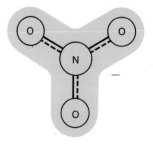

As with the carbonate ion, the negative charge remaining behind on the nitrate ion after the proton is lost is delocalized over the entire ion.

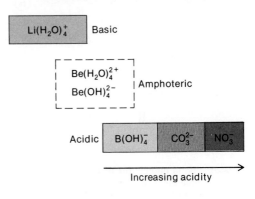

ACID-BASE TRENDS IN THE OXIDES

$Li(H_2O)_4^+$ — Basic

$Be(H_2O)_4^{2+}$
$Be(OH)_4^{2-}$ — Amphoteric

Acidic — $B(OH)_4^-$ — CO_3^{2-} — NO_3^-

Increasing acidity

TRENDS IN PROPERTIES OF THE OXIDES

The trends that we have seen in chemical properties of the second-row elements and their oxides can be extended to the heavier elements as well. Atoms with few outer electrons are metals, and their oxides are basic (left). In solution the metal ions surround themselves with a hydration shell of water molecules, attracted to the ions only by electrostatic forces. Somewhat more electronegative atoms are at the borderline between metals and nonmetals. Their oxides are both acidic and basic, and are termed amphoteric.

Even more electronegative atoms are clearly nonmetals, and complete their outer electron shell by either sharing electrons, or becoming ions by picking up the missing electrons if only one or two are needed. Their oxides are acidic. In solution, the attraction for oxygen is so strong that each central atom is surrounded by a shell of covalently bonded O atoms. The result is an oxyanion such as carbonate, CO_3^{2-}, and nitrate, NO_3^-. The acidity of such compounds is increased by stabilization of the ions via delocalized electrons.

Finally, if the electronegativity of the atom is greater than that of oxygen (true only for F), then the electrons are not shared between the central atom and O in covalent bonds, but are pulled away from the O atoms entirely. The result is not an oxyion, but a simple F^- ion. This behavior will not be seen again in heavier elements, because none of them are more electronegative than oxygen.

IONS AND METALS

Atoms with small electronegativities, which have strong tendencies to lose one, two, or three electrons and become positive ions, can associate in a special kind of solid without the presence of negative ions. These are the metals. A metal is an orderly crystalline packing of positive ions, each one having given up electrons from its outermost, incomplete electron shell (top of next page). These electrons are mobile, and are free to wander from one end of the metal to the other. The electrons surround the positive ions and hold the metal together. Without them, the full force of electrostatic repulsion between positive ions would blow the metal apart. With them, the positive ions can be packed together like marbles in a box. The structures of most metals are really just as simple as that: they represent efficient ways of packing spheres in a limited space.

Lithium metal is held together by one electron per positive ion, and beryllium by twice as many electrons. The additional electrons help to hold the positive ions together more strongly and make beryllium a harder metal than lithium. These electrons, instead of being confined to the vicinity of one atom as in a gas, are completely delocalized. As we already have seen for benzene and for carbonic and nitric acids, delocalization enhances stability. Part of the forces that hold a metal together comes from this delocalization.

Most of the physical properties that we associate with metals can be explained in terms of this model of closely packed positive ions held

86

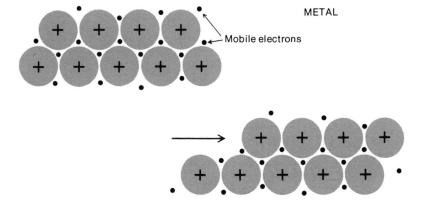

METAL

Mobile electrons

Positive ions in a metal can be pushed past one another without flying apart because they are held together by a "sea" of negative electrons.

together by delocalized electrons. When pressure is applied to a metal, the positive ions can roll past one another with little opposition, like marbles in mineral oil. The delocalized electrons "lubricate" this flow by shielding each positive ion from the charge of its neighbors. Layers of atoms can be bent, pushed out of shape, or pulled into a thin column without breaking the attraction between atoms. Hence metals are flexible, malleable (capable of being hammered into new shapes), and ductile (capable of being drawn into wires). If a foreign object such as a knife blade is intruded between layers of atoms in a soft metal like copper, the bonding of metal atoms on either side of the knife cut is unimpaired. In view of the role that electrons play in holding metals together, perhaps a better image of metal structure than marbles in mineral oil would be marbles in molasses.

Salt crystals react quite differently to mechanical stress. Rather than yielding to stress, they first resist, then either cleave cleanly along layers or crack and shatter. This is because positive and negative charges alternate in the crystal lattice of a salt. In an undeformed salt crystal these charges interlock in a stable way. But if one sheet of atoms is pushed over another, similar charges on the two sheets are brought closer together (see illustration at the bottom of the page). The strong electrostatic repulsion between similar charges pushes the sheets apart, and the crystal shatters.

Melting and boiling points of metals vary widely, but generally are lower than for salts. Melting a metal requires only that the positive ions be given enough thermal energy to shake loose from their close-packed positions and slide past one another in a liquid. Since salt crystals are careful balances of positive and negative charges, disturbing this bal-

If the layers of a salt crystal are pushed past one another, the resulting repulsion by like charges will push the layers apart, thereby breaking the crystal.

SALT CRYSTAL

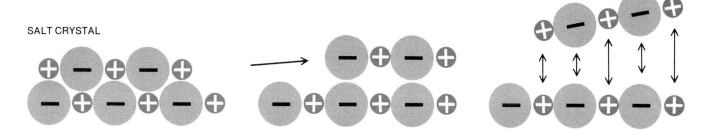

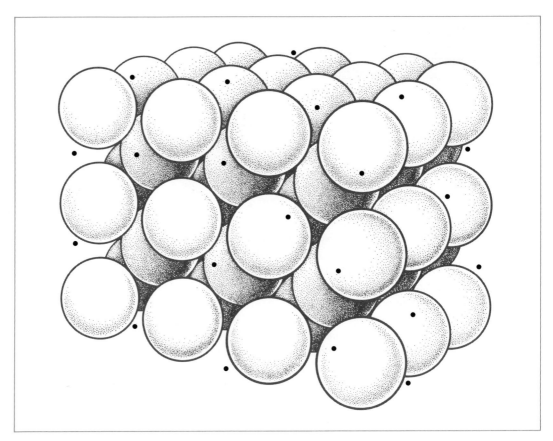

THE STRUCTURE OF LITHIUM METAL

Lithium metal, and other metals with one mobile electron per metal atom such as sodium and potassium, pack together in a cubic structure in which ions sit at the corners and at the center of a cube. This is called body-centered cubic or bcc packing.

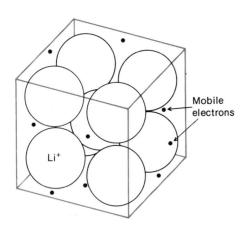

Mobile electrons

Li⁺

ance and melting the crystal brings like charges nearer to one another more often, and this requires energy. Vaporizing a metal requires only that each positive ion recapture its outer electrons from the general sea of electrons, but vaporizing a salt requires that electrons be forced back from the negative ions toward the positive ions during the formation of neutral gas molecules.

The mobile electrons in a metal can move from one end of the block to the other, and conduct electricity. Salts do not conduct electricity when crystalline, because the ions then are locked in place. If a salt is either melted or dissolved in water, then it can conduct electricity through the migration of entire ions, not electrons.

Heat is simply motion at the atomic or molecular level. If a match is touched to one end of a solid, the molecules or atoms at that end begin to vibrate more rapidly, and as each rapidly vibrating atom induces a slower neighbor to vibrate faster, heat flows along the solid object. The mobile electrons in a metal are very good carriers of this vibrational energy, so metals are good conductors of heat as well as electricity. Metals feel cold to the touch because they conduct heat away from your fingertips so fast. In salts each ion is held in place by the pull from neighboring ions of opposite charge, thereby forming a rigid framework. The vibrations of ions are damped down quickly by the attraction of

88

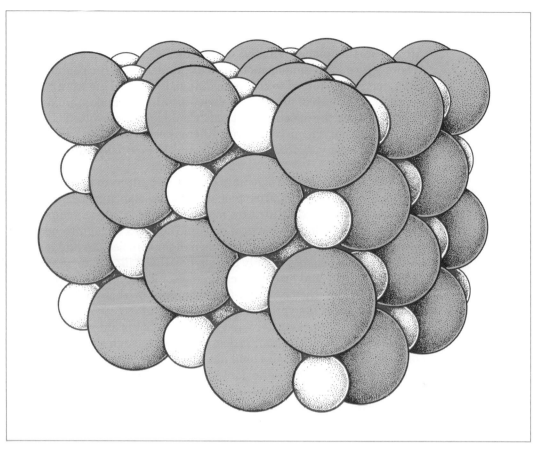

THE STRUCTURE OF A TYPICAL SALT

neighboring ions, and vibrations are passed down the crystal lattice inefficiently. Salts therefore are poor conductors of heat.

Even metallic sheen can be explained by structure. A glass surface or a mirror appears bright because the light that falls on it is reflected efficiently. Mirrors are simply glass, with a thin metal layer as a backing. When light strikes a metal, it is absorbed and the light energy raises electrons to excited (higher) energy states. There are many mobile electrons in a metal, and many closely spaced energy levels. The excited electrons can move about, and can drop back to their original low-energy states, giving back the energy as photons of light. Nonmetals lack these closely spaced electronic energy states, so light, once absorbed, is less likely to be reemitted.

Melting points are useful measures of the forces between molecules or ions. Molecular solids, in which covalently bonded molecules are packed together with nothing but van der Waals forces between them, have low melting points. Solid O_2, for example, melts at $-218°C$. Lithium metal, which has mobile electrons holding it together, melts at $179°C$, and LiF, a typical salt, melts at a much higher $842°C$. Solids that are held together completely by covalent bonds in a three-dimensional network are the most tightly knit of all, and carbon in the form of diamond has a melting point of over $3600°C$.

Lithium fluoride, sodium chloride, and many other salts have the structure shown here, in which positive and negative ions alternate along the three directions through the cubic lattice.

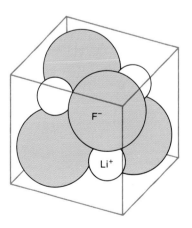

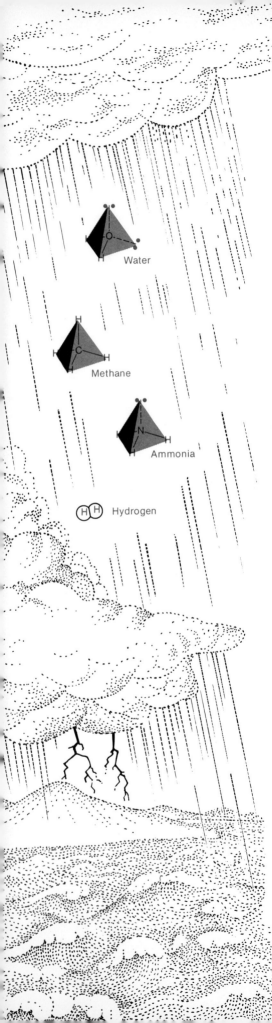

Water

Methane

Ammonia

Hydrogen

POSTSCRIPT: THE ELEMENTS OF LIFE

All life on this planet is based on the four elements C, N, O, and H. Wherever we look, similar molecules are undergoing such similar reactions that we are forced to conclude that all terrestrial life has a common ancestry. The web of life on this planet is universal and unbroken. Before we can ask the difficult question, "Could life have evolved elsewhere using a different chemistry or even different elements?" we must answer the simpler query, "How are C, N, O, and H especially suitable as the elements of life?"

Efficient computing machines cannot be built from ratchets, gears, and pulleys, as the computer pioneer Charles Babbage learned to his sorrow a century ago.[1] Intricate machines need intricate components. It is hard to imagine a biological machine complex enough to be classified as *living*, as made up from simple inorganic molecules and ions. Of all the chemical elements, only carbon has the ability to form virtually endless straight- and branched-chain molecules of infinite variety. We will develop this theme in the final chapters of this book. Nitrogen could never build the variety and complexity of molecules needed for a living organism, for long —N—N—N—N— chains are explosively unstable. Neither could boron; it does not have enough electrons to form continuous chains. Metals could not become the basis of the molecules of life, because electrostatic forces are nondirectional, and the only structure found in salts and metals comes from the packing of ions. Only carbon, with four electrons per atom available for making four electron-pair bonds, can construct the scaffolding needed for elaborate molecules.

Many of the second-shell atoms are special in that they are small enough to come close together and share more than one electron pair in double bonds. This, as we shall see later, is crucial in molecular architecture and the absorption of light. Double bonds contribute structural rigidity to large molecules. Rings and chains of carbon atoms with delocalized electrons have electronic energy levels close enough together to absorb and trap visible light. Chlorophyll, the key molecule in photosynthesis, is a large molecule with many delocalized electrons. The ability to trap light is important, because the most abundant source of energy available to life on any planet is radiation from that planet's star. These second-row atoms are small enough to make double bonds, but the larger atoms that we shall see in the next two chapters can do this only with difficulty, or not at all. For this reason alone, life based on third-shell or heavier elements is unlikely. The third-shell atoms are too big, and the first-shell atoms, H and He, are too simple by themselves. *Life appears to be a property of second-shell atoms.*

---

[1] Charles Babbage (1792–1871) is an interesting case of a man born a century too early. He was an English mathematician who, in 1822, proposed the concept of a digital computer with an internally stored and alterable program. He then spent the rest of his life and considerable sums of his own and government money in an unsuccessful effort to build one with the nonelectronic technology of his era. His great "calculating engine" was a failure, but his principles were used by John von Neumann and others in the 1940's when they invented the electronic digital computer. Babbage's calculating engine, like Leonardo da Vinci's helicopter, was sound in principle but technologically premature.

The energy for life may come ultimately from the sun, but it is stored in carbon–hydrogen–oxygen compounds, and released by the combination of these molecules with oxygen. Oxygen is almost unique in its chemical reactivity, and in the energy that it gives off when it combines with other atoms. This arises from its high affinity for electrons, or its electronegativity. Only fluorine is more reactive, but it is a thousand times rarer than oxygen on the crust of the Earth, and thus was bypassed as a reactant for the energy-releasing machinery.

Reactions in solution are so much more rapid than solid-state processes that we can hardly imagine life evolving on a planet without large amounts of a liquid that is a good solvent for other chemical substances. One of the most common oxygen compounds on Earth is water. Because its molecules are polar, water is an excellent solvent for salts and molecules with polar bonds. It dissolves carbon dioxide with the release of acidic protons, and ammonia with the creation of basic hydroxide ions. These protons and hydroxide ions in turn catalyze, or speed up, reactions that otherwise would proceed extremely slowly. Many other compounds are acids or bases in aqueous solution. Liquid ammonia has solvent properties similar to those of water, and has been suggested as a possible medium for extraterrestrial life on a cold planet. Ammonia has one disadvantage that affects its usefulness as a solvent medium in which life might evolve: Water ice floats on water, but ammonia ice sinks in liquid ammonia.

There is another reason why H, C, N, and O were used in the development of life: Like Mt. Everest, they were there. The primary atmosphere on the Earth that was present when it was formed by accretion of material from the primal dust cloud around the young sun, was mainly hydrogen, helium, and some other inert gases. In time, these light atoms were lost from the planet's weak gravitational field, and the Earth became an airless ball of rock. The secondary atmosphere, in which life evolved, arose later by outgassing of the interior of the planet. This atmosphere was mainly a mixture of hydrogen, and of methane, ammonia, and water, the hydrogen compounds of the second-row nonmetals. Only such small, covalently bonded molecules as these were gases and hence were exuded into the secondary atmosphere. The heavier elements, and the elements that favored ionic compounds, remained locked in the minerals of the crust. It is natural that if life develops on a planet, it makes use of materials that are readily available.

To complete the story in capsule form, the best evidence we have suggests that lightning discharges, ultraviolet radiation, heat from vulcanism, and energy from radioactive decay caused the molecules of the primitive atmosphere to react and to condense (polymerize) into formaldehyde, amino acids, and other simple organic compounds, which were washed into the seas by rain. This thin "organic soup" then was the medium in which self-perpetuating chemical systems sufficiently complex to be called "living" gradually developed. Our planet did not decide, 4.5 billion years ago, to bring forth life. Instead, the Earth was fortunate enough to have in abundance the kinds of chemical elements that could form the types of compounds that led to the reactive systems of living organisms. It is possible that, given the right conditions on a young planet, life develops as inevitably as crystals develop in evaporat-

Sun

Mercury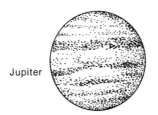

Venus

Earth

Mars

ing salt water. Life is a matter of physical forces and chemical reactions. We cannot yet define these "right conditions" with assurance, and the prime reason for the unmanned probes of Venus and Mars has been to search for some other form of life, and to give us more data on the limits within which life can evolve. We are apparently out of luck with Venus, which has surface temperatures close to that of molten lead. Mercury is a lifeless ball of rock baked by the sun. Mars is our best remaining hope as a home for extraterrestrial life, although it apparently is a dry, cold, and relatively inhospitable planet. We can imagine life surviving under present Martian conditions (even human life), but it is hard to imagine it *evolving* under such conditions. Perhaps Mars was a quite different planet earlier in its history.

Jupiter is rich in hydrogen, with lesser amounts of ammonia and methane, and it is not ridiculous to imagine liquid ammonia as a medium for life there instead of water. But we have no data or experience to make this more than pure speculation. Even this would still be "second-shell" life, using the same group of chemical elements as on Earth. Beyond Jupiter, the low temperatures and resulting slowdown in chemical reactions make life hard to imagine. All that we can say is that, wherever life is found, we would expect it to be based on the first- and second-shell elements, hydrogen through fluorine. Whether there is more than one pattern of reactions or choice of elements for life within this range, is impossible to say.

Jupiter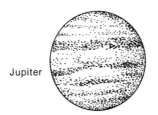

Saturn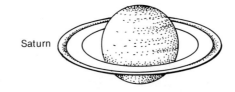

QUESTIONS

1. What is different about the forces between atoms in gaseous diatomic HF and LiF?

2. What types of forces hold the liquid together in liquid HF? In liquid LiF?

3. Why is the boiling point of LiF so much higher than that of HF?

4. Why is the melting point of LiF so much higher than that of HF?

5. Which liquid, HF or LiF, is more like liquid benzene? Why?

6. In which of the three phases—solid, liquid, or gas—will you find discrete molecules of HF? Is the situation the same for LiF?

7. What is the term for substances that behave like LiF?

8. Will LiF conduct electricity as a solid? Will it do so after being melted? What carries the electric current? Compare this with the conduction of electricity by a metal.

9. What role do the water molecules play when LiF is dissolved in water? Will LiF dissolved in water conduct electricity? If so, what carries the current?

10. What combines with what in the neutralization process? In what sense is neutralization the "canceling out" of an acid and a base?

11. When sodium hydroxide (NaOH) is neutralized by hydrochloric acid (HCl), what happens to the sodium ions? What would be left behind if the neutralized solution were evaporated to dryness?

12. What is meant when nitric acid is described as a strong acid, carbonic acid as a weak acid, and boric acid as extremely weak?

13. How do the relative electronegativities of atoms help to bring about the situation described in Question 12?

14. Why is beryllium oxide described as "amphoteric"? What kind of bonding holds crystalline BeO together?

15. How does acid cause crystalline BeO to dissolve? How does base produce a similar effect?

16. What is the formula of the beryllium ion in acid solution? What is it in basic solution? What would happen to the ion if one began with an acid solution of beryllium ions and slowly made it basic?

17. Why does fluorine not form an oxion analogous to NO_3^- or CO_3^{2-}?

18. What is the difference between a crystalline solid and a glass? Which of the oxides of second-row elements forms a glass? How do crystals and glasses differ in melting points?

19. Why is the carbon dioxide molecule linear, whereas the water molecule is bent at an angle of 105°?

20. What is the dipole moment of the carbon dioxide molecule?

21. Write at least three possible bond models for the carbonate ion. What would each of your models predict about the three carbon–oxygen bonds? How do the carbon–oxygen bond lengths in the real carbonate ion compare with those in your model structures?

22. In ethylene, $H_2C=CH_2$, all six atoms lie in a plane. Is this also true for hydrazine, H_2N-NH_2? Use VSEPR theory to sketch what the hydrazine molecule should look like.

23. In ethylene, the H—C—H bond angle at either end of the molecule is 120°. Roughly what should the corresponding H—N—H angle be in hydrazine?

24. What holds the ions together in a salt? What holds them together in a metal?

25. Why will metals bend when pushed upon, whereas salts usually crack? Explain in terms of ionic forces.

26. Explain the easy conductivity of electricity by most metals. Why do metals conduct heat well? What gives them their typical "metallic" luster or sheen? Explain the metallic black sheen in graphite. Why does diamond not have the same appearance?

27. Why does liquid ammonia (boiling point −33°C) have solvent properties similar to those of water? Sketch what happens when sodium chloride is dissolved in liquid ammonia. Do the same for methyl alcohol in liquid ammonia.

28. If we were to search through the solar system for life that evolved in liquid ammonia like it evolved in liquid water on Earth, should we begin searching on planets nearer to, or farther from, the sun?

29. What nearly unique physical property does water have that liquid ammonia does not have? How would this affect the temperature distribution at different depths in oceans of liquid ammonia versus oceans of water?

PROBLEMS

1. What are the molecular weights of lithium hydroxide and hydrogen fluoride?

2. In the neutralization of lithium hydroxide solution by hydrofluoric acid solution, how many moles of HF are required for each mole of LiOH?

3. How many moles of HF will be required to neutralize 100 g of LiOH? How many grams of HF will this correspond to?

4. If the neutralized solution of the preceding problem is evaporated to dryness, how many moles of crystalline lithium fluoride will result? How many grams of LiF will there be?

5. How much water will be produced during neutralization of 100 g of LiOH? How does the total weight of lithium hydroxide plus hydrogen fluoride starting materials compare with the weight of water plus LiF at the end of the experiment?

6. If, in the lunar excursion module propulsion system, one molecule of N_2O_4 reacts with two molecules of hydrazine to yield three molecules of N_2 and four molecules of H_2O, write an equation for this reaction. Check your result against the equation given previously in this chapter. Count the numbers of atoms of N, H, and O

on both sides of the equation. Are they the same for each kind of atom? If this is so, then the equation is said to be "balanced."

7. Calculate the molecular weights of N_2O_4 and hydrazine. How many moles of hydrazine would be required to react with one mole of nitrogen tetroxide?

8. How many moles of hydrazine will be required to react with 500 g of N_2O_4? How many grams of hydrazine will this be? How many grams of N_2 and water vapor will be ejected through the rocket nozzle? How does this compare with the original weight of hydrazine and nitrogen tetroxide?

9. In metallic iron, the atoms are arranged at the corners and the center of a cube of edge 2.866 Å, in the same body-centered cubic structure shown in this chapter for lithium. What is the volume of this unit cube, and how many iron atoms are there per unit volume of this size? (Be careful. If an iron atom is shared between four unit volumes, then only one quarter of the atom can be counted for a given unit volume. What is the situation with regard to sharing for one of the atoms at the corners of the cube? What about the atom in the center of the cube?)

10. What is the atomic volume for iron, in $Å^3$ per atom? What is the atomic density, in atoms per $Å^3$? How many atoms are there per cubic centimeter in iron?

11. The measured density of iron is 7.86 g cm^{-3}. If the atomic weight of iron is 55.85, how many moles of iron are there per cubic centimeter?

12. Use the answers to Problems 10 and 11 to obtain an experimental value for Avogadro's number. How does it compare with the value that we have used before?

13. The structure of crystalline sodium chloride can be thought of as being built from cubes with Na^+ and Cl^- ions on alternating corners, as in the diagrams seen previously in this chapter. The distance between the centers of Na^+ and Cl^- ions along an edge of the cube is 2.820 Å. (These crystal spacings can be obtained from x-ray diffraction experiments.) How many NaCl units are there in a cube 2.820 Å on a side? (Remember the sharing of ions with several adjacent cubes. You should come up with an answer of one half unit of NaCl per cube of edge 2.820 Å.) What is the density of sodium chloride, in NaCl pairs per $Å^3$? What is the density in NaCl pairs per cm^3?

14. The measured density of rock salt is 2.165 g cm^{-3}. Calculate the molecular weight of NaCl from the atomic weights on the inside back cover, and calculate the density of NaCl in moles cm^{-3}.

15. Use your answers to Problems 13 and 14 to calculate Avogadro's number. How does it compare with the value we have been using?

ELECTRON SHELLS

Electrons in filled shells are shown as gray dots on a colored background. Outer-shell electrons are black dots on a white background. In the Lewis dot notation below each atom, each of the four compass points represents a position for one of four possible electron pairs.

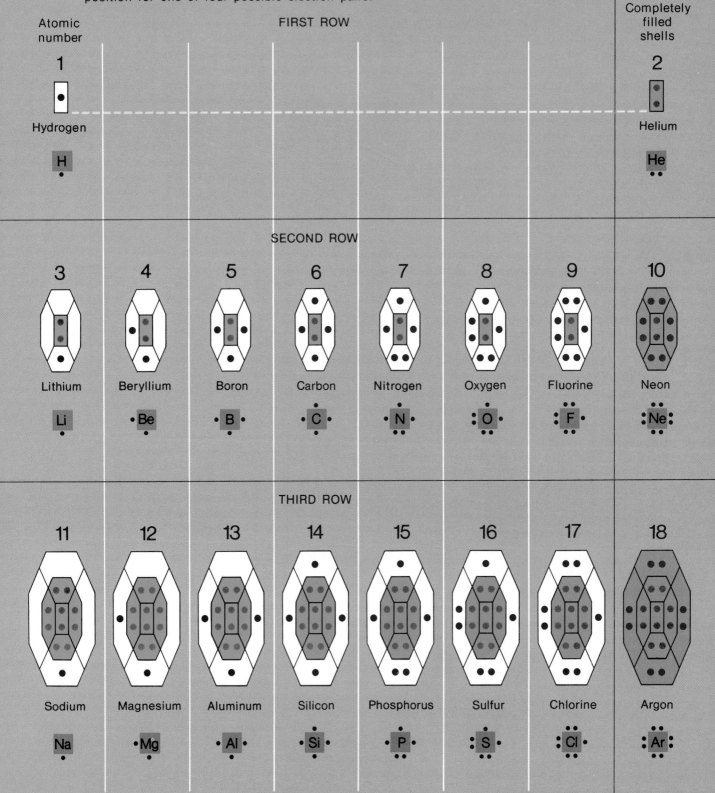

CHAPTER 6

Periodicity of Behavior; Sodium Through Argon

The preceding three chapters have been a brief primer of chemistry, with most of the central ideas that will be needed to explain how all atoms behave: electronegativity; ions and atoms; metals and non-metals; ionic and covalent bonds; gases, liquids, and solids; acids and bases; salts and molecular compounds. The most encouraging single fact of chemistry is that once you understand the properties of these first ten elements, you have a very good idea of how the next eight should react, and the heavier atoms as well. In this chapter we really will not be breaking new ground in looking at the third-shell elements, but merely tying together the ideas in Chapters 3 through 5 and showing how they apply to atoms with more electrons.

In Chapter 3 we imagined a process in which we built up heavier and heavier atoms by increasing the charge on the nucleus (by adding more protons) and adding more electrons around the nucleus to keep the atom electrically neutral. The first two electrons went into the inner electron shell, in the elements H and He. The next eight electrons were added one at a time to form Li through Ne, while filling a second electron shell. Now if we add more electrons, the next eight can go into a third electron shell to build elements with atomic numbers 11 through 18. The nineteenth electron has to be placed in a fourth shell because the third shell has room for only eight electrons at this point in the periodic table. Thus it is logical to look at elements 11 through 18 as a unit.

The electronic structures of the first eighteen elements are shown on the facing page, arranged in three rows of the periodic table as it was introduced at the end of Chapter 3. These are not pictures of the atoms, but are schematic diagrams of electron-shell structure. Electrons are represented by black dots. Each shell is shown in white while it is being filled, and with a colored background when full, so that attention will be

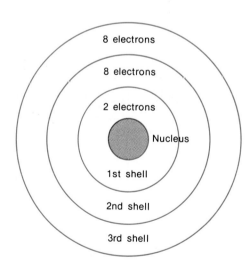

Shell diagram of a neutral atom. The positively charged nucleus is surrounded by clouds of negatively charged electrons, arranged in successive shells. The first (inner) shell holds a maximum of 2 electrons; the second and third shells can hold 8 outer electrons each.

97

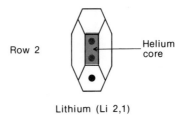

Row 2

Helium core

Lithium (Li 2,1)

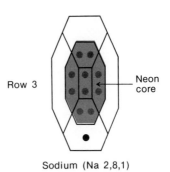

Row 3

Neon core

Sodium (Na 2,8,1)

Lithium and sodium both have a lone outer electron around a filled inner core, but the core consists of two electrons in Li and ten electrons in Na. Similarly, the same outer-shell structure is found in carbon and silicon, in fluorine and chlorine, and in neon and argon (below).

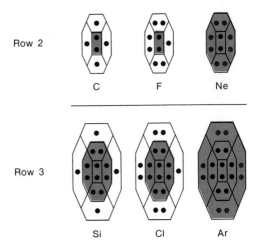

Row 2

C   F   Ne

Row 3

Si   Cl   Ar

focused on the next shell being filled. The second and third shells are divided into four boxes as a reminder that the eight electrons in a full shell occur as four electron pairs. Below each shell diagram is a Lewis electron-dot diagram of the atom, which conveys the same information about outer-shell electrons. Each of the four compass points around the atom symbol in a Lewis diagram represents one of the four possible positions for electron pairs.

Second- and third-shell atoms with the same number of outer electrons are placed in the same vertical column in the drawing at the beginning of the chapter. Lithium and sodium have one outer electron each around a filled inner core. In lithium this core consists of two electrons in the first shell, whereas in sodium the core is made up of ten electrons in the first and second shells (left). Lithium has one electron outside a "helium" core, and its electronic structure can be written Li 2,1. Sodium has one electron outside a filled "neon" core, and is represented as Na 2,8,1. Carbon has four electrons outside a helium core, and silicon has four electrons outside a neon core. Fluorine and chlorine have seven electrons each surrounding a two-electron or ten-electron core. At the end of the rows, neon has a filled eight-electron second shell and argon has a filled eight-electron third shell. The argon electrons serve as a core for the heavier fourth-shell elements.

Atoms with the same outer-shell structure have similar chemical properties. These outer electrons are the most significant features that a neighboring atom sees. Sodium behaves like lithium, silicon and carbon have many properties in common, and chlorine and fluorine are very much alike. This is the most important single fact in this chapter, and we will develop this theme at length.

Having said this, we must qualify matters by saying that there are important differences in the chemical behavior of second-shell and third-shell elements, which arise because the third-shell atoms are bigger and have a weaker hold on their outer electrons. Each third-shell atom has a lower first ionization energy than the corresponding atom in the row above it. This property makes every third-shell element *less* electronegative than its second-shell analogue, and more metallic. This is the key to the chemistry of the third-shell elements.

The three rows in the opening diagram, which represent the first three electron shells, are the beginning of a very important means of classifying chemical properties of atoms, the *periodic table*. The periodic table is organized such that the successive addition of electrons to the same shell occurs across horizontal rows (or periods), and similar outer electron-shell structures and chemical properties are found in vertical columns (or groups). In this chapter and the following two, we shall see the complete periodic table gradually developed for all 106 chemical elements. The periodic table was devised a century ago as a memory aid, to make chemistry easier. It eventually became the great statement of chemical reality, against which any theory of atomic structure and properties had to be tested. The predictions of the most successful theory to date, quantum mechanics, will be tested against the periodic table in the next two chapters.

The second-shell elements are the elements of living organisms, and the third-shell elements make up the framework of our planet. The crust of the Earth is 60 atomic percent oxygen. The other 40% is di-

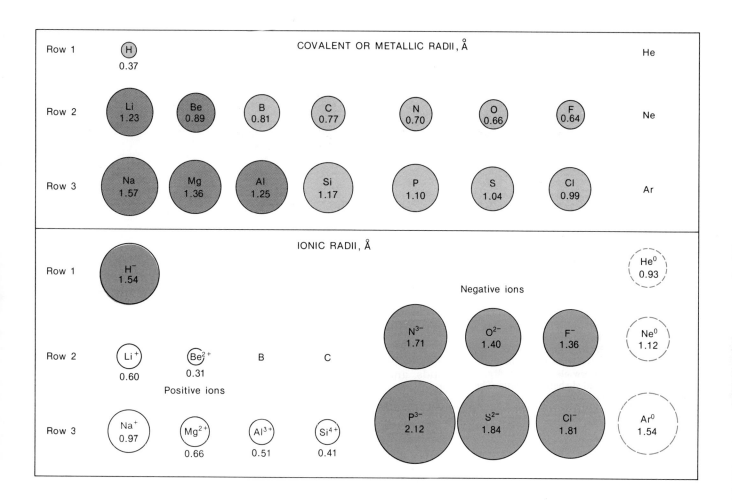

COVALENT OR METALLIC RADII, Å

| Row 1 | H 0.37 | | | | | | | He |

| Row 2 | Li 1.23 | Be 0.89 | B 0.81 | C 0.77 | N 0.70 | O 0.66 | F 0.64 | Ne |

| Row 3 | Na 1.57 | Mg 1.36 | Al 1.25 | Si 1.17 | P 1.10 | S 1.04 | Cl 0.99 | Ar |

IONIC RADII, Å

Negative ions

Positive ions

| Row 1 | H^- 1.54 | | | | | | | He^0 0.93 |

| Row 2 | Li^+ 0.60 | Be^{2+} 0.31 | B | C | N^{3-} 1.71 | O^{2-} 1.40 | F^- 1.36 | Ne^0 1.12 |

| Row 3 | Na^+ 0.97 | Mg^{2+} 0.66 | Al^{3+} 0.51 | Si^{4+} 0.41 | P^{3-} 2.12 | S^{2-} 1.84 | Cl^- 1.81 | Ar^0 1.54 |

vided among silicon (21%), hydrogen (3%), and third- and fourth-shell metals (16% together): sodium, magnesium, and aluminum in the third shell; and potassium, calcium, and iron in the fourth. All of the remaining elements taken together make up less than half of one percent of the Earth's crust. The six metals just mentioned occur in combinations with oxygen as silicate minerals, water, and the various metal oxides, carbonates, and nitrates. The third-shell elements are the stage on which the chemistry of life is played.

ELECTRONIC STRUCTURE AND CHEMICAL PROPERTIES

Everything that we have learned in the preceding three chapters about the properties of elements applies to the heavier atoms, with one key difference: The atoms of the third row are larger, so their outer electrons are farther from the nucleus. The top section of the diagrams above shows the relative sizes of atoms when they are involved in metallic or covalent bonds. We saw these radii for the first ten elements in Chapter 3. The ionic radii in the second section represent the sizes of ions having the closed-shell configuration of the nearest noble gas, positive ions for metals and negative ions for nonmetals. These radii are the sizes of ions in salts.

Metallic radius in sodium metal

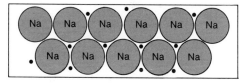

Covalent radius in chlorine gas

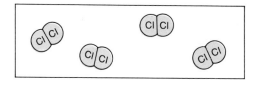

The ionic radius of Na^+ in salts is smaller than the Na metallic radius; the ionic radius of Cl^- is larger than the Cl covalent radius.

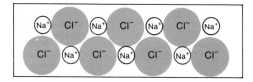

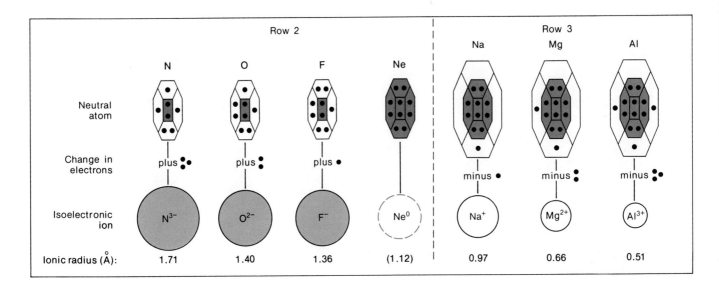

Ionic radius (Å): | N 1.71 | O 1.40 | F 1.36 | Ne (1.12) | Na 0.97 | Mg 0.66 | Al 0.51

ISOELECTRONIC IONS

All of the ions above have ten electrons, as does neon. The second-row elements N, O, and F have gained enough electrons to fill their second shell. The third-row elements Na, Mg, and Al have lost their third-shell electrons. The steadily increasing charge on the nucleus from N^{3-} to Al^{3+} pulls the electrons closer in, and makes the ions smaller.

Metallic bonding radii for metals and covalent bonding radii for nonmetals form a smooth, continuous series because both kinds of bonding involve electron sharing; between pairs of atoms in covalent bonds, and throughout the entire block of metal in metallic bonding. Metallic radii are larger than ionic radii for the corresponding positive ions in salts. The effective radius of sodium, for example, is greater when mutually repelling positive ions are packed together in a metal and held by a "glue" of electrons, than when an ion which has completely lost its outer electron is packed in a NaCl salt crystal next to ions of opposite charge. Thus the metallic radius of sodium in the metal is 1.57 Å, whereas its ionic radius in NaCl is only 0.97 Å.

Covalent radii of nonmetals are smaller than their corresponding ionic radii, both because the ions have added one or more electrons to complete their outer shell, and because atoms can come closer to one another in covalent bonds. For example, F and Cl (covalent radii) are smaller than F^- and Cl^- (ionic radii). The change in radius between atoms and ions is illustrated for Na and Cl at the bottom of Page 99.

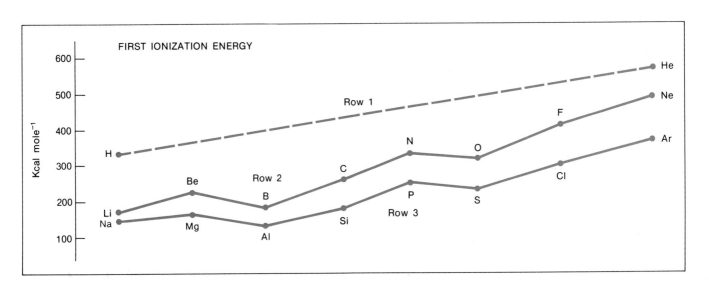

The hydrogen atom has essentially no size at all when it loses an electron and becomes a bare hydrogen nucleus, or H^+ ion. In covalent compounds of hydrogen such as methane, CH_4, the atomic radius of hydrogen is 0.37 Å. In LiH, the *less* electronegative lithium gives its electron to hydrogen, and the H^- ion, with a filled first-electron shell, has an ionic radius of 1.54 Å.

Each atom from Na to Ar is larger than its second-row counterpart because of the additional shell of electrons in its core. Within each row, atoms become smaller with increasing atomic number because of the increased charge on the nucleus. This is illustrated well by the ions in the series

$$N^{3-} \qquad O^{2-} \qquad F^- \qquad Ne^0 \qquad Na^+ \qquad Mg^{2+} \qquad Al^{3+}$$

which extends through the end of the second row and the beginning of the third. The ions and Ne are isoelectronic because they all have the identical 2,8 electron-shell structure. The only difference between them is the charge on the nucleus: +7 for nitrogen through +13 for aluminum. This increasing charge causes the ions to shrink in steady progression, as shown at the top of the opposite page. The "ionic radius" of neon has been set at its van der Waals packing radius, because neon can be considered as a 2,8-electron ion with zero charge. By the same logic, the ionic radii listed for He and Ar also are their van der Waals radii. There are no covalent radii for these atoms because they make no covalent bonds.

Because the third-shell electrons are farther from the nucleus, they are held more weakly. The first ionization energies, plotted at the bottom of the left page, demonstrate this. Within each shell, the first IE increases with atomic number because of the increased charge on the nucleus, but each third-row element has a lower first IE than its second-row analogue.

Electronegativity values also follow this trend (see below). For the second-row atoms they range from 1.0 for Li to 4.0 for F. In the third shell the span is only from 0.9 for Na to 3.0 for Cl. Every third-row element is less electronegative than its counterpart above it in the periodic table, and therefore is more metallic. Sodium, for example, is a

Electronegativities, based on the Pauling scale in which Li is 1 and F is 4

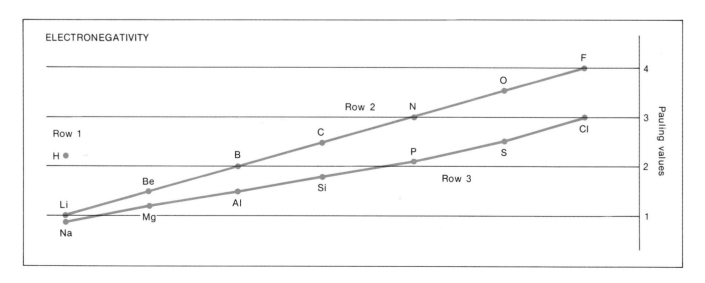

ELECTRONEGATIVITY

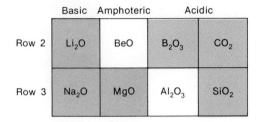

	Basic	Amphoteric	Acidic	
Row 2	Li_2O	BeO	B_2O_3	CO_2
Row 3	Na_2O	MgO	Al_2O_3	SiO_2

Each third-row oxide resembles the second-row oxide above it and to the left.

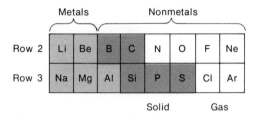

	Metals		Nonmetals				
Row 2	Li	Be	B	C	N	O	F	Ne
Row 3	Na	Mg	Al	Si	P	S	Cl	Ar

Solid   Gas

Diagonal trends also show up in the metallic versus nonmetallic behavior of the elements.

Nitrate ion
Row 2
NO_3^-

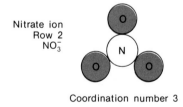

Coordination number 3

Phosphate ion
Row 3
PO_4^{3-}

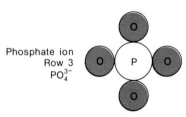

Coordination number 4

more reactive metal than lithium. Lithium reacts moderately fast with water:

$$Li + H_2O \rightarrow Li^+ + OH^- + \tfrac{1}{2}H_2 \qquad \text{(some heat emitted)}$$

The analogous reaction with sodium is so vigorous and gives off so much heat that the emitted hydrogen gas is ignited in an explosion:

$$Na + H_2O \rightarrow Na^+ + OH^- + \tfrac{1}{2}H_2 \qquad \text{(much heat emitted)}$$

$$H_2 + \tfrac{1}{2}O_2 \rightarrow H_2O \qquad \text{(explosively fast combustion)}$$

Magnesium (Mg) metal is held together by two electrons per atom, as is beryllium metal, but magnesium loses these electrons more easily and therefore is more metallic. In many ways magnesium resembles lithium more than it does beryllium. Among atoms with three outer-shell electrons, boron is nonmetallic, but aluminum (Al), in the next row, is a metal. For the second-row elements, BeO is an amphoteric oxide on the borderline between bases and acids, and boron oxide is acidic. For the third row, MgO is still basic, and the amphoteric borderline does not occur until aluminum oxide, Al_2O_3 (see top left).

Atoms become more electronegative with increasing atomic number within a shell, but less electronegative from one shell to the next. In the diagram with which this chapter opened, each element resembles the one below it and to the right, more than it does the one directly below.

Electronegativities

Second row:	Li	Be	B	C	N	O	F
	1.0	1.5	2.0	2.5	3.0	3.5	4.0
Third row:	Na	Mg	Al	Si	P	S	Cl
	0.9	1.2	1.5	1.8	2.1	2.5	3.0

The elements therefore show a *diagonal trend* in many chemical properties (left). Lithium is a moderately reactive metal like magnesium, but not as reactive as sodium. Beryllium has an amphoteric oxide like aluminum, rather than a basic oxide like magnesium. Boron is a nonmetal like silicon, diagonally below it to the right, whereas aluminum, directly below it, is a metal. This diagonal trend of chemical properties is important, and we will encounter it often.

Among the nonmetals, the increase in size of atoms accounts for the larger number of oxygen atoms that can be accommodated around the central atom. Only three oxygens can be fitted around carbon in the carbonate ion, CO_3^{2-}, or nitrogen in the nitrate ion, NO_3^-. The larger third-row atoms have room for four oxygens in the silicate ion, SiO_4^{4-},

As the size of an atom increases from the second row to the third, the coordination number also increases.

102

phosphate ion, PO_4^{3-}, and sulfate ion, SO_4^{2-}. As we mentioned in the preceding chapter, fluorine is so electronegative that it tears electrons away from oxygen and forms F^- ions, instead of sharing electrons with oxygen in an oxyacid ion of the type we have been considering. Chlorine is not as strongly electronegative, and is content to share bonds with oxygen, as in the perchlorate ion, ClO_4^-.

The number of atoms that a central atom has around itself in a particular molecule or ion is its *coordination number*, CN (bottom, left page). For the second-shell elements Li through B, the maximum coordination number with oxygen is four, but the smaller carbon and nitrogen atoms have room for no more than three oxygen atoms. In the third row, Si through Cl have a maximum CN of four with oxygen, but the larger Na, Mg, and Al atoms at the beginning of the row all have a maximum CN of six. Thus a sodium ion in solution has six water molecules around it in octahedral coordination (i.e., like the six Cl^- ions around a Na^+ ion in a salt crystal—at the four corners of a square plus one above and one below). When amphoteric aluminum hydroxide is dissolved by a sufficiently strong base, Al^{3+} is surrounded by an octahedron of six hydroxide ions to form an $Al(OH)_6^{3-}$ ion, rather than four hydroxide ions as with beryllium, $Be(OH)_4^{2-}$. The difference in coordination number arises from the relative sizes of the ions.

THE THIRD-ROW METALS: Na, Mg, and Al

Of the second-row elements, only Li and Be are metals. The metal–nonmetal borderline moves diagonally one column to the right from Row 2 to Row 3, and three of the third-row elements are metals: Na, Mg, and Al (right). Sodium (electronic structure Na 2,8,1) is a silvery metal resembling lithium (Li 2,1), but is even softer than Li because the atoms are larger and cannot be held together as strongly by the mobile electrons. A piece of lithium metal can be cut only with difficulty even with a sharp steel knife, but sodium has the consistency of a block of pine wood or a hard cheddar cheese. The weaker bonds between atoms in sodium also are manifested by melting points: 181°C for Li, but only 98°C for Na. The same trend (see right) is observed for beryllium (Be 2,2) and magnesium (Mg 2,8,2). Both are harder and higher-melting than Li and Na because they have twice as many binding electrons per ion, but Mg is softer than Be because of its greater atomic size and weaker hold on its electrons. Their melting points are consistent with the trend: 1278°C for Be and only 650°C for Mg.

Boron (B 2,3) holds its three outer electrons strongly because the B^{3+} ion is small, and electrons can come close to the central positive charge. Hence boron is nonmetallic. Aluminum (Al 2,8,3), below boron in the third row, is larger. Its attraction for the three outer electrons is weak enough that the electrons are lost easily, so the atom is metallic. Solid aluminum has a close-packed spherical-ion structure typical of a metal, and melts at 660°C, almost as low as magnesium.

Metals generally become more reactive as the number of electron shells increases, because their outer electrons are held more weakly and thus are lost more easily. The increase in reactivity with water, from Li

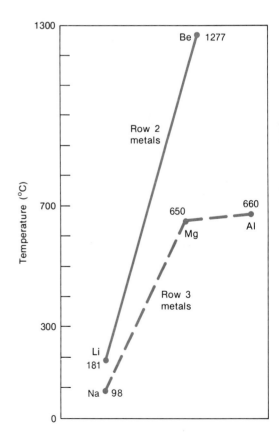

The third-row metals are larger and more reactive than their second-row counterparts.

Melting points of second- and third-row metals

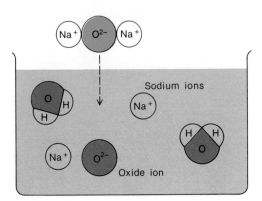

Crystals of sodium oxide break apart in water to form Na^+ and O^{2-} ions.

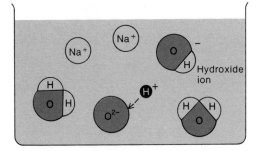

Oxide ions (O^{2-}) pull protons from water molecules, leaving hydroxide ions.

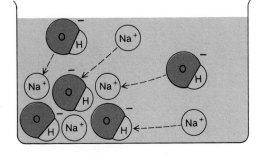

Upon drying, sodium ions join hydroxide ions to form crystalline sodium hydroxide, or lye.

to Na, already has been mentioned. Metals also become less reactive as atomic number increases within a shell. Sodium burns in air with an intense yellow color, which is also seen in sodium vapor lamps. Magnesium burns readily enough that it is used in photoflash bulbs and flares, and must be handled with care when used as a structural metal in aircraft. In contrast, aluminum is relatively inert, in part because it is intrinsically less reactive than sodium, but mainly because its oxide, Al_2O_3, adheres tightly to the surface of the metal and protects it from further corrosion. (One of the curses of iron is that its oxide, Fe_2O_3, does *not* stick to the surface of the metal. It flakes away as rust, continually exposing fresh metal to attack by oxygen.) In some ways, magnesium is the ideal metal for aircraft. It is less reactive than Li and Na, reasonably strong (thanks to its two electrons per atom), more ductile and easier to machine than the ultra-light but partly covalent Be, and lighter than nearly every other metal. Aluminum runs a close second to magnesium, with the great advantage of being less combustible or reactive with oxygen because of its protective coating of Al_2O_3. Neither magnesium nor aluminum is active enough to react with water and to decompose it at room temperature, although any attempt to put out a magnesium flare or incendiary bomb with water will lead to the reaction of magnesium with steam to generate hydrogen, followed by an explosion.

The oxide Na_2O is strongly basic, like Li_2O. It forms ionic crystals of two Na^+ to each O^{2-} ion, with the same structure as Li_2O. Because Na_2O is very hygroscopic (meaning that it will absorb water from the atmosphere), it is a good drying agent. It dissolves in water to produce a strongly basic solution of Na^+ and OH^- ions, which upon drying yields crystalline sodium hydroxide (left):

$$Na_2O + H_2O \rightarrow 2Na^+ + 2OH^- \xrightarrow{\text{drying}} 2NaOH$$

sodium oxide   sodium ions   sodium hydroxide

Sodium hydroxide, commonly known as caustic soda or lye, is the most common laboratory and industrial source of hydroxide ions.

The oxide of the second-row element beryllium, BeO, is amphoteric, but MgO is basic. The bonds between Mg^{2+} and O^{2-} ions in the crystal are almost entirely ionic. Crystalline magnesium oxide is a close-packed array of oxide ions, held together by an equal number of tiny Mg^{2+} ions slipped into niches between layers of oxide ions. The solubility of ionic salts represents a competition between the attractions of ions for one another, and the attractions of polar water molecules for both. Ionic salts of magnesium generally are less soluble than their sodium counterparts, because the smaller size and doubled charge of the Mg^{2+} ion helps them to hold the crystal together more tightly. MgO is nearly insoluble in water, but soluble in acid:

$$MgO + 2H^+ \rightarrow Mg^{2+} + 2H_2O$$

magnesium oxide   magnesium ion

The borderline between acidic and basic oxides of the third-row elements comes at aluminum, and Al_2O_3 and $Al(OH)_3$ are amphoteric. Aluminum hydroxide is insoluble in pure water, but dissolves in either acid or base:

$$Al(OH)_3 + 3H^+ + 3H_2O \rightarrow Al(H_2O)_6^{3+}$$
solid aluminum   acid   hydrated
hydroxide   aluminum ion

$$Al(OH)_3 + 3OH^- \rightarrow Al(OH)_6^{3-}$$
solid aluminum   base   aluminum hexahydroxo
hydroxide   complex ion

In basic solution, six hydroxide ions are coordinated around the central Al^{3+} ion. VSEPR theory predicts that six mutually repelling equal charges at fixed distances around a central ion will be most stable when positioned at the north and south poles and 90° apart around the equator, as shown at the right. Since these are the six directions of the vertices of a regular octahedron, this is known as *octahedral coordination*. Unless special features intervene, sixfold coordination of atoms, ions, or molecules around a central atom is always octahedral, as this represents the least clash or interference between neighboring groups.

The attractions between hydrating water molecules and the central ion are mainly electrostatic for Na^+ and Mg^{2+}, as they are for Li^+. For Al^{3+}, as for Be^{2+} in the second row, the metal–oxygen bonds have a more covalent character, which in turn weakens the O—H bonds of the hydrating water molecules. Electrostatic repulsion between ions plays a large part in keeping $Al(H_2O)_6^{3+}$ or $Al(OH)_6^{3-}$ ions in solution. If we begin with an acid solution of hydrated Al^{3+} ions and gradually lower the acidity, or amount of H^+ present, several of the weakened water molecules coordinated to aluminum will give off a proton each, leaving hydroxide ions bound to the metal. The charge on the complex ion will decrease by one each time a proton is released:

$$Al(H_2O)_6^{3+} \xrightarrow{-H^+} Al(H_2O)_5(OH)^{2+} \xrightarrow{-H^+}$$

$$Al(H_2O)_4(OH)_2^+ \xrightarrow{-H^+} Al(H_2O)_3(OH)_3^0$$
aluminum
hydroxide

With no electrostatic repulsion to keep the ions apart in solution, aluminum hydroxide comes out of solution as a gelatinous, water-containing precipitate. The same behavior is seen if a basic solution of $Al(OH)_6^{3-}$ ions is gradually acidified. Some of the added protons combine with hydroxide ions and turn them into water molecules. The charge on the ions is gradually reduced, and hydrated $Al(OH)_3$ again precipitates as a gel. Similar behavior was mentioned for beryllium in Chapter 5. $Be(H_2O)_4^{2+}$ ions are soluble in acid, and $Be(OH)_4^{2-}$ in base; but beryllium oxide is insoluble in pure water. Only four groups are coordinated around beryllium, rather than six, because Be^{2+} is smaller than Al^{3+}. Both beryllium and aluminum oxides are amphoteric, and are at the borderline between basic and acidic oxides in their respective rows.

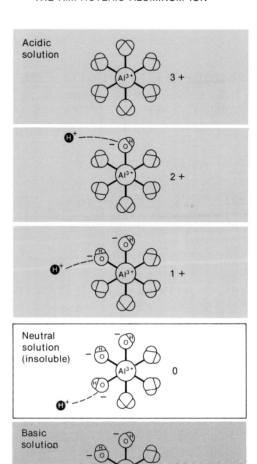

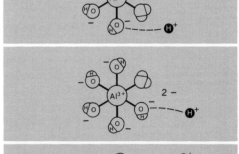

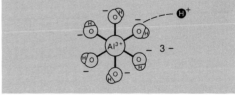

Al^{3+} is large enough to accommodate six H_2O or OH^- around it. Starting from $Al(H_2O)_6^{3+}$ in strong acid, one after another of the six H_2O loses a proton as the solution is made more basic. $Al(OH)_3(H_2O)_3$ precipitates in neutral solution because there are no charges to repel the ions, but it redissolves in base.

105

METAL SALTS

$$2\text{NaOH} + \text{H}_2\text{CO}_3 \rightarrow \text{Na}_2\text{CO}_3 + 2\text{H}_2\text{O}$$

sodium   carbonic   sodium
hydroxide   acid   carbonate

(1) $\text{Na}_2\text{CO}_3 \rightarrow 2\text{Na}^+ + \text{CO}_3^{2-}$

(2) $\text{CO}_3^{2-} + \text{H}_2\text{O} \rightarrow \text{HCO}_3^- + \text{OH}^-$

carbonate   bicarbonate
ion   ion

(almost
completely)

(3) $\text{HCO}_3^- + \text{H}_2\text{O} \rightarrow \text{H}_2\text{CO}_3 + \text{OH}^-$

bicarbonate   carbonic
ion   acid

(about
halfway)

All of the second- and third-row metals are found in the crust of the Earth in the form of silicates (which we will discuss in the next section), carbonates, oxides, and nitrates. Sodium carbonate, Na_2CO_3, is the salt of a strong base, NaOH, and a weak acid, H_2CO_3 (left). Carbonic acid is weak because the carbonate ion has nearly as strong an affinity for protons as water does. About half of the carbonic acid remains in undissociated form in water solution, half exists as bicarbonate ion, HCO_3^-, and very little CO_3^{2-} is present.

When sodium carbonate is dissolved in water, the carbonate ions thus released take protons away from water molecules and make bicarbonate and hydroxide ions (left). This is called *hydrolysis*, or "cleaving with water," under the original but erroneous impression that water simply takes sodium carbonate apart, rather than the carbonate ion pulling the water molecule apart. A solution of sodium carbonate, or of any salt of a strong base and weak acid, will be mildly basic. Na_2CO_3, or washing soda, is used as a mild source of hydroxide ions in the home and in industry. It dissolves grease and oils by turning them into soaps that can be washed away, but is not as corrosive to people or property as sodium hydroxide is. Sodium bicarbonate, NaHCO_3, is an even weaker base because only the second hydrolysis (Reaction 3, left) can take place:

$$\text{Na}^+ + \text{HCO}_3^- + \text{H}_2\text{O} \rightarrow \text{Na}^+ + \text{H}_2\text{CO}_3 + \text{OH}^-$$

Sodium bicarbonate is weak enough to be taken internally as an antacid. It is useful in baking because even weak acetic acid or tartaric acid can liberate CO_2 gas from it, and make biscuit dough rise:

$$\text{H}^+ + \text{HCO}_3^- \rightarrow \text{H}_2\text{CO}_3 \rightarrow \text{H}_2\text{O} + \text{CO}_2$$

The foaming produced when vinegar is poured over bicarbonate of soda (the old name for sodium bicarbonate) arises from this generation of CO_2. A soda–acid fire extinguisher is a simple device for manufacturing a stream of carbon dioxide by dumping acid onto sodium bicarbonate when the container is turned upside down.

Sodium nitrate, NaNO_3, is extremely soluble. It is found naturally only in deposits where rain never occurs, as in caves and in parts of the Chilean desert. It is an important source of nitrate both for fertilizers and for explosives. The Allies came very close to ending World War I early when their naval blockade cut Germany off from its supply of Chilean nitrate for munitions. Chemistry came to the rescue (a dubious honor) when the brilliant German chemist Fritz Haber found a way to manufacture ammonia from atmospheric nitrogen ("nitrogen fixation") and bypass the need for nitrate.

The most plentiful source of sodium is the NaCl of sea water. Centuries of leaching sodium out of weathered minerals and soils have raised the sodium-ion content of the Earth's oceans to three parts per thousand. Our own body fluids have approximately the same salinity as sea water, which probably reflects the oceanic origin of life. The other main salt constituent of sea water is magnesium chloride, MgCl_2, in approximately one third of a part per thousand.

106

THE FRAMEWORK OF THE PLANET: SILICATES

In the center of the third row of the periodic table sits silicon (Si 2,8,4), with four outer electrons like carbon (C 2,4). The rocks of our planet are derived from silicon dioxide, SiO_2, and are surrounded by an atmosphere composed in part of carbon dioxide gas, CO_2. This does not seem remarkable until we recognize that silicon and carbon, which have the same outer electronic structure, should have similar chemical properties. Why the gross difference in properties of their oxides?

The difference in properties arises because a silicon atom is larger than a carbon atom. Sharing two electron pairs with another atom in a double bond requires a closer approach of atoms than for a single bond. Silicon, with an inner core of ten electrons, cannot get close enough. Carbon, with a two-electron inner core, is smaller and can make C=O bonds. Two such double bonds build a CO_2 molecule, O=C=O. Rather than making double bonds to two oxygen atoms, it is easier for silicon to make single bonds to four oxygens, arranged around the Si atom at the corners of a tetrahedron (below). Each of these oxygen atoms can bridge two silicon atoms, and the result is an endless three-dimensional lattice of silicate tetrahedra as in quartz, shown below. If silicon were smaller and could make double bonds to oxygen, there would be no reason not to expect discrete molecules of O=Si=O. Quartz would be a gas instead of a very hard mineral, and the history of our planet would be vastly different.[1] There is another factor: the smaller electronegativity of Si as compared with O, 1.8 versus 3.5. The Si—O bond has a considerable ionic character, and most of the electrons in the Si—O bond are drawn away from Si toward O. Ionic bond radii, with large O^{2-} and small Si^{4+} ions (O^{2-}, 1.40 Å; Si^{4+}, 0.41 Å), give a better picture of silicate structures than covalent radii with relative sizes reversed (O, 0.66 Å; Si, 1.17 Å).

Pure quartz, with the overall composition of SiO_2, is an endless framework of Si and O atoms. Each Si is surrounded by four O atoms at the corners of a tetrahedron, and each O atom is shared between two

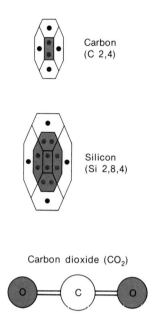

Carbon
(C 2,4)

Silicon
(Si 2,8,4)

Carbon dioxide (CO_2)

---

[1] James McNeill Whistler, the American painter, came from a long line of military ancestors, but turned to art when he flunked out of West Point. In later years he remarked, "If silicon had been a gas, I would have been a General."

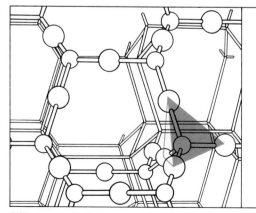

Silicate tetrahedra in quartz

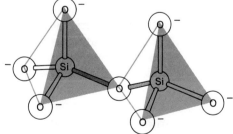

Silicate tetrahedra are linked by sharing corner oxygen atoms. Any unshared oxygens are left with a negative charge.

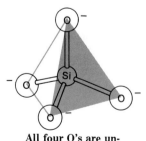

All four O's are unshared in the SiO_4^{4-} ion.

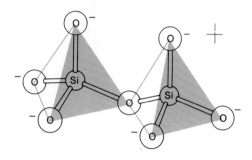

Linked tetrahedra of silicates are the motif for the framework of the planet.

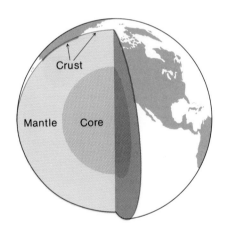

Composition of Earth in atomic percent

Row	Element	Whole earth	Outer crust
1	H	0.1	2.9
2	O	48.9	60.1
3	Na	0.6	2.2
	Mg	12.5	2.0
	Al	1.3	6.3
	Si	14.0	20.8
	P	0.1	0.1
	S	1.4	—
4	K	0.1	1.1
	Ca	0.5	2.1
	Fe	18.9	2.1
	Ni	1.4	—
		99.8%	99.7%

adjacent tetrahedra (left). One silicon atom has "half a share" in each of four oxygen atoms around it, so the number of O atoms per Si atom is $\frac{1}{2} + \frac{1}{2} + \frac{1}{2} + \frac{1}{2} = 2$, thereby accounting for the overall composition of SiO_2. In other types of silicates, one or more of the four oxygens around a silicon atom may not be shared with other silicons, and the unshared oxygen atoms each carry one negative charge.

The smallest freestanding unit of silicon and oxygen is the silicate ion, SiO_4^{4-}, with none of the four oxygen atoms shared, and with each of them negatively charged. These silicate tetrahedra can be linked together by sharing oxygens to form one-dimensional chains, two-dimensional double chains (or ladders) and sheets, and three-dimensional frameworks such as quartz. These one-, two-, and three-dimensional structures are the basis for all silicate minerals. Any negative charges arising from unshared oxygen atoms are balanced by positive metal ions inserted alongside the chains or between the layers.

Our planet is a three-layered ball of silicates (left). It passed through a stage with a molten interior soon after its formation, and the heaviest materials sank to the center to build an iron–nickel *core* 3500 kilometers (km) in radius. Around this core, various metal silicates stratified according to density. The *mantle*, nearly 3000 km thick, consists mainly of a dense crystalline aggregate of olivine, an iron–magnesium silicate. Olivine has the formula X_2SiO_4, in which X can be Mg^{2+} or Fe^{2+} in any proportions. SiO_4^{4-} silicate tetrahedra are packed together in the tightest possible way in olivine; thus the mineral is very dense. A combination of high pressure and high temperature makes the material of the mantle semifluid even today, and convection currents in the mantle are the principal forces in continent-building.

Less dense silicate minerals are produced if the SiO_4^{4-} tetrahedra are linked into long chains. Each Si then shares two of its O atoms with two other Si atoms, leaving it with a net of $1 + 1 + \frac{1}{2} + \frac{1}{2} = 3$ oxygens, and two negative charges on its two wholly owned oxygen atoms. The overall (empirical) composition of these chain silicates is SiO_3^{2-} (opposite page, top). These chains have only half the negative charge per Si atom that olivine has, and hence need fewer metal ions to counterbalance the charge. Because of this, and also because of the open way in which the chains are packed in the mineral, chain silicates are less dense than olivine. Many of them floated to the top of the mantle and helped build the *crust*, the outer layer of the planet, which is about 33 km thick under the continents but only 5 km thick beneath the ocean basins. Pyroxenes are single-chain silicates, with the chains held together by positive ions. Amphiboles are double-chain, or ladder, structures (opposite page). All these minerals cleave easily along the chain direction, but the covalent Si—O bonds within a chain are not easily broken. This is why asbestos (an amphibole) is fibrous and stringy.

Silicate tetrahedra also can be linked into endless sheets, with three of the four oxygen atoms shared, and only one O atom per Si left with a negative charge (bottom right). This negative O is fully owned

The entire planet Earth has an atomic composition very close to $FeMgSiO_4$ of olivine, with extra iron and nickel for the core. The crust has less iron and proportionately more third-row metals. All of the second-row elements except oxygen are scarce, even in the crust, yet it is mainly from C, N, and O that life has evolved.

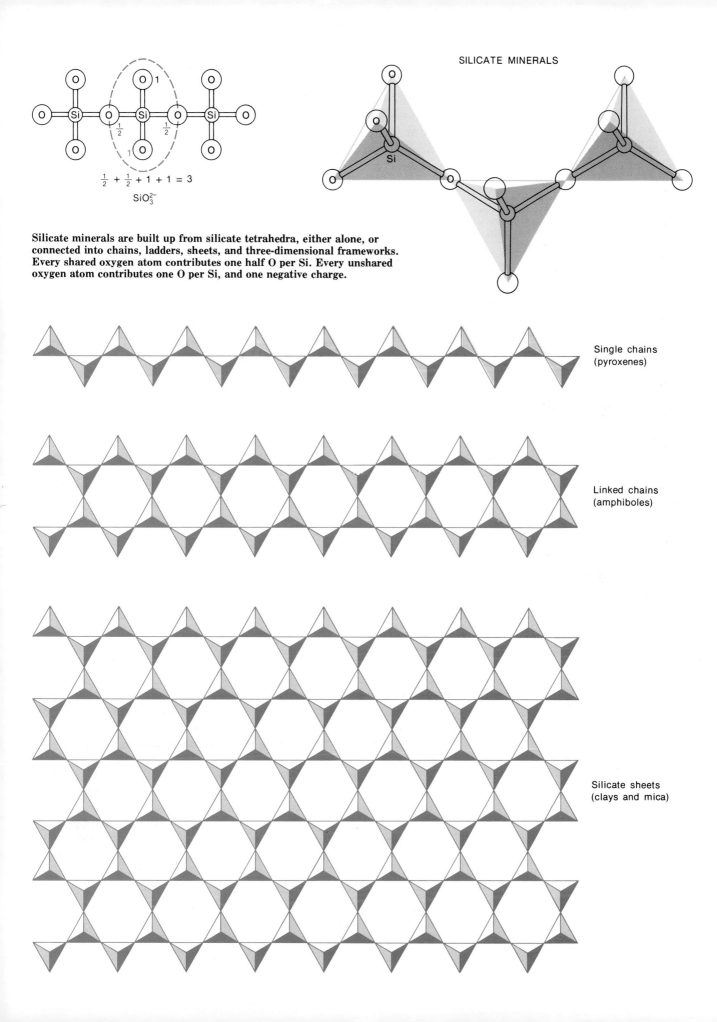

$$\frac{1}{2} + \frac{1}{2} + 1 + 1 = 3$$

$$SiO_3^{2-}$$

SILICATE MINERALS

Silicate minerals are built up from silicate tetrahedra, either alone, or connected into chains, ladders, sheets, and three-dimensional frameworks. Every shared oxygen atom contributes one half O per Si. Every unshared oxygen atom contributes one O per Si, and one negative charge.

Single chains
(pyroxenes)

Linked chains
(amphiboles)

Silicate sheets
(clays and mica)

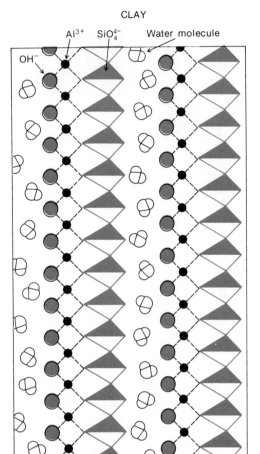

CLAY

Al³⁺   SiO₄⁴⁻   Water molecule

OH⁻

Kaolinite is an especially regular form of clay. Two-dimensional sheets of silicate tetrahedra (seen in edge view here) have one unshared O and one negative charge per Si. Associated with each tetrahedron are one Al³⁺ and two OH⁻ to balance charges. Water molecules separate the sheets. Other forms of clays and micas have different sheet arrangements but are similar in principle.

by one Si, while the other three are shared; thus the overall ratio of O to Si is $1 + \frac{1}{2} + \frac{1}{2} + \frac{1}{2} = 2\frac{1}{2}$ to one. The silicate sheet has the composition $SiO_{2\frac{1}{2}}$ or $Si_2O_5^{2-}$. Even fewer metal ions are required to balance the negative charges than in olivines or pyroxenes, so micas and clays with sheet structures are lighter yet. They are believed to be present only in the crust of the Earth. The familiar flaking of mica arises because it is easy to separate silicate sheets, but much harder to break bonds within the sheets. (Recall the similar behavior of graphite.)

Kaolinite (diagramed at left) is a typical clay mineral. It has one Al^{3+} associated with the negative charge on each silicate tetrahedron in the sheet, and two $OH^=$ ions balance the other two charges on Al^{3+}. It is a layer structure, with the negatively charged oxygen atoms all pointing out on one side of the sheet of tetrahedra, aluminum atoms coordinated to these negative oxygens, and hydroxide ions on the other side of the Al^{3+}. This sandwich of silicate, Al^{3+}, and OH^- is stacked in layers to build up the three-dimensional structure. Water and other small molecules can get between the layers of kaolinite. Because the layers can slip past one another easily, wet clay is pliable and slippery. When clay is baked, or fired, in a kiln, water is driven out and the layers lock into a rigid structure. A primitive pottery maker is a true technologist, in the sense that he takes a natural material that is unsuitable for his purposes, fires it in a kiln, and transforms it into a material with quite different physical properties. Pottery making ranks with brewing as one of the oldest chemical technologies of mankind.

Many of the most interesting chemical properties of clays result from their enormous surface areas. Since both sides of each layer are accessible to water and other small molecules, the effective surface area of a clay mineral is enormous. A cube of material one centimeter on a side has an outside surface area of 6 cm². If the material is ground to a fine powder of spheres 0.01 mm in radius, the total surface area of the powder grains increases to 3000 cm², or a little more than three square feet. But with layers 7.1 Å (7.1×10^{-8} cm) apart, a cube of kaolinite one centimeter on a side has a total layer surface area of 28,000,000 cm², or two thirds the size of a football field! This means that wherever large surface areas are important, clays can be useful. They can absorb organic molecules, and can be used in extracting impurities from the air and removing grease and stains from fabrics. Fuller's earth is a dried clay powder that is the basis of common spot removers. When rubbed into fabrics, it will lift out grease stains by absorbing the grease molecules onto the silicate layers. Fuller's earth is used in large amounts in the textile industry as a means of removing unwanted oils from new wool.

Clays are useful components of soils because they can trap water, ions, and organic matter, which are needed for plant growth. Certain types of clays can be used as ion-exchange compounds. If a solution is passed through an ion-exchange column packed with the material, one kind of positive ion can be flushed out of the column and replaced by another from the solution. The petrochemical industry takes advantage of the great surface areas of kaolinite clays by using them as beds, or supports, for metallic catalysts in petroleum cracking and refining. The great British biochemist J. D. Bernal proposed clay minerals as

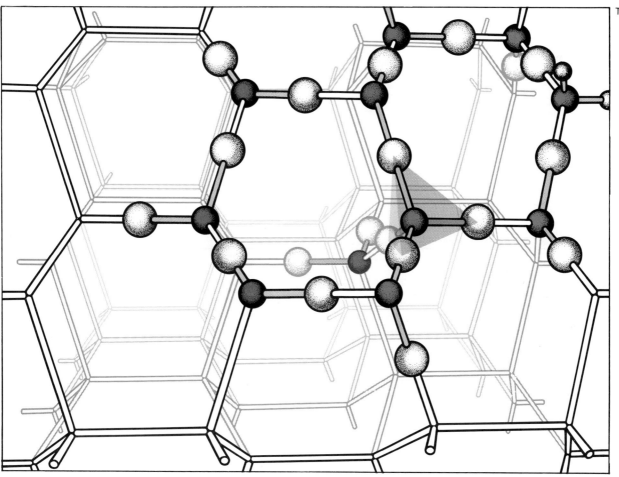

Tridymite is the form of SiO_2 in which the silicon atoms occupy the positions that oxygen atoms do in ice, and oxygen atoms are located between silicons, like the O—H—O bridges in ice. Crystobalite, another form of SiO_2 has a structure resembling diamond. The basic structural unit, in SiO_2 as in ice and diamond, is a tetrahedron.

the catalytic surfaces at which the first reactions ultimately leading to the evolution of life occurred. By this argument we indeed are formed "from the dust of the Earth," although in a high state of hydration.

The most common materials in the crust of the Earth are the framework silicates: quartz and feldspars. In these, all four corners of each silicate tetrahedron are linked in a three-dimensional framework. In common hexagonal quartz, the tetrahedra are linked in a six-fold helix, a spiral staircase with six silicate steps per turn. These helices then are packed parallel to one another in the quartz crystal and connected by sharing oxygen atoms in the silicate tetrahedra. Hence quartz is held together completely by covalent Si—O bonds, and is a hard mineral. There are left-handed and right-handed quartz crystals, depending on the direction or "handedness" of the helices. Another form of SiO_2, tridymite, has the structure that we already have encountered for ice, with the oxygen atoms of ice replaced by silicons, and with each O—H $\cdots$ O bond replaced by Si—O—Si bonds. Tridymite is shown at the top of the page.

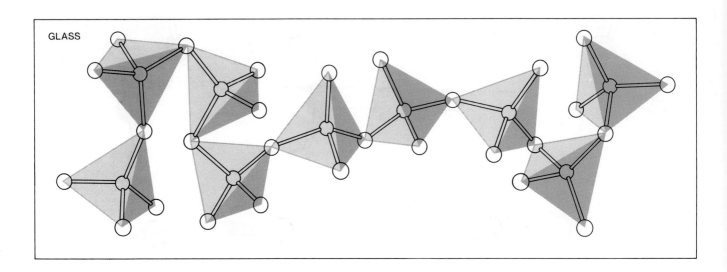

GLASS

In a glass, the silicate tetrahedra are not connected in a regular manner, but are in snarls of tangled chains. Glasses are not as hard as quartz, and melt slowly over a broad temperature range because the thermal energy gradually unsnarls the chains.

If quartz is heated above its melting point of $1610°C$ and then cooled rapidly, the silicate chains do not have time to return to a perfectly crystalline array, so they harden into a disordered silicate *glass* instead (above). Glass really is a liquid, although an extremely viscous one. Given enough time, glass will flow, as the thickening of the bottom of panes of glass in very old European buildings demonstrates. Special forms of glass are prepared with oxides of lead, boron, aluminum, sodium, and calcium mixed with the SiO_2 from sand. In general, the less electronegative elements Na and Ca, with ionic bonds to the silicate oxygens, produce a softer and lower-melting glass. Pyrex glass includes oxides of B and Al, with more covalent bonding to oxygen. This makes Pyrex almost as strong and heat-resistant as pure silicate glass, or fused quartz.

Feldspars are silicates in which one fourth to one half of the Si^{4+} ions in the tetrahedra have been replaced by Al^{3+}, thereby requiring one additional $+1$ charge from a positive ion for each such substitution. Since feldspars are open, three-dimensional cage structures, they are lighter than pyroxenes and olivine. In the original stratification of the planet, feldspars floated to the top, and today make up 60% of the crust of the Earth by weight. Quartz, which also is light, is responsible for another 12%. Micas and clays contribute 5%, the heavier pyroxenes 12%, and dense olivine only 3% of the crust, with the last 8% being iron oxides and miscellaneous minerals. Granite, probably the most familiar of all rocks, is a mixture of fine crystals of quartz, feldspar, and mica.

It is interesting to reflect that all of this silicate geology arose because silicon cannot make double bonds with oxygen. If by some cosmic readjustment, the size of a silicon atom were to decrease by 25%, then such a double bond would become possible. All of the silicates in our planet would boil away in clouds of SiO_2 gas, leaving behind only a metallic core of half the present radius, covered by a scum of metal oxides. It is easy to see why the "fitness of the world" was used by theologians of the past century as a scientific demonstration of the existence of a Designer in the universe. The "fitness" of carbon and silicon for the separate roles they play on our planet is uncanny.

112

THE ACIDIC NONMETALS: P, S, AND Cl

In comparing carbon in the second row with silicon in the third, we were looking at a common theme with striking variations. These arose from the larger size of Si and the lesser ability to form multiple bonds with like neighbor atoms. This trend also is seen in comparing nitrogen (N 2,5) with phosphorus (P 2,8,5), oxygen (O 2,6) with sulfur (S 2,8,6), and fluorine (F 2,7) with chlorine (Cl 2,8,7). Nitrogen gas, N_2, has a triple bond between two atoms, with a lone electron pair on each atom. Phosphorus atoms are too large to form triple bonds, so in P_4 molecules, which are found in the gas, liquid, and one solid form of phosphorus, each P atom makes a single bond to three others at the corners of a tetrahedron (below). Similarly, oxygen gas has a double bond in the O_2 molecule, but solid sulfur is made up of eight-membered rings of S_8, in which each S atom is singly bonded to two others in the ring. Chlorine is singly bonded in Cl_2 gas molecules, as is F_2.

As we saw in the preceding chapter, carbonic acid is a weak acid. Carbon has room for no more than three oxygen atoms around it, as in the carbonate ion, CO_3^{2-}. The larger silicon atom can accommodate four oxygens in silicic acid, H_4SiO_4, and the silicates. In aqueous solution, silicic acid is extremely weak and hardly ionized at all. This is because silicon is less electronegative than carbon, and pulls the four negative charges in the silicate ion only weakly toward itself. The negative charges remain mainly on the oxygens of the SiO_4^{4-} ion, where they are able to attract protons easily and form undissociated silicic acid molecules. Also, SiO_4^{4-} is not stabilized by delocalization of electrons. Each electron pair in the ion is pinned down either in an oxygen lone pair or a Si—O single bond.

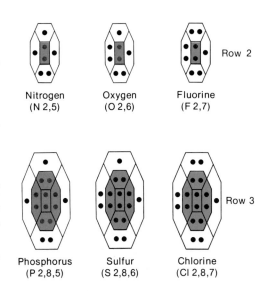

Phosphorus, sulfur, and chlorine have the same outer electron-shell structure as nitrogen, oxygen, and fluorine in the second row, but are larger atoms with weaker holds upon their outer electrons. Many of their chemical properties follow from this fact.

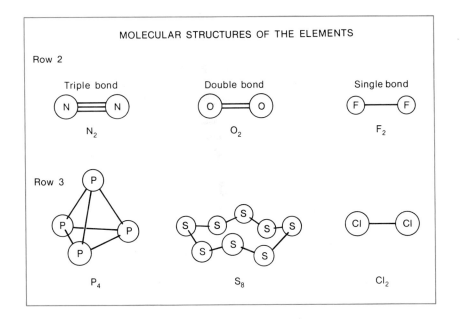

N and P both form three bonds to neighboring atoms, and O and S both form two. However, the second-row atoms are small enough to make multiple bonds to a single neighbor, whereas the larger third-row atoms must make single bonds to several other atoms.

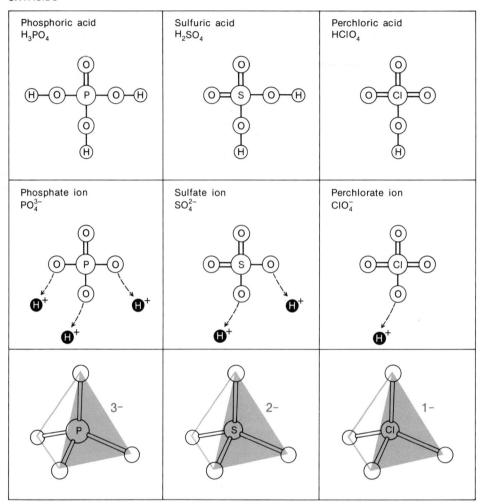

Phosphoric acid H_3PO_4	Sulfuric acid H_2SO_4	Perchloric acid $HClO_4$
Phosphate ion PO_4^{3-}	Sulfate ion SO_4^{2-}	Perchlorate ion ClO_4^-

Phosphorus, sulfur, and chlorine form oxyacids that can be represented as having 1, 2, and 3 double bonds to O atoms, respectively; and 3, 2, and 1 single bonds to —OH. The H of each —OH group dissociates to yield ions with maximum charges of −3, −2, and −1. In each case the oxygens are arranged tetrahedrally around the central atom.

Aside from illustrating the beginning of a trend, silicic acid is of minor importance. The elements P, S, and Cl do form important oxyacids, each with four oxygens around the central atom. These acids are phosphoric acid, H_3PO_4, sulfuric acid, H_2SO_4, and perchloric acid, $HClO_4$. Each of these is capable of losing all of its protons to form, respectively, the ions shown above: phosphate, PO_4^{3-}; sulfate, SO_4^{2-}; and perchlorate, ClO_4^-. As with carbonate and nitrate ions, no simple single-and-double bond model is entirely satisfactory for these ions. Models can be drawn with single and double bonds to O, because it is possible with these larger atoms to put more than four electron pairs around the central atom. However, such models suggest that not all the bonds to oxygen are the same length, which is in disagreement with experimental results. If this difficulty is avoided by making a model with one single bond to each O, then the central ions wind up

114

with positive charges, an undesirable state of affairs (see right margin). The best description of reality is to say that negative charge is delocalized over the entire ions, with the X—O bonds being approximately $1\frac{1}{4}$ bonds in phosphate, $1\frac{1}{2}$ bonds in sulfate, and $1\frac{3}{4}$ bonds in perchlorate. All three ions are stabilized by delocalization, which makes the acids stronger than we might expect. Silicic acid, lacking this delocalization, is extremely weak.

Acidity increases in the series from P to S to Cl, because of the increasing electronegativity of the central atom. In aqueous solutions of the two strongest acids, perchloric and sulfuric, one proton is completely dissociated:

$$HClO_4 \rightarrow H^+ + ClO_4^-$$
perchloric   perchlorate
acid   ion

$$H_2SO_4 \rightarrow H^+ + HSO_4^-$$
sulfuric   bisulfate
acid   ion

The bisulfate ion can dissociate again, but does so to a smaller extent because this requires the removal of a positive charge from an entity that already has one negative charge:

$$HSO_4^- \rightarrow H^+ + SO_4^{2-}$$
bisulfate   sulfate
ion   ion

The weaker phosphoric acid loses its first proton with roughly the same reluctance as sulfuric acid loses its *second* proton:

$$H_3PO_4 \rightarrow H^+ + H_2PO_4^-$$
phosphoric   dihydrogen
acid   phosphate ion

The second and third dissociations of phosphoric acid are even weaker. Like carbonic acid, phosphoric acid is weak enough to be used in soft drinks. In an earlier era, every soda fountain offered "phosphates," in which a small amount of phosphoric acid was added to the carbonic acid to give a special tang to the drink. Orange phosphates, regrettably, have become one of the casualties of progress.

The second- and third-row oxyacids show "diagonality" in their chemical properties, with each acid in the second row being most like the one below it and to the right:

Oxyacids

$HB(OH)_4$ H_2CO_3 HNO_3
boric   carbonic   nitric

H_4SiO_4 H_3PO_4 H_2SO_4 $HClO_4$
silicic   phosphoric   sulfuric   perchloric

Boric and silicic acids are not strengthened by delocalization of electrons in their ions, and are so weak that they seldom are thought of as acids at all. Carbonic and phosphoric acids are so weak that only the first proton dissociation is important, and both are weak enough for use

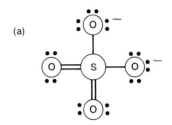

(a)

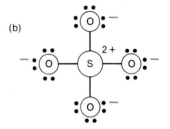

(b)

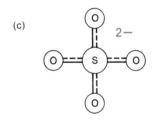

(c)

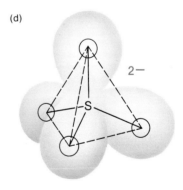

(d)

As with carbonic and nitric acids, delocalization is a factor in making sulfuric acid stronger than it would be otherwise. (a, b) Two possible simple bond models with single and double bonds. (c) A $1\frac{1}{2}$ bond model, which accounts better for the observed S—O bond lengths and the equal length of all four. (d) Tetrahedral model of SO_4^{2-} with electrons delocalized over the entire ion.

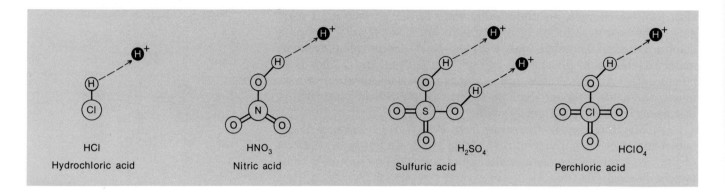

The four most common strong laboratory acids

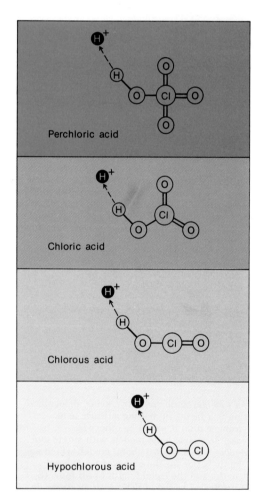

The four chlorine oxyacids, with strong perchloric acid at the top and weak hypochlorous acid at the bottom

in beverages. Nitric and sulfuric are very strong, and are the two most common laboratory acids. Perchloric acid is the strongest of all (above).

The elements that form strong oxyacids, N, P, S, and Cl, also can form weaker acids that have fewer oxygen atoms present in the molecules. Nitrous acid, HNO_2, is weaker than nitric acid, HNO_3; and phosphorous acid, H_3PO_3, is weaker than phosphoric acid, H_3PO_4. Sulfurous acid, H_2SO_3, is not as strong as H_2SO_4. Chlorine can form an entire series of oxyacids with decreasing oxygen content and decreasing acid strength:

$HClO_4$ or H—O—ClO_3 perchloric acid

$HClO_3$ or H—O—ClO_2 chloric acid

$HClO_2$ or H—O—ClO   chlorous acid

HClO or H—O—Cl   hypochlorous acid

In each of these acids, shown at the left, the dissociating proton is bonded to an oxygen atom; thus the second structure given above for each acid is a more accurate model of the molecule. The greater the number of oxygen atoms bonded to the Cl, the greater is the attraction by the rest of the molecule for the electrons of the H—O bond, and the more likely the acid molecule is to dissociate into H^+ and an oxyanion. Perchloric acid is the strongest common inorganic acid known, but hypochlorous acid is weak.

The third-row nonmetals also form acids other than oxyacids, in which the protons are attached directly to the central atom, as in HF. Hydrochloric acid, HCl, is a strong acid and, with HNO_3 and H_2SO_4, makes up the trio of acids that you are most likely to encounter in the laboratory. Sulfur is less electronegative than chlorine, therefore hydrogen sulfide, H_2S, is a much weaker acid. Even so, it is stronger than its second-row analogue, H_2O. This is so because the sulfur atom is large enough that the protons cannot get as close to the center of charge on the sulfur atom, and the attraction between S and H is weakened. By the same token, HCl is stronger than HF, even though fluorine is more electronegative and pulls electrons toward itself more than Cl does. H_2S formed from the sulfur of decomposing proteins is responsible for the odor of rotting eggs. HCl is the principal acid found in the digestive system and breaks the bonds between amino acid subunits in the proteins we eat.

116

OXIDATION STATES AND OXIDATION NUMBERS

One of the most important unifying concepts in chemistry is that of electronegativity, and we have used it frequently. When two atoms compete for the same electrons, their relative electronegativities tell us which will win. The end result can be described as an oxidation and a reduction. When atoms lose electrons and become positive ions, they are *oxidized*. The terminology comes from combination with oxygen, which for every element except fluorine means a shift of electrons toward the more electronegative oxygen atom. (If fluorine were as common as oxygen on our planet, we probably would call the loss of electrons fluoridation instead of oxidation.)

When electrons are given to a substance, the substance is *reduced*. Again, the terminology is historical. It comes from the process of reducing ores to pure metals, during which oxygen is removed from the ore, and the metal ions are given electrons and converted to neutral atoms. The terms have become generalized beyond their original meanings, and today any loss of electrons is called an *oxidation*, and any gain of electrons is called a *reduction*, even if oxygen is not involved. Since electrons are neither created nor destroyed in chemical reactions, whenever one substance is oxidized, something else must be reduced. In the reaction of metallic sodium with chlorine gas, sodium is oxidized and chlorine is reduced:

$$Na + \tfrac{1}{2}Cl_2 \rightarrow Na^+ + Cl^-$$

An electron is transferred from sodium to chlorine (right).

Oxidation and reduction are such useful concepts that they have been extended from cases of outright electron gain or loss, to reactions involving varying degrees of electron sharing. When copper oxide ore is reduced to metallic copper by roasting with charcoal (below), copper ions are reduced and carbon is oxidized:

$$2Cu_2O + C \rightarrow 4Cu + CO_2$$

The reduction of copper is obvious; each Cu^+ ion accepts one electron and becomes a copper atom. But in what sense is carbon oxidized? It does not give up its outer electrons and become a C^{4+} ion in CO_2.

Each carbon atom of coke initially shared its four electrons equally with other carbon atoms. It continues to share electron pairs with oxygen in CO_2, but on an *unequal* basis. The bonding electrons in CO_2 are

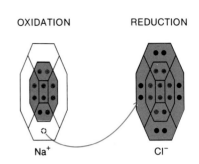

OXIDATION   REDUCTION

Na$^+$ Cl$^-$

Sodium loses an electron and is *oxidized* to Na$^+$.

Chlorine gains an electron and is *reduced* to Cl$^-$.

Electrons from oxygen are released to the Cu^+ ions, *reducing* them to pure metallic copper (Cu).

HOW COPPER OXIDE ORE IS REDUCED

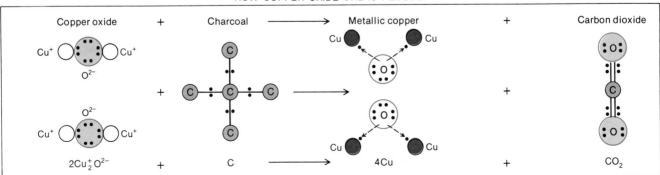

117

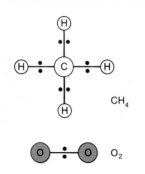

CH_4

O_2

Equal sharing of electrons in methane and oxygen

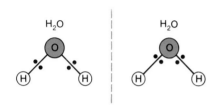

H_2O H_2O

In water, the bonding electrons (left) actually are attracted closer to the oxygen atom (right).

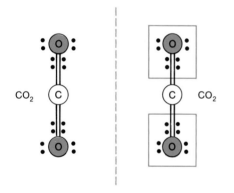

CO_2 CO_2

In carbon dioxide, four electrons are shared between C and O in each double bond. All of these shared electrons in reality are pulled closer to the more electronegative oxygen atoms.

PSEUDO-IONS AND OXIDATION NUMBER

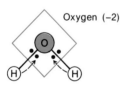

Oxygen (−2)

Hydrogen (+ 1)   Hydrogen (+ 1)

pulled closer to O because it is more electronegative than C. Although carbon does not give up its electrons, it does relinquish them to an extent when they shift toward the more electronegative oxygen atoms. If an atom abandons an environment in which its electron pairs are shared equally with a neighbor, and forms a new bond with a more electronegative atom in which the electron pair is more tightly bound to the new neighbor, then we consider that the original atom has been oxidized, even though no actual loss of electrons occurs. In the combustion of methane, C and H atoms combine with oxygen to produce CO_2 and H_2O:

$$CH_4 + 2O_2 \rightarrow CO_2 + 2H_2O$$

The electron pairs in the four bonds of methane initially are shared equally between the almost equally electronegative C and H (left). Electrons also are shared equally in the O_2 molecules, of course, because the two atoms are identical. After reaction, carbon and hydrogen each are bonded to the more electronegative atoms of oxygen. The electron pairs in the single and double bonds of H—O—H and O=C=O all will be shifted away from H or C, and closer to O. Although there has been only a *tendency* toward removal of electrons instead of outright removal, C and H still have been oxidized. Each O atom has had electrons shifted toward it, and therefore has been reduced. A substance such as O, which itself is easily reduced, is a good *oxidizing agent* for other materials; conversely, a substance that is easily oxidized will be a good *reducing agent*.

How much oxidation can a given amount of a reducible substance accomplish? How many molecules of methane can one molecule of oxygen gas oxidize? For a simple example like this one, the answer can be found merely by balancing the equation, or making sure that there are the same numbers of C, H, and O atoms before and after a reaction. But for more complicated reactions it is helpful to use a concept called the *oxidation number*.

For a single-atom ion, the oxidation number is simply the charge on the positive or negative ion. Thus Na^+ has an oxidation number (ON) of +1, and Cl^- has an ON of −1. An atom in a metal, such as magnesium, has a zero ON. In calculating oxidation numbers, each mobile electron in the metal is "given back" to its original ion, since all ions in the metal have the same attraction for electrons. When magnesium is oxidized to Mg^{2+}, it acquires an ON of +2. Oxidation numbers are merely a means of keeping track of oxidation–reduction processes.

Oxidation numbers of atoms are only slightly more complicated to calculate when the atoms are covalently bonded in molecules. In this case, one pretends that the covalent compounds are totally ionic, *with each electron pair in a bond being given completely to the more electronegative of the two atoms.* Thus in the water molecule, oxygen is more electronegative (EN = 3.5) than hydrogen (EN = 2.1), and in figuring oxidation numbers, the covalent molecule H—O—H is thought of as $H^+ O^{2-} H^+$ (left). The oxidation number of each atom is the net charge on each of the pseudo-ions. Oxygen in water has an ON of −2, and each of the hydrogens has an ON of +1. The sum of the oxidation numbers of all the atoms in a neutral molecule is zero.

118

Hydrogen is less electronegative than chlorine, so in HCl the electron pair of the bond is assigned entirely to chlorine to make the pseudo-ionic molecule H⁺ Cl⁻ (right). Hydrogen in HCl has an ON of +1, and chlorine has an ON of −1. This pseudo-ionic state becomes real when HCl is dissolved in water and the molecule dissociates. The oxidation numbers, however, are equally valid even for gaseous HCl, which consists of un-ionized H—Cl molecules.

If two atoms connected by a bond have identical electronegativities, as in the O—O bond in hydrogen peroxide, H—O—O—H, or in a diatomic gas, F—F, then in calculating oxidation numbers the electron pair is divided between them (center right). Each oxygen in hydrogen peroxide, H_2O_2, is assigned both electrons from its H—O bond and one of the two electrons from the O—O bond. The pseudo-ions corresponding to hydrogen peroxide are $H^{+1} O^{-1} O^{-1} H^{+1}$. Hence H has an ON of +1, oxygen has an ON of −1, and the total ON for all the atoms in the molecule is zero. Giving one of the bond electrons to each atom in hydrogen gas, H—H, would produce two neutral atoms, $H^0 H^0$, so the ON of each atom is zero. This is true for other diatomic gases such as Cl_2, N_2, and O_2, and in fact is true for any pure element. For a pure element, in which every atom has the same attraction for electrons, each atom has an ON of zero.

An element can have several different oxidation numbers, or oxidation states, in different compounds. Nitrogen has an ON of zero in N_2 gas, and −3 in ammonia, NH_3. What is its ON in the nitrate ion? A bond diagram for one model of the NO_3^- ion is shown at the bottom right. Oxygen is more electronegative than nitrogen, and if all of the bonding electrons are assigned to oxygen, each oxygen atom has a pseudo-ionic charge of −2, and the central nitrogen, a pseudo-ionic charge of +5. This is the charge that each atom would have if nitric acid were a purely ionic compound instead of a covalently bonded molecule. The delocalization of electrons makes no difference. If you start from any of the bond models of nitric acid presented in Chapter 4, and assign all of the bonding electrons to the more electronegative of the two atoms bonded, the result will be the same. Oxygen has an ON of −2 in the nitrate ion, and nitrogen has an ON of +5. The total overall ON is the sum of −2, −2, −2, +5 = −1, the same as the charge on the nitrate ion. If we add a proton with an ON of +1, a neutral HNO_3 molecule is the result, with an overall ON of zero.

Three shortcuts can save a lot of work in figuring out oxidation numbers:

1. Whenever oxygen is bonded only to atoms less electronegative than itself (which rules out only O—F and O—O bonds), oxygen has an ON of −2.

2. Except when bonded to metals in metal hydrides, or to itself in H_2, hydrogen has an ON of +1.

3. The sum of the ON of all atoms in a neutral molecule is zero, and the sum of ON of all atoms in an ion is equal to the charge on the ion.

The last rule follows from the fact that oxidation numbers reflect the pushing and pulling of electrons between atoms, and that the total

HCl

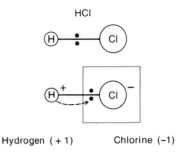

Hydrogen (+ 1)   Chlorine (−1)

The bonding pair in HCl is assigned to the more electronegative Cl to produce the pseudo-ionic molecule H⁺ Cl⁻, with oxidation numbers of +1 for H and −1 for Cl. In this molecule, the pseudo-ions become real ions if HCl is dissolved in water.

H_2O_2

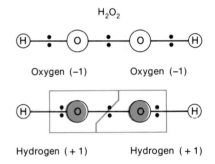

Oxygen (−1)   Oxygen (−1)

Hydrogen (+ 1)   Hydrogen (+ 1)

The equally shared electrons between the two equally electronegative oxygen atoms in hydrogen peroxide are divided evenly between them.

HNO_3

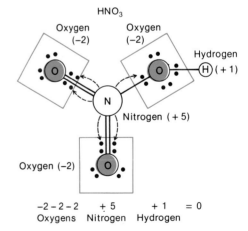

All the electrons in the N—O and the two N═O bonds are assigned to O atoms because they are more electronegative than N. This leaves N with a fictional +5 charge, which is its oxidation number. The sum of all the oxidation numbers of atoms in the nitric acid molecule is zero because the molecule has no net charge.

119

number of electrons must remain constant during any chemical process, such as the building of a molecule from its component atoms.

With these three short cuts, you can see quickly how the ON of chlorine varies in its acids and oxyacids:

Molecule	ON of Cl	Check of zero overall ON			
		H	Cl	O	Sum
HCl	-1	$(+1)+(-1)$			$=0$
Cl_2	0	$(0) +(0)$			$=0$
HClO	$+1$	$(+1)+(+1)+$		(-2)	$=0$
$HClO_2$	$+3$	$(+1)+(+3)+$		$2(-2)$	$=0$
$HClO_3$	$+5$	$(+1)+(+5)+$		$3(-2)$	$=0$
$HClO_4$	$+7$	$(+1)+(+7)+$		$4(-2)$	$=0$

The physical meaning of these oxidation numbers is that, in the series from HCl to $HClO_4$, the chlorine atom loses more and more of its grasp over the electrons that it shares with other atoms. In HCl it easily dominates over the weakly electronegative proton, but in $HClO_4$ it does an ineffective job of competing against the stronger electron-pulling power of the oxygen atoms. Chlorine is oxidized in going from Cl_2 to $HClO_4$, even though the change represents only a shifting away of

The neutral chlorine atom has 7 outer electrons. When one is "lost," the charge on the Cl atom is +1 and when all are "lost," the charge on the atom is +7.

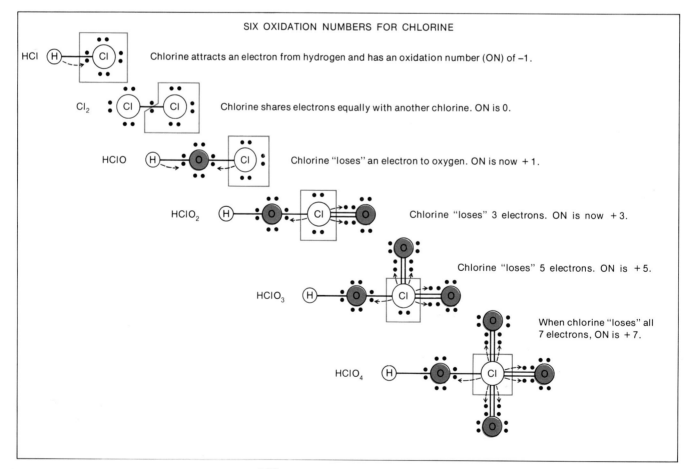

SIX OXIDATION NUMBERS FOR CHLORINE

HCl — Chlorine attracts an electron from hydrogen and has an oxidation number (ON) of −1.

Cl_2 — Chlorine shares electrons equally with another chlorine. ON is 0.

HClO — Chlorine "loses" an electron to oxygen. ON is now +1.

$HClO_2$ — Chlorine "loses" 3 electrons. ON is now +3.

$HClO_3$ — Chlorine "loses" 5 electrons. ON is +5.

$HClO_4$ — When chlorine "loses" all 7 electrons, ON is +7.

electrons and not their outright removal. Whenever an atom is oxidized, its ON increases, and whenever it is reduced, its ON decreases. Chemists commonly refer to the *oxidation state* of an atom, meaning its oxidation number in a specified compound.

The most commonly encountered oxidation states for the nonmetals are shown in the table below, along with examples. The highest possible positive oxidation state of an atom is the charge that it would have if it lost all of the electrons in its outer, incomplete electron shell. Thus carbon and silicon have maximum oxidation numbers of +4 because they both have four electrons to lose. Nitrogen and phosphorus have a maximum ON of +5, as in HNO_3 and H_3PO_4. Sulfur has a maximum of +6, as in H_2SO_4. You might expect oxygen to behave the same way, but oxygen is too small and holds its outer electrons too tightly. (Compare the first ionization energies of O and S on Page 100.) No oxygen compounds are known in which oxygen has an ON as high as +6. The size effect seen with oxygen applies even more strongly to fluorine. Chlorine in $HClO_4$ shows an ON of +7, the expected maximum; but the smaller fluorine atom holds its electrons very tightly and has no compounds with positive oxidation states.

The lowest possible negative oxidation state of an atom is the charge that the ion would have if it picked up enough electrons to fill its outer shell completely and produce the electronic configuration of the next heavier noble gas. For F and Cl, this means a minimum ON of −1 as in HF and HCl; for O and S, −2 as in H_2O and H_2S; for N and P, −3 as in NH_3 and PH_3; and for C and Si, −4 as in CH_4 and SiH_4. The two extreme maximum and minimum values, plus ON = 0, are the most common oxidation states for the elements we have discussed so far. Intermediate states are less common and usually occur at intervals of two in ON, representing shifts of pairs of electrons. Thus sulfur has common oxidation states of −2, 0, +4, and +6; and chlorine shows states −1, 0, +1, +3, +5, and +7.

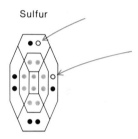

Silicon

The highest positive oxidation number an atom can have is that which completely empties its outermost, partially filled electron shell. For silicon, this is +4.

Sulfur

The lowest negative oxidation number is the charge that the atom would have by filling its outer electron shell completely. For sulfur, this is an oxidation number of −2.

Oxidation states of nonmetals, with examples

	Second row				Third row			
	C	N	O	F	Si	P	S	Cl
+7			—					ClO_4^-
+6			—				SO_4^{2-}	
+5		NO_3^-	No positive oxidation states	No positive oxidation states		PO_4^{3-}		ClO_3^-
+4	CO_3^{2-}	(NO_2)			SiO_4^{4-}		SO_3^{2-}	
+3		NO_2^-				PCl_3		ClO_2^-
+2	CO	(NO)			(SiF_2)			
+1		N_2O						ClO−
0	C	N_2	O_2	F_2	Si	P_4	S_8	Cl_2
−1		NH_2OH	H_2O_2	HF				HCl
−2		(N_2H_4)	H_2O				H_2S	
−3		NH_3				PH_3		
−4	CH_4				—			

Heavy type = Most common oxidation states
Light type = Less common oxidation states
(Brackets) = Rare oxidation states

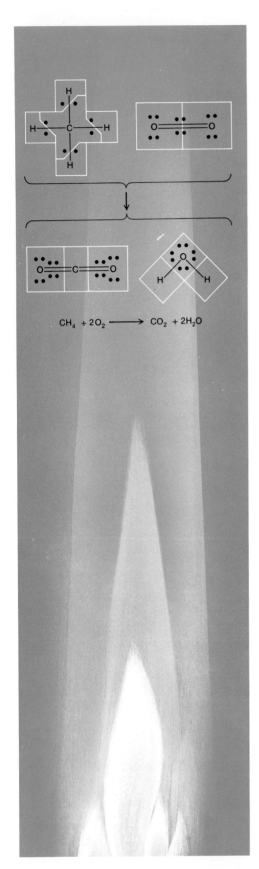

$$CH_4 + 2O_2 \longrightarrow CO_2 + 2H_2O$$

WHY IS FIRE HOT?

We can tie together these ideas about oxidation number and at the same time answer what may seem to be a simple-minded question: Why is fire hot? Burning is an oxidation process; in fact, it is from burning, or combination with oxygen, that we obtained the term now used to cover all removal or shifting away of electrons. At the same time that the C, H, and N atoms of the substance being burned are oxidized, oxygen atoms are reduced from O_2 to combinations with the original atoms such as CO_2, H_2O, and NO_2.

We can rephrase the original question more soberly (but no more meaningfully) as: Why do oxidations with O_2 give off energy, and reductions absorb energy? This is important in more than just bonfires and steam engines. All energy-yielding processes in living organisms are oxidations, and energy is stored by synthesizing reduced molecules such as fats and sugars. Respiration is the oxidation of these stored fuels with oxygen, and photosynthesis is the use of the energy of sunlight to make reduced sugar molecules.

To ask why oxidation releases energy is to ask why oxidized compounds have lower energy than the reduced compounds from which they came, because any energy given off must represent a loss of energy as products are formed from reactants. In the combustion of methane gas,

$$CH_4 + 2O_2 \rightarrow CO_2 + 2H_2O + \text{heat}$$

heat energy is given off because a carbon dioxide molecule and two waters have less energy than one molecule of methane and two of O_2. Why should this be so?

We can give a more precise answer to this in Chapter 12, after we have introduced quantitative measures of heats of reactions, but the outlines of an answer can be given now. In methane molecules, the electronegativities of carbon and hydrogen are nearly the same (2.5 for C, 2.1 for H). Although by strict application of the rules given earlier, carbon would have a formal ON of -4 and each hydrogen of $+1$, in reality the electrons in the C—H bonds are shared almost equally between atoms. Similarly, the electrons in the O=O double bonds are shared equally. In the product molecules, O=C=O and H—O—H, carbon and hydrogen both are paired with much more electronegative oxygen atoms (EN = 3.5). In both C=O and H—O bonds, electrons are pulled toward the oxygen atoms. From an energy standpoint the electrons have "rolled downhill" to a more stable situation nearer to the oxygen atoms. It takes energy to pull them away from the oxygen atoms again and to distribute them equally between two atoms (C and H) that do not especially want them. The energy liberated as heat during combustion arises mainly from the strong attraction of electrons to oxygen. In photosynthesis, when sugars are made from CO_2 and water, these electrons are pulled farther away from the oxygen atoms. The energy re-

In the combustion of methane gas, methane and oxygen molecules, in which bonding atoms are shared equally between the bonded atoms, react to form water and carbon dioxide, in which the bonding electrons are pulled toward the oxygen atoms and away from C and H. As the electrons "relax" toward atoms that attract them strongly, the energy released is given off as the heat of the flame.

quired to do this, obtained from light, can be released later for useful purposes via combustion (oxidation). Thus oxidation numbers and oxidation states are not devices invented by chemists to torment the beginner. They tell us what is happening in chemical reactions, and are closely tied in with some of the most vital energy processes in living organisms.

QUESTIONS

1. In what way are the third-row elements like the corresponding second-row elements? In what ways are they different?

2. Why is aluminum more metallic than boron, even though they both have the same outer electron-shell structure?

3. Is the metallic radius of magnesium larger, or smaller, than its ionic radius? Why?

4. Is the covalent bond radius of sulfur larger, or smaller, than its ionic radius? Why?

5. Why is the electronegativity of boron more like that of silicon than that of aluminum? Which third-row element has the same electronegativity as carbon? What is this pattern of similarity between rows called?

6. If F^- and Na^+ are isoelectronic, and have the same electron arrangement, why is Na^+ smaller?

7. Why is sodium metal softer than lithium? Why is sodium softer than magnesium?

8. Why is the maximum oxygen coordination number of sodium 6, whereas that for phosphorus, in the same third row, is only 4? Do any second-row elements have maximum coordination numbers of 4 for oxygen?

9. What makes aluminum especially unreactive? Does iron have the same advantage?

10. In what way is MgO more like Li_2O than like BeO? Which third-row oxide most resembles BeO?

11. What arrangement about a central ion does VSEPR theory predict for four electron pairs, either lone pairs or bonding pairs? What arrangement is predicted for six electron pairs? Give an example of a third-row compound with this geometry.

12. What species of aluminum–oxygen ion is found in strongly acid solutions? What species is present in a strong base? Why is aluminum oxide insoluble in pure water? Which second-row element behaves in a similar way, and what is this behavior called?

13. Why is a solution of sodium carbonate basic? What is the process of producing OH^- ions in this way called?

14. Why is sodium bicarbonate less basic than sodium carbonate?

15. When carbonic acid is dissolved in water, what are the relative amounts of H_2CO_3, HCO_3^-, and CO_3^{2-} present?

16. When sodium nitrate is dissolved in water, would you predict the solution to be basic, acidic, or nearly neutral? Why? (Recall why sodium carbonate solution is basic, and the differences between behavior of carbonate ion and nitrate ion from Chapter 5.)

17. Why is SiO_2 a hard solid when CO_2, from the element just above silicon in the second row, is a gas?

18. Why is the overall (empirical) formula for quartz SiO_2, when each silicon atom is surrounded by *four* oxygens?

19. How do quartz and olivine differ in their silicate framework? What other kinds of silicate frameworks are there?

20. What counterbalances the negative charges in silicate frameworks?

21. What is the difference between the types of silicates that are found in the mantle and in the crust of the Earth? Why does this difference occur?

22. What is the silicate framework in asbestos? In mica? In quartz? How are these structures reflected in the physical properties of the three minerals?

23. Why are clays useful in catalysis?

24. How does the molecular structure of clays make them useful in ceramics? What happens when pottery is fired?

25. Why are clays good adsorbants for greases and other substances?

26. What is the difference in atomic arrangement in quartz and in silicate glass? Why is quartz harder?

27. Why are feldspars found typically in the crust, whereas olivine is more characteristic of the mantle? (*Clue*: Why does ice float?)

28. Why do phosphorus and sulfur form multiatomic P_4 and S_8 molecules, whereas nitrogen and oxygen in the second row form diatomic molecules?

29. Compare the oxyacids of P, S, and Cl with those of the second-row elements for coordination number and acidity. Why is phosphoric acid weaker than nitric acid? Which third-row oxyacid is more similar to nitric acid in strength?

30. Which third-row oxyacid is most like carbonic acid? In what ways?

31. What does "diagonality" of chemical properties mean when applied to the periodic table? Give examples involving metals, amphoterism, and oxyacid properties.

32. Why does the acidity increase among chlorine oxyacids in the series hypochlorous acid, chlorous acid, chloric acid, and perchloric acid?

33. Why is HCl a stronger acid than HF, even though fluorine is more electronegative than chlorine and presumably would pull the bonding electron pair away from the proton more strongly?

34. Which is a stronger acid, H_2S or H_2O? Why? Which is stronger, H_2S or HCl? Why?

35. When sodium metal reacts with chlorine gas, what is oxidized and what is reduced? What do the terms oxidation and reduction mean in this reaction?

36. When a piece of metallic sodium is dropped into water, the first step of the reaction is one in which hydrogen gas is given off. In this step, which substance is oxidized and which is reduced?

37. The next and more dangerous consequence of dropping sodium in water is that the heat liberated ignites the hydrogen gas, which explodes. In this second step, what is oxidized and what is reduced?

38. In the reaction of hydrogen with oxygen, unlike that of sodium with chlorine, no ions are produced, and the sole product is covalently bonded water molecules. In what sense can one then say that oxidation and reduction have occurred?

39. When gasoline is burned, carbon and hydrogen are oxidized. Oxidation and reduction always must take place together. Then what substance is reduced in the burning of gasoline?

40. What is the oxidation number of lithium in lithium metal? In lithium chloride? In lithium hydroxide? In lithium oxide?

41. What is the oxidation number of fluorine in F_2? In HF? In LiF?

42. What is the oxidation number of hydrogen in H_2? In HF? In LiH (lithium hydride)?

43. What must be the sum of the oxidation numbers of all the atoms in a neutral molecule? In an ion with a charge of -3?

44. Is a good oxidizing agent a substance that is easily oxidized, or easily reduced? Is O_2 a good oxidizing agent, or a good reducing agent?

45. What is the "pseudo-ion" method for calculating oxidation numbers of atoms in a molecule? What is done with bonding electron pairs between atoms of unequal electronegativity? Between atoms of the same electronegativity?

46. How do the oxidation numbers of Cl compare in HCl and the four oxyacids of chlorine?

47. How do the oxidation numbers of O compare in O_2, water, and hydrogen peroxide, H_2O_2? What is the highest oxidation number that oxygen exhibits in its compounds? What is its lowest oxidation number?

48. In what way are the maximum and minimum oxidation numbers of an element often related to its electronic structure? What usually are the most common oxidation numbers for an element?

49. Why do O and F not show the same maximum oxidation numbers that S and Cl in the third row do? Explain in terms of atomic properties.

50. What are the oxidation numbers of nitrogen in the various oxides of nitrogen mentioned in Chapter 5, Page 84? In what common nitrogen compound does N have an oxidation number of -3?

51. When hydrazine is burned in oxygen, is nitrogen oxidized, or reduced? (Assume that the products are nitrogen gas and water. What substance is reduced, or oxidized, at the same time?)

52. When molten LiF is subjected to electrolysis (see Chapter 5), is lithium oxidized, or reduced? What happens to the fluorine?

PROBLEMS

1. The formula for an isolated silicate tetrahedron as it exists in minerals such as olivine is SiO_4^{4-}. Draw a Lewis electron-dot model of this ion, and indicate why each oxygen atom has a negative charge.

2. From atomic radii given in this chapter, calculate the Si—O bond distance assuming (a) a covalent bond between Si and O atoms, and (b) an ionic bond between Si^{4+} and O^{2-} ions. How different are these two Si—O distances? (Bond lengths can be measured by x-ray crystallography or spectroscopic methods, but it often is harder to decide how much of an observed bond length "belongs" to each of the atoms it connects. This requires looking at bonds between a given atom and many other different kinds of atoms, and arriving at a self-consistent set of bond radii that will reproduce all the observed bond lengths reasonably well.)

3. Zircon is a semiprecious stone, which sometimes is used to imitate diamond. It is made up of isolated silicate tetrahedra like olivine is, but with the charge balanced by ions of zirconium (a transition metal that we will see more of later) instead of iron and magnesium. The empirical formula of zircon is $Zr(SiO_4)$. What is the oxidation number of zirconium in zircon?

4. The mineral melilite is built from silicate units that are two tetrahedra connected together. If one silicate tetrahedron is SiO_4^{4-}, why is the melilite unit $Si_2O_7^{6-}$ rather than $Si_2O_8^{8-}$? One of the following is an acceptable formula for one type of melilite:

$NaCaAl(Si_2O_7)$ or $MgCaAl(Si_2O_7)$

Which one of the above is impossible? Why?

5. One of the two minerals that commonly are classified as the semiprecious jade is jadeite, a pyroxene made from infinitely long chains of silicate tetrahedra. Show that the empirical formula for such chains is $Si_nO_{3n}^{2n-}$, in which n is the number of tetrahedra in the chain, or more simply, the number of SiO_3^{2-} units. The empirical formula for jadeite is $NaAlSi_2O_6$. Why is this written with Si_2O_6 instead of SiO_3? (Pure jadeite with this composition is a milky white. The color in green jadeite comes from traces of chromium, as in emerald.)

6. The other mineral that traditionally is called jade is nephrite, a double-chain amphibole. What is the empirical formula for the amphibole chain? How many positive charges are needed per silicon atom to balance the negative charge on the double chains? Pure nephrite has counterbalancing calcium and magnesium ions in a ratio of one Ca to two Mg. What is the simplest overall for-

mula for nephrite? (Pure nephrite is colorless, and the green color of nephrite jade comes from trace amounts of iron, not chromium.)

7. From their structures, why would you expect that the different forms of jade would be more suitable materials for sculpture than quartz?

8. What are the oxidation numbers of H and C in methane, CH_4?

9. What is the oxidation number of beryllium in the metal and in BeO?

10. What is the oxidation number of carbon in the following substances: diamond, graphite, carbon monoxide, carbon dioxide, and carbon disulfide (CS_2)? (The latter is a somewhat special case.)

11. What is the oxidation number of carbon in the bicarbonate ion? What are the oxidation numbers of O and H? How does the sum of oxidation numbers of all the atoms in the bicarbonate ion compare with the charge on the ion?

12. What is the oxidation number of silicon in olivine? What are the oxidation numbers of O, Mg, and Fe? What is the sum of oxidation numbers for all atoms in the mineral? What is the sum of ON for the atoms in the silicate tetrahedra? How does this compare with the charge on a tetrahedron?

13. When aluminum oxide is dissolved in a strong base, what ions are produced? What are the oxidation numbers of each type of atom in these ions? What is the total oxidation number, and how does it compare with the charge on the ion?

14. Compare the oxidation numbers of N in nitrous acid and nitric acid. Of P in phosphorous acid and phosphoric acid. Of S in sulfurous acid and sulfuric acid. Of Cl in its four oxyacids. What generalization can you make about the strengths of oxyacids and the oxidation state of the central atom? Explain this in terms of electron-pulling power and the attraction of the acid anions for protons in solution.

15. What are the oxidation numbers of nitrogen in hydrazine and in dinitrogen tetroxide? (Assume that the ON for H is +1 and that for O is −2 in these molecules.) In the hypergolic reaction used to propel the lunar excursion module,

$$2N_2H_4 + N_2O_4 \rightarrow 3N_2 + 4H_2O$$

how does the ON of the hydrazine nitrogen atoms change during the course of the reaction? How does the ON of the nitrogen atoms of dinitrogen tetroxide change during reaction? How would these numbers suggest that you would need two hydrazine molecules for each dinitrogen tetroxide molecule? If you answered this correctly, you used a form of a conservation principle: the idea that electrons are not created or destroyed in a chemical reaction, and that all electrons that are taken up by one substance (reduction) must be yielded by something else (oxidation). We will come back to the *balancing* of oxidation–reduction equations in Chapter 11.

$n=5$ Stable orbit

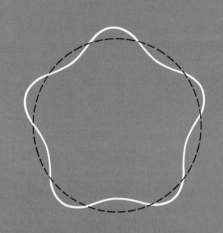
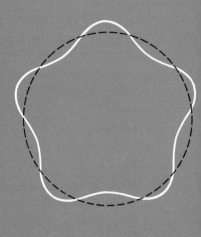

$n=5\frac{1}{3}$ Unstable orbit

$n=6$ Stable orbit

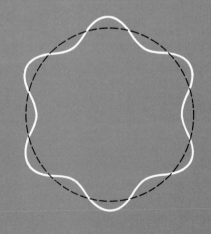
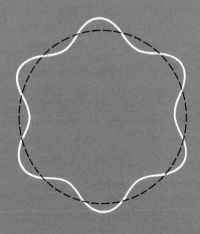
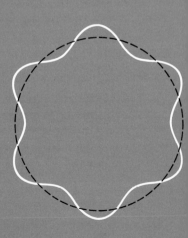

CHAPTER 7

Particles, Waves, and Paradoxes

Chemistry was in bad shape at the beginning of this century. Most of the knowledge of chemical properties that we have covered in the first six chapters was available, but without the underlying models that would tie it together. The usefulness of concepts of atoms, molecules, and moles was recognized, but there were still respectable chemists who doubted whether atoms had a real existence other than as conceptual models to account for observations. The periodic table organized chemical properties in a sensible manner, and had led to the successful prediction of properties of new elements, but no one knew why the table had the structure that it did. Ideas about the shapes of molecules were in their infancy. Van't Hoff used the number of different substituted methane compounds that could be made to argue for tetrahedral bond geometry around carbon atoms, but there was no theory of chemical bonding to explain why this should be true. Kekulé's flash of inspiration about the flat ring structures for benzene and other aromatic molecules was as much of a turning point for organic chemistry as Dalton's atoms had been a century earlier for chemistry in general. Organic chemistry, considered as the art of knowing what valuable dyes and drugs could be extracted from what natural or synthetic sources, was doing well in Germany, but chemistry remained principally a body of empirical knowledge. It was as much a trade as a science.

The British scientist Lord Rutherford expressed the disdain of the physicist for such empirical sciences, by dividing all science arrogantly into two branches: physics and stamp collecting. At the turn of the century, the field of chemistry was a large and loose stamp collection without an album.

Rutherford had no right to be arrogant, because physics was in just as bad shape. For a few years around 1890 it had begun to look like a closed and finished subject, with well-behaved "billiard ball" atoms moving according to Newton's laws of motion. The dilemma of

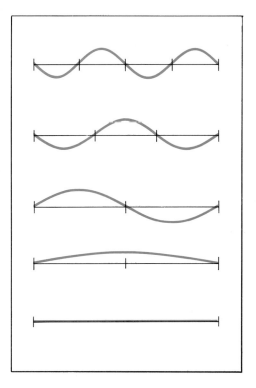

A violin string with fixed ends can vibrate only with certain frequencies: those which set up 0, 1, 2, 3, ⋯ half-cycles along the string. All other modes of vibration are forbidden because they violate the physical fact that the ends of the string are fixed. Violin strings and atoms both are examples of quantization in nature.

Top view

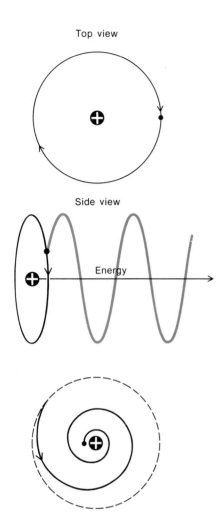

Side view

Energy

An electron moving in a circular orbit (top) should radiate energy (side view, center), according to classical physics. As it loses energy, it should spiral into the nucleus (bottom) and the atom should self-destruct. Stable atoms with electrons surrounding a nucleus are violations of the laws of classical physics, and are explainable only by quantum physics.

Red light has longer wavelength than green, and green longer than violet. The visible wavelengths and the colors that we associate with them are shown on the opposite page. This is a *linear* scale in wavelength.

the wave or particle nature of light was a puzzle, but surely only a minor one. Then in the space of a few years, the world of physics came unstuck at the seams. The Curies discovered that atoms could decompose. Max Planck and Albert Einstein showed that waves behaved like particles, and that "solid" particles had wave properties. The differences between mass and energy began to blur, and the substantial atom began to fade like the Cheshire cat.

The theory that "saved" physics was quantum mechanics, from which an entirely new picture of the nature of atoms and of matter developed in the first quarter of this century. In quantum mechanics, matter became only a special, condensed form of energy. The hard, billiard-ball atoms changed to standing waves, like waves in a vibrating violin string. The question of whether atoms *really* were particles or waves was rejected with a denial that the question had any meaning at the atomic level. The change was a profound philosophical wrench for most scientists. Although the really good physicists adopted quantum mechanics because it explained so many things that classical mechanics did not, the average nonscientist neither believed in nor even thought much about quantum physics until the atomic bomb burst over Japan in 1945. If the twilight world of half-waves, half-particles could produce something as awesome as an atomic bomb, then it must be real, and not just an elegant mathematical theory that physicists use to tie their data together.

It is this twilight zone that we will investigate in the next three chapters, because the quantum picture of the atom changed chemistry as much as it did physics. Erwin Schrödinger began applying quantum ideas to chemistry around 1926. It was soon apparent that the new theory gave a correct explanation for all of the chemical phenomena we have discussed so far, and more: electronic shell structure, chemical properties of atoms, the structure of the periodic table, the chemical bond, the shapes of molecules, and chemical reactivity. This chapter will lay the foundation for the new theory, Chapter 8 will apply it to atomic structure and the periodic table, and Chapter 9 will give the first satisfactory explanation for molecular structure and bonding.

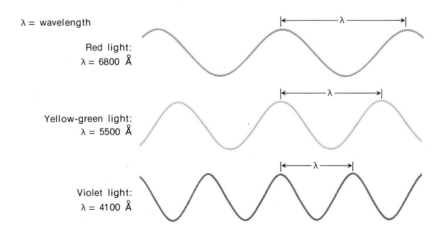

λ = wavelength

Red light:
$\lambda = 6800$ Å

Yellow-green light:
$\lambda = 5500$ Å

Violet light:
$\lambda = 4100$ Å

THE IMPOSSIBLE ATOM

By 1910 a picture of an atom had emerged as a tiny nucleus containing most of the mass of the atom and bearing a positive charge, surrounded by a swarm of electrons with enough negative charge to make the atom electrically neutral. The only problem was: What were these electrons doing? If they were motionless, then electrostatic attraction between the positive nucleus and the negative electrons should instantly cause the atom to collapse. This obviously was wrong.

The electrons could be moving in circular orbits with just enough centrifugal force to balance the pull of the nucleus, like planets around the sun (top left). This was the basis of an atomic theory proposed by the Danish physicist Niels Bohr in 1913. But this theory also had a fatal flaw. A positive nucleus with a negative electron orbiting around it, seen from the plane of the orbit, would appear as an oscillating electric dipole, as shown at center left. By all the laws of classical physics and electromagnetic theory, an oscillating electric dipole should radiate electromagnetic energy. If this were not so, the whole theory behind wireless telegraphy and radio would be wrong. *If* the atom did radiate energy, however, then the electron would fall to a lower-energy orbit, closer to the nucleus. It would radiate still more energy, and the process should end only when the electron had whirled down and collided with the nucleus, as shown in lower left margin. According to classical theory, every atom in the universe should long since have collapsed, because its electrons had spiraled into the nucleus. Thus whether electrons were stationary or orbiting, atoms should not exist. What was wrong with classical physics?

PARTICLES OF LIGHT

Even more unpleasant dilemmas faced physicists in the early years of this century. Light itself seemed to be misbehaving. The question as to whether light was made up of waves or particles had seesawed back and forth for several hundred years. Isaac Newton, who discovered in 1672 that light could be split into many colors by a prism, favored a particle theory of light. Others before and after Newton preferred a wave theory to explain the bending of light by lenses, the interference of light passed through adjacent pinholes, and the diffraction of light by gratings. By the end of the nineteenth century few people doubted the wave nature of light and of all other forms of electromagnetic radiation. James Maxwell developed an elegant theory by which such radiation was thought of as arising from vibrating electric and magnetic fields in space. Visible light was recognized as being just the range of wavelengths of electromagnetic radiation that the eye is sensitive to, with radiation of longer or shorter wavelengths being invisible but present.

Three typical vibrations (waves) are shown in the left diagram. The *wavelength* is the distance in centimeters, angstroms, or any other unit of length, from one wave crest to the next, and is represented by

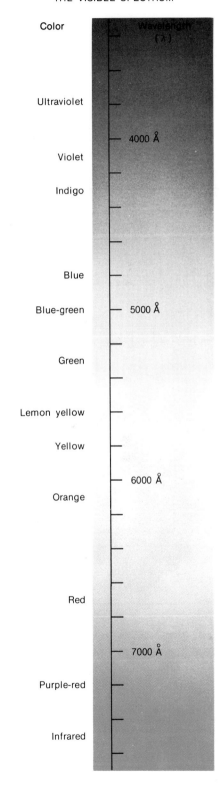

THE VISIBLE SPECTRUM

Color   Wavelength (λ)

Ultraviolet

— 4000 Å

Violet

Indigo

Blue

Blue-green   — 5000 Å

Green

Lemon yellow

Yellow

— 6000 Å

Orange

Red

— 7000 Å

Purple-red

Infrared

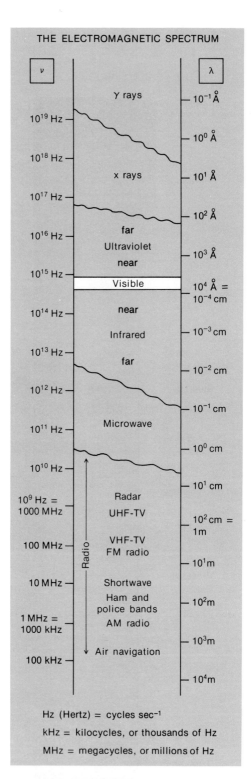

THE ELECTROMAGNETIC SPECTRUM

ν | λ

- 10^{19} Hz — γ rays — 10^{-1} Å
- 10^{18} Hz — — 10^0 Å
- 10^{17} Hz — x rays — 10^1 Å
- 10^{16} Hz — far / Ultraviolet / near — 10^2 Å
- 10^{15} Hz — — 10^3 Å
- Visible — 10^4 Å = 10^{-4} cm
- 10^{14} Hz — near / Infrared — 10^{-3} cm
- 10^{13} Hz — far — 10^{-2} cm
- 10^{12} Hz — — 10^{-1} cm
- 10^{11} Hz — Microwave — 10^0 cm
- 10^{10} Hz — — 10^1 cm
- 10^9 Hz = 1000 MHz — Radar / UHF-TV — 10^2 cm = 1m
- 100 MHz — VHF-TV / FM radio — 10^1m
- 10 MHz — Shortwave / Ham and police bands — 10^2m
- 1 MHz = 1000 kHz — AM radio — 10^3m
- 100 kHz — Air navigation — 10^4m

Radio

Hz (Hertz) = cycles sec^{-1}
kHz = kilocycles, or thousands of Hz
MHz = megacycles, or millions of Hz

The entire electromagnetic spectrum, from radio waves (low frequencies, long wavelengths) to gamma rays (high frequencies, short wavelengths). The entire visible spectrum of the preceding page is compressed into a narrow band here. This is a *logarithmic* scale in both frequency and wavelength.

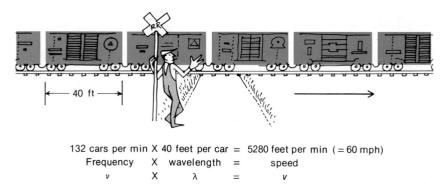

40 ft

132 cars per min X 40 feet per car = 5280 feet per min (= 60 mph)
Frequency   X   wavelength   =   speed
ν X λ = v

Speed equals frequency times unit length, whether the units are boxcars or waves of orange light.

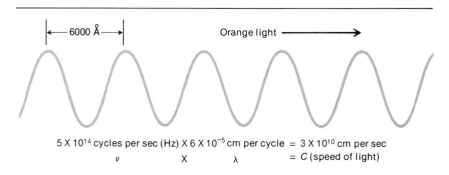

6000 Å   Orange light ⟶

5×10^{14} cycles per sec (Hz) X 6×10^{-5} cm per cycle = 3×10^{10} cm per sec
ν X λ = C (speed of light)

the Greek letter lambda (λ). Red light is electromagnetic radiation of wavelengths around 6800 Å, and progressing through the visible spectrum of red, orange, yellow, green, blue, and violet, the waves become shorter. Violet light has wavelengths around 4100 Å. Radiation shorter than this cannot be perceived by the eye, and is in the *ultraviolet* region. Wavelengths longer than 7000 Å also are invisible and are termed *infrared*. The entire visible spectrum is shown in the margin of the preceding page, with the wavelengths that correspond to the various colors.

The visible region is only a minute part of the entire electromagnetic spectrum, which is shown at the left. Because of the vast range of wavelengths involved, a logarithmic, or power-of-ten, scale has been used instead of a linear scale. The first scale division represents the change from 1 cm to 10 cm, the next equal division represents 10 cm to 100 cm, and the next, 100 cm to 1000 cm. Each successive division corresponds to a tenfold increase in wavelength.

At wavelengths shorter than violet, the ultraviolet continues to approximately 100 Å, where an ill-defined border separates far ultraviolet from x rays. Radiation at atomic dimensions, around 1 Å, is called x radiation, but when these and finer waves are generated in atomic reactions they are called gamma (γ) rays. At longer wavelengths, the far infrared gives way to microwaves and then to radio waves, of which several of the more familiar types are shown on the spectrum. The shortest gamma rays represented on the spectrum are only a few hundredths the size of an atom, and the longest radio waves shown are seven miles long.

Moving waves can be described by their *frequency*, or number of waves per second, as well as by their wavelength. If a train of waves is moving past a stationary observer at a frequency of ν (nu) complete cycles, or waves per second, and if each of these has a wavelength of λ (lambda) centimeters per cycle, then the wave must be moving at a speed of $\nu\lambda = v$ cm per second. This is illustrated with boxcars and with orange light on the opposite page. It is an important observation that *all* electromagnetic radiation, radio waves through gamma rays, moves at the same universal speed. This is the speed of light, $c = 3 \times 10^{10}$ or 30,000,000,000 centimeters per second. For any such radiation we can write $\nu\lambda = c = 3 \times 10^{10}$ cm sec⁻¹. Because the speed of light is constant, if we know either the frequency or the wavelength of electromagnetic radiation we can calculate the other quantity. Frequencies are listed at the left of the electromagnetic spectrum on the opposite page. They range from a few hundred thousand hertz (Hz), or cycles per second (cps), to ten million million million cps.

Example. The orange light in the diagram provides one example of a wavelength calculation. As another example, what is the wavelength used by the FM station KPFK in Los Angeles, which has a frequency of 90.7 megahertz (MHz), or megacycles (Mc) per second?

Solution.

$$\nu = 90.7 \text{ Mc or } 90.7 \times 10^6 \text{ cycles sec}^{-1}$$

$$\lambda = \frac{c}{\nu} = \frac{3.00 \times 10^{10} \text{ cm sec}^{-1}}{90.7 \times 10^6 \text{ cycles sec}^{-1}} = 330 \text{ cm cycle}^{-1}$$

KPFK has a broadcast wavelength of 330 cm or 3.3 meters.

All of this discussion is straightforward and agrees with classical physics. It suggests that light and other electromagnetic radiation are *waves*. It was very disturbing, therefore, when phenomena were discovered (around 1900) that clearly indicated that light was made up of particles. One such phenomenon involved the photoelectric effect. It was known that if one shines a beam of light on a clean surface of a metal of low electronegativity, electrons will be knocked from the metal. This is familiar to us today from the use of cesium metal in photocells, electric eyes, and vidicon TV cameras (right). The electrons that are ejected from the metal by light in these devices are used to trigger a signal or to record an image.

What happens when light knocks electrons out of a metal surface? The process is shown in the margin of the next page. Some of the energy of the light is required to pull the electrons away from the metal (in fact this is one way of measuring the ionization energy of a metal atom). Unless the beam of light has at least this much energy, it will not be able to remove electrons from the metal surface at all. If the light has more than the minimum energy required, then the extra energy will be given to the ejected electrons as kinetic energy of motion. Therefore, it was expected that the more energy a light beam contains, the faster the ejected electrons would move.

It was assumed that the more intense the beam of light was, the greater its energy. Hence it was deeply disturbing in 1900 to discover that a light beam of greater intensity did *not* make the electrons move

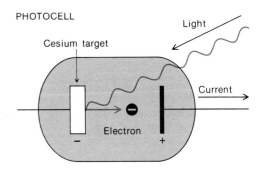

PHOTOCELL

Light striking the cesium target causes electrons to be ejected from the metal surface. Some of the energy of the incoming light is used to remove the electrons from the metal; the remainder gives kinetic energy to the electrons. The current thus set up by the light can be used in electronic circuits.

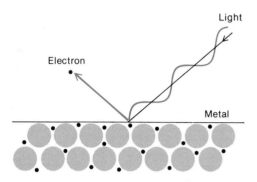

Incident light knocks electrons out of the metal. The greater the energy of the light, the faster the ejected electrons travel.

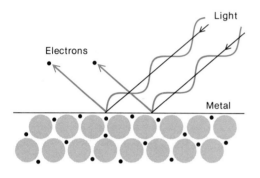

A more intense beam of light does not mean faster moving electrons, only more of them at the same speed.

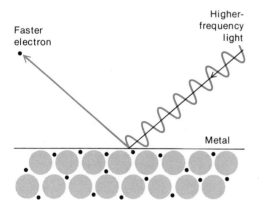

Faster electrons are obtained only with light of higher frequency (shorter wavelength).

faster after emission; it only caused more of them to be emitted (see center left). Light behaved as if it consisted of separate particles all with the same energy, with each ejected electron being the result of a collision between one particle of light and one electron in the metal. Greater intensity of light meant only that more light particles were hitting the metal per second, not that there was more energy per particle.

Then what could be done to increase the energy of each incident light particle, so that the electrons emitted by collision had more kinetic energy? The answer was that the speed of the outgoing electrons depended on the *frequency* of light used. The higher the frequency, the faster the electrons moved (lower left). The ejected electrons behaved as if the energy (E) of the incoming particles of light was directly proportional to the light frequency: $E \propto \nu$ or $E = h\nu$, in which h is a constant.

Max Planck first proposed this relationship between energy and frequency in 1900 as part of his study of the way in which heated solids emit radiation. The constant h is called *Planck's constant* in his honor. It was Albert Einstein who successfully explained the photoelectric effect. He showed that Planck's constant also was applicable to the photoelectric effect, and appeared to be a universal constant relating energy to frequency of radiation.

Here the paradox arose. How could light simultaneously be a wave with frequency ν, and a collection of particles with individual energies E? How could a wave act like particles, or particles simulate a wave? Was light really a wave, or a stream of particles? It took a considerable philosophical wrench to recognize that these questions were unanswerable because they were the wrong questions. "Wave" and "particle" are labels for things that exhibit certain behavioral patterns at the macroscopic size level. Things that we call "waves" do not show particle behavior in our familiar world, and things that we call "particles" do not act in a wavelike manner. This is only a matter of scale. At the level of atomic dimensions, we cannot say "This is a wave and that is a particle." The same "thing" can show both behaviors under appropriate conditions, and this is what light does. Someone has coined the term "wavicle" for these ambiguous things, but the "particles" of light ordinarily are called either *photons* or light *quanta*.

WAVES OF MATTER

If you look through a window screen at a distant street light, you will see the pinpoint of light broken into a crosslike pattern of spots. The same effect can be obtained with a geologist's wire-mesh sieve and a pinhole light source behind it, as shown at the upper right on the next page. This is the phenomenon of diffraction. The wires of the screen scatter the light waves. These scattered waves reinforce in certain directions to produce spots of light, and cancel or interfere in other directions to produce darkness. From the pattern of light and darkness in the diffraction pattern, a physicist can determine the spacings between wires in the original screen. In the same way, x rays passed through a single crystal produce a pattern of rows of spots. A metal foil will produce a set of diffraction rings instead (center right), because the metal is made up of many tiny crystals oriented at random. The spacings of the rings tells us how closely the atoms are packed together in the metal. X-ray diffraction by crystalline solids currently is the most accurate method of determining the structures of molecules.

This is the way that waves behave, yet we know that light and x rays also have particle properties. Nature often is symmetrical and, in retrospect, it was no great flash of insight for physicists to ask themselves, since waves are also like particles, whether entities such as electrons might not also be wavelike. Davisson and Germer at Bell Telephone Laboratories tested this idea, in 1927, by passing a thin beam of accelerated electrons through a metal foil. The pattern that they obtained, like that shown at the right, obviously is a pattern produced by diffraction of some kind of waves by the metal atoms. Knowing the wavelength of the x rays used, a physicist can measure the radii of the diffraction rings in an x-ray pattern, such as that shown at center right, and calculate the spacings between atoms in the metal. With this information, he then can work backward from the radii of the corresponding rings in the electron-diffraction pattern (lower right) to calculate the effective wavelength of the beam of electrons. It was found that the wavelength of a beam of electrons depends on the speed of the electrons. The faster the electrons the shorter their wavelength. Electrons accelerated through a potential of 40,000 volts, or given a kinetic energy of 40,000 electron volts, have a wavelength of 0.06 Å.

The relationship between mass, m, velocity, v, and wavelength, λ, is known as the de Broglie relationship, after the man who first proposed it on theoretical grounds three years before the Davisson–Germer experiment. This relationship is $\lambda = h/mv$ in which h is Planck's constant, the same constant we encountered previously in the photoelectric effect. Since both mass and speed are in the denominator of the expression, we can see that a heavy particle or a rapidly moving one will have a short wavelength.

The de Broglie wavelength relationship does not apply only to electrons. It is valid for every particle in the universe, but the only particles that have small enough mass that their wavelengths are long enough to detect are electrons, protons, and neutrons. In addition to x-ray and electron diffraction, neutron diffraction is one of the standard tools of molecular structure analysis today. Experimentally useful electron and neutron beams have wavelengths from 1 Å to a few hundredths of an angstrom. In contrast, a baseball thrown at 30 meters per second has a de Broglie wavelength of only 10^{-24} Å. This is less than one billion-billionth the diameter of an atomic nucleus, and no experiment that we could ever design would reveal the wave properties of a stream of baseballs. Wave properties of particles only become apparent at the subatomic level.

The principle remains, however: All things in this universe are both waves and particles, and have both a wavelength and an energy per particle. At the size level encountered in everyday life, either one or the other behavior predominates, which is why the wave–particle duality was overlooked until this century. But at the atomic and sub-

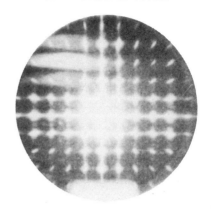

Diffraction of light by a wire-mesh screen, analogous to diffraction of x rays by a single crystal

Diffraction of x rays by a thin aluminum foil, with crystalline regions oriented in all directions. Each diffraction spot from the pattern above is smeared out into a ring.

Diffraction of an electron beam by the same thin aluminum foil. The ring pattern is the same, but the spacings differ because the wavelengths of x rays and electrons are not the same. Nevertheless, the electron beam is just as wavelike as the x-ray beam. Courtesy Education Development Center, Newton, Massachusetts.

135

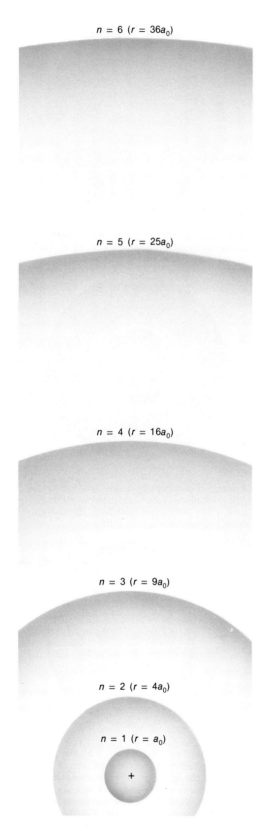

$n = 6 \; (r = 36a_0)$

$n = 5 \; (r = 25a_0)$

$n = 4 \; (r = 16a_0)$

$n = 3 \; (r = 9a_0)$

$n = 2 \; (r = 4a_0)$

$n = 1 \; (r = a_0)$

$+$

Radii of allowed orbits in the Bohr model of the hydrogen atom, $r_n = n^2 a_0$

atomic level, both wave and particle behavior can be detected under the right experimental conditions. The dualism is real. Electrons do not just assume wavelike behavior now and again like a disguise; electrons *are* waves as well as particles. This is important in the first modern theory of atomic structure, the Bohr picture of the hydrogen atom.

THE DISCONTINUOUS ATOM

In 1913 Niels Bohr proposed a model for the hydrogen atom in which the electron moved in a circular orbit around the nucleus, with the centrifugal force of the electron in the orbit just balanced by the electrostatic attraction of the nucleus. To the question "Why doesn't the electron radiate energy and fall into the nucleus as electromagnetic theory predicts?", Bohr gave the blunt reply "It just doesn't." The theory of oscillating dipoles and radiation may apply to radio antennae, he proposed, but not to things the size of atoms; just as the separate categories of wave and particle do not apply at that level. For a cornerstone of his theory Bohr assumed that stable atoms could exist with electrons in circular orbits.

Not all orbits were possible, according to Bohr, but only those that met certain conditions. Although his original conditions were more complicated, in essence he proposed that the only stable electronic orbits were those that corresponded to *standing*, or *stationary*, *electron waves around the orbit*, with an integral number of complete wavelengths. (See illustration at the beginning of this chapter.) The orbit with the smallest size and lowest energy would have one complete electron wave around its circumference; the next allowable orbit would have two complete waves, and then three, four, and so on. An intermediate orbit that corresponded to $2\frac{1}{4}$ or $5\frac{1}{3}$ waves per circuit would lead to destructive interference between waves from successive turns around the orbit, as shown at the beginning of this chapter. The only allowed orbits were those for which the total circumference was an integral number, n, of wavelengths:

$$\text{circumference} = 2\pi r = n\lambda = n\frac{h}{mv} \qquad n = 1, 2, 3, 4, \cdots$$

Each of these allowed orbits, or states, was called a *quantum state*, characterized by a *quantum number*, n, which was a positive integer.

If you write the expression for the balance between electrostatic attraction and centrifugal force for a stable orbit, and include the restriction among radius, mass, and speed given by the above equation, you can obtain expressions for the radii of the allowed quantum orbits (r) and the energies of the electrons in them (E). The sizes of the allowed orbits are given by

$$r_n = n^2 a_0$$

in which r_n is the radius of the nth permitted orbit, and a_0 is a collection of physical constants, which for the hydrogen atom has a numerical value of 0.53 Å. The size of the radius increases as the *square* of the quantum number; thus the smallest (and lowest-energy) orbit has a radius of 0.53 Å, the next has a radius of 2.12 Å, and so on. These orbits are illustrated at the far left.

The energy corresponding to the quantum state n is given by

$$E_n = -\frac{E_0}{n^2}$$

E_0 is another collection of physical constants, which for hydrogen has a value of 313 kcal mole^{-1}. The allowed energy levels for hydrogen are diagramed at the right. By convention, energy is expressed relative to that of an ionized atom, with the electron at rest but infinitely far away. The energy of any atom with its electron still bound to it must be less than zero, or negative. Positive energy refers to the kinetic energy that the removed electron has, if it is not at rest.

For atomic hydrogen, the lowest-energy state, with the 0.53 Å radius orbit, has an energy of $E_1 = -313$ kcal mole^{-1}. Atomic hydrogen in this state is 313 kcal mole^{-1} more stable than an ionized atom. This 313 kcal mole^{-1} is the ionization energy of atomic hydrogen. Although the numerical value is calculated from first principles in the Bohr theory (using quantities such as Planck's constant and the mass and charge of the electron), it agrees exactly with the measured value of the ionization energy of hydrogen given in Chapter 3. This is the kind of agreement that builds confidence in any theory.

In the $n = 2$ quantum state, atomic hydrogen has an energy of

$$E_2 = -\frac{313 \text{ kcal mole}^{-1}}{2^2} = -78 \text{ kcal mole}^{-1}$$

This is a higher (less negative) energy than the $n = 1$ state. In this state, the atom is only 78 kcal mole^{-1} more stable than the ion. The higher the quantum number, n, the closer the energy comes to that of the ionized atom. Ionization, or removal of the electron, can be considered as placing the electron in quantum state $n = \infty$ (i.e., the electron is an infinite distance from the nucleus), with energy

$$E_\infty = -\frac{E_0}{\infty} = 0$$

Bohr's picture of the hydrogen atom can be summarized in a set of assumptions:

1. The electron moves in one of a set of circular orbits around the nucleus, with centrifugal force and nuclear attraction exactly balanced.

2. An electron in an orbit has a wavelength given by the de Broglie relationship, $\lambda = h/mv$. The only stable orbits are those that represent standing waves, with an integral number, n, of waves in the complete orbit.

3. These standing-wave orbits are truly stable—the atoms do not radiate energy and collapse, as would be predicted from classical physics.

From these assumptions, one arrives at the following statements about the size of orbits and energy of atoms:

4. The radius of the nth orbit is given by

$$r_n = n^2 a_0$$

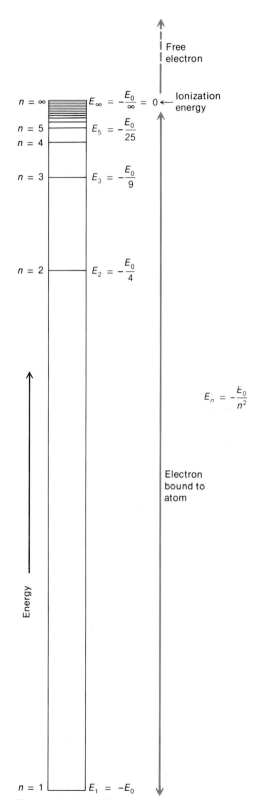

$$E_n = -\frac{E_0}{n^2}$$

Energy levels of allowed orbits in the Bohr model of the hydrogen atom,

$$E_n = -\frac{E_0}{n^2}$$

137

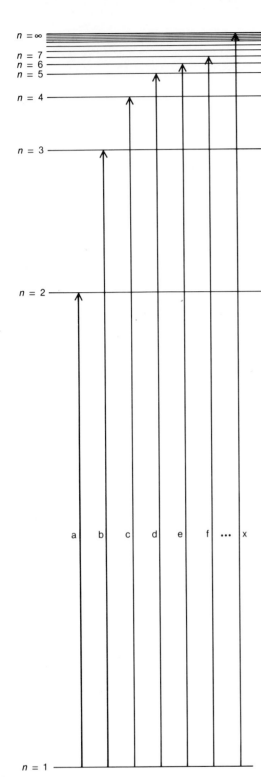

Energy-level diagram for the hydrogen atom, showing allowed jumps to higher quantum levels as energy is absorbed. Frequencies of energy absorbed are proportional to energy differences between initial and final levels. Letters by transition lines correspond to lines in the hydrogen spectrum shown on Page 140.

5. The energy of an atom with its electron in the nth orbit is given by

$$E_n = -\frac{E_0}{n^2}$$

Both a_0 and E_0 can be calculated in the Bohr theory from Planck's constant and the charge and mass of the electron, and checked against experimental values. The most important new idea in Bohr's model of the atom is the conclusion that not every energy is possible for the atom. The energy of an atom is restricted, or *quantized*. This quantization of energy arises from Assumption 2 (standing waves around the circumference of the orbit) just as the overtones that one can get from a vibrating violin string are determined by its length (standing waves along the string).

ATOMS, ENERGY, AND RADIATION

To physicists, the proof of Bohr's model of the hydrogen atom was its ability to explain exactly how atoms absorb and emit energy (called their atomic spectra). If we heat a substance to the point at which its molecules are broken down into gaseous atoms, and then pass electromagnetic radiation of many frequencies through it, most of the frequencies will pass through the gas unimpeded, and only a certain set of frequencies of radiation will be absorbed. Conversely, if we add energy to the atoms by heating them even further, they will emit radiation at this same characteristic set of frequencies. (These same general comments apply at lower temperatures to molecules, but molecular spectra are more complicated than atomic spectra.) We now know that the different frequencies of radiation absorbed or emitted by atoms represent jumps between different energy states that the electrons can be in (above). There are times when a physicist must settle for inaccurate measurements, but these spectral frequencies are among the most accurate quantities that can be measured. Atomic spectra had been observed, measured, and cataloged in detail prior to the development of quantum mechanics, but the reasons for them were not understood at all.

138

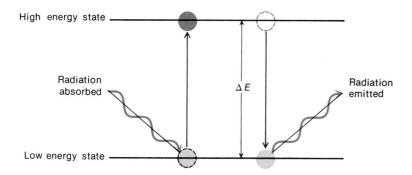

High energy state

Low energy state

Radiation absorbed

Radiation emitted

ΔE

An electron can jump from a lower to a higher energy level with energy difference ΔE if the atom absorbs a quantum (photon) of radiation of frequency ν; $\Delta E = h\nu$. The electron then can drop back to the lower energy level, with the emission of a photon of the same frequency.

Bohr proposed that an atom can absorb radiation *only* at a frequency, ν, that corresponds to the difference in energy, ΔE, between two allowed quantum states:

$$\Delta E = h\nu$$

This is illustrated above. An electron cannot jump from a lower to a higher energy state unless this exact amount of energy is supplied to it. Conversely, when an atom in a higher state falls to a lower state, the frequency of radiation given off is dictated by the relationship just given.

In the energy diagram for a hydrogen atom at the far left, the vertical lines marked a, b, c, ··· represent transitions from the lowest energy level, $n = 1$, to various higher levels. A certain fraction of atoms at any given temperature already will be in the first excited state (i.e., $n = 2$) and these atoms can absorb radiation as indicated by vertical lines g, h, i, ··· and go to even higher states. Those few atoms already in an $n = 3$ state can absorb radiation as shown by lines l, m, n, ··· and the progression can continue. Each of these series of absorptions, starting with a different initial quantum state, has an upper limit, which is the energy needed to ionize the atom. These are shown as lines x, y, and z for absorptions from $n = 1, 2,$ and 3 to $n = \infty$.

When atomic absorption spectra are measured, a beam of radiation of all frequencies is passed through the sample of hot gas, and then is dispersed by a prism or diffraction grating, as shown below. The separated frequencies are recorded on photographic film, and absorp-

SPECTROMETER

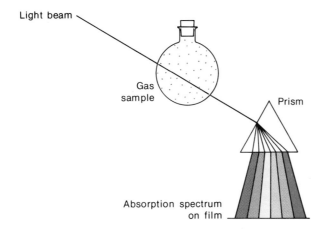

Light beam

Gas sample

Prism

Absorption spectrum on film

In absorption spectroscopy, a beam of light of many frequencies is passed through the sample, and the light that is not absorbed is spread out by a prism so the absorption frequencies can be measured.

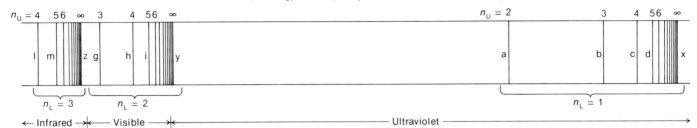

Energy and frequency ⟶

$n_U = 4$ 5 6   ∞   3   4 5 6   ∞ $n_U = 2$ 3   4 5 6 ∞

l   m   z g   h   i   y   a   b   c   d   x

$n_L = 3$ $n_L = 2$ $n_L = 1$

← Infrared →|← Visible →|←————————————— Ultraviolet —————————————→

Absorption spectrum of the hydrogen atom. Each absorption line corresponds to one vertical jump in the energy-level diagram on Page 138. Quantum numbers of the low-energy level, n_L, are indicated for each line below the spectrum, and quantum numbers of the upper level, n_U, are indicated above.

tions are indicated by lines across the film where no light reached the photographic emulsion because radiation of that frequency was absorbed by the gas. The complete absorption spectrum of hydrogen atoms, based on the energy-level transitions shown on Page 138, is diagramed above. Each line on this spectral diagram represents one absorption, or transition upward between quantum states, and the letters beside some of the lines correspond to the lettering of vertical transition lines on the energy-level diagram.

If subscripts L and U signify the lower and upper quantum levels between which a transition occurs, then the energy difference is

$$\Delta E = E_U - E_L = -E_0 \left(\frac{1}{n_U^2} - \frac{1}{n_L^2} \right) = h\nu$$

Absorptions or emissions involving the same lower quantum state belong to the same *series* because their spectral lines appear near one another. The spacings between quantum levels in hydrogen are so great that all lines of the $n_L = 1$ series fall in the high-energy ultraviolet region. Most of the $n_L = 2$ series of absorption lines fall in the visible region, and the $n_L = 3$ lines are found in the near infrared region. The actual visible spectrum of the hydrogen atom is shown below. This spectrum, and its exact match with that predicted by the Bohr theory at a time when no other explanation of atomic spectra was available, was convincing evidence that Bohr was on the right track.

The main flaw in Bohr's theory was that, although it explained the hydrogen atom perfectly, it explained nothing else. All attempts to extend the theory to atoms with more than one electron failed until Schrödinger developed wave mechanics a decade later. However, the following ideas of the Bohr theory, which were so startling to contemporary physicists, remained valid even in the later theory: the wave nature of the electron, quantization of energy in atoms, quantum numbers to describe particular energy states of an atom, and absorption and emission of energy as the atoms jump from one quantum level to another.

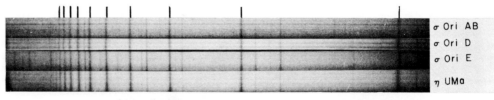

σ Ori AB
σ Ori D
σ Ori E
η UMa

Actual photographs of the visible portion ($n_L = 2$) of the hydrogen absorption spectrum. These spectra are from four stars in our galaxy. Hydrogen lines are marked, and the other lines mostly are for helium. Courtesy John Oke, California Institute of Technology.

ATOMIC SPECTRA AND EXPANDING GALAXIES

What we have said about the atomic spectrum of hydrogen holds for other elements as well. Every chemical element, when heated to an incandescent gas, emits radiation at a particular set of frequencies, which is just as characteristic of the element as are the fingerprints of a person. This is the element's atomic *emission spectrum*. Conversely, if radiation of all wavelengths is passed through a somewhat cooler atomic gas of an element, the gas can absorb or remove radiation at the same set of frequencies, to produce an atomic *absorption spectrum*. These frequencies, which represent transitions between quantum levels of the atom, can be used to construct an energy-level diagram for that kind of atom.

When the "white" or all-wavelength radiation emitted in the hot center of a star passes through its somewhat cooler outer layers, these layers absorb certain frequencies corresponding to the elements present. Therefore, dark lines are seen in the spectrum of a star, which represent the sum of the absorption spectra of the elements in its outer region. The spectrum of a given element is the same whether seen in a laboratory or in light from a distant star. We do not need to go to a star to determine its composition; it sends its analysis to us. This is why we can speak so confidently about the atomic composition of stars. It also is evidence for the statement, universally accepted but inherently untestable by direct means, that the basic laws of physics are the same throughout the universe.

There is one important exception to this statement about the constancy of atomic spectra. Spectra from very distant galaxies show lines that obviously belong to hydrogen, helium, and other recognizable elements, but the lines are shifted to lower frequencies, toward the red end of the visible spectrum (right). The American astronomer Edwin Hubble interpreted this lowering of frequencies as a cosmic Doppler shift, or "red shift," produced because the galaxies are moving away from us, like the lowering of pitch of the whistle of a rapidly departing train. This red shift of the galaxies has enabled astronomers to calculate how far each galaxy is from our own. The more distant a galaxy, the faster it moves away from us, and the more its atomic spectra are shifted toward the red, or longer wavelengths.

If the history of this expanding universe were plotted backward in time, the galaxies would meet at a common locale approximately 15 billion years ago. This is the basis for the "big bang" theory of the universe, which proposes that everything began in a cosmic explosion 15 billion years ago, and that the galaxies are island universes of stars that represent the expanding debris from this first cosmic event. All this from shifted frequencies in atomic spectra!

THE QUANTIZED ATOM: A SUMMARY

This has been a chapter of ideas, and very strange ideas they were when they first appeared: light waves that came in bundles, beams of electrons that were also waves, atoms that didn't radiate like they were supposed to by classical theory, and atoms that jumped discontinu-

RELATIONSHIP BETWEEN RED SHIFT AND
DISTANCE FOR EXTRAGALACTIC NEBULAE

Location of nebula and distance in light years	Speed away from our galaxy

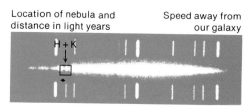

Virgo: 78 million   1,200 km sec⁻¹

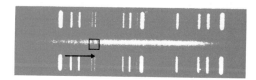

Ursa Major: 1 billion   15,000 km sec⁻¹

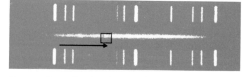

Corona Borealis: 1.4 billion   22,000 km sec⁻¹

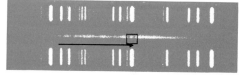

Bootes: 2.5 billion   39,000 km sec⁻¹

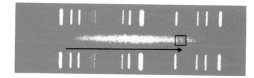

Hydra: 3.96 billion   61,000 km sec⁻¹

Red shifts in the H and K lines of the calcium spectrum from five galaxies at increasing distance from our own. Each galactic absorption spectrum is bracketed top and bottom by iron emission spectra from the laboratory for calibration purposes. The horizontal arrow below each galactic spectrum indicates the shift of the two calcium absorption lines from their normal position relative to the iron lines. Courtesy of The Hale Observatories.

ously from one energy state to another, with the intermediate energies being forbidden. These bundles of light energy were called light *quanta*, from the same root word that gave us "quantity." Atoms that could exist only in certain energy states, and which could jump from one state to another by absorbing or emitting quanta of electromagnetic energy, were termed *quantized* atoms, and the new mechanics based on such ideas was *quantum mechanics*.

The simplest quantum theory was that of Niels Bohr, which we have been examining in this chapter. His theory explained the hydrogen atom perfectly, but that was all it explained. Any atom or ion with more than one electron was too complicated for the Bohr theory, and all attempts to patch the theory failed. Schrödinger took the next step, around 1926, with his improved quantum theory, *wave mechanics*. This was the missing key to atomic structure. Wave mechanics led to an explanation for the structure and properties of all the atoms, and for interatomic bonding in molecules as well. This is the subject of the next chapter.

QUESTIONS

1. Why is the model of an electron moving in a circular orbit around a central positive nucleus a violation of classical physics? What should happen to such an atom?

2. What would happen if the electron were stationary instead of moving in orbit?

3. What is the wavelength of a wave? Illustrate with a diagram. What is the frequency of a wave, and in what units is it expressed? How are these two quantities related to the speed with which the wave travels?

4. What is a typical wavelength for light that we see as red? What is the frequency of this light? What color is the light that has a wavelength two thirds as long? How does its frequency compare with that of red light?

5. Which light in the preceding problem has more energy per photon? What is the ratio of energy per photon for the two wavelengths?

6. In what way are the names VHF and UHF (very-high frequency and ultra-high frequency) chosen appropriately for television channels? Short-wave radio is "short" relative to what?

7. Explain the relative health hazards of light waves, ultraviolet radiation, and x rays, in terms of the relative energy per photon.

8. From the use of cesium metal in photoelectric devices, would you expect Cs to have a larger, or smaller, first ionization energy than lithium and aluminum?

9. When cesium metal is used in a photocell in an automatic door-opening circuit, what happens to the electrons that are knocked out of the cesium metal? How does the cesium ultimately get electrons back again? Does the signal from the photocell circuit hold the door closed, or hold it open?

10. The voltage output of a photocell is proportional to the energy of the electrons ejected from the metal target. In contrast, the current output is proportional to the rate at which electrons are emitted from the target. What happens to the voltage of the photocell when the intensity of light falling on it is doubled? What happens to the current?

11. What happens to the voltage and current from the photocell when light of shorter wavelength but the same intensity as Question 10 is used?

12. How do your answers to the two previous questions provide evidence for the particle nature of light?

13. What evidence is there for the wave nature of light?

14. What are the fundamental units of light called? Is light made up of waves, or particles?

15. In the expression relating energy to frequency, what is the constant, h?

16. What evidence is there for wavelike behavior of matter?

17. If the speed of a beam of electrons is doubled, what happens to its wavelength?

18. To x-ray diffraction and electron diffraction, the structural chemist can add a third related technique, neutron diffraction. If a beam of electrons and a beam of neutrons are moving with the same speed, which has the longer wavelength? By approximately what factor?

19. In the Bohr theory of the hydrogen atom, an electron travels in a circular orbit around the nucleus. How did Bohr answer the objection that such an atom should radiate away all its energy and collapse?

20. What restrictions did Bohr place on permissible orbits of the electron around the nucleus? How did it affect the energy that the hydrogen atom can have?

21. Why is the energy of the hydrogen atom in its ground state a negative number?

22. What is wrong with a Bohr orbit corresponding to $n = 3\frac{1}{2}$?

23. In what way is Bohr's hydrogen atom "quantized"? In what way is a vibrating violin string "quantized"? How do the fingers of a violinist's left hand help him to get around this quantization?

24. What happens to the electron when the hydrogen atom absorbs radiation? What is the spectrum called that represents the selective removal of certain frequencies from the initial beam of radiation?

25. What happens when hydrogen atoms emit radiation? How is the frequency of radiation related to energy levels within the atom?

26. In what part of the spectrum do the lines occur that correspond to transitions between the $n = 1$ and higher levels? Where do the $n = 2$ to higher transitions appear in the spectrum? Where are the $n = 3$ to higher absorptions or emissions found?

27. What happens to the spectrum of a galaxy that is moving rapidly toward us? What happens if the galaxy is moving rapidly away? Which of these is a blue shift, and which is a red shift, and why?

28. Hubble discovered that the speed with which a galaxy is moving away from us is proportional to its distance from us. Show that this implies that the expanding universe arose from a relatively restricted region of space.

PROBLEMS

1. In the American midwest, rural roads are laid out in a square grid one mile on a side. A passenger on an eastbound airliner braces his head against a window frame and observes that one of these grid roads passes the edge of the window every six seconds. How fast is the airplane traveling relative to the ground?

2. The preceding problem used the relationship $v = \lambda\nu$. If the wavelength of the repeating road pattern is 1 mile, what is the frequency in roads per second? Show that $v = \lambda\nu$ leads to the answer of Problem 1.

3. Chlorophyll in green plants absorbs light especially well at wavelengths around 6600 Å. What color is this light? What is the frequency of the light? (1 cm = 10^8 Å)

4. What is the energy in ergs of one photon of light of wavelength 6600 Å? (Planck's constant is $h = 6.626 \times 10^{-27}$ erg sec.) What is the energy in ergs of one mole of these photons?

5. If 1 erg = 2.390×10^{-11} kcal, what is the energy in kilocalories of one mole of photons of wavelength 6600 Å?

6. If the energy of one photon is given by $E = h\nu$, then the energy of a mole of photons, a chemically useful piece of information, is given by $E = Nh\nu$, in which N is Avogadro's number. From the conversion factors given in Problems 3 through 5, calculate Nh in kcal mole^{-1} sec. Use this number directly with the frequency of 6600-Å light to calculate the energy per mole of photons, and verify that the answer is the same as for Problem 5.

7. An even easier way of converting wavelength to energy per mole of photons is

$$E = Nh\nu = \frac{Nhc}{\lambda}$$

Calculate the constant Nhc in units of kcal mole^{-1} cm and kcal mole^{-1} Å. (Your answer should be $Nhc = 286,000$ kcal mole^{-1} Å.) Use this to verify again the energy in kilocalories of a mole of 6600-Å photons.

8. Carbon–carbon single bonds in organic and biological molecules have energies around 83 kcal mole^{-1}. From the answers to Problems 5–7, would you expect that red-orange light is capable of breaking carbon–carbon bonds and disrupting molecules?

9. What is the energy per mole of photons of ultraviolet light of wavelength 2400 Å? (See Problem 8.) Should this radiation be capa-

ble of disrupting organic molecules? Why are UV lamps used as germicidal sterilizers?

10. When light of frequency ν falls on a photocell, an individual electron in the metal surface is given an energy kick of $E = h\nu$. The kinetic energy that the ejected electrons will have is given by $KE = h\nu - \phi$, in which ϕ is called the "work function" of the metal, and is the energy needed to pull an electron out of the metal surface. The work function is similar to the first ionization energy, but applies to the removal of an electron from a block of metal instead of from an isolated gaseous atom. The incoming photons of light must have energy at least as large as ϕ, or they cannot remove electrons at all. Does this mean that there is a maximum wavelength, or a minimum wavelength, for photoemission of electrons from a metal surface?

11. The work function (see Problem 10) for lithium metal is 55.7 kcal mole^{-1}. How does this compare with the first ionization energy of gaseous Li atoms? What is the longest-wavelength light that could be used in a lithium photocell?

12. Copper has a work function of 92.3 kcal mole^{-1}. Can electrons be ejected from copper by visible light? If not, what types of radiation could?

13. The maximum wavelength for emission from a cesium photocell is 6200 A. What is the work function for cesium metal?

14. In the Bohr model of the hydrogen atom, what is the radius of the electron orbit for quantum number $n = 2$? What is the energy of this quantum state? What is the energy of state $n = 3$?

15. What is the energy difference between states $n = 2$ and $n = 3$ of the hydrogen atom? What is the wavelength of radiation absorbed when the hydrogen atom jumps from $n = 2$ to $n = 3$? In what part of the electromagnetic spectrum does this occur?

16. Calculate the wavelengths of the hydrogen atom transitions from $n = 2$ to $n = 3, 4, 5, 6, 7$, and ∞ (infinity). Plot these along a wavelength scale. Notice how the lines become closer and closer together as the upper quantum number n increases.

17. If our galaxy and any of the ones whose spectra were shown previously in the chapter began rushing apart with speed v just after the big bang that started the universe going, then after a time t they should be a distance d apart, where $d = vt$. From the distance, d, and relative velocity, v, for any of the galaxies mentioned, calculate the age of the universe, t. (1 light year $= 9.46 \times 10^{12}$ km, and 1 year $= 3.15 \times 10^7$ sec)

QUANTUM NUMBERS	ORBITALS

n

Principal quantum number always is a positive integer; thus n = 1, 2, 3, 4, 5, · ·

Principal quantum number n determines size of orbitals, and is a rough indication of energy.

$l = 0$

Azimuthal quantum number l indicates shape, and magnetic quantum number m indicates orientation in space. For $l = 0$, m can only be 0. An orbital with $l = 0$ is an s orbital, and is always spherical.

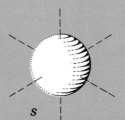

s

Commo
name

s orbit

$l = 1$

For $l = 1$ (p orbitals), m can have values of –1, 0, or + 1. The three p orbitals are identical in shape, but are oriented in three mutually perpendicular directions in space.

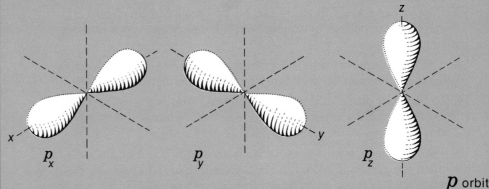

p_x p_y p_z

p orbita

$l = 2$

For $l = 2$ (d orbitals), m can have five different values: –2, –1, 0, + 1, or + 2. The five different d orbitals are shown at the right.

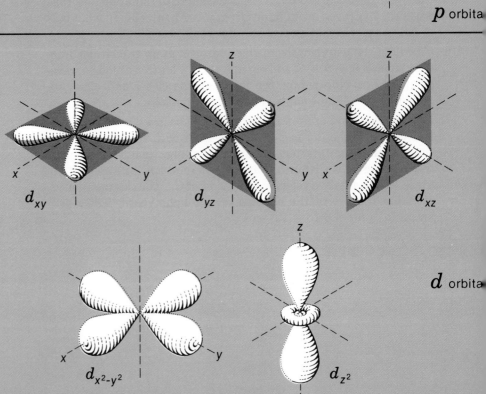

d_{xy} d_{yz} d_{xz}

$d_{x^2-y^2}$ d_{z^2}

d orbita

CHAPTER 8

The Machinery Behind the Periodic Table

Scientific theories are labor-saving devices. If you can replace twenty facts with five rules, and five rules with one good theory, then you obviously have made life easier. Mark Twain once remarked, "There is one big advantage to telling the truth: you don't have to have such a good memory." The same can be said for constructing theories.

The greatest single achievement in chemistry after the discovery of atoms was the working out of the periodic table, by Mendeleev in Russia in 1869, and independently by Meyer in Germany later that same year. Both men realized that similar chemical behavior recurred periodically if the elements were listed by increasing atomic weight (actually atomic number). They both devised the same scheme in which the elements were arranged so as to display this common chemical behavior. Chemists no longer had to remember the properties of every element in isolation. The "twenty facts" of the opening remark had given way to a few simple rules. But where was the theory that would explain these rules and account for the rather strange structure of the periodic table? The unifying theory would have to wait for nearly another half century, until physicists began applying the new quantum mechanics to chemistry. Nevertheless, with the periodic table the first big step toward placing chemistry on a rational basis had been taken.

THE BETTER THEORY: WAVE MECHANICS

A new and better quantum theory was developed in the 1920's by an Austrian and a German physicist, Erwin Schrödinger and Werner Heisenberg. Their *wave mechanics* is mathematically intimidating, and almost seems to view the world as a set of solutions of differential equations. It succeeded in explaining the structure of multielectron atoms, the structure of the periodic table, and the theory of bonding between

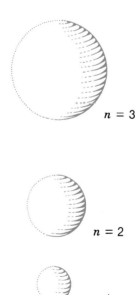

$n = 3$

$n = 2$

$n = 1$

As the principal quantum number n increases, the size and energy of the orbital both increase, but the shape remains essentially the same.

147

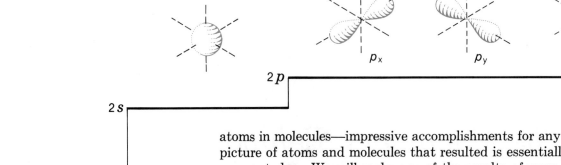

$2p$

$2s$

$1s$

The 2s energy level is considerably higher than the 1s, and the three 2p levels are slightly higher in energy than the 2s.

atoms in molecules—impressive accomplishments for any theory. The picture of atoms and molecules that resulted is essentially that which we use today. We will make use of the results of wave mechanics—energy levels and atomic structure—without going through the mathematics that led to those results.

As in the simpler Bohr theory, the energy of an electron in an atom is restricted to certain values, or is quantized. Three quantum numbers instead of one are required to describe an electron, and they are designated n, l, and m. The average distance of the electron from the nucleus depends primarily on n, which is called the *principal quantum number*. The geometry of bonding around the atom depends primarily on quantum number l, called the orbital-shape, or *azimuthal, quantum number*. The energy of an electron in an atom is a function of n and to a lesser degree of l. The orbital-orientation, or *magnetic quantum number*, m, describes how the electron's orbit is oriented in space relative to some external reference such as a magnetic or electric field. In the absence of such fields, all m states for a given n and l value have the same energy.

There are special limitations on the values of n, l, and m that an electron in an atom can have. As with the Bohr theory for the hydrogen atom, n only can be a positive integer:

$$n = 1, 2, 3, 4, 5, 6, 7, \cdots$$

Quantum number l can be zero or any positive integer *less than n*. States with $l = 0$, 1, 2, 3, 4, 5, 6, $\cdots$ are identified by the lower case letters s, p, d, f, g, h, i, $\cdots$ respectively. A state with $n = 3$ and $l = 2$ is called a $3d$ state. The possible n and l combinations for $n = 1$ through 4 are shown in the table at the top of the next page.

The magnetic quantum number, m, can have any integral value from $-l$ to $+l$, including zero. These values are less important at the moment than are the number of such m states that exist. For each l value there are $(2l + 1)$ different m states:

Type of l state	Value of l	m values	Number of m states
s	0	0	1
p	1	$-1, 0, +1$	3
d	2	$-2, -1, 0, +1, +2$	5
f	3	$-3, -2, -1, 0, +1, +2, +3$	7

These quantum numbers describe electronic states of different energy and geometry. One radical difference between the new quantum theory and the Bohr theory is that we have to abandon forever any hope

148

Quantum states available to electrons in an atom

Principal Q.N., n	Orbital-shape Q.N., l	Common name	Number of m states	Total states for Q.N., n
1	0	1s	1 ------------ 1	
2	0	2s	1 ⎫	
2	1	2p	3 ⎬ ------------ 4	
3	0	3s	1 ⎫	
3	1	3p	3 ⎬ ------------ 9	
3	2	3d	5 ⎭	
4	0	4s	1 ⎫	
4	1	4p	3 ⎪	
4	2	4d	5 ⎬ ------------ 16	
4	3	4f	7 ⎭	
5	0	5s	1 ⎫	
5	1	5p	3 ⎪	
5	2	5d	5 ⎬ ------------ 25	
5	3	5f	7 ⎪	
5	4	5g	9 ⎭	

SHAPES OF ORBITALS

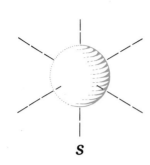

s

s Orbitals always are spherical.

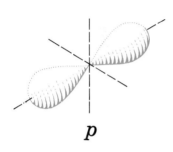

p

p Orbitals point out in opposite directions along one line.

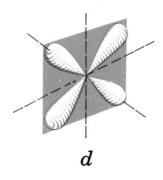

d

d Orbitals have lobes of probability density in different directions.

See the opening illustration of the chapter for detailed shapes.

of knowing the exact path of an electron around the nucleus. Classical mechanics would have led us to believe that if we were skillful enough, we could know the position of the electron at every instant in time, and plot its precise trajectory. The Bohr theory replaced a billiard-ball electron by a stationary wave around a circular orbit, but still let us give a precise numerical value for the radius of the orbit. Wave mechanics take even this away from us. Instead of an electron's position, all that we know is the *probability* that an electron will be at any selected point in space. Solving the mathematical wave equations for an electron in a particular quantum state (n,l,m) around an atom yields a wave function, $\psi(x,y,z)$, which varies from one point in space (x,y,z) to another. The wave function, ψ, has no direct physical meaning, but the *square* of the wave function, ψ^2, is proportional to the probability of finding the electron at point (x,y,z) rather than somewhere else. The end result, when plotted, is a fuzzy cloud of electron probability around the nucleus for each (n,l,m) quantum state. The density of the probability cloud at each region in space represents the probability that the electron will be found there, and not elsewhere.

These ψ^2 electron probability clouds are sketched at the right for $l = 0$, 1, and 2, or for s, p, and d states. The corresponding l states for different values of n look very much the same, except that they increase in size as n increases. Because we cannot know the exact path of the electron, these electron probability clouds should not be called orbits, but the similarity to the older theory is maintained by calling them *orbitals*. Every allowed combination of n, l, and m describes an atomic orbital of a certain shape and energy.

All s (or $l = 0$) orbitals—1s, 2s, 3s, 4s, or higher—are spherical (upper right). The electron in such an orbital has an equal probability of being found in any direction from the nucleus. In contrast, the three p orbitals $(l = 1)$, each with a different value of magnetic quantum number m, have maximum electron probabilities in three mutually perpendicular directions, which we can call the x, y, and z axes. All three are illustrated at the beginning of the chapter. There is no point in try-

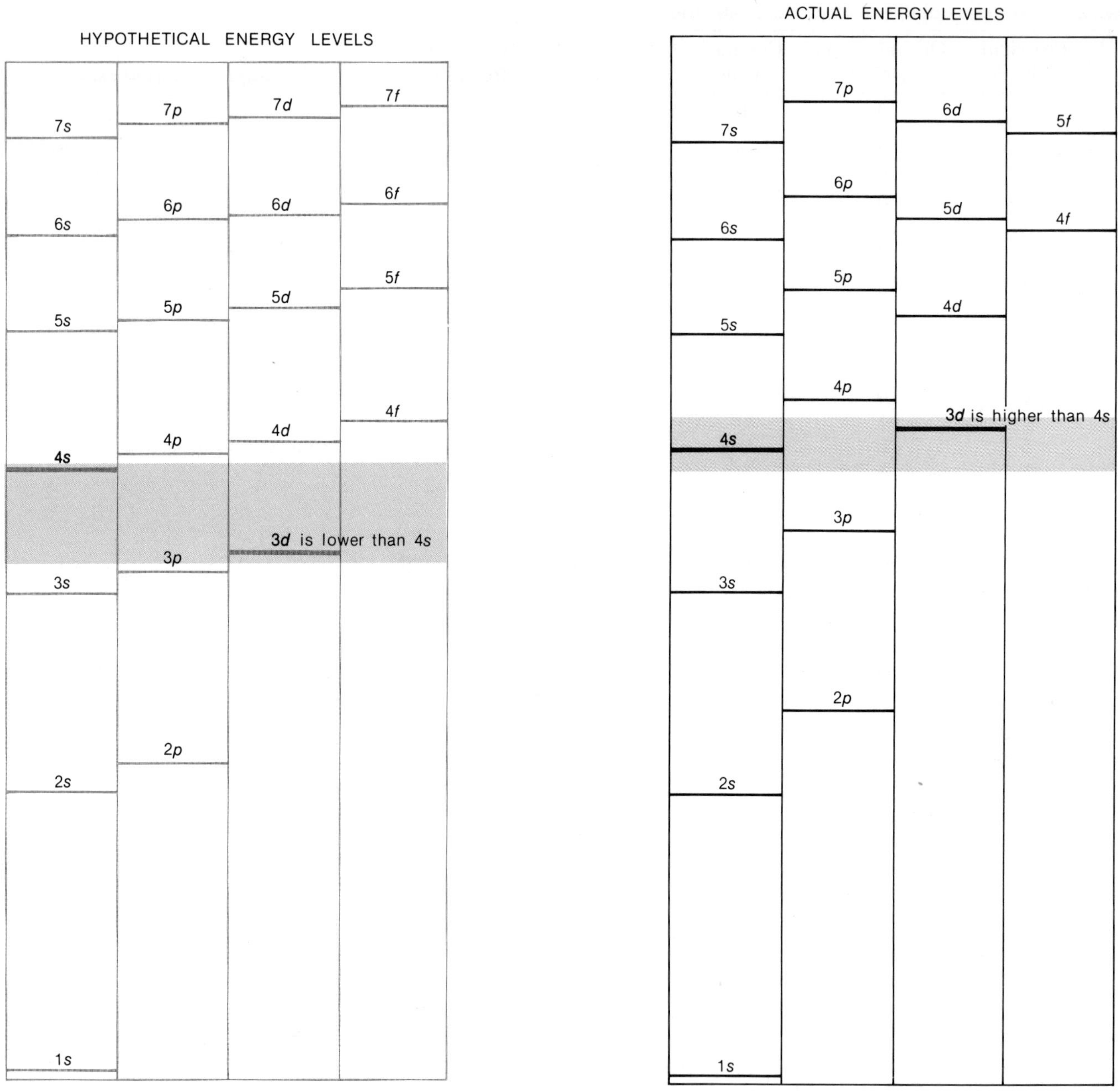

Hypothetical energy-level diagram (left) in which levels with the same principal quantum number n are closely spaced. Actual order of levels (right), with overlap of energies between levels with different n

ing to associate the orbitals individually with the m values -1, 0, and $+1$, because all three have the same energy in the absence of an outside magnetic field. The important feature is not the numerical value of m, but the shape and orientation of the orbitals.

The five orbitals for $l = 2$, or d orbitals, are more complicated. If we define a set of perpendicular x, y, and z coordinates, then three of the orbitals, d_{xy}, d_{yz}, and d_{xz}, have cloverleaf electron probability distributions in the xy, yz, and xz planes, respectively, as shown at the beginning of the chapter. The $d_{x^2-y^2}$ orbital has highest probability along the x and y axes, and the d_{z^2} has maximum electron probability along the z axis. The f and higher orbitals are even more complicated, but never need to be visualized in any practical chemical situation. The s, p, and d orbital shapes are sufficient for our purposes, and you should know these well.

150

The drawings at the beginning of the chapter represent electron probabilities, or values of the square of the wave function, ψ^2. These values always are positive, whereas the original wave function, ψ, can be positive or negative. The signs of ψ in various lobes of the probability functions are indicated by colored $+$ and $-$ signs. Whether the sign is positive or negative is not significant, but the *change* in sign from one lobe of probability to the next is. The signs of the wave functions become necessary as soon as we begin to combine atoms to form molecules, as in the next chapter.

So far we have said very little about the energies of these quantum states of an atom. The energy depends mainly on the principal quantum number, n, and to a lesser extent on the orbital-shape quantum number, l. Within a given n state, a higher l value corresponds to a higher energy for atoms with more than one electron. This l dependence can be thought of as producing a splitting of the principal quantum levels. If this splitting were zero, then wave mechanics would reduce to the old Bohr theory, with the same expression relating energy, E, to principal quantum number, n. (This is true only for hydrogen.) If the splitting were small, so the upper states from one n level did not overlap with the lower states of the next, then the energy levels would appear as at the far left. The sequence of levels of increasing energy would be very orderly: $1s$; $2s$, $2p$; $3s$, $3p$, $3d$; $4s$, $4p$, $4d$, $4f$; $5s$, $\cdots$.

In reality the splitting of n levels is more severe, as shown at the nearer left. From $n = 3$ onward, each n level overlaps with the next, and the order of increasing energies is more involved: $3s$, $3p$; $4s$, $3d$, $4p$, $\cdots$. This is not as complicated as it first appears. If the orbitals are written in a triangular array as below, the order of increasing energy is indicated by the diagonal colored arrows. As we shall see in the next section, this sequence of energy levels in an atom provides a complete explanation of the observed structure of the periodic table.

The results of the qualitative treatment of wave mechanics in this section are three essential pieces of information about electrons in atoms: (1) quantum numbers (n, l, m) and their relationships among one another, (2) the electron probability clouds for each (n, l, m) orbital, and (3) the energy levels corresponding to different (n, l, m) orbitals.

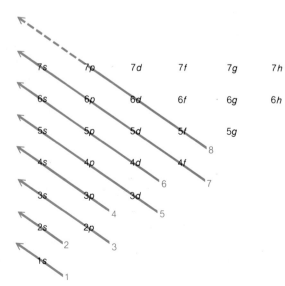

The order of increasing energy of levels as shown at the right of the opposite page can be obtained by following the diagonal colored arrows: $1s$, $2s$, $2p$, $3s$, $3p$, $4s$, $3d$, $4p$, $5s$, $4d$, $5p$, $6s$, $4f$, $5d$, $6p$, $7s$, $5f$, $6d$, and $7p$. Although of no deep theoretical significance, this diagram is a handy memory aid. The structure of the entire periodic table of the elements follows from this order of levels.

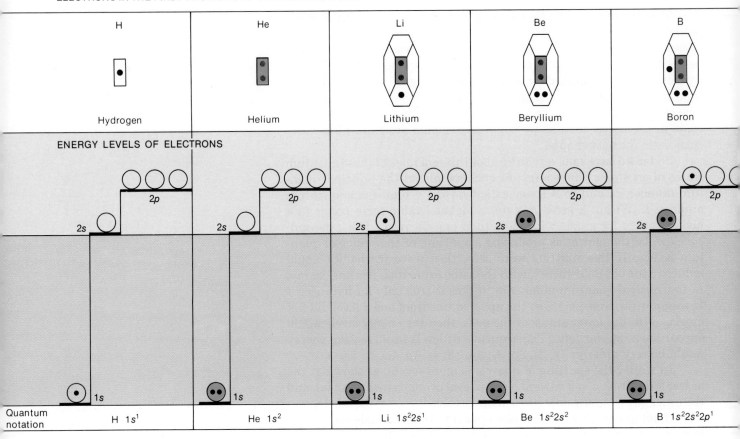

H	He	Li	Be	B
Hydrogen	Helium	Lithium	Beryllium	Boron

ENERGY LEVELS OF ELECTRONS

| H 1s¹ | He 1s² | Li 1s²2s¹ | Be 1s²2s² | B 1s²2s²2p¹ |

Quantum notation

| H $1s^1$ | He $1s^2$ | Li $1s^2 2s^1$ | Be $1s^2 2s^2$ | B $1s^2 2s^2 2p^1$ |

Atoms are successively built up by increasing the charge on the nucleus, and then feeding electrons into the lowest available orbitals until the nuclear charge is counterbalanced. Each orbital can hold a maximum of two electrons with opposite spins.

QUANTUM LEVELS AND ATOMIC BUILDUP

We now can return to the shell models discussed in the first six chapters, and reinterpret them in terms of quantum levels of the atom. The first ten elements are diagramed across the top of these two pages. The hydrogen atom has only a single electron, and in its lowest-energy state, or *ground state*, the electron occupies the 1s quantum level.

The helium atom has two electrons, and in its ground state both will occupy the 1s orbital as shown. Electrons have one more property that has not been mentioned so far, *spin*. Electrons behave magnetically as if they were tiny spinning spheres of negative charge, with the north pole pointing either up or down. Two electrons can occupy the same orbital if, and only if, they have opposite spin directions. Hence we say that the 1s orbital in helium is occupied completely by a pair of electrons of opposite spins.

The remaining eight elements shown are built up by adding more electrons, one at a time, and placing them in the lowest-energy orbital that is still unfilled. The 2s orbital is slightly lower in energy than the 2p, so it is filled with two electrons (Be) before the third electron goes into the first of three 2p orbitals in boron. Because placing two electrons in the same orbital means placing them close to one another in space, there is an electron–electron repulsion between them. This

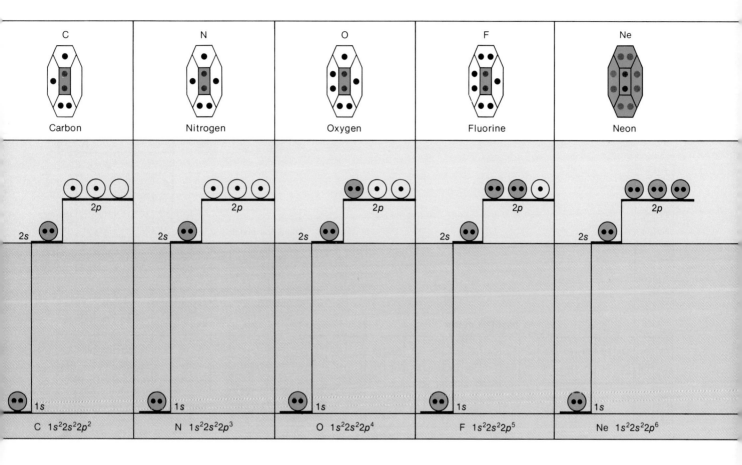

C	N	O	F	Ne
Carbon	Nitrogen	Oxygen	Fluorine	Neon

2s	2s	2s	2s	2s
1s	1s	1s	1s	1s
C $1s^2 2s^2 2p^2$	N $1s^2 2s^2 2p^3$	O $1s^2 2s^2 2p^4$	F $1s^2 2s^2 2p^5$	Ne $1s^2 2s^2 2p^6$

means that the first three electrons in $2p$ orbitals (B through N) go into the three different $2p$ orbitals, before a pairing of two electrons in one orbital (in an O atom) is forced by the lack of more empty orbitals of the same energy.

The electronic configuration is given by listing the orbitals in order of increasing n and l values, and indicating the number of electrons in each orbital with a superscript. Thus hydrogen has the electronic configuration $1s^1$, helium $1s^2$, and lithium $1s^2 2s^1$. The other electronic configurations proceed in a systematic way, and are shown at the bottom of the diagrams on these two pages. Neon has both the $n = 1$ and $n = 2$ orbitals completely occupied, and the electronic configuration is $1s^2 2s^2 2p^6$. This is a more elaborate (and more informative) version of the configuration that was given in Chapter 3 as merely Ne 2,8.

There is one difference between the diagrams on these pages and previous diagrams. Carbon, for example, was shown with four unpaired electrons, rather than $2s^2 2p^2$, as shown above. Because the energy difference between s and p orbitals is small, and since two electrons in the same s orbital repel one another, the actual difference in energy between the two arrangements is small. Isolated carbon atoms in the gas phase do have the paired $2s^2 2p^2$ configuration, but carbon atoms involved in tetrahedral bonding can be thought of as adopting the unpaired $2s^1 2p^3$ arrangement before the bonds are formed. The small cost in energy is more than compensated for by the extra stability of the bonds.

Only a small amount of energy is needed to promote one of the two $2s$ electrons in carbon into the empty $2p$ orbital, both because the energy difference between $2s$ and $2p$ levels is small, and because electrostatic repulsion between two electrons in the same orbital is eliminated by the promotion.

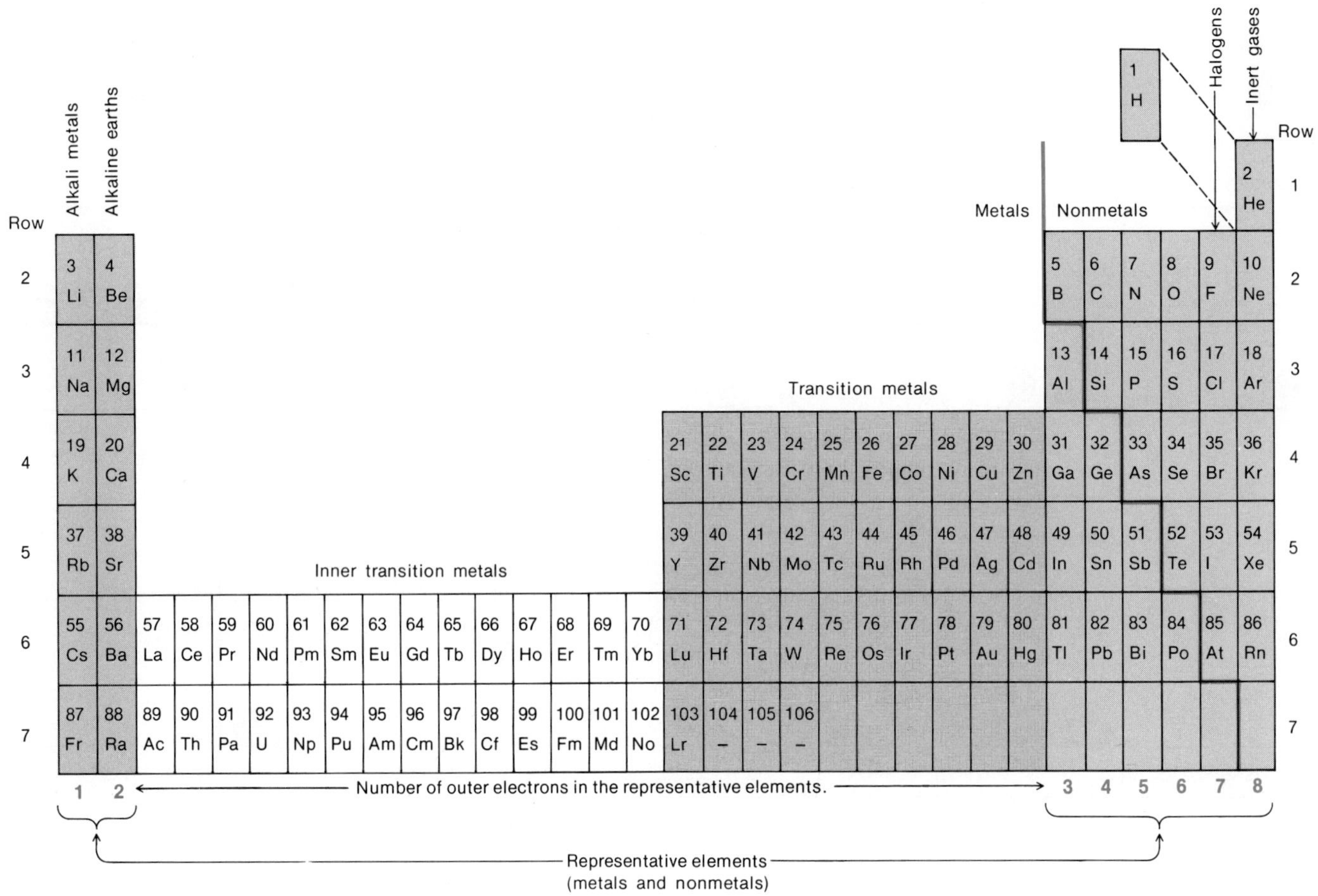

The full periodic table as it has been deduced from observation of the properties of the elements. The eight-electron rows of the *representative elements* (color) are interrupted in Rows 4 and 5 by ten *transition metals,* and in Rows 6 and 7 by fourteen *inner transition metals* and ten *transition metals.* The inner transition metals are named lanthanides and actinides after the first member in each series. The lanthanides also are called rare earths.

BUILDUP OF ATOMS AND THE PERIODIC TABLE

The periodic table of the elements in its most complete form as it has been developed since Mendeleev's time is shown above. It summarizes the observed chemical behavior of atoms. In essence it is a series of eight-element rows, representing shells containing one to eight electrons. To this extent, the eight-electron shell model of previous chapters has been correct. The first row contains only two elements, hydrogen and helium. The second and third rows contain eight elements each. The fourth row is interrupted after the second element, and a series of ten additional metals is inserted, the *transition metals* scandium (Sc) through zinc (Zn). Similarly, the fifth row is interrupted by the insertion of another series of ten transition metals, yttrium (Y) through cadmium (Cd). The sixth row has a double interruption: a set of fourteen *inner transition metals* (also called lanthanides or rare earths), and a series of ten more transition metals. The seventh and last row again has fourteen inner transition metals, and the beginning of another series of transition metals. Only the first four of these transition metals have been prepared artificially, and none of them exists in nature.

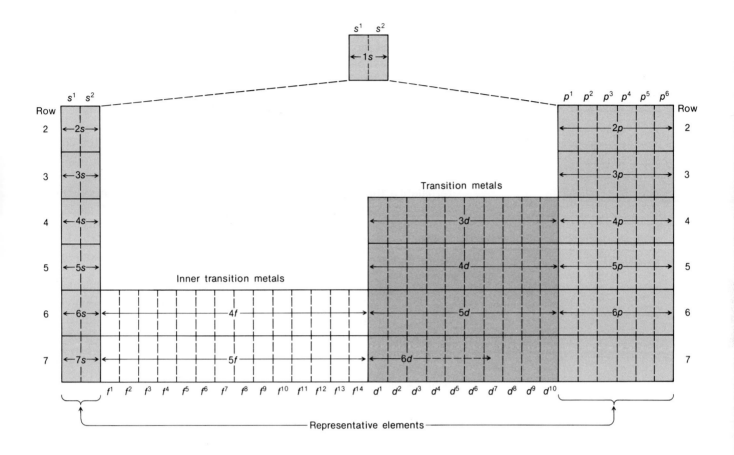

The "eight-electron" elements—all of the elements except transition metals and inner transition metals—show the widest variety of chemical properties. They range from metals to nonmetals, and the boundary between these categories runs diagonally from upper left to lower right in the table. Because they illustrate the entire range of chemical properties, they are called the *representative elements*. The transition metals, although easily distinguishable from one another, are much more similar in behavior. All are metals, with a tendency to lose one to three electrons easily in chemical reactions. Iron (Fe), copper (Cu), tungsten (W), and gold (Au) are not difficult to distinguish, but neither are they as different, for example, as hydrogen, lithium, chlorine, and carbon. The inner transition, or rare earth, metals are so similar to one another that they can be separated only with great care. One rare earth, "didymium," discovered in 1885, later was found to be a mixture of two elements, which were christened neodymium (Nd) and praseodymium (Pm).

Elements in the same vertical column in the periodic table have similar chemical properties and, for the representative elements at least, the same outer electronic configuration. This systematic arrangement of elements, as shown at the top of the opposite page, is the periodic

The experimentally observed structure of the periodic table on the opposite page follows naturally from the successive filling of orbitals from lowest to highest energy, in the order explained by wave mechanics: $1s$, $2s$, $2p$, $3s$, $3p$, $4s$, $3d$, $4p$, $5s$, $4d$, $5p$, $6s$, $4f$, $5d$, $6p$, $7s$, $5f$, and $6d$. The interruptions within eight-electron rows for the transition and inner transition metals occur during the filling of the relatively buried d and f orbitals.

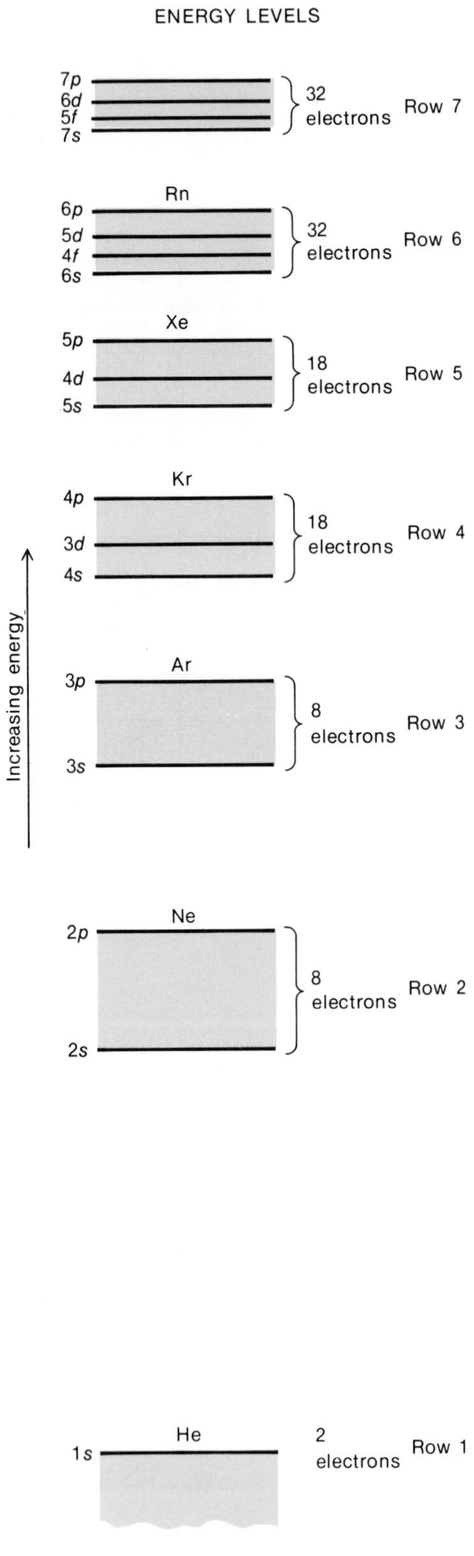

ENERGY LEVELS

7p
6d } 32
5f } electrons Row 7
7s

Rn
6p
5d } 32
4f } electrons Row 6
6s

Xe
5p
4d } 18
5s } electrons Row 5

Kr
4p
3d } 18
4s } electrons Row 4

Ar
3p } 8
3s } electrons Row 3

Ne
2p } 8
2s } electrons Row 2

He   2
1s   electrons Row 1

Increasing energy

Energy levels accounted for by wave
mechanics, as seen previously, but now plotted
on a single vertical energy scale to emphasize
their energy sequence.

table, based on chemical experience rather than theory, that any serious atomic theory must explain satisfactorily.

The wave mechanics discussed in the previous section provides this explanation. The energy-level diagram that we saw on Page 150, and which is repeated at the left, describes the different energy states that are available to an atom. As the atomic number and the positive charge on the nucleus increase, all of these levels are lowered in energy because the nucleus pulls on the electrons more tightly. In spite of this, the relative order of levels remains much the same. With minor differences, this sequence of levels holds for all atoms.

We can think of building up an atom by first placing the correct positive charge on the nucleus, and then adding electrons around the nucleus, one at a time, until enough electrons have been added to counterbalance the positive charge. In the ground state, or lowest-energy state of the atom, each additional electron will go into the lowest energy level still available. In this way the electronic structure of any atom is determined by the successive filling of energy levels from the lowest upward. We already have used this process to show the buildup of the first ten elements.

How many electrons can each energy level hold? This is the last link needed to complete the chain leading to the periodic table. Each orbital, or quantum state, identified by a particular combination of n, l, and m values, can hold a pair of electrons with opposite spins. The $1s$ orbital has room for two electrons, the $2s$ orbital can hold two more, the three $2p$ orbitals can hold a total of six, and so on. The five $3d$ orbitals have room for ten electrons, and the seven $4f$ orbitals can accommodate fourteen electrons. When several orbitals have the same energy but different orientations, as the p_x, p_y, and p_z orbitals, each one adds a single electron before any of them becomes filled with two. This permits the electrons to remain as far from one another as possible, and minimizes the repulsions between their negative charges.

If the ten-electron d orbitals suggest the ten transition metals to you, and the fourteen-electron f orbitals suggest the inner transition metals, you are on the right track. Filling the energy levels depicted at the left from the bottom up, with two electrons per orbital, creates the periodic table as it was shown on the previous two pages. The connection is easier to see with the aid of a "filling diagram" showing which orbitals are being filled in the various regions of the table (see preceding page).

As we saw earlier, hydrogen and helium are created by the filling of the $1s$ orbital. Lithium and beryllium arise from the placing of the third and fourth electrons in the $2s$ orbital, and boron through neon represent the subsequent filling of the three $2p$ orbitals with six more electrons. This completes the second row of the table. The next lowest orbitals are the $3s$ and the three $3p$, and filling these orbitals produces the third row of the table. It is common to write the electronic structure of an atom by listing the orbitals in order of increasing n and l values, and indicating the number of electrons in each state with a superscript. As we have seen before, hydrogen has the arrangement $1s^1$, and helium $1s^2$. Lithium is $1s^22s^1$, nitrogen is $1s^22s^22p^3$, and phosphorus, just below nitrogen in the third row, is $1s^22s^22p^63s^23p^3$, with the same s^2p^3 outer electronic configuration. The electronic structures of all of the ele-

156

ments in the first four rows of the periodic table are shown at the right. Orbitals being filled are depicted with a white background, and completely filled orbitals are in color. An outer s^2p^6 arrangement with full s and p orbitals is the hallmark of a noble gas:

He: $\underline{1s^2}$

Ne: $1s^2\underline{2s^22p^6}$

Ar: $1s^22s^22p^6\underline{3s^23p^6}$

Kr: $1s^22s^22p^63s^23p^63d^{10}\underline{4s^24p^6}$

Xe: $1s^22s^22p^63s^23p^63d^{10}4s^24p^64d^{10}\underline{5s^25p^6}$

The energy gap between a p level and the next higher s level is always greater than the gaps between other nearby levels. This can be seen when the levels are stacked vertically, as at the far left. An unusually large amount of energy is required to add another electron to an atom that already has a filled set of s^2p^6 orbitals, which is one reason why the noble gases are so unreactive. Each p level on the stacked energy-level diagram is labeled with the symbol of the noble gas that results when that level is filled. Both the noble gases and the natural breaks between rows of the periodic table are dictated by these larger energy spacings between p and s levels.

The interruptions for insertion of ten transition metals in rows four and five of the table arise because the $3d$ energy level lies between the $4s$ and $4p$ levels (see left), and the $4d$ level lies between the $5s$ and $5p$ levels. In rows six and seven, the inner transition metals result from the filling of a set of seven f orbitals with fourteen electrons. The order of filling of levels in row six is $6s$, $4f$, $5d$, $6p$, and in row seven of the table the order is $7s$, $5f$, $6d$, $7p$.

The closely related chemical properties of the transition metals, and the near-identity of the inner transition metals, can be explained in terms of orbital structure. The chemical behavior of an atom is dictated primarily by its outermost electrons, since these are what a neighboring atom "sees" and may react with. Even though the $3d$ orbitals have slightly higher energy than the $4s$ orbital, and hence come later in the filling sequence, they do not extend as far out from the nucleus as the $4s$ orbitals do. From the vantage point of a neighboring atom, there is less difference between iron and cobalt (filling of $3d$) than between potassium and calcium (filling of $4s$), because the orbitals in which the changes are occurring are less exposed. Hence less difference in chemical properties is seen between two horizontally adjacent transition metals than between neighboring representative elements. The f orbitals are buried even more deeply, and adjacent inner transition metals show almost no difference in chemical behavior.

The electronic configuration of any atom, and the structure of the periodic table, both are consequences of the energy-level diagram obtained from spectroscopy and wave mechanics. The idealized electron arrangement of any atom can be worked out from its place in the periodic table.

Example 1. Tin (Sn) is found in the p^2 column of the representative elements, in row five of the periodic table. What is its electronic configuration?

ELECTRONIC STRUCTURES OF ELEMENTS 1–36
(Rows 1–4 of the periodic table)

Filled electron shells are shown on colored background

Atomic number ↓

1	H	$1s^1$						
2	He	$1s^2$	Helium					
3	Li	$1s^2$	$2s^1$					
4	Be	$1s^2$	$2s^2$					
5	B	$1s^2$	$2s^2$	$2p^1$				
6	C	$1s^2$	$2s^2$	$2p^2$				
7	N	$1s^2$	$2s^2$	$2p^3$				
8	O	$1s^2$	$2s^2$	$2p^4$				
9	F	$1s^2$	$2s^2$	$2p^5$				
10	Ne	$1s^2$	$2s^2$	$2p^6$	Neon			

←Neon core→

11	Na	$1s^2$	$2s^2$	$2p^6$	$3s^1$			
12	Mg	$1s^2$	$2s^2$	$2p^6$	$3s^2$			
13	Al	$1s^2$	$2s^2$	$2p^6$	$3s^2$	$3p^1$		
14	Si	$1s^2$	$2s^2$	$2p^6$	$3s^2$	$3p^2$		
15	P	$1s^2$	$2s^2$	$2p^6$	$3s^2$	$3p^3$		
16	S	$1s^2$	$2s^2$	$2p^6$	$3s^2$	$3p^4$		
17	Cl	$1s^2$	$2s^2$	$2p^6$	$3s^2$	$3p^5$		
18	Ar	$1s^2$	$2s^2$	$2p^6$	$3s^2$	$3p^6$	Argon	

←——— Argon core ———→

19	K	$1s^2$	$2s^2$	$2p^6$	$3s^2$	$3p^6$		$4s^1$
20	Ca	$1s^2$	$2s^2$	$2p^6$	$3s^2$	$3p^6$		$4s^2$
21	Sc	$1s^2$	$2s^2$	$2p^6$	$3s^2$	$3p^6$	$3d^1$	$4s^2$
22	Ti	$1s^2$	$2s^2$	$2p^6$	$3s^2$	$3p^6$	$3d^2$	$4s^2$
23	V	$1s^2$	$2s^2$	$2p^6$	$3s^2$	$3p^6$	$3d^3$	$4s^2$
24	Cr	$1s^2$	$2s^2$	$2p^6$	$3s^2$	$3p^6$	$3d^5$	$4s^1$
25	Mn	$1s^2$	$2s^2$	$2p^6$	$3s^2$	$3p^6$	$3d^5$	$4s^2$
26	Fe	$1s^2$	$2s^2$	$2p^6$	$3s^2$	$3p^6$	$3d^6$	$4s^2$
27	Co	$1s^2$	$2s^2$	$2p^6$	$3s^2$	$3p^6$	$3d^7$	$4s^2$
28	Ni	$1s^2$	$2s^2$	$2p^6$	$3s^2$	$3p^6$	$3d^8$	$4s^2$
29	Cu	$1s^2$	$2s^2$	$2p^6$	$3s^2$	$3p^6$	$3d^{10}$	$4s^1$
30	Zn	$1s^2$	$2s^2$	$2p^6$	$3s^2$	$3p^6$	$3d^{10}$	$4s^2$

Transition metals (Row 4)

31	Ga	$1s^2$	$2s^2$	$2p^6$	$3s^2$	$3p^6$	$3d^{10}$	$4s^2$	$4p^1$
32	Ge	$1s^2$	$2s^2$	$2p^6$	$3s^2$	$3p^6$	$3d^{10}$	$4s^2$	$4p^2$
33	As	$1s^2$	$2s^2$	$2p^6$	$3s^2$	$3p^6$	$3d^{10}$	$4s^2$	$4p^3$
34	Se	$1s^2$	$2s^2$	$2p^6$	$3s^2$	$3p^6$	$3d^{10}$	$4s^2$	$4p^4$
35	Br	$1s^2$	$2s^2$	$2p^6$	$3s^2$	$3p^6$	$3d^{10}$	$4s^2$	$4p^5$
36	Kr	$1s^2$	$2s^2$	$2p^6$	$3s^2$	$3p^6$	$3d^{10}$	$4s^2$	$4p^6$ Krypton

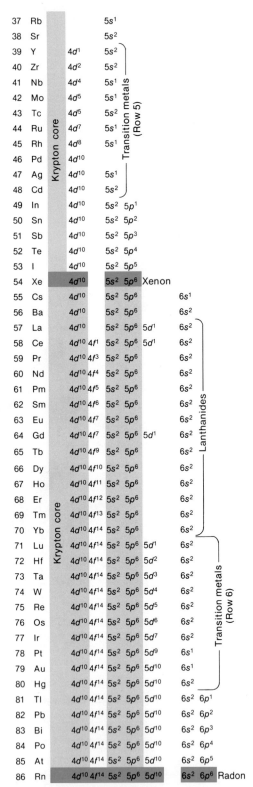

		Krypton core	Transition metals (Row 5) / Lanthanides / Transition metals (Row 6)	
37	Rb		$5s^1$	
38	Sr		$5s^2$	
39	Y	$4d^1$	$5s^2$	
40	Zr	$4d^2$	$5s^2$	
41	Nb	$4d^4$	$5s^1$	
42	Mo	$4d^5$	$5s^1$	
43	Tc	$4d^5$	$5s^2$	
44	Ru	$4d^7$	$5s^1$	
45	Rh	$4d^8$	$5s^1$	
46	Pd	$4d^{10}$		
47	Ag	$4d^{10}$	$5s^1$	
48	Cd	$4d^{10}$	$5s^2$	
49	In	$4d^{10}$	$5s^2\ 5p^1$	
50	Sn	$4d^{10}$	$5s^2\ 5p^2$	
51	Sb	$4d^{10}$	$5s^2\ 5p^3$	
52	Te	$4d^{10}$	$5s^2\ 5p^4$	
53	I	$4d^{10}$	$5s^2\ 5p^5$	
54	Xe	$4d^{10}$	$5s^2\ 5p^6$	Xenon
55	Cs	$4d^{10}$	$5s^2\ 5p^6$	$6s^1$
56	Ba	$4d^{10}$	$5s^2\ 5p^6$	$6s^2$
57	La	$4d^{10}$	$5s^2\ 5p^6\ 5d^1$	$6s^2$
58	Ce	$4d^{10}\ 4f^1$	$5s^2\ 5p^6\ 5d^1$	$6s^2$
59	Pr	$4d^{10}\ 4f^3$	$5s^2\ 5p^6$	$6s^2$
60	Nd	$4d^{10}\ 4f^4$	$5s^2\ 5p^6$	$6s^2$
61	Pm	$4d^{10}\ 4f^5$	$5s^2\ 5p^6$	$6s^2$
62	Sm	$4d^{10}\ 4f^6$	$5s^2\ 5p^6$	$6s^2$
63	Eu	$4d^{10}\ 4f^7$	$5s^2\ 5p^6$	$6s^2$
64	Gd	$4d^{10}\ 4f^7$	$5s^2\ 5p^6\ 5d^1$	$6s^2$
65	Tb	$4d^{10}\ 4f^9$	$5s^2\ 5p^6$	$6s^2$
66	Dy	$4d^{10}\ 4f^{10}$	$5s^2\ 5p^6$	$6s^2$
67	Ho	$4d^{10}\ 4f^{11}$	$5s^2\ 5p^6$	$6s^2$
68	Er	$4d^{10}\ 4f^{12}$	$5s^2\ 5p^6$	$6s^2$
69	Tm	$4d^{10}\ 4f^{13}$	$5s^2\ 5p^6$	$6s^2$
70	Yb	$4d^{10}\ 4f^{14}$	$5s^2\ 5p^6$	$6s^2$
71	Lu	$4d^{10}\ 4f^{14}$	$5s^2\ 5p^6\ 5d^1$	$6s^2$
72	Hf	$4d^{10}\ 4f^{14}$	$5s^2\ 5p^6\ 5d^2$	$6s^2$
73	Ta	$4d^{10}\ 4f^{14}$	$5s^2\ 5p^6\ 5d^3$	$6s^2$
74	W	$4d^{10}\ 4f^{14}$	$5s^2\ 5p^6\ 5d^4$	$6s^2$
75	Re	$4d^{10}\ 4f^{14}$	$5s^2\ 5p^6\ 5d^5$	$6s^2$
76	Os	$4d^{10}\ 4f^{14}$	$5s^2\ 5p^6\ 5d^6$	$6s^2$
77	Ir	$4d^{10}\ 4f^{14}$	$5s^2\ 5p^6\ 5d^7$	$6s^2$
78	Pt	$4d^{10}\ 4f^{14}$	$5s^2\ 5p^6\ 5d^9$	$6s^1$
79	Au	$4d^{10}\ 4f^{14}$	$5s^2\ 5p^6\ 5d^{10}$	$6s^1$
80	Hg	$4d^{10}\ 4f^{14}$	$5s^2\ 5p^6\ 5d^{10}$	$6s^2$
81	Tl	$4d^{10}\ 4f^{14}$	$5s^2\ 5p^6\ 5d^{10}$	$6s^2\ 6p^1$
82	Pb	$4d^{10}\ 4f^{14}$	$5s^2\ 5p^6\ 5d^{10}$	$6s^2\ 6p^2$
83	Bi	$4d^{10}\ 4f^{14}$	$5s^2\ 5p^6\ 5d^{10}$	$6s^2\ 6p^3$
84	Po	$4d^{10}\ 4f^{14}$	$5s^2\ 5p^6\ 5d^{10}$	$6s^2\ 6p^4$
85	At	$4d^{10}\ 4f^{14}$	$5s^2\ 5p^6\ 5d^{10}$	$6s^2\ 6p^5$
86	Rn	$4d^{10}\ 4f^{14}$	$5s^2\ 5p^6\ 5d^{10}$	$6s^2\ 6p^6$ Radon

Solution. Building up the atom, following the orbital-filling diagram shown on Page 155, until $5p^2$ is reached, you can see that the electronic structure of the tin atom must be

Sn: $1s^2 2s^2 2p^6 3s^2 3p^6 3d^{10} 4s^2 4p^6 4d^{10} 5s^2 5p^2$

This can be simplified by using the symbol [Kr] to represent the inner core of electrons of the noble gas krypton:

Kr: $1s^2 2s^2 2p^6 3s^2 3p^6 3d^{10} 4s^2 4p^6$

The tin configuration then can be written $[Kr]4d^{10}5s^25p^2$. (*Note:* Electronic configurations customarily are written with orbitals in sequence of increasing n and l values (left). Thus $3d$ would come before $4s$, and $4d$ (and $4f$ if used) before any $n = 5$ orbitals. This corresponds with the average distance of electrons in these orbitals from the nucleus, and emphasizes that $3d$, $4d$, and $4f$ orbitals are buried in the atom even though they are filled late.)

Example 2. What are the electronic arrangement and atomic number of bromine, the element one row below chlorine in the periodic table?

Solution. The outer electronic structure of chlorine is $3s^23p^5$, so we would expect that of bromine to be $4s^24p^5$. Hence we can write

Br: $1s^2 2s^2 2p^6 3s^2 3p^6 3d^{10} 4s^2 4p^5$

Counting electrons gives an atomic number of 35.

Example 3. Iron (Fe) is the sixth transition metal from the left in row four of the table. What is its electronic structure?

Solution. The previous noble gas is argon (Ar) at the end of the third row. Its unchanging inner core will be present in all fourth-row atoms:

Ar: $1s^2 2s^2 2p^6 3s^2 3p^6$

Beyond this core, the filling diagram shows that iron will have two electrons in the $4s$ orbital and six electrons in the $3d$ orbitals:

Fe: $[Ar]3d^6 4s^2$

The transition metals and inner transition metals sometimes deviate from this ideal filling scheme, by dropping one electron from the outer s orbital into the nearby d orbitals, or from the outermost d orbitals to an f orbital. This arises because half-filled shells, d^5 and f^7, with one electron in each orbital, or filled d^{10} and f^{14} shells, are especially stable. If an atom is one electron short of these states, that is, d^4, f^6, d^9, or f^{13}, it can steal an electron from a nearby level and achieve the more stable arrangement. This is possible only because the s, d, and f orbitals have very nearly the same energy, particularly in later rows. Hence chromium (Cr) has the structure $[Ar]3d^54s^1$ instead of $[Ar]3d^44s^2$, as would be expected from its place in the table, and gold (Au) has the structure $[Xe]4f^{14}5d^{10}6s^1$, rather than $[Xe]4f^{14}5d^96s^2$. These minor irregularities are not nearly as important as is the understanding of the overall pattern of electron filling, and how it can be obtained from the table. The table always will give the right answer for the representative elements.

ELECTRONIC STRUCTURES OF ELEMENTS 87–106

(Row 7 of the periodic table)

		(Krypton core →)		
87	Fr	$4d^{10}\,4f^{14}\,5s^2\,5p^6\,5d^{10}$	$6s^2\,6p^6$	$7s^1$
88	Ra	$4d^{10}\,4f^{14}\,5s^2\,5p^6\,5d^{10}$	$6s^2\,6p^6$	$7s^2$
89	Ac	$4d^{10}\,4f^{14}\,5s^2\,5p^6\,5d^{10}$	$6s^2\,6p^6\,6d^1\,7s^2$	
90	Th	$4d^{10}\,4f^{14}\,5s^2\,5p^6\,5d^{10}$	$6s^2\,6p^6\,6d^2\,7s^2$	
91	Pa	$4d^{10}\,4f^{14}\,5s^2\,5p^6\,5d^{10}\,5f^2$	$6s^2\,6p^6\,6d^1\,7s^2$	
92	U	$4d^{10}\,4f^{14}\,5s^2\,5p^6\,5d^{10}\,5f^3$	$6s^2\,6p^6\,6d^1\,7s^2$	
93	Np	$4d^{10}\,4f^{14}\,5s^2\,5p^6\,5d^{10}\,5f^4$	$6s^2\,6p^6\,6d^1\,7s^2$	
94	Pu	$4d^{10}\,4f^{14}\,5s^2\,5p^6\,5d^{10}\,5f^6$	$6s^2\,6p^6$	$7s^2$
95	Am	$4d^{10}\,4f^{14}\,5s^2\,5p^6\,5d^{10}\,5f^7$	$6s^2\,6p^6$	$7s^2$
96	Cm	$4d^{10}\,4f^{14}\,5s^2\,5p^6\,5d^{10}\,5f^7$	$6s^2\,6p^6\,6d^1\,7s^2$	Actinides
97	Bk	$4d^{10}\,4f^{14}\,5s^2\,5p^6\,5d^{10}\,5f^9$	$6s^2\,6p^6$	$7s^2$
98	Cf	$4d^{10}\,4f^{14}\,5s^2\,5p^6\,5d^{10}\,5f^{10}$	$6s^2\,6p^6$	$7s^2$
99	Es	$4d^{10}\,4f^{14}\,5s^2\,5p^6\,5d^{10}\,5f^{11}$	$6s^2\,6p^6$	$7s^2$
100	Fm	$4d^{10}\,4f^{14}\,5s^2\,5p^6\,5d^{10}\,5f^{12}$	$6s^2\,6p^6$	$7s^2$
101	Md	$4d^{10}\,4f^{14}\,5s^2\,5p^6\,5d^{10}\,5f^{13}$	$6s^2\,6p^6$	$7s^2$
102	No	$4d^{10}\,4f^{14}\,5s^2\,5p^6\,5d^{10}\,5f^{14}$	$6s^2\,6p^6$	$7s^2$
103	Lr	$4d^{10}\,4f^{14}\,5s^2\,5p^6\,5d^{10}\,5f^{14}$	$6s^2\,6p^6\,6d^1\,7s^2$	
104	—	$4d^{10}\,4f^{14}\,5s^2\,5p^6\,5d^{10}\,5f^{14}$	$6s^2\,6p^6\,6d^2\,7s^2$	Transition metals (Row 7)
105	—	$4d^{10}\,4f^{14}\,5s^2\,5p^6\,5d^{10}\,5f^{14}$	$6s^2\,6p^6\,6d^3\,7s^2$	
106	—	$4d^{10}\,4f^{14}\,5s^2\,5p^6\,5d^{10}\,5f^{14}$	$6s^2\,6p^6\,6d^4\,7s^2$	

An old-fashioned melodrama playing every night at the $[Kr]4d^{10}$. Try to solve it first with only a periodic table (see inside back cover). Then if you don't want to $[Ne]3s^23p^4$ any further, refer to electronic structures on Pages 157–159.

POSTSCRIPT: THE MAKING OF A UNIVERSE

Now that we have seen the entire range of chemical elements, we can reasonably ask where they all came from. Were they all made at once when the universe was formed, or did they develop gradually? This is outside the mainstream of chemistry, but is too interesting a line of thought to pass by.

There are two rival theories for the origin of the universe, the big-bang and the steady-state theories. Both agree that the red shift in atomic spectra indicates that the universe is expanding rapidly, and that the original matter of the universe consisted of hydrogen gas. The big-bang theory proposes that our material universe started its odyssey approximately 15 billion years ago in a violent fireball explosion at a billion degrees. In contrast, the steady-state theory proposes that new hydrogen gas is being created continuously in interstellar space to fill the gaps in an expanding but infinitely old universe. Although the issue is not yet completely settled, it is beginning to look as if the big-bang theory is correct. For example, radio astronomers have found that our universe is bathed in electromagnetic radiation around 1 mm in wavelength, possibly the last traces of the big fireball explosion. Nothing can be said about the state of the universe before this cataclysmic event. It could have begun then, or could have gone through an unknown series of earlier expansions and contractions in a "pulsating universe" model.

If the original universe were made up only of hydrogen, where did helium and the heavier elements come from? We know that the primary energy source in our sun is a fusion process in which four hydrogen nuclei coalesce to a helium nucleus, thereby releasing a great quantity of energy:

$$4 \ ^1\text{H} \rightarrow \ ^4\text{He} + \text{energy}$$

(Recall that the superscript is the atomic mass number, or total number of protons and neutrons in the nucleus.) This fusion process begins at temperatures of around 10 to 20 million degrees.

How did the heavier elements arise? Hydrogen fusion is a dead-end process. Helium does not combine with hydrogen to produce lithium, nor does lithium combine with hydrogen to produce beryllium. If the heat from the hydrogen-fusion process is partially confined in the interior of a big star and the temperature increases to 100–200 million degrees, then a second process can begin. Three helium nuclei can fuse to produce a carbon nucleus and release more energy:

$$3 \ ^4\text{He} \rightarrow \ ^{12}\text{C} + \text{energy}$$

In this same temperature zone, carbon nuclei can combine with more helium to make oxygen:

$$^{12}\text{C} + \ ^4\text{He} \rightarrow \ ^{16}\text{O} + \text{energy}$$

At even higher temperatures, higher than can be reached in our sun, further buildup is possible. Carbon and oxygen begin to fuse at

160

500–1000 million degrees:

$$2\ ^{12}C \rightarrow\ ^{20}Ne +\ ^4He + energy \qquad (neon)$$
$$2\ ^{12}C \rightarrow\ ^{24}Mg + energy \qquad (magnesium)$$
$$2\ ^{16}O \rightarrow\ ^{28}Si +\ ^4He + energy \qquad (silicon)$$
$$2\ ^{16}O \rightarrow\ ^{32}S + energy \qquad (sulfur)$$

One of the main products of carbon and oxygen fusion is silicon-28, which has a particularly stable nucleus. As temperatures increase to 2000 million degrees and more, silicon itself begins to react by a complicated set of fusion processes:

$$^{28}Si + x\ ^4He \rightarrow heavy\ elements\ to\ ^{56}Fe + energy$$

Only if a star is big enough to trap heat in its interior and generate these enormous temperatures will these reactions occur.

The energy in these reactions comes from a loss of mass during the fusion process. One helium nucleus is lighter than four hydrogen nuclei, and an oxygen nucleus is lighter than the sum of a carbon nucleus and a helium nucleus. The missing mass is converted to energy, according to Einstein's conversion formula, $E = mc^2$.

These reactions cannot continue building up heavier atoms indefinitely. The process stops with iron, ^{56}Fe. The iron nucleus is the most stable of all. Energy is given off whenever nuclei lighter than iron *fuse* to produce elements closer to iron, or when heavier nuclei, such as uranium, produce lighter elements near to iron by *fission*. The process

$$^{56}Fe +\ ^4He \rightarrow\ ^{60}Ni$$

does not give off energy, it absorbs it. Fusion as an energy source, whether for us or for the stars, will work only with elements lighter than iron. Synthesis of elements beyond ^{56}Fe probably was a slower process of reactions involving neutron capture.

Now we have a set of primary reactions that will produce the elements at least through iron. But how did these reactions occur during the evolution of the universe? These elements are synthesized in the interiors of stars. The first generation of stars began as hydrogen, and generated helium and the heavier elements by their fusion processes. Our own sun is a second-generation star; it was formed from the debris of the breakup of earlier stars. Hence it and the planets around it are enriched in the heavier elements.

The probable life history of a star, considered as an element-factory, is told on the following page. Depending on the size of the star, it can go successively through several of the element-generating reactions described previously. For each reaction, burning begins at the center of the star, and spreads slowly to the surface as fuel in the core is depleted. If the star is massive enough, the heat generated by one reaction may be enough to trigger the next. The minimum size for helium burning appears to be 0.7 times the mass of our sun, and for carbon and oxygen burning, 5 solar masses. A star of 30 solar masses will run the entire element-generating gamut from hydrogen to iron.

THE ELEMENT FACTORY

1. First-generation star forms from hydrogen gas. As it contracts, it is heated by release of gravitational energy.

2. Heat from contraction ignites the hydrogen fusion reaction at the center of the star:

   $4\ ^1\text{H} \rightarrow\ ^4\text{He} + \text{energy}$

   Stable burning period.

3. Hydrogen fuel at the center is exhausted, and burning spreads to the outer layers. The star expands to a red giant, and the total energy output increases.

4. The star collapses when its hydrogen is expended, and either dies or touches off the fusion of helium (helium flash):

   $3\ ^4\text{He} \rightarrow\ ^{12}\text{C} + \text{energy}$

   Helium burning spreads from the center to the outer layers. Carbon, oxygen, and silicon reactions are ignited successively in the core and spread outward as their fuel supplies are depleted. The star develops a layered structure, ultimately with iron at the core if the star is large enough.

5. Burning halts in the center of the star with the production of ^{56}Fe, since iron fusion reactions absorb heat rather than emitting it. The center of the star cools, and it collapses (implodes) violently.

6. Heat from gravitational energy of the collapse explodes the star in a supernova. The material of the star is dispersed throughout interstellar space.

7. Dispersed matter, including heavier elements, gradually collects into a second-generation star.

8. The planets of this second-generation star, if present, are enriched in the heavy elements through iron.

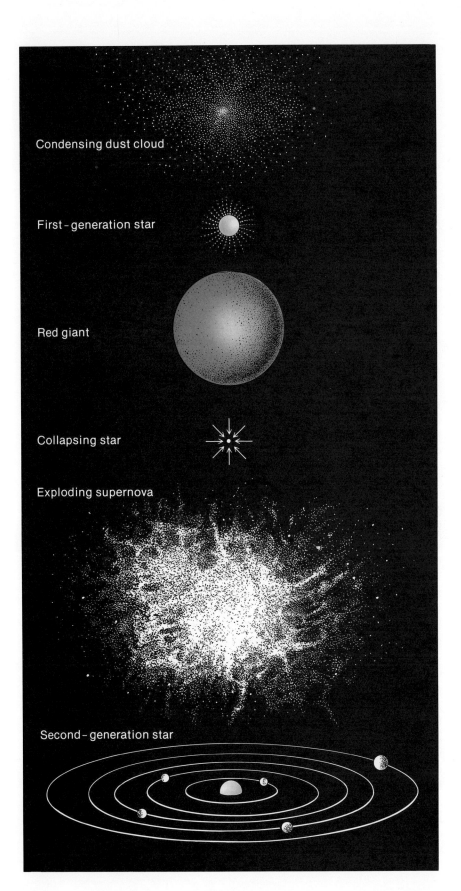

Condensing dust cloud

First-generation star

Red giant

Collapsing star

Exploding supernova

Second-generation star

If the next reaction in the series cannot be touched off, then the star becomes a white dwarf—a stellar cinder. Our own sun is approximately 4.5 billion years old. In another 5 billion years, it will swell to a red giant, annihilating life on Earth, and then shrink and touch off the "helium flash"—the burning of helium to carbon. The sun is too small to ignite the carbon reaction when helium is depleted at the core, so in a short 30 million years after the helium flash, it will swell again to engulf the orbit of Mars, puff off material, then shrink and die as a white dwarf.

Something radical, and fundamentally important to the distribution of elements through the universe, happens if the star is massive enough to continue to synthesize heavy elements until iron is reached. Since fusion involving iron absorbs energy rather than emitting it, the "fire" goes out. No more fusion reactions are available as energy sources. Paradoxically, this does not mean that the star cools to a dwarf, but that it explodes as a supernova. When the fuel at the core is finally and totally depleted, the center cools. Some of the iron at the center may break down again into helium, and by absorbing energy, make the cooling process even faster:

$$^{56}\text{Fe} + \text{large amounts of energy} \rightarrow 14\ ^{4}\text{He}$$

The star collapses in upon itself in a matter of *seconds* (a far cry from the million- and billion-year time scales used so far), and a tremendous amount of gravitational energy is released. (There is nothing mysterious about this gravitational energy. When lead shot is dropped from a height onto a steel plate, and the metal is warmed from the impact, this is the conversion of gravitational potential energy into heat. On a much larger scale, it is gravitational energy that heats the interior of an infant star and touches off the hydrogen-fusion process.) The enormous heat generated in this final collapse detonates more nuclear reactions in the outer layers of the star, and literally blows it apart in a supernova. The material of the former star is spread far and wide across interstellar space, with heavy elements arising both from the interior of the star and from the supernova explosion itself.

First-generation stars therefore turn hydrogen into heavier elements. After a supernova explosion, these elements are mixed with the original hydrogen of interstellar space, ready to serve as the raw material for a new generation of stars like our sun. As these second-generation stars coalesce, they may form planets around them, and if so, these planets are enriched in the heavier elements. The core of Earth, for example, is believed to be made up of metallic iron.

One of the most striking objects in the sky is the Crab Nebula in the constellation of Taurus, shown on the next page. This is a supernova in our galaxy, the remnants of a particularly violent stellar explosion that occurred in the summer of 1054 A.D. Western Europe was too primitive to notice such things then, although it is surprising that Arabian astronomers missed it. But the Japanese and the royal astronomers of the Sung Dynasty in China took note of it. Three such violent supernovae have been observed in our own galaxy in recorded history, in 1054, 1572, and 1604, but a search for supernovae in other galaxies conducted at the Palomar Observatory for many years suggests that a

The remains of a supernova explosion, the Crab Nebula in the constellation Taurus, which was recorded by Chinese astronomers in 1054 A.D. At the heart of this collection of cosmic debris is a pulsar, a tiny star only a few thousand miles in diameter that emits pulses of x rays, light, and radio waves 30 times a second. Heavy elements formed in such a supernova explosion are the raw materials for future star-building. Courtesy of The Hale Observatories.

辛未司天監言、自至和
元年五月客星晨出東方、
守天關、至是沒。

The Annals of the *Sung-shih* (treatise on Chinese astronomy) report a "guest star" of unusual interest, visible in the eastern heavens for the period from July 4, 1054 to April 17, 1056.

typical galaxy might produce a supernova every thirty years. The Crab Nebula is a hotbed of turmoil, emitting radio noise and x rays as well as light, and having a pulsar at its core. The theoretical astronomer has no trouble explaining why stars become supernovae; rather the problem is to explain why such catastrophes are not seen more often.

The composition of the universe reflects this evolutionary origin, as shown in the table on the opposite page. The universe is 93% hydrogen and 7% helium, with all of the other elements amounting to only 0.10%. A gap in natural abundance exists between He and C, reflecting the jump in synthesis:

$$3\ ^4He \rightarrow\ ^{12}C$$

Lithium, beryllium, and boron are formed later in secondary reactions involving the breakup of larger nuclei. Hence they are scarce in comparison with the elements on the direct line of synthesis. Beyond carbon, there is an alternation of abundance, with atoms of even atomic numbers more common than odd, as seen on the graph at the right. Again, this reflects the synthesis of the even elements by addition of alpha particles, ^4He. The odd elements, just like Li, Be, and B, must be made by side reactions and hence are not as prevalent. This is the primary reason why oxygen is used for the energy-producing reactions of life on Earth, even though fluorine is more electronegative; fluorine is simply too rare to be depended on as a biological oxidant. If this were not so, we probably would burn our foods with F_2 rather than O_2, and call the process fluoridation instead of oxidation.

The universe began as an unequal mixture of elements: few atoms of high atomic number, fewer with odd atomic numbers, and almost no Li, Be, or B. It was then subjected to further fractionation at several stages, as indicated by the last four columns of the atomic composition table at the right. The interstellar debris from which second-generation stars like our sun condensed already was enriched in the heavier elements. As the Earth was built up by accretion of dust, rocks, and debris, it too acquired an unusually rich supply of iron and other heavy elements. The energy from collisions of accreting particles, and from radioactive decay, was sufficient to melt the interior of the early Earth and create high surface temperatures. At these temperatures, the gravitational field of such a small planet was insufficient to hold onto its original gaseous atmosphere. This is why the Earth is so poor in the noble gases helium, neon, argon, and xenon, even though these elements are not particularly rare in the universe as a whole. Unable to form solid or high-melting compounds, they leaked into interplanetary space during this high-temperature era. Oxygen was retained in large quantities because it is a reactive element and was combined in many solid oxides, carbonates, phosphates, and silicates. Nitrogen, being less reactive and having fewer solid compounds, was largely lost. As you can see from the abundance table, the ratio of oxygen to nitrogen in the entire universe is only three to one, but on Earth the ratio is 160,000 to one! The fact that 80% of our atmosphere today is nitrogen gas is deceptive; most of the oxygen on our planet is locked up in solid compounds beneath our feet, not as O_2 gas in the atmosphere.

The final fractionation and enrichment took place within the early fluid planet. This was the stratification into core, mantle, and crust,

The abundance of the elements

	Composition in atoms per 100,000				
	Entire universe	Entire Earth	Crust of Earth	Ocean water	Human body
Row 1					
H	92,760	120	2,880	66,200	60,560
He	7,140	—[a]	—[a]	—[a]	—[a]
Row 2					
Li	—[a]	—	—	—	—
Be	—	—	—	—	—
B	—	—	—	—	—
C	8	99	34	1.4	10,680
N	15	0.3	3	—	2,440
O	49	48,880	60,110	33,100	25,670
F	—	3.8	68	—	—
Ne	20	—	—	—	—
Row 3					
Na	0.1	640	2,160	290	75
Mg	2.1	12,500	1,960	34	11
Al	0.2	1,300	6,300	—	—
Si	2.3	14,000	20,800	—	0.9
P	—	140	70	—	130
S	0.9	1,400	17	17	130
Cl	—	45	8	340	33
Ar	0.4	—	—	—	—
Heavier elements					
K	—	56	1,100	6	37
Ca	0.1	460	2,100	6	230
Ti	—	28	250	—	—
Mn	—	56	35	—	—
Fe	1.4	18,870	2,100	—	0.4
Ni	—	1,400	3	—	—
	99,999.5	99,998.1	99,998	99,994.4	99,997.3

[a] A — indicates less than 0.1 atom per hundred thousand.

The entire universe is mainly hydrogen and helium. Elements with even atomic numbers are more common in the universe than those with odd atomic numbers (below) because of the way in which the elements were made. The Earth has lost most of its volatile substances, and retained an iron core and the elements of silicate minerals, which have high melting and boiling points. The crust is especially rich in the metals found in pyroxines, amphiboles, and feldspars. Sea water is essentially a dilute solution of NaCl and $MgCl_2$, and the human body in gross terms is an aqueous solution of carbon and nitrogen compounds.

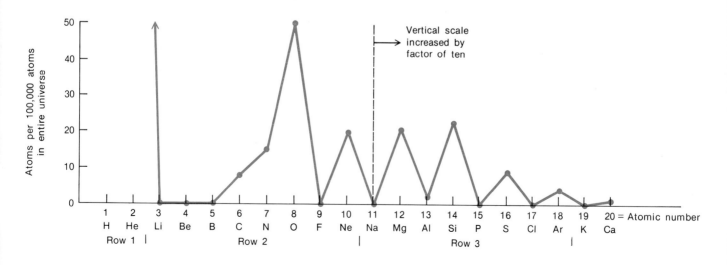

mentioned in Chapter 6. The planet as a whole has a composition approximately that of an iron core plus $FeMg(SiO_4)$, or olivine. In contrast, the crust is enriched in the cations found in feldspars, Na, Al, K, and Ca, and poorer in Mg and Fe. Two elements, oxygen and silicon, make up 81% of the crust, including the oceans, atmosphere, and all living matter. Hydrogen and the third-row metals raise this total to 94%, and K, Ca, and Fe in the fourth row bring it to 99.5%. The eighteen elements for which values are given in the abundance table account for all but two atoms per 100,000. Notice that no representative elements beyond the third row are included aside from the light metals K and Ca, that only the lightest transition metals are plentiful, and that the inner transition metals do not figure among the common elements of the crust at all. A chemistry textbook should not be based on a "popularity rating" of the elements. But since the crust of the Earth is the only part about which we have extensive chemical knowledge, and is the stage on which all the chemical reactions of living organisms evolved, it is natural that we should focus attention on the elements that seem to be doing interesting things around us.

QUESTIONS

1. What does wave mechanics substitute for the circular orbits of the Bohr theory?

2. What is meant when a picture of an orbital is described as an "electron probability cloud"?

3. What quantum numbers are needed to describe the state of an electron in wave mechanics?

4. How do the possible values of quantum number l depend on n?

5. How do the possible values of quantum number m depend on l?

6. Which quantum number is most closely associated with the size of the orbital?

7. Which quantum number is most closely associated with the shape of the orbital?

8. What property is associated with quantum number m?

9. How do the p_x, p_y, and p_z orbitals differ? Sketch them.

10. How do the d_{xy}, d_{yz}, and d_{xz} orbitals differ? How do they differ from the $d_{x^2-y^2}$ and d_{z^2} orbitals? Sketch all five d orbitals.

11. In an isolated atom, how do the energies of the three p orbitals with the same n values compare? How do the energies of the five d orbitals with the same n values compare?

12. For a given n value, how do the energies of s, p, d, and f orbitals compare?

13. How is the total number of orbitals of a given n value related to n?

14. Write the orbitals (n and l values) in order of increasing energy. How is this order related to the observed structure of the periodic table?

15. How many electrons can each atomic orbital hold? What property do the electrons have opposite values of when paired in an orbital?

16. Do two electrons in the same atomic orbital attract, repel, or have no effect upon one another?

17. Why, in terms of electron probability clouds, are two electrons in the p_x orbital forced close to one another, whereas an electron in a p_x and one in a p_y orbital are farther apart? Why does this lead to the prediction that all three p orbitals will be occupied with one electron each before any one of them receives a second electron?

18. What orbitals are being filled across the representative elements in the periodic table? What orbitals are associated with the transition metals? With the inner transition metals?

19. What are two alternative names for the first series of inner transition metals? What is another name for the second series of inner transition metals?

20. Why, based on electronic configurations, will elements in the same vertical column of the periodic table tend to have similar chemical properties?

21. What is common to the electronic structures of all of the noble gases? How does this contribute to their chemical behavior?

22. What is the big-bang theory of the origin of the universe, and how does it differ from the steady-state theory? Which is more likely to be correct, according to what we know now?

23. Why does hydrogen fusion give off energy? Where does this energy come from? What are the product nuclei?

24. Where does most of the synthesis of helium and heavier elements take place?

25. How are Li, Be, B, and C made during natural synthesis? How does your answer explain the rarity of the first three in the universe, and the relative abundance of carbon?

26. By what reactions are the elements from oxygen to silicon formed? How are the heavier elements to iron formed? What role does temperature play in determining how far this process will go?

27. Why does this elemental synthesis process stop at iron? What happens when iron and other nuclei fuse to make even heavier elements?

28. Are *all* the elements between carbon and iron formed by the reactions you outlined in response to Question 26? If not, what types of elements are systematically omitted from this scheme? How are they formed?

29. In what way does the size of a star determine how far down the set of reactions of Question 26 stellar synthesis will proceed? What eventually happens to the star if it falls short of synthesis of iron? What happens eventually if it does synthesize iron in its interior?

30. How far down the set of stellar synthesis reactions will our own sun go?

31. Where did the heavy elements in our planet (and in the solar system) come from? Were they made in the interior of our sun?

32. Why is helium so rare on Earth, although common in the universe as a whole?

33. Why is the nitrogen content of the Earth less than in the entire universe, whereas the oxygen content is a thousand times greater?

34. Why is the composition of a living organism enriched in carbon and nitrogen relative to the other elements?

PROBLEMS

1. What are the electronic configurations for fluorine and the fluoride ion?

2. What element is the third-row analogue of oxygen? What are the corresponding elements in the fourth and fifth rows? Write the electronic configurations of all four elements, and point out the common features that give them similar chemical properties. What are their atomic numbers? As the atomic number increases, will the elements in this set of four become more, or less, metallic? Why?

3. What are the electronic configurations of the following: P, K$^+$, Mg^{2+}? What would the electronic configuration of each be in the first excited state (i.e., one electron promoted to an unoccupied orbital by the least possible addition of energy)?

4. Name two positive ions, a negative ion, and a neutral atom that are isoelectronic with Cl$^-$. What is their electronic configuration? For the ions, what is the corresponding neutral-atom configuration of each?

5. Which of the following electronic configurations represents a ground state of an atom, an excited state, and an impossible state:

   (a) $1s^2 2s^2 2p^6 3s^2 3p^5$
   (b) $1s^2 2s^2 2p^6 3s^3 3p^6$
   (c) $1s^2 2s^2 2p^5 3s^1$
   (d) $1s^2 2s^2 2p^6 3s^1$

   Assuming that these all represent neutral atoms and not ions, identify the atoms (except for impossible combinations, of course).

6. Ten elements and their electronic configurations are given below. For each, decide whether a neutral atom, or a positive or negative ion, is represented. In addition, specify whether the electronic state represented is a ground state, an excited state, or an impossible state.

   (a) Li: $1s^2 2p^1$
   (b) H: $1s^2$
   (c) S: $1s^2 2s^2 2p^6 3s^2 3p^4$
   (d) C: $1s^2 2s^2 2p^1 2d^1$

(e) Ne: $1s^22s^12p^7$

(f) N: $1s^22s^12p^3$

(g) F: $1s^22s^22p^53s^1$

(h) He: $1p^1$

(i) Sc: $1s^22s^22p^63s^23p^63d^14s^2$

(j) O: $1s^22s^22p^3$

Explain what is wrong with each impossible state.

7. If the filling of electron shells occurred in the most straightforward way implied by the structure of the periodic table, what would be the electronic configuration of chromium (Cr, atomic number 24)? What is its actual configuration? Why the difference?

The *s* and three *p* orbitals are the starting materials for bonding in methane.

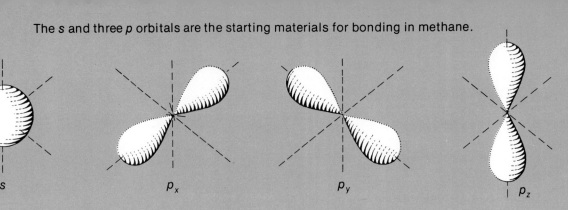

s p_x p_y p_z

These orbitals are hybridized, or combined, to form four equivalent sp^3 atomic orbitals directed toward the corners of a tetrahedron.

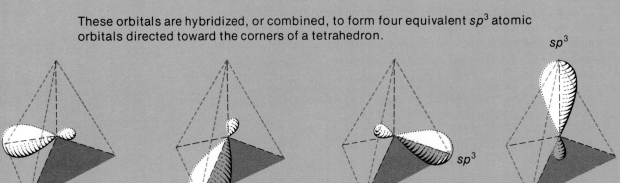

sp^3 sp^3 sp^3 sp^3

sp^3

MOLECULAR ORBITALS IN METHANE

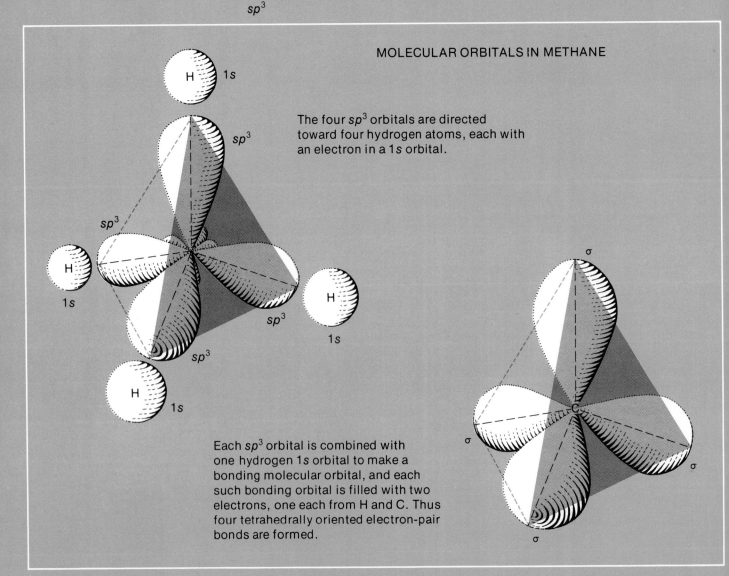

H 1*s*

sp^3

sp^3

H
1*s*

H
1*s*

sp^3

H
1*s*

sp^3

The four sp^3 orbitals are directed toward four hydrogen atoms, each with an electron in a 1*s* orbital.

σ

σ   C   σ

σ

Each sp^3 orbital is combined with one hydrogen 1*s* orbital to make a bonding molecular orbital, and each such bonding orbital is filled with two electrons, one each from H and C. Thus four tetrahedrally oriented electron-pair bonds are formed.

CHAPTER 9

Molecular Orbitals and Molecular Structure

So far we have used two models for chemical bonding and molecular geometry: Lewis' electron pairs to explain how atoms are held together, and valence-shell electron-pair repulsion theory (VSEPR theory) to account for the geometry of bonding. These are simple ideas, but we have pushed them about as far as they will go. The cracks and seams in the bonding theory have begun to show through—the need for delocalized electrons is one example—and rather than trying to patch over the cracks, it is wiser to develop a better theory of bonding that will include the old ideas and permit us to go beyond them. Now that we have the atomic orbitals of Chapter 8, we can use these to develop a theory of molecular orbitals that will do a much better job of accounting for the structures and properties of molecules.

The central idea in molecular orbital theory (or MO theory) is that of combining atomic orbitals (or AO's) from all the atoms in a molecule into the same number of molecular orbitals. The process is illustrated at the left for methane. Like the atomic orbitals of the preceding chapter, these molecular orbitals will have different shapes, sizes, and energies. The next step is to feed all of the electrons available from the atoms into these molecular orbitals one at a time with a maximum of two per orbital, starting with the lowest-energy orbital and progressing upward. This buildup of the molecule by the filling of molecular orbitals is exactly analogous to the buildup of atoms in the preceding chapter, by the filling of atomic orbitals. The main practical problem in this theory is one of deciding how the MO's are to be constructed from the available AO's, and what their energies are. The principal difficulty of MO theory is that orbitals for molecules with more than a small number of atoms become too complicated to calculate, even with the help of high-speed digital computers. Fortunately, instead of considering the entire molecule at once, one often can drop back to the easier approach of looking at bonds between pairs of atoms. This is called *localized MO*

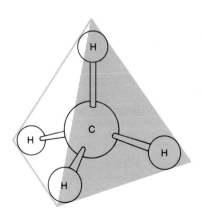

Ball-and-stick model of the methane molecule, showing its tetrahedral geometry

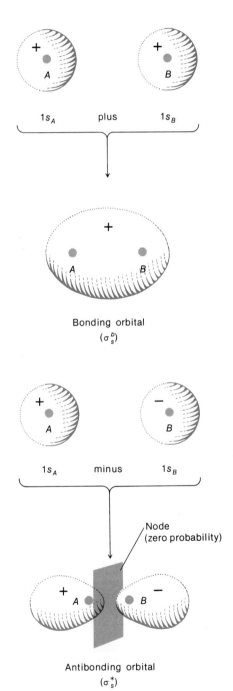

BONDING AND ANTIBONDING
MOLECULAR ORBITALS IN H_2 MOLECULE

$1s_A$ plus $1s_B$

Bonding orbital
(σ_s^b)

$1s_A$ minus $1s_B$

Node
(zero probability)

Antibonding orbital
(σ_s^*)

theory, and it has the advantages of being mathematically simpler, very pictorial even without mathematics (which will be our approach), inherently sensible, and fairly accurate. We shall use complete MO theory for some simple two-atom molecules such as H_2, O_2, and HF, and then show how a localized MO theory can work with larger molecules, and how it fails for molecules with delocalized electrons.

HYDROGENLIKE MOLECULES

The simplest molecules that could be imagined would have two atomic nuclei surrounded by one to four electrons derived originally from the two $1s$ atomic orbitals. We shall look at such molecules first, and what we learn about combining $1s$ orbitals will carry over into the combining of other orbitals for more complicated molecules.

The most familiar example of a molecule built from $1s$ atomic orbitals is hydrogen, H_2, which has two electrons. The hydrogen molecule-ion, H_2^+, also can exist with only one electron to hold the nuclei together. The bond is weak, and the molecule-ion is hyperreactive, seizing an electron where it can and turning into a neutral hydrogen molecule again. Another short-lived but observable molecule-ion is He_2^+, with two nuclei and three electrons. As we shall see shortly, two of these electrons help to bond the nuclei together, and the third electron weakens the bond. The molecule with four electrons, He_2, is only imaginary, because with two electrons holding the nuclei and two repelling them, He_2 would fall apart into two helium atoms. These four molecules, one stable, two less stable, and one nonexistent, offer a simple test of the MO theory because they all use the same orbitals and energy levels.

How can we combine the $1s$ atomic orbitals from two atoms to obtain two molecular orbitals? Recall that the electron density or probability clouds that we have been using are the *squares* of wave functions, which came out of quantum theory. It is these wave functions, not the probability clouds themselves, that are combined into molecular orbitals. The probability clouds always are positive (probabilities for anything only can be positive or zero), but different parts of the wave functions can have positive or negative signs. These signs are important in deciding whether and how a given pair of AO's can be combined.

There are two ways of combining two $1s$ atomic orbitals in the hydrogenlike molecules: with the same sign on the two wave functions, or with opposite signs. This amounts to adding the two wave functions or subtracting one from the other, which leads to the electron densities shown at the left. If the wave functions are added, the resulting molecular orbital has a pileup of electron density between the nuclei. When a pair of electrons is placed in this orbital, the negative charge on the electrons attracts both nuclei, and shields each nucleus from repulsion by the other. This is the electron-pair bond introduced in Chapter 4. This ($1s_A + 1s_B$) MO is called a *bonding orbital* because electrons placed in it help to hold the nuclei together. Two electrons in such a bonding orbital are more stable (lower energy) than one electron in each of the two isolated atomic orbitals.

172

Electrons also can pull a molecule apart, an idea that could not be accounted for with the old Lewis theory. The other way of combining the $1s$ wave functions, with opposite signs, leads to an MO in which the greatest electron density lies on the outside of the nuclei, away from the bond. In such a molecular orbital, there is zero probability of finding electrons on a plane halfway between the nuclei (see bottom left on the opposite page). Electrons in this $(1s_A - 1s_B)$ orbital not only fail to shield the nuclei from one another, they actively pull the molecule apart from each end. Such an MO is called an *antibonding orbital* because it is less stable (higher energy) than the orbitals of the separated atoms.

Some terminology must be introduced at this point to make the subsequent discussion easier. If a molecular orbital is completely symmetrical about the line connecting the nuclei, it is called a σ (sigma) MO. Bonding MO's are further indicated by a small superscript b, and antibonding orbitals by a small asterisk. (Think of the asterisk as a miniexplosion, representing instability.) The kind of AO's from which the MO's came is indicated by a subscript. Then we can write the two molecular orbitals as

$$\sigma_s^b = 1s_A + 1s_B \qquad \sigma_s^* = 1s_A - 1s_B$$

$$\text{I} \qquad\qquad\qquad \text{II}$$

(These are expressions for the wave functions, and the electron densities in the two MO's are found by squaring them.) These two concise equations can be translated into words as

I: A sigma bonding MO from s atomic orbitals is obtained by adding the $1s$ AO's from atoms A and B.

II: A sigma antibonding MO from s atomic orbitals is obtained by subtracting the $1s$ orbitals, or combining the wave functions with opposite signs.

These are the orbitals that have been drawn at the far left. Together they can hold a maximum of four electrons. By adding one electron at a time we can build up the four molecules or molecule-ions mentioned previously.

The energy levels of these two MO's are shown schematically below. The bonding MO is more stable than the original $1s$ atomic orbitals, and the antibonding MO is less stable; so in effect the original energy level of the $1s$ AO's is split into two levels, one lower and one

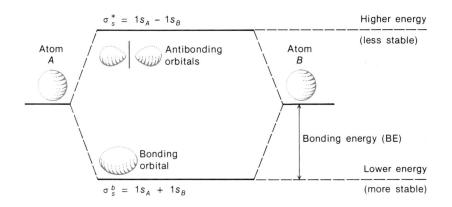

The two atomic orbitals combine to form a bonding orbital of lower energy and an antibonding orbital of higher energy. Two electrons paired in the bonding orbital constitute a bond, and the extra stability of the bonding orbital over the original atomic orbitals represents the bonding energy, BE.

	H_2^+	H_2	He_2^+	He_2
Antibonding (σ_s^*)	—	—	●—	●●—
Bonding (σ_s^b)	●—	●●—	●●—	●●—

	H_2^+	H_2	He_2^+	He_2
Antibonding electrons	0	0	1	2
Bonding electrons	1	2	2	2
Net bonding	1	2	1	0
Bond type	Half	Single	Half	None

	H_2^+	H_2	He_2^+	He_2
Bond length (Å)	1.06	0.74	1.08	——
Bond energy (kcal mole^{-1})	61	103	60	——

higher. These energy levels now can be occupied by as many electrons as are available in a molecule, just as the atomic energy levels were occupied in Chapter 8. This molecular buildup is tabulated above. The H_2^+ molecule-ion has only one electron, which occupies the bonding σ_s^b orbital by itself. This electron spends most of its time between the nuclei, shielding them from one another and holding them together like half of a Lewis electron-pair bond. Two electrons are present in H_2, and they completely fill the bonding MO. This is the ordinary electron-pair bond discussed in Chapter 4. He_2^+ has three electrons, and since two of them fill the σ_s^b MO, the third is forced into the antibonding σ_s^* orbital. The molecule has two electrons holding the nuclei together, and one pulling them apart, for a net of one bonding electron. The antibonding electron weakens the molecule. He_2 would have two electrons in the bonding orbital and two in the antibonding orbital. The push and pull of these electrons cancel, and no net bonding is left in the He_2 molecule, which therefore does not exist.

This bonding–antibonding arithmetic is summarized below the filling diagrams at the top of the page. We can calculate the number of electron-pair bonds by counting the *net* number of bonding electrons and dividing by two. If we refer to an electron-pair bond as a "single bond" then H_2 has a single bond, H_2^+ and He_2^+ have one half bonds, and He_2 has no bond at all. The number of bonds between two atoms in a molecule is termed its *bond order*: H_2^+ and He_2^+ have bond order $\frac{1}{2}$, H_2 has bond order 1, and the C=C double bond in ethylene has bond order 2. Bond order is related to bond length and bond energy. The measured experimental bond lengths, r, and bond energies, BE, are given below the filling diagrams. The single bond in H_2 is 0.74 Å long, and 103 kcal mole^{-1} of energy is required to break the bonds and turn a mole of H_2 molecules into H atoms. The half bonds of the two molecule-ions require approximately half as much energy to break them, and are weak enough to allow the bond length to stretch from 0.74 Å to a little over 1 Å. Simple MO theory is correct in predicting trends in bond lengths and bond energies for these small molecules, and this should give us confidence that the basic approach to bonding is correct.

LARGER DIATOMIC MOLECULES

Where do we go from here? How do we combine 1s, 2s, and the different 2p atomic orbitals into MO's in larger molecules? The principles remain the same:

1. Combine the available AO's properly to produce the same number of MO's of different energies, some bonding, others antibonding.
2. Fill the MO's from the lowest energy upward with all the available electrons, two per orbital.

The immediate problem is the meaning of the word "properly" in the first step above. How are the atomic orbitals combined?

You can go a long way in MO theory with common sense and three combination principles:

1. Two AO's must be close enough in space to overlap appreciably before they can be combined into an MO.
2. The combining AO's must be of similar energy.
3. The orbitals must have the same symmetry around the bond axis.

The first principle is reasonable. Atoms cannot combine when they are far from one another. However, there is a more practical aspect. A 2s orbital is larger than a 1s, and when two atoms are brought close enough for overlap between 2s orbitals, the smaller 1s orbitals are still too far away to overlap appreciably. We can leave them as separated atomic orbitals, each with a pair of electrons around each atomic nucleus. This is another way of saying that when the outer electron shells of an atom are involved in bonding, the filled under shells take no part and can be ignored. For an atom in any row of the periodic table, the electrons of the noble gas that brought the preceding row to a close can be regarded as an unchanging atomic core, and neglected in bonding. This makes life much simpler.

The principle of similar energies would have ruled out combinations between 1s orbitals and 2s or 2p orbitals from the same kind of atoms. It can even take us one step further, and tell us that in the simplest treatment we do not have to worry about combining 2s and 2p orbitals on different atoms of the same type; the energy difference between s and p orbitals is enough to make their combination unlikely.

The most stringent and most helpful rule is the third one, which demands the same symmetry of orbitals around the bond axis, or the line connecting atoms. The logic behind this is shown at the right. Two atomic s orbitals have total symmetry about the bond axis, and can be combined into a σ MO as shown at (a). Two p orbitals oriented as in (b) have what is termed π (pi) symmetry about the bond axis. If you rotate them 180° around this axis, the electron density will look the same, but the *signs* of the wave functions in all of the density lobes will be reversed. Each atomic p orbital has one positive lobe and one negative lobe, and there is a surface plane halfway between on which the electron probability falls to zero. Such a zero-probability surface in a wave function is called a *node*. The resulting π MO also has a positive lobe, a negative lobe, and a zero-probability node halfway between.

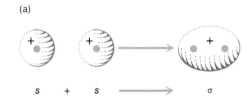

(a)

s + s ⟶ σ

Sigma (σ) symmetry: Complete identity upon rotation about the bond axis

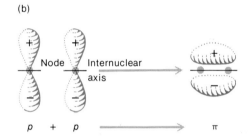

(b)

p + p ⟶ π

Pi (π) symmetry: Change of sign of the wave function upon rotation about the bond axis

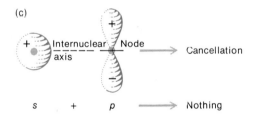

(c)

s + p ⟶ Nothing

Different symmetries of atomic orbitals; no combination is possible

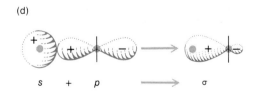

(d)

s + p ⟶ σ

Same two orbitals but reoriented so as to have the same symmetry around the potential bond axis. Combination into a molecular orbital now is possible as shown.

Atomic orbitals (AO)   Molecular orbitals (MO)

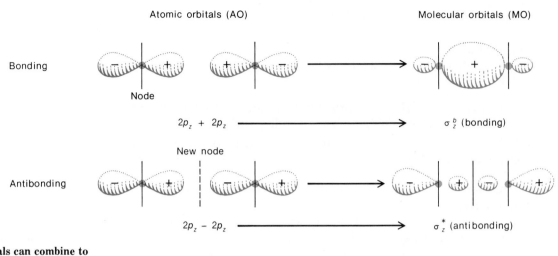

Bonding

Node

$$2p_z + 2p_z \longrightarrow \qquad \sigma_z^b \text{ (bonding)}$$

New node

Antibonding

$$2p_z - 2p_z \longrightarrow \qquad \sigma_z^* \text{ (antibonding)}$$

The two p_z atomic orbitals can combine to form a bonding and an antibonding molecular orbital, each with σ symmetry about the bond axis.

SIGMA (σ) ORBITALS

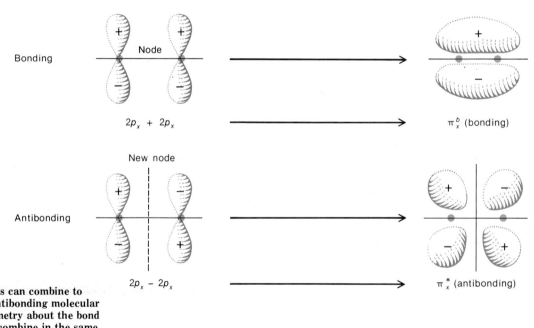

Bonding

Node

$$2p_x + 2p_x \longrightarrow \qquad \pi_x^b \text{ (bonding)}$$

New node

Antibonding

$$2p_x - 2p_x \longrightarrow \qquad \pi_x^* \text{ (antibonding)}$$

The two p_x atomic orbitals can combine to form a bonding and an antibonding molecular orbital, each with π symmetry about the bond axis. The two p_y orbitals combine in the same way, but at right angles to these orbitals out of the plane of the page.

PI (π) ORBITALS

An s and a p orbital oriented as in (c) cannot be combined, because they have different bond-axis symmetries. Any positive overlap between the s and the upper lobe of the p would be canceled exactly by negative overlap between s and the bottom lobe, and nothing would result. If the p orbital is turned $90°$ so one lobe points toward s along the bond axis as in (d), then both AO's have σ symmetry along the bond axis. They can be combined without canceling, provided the similar-energy requirement is met.

176

With these three principles, we are now ready to build MO's from the $2s$, $2p_x$, $2p_y$, and $2p_z$ atomic orbitals of two atoms. The two $2s$ orbitals are added and subtracted to produce bonding and antibonding MO's in the way seen previously for H_2:

$$\sigma_s^b = 2s + 2s \qquad \sigma_s^* = 2s - 2s$$

These look so much like slightly larger versions of the H_2 orbitals that it is unnecessary to draw them again. If the bond axis is chosen as the z axis, then the two $2p_z$ orbitals can be combined, as in the left drawing, to yield a bonding σ_z^b orbital and an antibonding σ_z^* orbital. The MO's are both σ orbitals because they are symmetrical about the bond axis. Each of the original p orbitals had one nodal plane of zero electron probability, and these nodes are preserved in the resulting bonding MO. When we bring density lobes of opposite signs together in making the antibonding MO, we introduce another change of sign, so the antibonding orbital has three nodal surfaces, as shown. The bonding σ_z^b is like the σ_s^b in concentrating most of the electron probability between the nuclei, where it helps to hold the atoms together. The antibonding σ_z^* resembles the σ_s^* in having most of the density on the outside of the nuclei, where it tends to pull the atoms apart.

The $2p_x$ and $2p_y$ atomic orbitals are at right angles to the bond line, and can be paired to make bonding and antibonding MO's as in the lower figure on the preceding page. Only p_x orbitals are shown, but the p_y orbitals look just like them, at right angles out of the page. These AO's lead to π MO's, with a change of sign upon $180°$ rotation around the bond axis. The bonding π_x^b and π_y^b orbitals preserve the nodal surface present in the original p_x and p_y orbitals, and the antibonding π_x^* and π_y^* add an extra node that is introduced when the p's are combined with opposite signs.

These are the molecular orbitals, or electron probability clouds, that a simple diatomic (two-atom) molecule can have. What can we say about their energies, other than that half of the MO's are bonding orbitals and half are antibonding? The energies all can be calculated from molecular orbital theory and given numerical values, but we can reach the same goal in our nonmathematical treatment by recognizing the significance of *nodes* in the wave functions. Other things being equal, the greater the number of nodes in any wave, the higher the energy. We have seen this principle before, but have not recognized it explicitly. A high-frequency light wave has more nodes per unit length (the wave returns to zero more often) than a low-frequency one (see upper right). By the relationship $E = h\nu$, higher frequency means higher energy. The same principle holds for atomic orbitals (right): An s orbital is spherically symmetrical, a p orbital has one nodal plane, and a d orbital has two nodal planes. The energy within one n level accordingly increases from s to p to d.

This principle can be used to draw an energy-level diagram for the molecular orbitals. The first consideration is the relative energies of the AO's from which the MO's are made. Then, among MO's built from AO's of the same energy, the relative order is dictated by the increasing number of nodes. Both the bonding and antibonding MO's from the $2s$ AO's are lower in energy than any of the $2p$-derived orbitals, but among

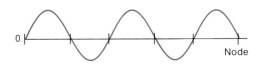

A low-frequency wave has fewer nodes (where the wave falls to zero) and lower energy, as given by $E = h\nu$.

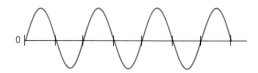

A higher-frequency wave has more zero nodes, and also has more energy.

Similar behavior is observed with atomic wave functions.

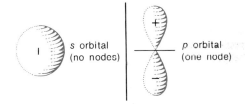

s orbital (no nodes) | *p* orbital (one node)

For the same value of n, an s orbital has no zero nodes and is lowest in energy; a p orbital has one nodal plane of zero electron probability and slightly greater energy.

A d orbital has two nodal surfaces, and higher energy still.

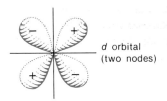

d orbital (two nodes)

Energy levels for *s*, *p*, and *d* orbitals

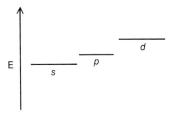

Energy levels

ENERGY LEVELS FOR SIMPLE
DIATOMIC MOLECULES

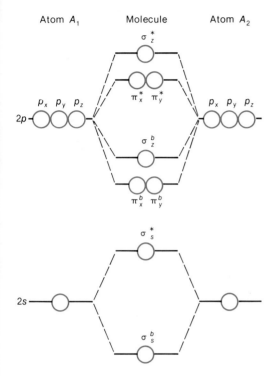

When two identical atoms, A_1 and A_2, are combined into a molecule, the energy levels of the initial atomic orbitals (left and right) are split into the new energy levels of bonding and antibonding molecular orbitals (center). In the ground state of the molecule, these orbitals are filled from the most stable orbital upward, with as many electrons as were present in s and p orbitals in the original atoms.

these latter, the node-counting rule is useful to determine relative energies. The π_x^b and π_y^b bonding orbitals have a single node and the lowest energy, followed by the σ_z^b bonding orbital, which has two nodes. All of these orbitals are more stable than the $2p$ AO's that led to them. Among the antibonding orbitals, the π_x^* and π_y^*, which have two nodes, are next, and the σ_z^*, which has three nodes, has the highest energy of all.

These energies are diagramed at the left, with each two-electron orbital being represented by a colored circle. It is worth emphasizing here that "bonding" and "antibonding" only imply that the MO is more, or less, stable than the AO's from which it arose, not that it is of low energy or high energy on an absolute basis. The antibonding σ_s^* orbital has lower energy than the bonding orbitals derived from $2p$; but it still is antibonding because if the atoms were pulled apart, the electrons in σ_s^* would drop down to the less energetic $2s$ atomic orbitals.

This set of molecular orbitals and the energy-level diagram are valid for all diatomic molecules made from second-row atoms, from Li_2, through CO, to F_2 and the nonexistent Ne_2. Although CO has two different atoms, the energy levels of the atoms are so similar that we can treat the molecule like we do N_2. Filling diagrams for most of these molecules are shown on the opposite page. Li_2 has two bonding electrons, which occupy the lowest σ_s^b molecular orbital. Be_2 has another two electrons, which fill the antibonding σ_s^* orbital, cancel the bonding of the first two electrons, and cause the molecule to fall apart. B_2 has two more electrons, and these go into the π_x^b and π_y^b bonding orbitals. Because of the repulsion between electrons, one goes into each orbital, giving B_2 two unpaired electrons. These two levels are filled by two more electrons in C_2, and all of the bonding orbitals are full in N_2 and CO. In O_2 one electron is added to each of the π_x^* and π_y^* antibonding states, in F_2 these states are filled, and the final antibonding orbital is filled in Ne_2.

As with H_2, H_2^+, and He_2^+, we can establish the number of bonds between atoms in these molecules by counting the *net* number of bonding electrons and dividing by two, since we are accustomed to calling two bonding electrons a "bond." Li_2, found when lithium metal is vaporized, has a single bond. Be_2 has no net bonding for the same reason He_2 has none, so vaporized Be consists of single atoms. B_2 has a single bond, C_2 a double bond, N_2 and CO triple bonds, and O_2 a double bond because of the disruptive effect of the π_x^* and π_y^* antibonding electrons. F_2 has only a single bond, and Ne_2 has no bond at all, like He_2 and Be_2.

These predictions about bond order from MO theory correspond quite well with the observed bond lengths and bond energies, which are tabulated below the filling diagrams. Bond lengths decrease and bond energies increase with increasing bond order from B to N, and then reverse their trends as the bond order decreases from N to Ne. N_2 and CO have the same bond structure and show similar bond lengths and bond energies. The single–double–triple–double–single sequence of bond orders for B_2 through F_2 is entirely the consequence of the order of energies of the MO's as diagramed at the left. If this sequence of energy levels had been different—if all the bonding MO's had come before the antibonding, for example—then the predictions of bonding in diatomic molecules by MO theory would have been quite wrong.

178

THE FILLING OF ORBITAL ENERGY LEVELS IN A DIATOMIC MOLECULE

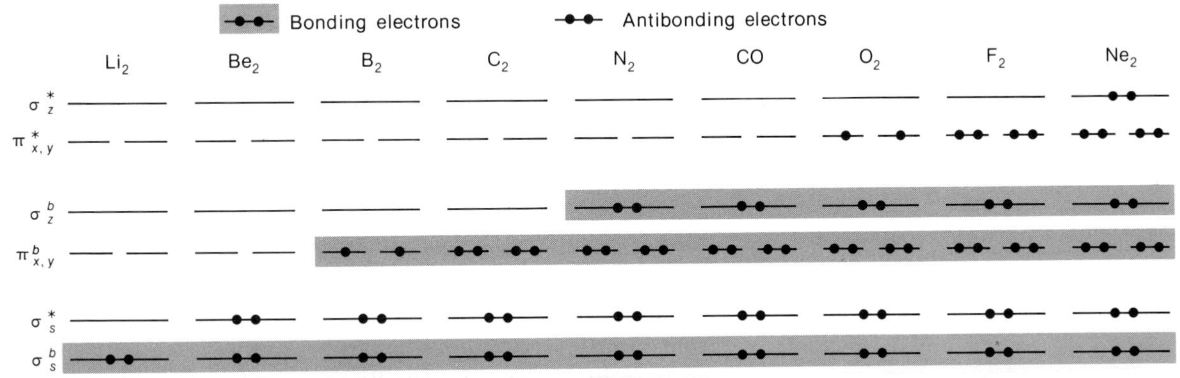

Bonding electrons ●─●   Antibonding electrons ●─●

	Li₂	Be₂	B₂	C₂	N₂	CO	O₂	F₂	Ne₂
Electrons:									
Bonding	2	2	4	6	8	8	8	8	8
Antibonding	0	2	2	2	2	2	4	6	8
Net bonding	2	0	2	4	6	6	4	2	0
Bond	Single	None	Single	Double	Triple	Triple	Double	Single	None
r (Å)	2.67	—	1.59	1.24	1.10	1.13	1.21	1.42	—
BE (kcal mole⁻¹)	26	—	66	144	225	256	118	33	—
Unpaired electrons	0	—	2	0	0	0	2	0	—
Lewis diagrams	Li—Li	—	:B—B:	:C=C:	:N≡N:	:C≡O:	:O=O:	:F—F:	—

How does the MO picture of these molecules compare with the old Lewis electron-dot models? This is shown at the bottom of the filling table above. The number of bonds predicted is the same in both theories, but the descriptions of what the electrons are doing are somewhat different. From B_2 onward, each Lewis model has at least one lone electron pair on each of the atoms. One lone pair from each atom, which contribute nothing to bonding, correspond to the self-canceling bonding and antibonding σ_s^b and σ_s^* orbitals in MO theory. Both theories say that two electron pairs make no contribution to bonding, but the Lewis model assigns one pair to each atom, whereas MO theory states that both are shared by the entire molecule. The sum of σ_s^b and σ_s^* does amount to one electron pair on each atom, so the two theories are not as different as they might seem at first.

The two theories differ in their predictions about the pairing of electrons. In the Lewis models, all electrons are paired, whereas with MO theory B_2 and O_2 each have *two* unpaired electrons in π orbitals of the same energy. Magnetic measurements of these molecules show that this is correct: B_2 and O_2 do have unpaired electrons. This experimental finding is consistent with MO theory, but cannot be explained by the simple Lewis models. In this respect, as in others involving quantitative calculations of energies, MO theory is a vast improvement over simpler electron-pair bond ideas.

As with the hydrogenlike molecules seen before, a maximum of two electrons can occupy each molecular orbital, bonding or antibonding. The total number of bonds (or bond order) is obtained by dividing the number of net bonding electrons by two. N_2 and CO are the stablest molecules, being held together by triple bonds. Notice the agreement between calculated bond order, and measured bond lengths and bond energies. The simple Lewis model cannot account for the presence of unpaired electrons in B_2 and O_2, whereas MO theory simply assigns them to different orbitals of the same energy.

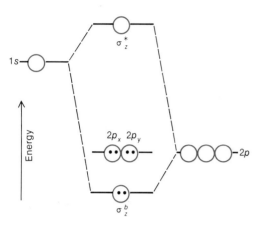

Atomic and molecular energy levels for the combination of H and F into HF. The $2p_x$ and $2p_y$ orbitals of F cannot combine with the $1s$ of hydrogen because they have the wrong bond-axis symmetry.

The $2p_z$ of F and the $1s$ of H can combine to form bonding and antibonding molecular orbitals because they have the same bond-axis symmetry.

BONDS BETWEEN DIFFERENT KINDS OF ATOMS

How would we combine atomic orbitals to make molecular orbitals for diatomic molecules such as HF? Would the $2s$ hydrogen orbital interact with the $2s$ orbital of fluorine, and the $2p$ of hydrogen with the $2p$ of fluorine? No, because the energies of orbitals with corresponding quantum numbers in H and F are very different. The increased nuclear charge of $+9$ on F, compared to $+1$ on H, pulls on the electrons in all the fluorine quantum levels and makes them more stable (lower energy). The $1s$ orbital of fluorine is so much lower in energy than the $1s$ of hydrogen that they cannot possibly interact.

The outer occupied orbital in F and the $1s$ H orbital are the ones that are of similar energy. The first ionization energy of each kind of atom is the energy needed to remove one electron from an outer orbital: the $1s$ of hydrogen, and the $2p$ of fluorine. The first ionization energy of hydrogen is 313 kcal mole^{-1}, and that of fluorine is 402 kcal mole^{-1}, so the $2p$ orbitals in F are approximately 89 kcal mole^{-1} lower in energy than the $1s$ orbital in H. These are the orbitals that are similar enough in energy to combine, and their relative energies are shown at the left and right of the energy-level diagram in the margin. The $2s$ orbital of fluorine is off scale at the bottom of the diagram, and the $1s$ is lower still. Molecular orbitals for HF are obtained by combining the $1s$ of H with the $2p$ of F.

The symmetry requirement makes things even simpler. If we choose the H—F bond as the z axis, then the p_x and p_y orbitals have the wrong symmetry and cannot combine with the $1s$ orbital of hydrogen. Electrons in these two orbitals remain as lone pairs on the fluorine atom. Only the $2p_z$ orbital has the proper symmetry, and it combines with the hydrogen $1s$ to form a bonding MO and an antibonding MO with σ symmetry: σ_z^b and σ_z^*. These are sketched below. The bonding MO is lower in energy than either the $1s$ of H or the $2p_z$ of F, and the antibonding MO is higher than either. These bonding and antibonding MO's and the $2p$ lone pairs, are represented in the center of the energy-level diagram at the left.

Ten electrons are available to the HF molecule, nine from F and one from H. Of these, two will fill the fluorine $1s$ atomic orbital and two more the $2s$, not shown on the energy-level diagram. The next two electrons fill the bonding σ_z^b MO and provide the attraction that holds the molecule together. The remaining four electrons occupy the $2p_x$ and $2p_y$ orbitals on fluorine, as lone pairs. The simple Lewis diagram of this

MOLECULAR ORBITALS FOR HYDROGEN FLUORIDE (HF)

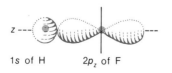

1s of H $2p_z$ of F

Atomic orbitals

Antibonding, σ_z^*

Bonding, σ_z^b

Molecular orbitals

molecule is accurate:

$$H—\overset{\cdot\cdot}{\underset{\cdot\cdot}{F}}:$$

The bond line represents the bonding σ_z^b orbital electrons, and the three lone pairs around F are in the $2s$, $2p_x$, and $2p_y$ orbitals.

This treatment of HF illustrates how two different quantum levels on different atoms can be combined if they have similar energies. It also illustrates the effect of difference in electronegativities on the character of the chemical bond. The bonding MO in HF is closer in energy to the $2p_z$ AO of fluorine from which it came, and less like the $1s$ AO of hydrogen. The antibonding MO, in contrast, is closer in energy to the hydrogen $1s$. If you worked out the mathematics of combining AO's into MO's, you would find that the bonding σ_z^b MO has a greater contribution from the fluorine $2p_z$, and the antibonding MO is more like the hydrogen $1s$ orbital. In H_2, of course, the two atoms are identical, and the bonding and antibonding MO's have equal contributions from both atoms.

The lower energy of the fluorine $2p$ AO, compared with that of the hydrogen $1s$, is a reflection of the fact that F is more electronegative than H, and holds onto its outer electrons more tightly. In general, when two atoms of different electronegativities are combined, the bonding MO's are more like the AO's of the more electronegative element in both shape and energy, and the antibonding MO's resemble those of the less electronegative atom. This trend is illustrated at the right for H_2 and HF, and in more exaggerated form for LiF. If the bonding MO has more of a contribution from F because of its electronegativity, then filling this orbital with an electron pair means giving the electrons more to F than to the other atom. The bonding pair is unequally shared, and the bond has a partial ionic character. The larger the energy spread between orbitals of the original atoms, the more the bonding orbital resembles the AO from the more electronegative atom, and the more ionic the bond will be. H—H is totally covalent, with equal sharing. H—F is partially ionic, with a partial displacement of the bonding electron pair toward F. In LiF the energy gap is so large that the bonding σ_z^b MO is almost indistinguishable from the $2p$ orbital of fluorine. The bonding electron pair is transferred almost completely to the F atom as a lone pair. Molecular orbital theory views covalent and ionic bonds as two extremes of a continuum of bond types, a matter of degree rather than kind. What determines the covalent or ionic character of a bond is the difference in energy between the atomic orbitals being combined, which in turn reflects the relative electronegativities of the two atoms.

LOCALIZED MOLECULAR ORBITALS

In principle, we could extend molecular orbital theory to larger molecules by the same procedures: combine the atomic orbitals from all atoms in the molecule into an equal number of MO's that extend over the entire molecule, then fill these MO's from the lowest energy up with as many electrons as are available. In practice, this rapidly exceeds the

EFFECT OF ELECTRONEGATIVITY DIFFERENCES
ON MOLECULAR ORBITALS

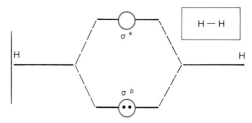

Same electronegativity: Bonding and antibonding MO's have the same contributions from each atom; pure covalent bond.

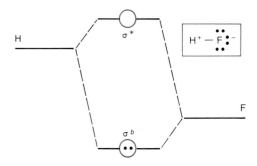

F more electronegative than H: Bonding MO is more like the AO from fluorine and antibonding MO is more like the AO from hydrogen; polar, partially ionic bond.

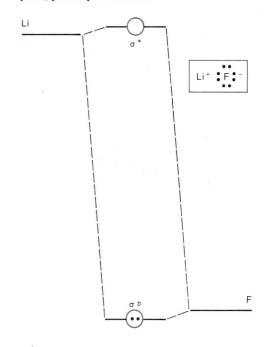

F much more electronegative than Li: Bonding MO is virtually identical to fluorine AO and the bonding electron pair is virtually given to fluorine; almost completely ionic bond.

The $2p_x$ and $2p_y$ orbitals of oxygen are used in bonds to the two hydrogens. The oxygen $2s$ and $2p_z$ orbitals are uninvolved in bonding and are filled by the two oxygen lone electron pairs.

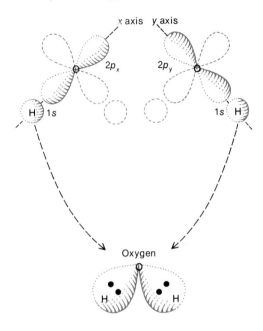

Bonding MO's in water, with electron pairs as black dots.

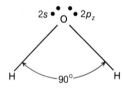

With pure *p*-orbital bonding from oxygen, the expected bond angle in water would be 90°. The observed angle is 105°, so this model cannot be the entire story.

calculating abilities of even the best digital computers, and some compromises and approximations are called for. The most important of these is the localized molecular orbital approximation, which brings us back from entire molecules to bonds between pairs of atoms.

The localized MO theory assumes that we can combine an AO from each of two atoms that share a bond to produce bonding and antibonding localized MO's extending only over the two atoms. If the bonding MO is filled with a pair of electrons, then a bond is formed between the atoms. The other atoms in the molecule, and even the other atomic orbitals on the two being bonded, are assumed not to matter very much to that particular bond. For example, the water molecule has five atomic orbitals from oxygen, $1s$, $2s$, $2p_x$, $2p_y$, and $2p_z$, and a $1s$ orbital from each of the two hydrogens. It also has ten electrons, eight from O and one each from H. By analogy with HF, we can assume that the $1s$ and $2s$ orbitals of oxygen are filled with electron pairs and take no part in bonding. Of the three $2p$ orbitals, two can be considered as interacting with one hydrogen $1s$ orbital each, as shown for $2p_x$ and $2p_y$ at the left. Each such interaction produces a bonding and an antibonding localized MO, and when the bonding MO is filled with an electron pair, a bond is formed between O and that H atom. The $2p_z$ orbital remains unused in bonding because it has the wrong orientation and symmetry to combine with the $1s$ orbitals of the hydrogen atoms.

In summary, the ten electrons are added to the MO's in order of increasing energy:

1. two to the oxygen $1s$, as an electron pair in the closed inner shell,
2. two to the oxygen $2s$, as a lone pair,
3. two each to the two H—O bonding orbitals,
4. two to the oxygen $2p_z$, as the second lone pair.

The Lewis diagram of a water molecule, at the bottom left, still holds, but MO theory identifies the two oxygen lone pairs explicitly as being in the $2s$ and $2p_z$ orbitals. However, something is badly wrong with the simple localized MO theory as it has been presented here, because it predicts that the H—O—H bond angle will be 90°, from the orientation of the p_x and p_y orbitals. This is reasonable for H_2S, for which the observed value is 92°, but is wide of the mark for H_2O with its measured 105° angle. One could give up the localized-bond approximation and go back to a full-molecule treatment of H_2O, but it is easier to introduce an idea that will be essential for carbon compounds: hybrid atomic orbitals.

sp^3 HYBRID ORBITALS

Most compounds of second- and third-row nonmetals involve tetrahedral or near-tetrahedral geometry around a central atom. We already have discussed methane, CH_4, which has ideal tetrahedral H—C—H angles of 109.5°; ammonia, NH_3, with H—N—H angles of 107°; and water with an H—O—H angle of 105°. Tetrahedral bonding geometry can be obtained by combining an *s* and three *p* atomic orbitals of the

One sp^3 hybrid atomic orbital (below)

Tetrahedral arrangement of four sp^3 hybrid atomic orbitals formed from the s, p_x, p_y, and p_z orbitals (right)

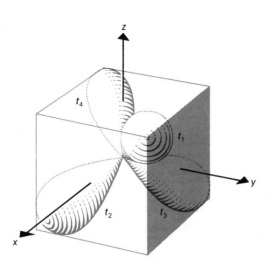

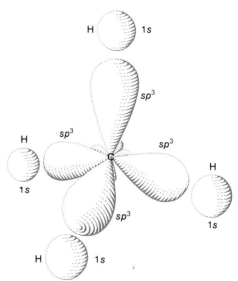

Carbon sp^3 and hydrogen $1s$ atomic orbitals prior to bonding

central atom before bringing in other atoms, to produce a set of four new orbitals called *hybrid atomic orbitals*, as at the right. These hybrid orbitals can be represented by t_1, t_2, t_3, and t_4, and can be written formally as

$$t_1 = s + p_x + p_y + p_z$$
$$t_2 = s + p_x - p_y - p_z$$
$$t_3 = s - p_x + p_y - p_z$$
$$t_4 = s - p_x - p_y + p_z$$

All four hybrid orbitals have an equal contribution from the spherical s orbital, but they point in different directions because they have different contributions from p_x, p_y, and p_z. The four hybrid orbitals extend out in the four directions of the vertices of a tetrahedron, or to four nonneighboring corners of a cube. The signs of the p terms in the set of four equations above are, in effect, the coordinates of each orbital. The t_3 orbital, for example, has its maximum electron probability in the x, $+y$, $-z$ direction, as can be seen in the drawing above.

These four tetrahedral hybrid atomic orbitals are less stable than the s and three p orbitals from which they came, because a small amount of energy is required to bring the s-orbital energy up to the energy of p before they can be hybridized. This energy is regained several times over when bonds are formed between these hybrid orbitals and orbitals from other atoms, so the mixing is possible. The four tetrahedral orbitals are called sp^3 *hybrid atomic orbitals*.

Bonding in methane is illustrated at the right. Each of the four sp^3 hybrid orbitals can combine with a hydrogen $1s$ atomic orbital to form a localized bonding and antibonding pair of MO's. The antibonding MO's are of no importance for methane because they are never occupied. But when one of the bonding orbitals is filled with a pair of electrons, a bond is formed between C and H. The sp^3 hybridization leads to the observed molecular geometry with bond angles of 109.5°. Formation of four such bonds uses all of the $1s$ orbitals of the four hy-

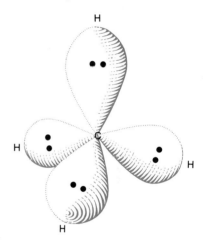

The four bonding MO's, each formed from a carbon sp^3 and a hydrogen $1s$, and each filled with one bonding electron pair. The four antibonding MO's are not shown, since they are unused.

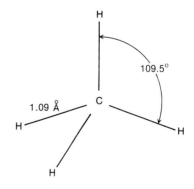

Tetrahedral geometry of the methane molecule

183

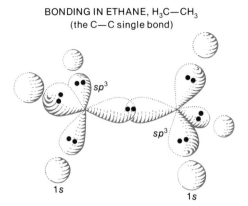

BONDING IN ETHANE, H₃C—CH₃
(the C—C single bond)

sp³

sp³

1s

1s

1s AO's from hydrogens, and *sp³* hybrid orbitals from carbons, arranged as they would be for combination into six C—H and one C—C electron-pair bonds. Electron pairs are shown in color.

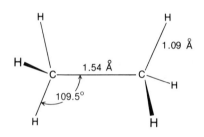

Tetrahedral geometry about carbon atoms in the ethane molecule

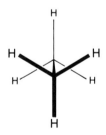

End view of the ethane molecule showing the most stable "staggered" arrangement of hydrogens on opposite carbons, which places them as far apart as possible

drogen atoms, and the s, p_x, p_y, and p_z orbitals from carbon. Filling the bonding orbitals requires all four H electrons and all four second-shell electrons from C. The $1s$ orbital of carbon and its electron pair are not involved in this bonding process.

The great simplification in this localized hybrid picture is that each C—H bond involves only one hybrid orbital from carbon, and what the other three sp^3 orbitals are doing is irrelevant. Bonds can be considered one at a time, and it is not necessary to throw all five atoms into one great mathematical pot. Consequently calculations of electron density and energy are greatly simplified.

The same sp^3 hybridization can be used for ethane, H₃C—CH₃, and for a great many other carbon compounds. In ethane, shown at the left, three of the four sp^3 hybrid atomic orbitals on each carbon are combined with atomic orbitals of hydrogen, as in methane, and the fourth is combined with one sp^3 from the other carbon atom. The sp^3 hybrid orbitals extend out farther from the nucleus than the $1s$ orbitals of hydrogen do, so a C—C bond is longer than a C—H bond: 1.54 Å versus 1.09 Å. Bond angles throughout the molecule still have tetrahedral values of 109.5°. The two ends of the molecule can rotate freely around the C—C bond, but the most stable arrangement of hydrogen atoms by a small amount of energy is that shown at the lower left. The hydrogen atoms are "staggered" so that the hydrogen atoms on one carbon atom are as far as possible from the hydrogens on the other carbon atom.

The sp^3 hybridization model also can be used for molecules involving N and O, with lone electron pairs filling some of the sp^3 orbitals. Thus an improved picture of water (below) employs two of the sp^3 orbitals in bonds with hydrogen, and the other two for the two lone electron pairs on O. This sp^3 model predicts a tetrahedral H—O—H bond angle of 109.5°. The smaller observed angle of 105° can be explained by the strong repulsion generated by the lone pairs, which are closer to the oxygen atom and to each other than are the bonding electron pairs.

sp^3 HYBRIDIZATION BONDING MODEL FOR WATER MOLECULE

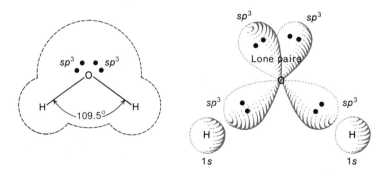

Two of the four sp^3 hybrid AO's are used in bonding to H, and the other two are filled by lone electron pairs. This model predicts that the H—O—H bond angle will be the tetrahedral 109.5°, close to the actual 105°. Lone-pair repulsions can explain the slight closing of the tetrahedral angle by 4.5°.

184

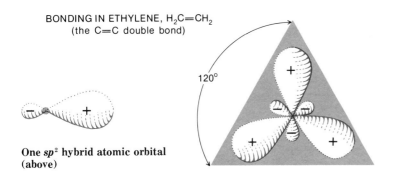

BONDING IN ETHYLENE, H_2C=CH_2
(the C=C double bond)

120°

One sp^2 hybrid atomic orbital
(above)

Trigonal arrangement of three sp^2 hybrid atomic orbitals, 120° apart in a plane. The remaining, unused p orbital, at right angles to the plane of the page, is not shown.

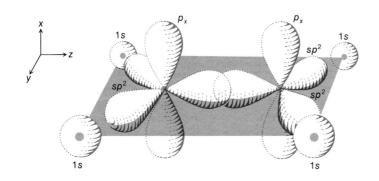

Atomic orbitals in ethylene, arranged as they would be for combination into four C—H single bonds, one C—C bond of σ symmetry, and one C—C bond of π symmetry. This bond model predicts a H—C—H bond angle of 120°, close to the actual 117°.

DOUBLE BONDS AND sp^2 HYBRIDIZATION

Ethylene, H_2C=CH_2, is typical of carbon compounds that have double bonds between atoms. The carbon–carbon bond length in ethylene is 1.34 Å, compared to 1.54 Å in ethane, and the bond energy, or energy required to pull the carbon atoms apart, is 147 kcal mole^{-1}, rather than 83 kcal mole^{-1} for ethane. Furthermore, the carbon–carbon double bond is rigid. No rotation is possible around the bond, and the two carbon atoms and four hydrogen atoms all are constrained to lie in one plane. The H—C—H bond angle at either end of the molecule is 117°. How can MO theory account for these characteristics of ethylene?

Ethylene has 12 outer-shell atomic orbitals involved in bonding: one s and three p orbitals from each carbon, and a $1s$ from each of the four hydrogens. It also has 12 outer-shell electrons to place in MO's: four each from the carbons and one each from the hydrogens. The $1s$ carbon orbitals are filled with electron pairs, do not overlap appreciably, and play no part in bonding. One solution to the bonding problem would be to begin with sp^3 hybrid orbitals around the carbons, and to assume that each carbon atom shares two such tetrahedral orbitals with the other, as shown at the lower right. This is unlikely, because of the severely bent bonds that would result between carbons. It is also wrong, because it predicts a H—C—H bond angle of 109.5° instead of the observed 117°.

Bond angles close to 120° suggest three equal orbitals in a plane. This geometry can be obtained by combining the s orbital and two of the three p orbitals of each carbon into a set of three sp^2 *hybrid atomic orbitals*, as shown at the top of the page. The third, unhybridized p

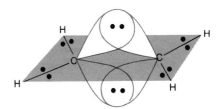

An attempted explanation of the double bond in ethylene using sp^3 orbitals of carbon. This model predicts a too-small 109.5° H—C—H bond angle.

185

THE π MO IN ETHYLENE

π_z^b orbitals

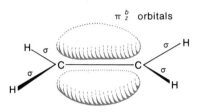

All σ bonds are represented by straight lines.

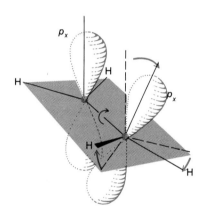

Twisting the ethylene molecules about its C—C axis does not affect the σ bond, but breaks the π bond. The double bond is reduced to a single bond, and the molecule no longer is planar.

orbital extends vertically above and below the plane of the page. In ethylene, two of the three sp^2 orbitals on each carbon are combined with hydrogen $1s$ orbitals, and the third is involved in the bond with the other carbon. These all are σ bonds because they are symmetrical about the individual bond axes. This σ framework of the ethylene molecule uses ten of the twelve available bonding electrons, and all of the outer-shell atomic orbitals except one unhybridized $2p_z$ orbital on each carbon.

The second half of the double bond in ethylene arises from a combination of these last two p orbitals into a π_z^b molecular orbital with lobes of density of opposite sign above and below the plane of the molecule. The double bond is shorter than a single bond because the p_z orbitals must come closer together before they overlap enough to bond. The π_z^b orbital also forces the molecule to be planar. Twisting about a bond axis is harmless to a symmetrical σ bond, but breaks a π bond by pulling the p orbitals out of alignment (see left). To twist one end of the ethylene molecule 90° relative to the other, one would have to supply energy equal to the difference between a C=C double bond and a single bond, or $147 - 83 = 64$ kcal mole^{-1}. The ideal H—C—H bond angle of 120° at each end of the ethylene molecule is decreased to 117° by electron-pair repulsion between the double bond and the two C—H single bonds.

Double bonds are of great importance in biological molecules, both because they help make proteins and other molecules rigid, and because of their unique ability to absorb light. We will come back to the structural rigidity aspects in the chapter on proteins, and to their light-absorbing properties in the postscript to this chapter.

TRIPLE BONDS AND *sp* HYBRIDIZATION

In a relatively small number of compounds, carbon is connected to another atom by a triple bond involving three electron pairs. This type of bond can be built from *sp hybrid orbitals* involving one s and one p orbital on each carbon atom, as shown at the bottom of the page. Two *sp* hybrid atomic orbitals extend out from an atom 180° apart, and the two remaining unhybridized p orbitals are at right angles to these and

BONDING IN ACETYLENE, HC≡CH (the C≡C triple bond)

One *sp* hybrid atomic orbital

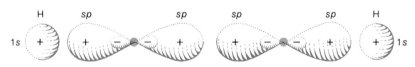

Atomic orbitals involved in σ molecular orbitals in acetylene. These form two C—H single bonds and one C—C single bond. The two unhybridized p atomic orbitals on each carbon atom are not shown.

186

to one another. In acetylene, H—C≡C—H, each of the two carbon atoms uses one *sp* hybrid orbital in a C—H bond and the other in the bond between carbons. Three electron pairs are employed in holding this σ-bonded framework together.

The remaining two thirds of the triple bond involves the *p* orbitals. If the C—C bond direction is chosen as the *z* axis, then the two p_x orbitals on carbon combine into one π^b MO, and the two p_y orbitals combine into another. This means that the carbon atoms are held together by three electron pairs, one in a σ bond and two in π bonds. The π_x^b and π_y^b MO's taken together form a symmetrical barrel of electron density around the carbon–carbon bond.

The acetylene molecule is linear, with all four atoms in a straight line. The C—H bond lengths are little different from those of other molecules, but the three electron pairs in the triple bond pull the carbon atoms together until they are only 1.21 Å apart, compared with 1.34 Å for a double bond and 1.54 Å for a single bond. If a nitrogen atom replaces one carbon, a triple bond is still possible, but then the C—H with an electron pair bond is replaced by N:, with its lone electron pair, and the result is HCN (hydrogen cyanide), which is shown at the right. If the other carbon atom also is replaced by N, the result is the triply bonded N_2 molecule.

This is the end of the road for bonds between most atoms. Quadruple bonds involving *s* and *p* orbitals are geometrically impossible. An absolute requirement for bonding is that the AO's from the two atoms overlap, and as the bond order increases from single to double to triple, the atoms have to be pushed closer together to achieve this overlap. No matter how the *s* and three *p* orbitals are hybridized, the only way to make all four orbitals overlap with the corresponding four from another atom is to push the atoms together until their nuclear centers coincide—an impossible thing to do. Hence, quadruply bonded C_2 gas molecules, sharing all four bonding electrons on one C with a single partner, are not found. This is one reason for the observed dramatic difference in properties of the pure elements, between solid diamond and N_2, O_2, and F_2 gases. The C_2 molecule can exist, but only with incomplete electron-sharing. This makes C_2 very reactive and stable only at high temperatures.

BOND LENGTHS AND BOND ANGLES

Single bond in ethane

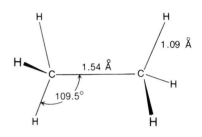

Double bond in ethylene

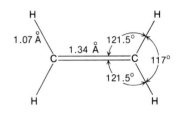

Triple bond in acetylene

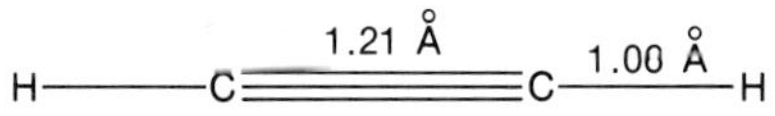

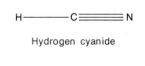

Hydrogen cyanide

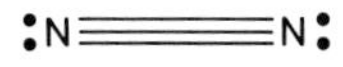

Nitrogen

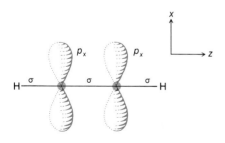

Two p_x atomic orbitals, which combine in acetylene to form a second C—C bond, a π_x bond. The two p_y orbitals perpendicular to the page combine to form the third bond, π_y.

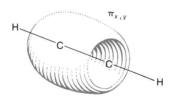

The two π_x and π_y MO's in acetylene add to produce a cylindrically symmetrical electron distribution around the bond axis.

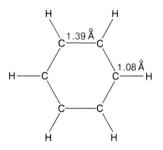

Hexagonal molecular framework and bond lengths in benzene, C_6H_6

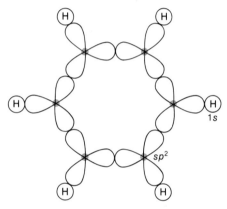

Carbon sp^2 and hydrogen 1s atomic orbitals that are involved in σ bonding in benzene

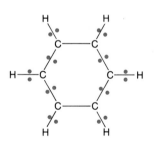

The electron pairs used in σ bonding in benzene

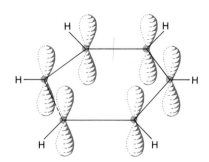

Six more electrons, and six carbon p orbitals perpendicular to the plane of the benzene ring (left), are not used in the σ-bonding skeleton of benzene. These electrons would be sufficient for three more localized carbon–carbon bonds.

AROMATICITY: DELOCALIZATION AND RESONANCE

What we have just gone through has been the outline of a very successful theory of molecular structure and bonding. What has not been covered is the quantitative calculation of shapes and energies of molecular orbitals that makes MO theory even more attractive. We began by abandoning the concept of a "bond" and looking at the entire molecule at once. It is perhaps fortunate for our computational sanity that such a procedure usually is excessive with larger molecules, and that the approximation of localized molecular orbitals and two-atom bonds can be used instead. Adding the concepts of hybridization and single, double, and triple bonds provides the framework of a theory that can explain most molecules.

One important class of molecules that cannot be explained in terms of two-atom bonds is the organic *aromatic* molecules, mentioned briefly in Chapter 4. Benzene, C_6H_6, is the most familiar example. It has six carbon atoms in a regular hexagonal ring, with all carbon–carbon bonds 1.39 Å long, which is intermediate between single and double bond lengths. Each carbon has one C—H bond of normal length. The skeleton of benzene is shown top left.

As soon as we try to make a localized MO model of benzene, we run into trouble. The planar hexagonal geometry of the molecule, with 120° bond angles, suggests sp^2 hybridization around the carbons, with one sp^2 orbital from each C pointed toward an H, and the other two directed toward the neighboring carbon atoms in the ring. This skeleton of σ bonds uses 24 of the 30 bonding electrons (6×4 from carbons plus 6×1 from hydrogens), and all of the outer orbitals except the six p orbitals perpendicular to the plane of the hexagon. This σ framework is drawn at center left.

What should be done with the six unused electrons and six remaining p orbitals? These are shown in perspective at the bottom left. Adjacent p orbitals could be combined in pairs around the ring to make every other carbon–carbon bond a double bond. There are two ways of doing this, represented schematically below. These are known as the Kekulé structures after the man who first proposed them, but they cannot be correct because we know that all of the carbon–carbon bonds are the same length. A somewhat less plausible way of pairing the p orbitals would be to connect two across the ring, and then pair the remaining two at either side, as in the three Dewar structures shown below the Kekulé rings.

Possible π double-bonded structures in Benzene

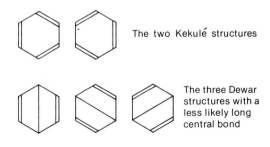

The two Kekulé structures

The three Dewar structures with a less likely long central bond

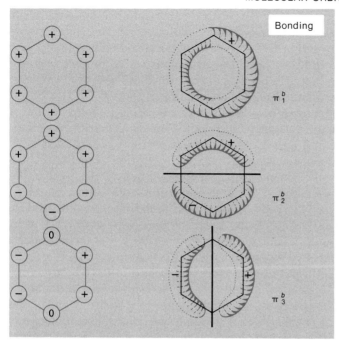

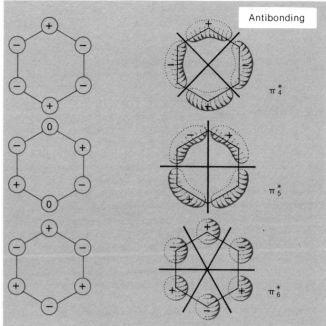

All five of these Kekulé and Dewar structures, considered individually, are wrong. There is no way to write the correct benzene structure as a set of single and double bonds, so the localized bond approximation, which has proven so useful for methane and other multi-atom molecules, breaks down. We must retreat a little way from localized bonds toward the whole-molecule approach again, at least where p electrons are concerned.

We can combine the six p orbitals around the benzene ring according to the rules of MO theory, and produce the six full-ring MO's sketched above. In the lowest-energy orbital, π_1^b, all six p AO's are combined with the same sign to produce two rings of electron density above and below the plane of the benzene skeleton. There is zero electron probability in this plane because the original p orbitals had zero probability there. Like the two lobes of density in the p orbitals from which they came, the two "doughnuts" of probability in the π_1^b MO have opposite wave-function signs.

The next most stable MO's, π_2^b and π_3^b, have the same energy and the same shape, with one horizontal or vertical plane of zero probability perpendicular to the benzene ring. Two antibonding orbitals with the same energy, π_4^* and π_5^*, each have two such zero-probability nodes at right angles, and the least stable antibonding orbital, π_6^*, has three such nodes.

The energy-level diagram for these six MO's appears at the right. As we have seen consistently in other AO's and MO's, the general principle holds that, other things being equal, the more nodes of zero probability in an orbital, the higher its energy. Six p atomic orbitals are combined to form six molecular orbitals—three bonding and three antibonding. The six electrons not used in the σ framework of the benzene

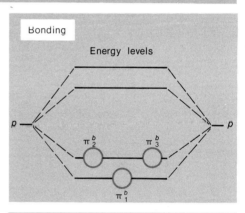

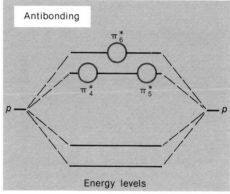

The six carbon p orbitals are combined to form three bonding MO's and three antibonding MO's. The six electrons remaining are used to fill the three bonding orbitals to form three more electron-pair bonds.

189

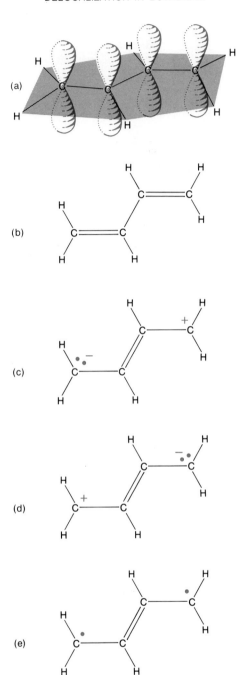

(a) σ-Bonding skeleton and the four unused *p* orbitals in butadiene; four electrons also remain unused in σ bonding. (b)–(e) Four resonance bond models for butadiene. (b) Two electrons in each of two π bonds, thus forming two double bonds. (c) and (d) Central double bond, lone pair at one end, and electron deficiency at the other. (e) Central double bond, and unpaired electron on each end carbon atom.

molecule are used to fill the three bonding MO's, and the antibonding orbitals are unused. The benzene ring therefore has three more bonds in addition to its σ-bonded skeleton, but these three bonds are spread around the entire ring rather than being localized between pairs of carbon atoms, as the Kekulé or Dewar models would predict. All of the carbon–carbon bonds in the ring are intermediate between "single" and "double," and their observed bond length verifies this.

There is another way of looking at bonding in benzene that preserves the language of single and double bonds. This is to say that all of the Kekulé and Dewar structures are partially correct, but that no one of them alone is a sufficiently good description of reality. The real benzene molecule in some way is a combination of all of them, like a mule is a combination of a horse and a donkey. Unfortunately, the term "resonance" has become associated with this viewpoint, and these partially correct structures are called *resonance structures*. This term gives the quite erroneous idea of a flipping back and forth among the several structures. The benzene molecule contains features of all five resonance structures, but it no more flips back and forth between them, than a mule "resonates" before your eyes from horse to donkey and back again. Nevertheless, the term resonance is so firmly embedded in the language of chemistry that we shall use it too. The 40 kcal mole^{-1} of extra stability of the molecules over that of a Kekulé structure is called the *resonance energy* of the benzene molecules.

Resonance structures provide a handy way of deciding how far delocalization extends in a molecule. A set of resonance structures for a molecule must have the atomic nuclei in the same places, and can differ only in the placement of electrons and hence of bonds and charges. When all possible resonance structures have been written for a molecule that cannot be described adequately by simple single and double bonds, then all atoms that are connected by double bonds in at least one of the resonance structures are involved in the delocalized electron system. For benzene these are the six carbon atoms, and the hydrogens play no part in delocalization. Delocalization in carbon compounds almost always involves the combination of a set of *p* orbitals perpendicular to the plane of a molecular skeleton connected by σ bonds.

The double bonds do not have to be alternating around a closed ring for delocalization to occur. In the butadiene molecule shown at the left, four carbon atoms are connected in a linear chain with two double bonds. Structure (b) is the one usually thought of for butadiene, but it cannot be completely right because all ten atoms in the real molecule lie in a plane, and this would not necessarily be true if the central carbon–carbon bond were a single bond.

After making the skeleton of σ bonds using sp^2 hybridization around carbons, four electrons and four *p* orbitals in butadiene remain unused, and the *p* orbitals are arranged as in the perspective drawing (a) at the upper left. As in benzene, these *p* orbitals can be combined in several ways to produce various resonance structures for the molecule. Four resonance structures are shown in drawings (b)–(e) at left. All four carbon atoms are linked in a delocalized electron system. Compounds with alternating single and double bonds, in which *p*-electron delocalization can occur, are called *conjugated* molecules. Whether linear or in closed rings, conjugated molecules somewhat larger than butadiene or benzene have the useful property of absorbing visible light, as we shall see in the postscript. Linear conjugated molecules are used in the photoreceptors of the eye, and both linear and aromatic conjugated molecules are put to work in trapping light in photosynthesis.

Delocalization has appeared several times in previous chapters, but only now can we give it an interpretation in terms of molecular orbitals. The benzene molecule was introduced in Chapter 4, and the carbonate and nitrate ions in Chapter 5. The various Lewis dot models for CO_3^{2-}, which assigned single- or double-bond character to different combinations of the three C—O bonds, were resonance structures for the carbonate ion, differing only in the positioning of electrons between atoms. The phosphate, sulfate, and perchlorate ions discussed in Chapter 6 also were examples of delocalization. In all of these examples, delocalization brought extra stability to the ion, and it is a good practical rule of thumb that the more resonance structures one can draw for a delocalized ion or molecule, the more stability this delocalization creates.

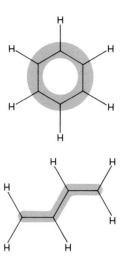

Comparison of the extent of delocalization in benzene (top) and butadiene (bottom). None of the resonance structures for butadiene shown on the opposite page is correct; the four electrons not used in σ bonding are delocalized over the entire four-carbon skeleton.

MOLECULAR ORBITAL PICTURE OF BONDS: A SUMMARY

In MO theory a bond is formed when atomic orbitals of similar energy and symmetry combine to form at least one molecular orbital of lower energy than that of the isolated AO's, and when that bonding MO then is filled by a pair of electrons. In principle, all bonds extend over the entire molecule, but in practice it is usually possible to consider only two atoms at a time, and to think of the bond between them as being independent of all other bonds in the molecule. This localized-bond picture sometimes fails us, especially when p orbitals are involved in delocalization along chains or rings of carbon atoms. When this occurs, the molecular skeleton can be treated as a set of σ bonds, and the p orbitals can be treated separately.

The filled inner shells in atoms can be ignored in bonding, and only the outer orbitals and outer-shell electrons need be considered. In localized, two-atom bonds, the s and three p atomic orbitals usually are not the best starting points in bonding. All four orbitals can be hybridized, before they are combined with orbitals from other atoms, to produce a set of four identical sp^3 hybrid orbitals pointing in tetrahedral directions. Alternatively, the s and two of the p orbitals can be hybridized into three sp^2 orbitals 120° apart in a plane; or the s and one p can be combined into two sp orbitals pointing in opposite directions from the atom. The best hybridization to use depends on the actual geometry of the molecule, and on the presence of double or triple bonds.

Bonding orbitals in MO theory always concentrate an excess of electron density between the atoms being bonded, and in this regard the MO theory is no different from the old qualitative electron-pair ideas of a bond. But only MO theory recognizes that electron pairs can tear a molecule apart as well, if they are placed in antibonding orbitals. The essential factor in determining bonding is the net *excess* of bonding electrons over antibonding electrons. If these bonding and antibonding electrons counterbalance one another, then the molecule will not form, as we saw for He_2, Be_2, and Ne_2.

Nothing in MO theory contradicts the simpler electron-pair theory, or we would have grave doubts about its validity. But even more, MO theory explains molecular properties about which the simpler theory has nothing to say—for example, the magnetic behavior of the O_2 molecule with its two unpaired electrons, and the planarity of molecules with double bonds. This chapter has been a pictorial and qualitative introduction to molecular orbital theory, but the theory also has a mathematical and quantitative side that permits the calculation of energy levels and of ionization energies, spectra, and reactivities of molecules.

POSTSCRIPT: DELOCALIZATION AND COLOR

Aromatic compounds are carbon-framework molecules in which the carbon skeleton is held together in flat rings by σ bonds, and the carbon p orbitals perpendicular to the rings are involved in extensive delocalized electron systems. Benzene is the simplest such molecule, but many rings can be fused together in larger molecules. Naphthalene, $C_{10}H_8$, has two fused rings; anthracene, $C_{14}H_{10}$, has three, and many larger molecules exist (see below). Replacing the peripheral hydrogens by other chemical groups gives rise to a rich and varied branch of organic chemistry, which includes many biologically important molecules, flavorings, dyestuffs, light receptors, and carcinogenic (cancer-producing) agents.

DELOCALIZATION AND COLOR

Molecule	Delocalized system	Absorption region	Color absorbed	Color seen
Benzene	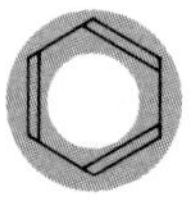	2550 Å	UV	——
Naphthalene	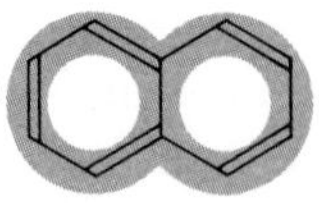	3150 Å	UV	——
Anthracene	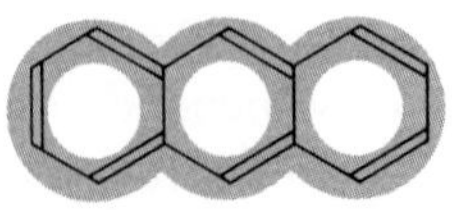	3800 Å	UV	——
Naphthacene	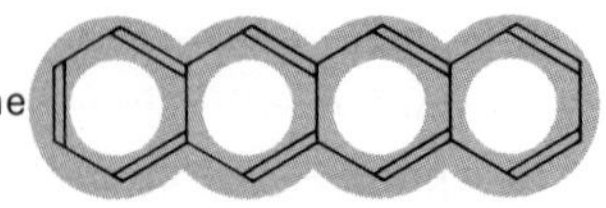	4800 Å	Blue	Orange
Pentacene	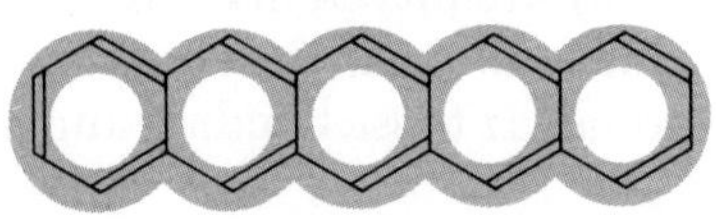	5800 Å	Yellow	Indigo

The larger the extent of delocalization, the smaller the spacing between energy levels, and the longer the wavelength of radiation absorbed by the molecule. The color seen is that which is left behind after some radiation is absorbed by the molecule.

192

A common property of aromatic molecules is their ability to absorb electromagnetic radiation in the near ultraviolet or even in the visible range, thereby making the molecules brightly colored. The effect of combining p orbitals in benzene into a set of delocalized MO's is to split the energy of the individual p orbitals into four closely spaced energy levels, which were diagramed previously. In benzene, the three bonding orbitals are filled and the antibonding orbitals are empty. If the right frequency of radiation is supplied, a benzene molecule can absorb it and promote one or more electrons from bonding to antibonding orbitals. The gap between levels is a measure of the energy needed to make the transition from the ground state (lowest energy) to an excited electronic state. An excited molecule can emit this energy later as a photon of radiation, and drop back to the ground state.

Nonaromatic molecules also can be electronically excited, but larger amounts of energy are required, and this means that absorption and emission take place farther into the ultraviolet. If enough energy is supplied, the σ single bonds can be broken and the molecules destroyed. The special property of aromatic molecules is that their π-orbital energy levels are closely spaced, which leads to absorption in the lower-energy, longer-wavelength region.

Delocalization leads to a lowering of energy levels and narrowing of the spacings between levels; and the larger the delocalized system, the greater this effect. This can be seen in the series of aromatic molecules compared at the bottom of the opposite page. Benzene has six atoms in its delocalized π-electron system, and the spacings between the π-orbital energy levels are such that it absorbs energy at a set of wavelengths in the ultraviolet region, centered around 2550 Å. The visible wavelengths pass through the molecule untouched, so benzene is colorless to our eyes. So are naphthalene and anthracene, which have 10 and 14 atoms in the delocalized system, although the larger rings shift the absorption to longer wavelengths or lower energies: 3150 Å and 3800 Å. In contrast, delocalization in naphthacene is so extensive that the splitting between π energy levels has narrowed to the point where blue light around 4800 Å is absorbed. With the blue light absorbed, the remaining visible wavelengths make naphthacene appear orange, the complement of blue. In pentacene, which has five rings, absorption is shifted down to even lower energies. Pentacene removes yellow light around 5800 Å and therefore appears indigo.

This "eyeball spectroscopy" is surprisingly informative in revealing what aromatic molecules are doing. The visible spectrum is shown at the right, with colors recorded as a function of wavelength from the ultraviolet to the infrared. If any of these wavelengths is absorbed by a molecule, the remaining wavelengths give the molecule the complementary color. Removal of green wavelengths around 5300 Å makes a molecule appear purple. If the molecule absorbs red light at around 6800 Å, we will see it as blue-green. By looking at what is left of the visible spectrum after absorption, we can decide approximately what visible wavelengths the compound is absorbing.

Any attached side group on the ring that increases the number of atoms in the delocalized system will shift the electronic absorption toward lower energy and longer wavelengths. Early industrial dyestuff chemists knew by experience that some chemical groups such as —OH

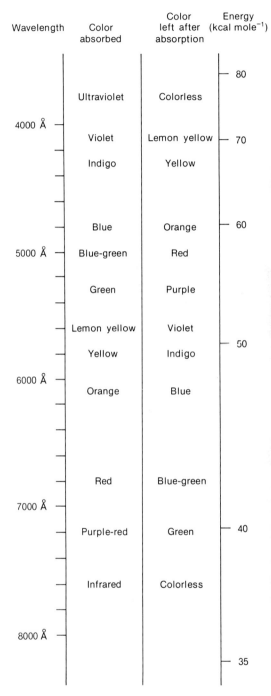

Wavelength	Color absorbed	Color left after absorption	Energy (kcal mole⁻¹)
	Ultraviolet	Colorless	80
4000 Å	Violet	Lemon yellow	70
	Indigo	Yellow	
	Blue	Orange	60
5000 Å	Blue-green	Red	
	Green	Purple	
	Lemon yellow	Violet	50
	Yellow	Indigo	
6000 Å	Orange	Blue	
	Red	Blue-green	
7000 Å	Purple-red	Green	40
	Infrared	Colorless	
8000 Å			35

As the spacing between electronic energy levels decreases, the radiation absorbed moves from the ultraviolet, through violet, blue, green, orange, red, and ultimately into the invisible infrared. The colors that we observe are the complement of the colors absorbed. The energy of a mole of photons or radiation is given at the right for visible wavelengths. (See Problems 4–9 in Chapter 7.)

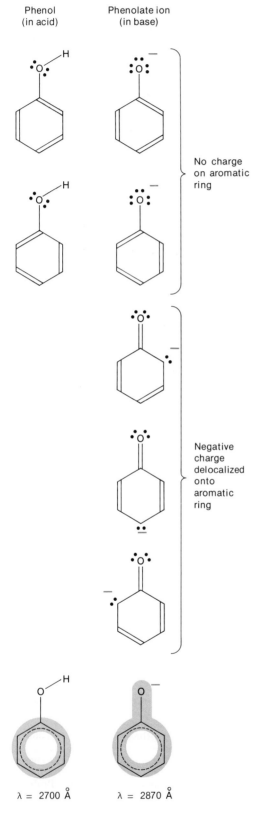

Phenol
(in acid)

Phenolate ion
(in base)

No charge
on aromatic
ring

Negative
charge
delocalized
onto
aromatic
ring

$\lambda = 2700$ Å

$\lambda = 2870$ Å

and —NH_2 would shift the colors of aromatic molecules down the series yellow–orange–red–purple–blue–green, the complement of the absorbed visible spectrum, violet–blue–green–yellow–orange–red, before they understood the relationship among color, frequency, and energy. Adding an —OH group to benzene to produce phenol, C_6H_5OH, shifts the center of the absorption band slightly, from 2550 Å to 2700 Å, since the oxygen in the —OH group is rich in electrons. Phenol is an acid, and can dissociate and lose the proton of the —OH to form the phenolate ion:

$$C_6H_5\!\!-\!\!OH \rightarrow C_6H_5\!\!-\!\!O^- + H^+$$
phenol   phenolate ion

In the phenolate ion the oxygen actually becomes part of the delocalized system and enlarges it from six atoms to seven. You can see this by comparing the various resonance structures for phenol and the phenolate ion at the left. Only benzenelike resonance structures are possible for phenol, since the —OH group really is not included in the delocalized system. The phenolate ion has resonance structures in which the oxygen has three lone pairs and a negative charge, and is attached to the ring by a single bond. But other resonance structures can be drawn in which one of the three lone pairs is shifted into a C=O double bond, and the negative charge shows up at different positions on the ring. These resonance structures tell us that in the ion the oxygen is part of the general seven-atom delocalized system. With greater delocalization, the spacings between π-orbital energy levels are decreased, and the electronic absorption band shifts from 2700 Å to 2870 Å. We cannot see this change because our eyes are insensitive to the ultraviolet, but if all the wavelengths were doubled, benzene would be red, phenol would be purple, and the phenolate ion would be blue-violet. Phenol then would be an *acid–base indicator*, revealing the acidity of its environment by its color. If added in small amounts to a solution, it would appear purple in acid, where its own dissociation was repressed by a plentiful H^+ supply, and blue-violet in base, where most of it had dissociated to the phenolate ion.

Phenol is not a usable acid–base indicator because it absorbs in the wrong part of the spectrum, but the same principles explain why slightly larger aromatic molecules make good indicators. Alizarin, shown at the top of the next page, is a derivative of anthracene. The two double-bonded oxygens on the center ring enlarge the delocalized system from 14 atoms to 16, and shift the center of absorption from 3800 Å in the ultraviolet to 4300 Å in the indigo part of the visible spectrum. The unabsorbed wavelengths make alizarin yellow.

The two —OH groups on the outer ring do not participate in the delocalized system until they dissociate, as they do in basic solutions in which H^+ ions are scarce. When this happens, the two hydroxyl oxygens become just as much a part of the delocalization as the original double-bonded oxygens. You can see this by drawing other resonance structures that give the hydroxyl oxygens the double bonds. This enlargement shifts the main absorption to around 4800 Å in the blue re-

Delocalization of phenol in acid (gray tint) and phenolate ion in base (color tint)

ALIZARIN, AN ACID-BASE INDICATOR

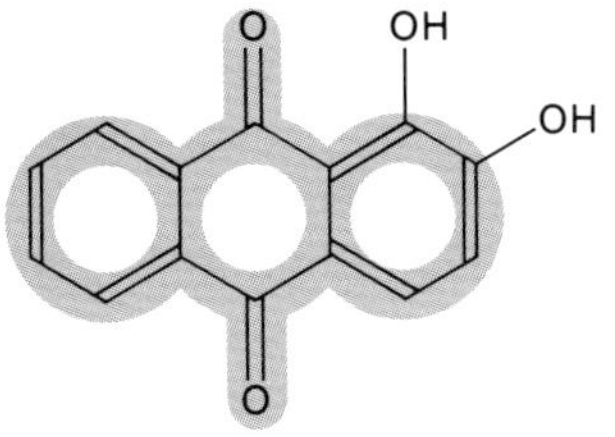

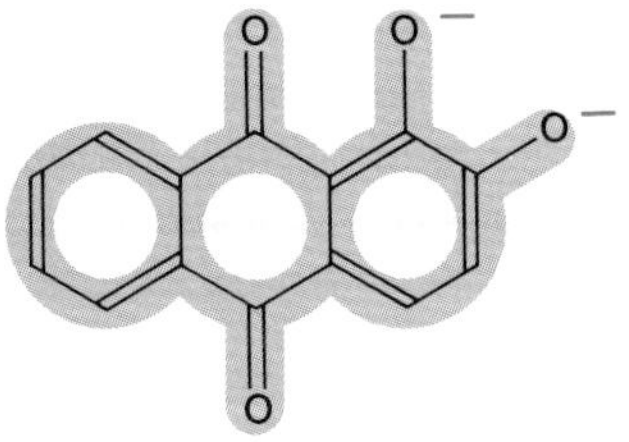

	Absorption region	Color absorbed	Color seen
Alizarin (in acid)	4300 Å	Indigo	Yellow
Alizarin ion (in base)	4800 Å	Blue	Orange

Alizarin and its ion behave like phenol and its ion, in that the more extended delocalization in the ion causes a shift in absorption to longer wavelengths. Unlike phenol, absorption in alizarin occurs in the visible region of the spectrum, so alizarin is a useful acid–base indicator, changing color with ionization state.

gion, and makes the solution of ions orange. Alizarin is one of the standard acid–base indicators, turning yellow in acid and orange in base. Phenolphthalein, which is colorless in acid and deep red in base, and methyl violet, which is yellow in acid and violet in base, are other examples of aromatic acid–base indicators.

Linear conjugated molecules with alternating single and double bonds also will absorb light if they are long enough. Carotenoids, which are "super butadienes" with 22 carbon atoms connected by alternating single and double bonds, are used as antennae by green plants to trap light and transfer the energy to chlorophyll for use in chemical syntheses. They are bright yellow-orange because they have evolved over the past 3.5 billion years to absorb light in the 5000-Å wavelength region (blue-green), which is the most intense part of solar radiation.

Living organisms use aromatic and straight-chain conjugated molecules to trap light energy, to transfer this energy from one molecule to another, and to recognize the presence of light so they can grow toward it, turn toward it, or use it for information gathering through vision. The radiation that reaches the surface of our planet covers a relatively narrow range. Ozone, O_3, in the upper layers of the atmosphere absorbs almost all wavelengths shorter than 2900 Å, and water vapor absorbs much of the infrared. Little infrared radiation longer than 13,000 Å remains by the time light reaches the surface of the Earth, and only five meters below the surface of the ocean all radiation longer than 8000 Å has been absorbed. The most intense radiation from the sun occurs in the blue-green region, around 5000 Å, the region for which the carotenes have evolved to absorb light.

The loss of the infrared is of no consequence, because these wavelengths contain so little energy per photon that they are not very good as energy sources. The spectrum on Page 193 shows that 8000-Å infrared radiation carries only 35 kcal of energy per mole of photons. At the short wavelength end of the solar spectrum, it is fortunate for us that everything shorter than 2900 Å is cut off by the ozone layer, because these "hard ultraviolet" photons are energetic enough to break the C—C and C—N single bonds that hold proteins and other biological macromolecules together. The energy of a C—C single bond, 83 kcal mole^{-1}, corresponds to a wavelength of 3500 Å. These and shorter wavelengths are potentially lethal, which is why ultraviolet lamps can be used to kill bacteria and other microorganisms.

Life evolved in the oceans, bathed in a "window" of electromagnetic radiation from about 2900 Å to 8000 Å, with maximum abundance around 5000 Å. It is no accident that living creatures developed means of using this radiation as an energy source, and as a means of sensing the environment through vision. The molecules that absorb energy in this wavelength range are the aromatic and linear conjugated molecules with delocalized double bonds. We will see in subsequent chapters how the chlorophylls and carotenoids in photosynthesis, and retinal in vision, all use the light-absorbing properties of delocalized π molecular orbitals.

QUESTIONS

1. When atomic orbitals are combined into molecular orbitals, how does the number of MO's obtained compare with the original number of AO's?

2. For a multiatom molecule, what approximation are we using when we combine atomic orbitals from atoms two at a time in forming bonds between pairs of atoms? Why is this approximation useful? Give an example of a molecule for which this approximation is valid, and another for which it breaks down.

3. What is the distinction between bonding and antibonding MO's? How is it that molecules such as N_2 and F_2 can have antibonding orbitals that are lower in energy than some bonding orbitals?

4. How many electrons can each MO hold? What is the relationship between the spins of electrons occupying the same MO? How does this compare with the occupancy of AO's by electrons in isolated atoms?

5. In the hydrogenlike diatomic molecules H_2^+, H_2, He_2^+, and He_2, why do the first two electrons increase the strength of the bond, and the third and fourth electrons weaken the bond? What is the bond order in each of the above molecules or molecule-ions?

6. Compare the theoretical predictions in Question 5 with the observed bond lengths and bond energies. Does the bond length increase, or decrease, with increasing bond order? Why?

7. How do filled bonding MO's tend to hold the two bonded atomic nuclei together? How do filled antibonding MO's tend to pull them apart? Explain in terms of electron probability distributions.

8. What are the requirements in terms of location, energy, and symmetry of two atomic orbitals if they are to be combined into molecular orbitals?

9. What is meant by σ and π symmetry in molecular orbitals? How is this nomenclature an obvious extension of the s and p notation for atomic orbitals? Explain in terms of 180° rotations and the signs of the wave functions.

10. How is the bond energy of an electron-pair bond related to the relative energies of the bonding and antibonding MO's and the AO's from which they were derived? Explain with a diagram. If the energy difference between the AO's and the bonding MO in H_2 is x kcal mole^{-1}, what is the bond energy of H_2?

11. What is the relative order of increasing energies for the six MO's derived from the six outer p AO's on two atoms in a diatomic molecule? How does this energy sequence account for the observed bond orders in the diatomic molecules obtained from second-row elements?

12. For which of the second-row elements do diatomic molecules not exist? Why, in terms of MO theory? For which of these elements do diatomic molecules occur only at high temperatures? What is their state at 298°K, and why? For which of these elements is the diatomic molecule the stable form at room temperature?

13. Which of the diatomic molecules of the second-row elements have unpaired electrons? How many unpaired electrons do they have? Why are these electrons not paired in the same orbital? How does the Lewis electron-dot model account for these unpaired electrons?

14. How do the observed bond lengths and bond energies of the second-row diatomic molecules correlate with the predicted bond order?

15. When AO's of different kinds of atoms are being combined to build an MO, what important energy criterion helps to decide which AO's on the two atoms will interact? What symmetry considerations are important? Illustrate with the HF molecule.

16. Draw the Lewis electron-dot model for the HF molecule. The F atom should be represented as having one bond to H, and three lone electron pairs. In MO theory, what orbitals do these three electron pairs occupy? Which fluorine AO is involved in the H—F bond?

17. To which MO does the fluorine $2p$ AO make the greatest contribution, the bonding MO or the antibonding? What does this imply in terms of the location of the bonding electron pair and the polarity of the bond? How is this related to the relative electronegativities of H and F?

18. How are the energy levels of the hydrogen $1s$ and fluorine $2p$ atomic orbitals related to the first ionization energies of H and F? (The correlation is approximate, but useful.)

19. In the limit of completely ionic bonding between two atoms of very high and very low electronegativities, how would the bonding MO compare with the AO's of the two atoms? What would this imply about the location of the bonding electron pair? Illustrate with NaCl.

20. Sketch the use of AO's in bonding in the water molecule, assuming that unhybridized s and three p orbitals of oxygen are used. What prediction does this model make about the H—O—H bond angle?

21. Sketch the use of AO's in bonding in the water molecule, assuming that hybrid sp^3 AO's are the starting point for the oxygen atom. What does this predict about the H—O—H bond angle? What is the observed bond angle, and what does this tell us about the relative merits of the bond models of this question and the preceding one?

22. What physical explanation can be given for the decrease of the H—O—H bond angle in water from its ideal tetrahedral value? How does this compare with the VSEPR explanation?

23. When an sp^3 hybrid AO on carbon interacts with a hydrogen $1s$ orbital, what is the symmetry of the resulting MO's? Why are the antibonding MO's from such combinations ordinarily ignored?

24. There is essentially free rotation about the carbon–carbon bond in ethane, although the "staggered" conformation, with hydrogens on one carbon rotated 60° away from those on the other carbon, is 3 kcal mole^{-1} more stable than the "eclipsed" conformation, in which the hydrogens on opposite carbon atoms overlap in a view down the carbon–carbon bond axis. Why should this energy difference, small as it is, exist?

25. Sketch the bonding in ethylene, assuming sp^3 hybridization around the carbon atoms. In what sense would the bonding between carbons be a double bond? What would this model predict for the H—C—H bond angle at each end of the molecule?

26. Sketch the bonding in ethylene, assuming sp^2 hybridization around the carbon atoms. Where does the double bond come from in this model? What would the prediction now be for the H—C—H bond angle? What is the observed value, and which hybridization model does it favor? How can you account for the small discrepancy that still exists between the best model and the experimental angle?

27. Use the sp^3 model and then the sp^2 model to predict what would happen to the double bond when the two ends of the ethylene molecule are twisted? How does the real molecule behave, and which model is most compatible with reality?

28. Sketch the σ-bond skeleton of the ethylene molecule. Draw in the π MO of the second bond. What is the electron probability density at each of the six atoms in ethylene from the electrons in this π MO? Draw the nodal surface for this orbital.

29. Sketch the σ-bond skeleton of the acetylene molecule. Draw in the π MO's of the second and third bonds between carbon.

30. How does the carbon–carbon bond length change between ethane, ethylene, and acetylene? How would you expect the bond energies to change?

31. Sketch the σ-bond skeleton of the benzene molecule. How many AO's and how many bonding electrons are used in this σ skeleton? What kind of hybridization is used around the carbon atoms?

32. How many bonding electrons, and how many and what kind of AO's, remain unused in benzene after the σ-bond skeleton is built? How are these electrons and AO's used for further bonding in benzene? How does this resemble the situation in ethylene and acetylene, and in what important way is it different?

33. How would the electrons and AO's not involved in the σ-bond skeleton be used in the Kekulé bond model for benzene? In a perspective view of the hexagonal C_6 ring, sketch the bonding π MO's.

34. Repeat the preceding question for one of the Dewar models of benzene.

35. In a similar perspective view of the benzene ring, sketch the actual π_1^b MO, showing the rings of electron probability above and below the C_6 benzene-ring plane.

36. For all of the π MO's in benzene, what is the electron probability density at the carbon and hydrogen atoms? How does this compare with the density at the C and H atoms for the π MO in ethylene? (See Question 28.)

37. In what sense does bonding in the benzene molecule represent a step backward from two-atom bonds to full-molecule orbitals? What is this called? What effect on the energy levels of a molecule accompanies such behavior? Give examples of inorganic oxygen-containing compounds that show the same behavior.

38. In what sense is it possible to think of the actual bonding in benzene as being a "mixture" of Kekulé and Dewar structures? What are these structures called? Is any actual alternation back and forth between structures implied?

39. In what ways can different resonance structures differ from one another, and in what ways must they be alike? How is the number of different resonance structures that can be drawn for a given molecule correlated approximately with the energy of the molecule?

40. Sketch the σ-bond skeleton of the butadiene molecule. How many electrons and AO's are used in this framework? What kind of hybridization is used around the carbon atoms?

41. How many bonding electrons, and how many and what kind of AO's, remain unused in butadiene after the σ-bond skeleton is built? How are these electrons and AO's used for further bonding in butadiene? Over which atoms in the molecule does delocalization extend?

42. Draw several resonance structures for butadiene. Show how each structure assigns the four electrons not involved in σ bonding among the four carbon atoms.

43. How do the energy levels in aromatic molecules change with an increase in the extent of delocalization, and how is this reflected in the energy wavelengths of absorption or radiation?

44. How is the color that we see in a chemical compound related to the energy that it absorbs? If a molecule absorbs wavelengths in the blue region, why does it appear orange to our eyes instead of blue?

45. Why does absorption shift to longer wavelengths when the phenol molecule dissociates to the phenolate ion? What prevents phenol from being a useful acid–base indicator?

46. Why is alizarin a good acid–base indicator, whereas phenol is not?

47. Why is the ability to absorb visible light useful to living organisms? In what way or ways is this ability especially useful to plants, and in what different way is it useful to animals?

48. One objection to the supersonic transport (SST) is that waste oxides of nitrogen emitted at high altitudes by the SST would combine with, and slowly destroy, the high-altitude ozone layer around the planet. Recent calculations have shown that a thermonuclear war would practically eliminate the ozone layer. Why would the destruction of the ozone layer be dangerous to life (in addition to the immediate hazards of the atomic war)?

49. What is the approximate wavelength range of the radiation that reaches the surface of the Earth at the present time? What absorbs the longer and shorter wavelengths and prevents them from reaching the surface?

PROBLEMS

1. Where such combination is possible, sketch the initial arrangement of AO's and final bonding and antibonding MO's for the combination of the following AO's into MO's:
   (a) two s AO's into two σ MO's
   (b) two p AO's into two π MO's
   (c) two s AO's into two π MO's
   (d) two p AO's into two σ MO's
   (e) an s and a p AO into two σ MO's
   (f) an s and a p AO into two π MO's
   For the impossible combinations, explain why they are impossible.

2. Add the nodes, or surfaces of zero electron probability, to the sketches of Problem 1. What relationship is there between the number of nodes in the bonding and antibonding orbitals from the same two AO's? How does this arise in the way the AO's are combined? How is this correlated with relative energies?

3. If θ is the angular coordinate around the H—C≡C—H molecular axis in acetylene, then the p_x wave functions (not the orbitals) have an angular dependence given by $\psi(\theta) = \sin\theta$, and the p_y wave functions have an angular dependence $\psi(\theta) = \cos\theta$. What then is the expression for the angular dependence of the p_x and p_y atomic orbitals? Plot the two wave functions, and the two atomic orbitals, on separate polar graphs and compare them.

4. In view of the angular functions given in Problem 3, prove the statement in the text that the combined π_x and π_y MO's in acetylene form a cylindrical barrel of electron density, the same in all directions, θ, around the molecular axis.

5. The bond energies for typical carbon–carbon single and double bonds are 83 kcal mole^{-1} and 147 kcal mole^{-1}, respectively. Which

of the following would you expect as the triple bond energy: 106, 150, or 194 kcal mole^{-1}?

6. The triple bond energies in acetylene, hydrogen cyanide, and nitrogen, are 194, 213, and 226 kcal mole^{-1}, respectively. Diagram these three molecules, showing the positions of all bonds and lone electron pairs. Why would one expect the observed progression of bond energies? In singly bonded —N—N—N—N— chains, it was stated previously that these were unstable in comparison with —C—C—C—C— chains because of repulsions between nitrogen lone electron pairs. Why is this apparently not a dominant factor in the comparison of HC≡CH, HCN, and N_2? Where are the lone pairs positioned in the N_2 molecule?

7. The conventional numbering system for a three-ring carbon skeleton such as that of alizarin is

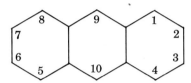

Hence the undissociated alizarin molecule shown previously in this chapter can be described as having carbonyl (C=O) groups at Positions 9 and 10, and —OH groups at Positions 1 and 2. The resonance model for the alizarin ion shown in this chapter has —O$^-$ groups at Positions 1 and 2. Draw another resonance structure with —O$^-$ groups at Positions 9 and 10 and carbonyl groups at 1 and 2. What would this imply about shifts of electrons to and from the various oxygen atoms?

8. Continuing a search for resonance structures for the alizarin ion from Problem 7, can you draw a structure in which carbonyl groups are present at Positions 9 and 2, and —O$^-$ at 1 and 10? What about carbonyl groups at 9 and 1, and —O$^-$ at 2 and 10? How many other resonance structures can you find that differ in assignment of the negative charges to different pairs of oxygen?

9. How many different resonance structures can you draw for the alizarin ion in which the negative charges are located on carbon atoms rather than on oxygen atoms?

10. As you try out various resonance models for the alizarin ion, you may come across the empirical observation that only those structures are possible for which the carbon atoms bearing negative charges (either directly or through an attached —O$^-$) are separated by an even number of other carbon atoms: 0, 2, 4, ···. Can you explain this in terms of single and double bonds between carbons in the three rings?

THE PERIODIC TABLE

(A) Representative Elements

	Group IA	IIA	IIIA	IVA	VA	VIA	VIIA	Group 0	Filled outer shell
Row 1	1 **H** Hydrogen							2 **He** Helium	$1s^2$
Row 2	3 **Li** Lithium	4 **Be** Beryllium	5 **B** Boron	6 **C** Carbon	7 **N** Nitrogen	8 **O** Oxygen	9 **F** Fluorine	10 **Ne** Neon	$2s^2 2p^6$
Row 3	11 **Na** Sodium	12 **Mg** Magnesium	13 **Al** Aluminum	14 **Si** Silicon	15 **P** Phosphorus	16 **S** Sulfur	17 **Cl** Chlorine	18 **Ar** Argon	$3s^2 3p^6$
Row 4	19 **K** Potassium	20 **Ca** Calcium	31 **Ga** Gallium	32 **Ge** Germanium	33 **As** Arsenic	34 **Se** Selenium	35 **Br** Bromine	36 **Kr** Krypton	$4s^2 4p^6$
Row 5	37 **Rb** Rubidium	38 **Sr** Strontium	49 **In** Indium	50 **Sn** Tin	51 **Sb** Antimony	52 **Te** Tellurium	53 **I** Iodine	54 **Xe** Xenon	$5s^2 5p^6$
Row 6	55 **Cs** Cesium	56 **Ba** Barium	81 **Tl** Thallium	82 **Pb** Lead	83 **Bi** Bismuth	84 **Po** Polonium	85 **At** Astatine	86 **Rn** Radon	$6s^2 6p^6$
Row 7	87 **Fr** Francium	88 **Ra** Radium							

Metals Borderline Nonmetals { Solid, Liquid, Gas }

(B) Transition Metals

Filled inner shell

	Group IIIB	IVB	VB	VIB	VIIB	VIIIB			IB	IIB	Filled inner shell
Row 4	21 **Sc** Scandium	22 **Ti** Titanium	23 **V** Vanadium	24 **Cr** Chromium	25 **Mn** Manganese	26 **Fe** Iron	27 **Co** Cobalt	28 **Ni** Nickel	29 **Cu** Copper	30 **Zn** Zinc	$3d^{10}$
Row 5	39 **Y** Yttrium	40 **Zr** Zirconium	41 **Nb** Niobium	42 **Mo** Molybdenum	43 **Tc** Technetium	44 **Ru** Ruthenium	45 **Rh** Rhodium	46 **Pd** Palladium	47 **Ag** Silver	48 **Cd** Cadmium	$4d^{10}$
Row 6	71 **Lu** Lutetium	72 **Hf** Hafnium	73 **Ta** Tantalum	74 **W** Tungsten	75 **Re** Rhenium	76 **Os** Osmium	77 **Ir** Iridium	78 **Pt** Platinum	79 **Au** Gold	80 **Hg** Mercury	$5d^{10}$
Row 7	103 **Lr** Lawrencium	104	105	106							

(C) Inner Transition Metals

Filled inner shell

															Filled inner shell
Row 6	57 La	58 Ce	59 Pr	60 Nd	61 Pm	62 Sm	63 Eu	64 Gd	65 Tb	66 Dy	67 Ho	68 Er	69 Tm	70 Yb	$4f^{14}$
Row 7	89 Ac	90 Th	91 Pa	92 U	93 Np	94 Pu	95 Am	96 Cm	97 Bk	98 Cf	99 Es	100 Fm	101 Md	102 No	$5f^{14}$

CHAPTER 10

Playing with a Full Deck: The Periodic Table

One of the triumphs of quantum mechanics was the successful explanation of the arrangement of electrons in atoms and the structure of the periodic table. Now that we have seen (Chapter 8) how the table is based on electronic structure, we can present an overview of the chemical elements that make up our universe. This is the full deck with which the game of chemistry is played. This chapter will be a wrap-up of the ideas presented in the first nine chapters.

The rows or *periods* of different length in the table represent the filling of different orbitals: s in Row 1; $s + p$ in Rows 2 and 3; $s + d + p$ in Rows 4 and 5; and $s + f + d + p$ in Rows 6 and 7. The fully developed table from Chapter 8 is shown in the right margin, with the representative elements (filling of s and p orbitals), transition metals (d orbitals), and inner transition metals (f orbitals) differentiated by color. Each period begins with the occupancy of a new s orbital and (after Row 1) ends with a noble gas with a closed $s + p$ electron shell. The representative elements are divided vertically into eight *groups*, labeled IA through VIIA, and 0 for the noble gases. The Roman numeral in the group number indicates the number of s and p electrons in the outer shell.

The transition metals are inserted between Groups IIA and IIIA, beginning with Row 4. They are given group numbers that continue the numbering of the representative elements, but their numbers are followed by B instead of A. Group IIIB follows IIA in Row 4, then comes IVB through VIIIB, followed by IB and IIB, and a resumption of the representative elements with IIIA. This numbering is shown on the table at the left. The inner transition metals are so much less important that they are not given group numbers at all. In this chapter we shall look for the last time at the representative elements as a whole, introduce the transition metals, and have very little to say about the inner transition metals.

THE PERIODIC TABLE

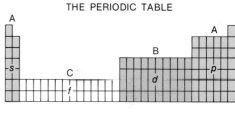

Extra-long form

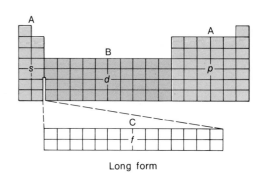

Long form

Representative elements reflect the filling of s **and** p **orbitals, transition metals of** d **orbitals, and inner transition metals of** f **orbitals. The extra-long form of the periodic table at the top shows the filling of orbitals in their proper order, but is large and clumsy. The standard long form of the table below it removes the inner transition metals to a separate block, and the short form on the facing page also separates out the transition metals.**

ATOMIC SIZE AND ELECTRONEGATIVITY

Two of the key factors in the chemistry of an atom are its size and the charge on its core (the nucleus plus the electrons of the preceding noble gas). The distance of the outer-shell electrons from the nucleus, and the charge on the core, jointly determine the pull that these electrons feel, and hence determine the electronegativity, or electron-holding power, of the atom.

In Chapters 3 and 6 we introduced several measures of atomic size: metallic and covalent radii, ionic radii, and van der Waals radii. Metallic and covalent radii form a smooth, continuous series across the periodic table because they both describe atoms held together by shared electrons. In metals the electrons are shared between many atoms, and it is natural to think of the metal ions and the bonding metallic electrons separately. In contrast, one seldom regards an O_2 molecule as consisting of two O^{2-} ions held together by four bonding electrons, but the distinction is more conventional than real.

Ionic radii are larger than covalent or metallic radii for negative ions, which have picked up more electrons, and smaller for positive ions, which have lost them. Van der Waals radii are important mainly for nonmetals, and are large because they represent packing of atoms without electron sharing.

Metallic and covalent radii for all the representative elements that form bonds are shown at the bottom of the page. Two trends are obvious: shrinkage from left to right across one row because of the pull of the increased nuclear charge, and expansion from top to bottom because of the higher quantum number of the outer shell being filled.

Metallic or covalent radii are the effective radii of atoms when they share electrons in bonds with neighboring atoms, either many atoms in a metal, or a restricted number of atoms in electron-pair bonds. Size increases with increasing number of filled electron shells, and decreases with increasing nuclear charge within each row.

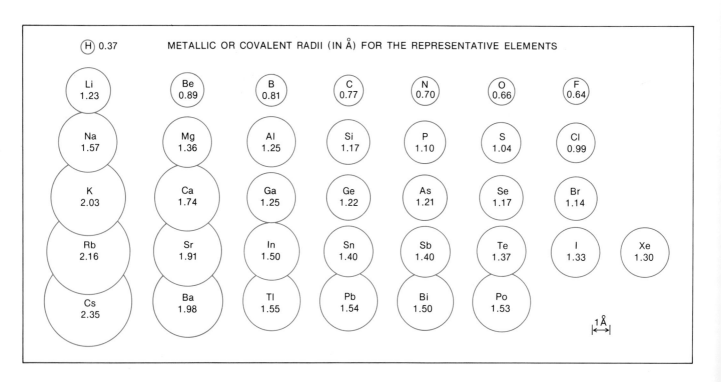

METALLIC OR COVALENT RADII (IN Å) FOR THE REPRESENTATIVE ELEMENTS

H 0.37

Li 1.23	Be 0.89	B 0.81	C 0.77	N 0.70	O 0.66	F 0.64	
Na 1.57	Mg 1.36	Al 1.25	Si 1.17	P 1.10	S 1.04	Cl 0.99	
K 2.03	Ca 1.74	Ga 1.25	Ge 1.22	As 1.21	Se 1.17	Br 1.14	
Rb 2.16	Sr 1.91	In 1.50	Sn 1.40	Sb 1.40	Te 1.37	I 1.33	Xe 1.30
Cs 2.35	Ba 1.98	Tl 1.55	Pb 1.54	Bi 1.50	Po 1.53		

1 Å

The transition metals add little to the trend and need not be shown, but their absence can be detected by the extra decrease in radii between Groups IIA and IIIA: Ca and Ga, Sr and In, Ba and Tl.

Size correlates beautifully with electronegativity. The larger the atom, the weaker its hold on its outer-shell electrons, and the easier it is for another atom to take them away. Electronegativities of the representative elements are shown in color below. They range from 0.7 for cesium at the lower left, to 4.0 for fluorine at the upper right. We encountered cesium in Chapter 7, in connection with the photoelectric effect, as the electron-losing metal that is employed in electric eyes and photocells. It was mentioned previously that the omission of the transition metals between Groups IIA and IIIA was detectable by the sudden decrease in metallic radii, as shown in the table on the lower left page. They also are responsible for the unusual increase in electronegativity values (below), from 1.0 in Ca to 1.6 in Ga, and from 1.0 in Sr to 1.7 in In.

Lines connecting elements of equal electronegativity would extend diagonally from the upper left of the table to the lower right. Since electronegativity is chiefly responsible for determining chemical behavior, the chemical properties of the elements also show diagonal trends, as we have seen previously. The elements with amphoteric oxides cut a diagonal swath down the table, from Be to Al, Ge, and Sb. Weak, barely acidic oxyacids are formed by B, Si, As, and Te, whereas the common strong laboratory oxyacids are derived from N and S. This diagonality of properties also extends to the metal–nonmetal boundary and the solid–gas boundary for nonmetals, as the table at the beginning of the chapter indicates. The elements become more metallic downward in each group, and to the left across each row.

Electronegativities show trends opposite to those of atomic radii. Small atoms with outer electrons close to the nucleus have strong attractions for these electrons, and hence are very electronegative. (The darker the tint, the higher the electronegativity value.) Large atoms with loosely held outer electrons have low electronegativities.

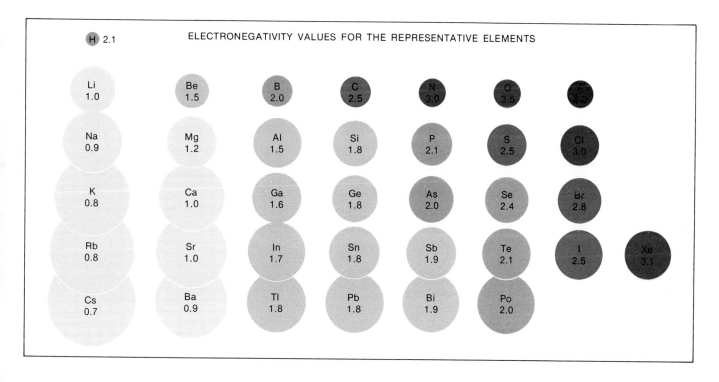

H 2.1   ELECTRONEGATIVITY VALUES FOR THE REPRESENTATIVE ELEMENTS

Li 1.0	Be 1.5	B 2.0	C 2.5	N 3.0	O 3.5	F 4.0
Na 0.9	Mg 1.2	Al 1.5	Si 1.8	P 2.1	S 2.5	Cl 3.0
K 0.8	Ca 1.0	Ga 1.6	Ge 1.8	As 2.0	Se 2.4	Br 2.8
Rb 0.8	Sr 1.0	In 1.7	Sn 1.8	Sb 1.9	Te 2.1	I 2.5	Xe 3.1
Cs 0.7	Ba 0.9	Tl 1.8	Pb 1.8	Bi 1.9	Po 2.0		

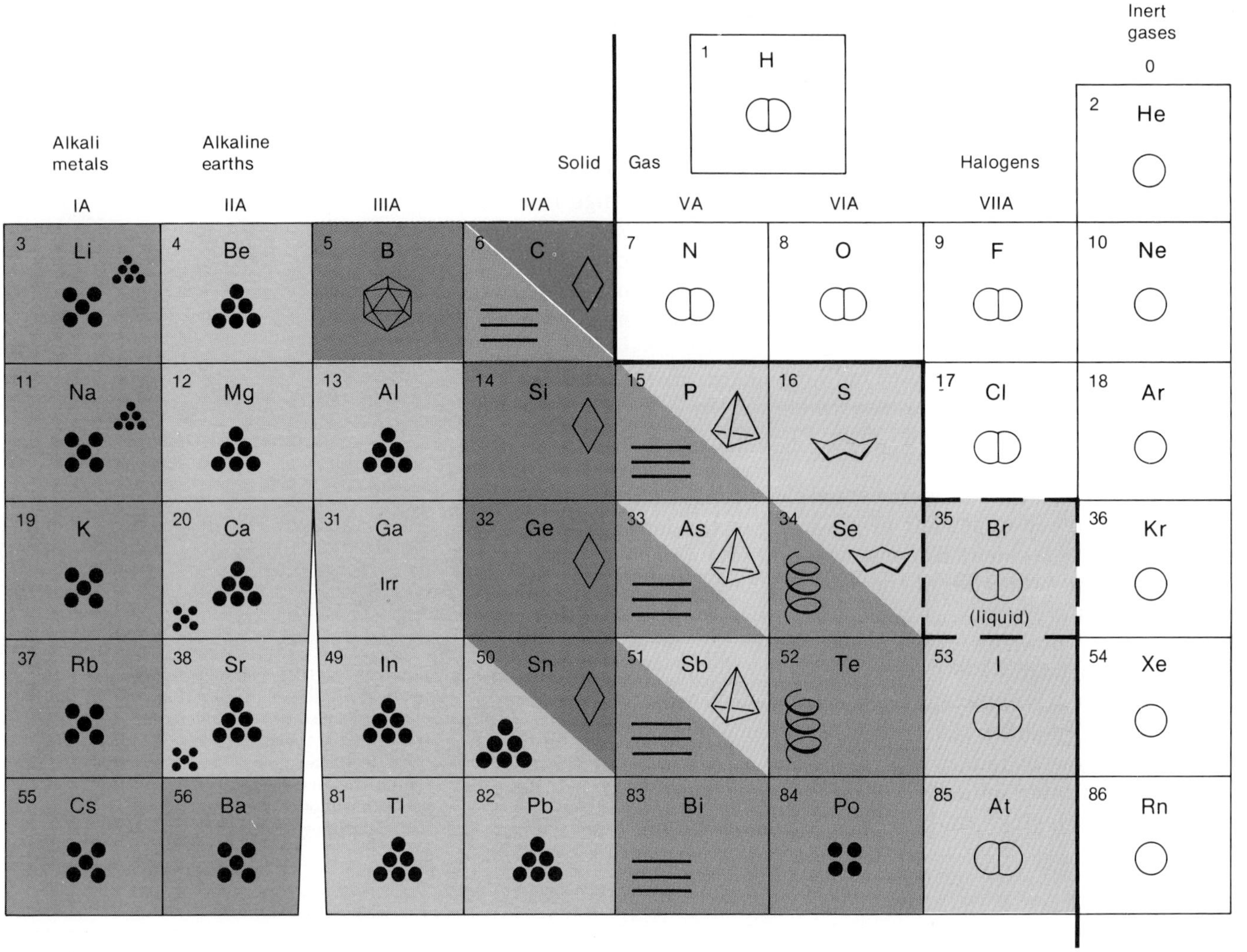

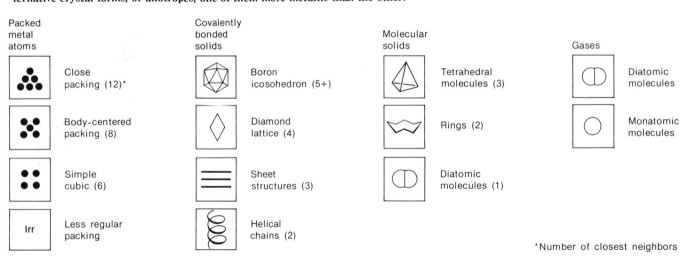

Bonding in metals extends over the entire piece of metal, and structure is dictated by the packing of spherical positive ions. The covalently bonded solids in the center of the table have each atom connected to two, three, or four neighbors by electron-pair bonds. Elements that form only single bonds, or small elements that can form double and triple bonds, exist as diatomic gases. The noble gases at the right are monatomic. Elements on the metal–nonmetal borderline can have two alternative crystal forms, or allotropes, one of them more metallic than the other.

Packed metal atoms

Close packing (12)*

Body-centered packing (8)

Simple cubic (6)

Irr — Less regular packing

Covalently bonded solids

Boron icosohedron (5+)

Diamond lattice (4)

Sheet structures (3)

Helical chains (2)

Molecular solids

Tetrahedral molecules (3)

Rings (2)

Diatomic molecules (1)

Gases

Diatomic molecules

Monatomic molecules

*Number of closest neighbors

THE STRUCTURES OF THE ELEMENTS

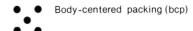

Body-centered packing (bcp)

We can use the structures of the elements as a means of surveying the entire table. The diagram at the left shows the structures of the representative elements, and the transition metals are similar to the metals shown.

The metals all are packed spheres of positive ions held together by mobile electrons. In close packing (cp), the densest way of packing marbles or other spherical objects, each atom has twelve nearest neighbors touching it, and 74% of the volume of the metal is occupied by atoms. (There are two main kinds of close packing, cubic and hexagonal, which differ only in the way that the individual close-packed layers of atoms are stacked.) In a slightly less dense form, body-centered packing (bcp), each atom has eight neighbors in contact with it in the directions of the corners of a cube, and the atoms occupy only 68% of the total volume. Close packing is favored in metals with small atoms and many electrons to hold them; body-centered packing is found in metals with larger atoms and fewer electrons to bind them together. It is not uncommon for a metal to show a close-packed structure at low temperatures, and change to a body-centered structure at higher temperatures when the atoms are vibrating more freely. The alkali metals in Group IA all have the bcp structure at room temperature; but the smallest two, Li and Na, change to close packing below −200°C. Among the alkaline earths (Group IIA), which are held together by two electrons per atom, the smallest two, Be and Mg, always use the dense cp structure. The next two, Ca and Sr, have close packing at room temperature, but change to body centering above 600°C; the largest alkaline earth, Ba, always uses the open bcp structure. The metals in Groups IIIA and IVA have a more-or-less distorted cp structure because the forces between atoms are more covalent than the forces in Group IA and IIA metals. The borderline with nonmetals is not far off.

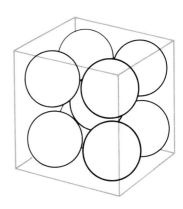

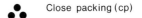

Close packing (cp)

(a) Cubic

The first nonmetal in Row 2, boron, is encountered at the top of Group IIIA. It has a complex three-dimensional covalent cage structure. The no-man's-land between metals and nonmetals is especially dramatic in Groups IVA, VA, and VIA, with the lighter elements being nonmetals, the heavier elements at the bottom of the table metals, and a transition zone separating them. In this zone, one element often has two different crystal forms, or *allotropes*, one metallic and the other nonmetallic. The nonmetallic allotrope is held together by covalent bonds with all electrons localized, whereas the metallic form usually will show the dark color and metallic luster that indicate the presence of mobile electrons.

Diamond and graphite illustrate this behavior for carbon; diamond is the nonmetallic allotrope, and graphite has some of the prop-

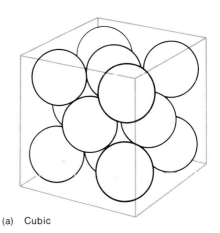

(b) Hexagonal

In body-centered packing, atoms occupy the corners and center of a cube. If perfect spheres are packed this way, only 68% of the volume is occupied by spheres, and 32% is empty space. In close packing, spheres are packed tightly together in layers and the layers are stacked against one another in the most economical way, so that the spheres take up 74% of the available space. Cubic and hexagonal close packing differ only in the manner in which the tightly packed layers are stacked.

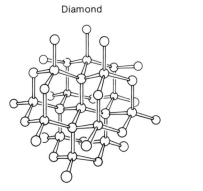

Diamond

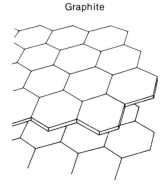

Graphite

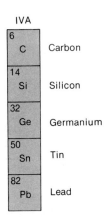

IVA

6 C	Carbon
14 Si	Silicon
32 Ge	Germanium
50 Sn	Tin
82 Pb	Lead

The diamond and graphite structures (above right), which we saw first in Chapter 4, now can be understood in terms of orbitals and bonding. Each carbon atom in diamond uses sp^3 hybridization to form four bonds to neighbors, and all bonding electrons are localized. In graphite, three electrons per carbon atom are localized in sp^2-derived bonds within one sheet, and the fourth electron is delocalized over the entire sheet as though in a "two-dimensional metal."

Mobile electrons, color, and metallic sheen

$$\langle\!\!\!\!\!\!\!\rangle\!\!-\!\!(\!-CH\!\!=\!\!CH\!-\!)_n\!\!-\!\!\langle\!\!\!\!\!\!\!\rangle$$

n	$\lambda(\text{Å})$	Color
1	3190	None
2	3520	Pale yellow
3	3770	Greenish yellow
4	4040	Orange-yellow
5	4240	Orange
6	4450	Orange-brown
7	4650	Copper-bronze sheen
8	4840	Bluish-copper sheen

erties of a metal (see above). The lack of color in diamond tells us that it has no closely spaced electronic energy levels to absorb visible light; all of its electrons are tied down in covalent bonds. In graphite the electrons are delocalized and free to wander within the layers of carbon atoms. The black color and metallic sheen of graphite result from the absorption and reemission of many wavelengths of light by these mobile electrons.[1]

Silicon, germanium, and tin, below carbon in Group IVA, all have the diamond structure but with increasing gray color and metallic luster. Tin also has a second, metallic allotrope. Gray tin, which has the nonmetallic diamond structure, is the stable form below 13°C, and metallic white tin is more stable above this temperature, although the rate of conversion from one to the other is very slow. These allotropes led to considerable grief for medieval metallurgists, who noticed every so often that tin objects left out in the cold would begin to decay in spots and crumble into a nonmetallic gray powder. They thought it was a disease of the metal, and called it "tin pest." Actually, it was only the slow conversion of white tin to gray tin at low temperatures. Because the change is slow, we ordinarily do not observe it; the tin remains metastable in the metallic form. Lead, at the bottom of Group IVA, occurs only in the metallic cp structure.

A similar borderline is crossed by the elements of Group VA. Having three unpaired outer electrons, these elements all prefer to make three bonds to other like atoms. Nitrogen is so small that one atom can form a triple bond to another atom, thereby making N_2 gas molecules.

---

[1] The connection between delocalized electrons and metallic luster can be illustrated in a simple way by looking at a series of linear conjugated molecules of the type encountered in Chapter 9:

$$\langle\!\!\!\!\!\!\!\rangle\!\!-\!\!(\!-CH\!\!=\!\!CH\!-\!)_n\!\!-\!\!\langle\!\!\!\!\!\!\!\rangle \qquad \text{with } n = 1, 2, 3, 4, \cdots$$

The maximum wavelength absorbed and the color seen in this series of molecules are given in the table at the left for molecules with chain lengths from $n = 1$ to 8. As the length of the delocalized chain increases, the absorption of radiation shifts from the ultraviolet into the visible, the complement of the absorbed color is seen, and at $n = 7$ or 8 a metallic luster begins to appear. Compounds of longer molecules in this series are a shiny black, like graphite, because the region of absorption is so broad that it encompasses virtually the entire visible spectrum. Graphite, with its endless hexagonal-mesh sheets, can be considered as the infinite extension of aromatic molecules like benzene and naphthalene.

Phosphorus is too large for triple bonds, so it makes single bonds to three other P atoms instead, at the corners of a P_4 tetrahedral molecule (see right). These P_4 tetrahedra are found in the vapor, liquid, and in solid white phosphorus. Black phosphorus also has each atom linked to three neighbors, but in sheets like a puckered version of graphite. The black color is a clue to the presence of mobile electrons within each of the stacked sheets, and this allotrope is more metallic. Red phosphorus is a third allotrope of uncertain structure, possibly an amorphous mixture. Arsenic and antimony also have two allotropes, very unstable yellow nonmetallic forms, with separate molecules of As_4 and Sb_4 tetrahedra, and metallic allotropes with stacked sheets like those of black phosphorus. The color of this metallic form changes from black in P, to gray in As, to a gunmetal blue sheen in Sb. Bismuth, at the bottom of the group, has only the sheet structure with a white metallic luster.

The Group VIA elements have two unpaired electrons and need to make two bonds to neighbors. Oxygen is small enough to make a double bond with a single neighboring atom in O_2 gas, but sulfur is too large to do so, and must settle for rings of eight atoms, each connected to two neighbors (lower right). This is the structure of molecules of yellow crystalline sulfur. In the darker, amorphous sulfur allotrope, these S_8 rings break open and link together into helical chains. These structures also are the basis for two crystalline allotropes of selenium: red, nonmetallic Se with eight-membered rings, and metallic Se with endless helices. In these Se helices the delocalization of electrons is confined to one chain, and selenium in effect is a "one-dimensional metal." Tellurium has only the metallic chain form, with the chains more closely packed. Polonium carries this compacting farther until the atoms form a simple cubic structure, the only example of such a structure known. (The radioactivity of Po makes it difficult to examine its crystal structure, because the alpha particles emitted during radioactive decay heat the crystal and destroy it.)

Allotropy and the metal–nonmetal borderline vanish in Group VIIA. (Astatine may be a borderline element, but is difficult to study for the same reason Po is.) All of the halogens form simple diatomic molecules and, depending on their size, are gases (F_2 and Cl_2), liquid (Br_2), or solids (I_2 and At_2) at room temperature. Iodine does have a metallic luster to its crystals, which indicates a less firm grip on electrons than the lighter halogens have. The noble gases in Group 0 all are monatomic.

As you look over the representative-element structure table again (Page 206), you can see the gradual diagonal change in properties from lower left to upper right: bcp and then cp metals, an intermediate zone of metallic and nonmetallic allotropes, and finally the covalently bonded discrete molecules of nonmetals. As the number of bonds formed between like atoms in Groups IVA, VA, and VIA changes from four, to three, to two, the metallic allotrope changes from packed atoms, to stacked layers or sheets, to helical chains; and the nonmetallic allotrope changes from a three-dimensional diamond lattice, to X_4 tetrahedra, to rings of eight atoms. Only the smallest atoms can form diatomic gases having multiple bonds, but singly bonded diatomic molecules are the rule for the halogens, in Group VIIA.

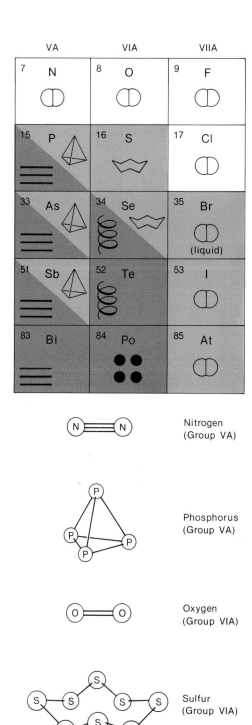

Nitrogen
(Group VA)

Phosphorus
(Group VA)

Oxygen
(Group VIA)

Sulfur
(Group VIA)

Nitrogen atoms are small enough to form triple bonds to a single neighbor atom, but the larger phosphorus atoms must make single bonds to three other neighbors. Similarly, oxygen forms a double bond to one neighbor, but sulfur must form two single bonds instead.

MELTING POINTS OF THE
REPRESENTATIVE ELEMENTS

As we have seen before, the melting point, or the temperature needed to break a solid apart into fluid atoms or molecules, is a convenient measure of the forces between these atoms or molecules. Melting points for the representative elements are plotted on the three-dimensional graph, with the periodic table as the base and temperature along the vertical axis. Along the left edge, the alkali metals in Group IA, having one electron per atom and an open bcp structure, are soft and low-melting. The hardness of the metal and its melting point increase in Group IIA, in which twice as many electrons are available. Al, Ga, and In are lower melting because of the imperfections and openness of their metal structures. Within one group, the heavier metals are softer and lower melting because their atoms are farther apart.

Melting points increase steeply from Li to Be to B to C because of the increasingly covalent character of the forces between atoms. Diamond is the hardest and highest-melting element known. Diagonally across the center of the table, from B to Si to As to Te, the borderline elements with three-, two-, and one-dimensional covalently bonded structures (frameworks, sheets, chains) are harder and have higher melting points because covalent bonds must be broken to disrupt the solid. At the far right of the table, the molecular compounds P_4, S_8, N_2, O_2, and the halogens have lower melting points because, although the molecules are covalently bonded internally, they have only weak van der Waals forces holding them together in the solid.

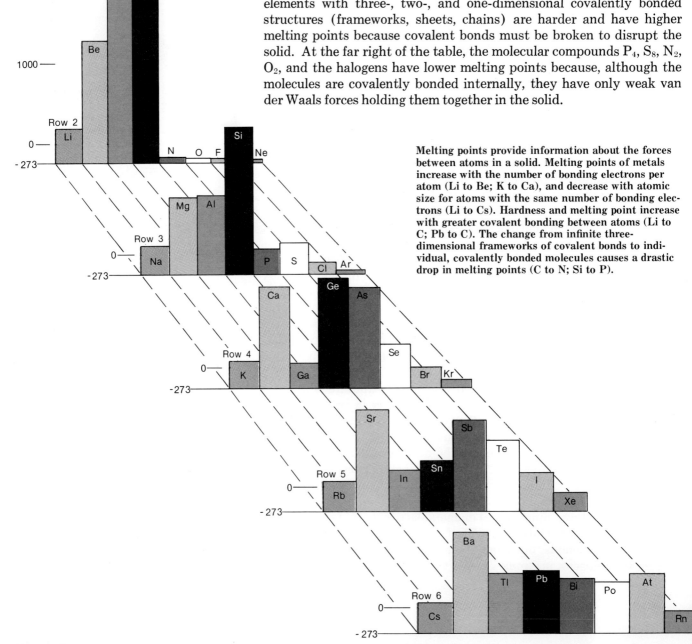

Melting points provide information about the forces between atoms in a solid. Melting points of metals increase with the number of bonding electrons per atom (Li to Be; K to Ca), and decrease with atomic size for atoms with the same number of bonding electrons (Li to Cs). Hardness and melting point increase with greater covalent bonding between atoms (Li to C; Pb to C). The change from infinite three-dimensional frameworks of covalent bonds to individual, covalently bonded molecules causes a drastic drop in melting points (C to N; Si to P).

CHEMICAL PROPERTIES; THE ALKALI METALS

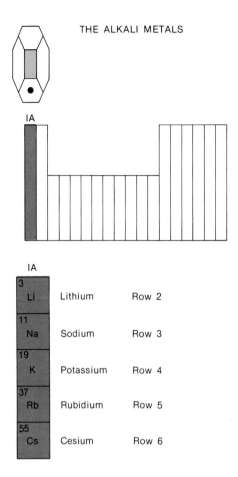

The alkali metals, in Group IA at the left of the table, all have a single electron outside of a filled noble-gas shell. They have low ionization energies, and hence a strong tendency to lose the outer electron and become oxidized to the +1 state. This tendency is so strong (it is stronger for the larger atoms at the bottom of the group) that the alkali metals always occur in nature as +1 ions, never as pure metals. They are found in sea water and brine wells, in deposits of soluble salts such as NaCl and NaNO$_3$, and as cations in many less soluble or insoluble minerals such as the silicates. Na$^+$ and K$^+$ make up a little over 3% of the atoms in the crust of the Earth. The heavier alkali metals rubidium and cesium are rarer, but are found in small amounts in KCl and NaCl deposits.

Because of their strong tendency to become ions, the alkali metals are extremely strong reducing agents. For example,

$$K \text{ (metal)} \rightarrow K^+ + e^-$$

The metals cannot be obtained from their salts by purely chemical means, and the only practical method is the electrolysis process introduced in Chapter 5, in which an electric current is passed through the appropriate molten salt (see lower right). Electrons from the outside circuit combine with the cations at the cathode and reduce them to pure metal. At the anode, electrons are donated by the anions and flow out to the external circuit again. For potassium chloride the reactions are

Cathode: $K^+ + e^- \rightarrow K$
Anode: $Cl^- \rightarrow \frac{1}{2}Cl_2 \text{(gas)} + e^-$

Positive and negative ions migrate between the electrodes within the molten salt. The energy needed to reduce the potassium ions and oxidize the chloride ions is supplied by outside electrical energy.

Once obtained as pure metal, the alkali metals then can be used as sources of reducing power in other chemical reactions. Sodium is the usual choice in industry because of its ready availability. All the alkali metals must be kept away from air and water because of their strong tendency to return to the +1 oxidation state. Thus when stored they must be immersed in kerosene or some other organic liquid. Cesium and rubidium have few uses, the most important being as electron-releasing metal surfaces in photoelectric devices.

Sodium and potassium ions are important in living organisms. Their contribution to the composition of a human is shown in the periodic table on the front end papers. Na$^+$ and K$^+$ help to keep the proper ionic balance inside and outside cells, so that the cells do not shrink or swell as their surroundings change in salt concentration. They also are involved in triggering nerve impulses down an axon of a neural cell, and hence are critical to the communication system of the body. The main positive ion inside cells is K$^+$, and Na$^+$ predominates in the blood and body fluids outside the cells. The ionic composition of these body fluids is close to that of sea water diluted with three volumes of pure water. This is not surprising, in view of the evolution

IA		
3 Li	Lithium	Row 2
11 Na	Sodium	Row 3
19 K	Potassium	Row 4
37 Rb	Rubidium	Row 5
55 Cs	Cesium	Row 6

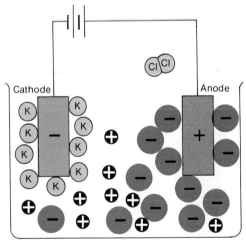

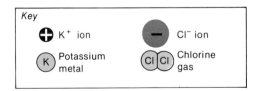

Electrolysis of molten potassium chloride to potassium metal and chlorine gas

211

of life in the oceans.[2] In a sense, our cells have found a way of carrying around a bit of ocean with them long after our ancestors left it physically.

The main alkali metal ion in plants is K^+ rather than Na^+. A traditional source of potassium hydroxide, KOH, has been the leaching, or extraction, of wood ashes with water. The name "potassium" for the metal comes from the old English term "pot ash" or "cooking ashes." "Alkali" has the same meaning in Arabic: "al Kali" means "the ashes." The Arabic word ultimately leads back to the Greek word for burning, which drifted off in a different direction via the Latin "caleo," to reach us again in "calorie" and "cauldron."

GROUP IIA: THE ALKALINE EARTHS

The alkaline earths resemble the alkali metals, but are less strongly reducing. They occur only in the zero or +2 oxidation states, and are always found naturally as +2 ions. They are found as soluble chloride salts in sea water, and in minerals such as sulfates, carbonates, phosphates, and silicates. Calcite, chalk, limestone, and marble all are forms of calcium carbonate, $CaCO_3$. Dolomite and some marbles are mixtures of $CaCO_3$ and magnesium carbonate, $MgCO_3$. Gypsum is a calcium sulfate. Approximately 4% of the Earth's crust is Ca and Mg ions. Beryllium, strontium, and barium are much rarer, the most common source of Be being emeralds and lesser forms of beryl, a beryllium–aluminum silicate.

Magnesium and calcium usually are obtained by electrolysis of fused salts such as molten $MgCl_2$, although these +2 salts also can be reduced by metallic Na or K:

$$2Na + Mg^{2+} + 2Cl^- \rightarrow 2Na^+ + Mg + 2Cl^-$$

Here the chloride ions play a passive role in the reaction, which involves only a transfer of electrons from sodium to magnesium ion.

Magnesium's light weight makes it useful in the aircraft industry, but the other metals in Group IIA have little application. The chief industrial use of Sr and Ba is to produce brilliant red and green flames for signal flares and fireworks. Barium sulfate, $BaSO_4$, being very dense to x rays and at the same time relatively harmless and not assimilated by the body, is useful for contrast in medical x rays of the stomach and intestinal tract.

Calcium and magnesium are twice as prevalent in living organisms as are sodium and potassium, but not primarily as soluble ions. Calcium phosphate is the main component of bones and teeth in vertebrates, and calcium carbonate is the material of shells. Ca^{2+} and Mg^{2+} ions are found in many enzymes, and Mg^{2+} surrounded by a delocalized aromatic ring (a porphyrin ring) is the light-trapping unit in chlorophyll.

THE ALKALINE EARTHS

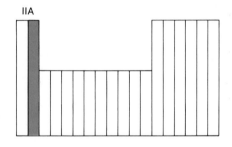

IIA

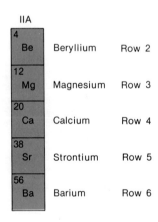

IIA		
4 Be	Beryllium	Row 2
12 Mg	Magnesium	Row 3
20 Ca	Calcium	Row 4
38 Sr	Strontium	Row 5
56 Ba	Barium	Row 6

---

[2] It has even been suggested that this 3:1 dilution reflects the lesser salinity of the early ocean at the time when life was evolving 3.5 to 4 billion years ago.

THE TRANSITION METALS

The *d*-electron elements have distinctive physical properties that make them useful as structural metals and catalysts, and distinctive electronic properties that find applications in the molecules of living organisms. The physical properties will be discussed in this section, and the electronic properties in the next.

The four series of transition metals, and the electron-filling process for the first of these, are shown below. Generally, each new transition metal along one row has two electrons in the outer *s* orbital, and an increasing number of electrons in the buried *d* orbital belonging to the preceding principal quantum number. In Row 4 chromium (Cr) and copper (Cu) are exceptions to this rule, stealing one of the two *s* electrons to half-fill or fill the *d* orbitals. These are minor exceptions, and it is the filling principle that is important.

In chemical reactions of the transition metals, the *s* electrons are lost most easily, and +1 and +2 oxidation states are common. Higher oxidation states also are possible for atoms that have *d* electrons and, in principle, the highest possible state would correspond to the loss of all of the outer *s* and *d* electrons: +3 for scandium, +4 for titanium, and +7 for manganese. Electron pairing complicates matters from iron onward, as we shall see.

Because of the way in which the elements were synthesized (see postscript to Chapter 8), elements in the first series of transition

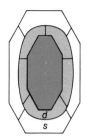

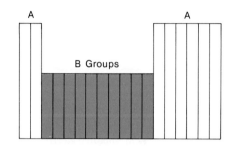

Electron-shell diagram for transition metals. The *s* orbital is the outer shell, and the *d* orbitals from the preceding principal quantum number are buried more deeply. (Row 4 is illustrated in the table below.)

The A-group representative elements in the periodic table are interrupted to accommodate the transition metals (B group).

Below: The four series of transition metals, occurring in Rows 4 through 7 of the table. Immediately below are electron-shell diagrams for the first transition metal series. The common argon core for these elements is represented by the solid color in the center.

	TRANSITION METALS									
IIIB	IVB	VB	VIB	VIIB		VIIIB		IB	IIB
Sc	Ti	V	Cr	Mn	Fe	Co	Ni	Cu	Zn

Electrons in outer shells: 3, 4, 5, 6, 7, 8, 9, 10, 11, 12

	IIIB	IVB	VB	VIB	VIIB	VIIIB	VIIIB	VIIIB	IB	IIB
Row 4	21 Sc Scandium	22 Ti Titanium	23 V Vanadium	24 Cr Chromium	25 Mn Manganese	26 Fe Iron	27 Co Cobalt	28 Ni Nickel	29 Cu Copper	30 Zn Zinc
Row 5	39 Y Yttrium	40 Zr Zirconium	41 Nb Niobium	42 Mo Molybdenum	43 Tc Technetium	44 Ru Ruthenium	45 Rh Rhodium	46 Pd Palladium	47 Ag Silver	48 Cd Cadmium
Row 6	71 Lu Lutetium	72 Hf Hafnium	73 Ta Tantalum	74 W Tungsten	75 Re Rhenium	76 Os Osmium	77 Ir Iridium	78 Pt Platinum	79 Au Gold	80 Hg Mercury
Row 7	103 Lr Lawrencium	104	105	106						

metals are much more common than those in later series, and hence are more familiar. All of these elements are metallic solids at room temperature except mercury, which is a liquid with a freezing point of −39°C.

The transition metals generally are hard, brittle, and have high melting points. Hardness and melting point correlate well with the number of unpaired d electrons, as can be seen from the melting point curve below. This correlation arises because bonding between atoms in these metals is partially covalent. Potassium and calcium at the beginning of the fourth row of the table lose all their outer electrons, to become +1 and +2 ions in the metal. Their electrons are free to wander through the solid. The first transition metal, scandium, also loses all three of its outer electrons, but as the number of electrons in the d orbitals increases in successive elements, complete loss of electrons becomes more difficult. Chromium does not become a Cr^{6+} ion completely in the metal, but retains a partial hold on its outer-orbital electrons, sharing them to an extent with neighboring ions. If we could watch the electrons in a block of chromium, we might see them moving through the metal, but spending a disproportionate amount of time in positions that correspond to covalent bonds between adjacent Cr atoms. This partial covalent behavior creates stronger attractions between atoms in chromium and makes it harder, tougher, and higher

Melting points of the transition metals rise as increasing numbers of unpaired electrons occupy d orbitals, and then fall once more as additional electrons pair with them and diminish their effectiveness in bonding in the metal.

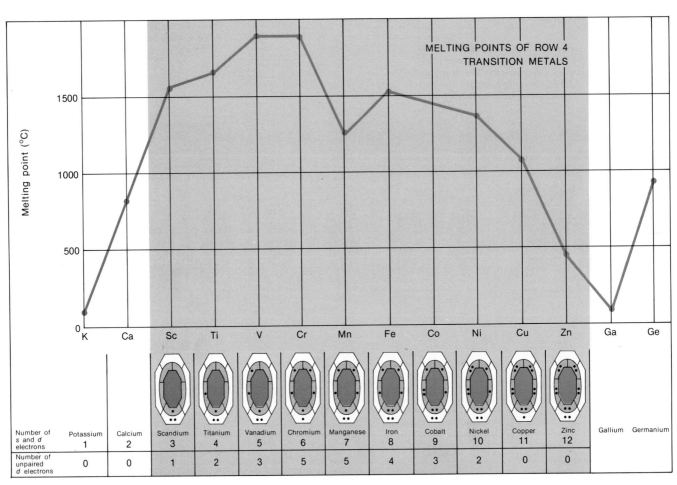

MELTING POINTS OF ROW 4 TRANSITION METALS

	K	Ca	Sc	Ti	V	Cr	Mn	Fe	Co	Ni	Cu	Zn	Ga	Ge
Number of s and d electrons	Potassium 1	Calcium 2	Scandium 3	Titanium 4	Vanadium 5	Chromium 6	Manganese 7	Iron 8	Cobalt 9	Nickel 10	Copper 11	Zinc 12	Gallium	Germanium
Number of unpaired d electrons	0	0	1	2	3	5	5	4	3	2	0	0		

214

IIIB	IVB	VB	VIB	VIIB		VIIIB		IB	IIB	Group number
Sc	Ti	V	Cr	Mn	Fe	Co	Ni	Cu	Zn	Element (Row 4)
3	4	5	6	7	8	9	10	11	12	Number of s and d electrons

Sc	Ti	V	Cr	Mn	Fe	Co	Ni	Cu	Zn	Oxidation states
−	−	−	−	−	−	−	−		−	+1
										+2
							−			+3
							−			+4
					−	−	−			+5
										+6
										+7

melting than potassium or calcium. In spite of this tendency toward covalency, the transition metals are good conductors of electricity because the outer-shell electrons are still mobile, and there are relatively many of them per atom.

Transition metals exhibit many different oxidation states, more than for any other class of elements. For reasons that we shall see in the next section, ions in many of these states are brightly colored, which indicates the electronic absorption of energy in the visible spectrum. The name "chromium" came from "chroma" for color. In principle, the maximum oxidation number for a transition metal would be the total number of outer s and d electrons, and this maximum indeed is found from scandium (Sc) to manganese (Mn), with 3 to 7 outer electrons (see above). Each d electron can go into a separate orbital in these elements, so pairing of two electrons with opposite spin in the same orbital is not necessary. Pairing to fill an orbital must begin with iron (Fe), and this pairing effectively removes both electrons from bonding activity. The maximum oxidation number decreases in the progression from iron to zinc (Zn) at the end of the first transition-metal series. The +2 and +3 states are most common for these latter transition metals.

Transition metals in Row 4 favor lower oxidation numbers because the atoms are smaller and their electrons are held more tightly. The elements in Rows 5 and 6 show more of the higher oxidation states because their larger atomic sizes loosens their grip on the outer d and s electrons. As an example, Fe usually is found in the +2 (ferrous) and +3 (ferric) oxidation states. Osmium, two rows below it, has oxidation states up to +8, as in osmium tetroxide. The elements are more metallic in their lower oxidation states, and their compounds are more ionic. Compounds in higher oxidation states are more covalent, with electrons being shared rather than lost entirely. Osmium tetroxide is a covalently bonded, volatile, tetrahedral molecule of OsO_4. (Osmium in this high oxidation state is so unstable that even weakly reducing organic molecules can reduce it to a black precipitate of lower-oxidation-

The most common oxidation states are shown in solid color. Other common states have a medium tint, and relatively rare oxidation states are lightly tinted. Metals with all d electrons unpaired tend to favor oxidation states involving all outer s and d electrons. Beyond manganese (Mn), electron pairing in d orbitals tends to inhibit the use of these electrons and favors lower oxidation states.

215

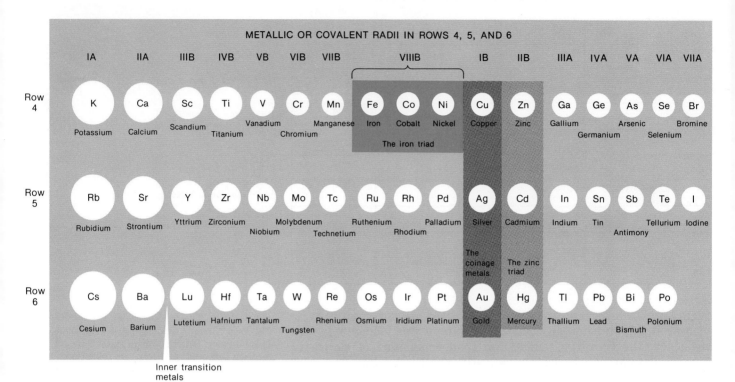

METALLIC OR COVALENT RADII IN ROWS 4, 5, AND 6

Inner transition metals

Increasing nuclear charge causes shrinkage of atomic radii from Groups IA through VIIB, and charge repulsion between electrons paired in the same *d* orbitals produces a slight subsequent increase in size through Group IIIA. Beyond the transition metals, shrinkage because of increasing nuclear charge predominates once more.

state compounds and the metal. This, plus the volatility of OsO_4, makes it useful as a tissue stain in electron microscopy. The vapor is potentially dangerous because it stains human tissue equally well, especially the eyes.)

Metallic and covalent radii of the elements in Rows 4–6 are shown above. If you cut out the transition metals from this plot and pushed calcium (Ca) and gallium (Ga) together, the size profile would not look radically different from that encountered in Rows 2 and 3; this is what we did in the radius drawings at the beginning of the chapter. Within the transition metals, shrinkage is unusually rapid from Sc to Mn, for which electrons are being added one at a time into empty *d* orbitals without pairing. The attractive charge on the nucleus increases steadily for these elements, yet the additional electrons are being placed in half-buried *d* orbitals where they have little compensating effect in increasing the atomic size. Only when electrons have to be paired with others, from Fe to Zn, does the repulsion between electrons in filled orbitals begin to increase the size of the atoms and bring the transition-metal radii back up to the main track at Ga and In.

The transition metals in Row 5 are larger than those in Row 4, as expected from their additional shell of electrons. But those in Row 6 are almost identical in size to the corresponding ones of Row 5, even though orbitals of higher principal quantum number are being filled. This phenomenon is known as the *lanthanide contraction* after lanthanum, the first metal in the series. The insertion of the fourteen *f*-orbital elements causes an increase in the nuclear charge of +14 by the time hafnium ($Z = 72$) is reached, thereby pulling all the electrons closer in. In Group VIB, molybdenum (Mo) has a nuclear charge +18 greater than chromium (Cr), but tungsten (W), below Mo, has a +32 greater

216

nuclear charge than molybdenum. The atomic radii accordingly are Cr, 1.18 Å; Mo, 1.30 Å; and W, 1.30 Å.

This near-identity in size between the second and third series of transition metals causes them to have similar chemical properties, which often are quite different than those of the metals above them in the first series. Niobium (Nb) and tantalum (Ta) are almost identical in behavior[3] and are less like vanadium (V). Ruthenium (Ru) and osmium (Os) are similar, but are quite different from iron (Fe). Iron, cobalt (Co), and nickel (Ni) in the first transition-metal series have more properties in common than with the six metals below them.

Titanium (Ti), manganese, iron, and nickel make up nearly 2.5% of the crust of the Earth, and the other transition metals are rarer. All of the Row 4 transition metals except Sc, Ti, and Ni are essential to living organisms, as is only one metal from later rows, molybdenum (Mo). (See front end papers.) Iron is used along with a delocalized aromatic ring as the oxygen-binding agent in hemoglobin, and as an oxidation–reduction carrier in the cytochromes, where it accepts and gives up an electron and fluctuates between the +2 and +3 oxidation states. Copper also is found in oxidation–reduction proteins, and goes from the +1 to the +2 state and back again. The other six essential transition metals (V, Cr, Mn, Co, Zn, and Mo) generally are bound in the +2 state to enzymes, in which they push and pull electrons in other molecules during catalysis.

The common transition metals can be thought of in four classes: the pre-iron elements in Groups IIIB through VIIB, the iron triad Fe, Co, Ni, and the elements below them in Group VIIIB, the coinage metals (Cu, Ag, Au), and the zinc triad in Group IIB (Zn, Cd, Hg). The pre-iron metals all are tough, hard, and high-melting. They are used mainly as catalysts for chemical reactions in industry, and as additives to iron to make steels with special hardness, elasticity, strength at high temperatures, and corrosion resistance. The iron triad share the unusual property of being magnetic. They also begin a downward trend in melting point and hardness, and an upward trend in size, caused by the pairing of electrons in *d* orbitals. This trend continues with the soft and malleable coinage metals.

The coinage metals are unusually good conductors of electricity because their electronic configurations are $d^{10}s^1$ instead of d^9s^2 as the periodic table would lead one to expect. In Chapter 8 we commented on the special stability of filled d^{10} orbitals. This advantage in energy is enough to permit copper to take one of the two electrons in the outer *s* orbital and use it to fill the last of the *d* orbitals. This leaves the *s* orbitals half empty, and facilitates the movement of *s* electrons through the solid metal. (Because the *d* orbitals are more deeply buried, electrons in these orbitals are not as free to wander as are *s*-orbital electrons.) The same mobility of *s* electrons makes Cu, Ag, and Au good

---

[3] The names niobium and tantalum reflect the frustrations felt by chemists in separating these elements. They were discovered in 1802, but were thought to be the same element until ways of distinguishing them were developed in 1844. Tantalus, according to Greek mythology, was punished for his misdeeds by being chained to a tree in hell, immersed to his neck in water. Whenever he tried to drink, the water level receded and eluded him, and whenever he tried to eat fruit from the tree, the wind would blow the branches away from his grasp. This legend also has given us the word "tantalize." Niobe was the daughter of Tantalus.

ELECTRON-SHELL DIAGRAMS
OF THE COINAGE METALS

Cu
(copper)

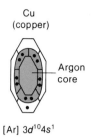

Argon core

[Ar] $3d^{10}4s^1$

Ag
(silver)

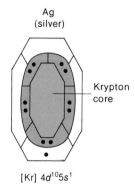

Krypton core

[Kr] $4d^{10}5s^1$

Au
(gold)

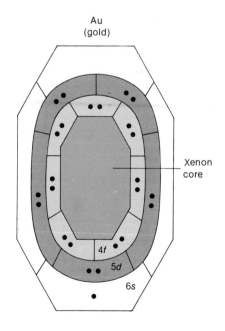

Xenon core

4f

5d

6s

All of the coinage metals have one electron in the outer *s* shell, and a filled *d* shell. Gold also has a filled *f* shell. All are good conductors of heat and electricity because of the mobility of their outer electrons.

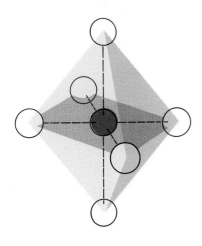

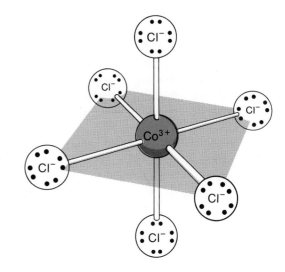

Six chloride ions octahedrally coordinated around a cobalt ion in $CoCl_6^{3-}$

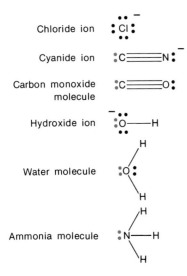

Chloride ion	$:\overset{\cdot\cdot}{\underset{\cdot\cdot}{Cl}}:^{-}$
Cyanide ion	$:C{\equiv}N:^{-}$
Carbon monoxide molecule	$:C{\equiv}O:$
Hydroxide ion	$\overset{\cdot\cdot}{\underset{\cdot\cdot}{O}}{-}H^{-}$
Water molecule	$:\overset{\cdot\cdot}{O}:$ (H, H)
Ammonia molecule	$:N{-}H$ (H, H)

For these common ligands in transition-metal complexes, the electron pair donated by the ligand for bonding to the metal ion is shown in color.

reflectors of light (absorption and immediate reemission at the same wavelengths) and conductors of heat. This is why copper and silver are employed as conductors in electronic circuitry, and why artificial satellites are sometimes gold-plated to reflect sunlight and keep the temperature down.

All of the s and d orbitals are filled in Zn, Cd, and Hg, thereby reducing the mobility of electrons from one atom to the next, and lowering the electrical and thermal conductivity of the metals. With all outer electrons paired, interactions between atoms are lessened, which makes the solids soft and low-melting. Mercury, the transition metal of largest atomic size, is a liquid above $-39°C$, but this is not a fundamental chemical difference because on a warm summer day cesium and gallium are liquids also.

d ORBITALS IN BONDING

With the transition metals, the use of d orbitals and electrons in chemical bonding is introduced. A great number of compounds known as *transition-metal complexes* are known. These are molecules or ions in which chemical groups that have lone electron pairs to share, share them with a central metal ion. The cobalt hexachloride ion shown above, $CoCl_6^{3-}$, is one example. It is built from a cobalt ion, Co^{3+}, with six chloride ions, Cl^-, around it at the corners of an octahedron (see above left). Each of the chloride ions is called a *ligand* and forms an electron-sharing bond with cobalt in which both electrons are provided by the ligand. This octahedral geometry is the most common one among transition metals, but square planar geometry is found in some compounds of Ni^{2+}, Pt^{2+}, and Au^{3+}, and tetrahedral coordination is observed for many ions, such as Co^{2+}. We will be concerned only with octahedral coordination in this section.

Deep red potassium ferricyanide, $K_3Fe(CN)_6$, and yellow potassium ferrocyanide, $K_4Fe(CN)_6$, are common laboratory reagents. They are remarkable because a mixture of the two, $KFeFe(CN)_6$, with one Fe^{2+} and one Fe^{3+}, leads to the very intense Prussian Blue pigment used in making blueprints. The ferricyanide ion, $Fe(CN)_6^{3-}$, and fer-

218

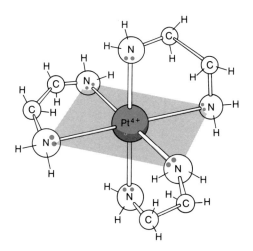

Three ethylenediamine molecules octahedrally coordinated to a platinum ion in Pt(en)$_3^{4+}$

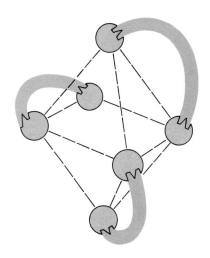

Arrangement of bidentate ligands. Each ligand has two "teeth."

rocyanide ion, Fe(CN)$_6^{4-}$, both are octahedral complexes in which Fe^{3+} or Fe^{2+} are surrounded by six cyanide ions, C≡N$^-$. Other common ligands in transition-metal complexes include the hydroxide and carbonate ions, and uncharged carbon monoxide, water, and ammonia molecules. The essential criterion for a ligand is the ability to provide an electron pair in a bond to the metal.

One ligating molecule or ion may donate more than one of the six electron pairs. Each carbonate ion provides two electron pairs in the complex Co(CO$_3$)$_3^{3-}$, and each molecule of ethylenediamine, H$_2$N—CH$_2$—CH$_2$—NH$_2$, does the same in Pt(en)$_3^{4+}$ ("en" is the standard abbreviation for ethylenediamine). These and other bidentate ("two-toothed") and tridentate ligands are shown at the right. In the Pt(en)$_3^{4+}$ complex drawn above, each ethylenediamine molecule bends back to occupy two of the six octahedral positions. There are two mirror-related ways of doing this, which leads to left-handed and right-handed complexes. Only two molecules of diethylenetriamine are needed to enclose a transition-metal ion completely, and one ethylenediaminetetraacetate ion (EDTA) (see next page) provides all six bonding electron pairs. EDTA completely encloses a metal ion in a molecular cocoon, and its attraction for metal ions is so strong that it will tear them away from many enzyme molecules. EDTA is used as a means of removing the last traces of metals from solutions in analytical and biochemical experiments where their presence would be confusing or harmful.

The antibiotic valinomycin and several other antibiotics work in the same way as EDTA. Valinomycin is known to make it easier for potassium ions to get through biological membranes, and x-ray crystallographers found out why recently when they solved the structure of the potassium salt of the antibiotic. The valinomycin molecule is a closed ring of 36 atoms, with 12 carbonyl (C=O) groups. It wraps around the potassium ion with six of the carbonyl oxygens as octahedral ligands, and effectively gives the ion an organic molecule "overcoat." The coated ion can slip through a membrane more easily because its charge is disguised. Part of the toxicity of this antibiotic to microorganisms is believed to lie in its upsetting of the natural balance of potassium ions within the cell membranes.

Carbonate ion

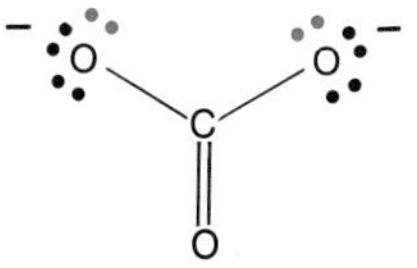

Oxalate ion

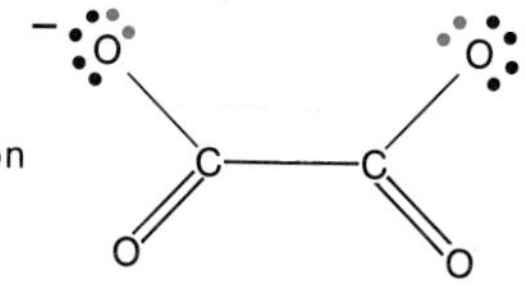

H$_2$N—CH$_2$—CH$_2$—NH$_2$

Ethylenediamine (en)

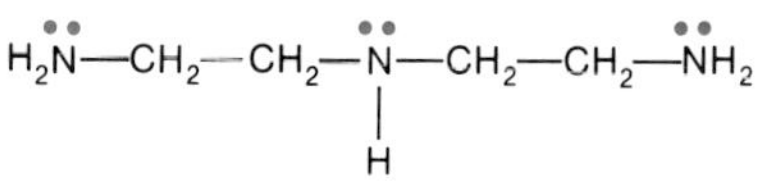

H$_2$N—CH$_2$—CH$_2$—N—CH$_2$—CH$_2$—NH$_2$
                         |
                         H

Diethylenetriamine (dien)

Shown above are three bidentate molecules, each of which can donate two electron pairs in ligand–metal bonds, and one tridentate ligand, which has three electron pairs for donation.

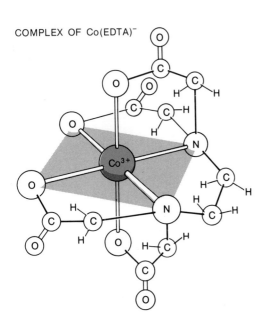

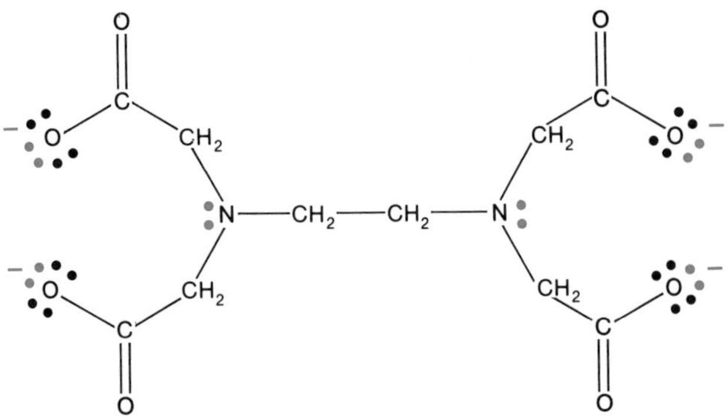

EDTA (ethylenediaminetetraacetate), shown diagrammatically above, and three-dimensionally at left. Each EDTA ion by itself can share six electron pairs with a metal ion in an octahedral complex.

THE HEME GROUP IN CYTOCHROME *c*

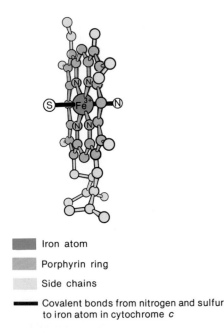

▮ Iron atom

▮ Porphyrin ring

▮ Side chains

▬ Covalent bonds from nitrogen and sulfur to iron atom in cytochrome *c*

Four of the six octahedral ligand positions of Fe^{3+} are occupied by four nitrogen lone pairs from the flat porphyrin ring, and the fifth and sixth positions are filled by other chemical groups. The double-bond electrons in the porphyrin ring actually are delocalized over the entire ring system.

The iron atom in the oxidation–reduction protein cytochrome *c* is octahedrally coordinated, with four of the six ligands coming from one large, planar porphyrin molecule, as shown below. This iron-porphyrin complex is called a *heme group*. In cytochrome *c* the fifth and sixth octahedral ligands, above and below the plane of the heme group, are provided by a nitrogen and a sulfur atom from the protein wrapped around the heme. The delocalized electrons in the porphyrin ring are shared with the iron, thereby changing its oxidation–reduction behavior. Hemoglobin is another combination of heme groups and protein, in which the fifth octahedral ligand is a nitrogen atom from the protein, and the sixth position is left open for binding the O_2 molecule that each hemoglobin molecule carries in the bloodstream.

One prominent characteristic of all transition-metal complexes is their wide variety of colors, which indicates the absorption of visible light by electrons within the complex. This happens because the six octahedral ligands alter the energies of the *d* orbitals of the metal unequally, and the resulting spacing between different *d*-level energies is small enough to fall in the visible region. In the absence of ligands, all five of these *d* orbitals in a transition-metal ion have the same energy. Now imagine that six negative charges (the electron pairs on the ligands) are brought in toward the ion from an infinite distance, along the octahedral directions $\pm x$, $\pm y$, and $\pm z$ (see opposite page). The negative charges will come directly toward the maximum-probability lobes of the d_{z^2} and $d_{x^2-y^2}$ orbitals. If electrons occupy these orbitals their energies will be raised because of repulsion from the incoming ligands. In contrast, the ligands move between the lobes of the d_{xy}, d_{yz}, and d_{xz} orbitals, so the energy of electrons in these orbitals is less perturbed. The original *d*-orbital energy level is split into two levels, as shown at the right, with an energy separation of Δ. These are called the *t* and *e* levels for reasons irrelevant to this discussion, but you can remember which is which by thinking of the letters as standing for "three-orbital" and "excited."

The way that the outer electrons in a transition-metal ion fill these two levels depends on the energy difference between the *t* and *e* levels, which is called the *crystal-field splitting energy*, Δ. The Cr^{3+} ion has

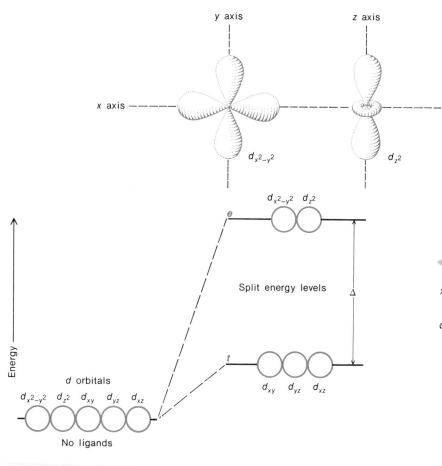

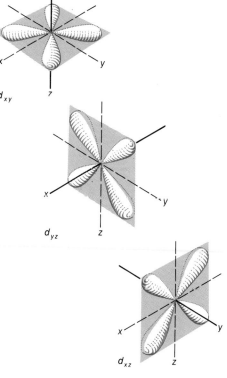

As ligands approach a metal ion along the octahedral directions ($\pm x$, $\pm y$, $\pm z$), electrons in the metal d orbitals are repelled. This repulsion is stronger in the $d_{x^2-y^2}$ and d_{z^2} orbitals (the two e orbitals), which point directly at the incoming ligand electron pairs, and weaker in the d_{xy}, d_{yz}, and d_{xz} orbitals (the three t orbitals), which are oriented 45° away. The energy difference between t and e levels when ligands are present is called the crystal-field splitting energy, Δ. Whether electrons will add to the e orbitals before pairing in the t orbitals depends on the relative strengths of electron–electron repulsion and the crystal-field splitting energy.

three outer electrons, and in the ground state of the ion each electron occupies one of the three d_{xy}, d_{yz}, and d_{xz} orbitals in the t level (right). Fe^{3+} has five outer electrons, and if the ligands around the iron produce only a small crystal-field splitting, Δ, then the electrostatic repulsion between electrons paired in the same orbital will ensure that one electron goes into each d orbital: three in the t level and two in the e. This is called a *high-spin complex* because the electron spins are not paired in the orbitals. These spins can be observed by magnetic measurements. If the ligands produce a large energy splitting, it may take less energy to pair electrons in the t orbitals than to place two electrons in the higher-energy e orbitals ($d_{x^2-y^2}$ and d_{z^2}) where they must come close to the electrons of the ligands. In such a case four electrons are paired in the lower orbitals, thus leaving only one electron unpaired and creating a *low-spin complex*, as shown at the right.

Split energy levels in Cr^{3+} and Fe^{3+} ions

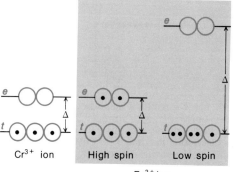

221

"Eyeball spectroscopy" of cobalt complexes

Co^{3+} Complex	Wavelength absorbed (Å)	Color absorbed	Color seen
CoF_6^{3-}	7000	Red	Green
$Co(CO_3)_3^{3-}$	6400	Red-orange	Greenish blue
$Co(H_2O)_6^{3+}$	6000	Orange	Blue
$Co(NH_3)_5Cl^{2+}$	5350	Yellow	Purple
$Co(NH_3)_5OH^{2+}$	5000	Blue-green	Raspberry red
$Co(NH_3)_6^{3+}$	4750	Blue	Yellow-orange
$Co(en)_3^{3+}$	4700	Blue	Yellow-orange
$Co(CN)_5Br^{3-}$	4150	Violet	Lemon yellow
$Co(CN)_6^{3-}$	3100	Ultraviolet	Pale yellow (tail of absorption in the visible region)

Stronger ligands, hence larger crystal-field splitting, cause absorption of radiation at shorter wavelengths, and a shift in the color absorbed and the residual color seen.

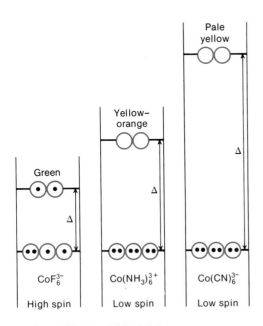

CoF$_6^{3-}$ absorbs red light and hence appears green. Co(NH$_3$)$_6^{3+}$, with stronger ligands, absorbs blue light and appears yellow-orange. The absorption maximum for Co(CN)$_6^{3-}$ occurs mainly in the ultraviolet region.

In both high-spin and low-spin complexes, electrons in the t level can absorb photons of light and jump to the upper e level. We can measure the value of the splitting energy, Δ, from the absorption spectrum of a complex, or we can get a rough idea of relative splittings from color alone. In the table above are listed several octahedral complexes of Co^{3+}, along with their main absorption wavelengths and colors. Knowing the relationship between color and energy in these and similar complexes, we can rank the various ligands for effectiveness in producing splitting in the d energy levels:

$$CN^- > en > NH_3 > OH^-, H_2O, CO_3^{2-} > F^- > Cl^- > Br^-$$

This list varies somewhat from one transition metal to another, but generally a more intense, concentrated packet of negative charge on a ligand causes a larger crystal-field splitting than does a large, diffuse cloud of negative density. For example, a localized lone electron pair on a nitrogen atom in ethylenediamine or ammonia is more effective than the diffuse negative charge on a bromide ion.

For Co^{3+}, fluoride ions as ligands cause such a small splitting that the six outer electrons in Co^{3+} can spread out among both levels to produce a high-spin complex with four unpaired electrons (see left). CoF_6^{3-} absorbs radiation of low-energy red wavelengths, and thus is green. Ammonia is a stronger ligand, and produces a large enough splitting to keep all six Co^{3+} electrons paired in the d_{xy}, d_{yz}, and d_{xz} orbitals, which point away from the lone pairs of the ammonia nitrogens. When electrons are promoted to the upper e state in $Co(NH_3)_6^{3+}$, blue light is absorbed, thereby giving solutions of the complex a yellow-orange hue. Because the cyanide ion, CN^-, is a strong ligand, capable of producing a large splitting, absorption for $Co(CN)_6^{3-}$ occurs in the ultraviolet. The small tail of absorption extending into the violet region gives $Co(CN)_6^{3-}$ solutions a washed-out yellow cast.

The same considerations apply to iron complexes in biological systems. Blood is red because the iron–porphyrin complex in hemoglobin absorbs green light. Chlorophyll is green because the magnesium-porphyrin complex absorbs light at the blue and red ends of the spectrum but not in the middle (see below). This rather paradoxical behavior of the main photosynthetic pigment in nature *not* absorbing light at wavelengths where solar energy is most abundant (5000 Å) is remedied by having carotene and similar molecules nearby to trap these more plentiful wavelengths and pass the electronic energy on to chlorophyll for use in synthesis. In previous chapters we saw the two main sources of closely spaced electronic energy levels—delocalized aromatic rings and transition-metal complexes—and the consequent absorption of visible light. Heme and chlorophyll combine both sources in a single molecule.

You may have wondered why this section was entitled "*d* Orbitals in Bonding," when we have seen no covalent bonding so far between metal ion and ligands. The simple *crystal field theory* that we have been using to explain energy-level splitting is indeed a purely electrostatic theory, which assumes that the metal remains an ion and the lone pairs remain on the ligands. In the more realistic molecular orbital treatment, six orbitals from the metal ion, one s, three p, and the two d orbitals that point toward the ligands, are combined with six ligand orbitals to produce twelve molecular orbitals, six of them bonding and six antibonding. The six electron pairs furnished by the ligands are used to fill the bonding orbitals and make covalent bonds from the metal to the ligands. The d_{xy}, d_{yz}, and d_{xz} metal orbitals are not involved in the combining process because they have the wrong symmetry to combine with the σ orbitals from the ligands. The end result is the same as obtained from crystal field theory. After six covalent bonds have been formed between metal and ligands, the three unused d orbitals and all of the outer electrons on the metal ion remain and can be given the kind of treatment we used with crystal field theory. The undisturbed energy level of these three orbitals corresponds to the t level, and the e level corresponds to the lowest two of the six antibonding molecular orbitals. Crystal field theory assumes that the bonds between metal and ligands are ionic, and molecular orbital theory assumes them to be covalent. As usual, the truth lies somewhere in between.

The chlorophyll molecule absorbs blue and red light (a) but not the wavelengths in between. With these absorbed wavelengths gone (b), the residual radiation gives chlorophyll a yellow-green color.

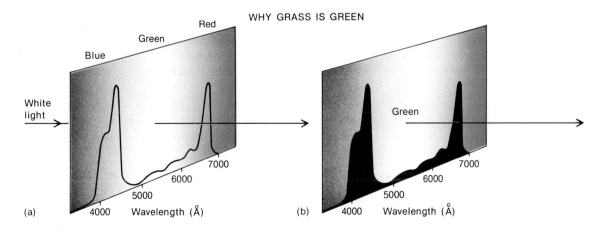

WHY GRASS IS GREEN

223

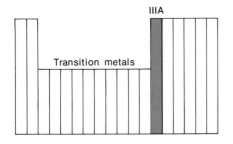

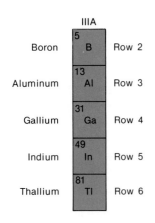

	IIIA	
Boron	5 B	Row 2
Aluminum	13 Al	Row 3
Gallium	31 Ga	Row 4
Indium	49 In	Row 5
Thallium	81 Tl	Row 6

BORON NITRIDE

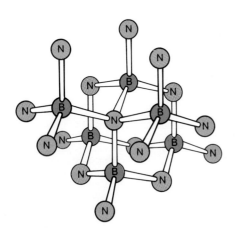

Boron nitride has the diamond structure, with each B atom surrounded by four N, and each N by four B. Each carbon atom in diamond has four bonding electrons. The deficit of one electron in each B atom is compensated by an excess of one electron in each N.

GROUP IIIA: B, Al, Ga, In, Tl

We encounter the borderline between metals and nonmetals for the first time in Group IIIA; boron at the top of the group is nonmetallic. Crystalline boron has atoms arranged at the twelve vertices of an icosahedron, and the various boron hydrides with formulas B_2H_6, B_4H_{10}, B_5H_{11}, B_9H_{15}, and so on, have boron frameworks that are fragments of icosahedra. They all have high heats of combustion with oxygen per unit of weight, and at one time were considered seriously as possible rocket fuels.

Boron makes very strong covalent bonds to C and N in crystals. Boron carbide, B_4C, and boron nitride, BN, are nearly as hard and as good abrasives as diamond. Boron nitride has the diamond structure (bottom left) and is isoelectronic with diamond. Every boron atom has one less electron than carbon, but every nitrogen atom has one more, so there are just enough electrons to hold the diamondlike structure together. Boric oxide, B_2O_3, is obtained from natural borax, $Na_2B_4O_7 \cdot 10H_2O$, which was made famous by the Death Valley twenty-mule teams that hauled it out of desert deposits.

Aluminum is a strong, light metal, especially corrosion-resistant because of its tightly adhering oxide coating of Al_2O_3 If aluminum metal lacked this oxide film, it would be sufficiently reactive to break down warm water as magnesium does:

$$Al + 3H_2O \rightarrow Al^{3+} + 3OH^- + \tfrac{3}{2}H_2 \rightarrow Al(OH)_3^- + \tfrac{3}{2}H_2$$

Crystalline aluminum oxide or corundum, Al_2O_3, is used as an abrasive. Rubies are Al_2O_3 crystals with a few of the Al^{3+} ions replaced by the transition-metal ion Cr^{3+}, which makes rubies deep red. Blue sapphires have a small amount of Ti^{3+} ions instead. Artificial rubies now are made in commercial quantities for use as bearings in watches and other precision instruments. Pure aluminum is obtained by electrolysis of bauxite, a hydrate of Al_2O_3. (Hydrates have definite amounts of water as part of a crystal structure, as in natural borax above.)

Among the Group IIIA elements, only aluminum is appreciably common in the Earth's crust (6%), and none of these elements is necessary to living organisms. Gallium, indium, and thallium are rare and relatively unimportant. Gallium sometimes is used in thermometers because of its great liquid range; it melts at 30°C but boils only above 2500°C. The boiling point is normal in comparison with nearby elements in the table, and it is the melting point that is unusually low. This probably arises because gallium has an open, irregular crystal structure that is easily disarrayed. The melting point of indium also is depressed, but not as much as gallium. Because gallium expands when it freezes (another indication of weak association of atoms in the solid) it finds a minor use in dental alloys and type metal. Both fillings and type must expand as they solidify to take a sharp impression of their moulds. Indium is used in some alloys, and thallium salts find their main use in odorless, tasteless rat poisons.

224

GROUP IVA: INSULATORS AND SEMICONDUCTORS

A sharp break in properties occurs between boron and carbon, and there is less of a discontinuity between Groups IIIA and IVA in later periods of the table. Carbon is a nonmetal with exactly the same number of outer electrons and orbitals, which facilitates the formation of the maximum number of bonds to other atoms. We will discuss carbon compounds in greater detail in Chapters 18–21. Silicon is more metallic than carbon, and we have compared carbonates and silicates in previous chapters. Germanium lies on the borderline between nonmetals and metals, and tin and lead both are metals. All of the Group IVA elements have common oxidation states of +2 and +4, which represent either the loss or sharing of half or all of their outer electrons. When the metals at the bottom of the group *lose* electrons, they favor losing only two of them to form the +2 state, whereas the nonmetals at the top, which only *share* electrons, more commonly occur in the +4 oxidation state.

About 21% of the atoms in the crust of the Earth are silicon; carbon accounts for 0.03%; and less than one atom per million is germanium, tin, or lead. The relative proportions for C and Si are reversed in a living organism: 11% of the body weight typically is C, and Si and Sn are needed in trace amounts; Ge and Pb are of no use. Lead, like most of the other heavy metals, is toxic.

Silicon and germanium are the cornerstones of transistor technology and the mini-electronics industry. Pure silicon and germanium are poor conductors of electricity because their outer electrons are tied up in the covalent bonds of the diamondlike framework. Diamond is an *insulator* because it is not easy to supply enough energy to pull the covalent-bond electrons loose and permit them to conduct electricity through the crystal. Less energy is required to free the electrons in silicon, and even less is required in germanium. These atoms are larger and hold their electrons less tightly. They are not conductors in the metallic sense of the word, but are *semiconductors*. At low voltages they are insulators, but they begin to conduct electricity if the applied voltage is high enough. Electrical conductivity decreases as temperature increases in metals because the vibrations of the atoms make passage of electrons more difficult. This effect is overshadowed in semiconductors by the greater number of electrons that are "shaken loose" from bonds at higher temperatures; thus semiconductors become better conductors as the temperature increases.

A better way of increasing electrical conductivity in these semiconductors is to purify them as much as possible, then "dope" them with small amounts of Al or P atoms to replace some of the Si atoms. (The replacements for Ge in the fourth row would be Ga and As.) Every aluminum atom substituted introduces a one-electron deficiency into the diamond framework, and every phosphorus atom brings with it an extra electron. Both of these controlled impurities make silicon a better conductor of electricity. With phosphorus, the extra electron fits into none of the covalent bonds of the diamond lattice, and can serve as the carrier of current. With aluminum, the cascading of electrons, tumbling domino-fashion into the electron vacancies, creates what physicists describe as an electron "hole," which migrates against the electric

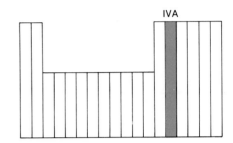

IVA

	IVA	
Carbon	6 C	Row 2
Silicon	14 Si	Row 3
Germanium	32 Ge	Row 4
Tin	50 Sn	Row 5
Lead	82 Pb	Row 6

MOBILE ELECTRONS AND "HOLES"
IN "DOPED" SILICON

p–silicon (positive)   n–silicon (negative)

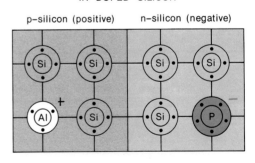

Each phosphorus atom (right) donates one excess electron, which is free to wander throughout the silicon lattice. Each aluminum atom (left) contributes an electron deficiency, which can be thought of as a positive "hole" that also is free to move about in the silicon lattice.

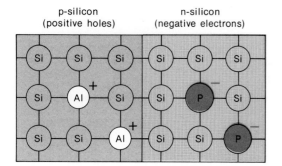

p-silicon
(positive holes)

n-silicon
(negative electrons)

A P–N SEMICONDUCTOR JUNCTION AS A CURRENT RECTIFIER

Left: p-silicon has aluminum atoms substituted occasionally for silicon atoms, and electron vacancies, or holes, which are mobile. n-Silicon has occasional phosphorus atoms that contribute extra electrons.

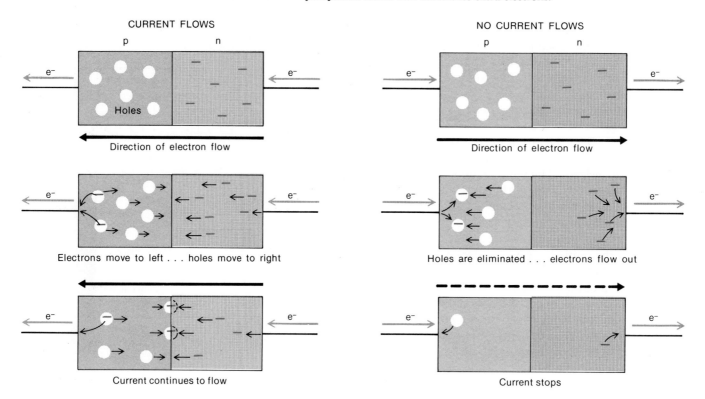

CURRENT FLOWS

NO CURRENT FLOWS

p   n

p   n

e⁻   e⁻

e⁻   e⁻

Holes

Direction of electron flow

Direction of electron flow

e⁻   e⁻

e⁻   e⁻

Electrons move to left . . . holes move to right

Holes are eliminated . . . electrons flow out

e⁻   e⁻

e⁻   e⁻

Current continues to flow

Current stops

More electrons come into the silicon from the wire at the right, and more holes are generated at the left as electrons migrate from the p-silicon into the wire of the external circuit. Continuous current flow is possible from right to left.

When holes and excess electrons have been eliminated, further current flow is impossible because there is nothing to carry the current through the silicon, which becomes an insulator. Continuous current flow from left to right is not possible.

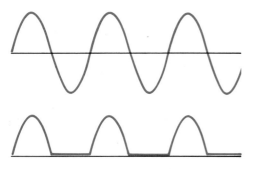

Before: Alternating current

After: Half-wave rectified direct current

A p–n junction transistor can act as a rectifier, which converts alternating current into direct current by eliminating current flow in one direction.

field rather than with it, but which also can carry a net electric current. Phosphorus-doped silicon is n-silicon (for negative electrons), and aluminum-doped silicon is p-silicon (for positive holes). When the two types are brought together, the result is a p–n junction. Electric current can be transmitted only one way across this p–n junction, as shown in the diagram above. The junction is a rectifier, capable of turning alternating current into pulses of direct current. Other semiconductor devices using p- and n-silicon have been designed, which can replace most of the old vacuum tubes with tiny and rugged transistors that operate on only a fraction of the power formerly required.

226

GROUP VA; THE NITROGEN CYCLE

We have discussed elemental nitrogen, ammonia, and nitric acid, and phosphorus and the phosphates, in previous chapters. Eighty percent of our atmosphere is N_2 gas. Although this amount represents only a tiny fraction of the planet as a whole, it is important because it is concentrated at the surface, where life evolved. Nitrogen and phosphorus are essential to living organisms; arsenic, antimony, and bismuth are not.

Nitrogen can form covalently bonded molecular compounds with carbon and is essential in many biological molecules. Proteins are long-chain polymers of amino acids with the backbone structure

$$-N-C-C-N-C-C-N-C-C-N-C-C-$$

Ammonia is a base because the nitrogen atom has a lone electron pair that can bind a proton:

$$:NH_3 + H^+ \rightarrow NH_4^+$$

A lone pair on a nitrogen atom also makes bases of many organic compounds such as pyridine, drawn at the lower right. Nitrogen-containing organic bases are the central stairsteps in the double-stranded DNA of the genes, where the bases provide the means of encoding genetic information. In the porphyrin ring, seen on Page 220, nitrogen atoms with their lone pairs are the ligands to the central iron atom. Many other nitrogen-containing ring compounds are bound to enzymes or are used as carriers of chemical energy.

In all of these biological nitrogen-containing molecules, nitrogen is in a reduced state with an oxidation number of -3, as in ammonia. Living organisms require a supply of reduced nitrogen to synthesize these molecules, but most of them cannot get it from atmospheric N_2. Fortunately, there are bacteria that can "fix" nitrogen by converting N_2 to NH_3. Energy is required to accomplish this, but this expenditure of energy is worthwhile to the bacterium because it provides a source of reduced nitrogen for synthetic purposes. When organisms die, most of the reduced nitrogen in proteins and other compounds remains reduced and is reused by other organisms. However, there are inevitable losses in this process, and new reduced nitrogen is required. The rest of the living world cannibalizes the efforts of nitrogen-fixing bacteria to keep the system going. Many such bacteria live in the root nodules of legumes such as soybeans, which is why agricultural land sometimes is replenished by growing a crop of soybeans and plowing the crop under at maturity. If given nitrates (with nitrogen ON = +5) instead of ammonia (with nitrogen ON = -3), plants can reduce them and incorporate them into protein. Thus the critical factor is not the oxidation state of nitrogen, it is the unreactivity of gaseous N_2 and the inability of plants or animals to do anything with it. The triple bond in the N_2 molecule is so stable and resistant to attack that reactions involving N_2, either oxidation or reduction, are hopelessly slow. Nitrogen-fixing bacteria, alone among living organisms, have catalytic enzymes that speed up these reactions.

VA

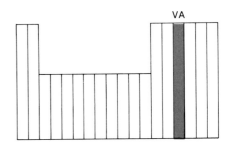

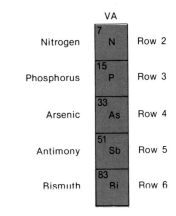

Nitrogen	7 N	Row 2
Phosphorus	15 P	Row 3
Arsenic	33 As	Row 4
Antimony	51 Sb	Row 5
Bismuth	83 Bi	Row 6

PYRIDINE BASE

A lone electron pair on a nitrogen atom in an organic ring can bond to a proton, just as in the conversion of NH_3 to NH_4^+. Like ammonia, pyridine and other such organic nitrogen compounds are bases.

A limited amount of N_2 is fixed in the atmosphere each year by electrical discharge in lightning, whereby the relative unreactivity of N_2 is overcome by energy from the lightning discharge. The products include acidic oxides of nitrogen, which means that the rain during a thunderstorm actually is a very dilute solution of nitric acid. More important as a rival to bacterial processes is industrial nitrogen fixation by methods involving catalysts and high pressures that were developed by Fritz Haber in Germany during World War I:

$$N_2 + 3H_2 \rightarrow 2NH_3$$

Once fixed as ammonia, nitrogen then can be used directly as fertilizers to grow crops, or oxidized to nitrates for explosives to blow them up.

Short of burning organic molecules in fluorine, the greatest amount of energy can be obtained from them by burning them in oxygen. In this combustion process, rapid in fire and slow and controlled in biological metabolism, oxygen with $ON = 0$ is reduced to H_2O and CO_2, which have an oxygen ON of -2, while hydrogen and carbon in the fuel molecules are oxidized from effective $ON = 0$ to $ON = +1$ and $+4$, respectively. *Denitrifying bacteria* (not the same organisms as nitrogen-fixing bacteria) can oxidize their foods with nitrate instead of O_2. If oxygen is scarce in soils, these bacteria can reduce nitrate to N_2, thereby reducing nitrogen from $ON = +5$ to 0. They only obtain 90% as much energy in this process because nitrate is not quite as good an oxidizing agent as is O_2 gas. The other 10% is not lost, however, for every scrap of energy is used in the interlocking network of life on this planet. After the *nitrogen-fixing bacteria* have reduced N_2 to NH_3, a third class of bacteria, the *nitrifying bacteria*, can use the fixed nitrogen of ammonia or amines as foods, thereby oxidizing them back to nitrates with O_2. With nitrates restored again, the net result of the activities of all three kinds of bacteria is the oxidation of the denitrifying bacteria's foods with O_2.

All of these relationships are summarized in the nitrogen cycle, diagramed at the top of the opposite page. The three-sided loop (a) represents the oxidation–reduction round-robin we have just considered, loop (b) represents the exchange of nitrogen at $ON = -3$ during growth and decay, and (c) represents the replenishment of the $ON = -3$ nitrogen by plants. We do not depend on nitrogen reactions for energy sources, nor do any of the higher plants or animals. From a purely human viewpoint, it might seem that loop (b) was sufficient, and that the other steps in the nitrogen cycle were wasted effort. But this is not true. Plants can use either ammonia or nitrate ion as a nitrogen source for protein synthesis, but ammonia has disadvantages. In the form of ammonium ions, as found in the soil, it is a cation very much like Na^+ and K^+. It is trapped easily between the silicate layers of clay minerals, and does not migrate rapidly toward the roots of the plants it could nourish. The negatively charged nitrate ions travel more freely through the soil. In this respect nitrates are better fertilizers than liquid ammonia. Nitrifying bacteria therefore help by converting ammonia into the more easily circulated nitrate ions.

Even so, are not the denitrifying bacteria dangerous parasites that turn useful nitrate into useless molecular N_2? This was thought to be

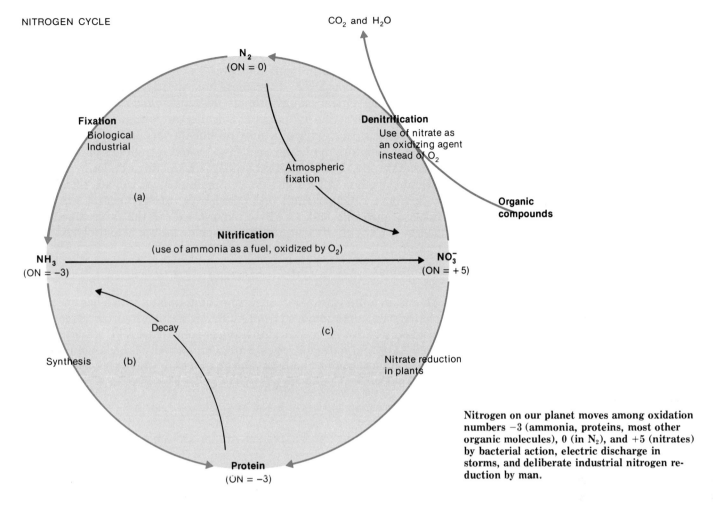

CO$_2$ and H$_2$O

N$_2$
(ON = 0)

Fixation
Biological
Industrial

Denitrification
Use of nitrate as
an oxidizing agent
instead of O$_2$

Atmospheric
fixation

(a)

**Organic
compounds**

Nitrification
(use of ammonia as a fuel, oxidized by O$_2$)

NH$_3$
(ON = −3)

NO$_3^-$
(ON = +5)

Decay

(c)

Synthesis   (b)

Nitrate reduction
in plants

Protein
(ON = −3)

Nitrogen on our planet moves among oxidation numbers −3 (ammonia, proteins, most other organic molecules), 0 (in N$_2$), and +5 (nitrates) by bacterial action, electric discharge in storms, and deliberate industrial nitrogen reduction by man.

true at the turn of the century when denitrifying bacteria first were discovered. A prominent British biochemist painted a bleak picture of world starvation unless an industrial process for fixing atmospheric nitrogen was found quickly. Fortunately, the race for survival between us and *Pseudomonas denitrificans* was a phony race. The denitrifying bacteria assist other life forms by preventing all of the world's nitrogen supply from slowly becoming locked up in mineral deposits such as nitrates. They keep the nitrogen circulating. The nitrogen gas that they produce eventually is fixed again by other bacteria, lightning discharges, and industrial chemistry, and ultimately feeds back into the biological cycle.

P. denitrificans is not a villain, but *we* may be when we upset the natural nitrogen cycle with huge supplies of industrially fixed ammonia and nitrates. When nutrients become too plentiful, algae and other life forms "explode" in population to the point where they deplete the available oxygen supply and all die. This process is known as eutrophication ("good" + "feeding"), and its ill effects have been seen already in Lake Erie, polluted both by industry and by runoff from agricultural fertilizers. The end result is a lake choked with algae, devoid of oxygen, and filled with dead fish. In the balance of nature, too much can be as disastrous as too little.

ADENOSINE TRIPHOSPHATE (ATP)

Adenine

Ribose
sugar

Adenosine

CH_2

OH

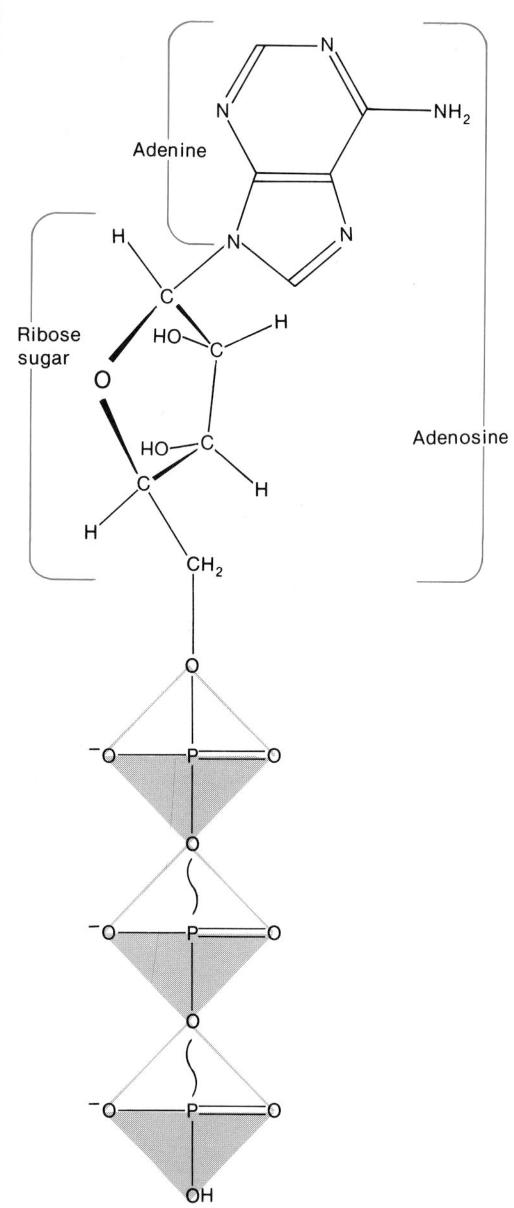

Adenine, an organic base, is linked covalently with ribose, a five-carbon sugar, to form adenosine. This in turn is connected to one, two, or three phosphates to make adenosine monophosphate (AMP), diphosphate (ADP), or triphosphate (ATP). The unusual amount of energy released when one or two of the phosphates are removed from ATP is symbolized by wavy bond lines instead of straight ones.

PHOSPHORUS AND ENERGY STORAGE

Phosphorus is as essential for life as is nitrogen, but for a different reason. It is absent in proteins, but present in the backbones of nucleic acid chains such as DNA. Even more importantly, phosphorus is at the heart of the central energy-storage molecule, *adenosine triphosphate* (ATP), shown at the left. Just as silicates can form polysilicate chains by sharing corner oxygen atoms of silicate tetrahedra, so PO_4^{3-} can polymerize into polyphosphates. Two linked tetrahedra build a pyrophosphate ion, $P_2O_7^{4-}$. Metaphosphates have rings or long chains of PO_4 tetrahedra. ATP consists of three linked phosphate tetrahedra, with ribose (a sugar ring) and adenine (a nitrogen-containing base) hooked onto one end. ATP is remarkable for the large amount of energy it gives off when one of the phosphate groups is hydrolyzed away by water:

$$ATP + H_2O \rightarrow ADP + phosphate + 7.3 \text{ kcal of energy per mole}$$

ADP is an abbreviation for adenosine diphosphate, which has one phosphate tetrahedron removed from ATP. Most other hydrolysis reactions yield only two or three kilocalories of energy. When ATP is synthesized from ADP and inorganic phosphate, an unusually large amount of energy can be stored in the final phosphate bond, which then is available for later use:

$$ADP + phosphate + 7.3 \text{ kcal of energy} \rightarrow ATP + H_2O$$

ATP is the central and universal storage molecule for energy in all living organisms. If energy is to be extracted from foods and stored as fats or sugars, the energy first is used to make ATP molecules, then these provide the push for the synthesis of other energy-storage molecules. Just as "money has no memory," so ATP molecules are freely interchangeable throughout an organism, and the energy extracted by various processes is in no way tied to its particular source or origin. ATP is the "laundering operation" of biological energy finances.

Biochemists sometimes write ATP as A—P~P~P, in which A stands for adenine plus ribose, or adenosine, each P represents a phosphate group, and the wavy lines represent bonds that liberate unusually large amounts of energy when hydrolyzed. Although the middle wavy bond is a "high-energy bond," also with a heat of hydrolysis of 7.3 kcal mole^{-1}, this bond is of little biological importance.

What is the chemical basis for the abnormally high energy of hydrolysis of these phosphate bonds? Why is ATP so unstable relative to ADP and phosphate? The answer lies in the charges on the polyphosphate chain. The triphosphate group has three to four negative charges, and the mutual repulsion of these charges makes the ATP molecule less stable than expected. The single- and double-bond structure of the phosphates drawn at the left is only schematic. In reality, the double-bond electrons are spread over the entire triphosphate group, thereby giving every P—O bond a partial double bond character. The negative charges also are delocalized over the entire chain. The drawings at the top of the opposite page are an attempt to illustrate a dynamic and constantly changing situation by one singly and doubly bonded struc-

230

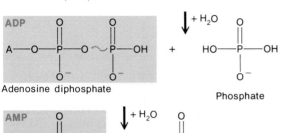

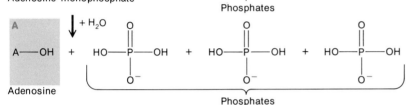

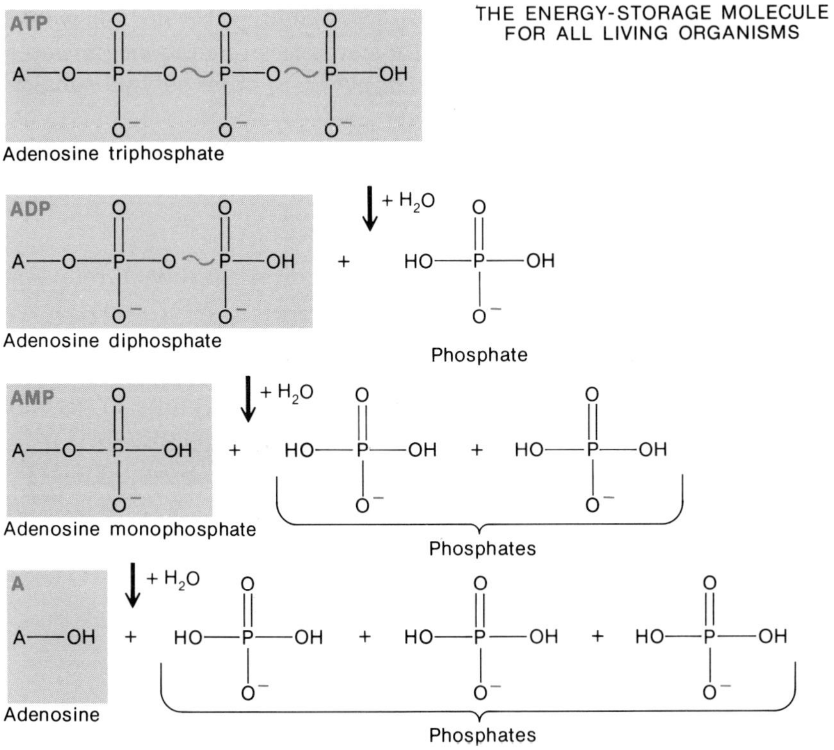

The two wavy bond lines symbolize the bonds that release unusually large amounts of energy when they are hydrolyzed, or cleaved by water. Cleavage of the first bond releases 7.3 kcal mole^{-1} of energy as ATP becomes ADP.

ADP has one remaining high-energy bond, which upon hydrolysis releases another 7.3 kcal mole^{-1} of energy in the formation of AMP.

The remaining bond between adenosine and phosphate in AMP releases a normal 3.4 kcal mole^{-1} when hydrolyzed.

ture, and are only approximately right. For example, in the roughly neutral conditions of a cell, half of the phosphate is found as HPO_4^{2-} and half as the $H_2PO_4^-$ ions drawn above. The ATP, ADP, and AMP structures drawn will be correct for approximately 50% of the molecules, and the others will have lost one more H^+ each. Nevertheless, the molecules as shown illustrate the principles of charge repulsion and energy in ATP.

When ATP is hydrolyzed and one phosphate group is split off by water, the charges on the ATP group are separated from one another, as shown at the middle of the sequence of drawings above. Less charge is left on ADP, and the two ions repel one another. Extra energy is given off—the energy that originally was needed to bring a negatively charged phosphate group up to the already negatively charged ADP and make them bond together. Another gain in stability is obtained when the repulsions of the remaining negative charges on ADP are relieved by splitting it into AMP and phosphate. The hydrolysis energy of the second phosphate bond likewise is correspondingly high:

$$ADP + H_2O \rightarrow AMP + phosphate + 7.3 \text{ kcal mole}^{-1}$$

Splitting the final phosphate group off adenosine produces no more charge separation, so this hydrolysis energy is normal:

$$AMP + H_2O \rightarrow adenosine + phosphate + 3.4 \text{ kcal mole}^{-1}$$

The key to short-term energy storage in every living organism on Earth thus is found in the charge repulsions on small polyphosphate ions of ATP. Because of this universality of ATP, it has been suggested that ATP hydrolysis is one of the oldest chemical reactions of living organisms. By this hypothesis, one of the first steps toward life would have been the acquisition of energy for synthetic or metabolic purposes by the degradation of naturally occurring ATP or other polyphosphates in the surrounding ocean. (Even today, some bacteria store energy in the form of small inclusions of polyphosphates within their cell fluid.) All of the other energy-extracting and energy-storing machinery would have evolved later to keep these ATP-using reactions going in the face of shortages of natural ATP.

In comparison with nitrogen and phosphorus, the other Group VA elements—arsenic, antimony, and bismuth—are of lesser importance. One of the reasons for the poisonous character of many arsenic compounds is that arsenic can almost, but not quite, mimic the chemical behavior of phosphorus. It can substitute for phosphorus in certain compounds, but then is unable to function as phosphorus can, with lethal consequences. Arsenic lies on the borderline between nonmetals and metals. Antimony and bismuth both are metals of relatively little use except in some alloys used in making metal type because they expand upon solidifying.

GROUP VIA: THE OXYGEN FAMILY

We have been discussing oxygen so continually that it seems superfluous to discuss it here in detail. Although we think of oxygen mainly as an atmospheric gas, only one oxygen atom in 600,000 on our planet is found in the atmosphere. The remainder are locked in the silicates and other minerals in the crust and mantle. If one assumes that the primitive Earth lost its original atmosphere during a high-temperature phase of its early history, the secondary atmosphere obtained by outgassing of the planetary interior would have contained little or no free O_2. This reduced atmosphere, in which life is believed to have evolved, would have consisted mainly of hydrogen and its compounds with the second-row nonmetals—CH_4, NH_3, and H_2O—with smaller amounts of H_2S. The best evidence that we have today suggests that our present oxygen-rich atmosphere was a by-product of life itself, from the splitting of water during photosynthesis:

$$\text{carbon source} + H_2O \xrightarrow[\text{energy}]{\text{light}} \text{reduced organic molecules} + O_2$$

If we think of how much oxygen is in the atmosphere and its importance to us, the turnover of the atmosphere from reducing to oxidizing seems like an immense change. If we regard it only as a freeing of less than two parts per million of mineral oxygen, then the turnover seems less revolutionary. But such a two-parts-per-million change is the basis for all O_2-breathing life.

The most common sulfur compounds are H_2S and various sulfates, SO_4^{2-}, and sulfites, SO_3^{2-}. Sulfur is found in living organisms mainly in disulfide —S—S— cross-links between chains in proteins. Photosynthesis in blue-green algae and all higher plants uses water as the source of hydrogen for synthesis, and liberates oxygen. Photosynthesis by purple and green sulfur bacteria depends on a supply of H_2S instead, and yields sulfate ions as a by-product. Other bacteria, the *Desulfo-*

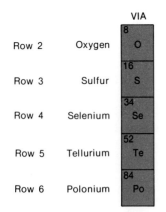

VIA

Row 2	Oxygen	8 O
Row 3	Sulfur	16 S
Row 4	Selenium	34 Se
Row 5	Tellurium	52 Te
Row 6	Polonium	84 Po

vibrio, use sulfate to oxidize their foods instead of nitrate or oxygen. Green plants and animals share an oxygen cycle in which photosynthesis oxidizes H_2O to O_2 in the process of storing energy in sugar molecules, and respiration reduces O_2 back to H_2O when energy is extracted from organic molecules. In a similar fashion, the sulfur bacteria and *Desulfovibrio* share a sulfur cycle, in which bacterial photosynthesis oxidizes H_2S to SO_4^{2-}, and bacterial respiration reduces SO_4^{2-} back down to H_2S. In both cases, the driving energy for the cycle is the radiation absorbed from sunlight. This sulfur cycle probably arose early in the Earth's history, and represents a process that did not become universal in the sense that water-using photosynthesis and oxygen respiration did. We will come back to these energy cycles and the evolution of metabolic processes in Chapters 23 and 26. Nitrate respiration, wherever it occurs in bacteria, always is an alternative to oxygen respiration, which the bacteria prefer if oxygen is available. Other than molecular oxygen, nitrate, and sulfate, no other chemical substance seems to have been used as an oxidant of foods in living organisms, at least not successfully enough to permit descendants of the organisms to survive to the present day.

The metal–nonmetal borderline in Group VIA comes at selenium. It exists in a metallic, chainlike allotrope as well as in Se_8 rings. Selenium is a "one-dimensional semiconductor" rather than a "one-dimensional metal" in the sense that electrons flow along the chains only with difficulty. Visible light shining on metallic selenium provides enough energy to get the electrons moving, therefore selenium has a greatly enhanced electrical conductivity when illuminated. This is the basis of the "Xerox" process. A selenium-coated cylinder is given a uniform electrostatic charge in the dark, and then has the image of a printed page or diagram cast on it. Where the original diagram was blank, light strikes the selenium cylinder, and the surface electrostatic charge leaks away. Only on the dark regions, representing the printing or design on the original, is the static charge retained. A black, fusible powder then is dusted onto the cylinder, and sticks only to the charged regions. The drum is rolled against a sheet of paper to transfer the powder, which then is bonded to the paper by heat. The result is an image, in fused black powder, of the dark areas on the original.

ELECTROSTATIC COPYING

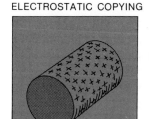  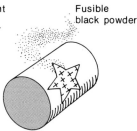 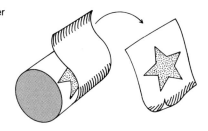

1. A selenium-plated drum is given an electrostatic charge in the dark.

2. Light casts an image onto the charged drum. Where the design is blank, light hits the selenium surface and the charge leaks away.

3. Electrostatic charge remains only in the regions corresponding to dark parts of the design. Black powder is dusted onto the drum, and sticks to the charged regions.

4. The powder is transferred to paper, and fixed permanently in place by heat. The original black on white design is reproduced.

GROUP VIIA: THE HALOGENS

THE HALOGENS

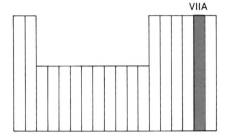

VIIA

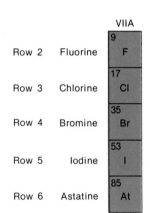

		VIIA
Row 2	Fluorine	9 F
Row 3	Chlorine	17 Cl
Row 4	Bromine	35 Br
Row 5	Iodine	53 I
Row 6	Astatine	85 At

After considering several columns in the periodic table containing both metals and nonmetals, we finally return to a homogeneous group. All of the halogens are nonmetals, although iodine's slight metallic sheen indicates some mobility of electrons in the crystalline solid. Radioactive astatine, if it were more than just a fleeting element seen in cyclotron bombardments, presumably would be even more metallic. (It has been estimated that the total amount of astatine in the Earth's crust at any one time, produced by radioactive decay of other elements, is approximately one ounce.)

The halogens all achieve a -1 oxidation state by gaining one electron per atom to complete their outer electron shell. Cl, Br, and I also occur in positive oxidation states as in perchloric acid, $HClO_4$, but fluorine is too electronegative for this to occur. The most common halogen compounds are salts with metal cations, and the name halogen itself means "salt-former." The hydroacids HF, HCl, HBr, and HI increase in acid strength as the halogen atom becomes larger and its proton becomes more weakly held. All but HF are completely dissociated in water.

Fluorine is the only element that is more electronegative than oxygen. Wood and rubber ignite spontaneously in F_2 gas, and even asbestos becomes incandescent. Copper and steel are attacked by F_2, but are quickly protected by adhering layers of CuF_2 and FeF_3, reminiscent of the protective Al_2O_3 coating on aluminum. The halogens all are too reactive to exist as pure elements in nature, and usually are found as their $ON = -1$ salts. They form compounds with every known element except the noble gases.

Even the noble gases are not totally immune from attack by fluorine. The most electronegative of all the elements, fluorine, can form covalent bonds with the least electronegative of all the noble gases, xenon, by sharing some of xenon's eight outer-shell electrons. Two F atoms can divide and share one of xenon's lone electron pairs between them to form XeF_2, which has ten electrons around the central Xe: two bonding pairs to the F atoms and three lone pairs. VSEPR theory predicts a linear F—Xe—F structure for this molecule, as shown at the top of the opposite page, with the strongly repelling lone pairs $120°$ apart in a plane perpendicular to the molecular axis. Two more F atoms can share a second xenon lone pair to produce XeF_4, with the xenon atom surrounded by four bonding pairs and two lone pairs. VSEPR theory predicts that this molecule will be most stable if the strongly repelling lone pairs are as far apart as possible, at opposite vertices of an octahedron, and the four F atoms lie in an equatorial plane, as drawn on the opposite page. A third xenon lone pair is shared by two more F atoms in XeF_6, with the xenon atom surrounded by seven electron pairs in a distorted octahedron. A few xenon and krypton compounds with the strongly electronegative oxygen atom also are known.

With the exception of compounds formed with Ag^+, Cu^+, Hg_2^{2+}, and Pb^{2+}, most of the halide salts are water-soluble. Ocean water essentially is a dilute solution of NaCl, $MgCl_2$, KCl, and $CaCl_2$ in the ratios of 50:6:1:1, with small amounts of other salts.

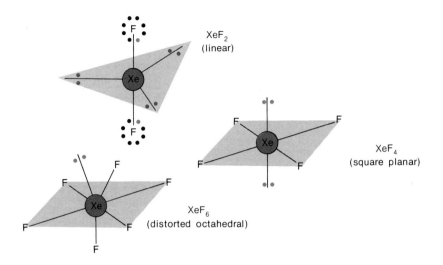

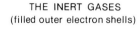

THE INERT GASES
(filled outer electron shells)

Exceptions to the general rule that noble gases make no chemical bonds. The least electronegative noble gas (Xe) and the most electronegative atoms (F and O) *can* form covalent bonds.

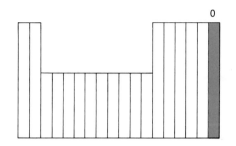

THE CHEMICAL UNIVERSE: A SUMMARY

In the "full deck" metaphor of the chapter opening, we now have inspected the deck and marked the most valuable cards for use in future games. There now are 106 elements in all, and more probably will be made artificially at the high atomic number end of the periodic table. These latter elements are only laboratory curiosities, however, and the elements of real importance to the planet and to life are known already. Only 18 of the 106 elements make up 99.98% of the Earth's crust, all from the first four rows of the periodic table. Only 11 of the 106 elements make up 99.99% of living organisms, again all from the first four rows. Another 13 elements are needed by living organisms in trace amounts, and the others, as far as we know, are not involved in life processes. The selection of these elements based on chemical properties has been superimposed on earlier selections based on chemical and physical properties, as the planet stratified, as the solar system formed earlier, and originally as the elements were synthesized in the stars.

We have tended to focus on the elements that are important to us and to our environment and to avoid the chemistry of the unusual elements. This is why we neglected many heavier elements, and all the inner transition metals. These first ten chapters are a study of matter and an introduction to the chemical elements. The next seven chapters are a study of energy and reactivity. These chapters will add quantitative and time dimensions to what so far has been only a descriptive science. They also will provide the necessary background for the last part of the book, the carbon compounds and the chemistry of living organisms.

		0
Row 1	Helium	2 He
Row 2	Neon	10 Ne
Row 3	Argon	18 Ar
Row 4	Krypton	36 Kr
Row 5	Xenon	54 Xe
Row 6	Radon	86 Rn

QUESTIONS

1. In terms of electronic structure, why are the transition metals more similar to one another than are the representative elements? Why are the inner transition metals even more similar to one another?

2. What is the relationship between group number and electronic structure for the representative elements? What is the relationship between group number and electronic structure for Groups IIIB through VIIB?

3. In what way are metallic and covalent radii similar—so similar, in fact, that they form a continuous series of size across one period of the table?

4. What is the difference between metallic or covalent radii, and van der Waals radii? How do these differ from ionic radii?

5. Why do metallic and covalent radii generally decrease across one period from left to right?

6. Why do metallic and covalent radii increase downward in each group or column of the table?

7. How is electronegativity related to atomic size? How is it related to nuclear charge? Account for the inverse relationship seen previously in this chapter between atomic radii and electronegativities.

8. How is the existence of the transition metals revealed by the atomic radii and electronegatives of the representative elements as given at the beginning of the chapter?

9. What diagonal trends can you see in atomic radii and electronegativities?

10. What is the difference between body-centered packing and close packing of spheres? Which form of packing is more compact?

11. How many nearest-neighbor atoms are in contact with one atom in the bcp structure? In the cp structure?

12. If a metal undergoes a cp to bcp structure transition at a certain temperature, which would you expect to be the high-temperature form, cp or bcp? Why?

13. Which should be the preferred packing type as the number of bonding electrons per metal atom increases, cp or bcp? Why?

14. Should an increase in atomic radius favor cp or bcp, other factors being equal? Why?

15. What is an allotrope? Which elements tend to have allotropes, and why, in terms of their positions in the periodic table? What is different about the two allotropes for such elements?

16. What is the difference in structure between the two allotropes of carbon? Which is more metallic, and why? Which is harder, and why?

17. What are the two allotropes of tin? Which structure is more metallic? Where is the nonmetallic allotropic structure of Sn encountered again among other elements?

18. How do nitrogen and phosphorus solve the need for three bonds to neighboring atoms differently? How is this behavior related to the relative sizes of the atoms?

19. In what way do oxygen and sulfur constitute another example of the situation of the preceding question?

20. How do the two allotropes of selenium differ, and why might you expect metallic properties from one but not the other? Which structure also is found in tellurium?

21. How is the extent of delocalization in a molecule related to relative spacings between energy levels, wavelengths of radiation absorbed, and color?

22. In what way do melting points tell us about bonding in solids? Why should molecular solids such as sulfur have lower melting points than structures such as diamond?

23. Why should Group IIA metals have higher melting points than Group IA metals?

24. Why should melting points generally decrease downward in Groups IA and IIA?

25. Why the abrupt drop in melting points in the middle of the second row, when no such drop is observed in Rows 5 and 6?

26. Why do the noble gases have low melting points? What forces keep their atoms together in a solid?

27. Why does a Group IIA metal have a higher first ionization energy than the Group IA metal in the same period?

28. Among the Group IA metals, why are Na and K more abundant than Rb and Cs? Why are they more abundant than Li?

29. Why are Group IA elements never found as the free metals in nature? Where, and in what form, are they found? How are the free metals prepared?

30. What is electrolysis? What happens when molten KCl is electrolyzed? What substance is oxidized, and what is reduced, in this process?

31. Where do Group IIA elements occur in nature, and in what form? How are they obtained as metals?

32. What oxidation states are most common in the first series of transition metals from Sc to Mn? What are the most common oxidation states from Fe to Zn? How are these states associated with electronic structure?

33. What trends in most common oxidation numbers are seen from the first series of transition metals to later series? Explain this in terms of other properties of the atoms.

34. For a given transition metal, are the lower, or higher, oxidation states more likely to involve covalent bonding? Why? Can you relate this to the chemical behavior of representative elements in the second row of the table?

35. Why do atomic radii along one row of the table containing transition metals decrease through a minimum and then increase, before

beginning a general decline again among the representative elements?

36. What is the lanthanide contraction? How does it affect chemical properties, and why does it occur?

37. What is meant by a ligand of a metal ion? What kind of a bond connects an ion and a ligand? Where do the bonding electrons come from?

38. How many Cl^- ions can be accommodated around one Co^{3+} ion? What is this *number* called, and what is its value in this example? What is the geometrical arrangement of Cl^- ions around a Co^{3+} called?

39. What do all of the other potential ligands mentioned previously in the chapter have in common that makes them ligands?

40. In what sense is ethylenediaminetetraacetate a *hexadentate* ligand? What happens when it associates with a metal ion?

41. How is ligation with a metal ion involved in the activity of antibiotics such as valinomycin?

42. What causes the splitting between t and e levels in octahedral coordination around a metal ion? Which d orbitals have the higher energy, and why, in terms of their shapes?

43. What is the difference between high-spin and low-spin complexes of Fe^{3+}? What factors determine whether a given complex will be high- or low-spin?

44. What factors affect the magnitude of the crystal-field splitting that a ligand will produce? Which ligand ordinarily produces a larger splitting, Cl^- or CN^-? Cl^- or NH_3?

45. How does the magnitude of the crystal-field splitting in a transition-metal complex affect the color of the complex?

46. Is the effect on color produced by exchanging Cl^- with CN^- as a metal ligand similar to that obtained by enlarging, or decreasing, the extent of delocalization in an aromatic ring system?

47. What biologically important chemical entity discussed in this chapter combines the electronic energy effects of transition-metal ligation and delocalized aromatic rings?

48. In what way are boron nitride and diamond similar? Can you imagine a boron–nitrogen analogue of benzene, C_6H_6? If you can't, look up *borazole* in a chemical handbook.

49. What is a semiconductor?

50. How do minute amounts of P atoms substituted for Si make silicon a better conductor of electricity?

51. Why is aluminum-doped silicon a better conductor than pure silicon, when each aluminum atom provides a shortage of one electron? What carries the current in such a silicon preparation?

52. How does the effect of temperature on conductivity differ between metallic conductors and semiconductors? Why?

53. What is a p–n junction? How does the silicon on either side of the junction differ?

54. How does a p–n junction function as an alternating current rectifier?

55. Which base more closely resembles organic bases: $LiOH$ or NH_3? Why?

56. What is the oxidation number of N in most of its organic compounds in living organisms?

57. How does the oxidation number of N change when nitrogen is "fixed" by electric discharge during thunderstorms?

58. How does the oxidation number of nitrogen change when nitrogen compounds instead of O_2 are used by denitrifying bacteria as sources of oxidizing power?

59. How do nitrogen-fixing bacteria change the oxidation number of nitrogen?

60. How do nitrifying bacteria use nitrogen compounds? What do they combine the compounds with? Is energy gained, or lost, by the bacterium in the process? How does the oxidation number of nitrogen change in the process?

61. Why does the structure of clay minerals make nitrates better fertilizers than ammonium ions?

62. What is eutrophication, and why is it potentially harmful?

63. What is ΛTP, and how is it especially suitable as an energy-storage molecule?

64. Why is the hydrolysis energy of two phosphate bonds in ATP abnormally high, and why is that of the third such bond normal?

65. What does arsenic mimic in some of its poisonous aspects, and why would this make arsenic poisonous?

66. Why is expansion upon solidification a useful property for a metal used in casting printer's type? What common nonmetallic compound has this same property?

67. What other substances besides O_2 have been used as oxidants in respiration by living organisms? What types of organisms use these oxidants?

68. What other substances besides water have been used as sources of reducing hydrogens for photosynthesis? What organisms use these substances?

69. When animals and green plants use O_2 from the atmosphere for respiration, how is this O_2 restored?

70. If green algae are grown in hydroponic tanks in a self-contained space station, what would the algae contribute to the environment in addition to artificial food for the astronauts?

71. In terms of molecular structure, why does light turn selenium into a conductor and permit electrostatic charge to leak away on a Xerox drum?

72. How is the image formed on paper in a Xerox copier?

73. If a noble gas were to form a compound with *any* other element, why would you expect that the noble gas would be xenon, and that the reacting atoms would be either O or F?

CONSERVATION OF ATOMS

How to balance an equation so that there will be the same number of atoms before and after a chemical reaction

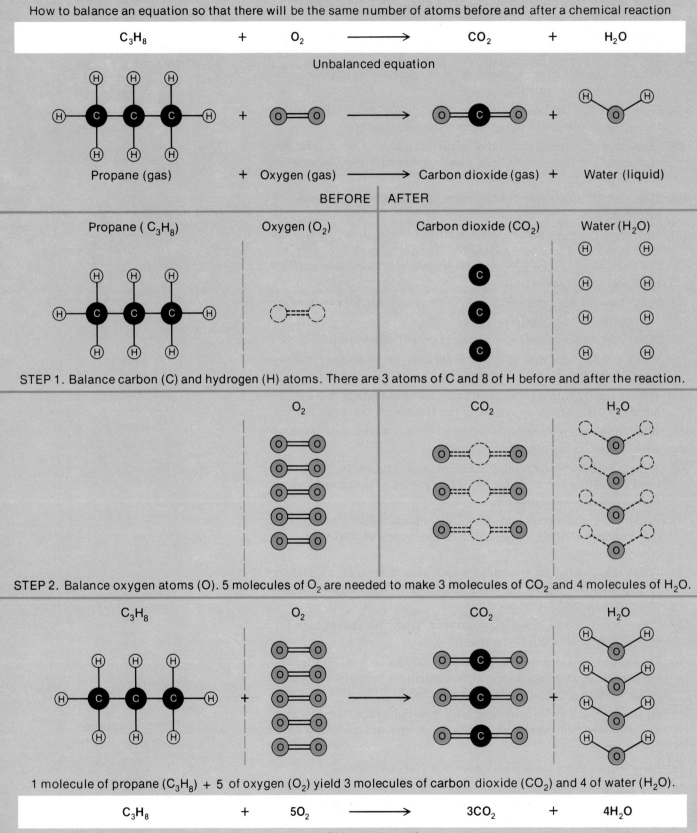

$$C_3H_8 \quad + \quad O_2 \quad \longrightarrow \quad CO_2 \quad + \quad H_2O$$

Unbalanced equation

Propane (gas) + Oxygen (gas) ⟶ Carbon dioxide (gas) + Water (liquid)

BEFORE | AFTER

Propane (C_3H_8)   Oxygen (O_2)   Carbon dioxide (CO_2)   Water (H_2O)

STEP 1. Balance carbon (C) and hydrogen (H) atoms. There are 3 atoms of C and 8 of H before and after the reaction.

O_2 CO_2 H_2O

STEP 2. Balance oxygen atoms (O). 5 molecules of O_2 are needed to make 3 molecules of CO_2 and 4 molecules of H_2O.

C_3H_8 O_2 CO_2 H_2O

1 molecule of propane (C_3H_8) + 5 of oxygen (O_2) yield 3 molecules of carbon dioxide (CO_2) and 4 of water (H_2O).

$$C_3H_8 \quad + \quad 5O_2 \quad \longrightarrow \quad 3CO_2 \quad + \quad 4H_2O$$

Balanced equation

◀ *There are precisely the same number of atoms on both sides of a balanced chemical equation*

CHAPTER 11

You Can't Get Something for Nothing: Conservation of Mass, Charge, and Energy

The first ten chapters of this book have been mainly descriptive. They have portrayed the material universe as seen by an observer who has the ability to adjust his field of view to encompass entire galaxies or single atoms. At the lowest level we have seen how electrons can be arranged around nuclei in atoms, and how this arrangement limits the different kinds of atoms that can exist. At a slightly higher level of organization we have seen the way in which electrons hold groups of atoms together in molecules of definite size and shape, and how the properties of matter depend on molecular structure. This is the essence of chemistry: to explain matter in molecular terms.

Like any other branch of science, chemistry eventually becomes trivial if it remains descriptive. The essence of science is control of matter by means of successful predictions of behavior; and predictions without measurement are hazy. Sooner or later we must adopt the viewpoint of William Thomson (Lord Kelvin), a pioneer in thermodynamics and electricity, who said in 1891:

> When you can measure what you are speaking about, and express it in numbers, you know something about it; but when you cannot measure it, when you cannot express it in numbers, your knowledge is of a meagre and unsatisfactory kind. It may be the beginning of knowledge, but you have scarcely, in your thoughts, advanced to the stage of science.

The next seven chapters will be devoted to using numbers in chemistry and making it exact. This will lead to an understanding of why substances react, why they appear to react only so far and no farther, and why they do so rapidly or slowly. One of the practical triumphs of chemistry is the ability to control the rates and course of chemical processes, to produce useful substances and energy. The advantages in

NONCONSERVATION OF VOLUME

$$C_3H_8 + 5O_2 \longrightarrow 3CO_2 + 4H_2O$$

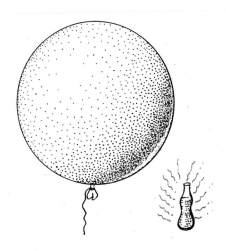

The number of atoms is conserved in the reaction above, but shape and volume can change dramatically. A balloon full of propane gas and oxygen, after combustion, becomes a soft drink bottle full of warm carbonated water (CO_2 and H_2O).

industrial synthesis are obvious; but the advantages in biosynthesis are no less important.

In the traditional way of organizing chemistry, the first ten chapters of this text can be regarded as an introduction to inorganic chemistry. These next seven chapters are an introduction to some aspects of physical chemistry, although quantum theory normally is included also as a part of physical chemistry. Chapters 18 through 21 introduce the subject of organic chemistry, and Chapters 22 through 26 bring us to biochemistry and the evolution of life. One should not pay too much attention to these categories, however, because the most active research today is being done in borderline areas that do not fall easily into any category. It is the overall view of the unity of chemistry that is important.

CONSERVATION PRINCIPLES

Science is full of principles of conservation: conservation of mass, conservation of energy, conservation of charge, conservation of symmetry or "parity," and others. These principles all are statements that, when physical and chemical changes take place, certain properties do not change. Throughout the first part of this book we have been using a conservation principle, although we have not spelled it out explicitly: In chemical reactions *matter* is neither created nor destroyed, within the limits of our ability to measure mass. The amount of material that comes out of any chemical process is no more and no less than the amount that went in, although the appearance of the material may be changed greatly. In the illustration at the beginning of the chapter, propane and oxygen gases react to produce another gas and a liquid. The substances produced look and behave differently, but the total number of atoms of each type is unchanged in the course of the reaction.

Energy also is conserved in chemical reactions, within the limits of our ability to measure it. The amount of energy in the universe at the end of the propane reaction is the same as at the beginning. If a process gives off energy (the propane reaction does), then the product molecules must have less energy than the reactants, by the amount given off.

A third, rather subtle quantity also is conserved during propane combustion. This quantity, the *oxidation number*, is a measure of the location of the electrons. Carbon and hydrogen atoms are oxidized, because they begin by sharing electrons equally with neighboring atoms, but end by forming C—O and H—O bonds in which oxygen exerts the greater pull on the electrons. Conversely, oxygen atoms are reduced because they begin by sharing electrons equally in O=O molecules and end by monopolizing electrons in their bonds with C and H. The sum of changes in oxidation numbers of all the atoms in propane combustion is zero, because every atom that loses its grip on an electron must be matched by another atom that pulls the electron toward it. In this chapter we consider the conservation of mass and oxidation number; the following chapters are devoted to energy.

If we look at mass and energy closely enough, the principles that they individually are conserved turn out to be only approximately true.

Mass and energy actually are interconvertible, and are different manifestations of the same thing. We can uncouple them in thinking about chemical reactions only because the quantities of energy involved in chemical processes correspond to infinitesimal amounts of mass. However, in the much more powerful nuclear reactions, these principles of separate conservation of mass and energy must be combined into the conservation of the *total* of mass and energy. Mass can be converted into energy and energy into mass according to Einstein's relationship $E = mc^2$, in which E is energy, m is mass, and c is the velocity of light. In the last half of this chapter we will discuss nuclear reactions for which this mass–energy conversion is important. The conversion of mass into energy is central to both nuclear fission and nuclear fusion, on this planet and in the sun.

In principle, if a reaction gives off energy, the products formed must have lower energy and *be lighter* than the reactants. But a release of 100 kcal mole^{-1} by a typical chemical reaction corresponds (via the Einstein relationship) to a mass loss of only 5×10^{-9} amu per molecule, or one hundred thousandth the mass of an electron. This amounts to only 5×10^{-9} gram per mole, which is far less than we can measure. This is why we can say that, for chemical reactions, mass and energy are conserved independently.

WEIGHT AND MASS

Many properties other than mass are not conserved in chemical reactions: volume, density, shape, thermal conductivity, hardness, color, and others. It was Antoine Lavoisier, the brilliant French chemist who revolutionized chemistry before he went to the guillotine in 1794, who realized that *mass* was more fundamental than any of these properties. When you ask "How much?" in chemistry, you basically are asking "What mass?".

Strictly speaking, mass is related to the inertia of a moving object and the effort needed to stop it. Even though two astronauts weigh only one sixth as much on the moon as on Earth, if they begin fighting the blows land just as hard and hurt just as much because the mass behind the blows is the same as on Earth. In contrast, weight is the force with which a planet pulls on a given mass. If m is the mass in grams and g is the gravitational acceleration in centimeters per second per second, the weight of the object, w, in g cm sec^{-2}, or dynes, is given by $w = m \times g$.

We ordinarily do not make the distinction between weight and mass. When we say that an object "weighs one gram," what we really mean is that it "weighs what a one-gram mass would weigh on Earth." The gravitational constant, g, is one sixth as large on the moon, so the same mass will have only one sixth the weight there that it has on Earth. When we say that a one-gram object "weighs only one sixth of a gram on the moon," we mean that it is pulled toward the moon with the same force that the Earth would exert on a one-sixth-gram mass. As long as we are making only Earth-bound comparisons, no confusion need arise between weight and mass. We will use the terms "atomic weights" and "atomic masses" interchangeably.

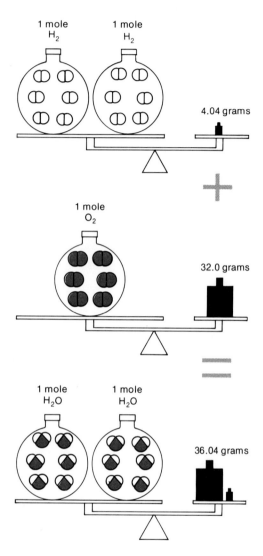

1 mole
H_2

1 mole
H_2

4.04 grams

+

1 mole
O_2

32.0 grams

=

1 mole
H_2O

1 mole
H_2O

36.04 grams

The total weight of reactants (H_2 and O_2) equals the weight of the product (H_2O). Mass is conserved.

CONSERVATION OF MASS IN CHEMICAL REACTIONS

In chemical processes, the most important property to be conserved is the number of atoms of each kind that are present. Unlike nuclear processes, chemical reactions do not create or destroy atoms, or change one kind of atom into another. They only reshuffle the atoms that were originally present into different molecular combinations. What we would like to be able to do is to count each kind of atom before and after a reaction and make sure that none has been gained or lost.

Counting atoms directly is not practical, but because mass–energy conversion is negligible in chemical reactions, conservation of the number of atoms effectively means the conservation of mass. From the discussion of moles and Avogadro's number in Chapter 2, we know that the mass of a substance divided by its atomic or molecular weight is the quantity of the substance in moles, and that one mole of any chemical substance contains the same number of particles. That number is Avogadro's number, N, which is 6.022×10^{23} particles per mole. Hence by weighing moles of a substance, we effectively can count atoms with a laboratory balance.

The symbols in a properly balanced chemical equation tell much more than just the identity of reactant and product molecules. The equation

$$2H_2 + O_2 \rightarrow 2H_2O$$

states that water can be made from hydrogen and oxygen molecules. In addition, it says that two moles of hydrogen and one mole of oxygen are required to produce two moles of water. As an expression of the conservation of atoms, it indicates that for every four atoms of hydrogen and two atoms of oxygen (in H_2 and O_2 molecules), only two molecules of water can be obtained, which contain the same total of four H and two O atoms.

From the balanced equation, one can obtain information about the relative amounts of reactants and products involved. The molecular weights of H_2, O_2, and H_2O are 2.02 g, 32.00 g, and 18.02 g, respectively. Hence 2×2.02 g of hydrogen react with 1×32.00 g of oxygen to form 2×18.02 g of water:

$$2(2.02) \text{ g} + 32.00 \text{ g} = 2(18.02) \text{ g}$$

$$36.04 \text{ g} = 36.04 \text{ g}$$

The total weight of reactants before the reaction is the same as the weight of the products after the reaction; mass has been conserved.

Example. Propane, C_3H_8, is a low-pollution fuel gas that can be burned in existing automobile engines with only minor engine adjustments. How many moles of O_2 are required to burn one mole of propane, and how many grams of O_2 are used with a kilogram of propane?

Solution. The unbalanced reaction, showing only the reactants and products, is

$$C_3H_8 + O_2 \rightarrow CO_2 + H_2O$$

since we know that the combustion products are carbon dioxide and water. The balancing process is given in the illustration at the beginning of the chapter. In brief, if three CO_2 molecules are formed from the three carbon atoms in one propane molecule, then six oxygen atoms or three O_2 molecules will be required. In addition, the eight hydrogen atoms in propane will lead to four water molecules, thereby requiring two more molecules of O_2. The balanced equation is

$$C_3H_8 + 5O_2 \rightarrow 3CO_2 + 4H_2O$$

The molecular weights of reactants and products are

C_3H_8: 3×12.01 g $+ 8 \times 1.01$ g $= 44.11$ g
O_2: 2×16.00 g $= 32.00$ g
CO_2: 1×12.01 g $+ 2 \times 16.00$ g $= 44.01$ g
H_2O: 2×1.01 g $+ 1 \times 16.00$ g $= 18.02$ g

From the balanced equation and these molecular weights we can verify that mass is conserved during the reaction:

$$44.11 \text{ g } C_3H_8 + 5(32.00) \text{ g } O_2 = 3(44.01) \text{ g } CO_2 + 4(18.02) \text{ g } H_2O$$

$$204.11 \text{ g} = 204.11 \text{ g}$$

The balanced equation indicates that each mole of propane gas burned requires five moles of oxygen. The problem as stated involved 1000 g of propane, and the number of moles is

$$\frac{1000 \text{ g propane}}{44.11 \text{ g mole}^{-1}} = 22.67 \text{ moles propane}$$

Five times this many moles of oxygen are needed:

$$22.67 \text{ moles propane} \times \frac{5 \text{ moles oxygen}}{1 \text{ mole propane}} = 113.4 \text{ moles oxygen}$$

The quantity of oxygen in grams then is

$$113.4 \text{ moles } O_2 \times 32.00 \text{ g mole}^{-1} = 3629 \text{ g } O_2$$

The entire calculation could have been set up in one step:

$$\frac{1000 \text{ g propane}}{44.11 \text{ g mole}^{-1} \text{ propane}} \times \frac{5 \text{ moles oxygen}}{1 \text{ mole propane}} \times 32.00 \text{ g mole}^{-1} O_2$$

$$= 3627 \text{ g } O_2$$

Note that we proceeded in five steps:

1. Write an unbalanced expression with the correct reactants and products.
2. Balance the equation properly, and obtain the ratio of number of moles of the reactants and products of interest.
3. Calculate molecular weights of the reactants and products of interest.
4. Calculate the number of moles of reactant used, and use the mole ratio from Step 2 to find the number of moles of product.
5. Use the molecular weight of the product to obtain the weight in grams.

Example. Glucose is a sugar with the chemical formula $C_6H_{12}O_6$, and is a common energy source for living organisms. How many moles of oxygen are required to burn a mole of glucose, and how many grams of O_2 are needed for a kilogram of glucose?

Solution.

1. Unbalanced expression with correct reactants and products:

$$C_6H_{12}O_6 + O_2 \rightarrow CO_2 + H_2O$$

2. Balancing process:
   The 6 C of glucose will produce 6 CO_2. The 12 H of glucose will produce 6 H_2O. Partial balancing:

$$C_6H_{12}O_6 + O_2 \rightarrow 6CO_2 + 6H_2O$$

   There are now 18 oxygen atoms on the right side and only 8 on the left, so 10 more are needed, or 5 more O_2. Balanced equation:

$$C_6H_{12}O_6 + 6O_2 \rightarrow 6CO_2 + 6H_2O$$

   Now we can say that *six* moles of oxygen are required for each mole of glucose.

3. Molecular weights:

   $C_6H_{12}O_6$:   180.18 g mole^{-1}
   O_2:   32.00 g mole^{-1}

   The molecular weights of the other reactants and products are not needed.

4. Moles of oxygen:

$$\frac{1000 \text{ g glucose}}{180.18 \text{ g mole}^{-1} \text{ glucose}} \times \frac{6 \text{ moles oxygen}}{1 \text{ mole glucose}} = 33.30 \text{ moles oxygen}$$

5. Grams of oxygen:

$$33.30 \text{ moles oxygen} \times 32.00 \text{ g mole}^{-1} = 1066 \text{ g oxygen}$$

In passing, observe that burning a kilogram of glucose requires only 1066 g of oxygen, whereas burning the same weight of propane requires 3627 g of oxygen. This is because glucose already is partially oxidized. You should not be surprised later when we calculate that the combustion of glucose produces only half as much heat per gram as combustion of propane. Glucose is a poorer fuel than propane on a weight basis. In Chapter 21 we will return to the question as to why plants selected glucose for energy storage (in plant starch), whereas animals developed fats as a kind of "solid propane."

CONSERVATION OF ELECTRONS

Mass is not the only property that is conserved in chemical reactions. In Chapter 6 we saw that, since oxidation and reduction represent only the moving of electrons away from or toward atoms, whenever something is oxidized something else must be reduced. Moving an electron away from one atom in a chemical reaction means moving it toward another one. Thus we can say that, in any chemical reaction in which oxidation and reduction take place, the *net* change in oxidation numbers of all of the atoms taking part is zero. Total oxidation number is conserved. This is merely an indirect way of saying that electrons are neither created nor destroyed during the reaction.

As an example, the combustion of foods during respiration in all oxygen-using forms of life requires the oxidation of carbon and hydrogen compounds. The hydrogen atoms in these compounds are assigned oxidation number zero, because each shares electrons equally with the atoms to which they are bonded. These zero-oxidation-state hydrogen atoms often are represented symbolically in brackets as [H], without reference to the particular source compound. The energy-yielding oxidation reaction taking place during respiration then can be written in unbalanced form as

$$[H] + O_2 \rightarrow H_2O$$

ON of H: 0   +1
ON of O: 0   −2

These oxidation numbers (ON) of H and O in H_2O arise because O is more electronegative than H, so both the electrons in each O—H bond are assigned to O. If you are unsure of this process, look back at Chapter 6. This is such a simple chemical reaction that it can be balanced by inspection—by making sure that the same number of atoms of H and O are on each side of the equation. The balanced equation is

$$2[H] + \tfrac{1}{2}O_2 \rightarrow H_2O \qquad \text{or} \qquad 4[H] + O_2 \rightarrow 2H_2O$$

We also could have balanced the equation by seeing to it that the net change in oxidation number of all substances was zero. If the oxidation number of one oxygen atom decreases by two, then two hydrogen atoms each must increase by one. In physical terms, if one oxygen atom pulls two electrons toward itself, then two hydrogen atoms are required to donate one electron each. In terms of changes in oxidation number,

$$2H \qquad O$$

Changes in ON: $2(+1) + (-2) = 0$

This was a trivial example, but the following example is not quite so trivial. If oxygen is in short supply, some bacteria can respire using nitrates as sources of oxidizing power instead of O_2. Rather than reducing oxygen to water, these bacteria reduce nitrates to NO_2^-, NO, or N_2. How can we write a properly balanced equation for the oxidation of foods with NO as the waste product?

The unbalanced reaction is

$$[H] + NO_3^- \rightarrow NO + H_2O$$

It might be tempting to balance by inspection along the following lines, making the number of each kind of atom the same on left and right:

$$2[H] + NO_3^- \rightarrow NO + H_2O + \tfrac{1}{2}O_2$$

OXIDATION-NUMBER METHOD OF BALANCING REDOX REACTIONS

Balance the oxidation–reduction equation for the oxidation of sulfite ion to sulfate by dichromate ion.

1. Write an unbalanced equation with correct reactants and products.

$$Cr_2O_7^{2-} + SO_3^{2-} \rightarrow Cr^{2+} + SO_4^{2-}$$

2. Assign oxidation numbers to those atoms that are oxidized or reduced. Calculate the change in oxidation state for each such atom.

Cr: $+6 \rightarrow +2$ (change of -4)

S: $+4 \rightarrow +6$ (change of $+2$)

3. Use enough oxidant and reductant so the changes in oxidation number cancel. In this example, use twice as many S atoms as Cr.

$$Cr_2O_7^{2-} + 4SO_3^{2-} \rightarrow 2Cr^{2+} + 4SO_4^{2-}$$

4. Balance this equation in the ordinary way with respect to numbers of atoms.

$$Cr_2O_7^{2-} + 4SO_3^{2-} + 6H^+ \rightarrow$$
$$2Cr^{2+} + 4SO_4^{2-} + 3H_2O$$

5. Check by verifying that the charges balance.

$$(-2) + 4(-2) + 6(+1) \overset{?}{=} 2(+2) + 4(-2)$$

$$-4 = -4$$

But this leaves an electron on the left side unaccounted for on the right side. The approach that is most nearly foolproof and at the same time shows you what is happening is the oxidation-number method. In nitrates, N has an oxidation number of $+5$ (verify this for yourself). In NO the oxidation number of N is $+2$, a decrease of three. Hydrogen, as before, goes from 0 to $+1$, an increase of one:

$$[H] + NO_3^- \rightarrow H_2O + NO$$

ON of H:	0	$+1$	(change of $+1$)
ON of N:	$+5$	$+2$	(change of -3)

For electrons to balance properly, three moles of H must be oxidized for every mole of NO_3^- reduced:

$$3(+1) + (-3) = 0$$

and the reaction can be written

$$3[H] + NO_3^- \rightarrow NO + what?$$

In any reaction in aqueous solution, one is at liberty to assume as many H_2O, H^+, or OH^- as are required to balance the reaction, using H_2O and H^+ under acidic conditions, or H_2O and OH^- if the solution is basic. The redox (oxidation–reduction) part of the balancing has been done, and what remains is only an accounting for O and H atoms. One possible answer is

$$3[H] + NO_3^- \rightarrow NO + H_2O + OH^-$$

This has accounted for the three hydrogen atoms and the negative charge. The equation is correct for basic solutions where OH^- ions are present. The corresponding equation for acidic solutions can be obtained by adding enough hydrogen ions to each side to eliminate the hydroxide ions:

$$3[H] + NO_3^- + H^+ \rightarrow NO + H_2O + OH^- + H^+$$

248

HALF-REACTION METHOD OF BALANCING REDOX REACTIONS

1. Separate the oxidizing agent from the reducing agent, and write them as individual half-reactions.

$$Cr_2O_7^{2-} \rightarrow Cr^{2+} \quad \text{(reduction)}$$

$$SO_3^{2-} \rightarrow SO_4^{2-} \quad \text{(oxidation)}$$

2. Balance each half-reaction separately with respect to number of atoms. Do not worry about charges at this point.

$$Cr_2O_7^{2-} + 14H^+ \rightarrow 2Cr^{2+} + 7H_2O$$

$$SO_3^{2-} + H_2O \rightarrow SO_4^{2-} + 2H^+$$

3. Add enough electrons to one side or the other of each half-reaction to make the charges balance.

$$Cr_2O_7^{2-} + 14H^+ + 8e^- \rightarrow 2Cr^{2+} + 7H_2O$$

$$SO_3^{2-} + H_2O \rightarrow SO_4^{2-} + 2H^+ + 2e^-$$

4. Multiply the half-reactions by factors such that when the half-reactions are added the electrons cancel. Then add the half-reactions.

$$Cr_2O_7^{2-} + 14H^+ + 4SO_3^{2-} + 4H_2O \rightarrow$$
$$2Cr^{2+} + 4SO_4^{2-} + 8H^+ + 7H_2O$$

5. Eliminate common substances on the two sides of the equation.

$$Cr_2O_7^{2-} + 4SO_3^{2-} + 6H^+ \rightarrow$$
$$2Cr^{2+} + 4SO_4^{2-} + 3H_2O$$

or

$$3[H] + NO_3^- + H^+ \rightarrow NO + 2H_2O$$

Example. Potassium permanganate, $KMnO_4$, is a common inorganic oxidizing agent, which becomes reduced to manganous ion, Mn^{2+}, in acidic solution. Write a balanced equation for the reaction in which permanganate oxidizes ferrous iron, Fe^{2+}, to ferric ion, Fe^{3+}.

Solution. The unbalanced equation is

$$MnO_4 + Fe^{2+} \rightarrow Mn^{2+} + Fe^{3+}$$

In the permanganate ion manganese has an oxidation number of $+7$, which decreases to $+2$ in the manganous ion, a change of -5. Iron increases in oxidation number by one:

	MnO_4^-	$+ Fe^{2+}$	$\rightarrow Mn^{2+}$	$+ Fe^{3+}$	
ON of Mn:	$+7$		$+2$		(change of -5)
ON of Fe:		$+2$		$+3$	(change of $+1$)

It is obvious that five iron atoms are required for every manganese atom, in order that the changes in oxidation numbers cancel:

$$MnO_4^- + 5Fe^{2+} \rightarrow Mn^{2+} + 5Fe^{3+}$$

Eight hydrogen ions are needed to use up the four oxygen atoms on the left, leading to four water molecules on the right:

$$MnO_4^- + 5Fe^{2+} + 8H^+ \rightarrow Mn^{2+} + 5Fe^{3+} + 4H_2O$$

In choosing a 1-to-5 ratio of Mn-to-Fe, we ensured that oxidation number was conserved. By adding the hydrogen ions we obtained an equation that balanced the number of each atom. As a final check, the net charge on each side of the equation can be tested, and found to be the same: $+17$. This oxidation–reduction equation now is balanced with respect to *electrons*, *atoms*, and *charge*.

There is another useful method for balancing redox equations: the half-reaction method. In this method each substance that changes its oxidation number is balanced separately in a half-reaction that includes electrons explicitly. The two balanced half-reactions then are combined in such a way as to cancel electrons from the final expression.

Example. Balance the iron and permanganate reaction by the half-reaction method.

Solution. The unbalanced permanganate half-reaction is

$$\underset{+7}{MnO_4^-} + 5e^- \rightarrow \underset{+2}{Mn^{2+}}$$

Five electrons are needed because manganese goes from +7 to +2 oxidation state. Water molecules are added on the right to balance the oxygen atoms in the permanganate, and protons are added on the left:

$$MnO_4^- + 8H^+ + 5e^- \rightarrow Mn^{2+} + 4H_2O$$

This half-reaction now is balanced with respect to both number of atoms and overall charge, +2 on each side.

The iron half-reaction is simple:

$$Fe^{2+} \rightarrow Fe^{3+} + e^-$$

The final step is to add these two individually balanced half-reactions and obtain an overall reaction in which electrons do not appear explicitly. To accomplish this, we must add one unit of the manganese reaction to five units of the iron reaction. The result is the same as before:

$$MnO_4^- + 8H^+ + 5Fe^{2+} \rightarrow Mn^{2+} + 4H_2O + 5Fe^{3+}$$

This overall equation now is balanced with respect to charge and number of atoms because the half-reactions were balanced, and with respect to oxidation number because the proper multiples of the half-reactions were chosen to make the electrons cancel.

Exercise. For practice, balance the following reactions by both the oxidation-number and half-reaction methods:

$$NH_3 + OCl^- \rightarrow N_2H_4 + Cl^- \quad \text{(basic solution)}$$
$$NO_3^- + Zn \rightarrow NH_4^+ + Zn^{2+} \quad \text{(acidic solution)}$$
$$H_3PO_4 + CO_3^{2-} \rightarrow PO_4^{3-} + CO_2 + H_2O \quad \text{(neutral solution)}$$

Although half-reactions have been introduced here merely as a means of obtaining a balanced overall reaction, they can have physical meaning of their own. If the iron oxidation and manganese reduction can be carried out in separate containers, and if these containers can be given suitable electrical connections, then we can make use of the energy released by this reaction as the electrons flow through a wire from the iron container to the manganese. This is the principle of the electrolytic cell or battery. An ordinary flashlight battery uses manganese reduction, and oxidation of the zinc battery casing. We will return to electrolytic cells and energy production in Chapter 17.

MASS AND ENERGY; NUCLEAR REACTIONS

With nuclear reactions, the energies involved are so great that the changes in mass become easily measurable. One no longer can assume that mass and energy are conserved separately, but must take into account their interconversion via Einstein's relationship, $E = mc^2$. If mass is in grams and the velocity of light is expressed as $c = 3 \times 10^{10}$ cm sec^{-1}, then the energy is in units of g cm^2 sec^{-2}, or ergs. A useful conversion is from mass in amu to energy in million electron volts (MeV):

1 amu = 931.4 MeV

What holds a nucleus together? If we attempt to bring two protons and two neutrons together to form a helium nucleus, we might reasonably expect the positively charged protons to repel one another violently. Then what keeps them together in the $_2^4$He nucleus? The answer, as we mentioned in Chapter 2, is that a helium atom is *lighter* than the sum of two protons, two neutrons, and two electrons. Some of the mass of the separated particles is converted into energy and dissipated when the nucleus is formed. Before the helium nucleus can be torn apart into its component particles, this dissipated energy must be restored and turned back into mass. Unless this energy is provided, the nucleus cannot be taken apart. This energy is termed the *binding energy* of the $_2^4$He nucleus.

The mass loss is not large, but is measurable.

Mass of 2 protons:	2(1.0073) amu	= 2.0146 amu
Mass of 2 neutrons:	2(1.0087) amu	= 2.0174 amu
Mass of 2 electrons:	2(0.00055) amu	= 0.0011 amu
Total mass of components:		4.0331 amu
Less mass of $_2^4$He atom:		−4.0026 amu
Missing mass in $_2^4$He atom:		0.0305 amu

Some mass is converted to energy and lost when protons, neutrons, and electrons combine to form a helium atom. The nucleus cannot be split apart again unless the missing energy is supplied from outside, so the mass loss can be made good. In this sense the 28.4 MeV is a "binding energy." *Energy* does not hold a nucleus together; *lack* of energy does.

MASS LOSS AND BINDING ENERGY

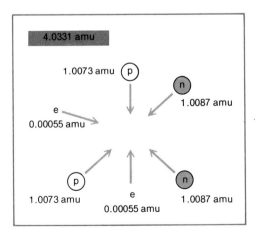

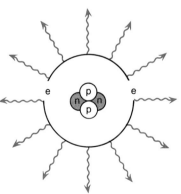

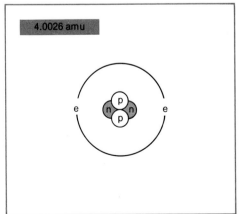

2p, 2n, and 2e together have a mass of 4.0331 amu   28.4 MeV energy given off $_2^4$He atom is 0.0305 amu lighter than its components

(We must include electrons in this calculation because 4.0026 amu is the mass of the helium-4 atom, not the nucleus.) This missing mass corresponds to 0.0305×931.4 MeV = 28.4 MeV of energy. If we could put together a helium atom directly from two neutrons, two protons, and two electrons, then 28.4 MeV of energy would be given off for every atom formed:

$$2p + 2n + 2e^- \rightarrow {}^4_2\text{He} + 28.4 \text{ MeV of energy}$$

Compared to common chemical reactions, this is an enormous quantity of energy. Since 1 electron volt per atom is equivalent to 23.06 kcal per mole,

$$\text{binding energy} = 28.4 \text{ MeV atom}^{-1} \times \frac{23.06 \text{ kcal mole}^{-1}}{1 \text{ eV atom}^{-1}}$$

$$= 655{,}000{,}000 \text{ kcal mole}^{-1}$$

(Compare this energy with the 83 kcal mole^{-1} required to break carbon–carbon bonds in chemical reactions.)

Protons and neutrons collectively are known as nuclear particles or *nucleons*. The number of nucleons in the nucleus is the sum of the number of protons and neutrons and, as was mentioned in Chapter 2, is known as the *mass number* of the nucleus. Every atomic nucleus is lighter than the sum of the masses of the nucleons from which it is built, and this mass loss corresponds to the binding energy of the nucleus. The relative stability of two nuclei with different numbers of nucleons can be assessed by comparing their *mass loss per nucleon.*

Example. What is the mass loss per nucleon for the ${}^4_2$He atom?

Solution. The total mass loss is 0.0305 amu, and since the nucleus has four nucleons, the mass loss per nucleon is 0.00763 amu.

Example. What is the mass loss per nucleon for the ${}^{56}_{26}$Fe atom, compared with its component protons, neutrons, and electrons?

Solution. The ${}^{56}_{26}$Fe atom contains 26 protons, 26 electrons, and 30 neutrons, so the mass calculation is

26 protons:	26(1.0073) amu =	26.190 amu
26 electrons:	26(0.00055) amu =	0.014 amu
30 neutrons:	30(1.0087) amu =	30.261 amu

Total mass of components:	56.465 amu
Less mass of ${}^{56}_{26}$Fe atom:	−55.935 amu
Total mass loss:	0.530 amu

Mass loss per nucleon: 0.530 amu/56 = 0.00946 amu

Notice that the mass loss per nucleon, and hence the binding energy per nucleon, is greater for iron than for helium. This means that the iron nucleus is more stable relative to protons and neutrons than the helium nucleus is. If some combination of helium nuclei could be induced to produce an iron nucleus, energy would be given off, which would correspond to the increased stability of the product nucleus per nuclear particle.

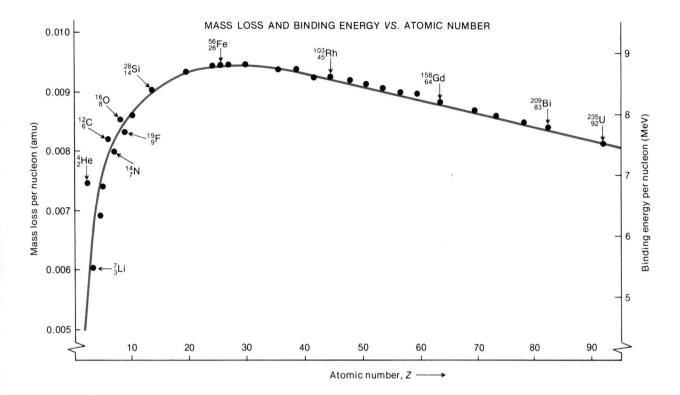

MASS LOSS AND BINDING ENERGY *VS*. ATOMIC NUMBER

The mass loss or binding energy per nuclear particle (protons and neutrons) rises
rapidly to a maximum at iron, then falls. Iron is the most stable nucleus of all.

The mass losses or binding energies per nucleon are plotted above
for all nuclei from hydrogen through uranium. After some initial minor
irregularities in the first- and second-row elements, the values settle
down to a smooth curve, which rises to a maximum at iron, then begins
a long descending slope through uranium and beyond. This curve gives
us information that was used in the discussion of stellar synthesis of
elements in Chapter 8. Iron is the most stable nucleus of all. For elements with smaller atomic numbers than iron, fusion of nuclei to produce heavier elements releases energy, because the products are lighter
and more stable on a per-nucleon basis than the reactants. In contrast,
beyond iron, fusion absorbs energy because the products are heavier on
a per-nucleon basis than the reactants. In this region, beyond atomic
number 26, energy is released by fission rather than fusion. At the far
left of the curve, hydrogen *fusion* in stars releases energy:

$$4\,^{1}_{1}\text{H} + 2\,^{0}_{-1}\text{e} \rightarrow\,^{4}_{2}\text{He} + \text{energy}$$

and at the far right, uranium *fission* in atomic reactors also releases
energy:

$$^{235}_{92}\text{U} + ^{1}_{0}\text{n} \rightarrow\,^{144}_{56}\text{Ba} + ^{89}_{36}\text{Kr} + 3\,^{1}_{0}\text{n} + \text{energy}$$

(This is only one of many ways in which the ^{235}U nucleus can break
down.)

The maximum stability of the iron nucleus is the reason why the element-building process by successive fusion reactions, outlined in Chapter 8, stops at iron. Beyond iron the fusion process is energy-requiring instead of energy-yielding. The heavier elements are built up by more indirect processes involving neutron capture.

In spite of the fact that mass is not conserved in nuclear reactions, conservation principles do apply to the total *number* of heavy particles (protons and neutrons) and total charge. This is implicit in the equations for the two previous nuclear reactions. In the fusion reaction $_1^1$H and $_2^4$He should be understood as representing nuclei, with total mass numbers given by superscripts, and nuclear charge (equal to the number of protons) given by subscripts. An electron is represented as $_{-1}^0$e, with a zero mass number (not counted among the nucleons) and a -1 charge. In the fusion equation four hydrogen nuclei (not atoms) combine with two of the four electrons around the atoms to form a helium nucleus. The two remaining original electrons, not shown in the equation, associate with the nucleus to build a neutral helium atom.

A proton in this representation is $_1^1$p, and a neutron is $_0^1$n. The uranium fission reaction tells us that a uranium nucleus, when bombarded by a neutron, breaks down into barium and krypton nuclei with the release of three more neutrons. Therefore this is a chain reaction, with more neutrons released than were used up. These neutrons can bombard neighboring ^{235}U nuclei and produce even more fission.

Mass number (superscripts) and charge (subscripts) are conserved in nuclear reactions of this type, just as the number of each kind of atom is conserved in a chemical reaction. You should verify that the sum of subscripts, and sum of superscripts, are constant on the two sides of the equation.

NUCLEAR STABILITY AND DECAY

What determines how many neutrons can exist in a nucleus along with a given number of protons? Some combinations are stable indefinitely, some combinations are never found, and intermediate ratios of neutrons to protons lead to unstable nuclei that decay in different ways into other nuclei. Nuclei are stable only if they have as many or more neutrons as protons; the only stable nucleus with a surplus of protons is $_1^1$H. The stable region of protons and neutrons is shown in the graph on the next page. Large colored circles indicate stable nuclei, and dots or crosses represent unstable nuclei that decay.

Nuclei with too many neutrons, below and to the right of the stable region in the graph, turn one neutron into a proton by emitting an electron or β^- particle from the nucleus. This is called *beta decay:*

$$_2^6\text{He} \rightarrow \ _3^6\text{Li} + _{-1}^0\text{e}$$

$$_6^{14}\text{C} \rightarrow \ _7^{14}\text{N} + _{-1}^0\text{e}$$

$$_{28}^{66}\text{Ni} \rightarrow _{29}^{66}\text{Cu} + _{-1}^0\text{e} \rightarrow _{30}^{66}\text{Zn} + 2 \, _{-1}^0\text{e}$$

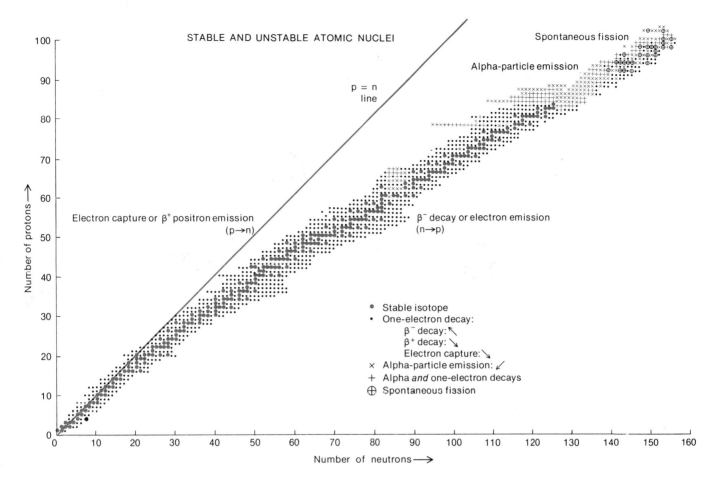

STABLE AND UNSTABLE ATOMIC NUCLEI

Number of protons →

p = n
line

Electron capture or β⁺ positron emission
(p→n)

β⁻ decay or electron emission
(n→p)

Spontaneous fission

Alpha-particle emission

- Stable isotope
· One-electron decay:
  β⁻ decay: ↖
  β⁺ decay: ↘
  Electron capture: ↘
× Alpha-particle emission: ↙
+ Alpha *and* one-electron decays
⊕ Spontaneous fission

Number of neutrons →

Stable nuclei form a belt across a p-n plot in the region of a slight excess of neutrons. Nearby unstable nuclei decay in such a way as to move back into this stable belt.

In the last example, nickel, which has 28 protons and 38 neutrons, emits a beta particle, or electron, and becomes copper, which has 29 protons and 37 neutrons. This is still too high a neutron-to-proton ratio, so the copper nucleus emits another electron and becomes a stable zinc nucleus, which has 30 protons and 36 neutrons. Note that each beta decay is a diagonal step one place up and to the left on the stability plot, and that this step brings the nucleus closer to the region of stability.

Nuclei with too many protons, above and to the left of the stable zone on the graph, can decay by two routes that lead to the same place. In some cases a positron is emitted from the nucleus, and one proton changes into a neutron. A positron is a particle with the mass of an electron but with a +1 charge, and is represented by $_{+1}^{0}e$ or sometimes by β^+. Examples of β^+ decay, or *positron emission*, are

$$_{5}^{8}B \rightarrow {}_{4}^{8}Be + {}_{+1}^{0}e$$

$$_{8}^{15}O \rightarrow {}_{7}^{15}N + {}_{+1}^{0}e$$

$$_{29}^{58}Cu \rightarrow {}_{28}^{58}Ni + {}_{+1}^{0}e$$

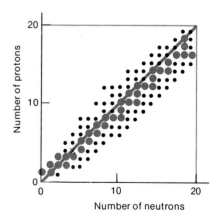

Enlarged 0–20 section of the top figure.

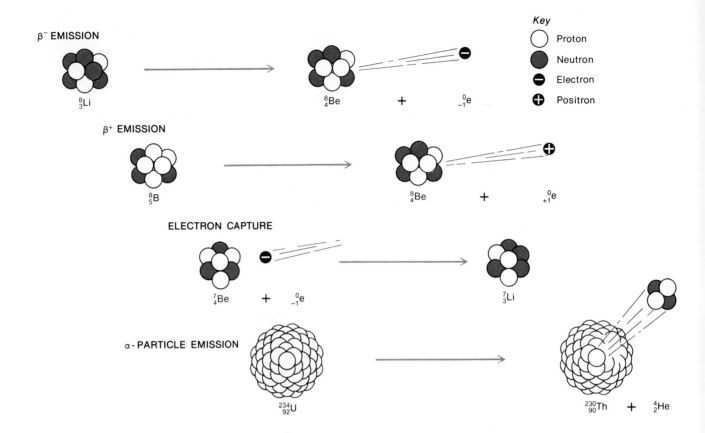

Key

○ Proton
● Neutron
⊖ Electron
⊕ Positron

β^- EMISSION

^8_3Li → ^8_4Be + $^0_{-1}\text{e}$

β^+ EMISSION

^8_5B → ^8_4Be + $^0_{+1}\text{e}$

ELECTRON CAPTURE

^7_4Be + $^0_{-1}\text{e}$ → ^7_3Li

α - PARTICLE EMISSION

$^{234}_{92}\text{U}$ → $^{230}_{90}\text{Th}$ + ^4_2He

Unstable nuclei can decay by ejecting electrons or positrons, capturing orbital electrons, or emitting helium-4 nuclei, depending on their proton-to-neutron ratio.

Alternatively, the same result can be obtained in other nuclei by capturing an electron orbiting around the nucleus and using it to convert a proton to a neutron. This is *electron capture*:

$$^7_4\text{Be} + {}^0_{-1}\text{e} \rightarrow {}^7_3\text{Li}$$

$$^{59}_{28}\text{Ni} + {}^0_{-1}\text{e} \rightarrow {}^{59}_{27}\text{Co}$$

Many nuclei can decay by either positron emission or electron capture. Both correspond to a movement down and to the right by one step in the stability graph, thereby bringing the nucleus closer to the stable region. In all of the reactions we have seen so far—beta emission, positron emission, and electron capture—notice that both mass number and charge are conserved.

A fourth kind of decay is observed in heavy nuclei that have too many of both protons and neutrons. Such nuclei are found at the upper right end of the stability plot. These nuclei decay by giving off an alpha particle, or helium nucleus (^4_2He). For example,

$$^{232}_{90}\text{Th} \rightarrow {}^{228}_{88}\text{Ra} + {}^4_2\text{He}$$

One thorium nucleus releases an alpha particle and becomes a radium nucleus. The mass number decreases by four, and the atomic number decreases by two.

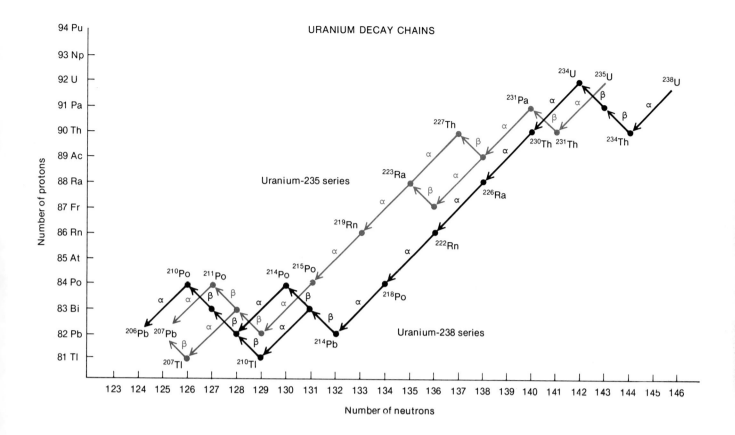

The product nucleus also may be unstable, and if so, a second and a third decay step can occur. Uranium-238 begins a multistep decay chain, which eventually stops at a stable isotope of lead:

$$\begin{aligned}
&{}^{238}_{92}\text{U} \overset{\alpha}{\to} {}^{234}_{90}\text{Th} \overset{\beta}{\to} {}^{234}_{91}\text{Pa} \overset{\beta}{\to} {}^{234}_{92}\text{U} \overset{\alpha}{\to} {}^{230}_{90}\text{Th} \overset{\alpha}{\to} {}^{226}_{88}\text{Ra} \overset{\alpha}{\to} \\
&{}^{222}_{86}\text{Rn} \overset{\alpha}{\to} {}^{218}_{84}\text{Po} \overset{\alpha}{\to} {}^{214}_{82}\text{Pb} \overset{\beta}{\to} {}^{214}_{83}\text{Bi} \overset{\beta}{\to} {}^{214}_{84}\text{Po} \overset{\alpha}{\to} \\
&{}^{210}_{82}\text{Pb} \overset{\beta}{\to} {}^{210}_{83}\text{Bi} \overset{\beta}{\to} {}^{210}_{84}\text{Po} \overset{\alpha}{\to} {}^{206}_{82}\text{Pb} \text{ (stable)}
\end{aligned}$$

In the transformations above, α indicates alpha-particle emission, and β represents beta decay. Write a few of the individual steps to check that mass number and charge are conserved. In this series of breakdowns, uranium emits an alpha particle to become an unstable isotope of thorium, which goes via β decay to protactinium and then to a different isotope of uranium. A series of α decays then descends through thorium, radium, radon, and polonium to an unstable lead isotope, and the process continues until a stable form of lead is reached. The entire ${}^{238}\text{U}$ decay chain represented on a p-n stability plot appears at the top of the page. Another decay chain shown in color leads from ${}^{235}\text{U}$ to ${}^{207}\text{Pb}$, and a third chain, not shown, begins with ${}^{232}\text{Th}$ and ends at ${}^{208}\text{Pb}$. Lead is just at the upper end of the stable region, as seen on Page 255, and the heavier elements beyond it to the upper right decay spontaneously back to lead.

Uranium-235 and uranium-238 each decay by a series of alpha particle and beta emissions to a stable isotope of lead. Thorium-232 and plutonium-241 have similar multistep decay chains.

ISOTOPES AND HALF-LIVES

The number of protons in a nucleus defines an element, but different numbers of neutrons lead to different isotopes of the same element. We encountered several isotopes of uranium, bismuth, and lead in the two uranium decay schemes just outlined. As another example, carbon has seven isotopes, which have been observed either in nature or in nuclear reactions.

Isotopes of carbon

Symbol	Protons	Neutrons	Atomic weight	Percent natural abundance	Radioactive half-life	Mode of decay
$^{10}_{6}$C	6	4	~10	—	19.45 sec	β^+
$^{11}_{6}$C	6	5	~11	—	20.3 min	β^+ or EC
$^{12}_{6}$C	6	6	12.00000	98.89	stable isotope	—
$^{13}_{6}$C	6	7	13.00335	1.11	stable isotope	—
$^{14}_{6}$C	6	8	~14	—	5570 years	β^-
$^{15}_{6}$C	6	9	~15	—	2.4 sec	β^-
$^{16}_{6}$C	6	10	~16	—	0.74 sec	β^-

Only two of the seven isotopes of carbon are stable; the others break down spontaneously with different rapidity. The unstable nuclei that are rich in protons, carbon-10 and carbon-11, decay by capturing an electron or ejecting a positron. The nuclei that are oversupplied with neutrons, carbon-14, -15, and -16, each eject an electron.

The *half-life* is the length of time required for half of any given amount of an element to decay into another element. For example, if one begins with a gram of carbon-10, 20 seconds later only half a gram will remain, after 40 seconds only a quarter gram will be left, after 60 seconds an eighth of a gram, after 80 seconds one sixteenth of a gram, and after 100 seconds have elapsed from the beginning of the experiment, only one thirty-second of the original carbon-10 will remain (left). Because it decays so fast carbon-10 is not found in nature, although it can be observed as the product of some nuclear reactions.

The half-lives of the five unstable isotopes of carbon differ greatly. Whereas half of any starting quantity of carbon-16 decays to nitrogen-16 in three quarters of a second, the same reaction for carbon-14 decaying to nitrogen-14 takes nearly six thousand years. Even so, carbon-14 is not a stable isotope, and will disappear in time. This slow decay of carbon-14 is the basis of a widely used dating method for archaeological materials. As long as any organism is alive, its carbon atoms are being exchanged continuously with the atmosphere. Plants and animals release CO_2 into the atmosphere during respiration. Plants use atmo-

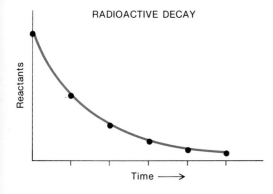

RADIOACTIVE DECAY

Reactants

Time ⟶

Since the probability of decay of every nucleus of an unstable isotope is the same, the number that decay in a given time period is just proportional to the number of nuclei left to decay. Half of the remaining material will decay in a time known as the decay *half-life*. If the half-life is one second, half the starting material will remain after 1 sec, a quarter after 2 sec, an eighth after 3 sec, a sixteenth after 4 sec, and so on.

spheric CO_2 during photosynthesis to make carbohydrates, and animals obtain these carbon atoms by eating the plants. A constant ratio of carbon-14 to stable carbon-12 is maintained in the atmosphere because of the continuous production of new carbon-14 by reactions with high-energy neutrons in the upper atmosphere:

$$^{14}_{7}N + ^{1}_{0}n \rightarrow ^{14}_{6}C + ^{1}_{1}H$$

To a first approximation, the carbon isotope ratio in the atmosphere and in all living organisms is fixed.

As long as the organism is alive, it maintains this same carbon-14 to carbon-12 ratio. But as soon as it dies, exchange with the atmosphere ceases. The slow decay of carbon-14 causes the isotope ratio to diminish by half every 5570 years. It is a simple matter in principle, although careful work is required to prevent contamination, to determine the actual carbon isotope ratio in any ancient sample of wood or other preserved organic matter, and to calculate from this how long ago the specimen died. In this way, surprisingly accurate chronologies can be constructed for the past 10,000 years. Radiocarbon dating has become one of the most important tools of archaeologists.

Similar dating methods can be used for geologic time spans by picking isotopes with longer half-lives. Potassium-40 decays with a half-life of 1.3 billion years to argon-40. Uranium-238 decays to lead-206 in a series of steps, of which the slowest has a half-life of 4.5 billion years, and rubidium-87 decays with a half-life of 500 billion years to strontium-87. Dating rock samples from the Earth and moon, and meteorite fragments, via potassium–argon, uranium–lead, and rubidium–strontium methods, has been an important tool in the study of our solar system.

NUMBER AND CHARGE: A SUMMARY

In both nuclear and chemical reactions, two physical quantities are seen to be conserved and unchanging: the number of particles and the total charge. A constant number of particles in nuclear reactions does not imply that mass is conserved. Three ^{4}He nuclei and one ^{12}C nucleus each have twelve nucleons (protons and neutrons), yet the three helium nuclei weigh 12.0078 amu, whereas the carbon nucleus weighs only 12.0000 amu. The difference represents the conversion of some of the mass into energy. In contrast, the energies involved in ordinary chemical reactions are so small that mass–energy conversions can be neglected, so equal numbers of atoms of each kind before and after a reaction takes place *do* imply conservation of mass.

Charge conservation in nuclear reactions means that no net positive or negative charge is created in the course of the reaction. If a positive charge appears somewhere, either another positive charge must disappear somewhere else, or a negative charge must appear to counterbalance it. For chemical reactions, charge conservation means that electrons in molecules are neither created nor destroyed. Whenever an electron moves away from one atom during an oxidation, it must move closer to another atom, which therefore is reduced. Conservation of oxidation number in chemical reactions is analogous to conservation of particle charge in nuclear reactions.

In this chapter we have seen two quantities that always are conserved in chemical reactions: mass and oxidation number. In the next chapter we shall see a third and very important conservation principle: the conservation of energy.

QUESTIONS

1. What is a conservation principle? Why is it useful in chemistry?

2. Which of the following properties of reactants and products are always conserved during a chemical reaction?
   (a) color
   (b) temperature
   (c) number of atoms
   (d) number of bonds
   (e) kinds of bonds: ionic, covalent, etc.
   (f) energy
   (g) molecular shape
   (h) mass
   (i) electrical conductivity
   (j) dipole moment
   (k) oxidation number
   (l) total of mass and energy

3. In what way does a zero net change in oxidation number for all participants in a reaction represent conservation of electrons?

4. What is the hidden assumption when we use conservation of mass as being equivalent to the conservation of the number of each kind of atom?

5. What is the difference between weight and mass? Which would change and which would remain the same on going from the Earth to the moon? Would the one that changes be greater, or less, on the moon?

6. How can we use the weighing operation to tell how many atoms are present in a sample of material, although the direct counting of atoms is impossible?

7. When we balance a chemical equation by making the number of each kind of atom the same on both sides, what conservation principle are we using?

8. When O_2 is combined with carbon to form CO_2, is the oxygen oxidized, or reduced? When chlorine gas is combined with carbon to form CCl_4, is the chlorine oxidized, or reduced? When O_2 and Cl_2 are combined to form the gas Cl_2O, which substance is oxidized and which is reduced?

9. Write the oxidation numbers for all atoms in the molecules H_2O, CO_2, CCl_4, and Cl_2O.

10. Strict application of the rules for calculating oxidation numbers, as given in Chapter 6, would lead to what values for C and H in methane, CH_4? Then why do we say, as we did in this chapter, that the oxidation numbers of these atoms are *effectively* zero in methane, in discussing the nature of combustions?

11. What are the oxidation numbers of the atoms in NaBr and ClBr? When these compounds are formed from pure elements, does an actual transfer of electrons occur from one atom to the other?

Which atom receives the electron, if transfer occurs? Are both of these compounds ionic salts? If not, what do the different oxidation numbers mean for atoms in the compound that is not a salt?

12. What are the oxidation numbers of the different atoms in potassium permanganate, $KMnO_4$? In manganese dioxide, MnO_2? In manganous sulfate, $MnSO_4$? Is manganese oxidized, or reduced, in going from manganese dioxide to potassium permanganate?

13. What are the oxidation numbers of the metal atoms in potassium chromate, K_2CrO_4? In potassium dichromate, $K_2Cr_2O_7$? In chromous chloride, $CrCl_2$? Is the chromium atom oxidized, or reduced, in going from dichromate to chromous chloride?

14. What is the difference between the oxidation-number method and the half-reaction method for balancing oxidation–reduction equations?

15. What three quantities must be accounted for in successfully balancing an oxidation–reduction equation? Which quantity is balanced *last* when using the half-reaction method, but *first* when using the other method?

16. In what sense do the principles of conservation of mass and conservation of energy fail when we turn from chemical to nuclear reactions? Why? What new conservation principle can be used instead?

17. How do the energies involved in a typical chemical reaction and a typical nuclear reaction compare?

18. In what sense can the mass loss observed upon forming a nucleus from subnuclear particles be considered a binding energy for the nucleus? Where has the missing mass gone?

19. How does the mass loss per nucleon change as atomic number changes? Which element has the greatest mass loss per nucleon? Does this make it especially stable, or unstable?

20. For elements with lower atomic number than that of the element in Question 19, is fission, or fusion, the energy-emitting process? Account for this in terms of binding energy and mass loss. Which is the energy-releasing process at higher atomic numbers?

21. What important quantities must be accounted for in balancing the equation for a nuclear reaction? How are these quantities represented in the symbols for atomic nuclei?

22. What is meant by a "stability zone" in a p-n plot?

23. How do nuclei with too many protons normally decay? What happens to the nuclear charge and mass number in this process? What does this decay process look like when represented on a p-n plot?

24. How do nuclei with too many neutrons normally decay? How do the nuclear charge and mass number change, and how does the position of the nucleus on a p-n plot change?

25. How do nuclei with too many neutrons *and* protons ordinarily decay? Show the change in nuclear charge and mass number on a p-n plot.

26. What happens if an unstable nucleus decays to another nucleus, which itself is unstable?

27. What is the half-life of an unstable element? In how many half-lives will the amount of an unstable element fall to less than 10% of its original value? In how many half-life periods will it disappear completely

28. How does the ratio of carbon isotopes tell us the age of an object?

PROBLEMS

1. Balance the following chemical equations properly. What principle of conservation is involved?
   (a) $NaOH + CO_2 \rightarrow Na_2CO_3 + H_2O$
   (b) $NH_3 + Fe_2(SO_4)_3 \rightarrow (NH_4)_2SO_4 + Fe(OH)_3$
   (c) $Mg(OH)_2 + HCl \rightarrow MgCl_2 + H_2O$
   (d) $Mg(OH)_2 + H_2SO_4 \rightarrow MgSO_4 + H_2O$
   (e) $NaHCO_3 \rightarrow Na_2CO_3 + H_2CO_3$
   (f) $Ca_3(PO_4)_2 + H_2SO_4 \rightarrow CaSO_4 + H_3PO_4$

2. Crystals of potassium chlorate, $KClO_3$, first will melt if heated, and then decompose to give oxygen gas and potassium chloride. (a) Write a balanced equation for the decomposition. (b) How many moles of potassium chlorate are needed to produce three moles of oxygen gas? (c) How many moles of potassium chlorate are needed to give 100 moles of oxygen gas? (d) How many moles and how many grams of oxygen gas would be produced by decomposing 100 g of potassium chlorate?

3. If plenty of oxygen is available, iron burns to form black Fe_3O_4. (a) Write the balanced equation for the reaction. (b) How many moles of O_2 are required to burn one mole of iron? (c) How many grams of O_2 are required to burn one mole of iron? (d) Can a piece of iron weighing 5.6 g burn completely in a vessel containing 0.05 mole of O_2?

4. Write the oxidation number for each atom in the following compounds:
   (a) nitric acid
   (b) potassium hydroxide
   (c) potassium oxide
   (d) ammonia
   (e) potassium permanganate
   (f) permanganate ion, MnO_4^-
   (g) cuprous oxide, Cu_2O
   (h) cupric oxide, CuO
   (i) magnetite, Fe_3O_4
   (j) iron pyrite, FeS_2

5. Write the oxidation number for each atom in
   (a) topaz, $Al_2SiO_4F_2$
   (b) lead sulfide, PbS
   (c) sulfur, S_8
   (d) borax, $Na_2B_4O_7 \cdot 10H_2O$
   (e) ammonium nitrate, NH_4NO_2
   (f) quartz, SiO_2
   (g) garnet, $Ca_3Al_2Si_3O_{12}$
   (h) hydrogen fluoride, HF
   (i) lithium hydride, LiH
   (j) oxygen difluoride, OF_2

6. Balance the following chemical equations properly by the oxidation-number method. Which substance is oxidized and which is reduced in each example?
   (a) $MnO_2 + Cl^- \rightarrow Mn^{2+} + Cl_2$ (acidic solution)
   (b) $NaCl + SO_3 \rightarrow Cl_2 + SO_2 + Na_2S_2O_7$

(c) $KBrO_3 + KI + H_2SO_4 \rightarrow KBr + K_2SO_4 + I_2$

(d) $Sb_2S_3 + HNO_3 \rightarrow Sb_2O_5 + H_2SO_4 + NO_2$

(e) $KI + H_2SO_4 \rightarrow I_2 + K_2SO_4 + SO_2$

(f) $Na_2CrO_2 + NaClO + NaOH \rightarrow Na_2CrO_4 + NaCl$

(g) $N_2O_4 + BrO_3^- \rightarrow NO_3^- + Br^-$ (acidic solution)

(h) $S_2O_4^{2-} + Ag_2O \rightarrow Ag + SO_3^{2-}$

(i) $NaBiO_3 + MnO_2 + H_2SO_4 \rightarrow$
$$Bi_2(SO_4)_3 + NaMnO_4 + Na_2SO_4$$

(j) $SnSO_4 + K_2Cr_2O_7 + H_2SO_4 \rightarrow$
$$Sn(SO_4)_2 + Cr_2(SO_4)_3 + K_2SO_4$$

(k) $H_2O_2 + KMnO_4 + H_2SO_4 \rightarrow O_2 + MnSO_4 + H_2SO_4$

(l) $As_2S_5 + KClO_3 \rightarrow H_3AsO_4 + KCl + H_2SO_4$

(m) $NaIO_3 + Na_2SO_3 + NaHSO_3 \rightarrow Na_2SO_4 + I_2$

7. Balance the chemical equations of Problem 6 by the half-reaction method.

8. Balance each of the following equations by any convenient method:

(a) $C_7H_{16} + O_2 \rightarrow CO_2 + H_2O$ (complete combustion)

(b) $C_7H_{16} + O_2 \rightarrow CO + H_2O$ (incomplete combustion)

(c) $C_7H_{16} + O_2 \rightarrow C_7H_{12} + H_2O$

9. The mass of the $^{16}_8O$ atom is 15.9949 amu. Calculate the mass loss per nucleon, and the binding energy per nucleon. How do these values compare with those for iron-56?

10. Write a balanced nuclear equation for the fusion of three helium-4 nuclei to form a carbon-12 nucleus. What quantities must be conserved in the balancing process?

11. When three helium-4 atoms fuse to form an atom of carbon-12, is there a gain, or loss, of mass, and how much? Is energy absorbed, or given off, and how much? (Recall that carbon-12 is the standard for the amu scale, with a mass of exactly 12 amu.)

12. When two oxygen-16 atoms fuse in a reaction at the centers of very heavy stars to produce an atom of sulfur-32, how much mass is lost, and how much energy is released? (Mass of $^{32}S = 31.9721$ amu; $^{16}O = 15.9949$.)

13. When an atom of nickel-60 and a helium-4 atom fuse to form zinc-64, what is the change in mass? Is energy given off, or absorbed, and how much?

14. Thorium-232 is the beginning of a radioactive decay series (similar to the two uranium series) in which six alpha particles and four beta particles are emitted before a stable isotope is reached. What is the final stable element, and what is its mass number?

15. Plutonium-241 is the beginning of a decay series during which eight alpha and five beta particles are emitted. What is the final stable element, and what is its mass number?

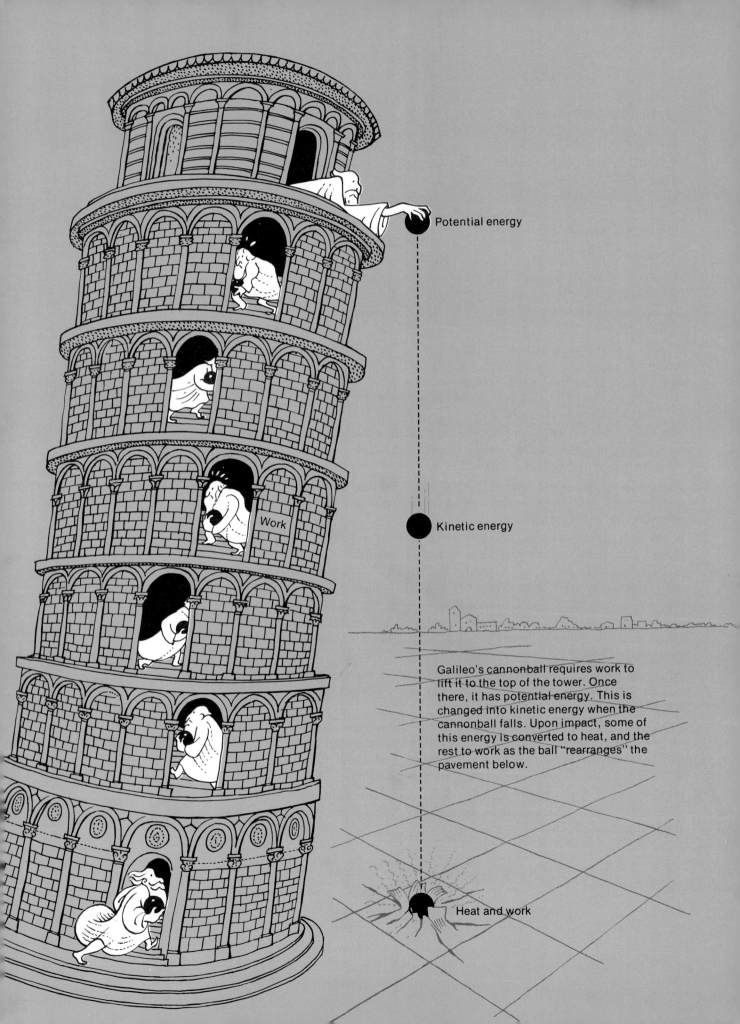

Potential energy

Kinetic energy

Work

Heat and work

Galileo's cannonball requires work to lift it to the top of the tower. Once there, it has potential energy. This is changed into kinetic energy when the cannonball falls. Upon impact, some of this energy is converted to heat, and the rest to work as the ball "rearranges" the pavement below.

CHAPTER 12

Heat, Energy, and Chemical Bonds

In Chapter 11 we saw two examples of principles of conservation, involving matter and charge, in chemical reactions. Neither the total mass nor the net oxidation number of reactants and products can change during a chemical transformation. Mass and oxidation number are more fundamental properties of substances than are volume, color, texture, density, or electrical conductivity. A third important property that is conserved is energy. Combustions and many other reactions give off energy in the form of heat, and this makes these processes useful to us. But if we draw an imaginary box around the reacting substances, large enough to contain the substances and everything else they interact with, then the total energy within that box will not change during the reaction. (This is one form of the first law of thermodynamics.) If the reaction gives off heat energy, then the products must have less energy than the reactants, because this difference is the only source of the heat. Conversely, if the products have more energy than the reactants, this extra energy must be supplied to the reaction from outside.

Energy can be thought of as the capacity to do work. *Potential energy* is energy that a motionless object has by virtue of its position. A rock poised at a great height has gravitational potential energy because it can do work while falling, if harnessed to a suitable apparatus. Galileo's cannonball had considerable potential energy before he dropped it (see opposite page). Two separated positive and negative charges have electrostatic potential energy, for they can do electrical work as they come together again. A bar magnet turned crosswise to a magnetic field has magnetic potential energy. Work is required to turn the magnet out of alignment with the field, and this work can be regained when the magnet aligns itself with the field once more.

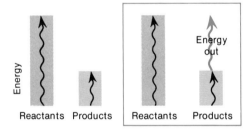

EXOTHERMIC REACTION gives off heat. Reactants have a *higher* energy than products. The difference between reactants and products equals the energy given off.

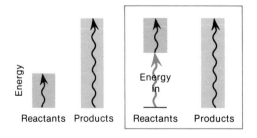

ENDOTHERMIC REACTION absorbs heat. Reactants have a *lower* energy than products. The difference must be supplied to the reaction by an outside energy source.

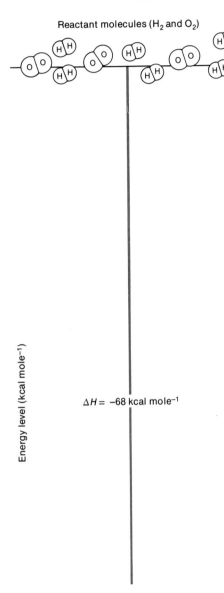

THE HEAT OF A REACTION

Reactant molecules (H_2 and O_2)

Energy level (kcal mole^{-1})

$\Delta H = -68$ kcal mole^{-1}

A mole of water molecules has 68 kcal less energy than the H_2 and O_2 molecules from which it was formed. The *change* in heat energy is negative, $\Delta H = -68$ kcal mole^{-1}, because heat is given off by the molecules to the outside world.

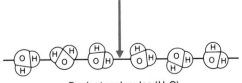

Product molecules (H_2O)

Kinetic energy is the energy that an object has because of its motion. Work is required initially to get the object going, and this work can be obtained again when the projectile collides with a target and comes to rest. If the moving object has mass m, and is moving with velocity v, its kinetic energy of motion is

$$E = \tfrac{1}{2}mv^2$$

Galileo's cannonball in the opening drawing converts potential energy to kinetic energy as it falls faster and faster.

Heat is a form of energy, too, but in a degraded form. On the molecular level, heat is the uncoordinated vibration or motion of individual molecules. It is easy to convert work or other kinds of energy into heat. If you rub one hand hard against another on a cold day, the warmth generated by friction is just a conversion of the work that you do into heat. When Galileo's cannonball strikes the pavement, the potential energy that had first changed into kinetic energy of motion as it fell, is changed again into heat as it collides with the ground. The reverse transformation of heat into motion, as in an automobile engine, is accomplished only with difficulty; not all of the heat can be converted. We will come back to these ideas when we talk about order and disorder in the next chapter. For the moment, the important idea is that potential energy, kinetic energy, heat, and work all are different kinds of energy, and with certain limitations they can be interconverted from one form to another.

HEAT AND CHEMICAL REACTIONS

One can think of a chemical reaction as proceeding by the pulling apart of all of the atoms in the reactant molecules, and then the reassembling of these isolated atoms in new ways to make product molecules. The difference between bond energies of products and reactants, ΔE, is essentially the energy of the reaction:

$$\Delta E = E_{\text{products}} - E_{\text{reactants}}$$

If the energy of the products is less than that of the initial molecules, the molecular energy decreases. The change in energy of the molecules and atoms during the reaction is negative, and heat is given off:

$$\Delta E = E_{\text{products}} - E_{\text{reactants}} = < 0$$

Conversely, if the product molecules have more energy than the starting materials, heat is absorbed, the total molecular energy increases, and ΔE is positive.

When gases are produced in a chemical reaction, work must be done in pushing against the pressure of the atmosphere to make room for them. Conversely, if gases disappear or condense to form liquids or solids during a reaction, work is done *on* the reacting substances by the external world. If we make a small correction for any work that gases in a reaction might do in pushing against the atmosphere when they are generated, then we obtain a modified energy, the *enthalpy, H*. Enthalpy is defined formally by $H = E + PV$, in which PV is the product of pressure and volume. When a reaction takes place at a constant surrounding pressure, which is true for reactions conducted in the open at the surface of the Earth (e.g., at a laboratory bench), then the heat of reaction is a measure of the change in enthalpy, $\Delta H = H_{\text{products}} - H_{\text{reactants}}$. The difference between energy and enthalpy is only a few percent, and enthalpy should be thought of as a "corrected" energy, with allowance made for atmospheric pressure. Whenever we talk about heats of reaction from now on, we shall be using enthalpies and not strictly molecular energies. You may think of H as standing for "heat" in reactions carried out at constant external pressure.

As an example, when one mole of hydrogen gas and one half mole of oxygen gas react to produce one mole, or 18 grams, of liquid water, 68 kilocalories of heat are given off (far left margin). When this energy escapes as heat, the total molecular enthalpy decreases by 68 kcal:

$$H_2(g) + \tfrac{1}{2}O_2(g) \rightarrow H_2O(l) + 68\,\text{kcal}$$

or in the more conventional way of writing the heat of reaction,

$$H_2(g) + \tfrac{1}{2}O_2(g) \rightarrow H_2O(l) \qquad \Delta H = -68 \text{ kcal mole}^{-1}\, H_2O$$

ΔH is negative because the enthalpy *of the chemicals taking part in the reaction* decreases. Because heat is given off, this reaction is described as *exothermic*. A reaction that absorbs heat is *endothermic*. If we regard hydrogen gas, with a molecular weight of 2 grams per mole, as a fuel, then the energy yield of this reaction is $68/2 = 34$ kcal per gram of fuel. This is a higher value than for any other chemical fuel burned in O_2. If hydrogen could be stored and handled more easily, we probably would use it instead of more conventional hydrocarbon fuels.

If the water in the combustion remained as a gas rather than condensing to a liquid, less heat would be given off (right margin):

$$H_2(g) + \tfrac{1}{2}O_2(g) \rightarrow H_2O(g) \qquad \Delta H = -58 \text{ kcal mole}^{-1}\, H_2O$$

The difference is the enthalpy or heat of vaporization:

$$H_2O(l) \rightarrow H_2O(g) \qquad \Delta H = +10 \text{ kcal mole}^{-1}$$

During vaporization at 25°C, water molecules absorb 10 kcal of heat energy per mole, so the enthalpy increases. This is necessary for liquids

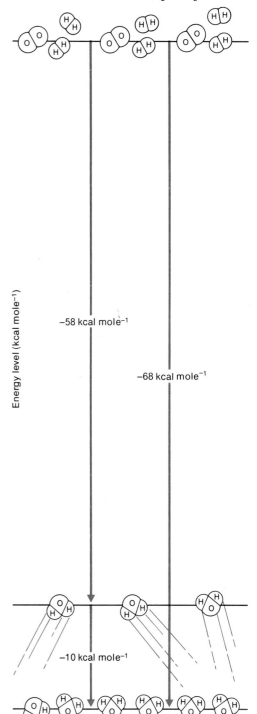

THE NATURE OF THE PRODUCTS

Reactant molecules (H₂ and O₂)

Energy level (kcal mole⁻¹)

-58 kcal mole⁻¹

-68 kcal mole⁻¹

Molecules of water vapor have 58 kcal less energy per mole than the H₂ and O₂ molecules from which they were formed.

H₂O (gas)

-10 kcal mole⁻¹

Liquid water is 10 kcal per mole lower in energy than vapor, or 68 kcal per mole more stable than the reactant H₂ and O₂ molecules.

H₂O (liquid)

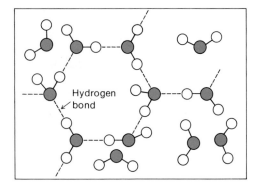

Hydrogen bond

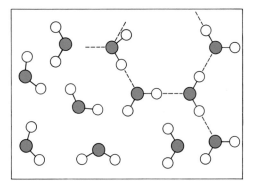

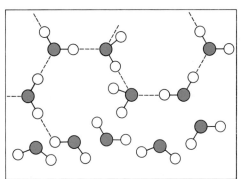

Three instantaneous "snapshots" of water molecules to illustrate the flickering cluster model of liquid water. Temporary hydrogen bonds are made and broken between O and H atoms in different molecules. The percent of H atoms involved in hydrogen bonding remains constant with time, but individual bonds change. One group of molecules may have an icelike cluster of hydrogen bonds at one instant, and a different group of molecules may be bonded in a cluster an instant later.

in general because gas molecules move faster and have more energy (and enthalpy) than molecules in a liquid. The same amount of heat energy is given off again when water vapor condenses:

$$H_2O(g) \rightarrow H_2O(l) \qquad \Delta H = -10 \text{ kcal mole}^{-1}$$

Water has the highest heat of vaporization *per gram* of any known liquid. A comparison of water with a few other common liquids is given below. The reason for the specially high value for water is the network of hydrogen bonds that holds the water molecules together, even in the liquid state. In the "iceberg" or "flickering cluster" picture of liquid water structure (mentioned on Page 61 of Chapter 4), small clusters of water molecules are held together by hydrogen bonds in a more or less icelike manner (left). Bonds are made and broken continually, and one particular molecule may be bonded to others at one instant and free the next. Throughout the liquid a certain percentage of the possible hydrogen bonds will be formed at a given moment. These bonds must be broken when the liquid is vaporized, and this requires energy. The result is a higher heat of vaporization than for liquids without hydrogen bonds. In the series O–S–Se–Te down Group VIA of the periodic table, hydrogen bonding becomes unimportant, because the atoms of S, Se, and Te are too large and their negative charge is too diffuse to attract a proton of a neighboring molecule strongly. Hence H_2S, H_2Se, and H_2Te have more "normal" boiling points and heats of vaporization (far right margin).

This anomalously high heat of vaporization of water has major consequences for life on this planet. Evaporation of ocean water in the tropics keeps the equatorial regions from being as hot as they would be otherwise, and the heat removed warms the more polar regions when the water vapor condenses. Liquid water therefore acts as a heat reservoir, moderating the extremes of temperature both at the equator and near the poles. The evaporation of ocean water at the equator appears to be approximately 2.3 meters of depth per year, corresponding to a

Heats of vaporization of several liquid compounds at their boiling points, in kilocalories per gram and per mole

Compound	Boiling point (°C)	ΔH_{vap} (kcal g^{-1})	ΔH_{vap} (kcal mole^{-1})
H_2O	+100	0.540	9.73
H_2S	−60.4	0.131	4.46
H_2Se	−41.5	0.058	4.70
H_2Te	−4	0.035	4.59
HF	+19	0.360	6.84
NH_3	−33	0.327	5.56
CH_3OH	+65	0.263	8.42
HCN	+26	0.210	5.67
CH_4	−162	0.122	1.95
C_6H_6	+80	0.094	7.33

The greater the polarity of molecules in a liquid, the greater the heat of vaporization per gram.

removal of 1.3 trillion (1,300,000,000,000) kilocalories of heat per square kilometer of surface area! To bring such a giant number into comprehensible range, a person not doing heavy labor normally needs the equivalent of 2000 kcal of energy from food per day. The energy removed annually by evaporation from every square kilometer of tropical ocean would correspond to enough energy to keep 2 million people going for a year.

Notice that we can add two of the previous reactions to yield the third:

$$H_2(g) + \tfrac{1}{2}O_2(g) \rightarrow H_2O(g) \qquad \Delta H = -58 \text{ kcal mole}^{-1} H_2O$$
$$H_2O(g) \qquad\qquad \rightarrow H_2O(l) \qquad \Delta H = -10 \text{ kcal mole}^{-1} H_2O$$
$$\overline{H_2(g) + \tfrac{1}{2}O_2(g) \rightarrow H_2O(l)} \qquad \overline{\Delta H = -68 \text{ kcal mole}^{-1} H_2O}$$

The heats of reaction also add in the same way. In general, if we can add or subtract two reactions to obtain a third, then the heat of this third reaction is obtained by adding or subtracting the heats of the first two. For those who particularly enjoy filing things away by name, this is *Hess' law of heat summation.* It actually is a natural consequence of the first law of thermodynamics.[1] We must be careful that the two reactions added really do yield the third, and that the heats used are for the reactions as they are written. For example, we could multiply the hydrogen combustion reaction by two to eliminate the fractional coefficient before the oxygen, but then the heat of reaction also would have to be doubled:

$$2H_2(g) + O_2(g) \rightarrow 2H_2O(g) \qquad \Delta H = -116 \text{ kcal}$$

The heat given off is 116 kcal for the molar reaction as written; that is, per two moles of hydrogen gas and one mole of oxygen used, and two moles of water vapor formed. If, without thinking, we were to add to this reaction, the reaction

$$H_2O(g) \rightarrow H_2O(l) \qquad \Delta H = -10 \text{ kcal mole}^{-1}$$

then the result would be not what we want at all:

$$2H_2(g) + O_2(g) \rightarrow H_2O(g) + H_2O(l) \qquad \Delta H = -126 \text{ kcal}$$

Although the equation would be true, it would not be particularly useful. One must keep the stoichiometry (the relative numbers of reactant and product molecules) correct for the heats of reaction to be meaningful.

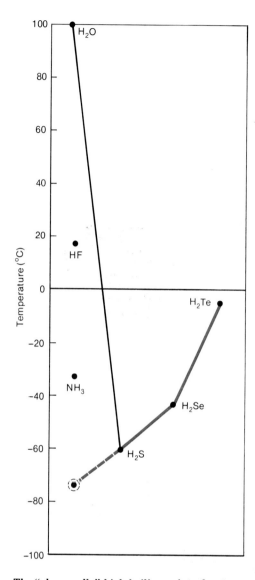

The "abnormally" high boiling point of water is explained by the energy that is required to break the network of hydrogen bonds. If there were no hydrogen bonding in water, and if the trend of boiling points seen with Group VIA elements in H_2Te, H_2Se, and H_2S continued, the expected boiling point of H_2O would be 75° below zero Centigrade instead of 100° above zero.

---

[1] Although we are not concerned here with formal thermodynamics, it might be well to introduce the first law in its thermochemical guise. The internal energy of a reacting system, E, is defined such that the change in energy during any process is the difference between the heat poured into the system, q, and the work done by the system on its surroundings, w, or $\Delta E = q - w$. The first law then states that the internal energy change, ΔE, depends only on the beginning and ending conditions and not on how the reaction was carried out. Because of the way that enthalpy is defined, this statement is true for ΔH also. In the example above, the reaction of hydrogen and oxygen gases to produce water vapor, followed by condensation of the vapor in a second step, must lead to exactly the same enthalpy change as the reaction of hydrogen and oxygen gases to produce liquid water directly. Hence the heats of the first two reactions must add to yield the heat of the direct process.

Starch grains
in plant cell

Plants store energy, derived from sunlight, in the form of starch grains. Animals store their excess energy in the form of fats, not starch.

FUELS, COMBUSTION, AND ENERGY

We mentioned previously that hydrogen gas was the most efficient of all fuels in terms of heat emitted per gram of fuel burned. Gasoline is less efficient by nearly a factor of three, as the table at the right shows. Hydrogen gas releases 34 kcal per gram upon combustion in air; gasoline yields less than 12 kcal per gram. Fats, the main energy-storage system in animals, produce 9.5 kcal per gram upon combustion, and are almost as efficient in energy storage as gasoline. Starch, the main energy-storage molecule in plants, is a long-chain polymer of glucose. Glucose can store only 3.7 kcal per gram, so on a weight basis, starch is an inefficient material for storing energy. Then why is the entire photosynthetic and energy-storage machinery of green plants based on starch?

The answer is that weight considerations are of minor concern to a stationary plant. There is no advantage in a lightweight fuel to an organism that is not going anywhere. The chemistry of assembling starch chains from glucose and recovering glucose again is particularly simple, whereas the metabolism of fats and fatty acids is more complicated. Plants store energy in starch because it is especially easy to get the energy in and out. Animals, which must move about and carry their fuel supplies with them, find the low energy-per-gram feature of starch to be a disadvantage. They put up with the more complicated chemistry of fats to achieve an energy-storage efficiency only slightly less than that of gasoline. The one big advantage of fats over gasoline is that fats are solids. It would be almost as disadvantageous for us to carry around liquid gasoline as an energy reserve as it would be to carry huge gas bags of hydrogen. (An organism that evolved bags of hydrogen gas for energy storage also would have come a long way in solving its locomotion problem. But thunderstorms and lightning would be hard on such a creature.)

Even animals cannot get along without the rapid-access feature of starch as an energy-storage agent. Animals have glycogen in their bloodstream as a quick-energy source, which serves as a buffer between the immediate energy needs of the organism and the slow production of energy from fats. Glycogen, or "animal starch," is a branched-chain polymer of glucose molecules very similar to plant starch.

The table of heats of combustion at the right also points out that we could do much better than to burn our fuels in oxygen. Combustion of methane in O_2 produces only 13 kcal of heat per mole of methane, whereas combustion in F_2 would yield 25 kcal, nearly twice as much. Chlorine gas is less favorable as an oxidant, yielding only 6.5 kcal per mole of methane consumed. These differences are purely a function of the electronegativities of F, O, and Cl, that is, the strength with which each atom pulls electrons toward itself. After combustion, the electrons that were shared equally between carbon and hydrogen in methane are drawn toward the Cl atoms when Cl_2 is the combustion medium, drawn more strongly toward O atoms, and most strongly of all toward F when F_2 is the combustion medium. The tighter the electrons are held after combustion, the more stable the product molecules are, and the more energy is given off as heat.

270

GLUCOSE

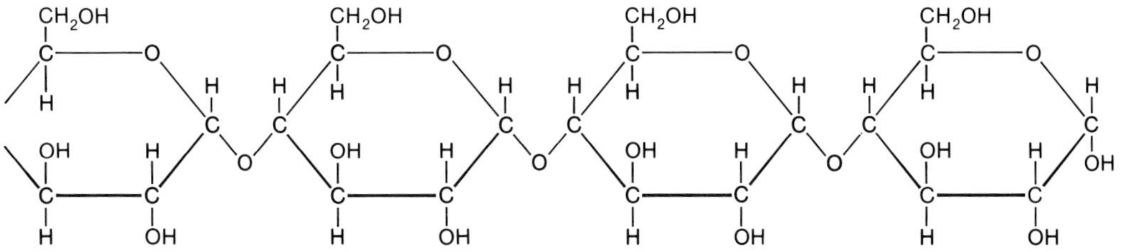

Starch is a long-chain molecule composed of repeating units of glucose, a sugar.

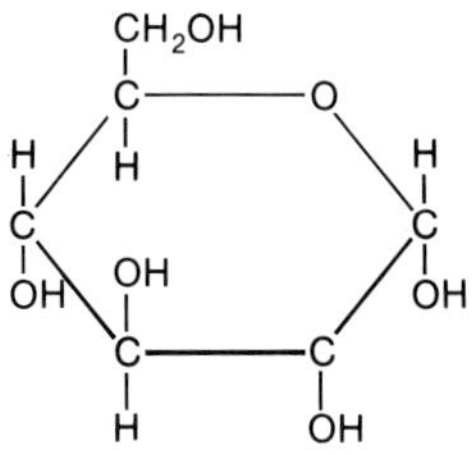

The chain is easily broken during digestion. Energy is obtained by the further breakdown of individual glucose molecules (see Chapter 23).

Combustion of various substances in O_2, F_2, and Cl_2

	Heat of combustion (kcal mole^{-1})	Molecular weight (grams)	Heat of combustion (kcal gram^{-1})
Hydrogen[a]:			
$H_2 + \frac{1}{2}O_2 \rightarrow H_2O\,(l)$	-68	2	-34.0
Methane gas:			
$CH_4 + 2O_2 \rightarrow CO_2 + 2H_2O\,(l)$	-213	16	-13.3
Gasoline (octane):			
$C_8H_{18}\,(l) + 12\frac{1}{2}O_2 \rightarrow 8CO_2 + 9H_2O\,(l)$	-1303	114	-11.5
Stearic acid (in animal fats):			
$C_{18}H_{36}O_2\,(s) + 26O_2 \rightarrow 18CO_2 + 18H_2O\,(l)$	-2712	284	-9.5
Ethyl alcohol:			
$C_2H_5OH\,(l) + 3O_2 \rightarrow 2CO_2 + 3H_2O\,(l)$	-327	46	-7.1
Glucose:			
$C_6H_{12}O_6\,(s) + 6O_2 \rightarrow 6CO_2 + 6H_2O\,(l)$	-673	180	-3.7
Magnesium metal:			
$Mg\,(s) + \frac{1}{2}O_2 \rightarrow MgO\,(s)$	-144	24.3	-5.9
Hydrogen in F_2:			
$H_2 + F_2 \rightarrow 2HF$	-128	2	-64.0
Methane in F_2:			
$CH_4 + 4F_2 \rightarrow CF_4 + 4HF$	-401	16	-25.0
Methane in Cl_2:			
$CH_4 + 4Cl_2 \rightarrow CCl_4 + 4HCl$	-104	16	-6.5

[a] All reactants and products are gases unless specified otherwise. The three columns at the right give the molecular weights in grams of the substances burned, and the heats of combustion in kilocalories per mole and per gram of those substances.

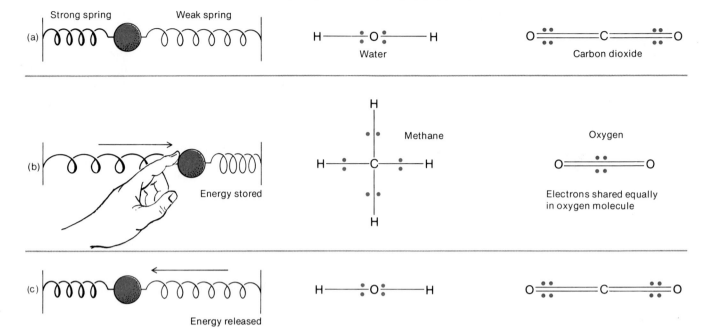

(a) Strong spring   Weak spring

Water

Carbon dioxide

(b) Energy stored

Methane

Oxygen

Electrons shared equally
in oxygen molecule

(c) Energy released

The strong spring symbolizes oxygen, which has a strong pull on electrons (symbolized by the ball). The weak spring represents the lesser pull of hydrogen and carbon. Electrons are close to oxygen in (a), a stable arrangement. They are pulled away from oxygen atoms in (b), thereby storing energy. During combustion (c), electrons are pulled back toward oxygen, releasing the stored energy, which is emitted as heat. [*Note:* Although bond lines ordinarily represent electron pairs, we also show dots here to emphasize where the electrons are between atoms.]

We can use the spring analogy above to illustrate why combustions in strongly electronegative media are exothermic, or heat-emitting. Let the ball in the middle symbolize the electrons, drawn either toward oxygen at the left, or carbon and hydrogen at the right. The stronger spring to the left represents the greater electronegativity of oxygen, and the weak spring at the right, the lesser electronegativities of carbon and hydrogen. If water and CO_2 were to react to form methane and O_2, electrons would be moved away from oxygen, against oxygen's natural electronegativity. This corresponds to using energy to push the ball to the right, thereby stretching the strong spring. This energy is stored in the spring (or in the methane molecules) as potential, or latent, energy. If methane is combined later with a strongly electronegative element, oxygen, and the electrons are permitted to relax toward more electronegative atoms again, the stored energy is released. In our spring model, combustion is analogous to releasing the constraints on the ball and letting the strong spring pull it back. In this model the spring is stronger for F than for O, so the energy released on combustion in fluorine is greater. One reason why all life on this planet uses a second-best oxidant, of course, is the natural rarity of fluorine, which in turn goes all the way back to elemental synthesis and the fact that fluorine has an odd rather than an even atomic number.

HEATS OF FORMATION

To summarize what has been said so far about heats of reaction, heats are always quoted *per mole* of an individual reactant or product. For the ethanol combustion in the table on the previous page,

$$C_2H_5OH(l) + 3O_2(g) \rightarrow 2CO_2(g) + 3H_2O(l)$$

the enthalpy change, or heat of reaction, can be quoted in three equivalent ways:

$\Delta H = -327$ kcal per mole of ethanol consumed,

$\Delta H = -164$ kcal per mole of CO_2 produced, and

$\Delta H = -109$ kcal per mole of O_2 used, or liquid water produced, since the numbers of moles are the same.

Moreover, each of the above heats would be different if any one of the reactants or products was in a different physical state: ethanol vapor, water vapor, ice, solid CO_2, and so on. The reverse reaction, synthesis of ethanol from carbon dioxide and water, would have the same heat but with opposite sign: +327 kcal per mole of ethanol produced.

Heats of reactions are additive in exactly the same way that the reactions they belong to are additive. From the information in the heat of combustion table, we can calculate how much heat would be given off by the combustion of a mole of water in fluorine gas, even though this reaction is not found in the table:

1. $H_2(g) + F_2(g) \rightarrow 2HF(g)$ $\qquad \Delta H = -128$ kcal
2. $H_2O(l) \qquad \rightarrow H_2(g) + \frac{1}{2}O_2(g)$ $\qquad \Delta H = +68$ kcal
3. $H_2O(l) + F_2(g) \rightarrow 2HF(g) + \frac{1}{2}O_2(g)$ $\quad \Delta H = -60$ kcal

This calculation tells us that 60 calories *more* heat are obtained by burning hydrogen in F_2 (Reaction 1) than in O_2 (reverse of Reaction 2). Even the "garbage" from O_2 combustion (H_2O) still is a fuel for F_2 combustion (Reaction 3), because F is more electronegative than O.

This additivity of heats of reaction is a tremendous labor-saving device. One might think that, to have available complete heat of reaction data for all possible chemical reactions, it would be necessary to measure and tabulate all of these heats. This is not the case. It is necessary to tabulate heats only for the minimum number of reactions from which all other reactions can be obtained by suitable combinations. There are several choices that could have been made; one example is the tabulation of the combustion reactions of all chemical compounds with O_2. The choice that was made and agreed upon by chemists is that of tabulating the *heat of formation* of every substance from its elements in standard reference states. The *standard state* of an element is the state in which it ordinarily is found—solid, liquid, or gas—at room temperature (298°K) and one atmosphere pressure. Therefore the heat of formation of any *element* in its standard state is zero by definition. If we have the heats of formation for all chemical compounds, all other reactions between compounds can be built up by the proper combination of formation reactions, and the heats of reaction can be built up in the same way.

Example. Calculate the heat of combustion of ethyl alcohol (ethanol) from heats of formation of reactants and products.

Solution. The balanced equation for combustion of ethanol is

$$C_2H_5OH(l) + 3O_2(g) \rightarrow 2CO_2(g) + 3H_2O(l)$$

The individual formation reactions for the substances appearing in the

Heats of formation of compounds at $298°K$ from elements in their standard states[a]

Compound	ΔH^0_{298} (kcal mole^{-1})
$H^+(aq)$, proton	0.0
$Na^+(aq)$, sodium ion	-57.28
$NaF(s)$, sodium fluoride	-136.0
$NaCl(s)$, sodium chloride	-98.23
$NaBr(s)$, sodium bromide	-86.03
$NaI(s)$, sodium iodide	-68.84
$C(s)$, diamond	0.453
$CO_2(g)$, carbon dioxide	-94.05
$CH_4(g)$, methane	-17.89
$C_2H_6(g)$, ethane	-20.24
$C_3H_8(g)$, propane	-24.82
$n\text{-}C_4H_{10}(g)$, n-butane	-29.81
$C_6H_6(g)$, benzene	19.82
$CH_3OH(g)$, methanol	-48.10
$C_2H_5OH(g)$, ethanol	-56.27
$C_2H_5OH(l)$, ethanol	-66.35
$NH_3(g)$, ammonia	-11.04
$NH_3(aq)$, ammonia	-19.32
$NH_4^+(aq)$, ammonium ion	-31.74
$NH_4Cl(s)$, ammonium chloride	-75.38
$OH^-(aq)$, hydroxide ion	-54.96
$H_2O(g)$, water	-57.80
$H_2O(l)$, water	-68.32
$F^-(aq)$, fluoride ion	-78.66
$HF(g)$, hydrogen fluoride	-64.20
$Cl^-(aq)$, chloride ion	-40.02
$HCl(g)$, hydrogen chloride	-22.06
$HCl(aq)$, hydrogen chloride	-40.02
$Br^-(aq)$, bromide ion	-28.90
$I^-(aq)$, iodide ion	-13.37

[a] More heats of formation are given in Appendix 2.

combustion process and their molar heats of formation, ΔH^0_{298}, are:

1. $2C(s) + 3H_2(g) + \frac{1}{2}O_2(g) \rightarrow C_2H_5OH(l)$ -66.4 kcal
2. $O_2(g) \rightarrow O_2(g)$ (already in standard state) 0
3. $C(s) + O_2(g) \rightarrow CO_2(g)$ -94.1 kcal
4. $H_2(g) + \frac{1}{2}O_2(g) \rightarrow H_2O(l)$ -68.3 kcal

The standard state for carbon is solid graphite, and that for all other elements on the left side of the equations is the gas at one atmosphere. The superscript zero on ΔH indicates standard states for reactants and products, and the subscript 298 (often omitted and assumed) indicates that the heats quoted are for reactions begun at $298°K$, with the products brought back to the starting temperature at the conclusion of the reaction. The heats are expressed, as they usually are, as kilocalories *per mole of compound formed*. Values for some representative substances are shown at the left.

How can we calculate the heat of combustion of ethanol from these data? Notice that the combustion reaction can be obtained by the following combination of formation Reactions 1 through 4:

combustion reaction = (products) − (reactants)

combustion = $2(R_3) + 3(R_4) - (R_1) - 3(R_2)$

From the additivity principle, it follows that the heat of combustion of ethanol is found from the corresponding combination of heats of formation:

$$\text{heat of reaction} = 2(-94.1) + 3(-68.3) - (-66.4) - 3(0)$$
$$= -326.7 \text{ kcal}$$

Notice that we can manipulate these heats of formation *as if* they were absolute enthalpies of molecules, rather than enthalpies of formation of the molecules from elements. Everything pertaining to the elements from which they came cancels out on both sides of the equation. For a general reaction of the type $A + 4B \rightarrow 3C + 2D$, in which A, B, C, and D are chemical substances, the heat of reaction can be calculated from $\Delta H^0 = 3\Delta H^0_C + 2\Delta H^0_D - \Delta H^0_A - 4\Delta H^0_B$, in which ΔH^0_C is the heat of formation of Compound C from its elements in their standard states. For example, if the reaction is the oxidation of glucose by nitrate, as is carried out by some nitrate-respiring bacteria

$$5C_6H_{12}O_6 + 24KNO_3 \rightarrow 6CO_2 + 24KHCO_3 + 12N_2 + 18H_2O$$

then the heat of reaction is obtained from the following combination of heats of formation of products and reactants:

$$\Delta H^0 = \underbrace{6\Delta H^0_{CO_2} + 24\Delta H^0_{KHCO_3} + 12\Delta H^0_{N_2} + 18\Delta H^0_{H_2O}}_{\text{products}} - \underbrace{5\Delta H^0_{C_6H_{12}O_6} - 24\Delta H^0_{KNO_3}}_{\text{reactants}}$$

Tables of standard heats of formation can be found in the CRC *Handbook of Chemistry and Physics*, in Lange's *Handbook of Chemistry*, and in Appendix 2. With such tables, the heats of all reactions involving the compounds can be calculated, including reactions that never have been carried out, or that for various reasons we cannot carry out easily in the laboratory.

274

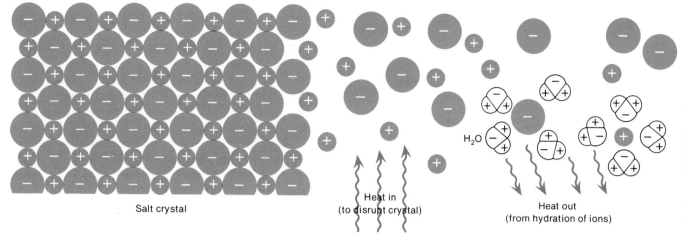

Salt crystal

Heat in
(to disrupt crystal)

H_2O

Heat out
(from hydration of ions)

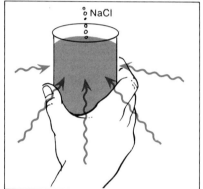

Endothermic reaction

Exothermic reaction

Whether this reaction will be endothermic or exothermic depends on a delicate balance between energy required to break up the crystal and energy given off when ions are hydrated (surrounded by water molecules).

A delicate balance determines whether the dissolving of a salt crystal in water will absorb or give off heat. Energy is required to pull apart the oppositely charged ions in the crystal, and this is called the lattice energy, ΔH_{lat}. In contrast, energy is liberated when the separated ions attract polar water molecules around themselves, and this is the heat of hydration, ΔH_{hyd}. The observed heat effect on solution depends on which factor predominates. Typical examples are

Salt	ΔH_{lat} (kcal mole^{-1})	$-$	ΔH_{hyd} (kcal mole^{-1})	$=$	ΔH_{sol} (kcal mole^{-1})
NaCl	186		185		+1
NaOH	176		186		−10
NH_4Cl	152.6		149		+3.6

Predictions about heats of solution (ΔH_{sol}) become tricky, because 5% errors in theoretical calculations of lattice and hydration energies will completely reverse a prediction. This table makes it look as if the ΔH_{sol} values were obtained from ΔH_{lat} and ΔH_{hyd}. In fact, the heats of solution are the experimentally measured quantities, and it is only with their help that we can get reasonable estimates of heats of hydration. The lattice energies are on somewhat firmer theoretical grounds.

These "small" heats of solution are large enough to have obvious physical consequences. The cooling when ordinary table salt is dissolved in water is small, but can be felt if one makes a concentrated solution and uses an aluminum tumbler. Ammonium chloride absorbs so much heat when it dissolves that hoar frost may form on the outside of the beaker. In contrast, sodium hydroxide generates so much heat that the mixing beaker may become too hot to touch.

To a certain extent, we can account for the trends in heats that we see in the table. Ammonium chloride has a weaker lattice energy than NaCl, because the NH_4^+ ion is larger than Na^+ and the binding attractions in the crystal are weaker. Unfortunately, the hydration energy also decreases with increasing ionic size, and it is difficult to predict whether lattice energy or hydration energy will show the greater change with larger ions. The heats of hydration of Cl$^-$ and OH$^-$ ions are similar, so in the comparison of NaOH with NaCl, the dominant effect comes from weaker crystal forces of NaOH in comparison with NaCl. The crystal structure of NaOH is in fact a badly distorted NaCl structure, with the distortion probably arising from the fact that the OH$^-$ ions are nonspherical. It is possible that this distortion makes the NaOH lattice easier to pull apart.

BOND ENERGIES

We began this chapter with a mention of making and breaking of bonds, but quickly began talking as if heats of reactions were nothing more than experimentally observable numbers, to be manipulated in whatever way was useful. Where do these heats come from? We can come a long way toward understanding chemical reactions by thinking of heats of reactions solely in terms of individual bond energies in molecules.

The water molecule, H—O—H, has two O—H bonds. How much energy is required to tear these bonds apart and form isolated H and O atoms? This process is represented diagrammatically in the picture story below. We can make an experimental measurement of the standard heat of the reaction

$$H_2O(g) \rightarrow H_2(g) + \tfrac{1}{2}O_2(g) \qquad \Delta H = +57.8 \text{ kcal mole}^{-1} \text{ H}_2O$$

This is not precisely what we were after, however. After the water molecule is pulled into H and O atoms, the situation is complicated by the

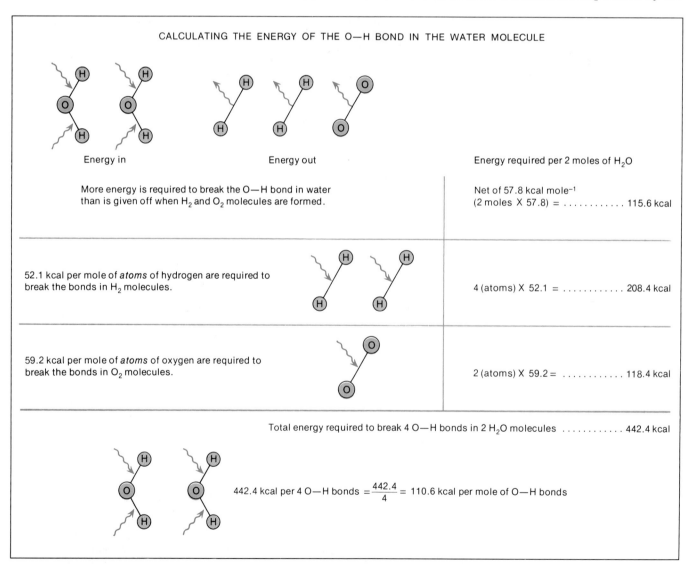

CALCULATING THE ENERGY OF THE O—H BOND IN THE WATER MOLECULE

Energy in   Energy out   Energy required per 2 moles of H₂O

More energy is required to break the O—H bond in water than is given off when H₂ and O₂ molecules are formed.

Net of 57.8 kcal mole⁻¹
(2 moles X 57.8) = ... 115.6 kcal

52.1 kcal per mole of *atoms* of hydrogen are required to break the bonds in H₂ molecules.

4 (atoms) X 52.1 = ... 208.4 kcal

59.2 kcal per mole of *atoms* of oxygen are required to break the bonds in O₂ molecules.

2 (atoms) X 59.2 = ... 118.4 kcal

Total energy required to break 4 O—H bonds in 2 H₂O molecules . . . . 442.4 kcal

442.4 kcal per 4 O—H bonds $= \dfrac{442.4}{4} = 110.6$ kcal per mole of O—H bonds

A. Heats of atomization of elements (kcal per mole of isolated atoms)

H	C	N	O	F	P	S	Cl
52.09	171.70	112.97	59.16	18.3	75.18	53.25	29.01

B. Approximate bond energies at 298°K (kcal per mole of bonds)[a]

	C	N	O	F	Si	P	S	Cl	Br	I
H—	98.8	93.4	110.6	134.6	70.4	76.4	81.1	103.2	87.5	71.4
C—	83.1	69.7	84.0	105.4	69.3		62.0	78.5	65.9	57.4
C=	147	147	174[b]				114			
C≡	194	213								
N—	69.7	38.4		64.5				47.7		
N=	147	100								
N≡	213	226								
O—	84.0		33.2	44.2	88.2			48.5		
O=	174		118.3							

[a] From L. Pauling, *The Nature of the Chemical Bond*, Cornell University Press, Ithaca, N.Y., 1960, 3rd ed. See also T. L. Cottrell, *The Strengths of Chemical Bonds*, Butterworths, London, 1958, 2nd ed.
[b] The energy of the C=O bond in CO_2 is 192 kcal because of resonance stabilization or delocalization of electrons. See text for explanation.

formation of H—H and O=O bonds. We must correct for the energy absorbed in taking these diatomic molecules apart:

$$H_2(g) \rightarrow 2H(g, atoms) \qquad \Delta H = +52.1 \text{ kcal per mole of H } atoms$$

$$O_2(g) \rightarrow 2O(g, atoms) \qquad \Delta H = +59.2 \text{ kcal per mole of O } atoms$$

The desired process and its ΔH can be determined from the previous reactions:

$$
\begin{array}{ll}
H_2O(g) \rightarrow H_2(g) + \tfrac{1}{2}O_2(g) & +57.8 \text{ kcal} \\
H_2(g) \rightarrow 2H(g) & +104.2 \text{ kcal} \\
\tfrac{1}{2}O_2(g) \rightarrow O(g) & +59.2 \text{ kcal} \\
\hline
H_2O(g) \rightarrow 2H(g) + O(g) & \Delta H = +221.2 \text{ kcal}
\end{array}
$$

This is what we were after: the energy required to tear a water molecule apart, not into elements in their standard states, but into isolated atoms. Half of this total energy can then be ascribed to each bond, giving an O—H *bond energy* of 110.6 kcal per mole of bonds.

From calculations such as this, we can obtain the table of bond energies shown above. These bond energies are not perfect for any one molecule, but are the best average values for a great number of molecules with the same kind of bond. The heats of atomization of elements are heats of dissociation of diatomic gas molecules such as H_2, N_2, O_2, or F_2, or of vaporization of solids such as graphite and sulfur into atoms. Since the standard state of sulfur is a solid made up of packed S_8 rings, atomization would entail first breaking van der Waals forces and evaporating the S_8 molecules, then taking them apart into isolated sulfur atoms.

Notice how the heats of atomization agree roughly with the number of bonds formed by each atom: four bonds in graphite, a triple N≡N bond in N_2, a double bond in O=O, and a single bond in F—F.

The single bond in H—H is almost as strong as the double bond in O=O because the H atoms are small and can get close to one another. The C=C double bond is not quite twice as strong as a single bond because the second shared electron pair does not have as favorable geometry for bonding as does the first pair. For the same reason, a triple bond is not three times as strong as a single bond. Carbon binds to hydrogen more strongly than to another carbon because of hydrogen's small size and the closer approach of atomic centers.

HEATS OF REACTIONS FROM BOND ENERGIES

How good are these approximate bond-energy values? How close can we come to reproducing measurable heats of reaction? As an example, let us calculate the heat of formation of ethanol vapor:

$$2C(graphite) + 3H_2(g) + \tfrac{1}{2}O_2(g) \rightarrow CH_3CH_2OH(g)$$

The ethanol molecule can be schematized as:

1 C—C bond:	$1 \times$ 83.1 kcal = 83.1 kcal
1 C—O bond:	$1 \times$ 84.0 kcal = 84.0 kcal
1 O—H bond:	$1 \times$ 110.6 kcal = 110.6 kcal
5 C—H bonds:	$5 \times$ 98.8 kcal = 494.0 kcal
	771.7 kcal

The individual atoms of C, H, and O are 771.7 kcal higher in energy than the assembled ethanol molecules. These same atoms are 715.1 kcal higher than carbon in graphite and H_2 and O_2 gases. The difference between 771.7 kcal and 715.1 kcal is the heat of formation of ethanol from graphite and H_2 and O_2 gases.

This is the heat of the hypothetical reaction

$$CH_3CH_2OH(g) \rightarrow 2C(g) + 6H(g) + O(g)$$

$$\Delta H = +771.7 \text{ kcal mole}^{-1} \text{ ethanol}$$

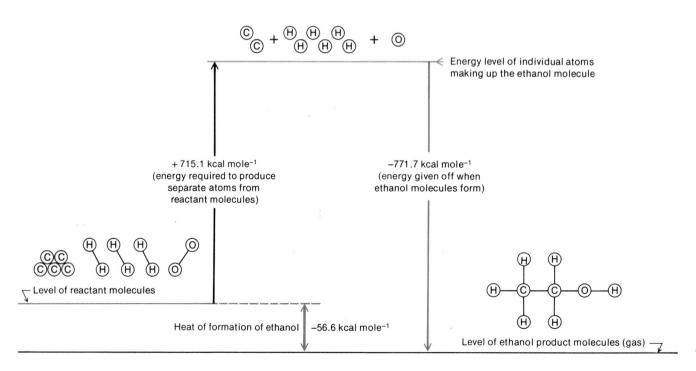

Energy level of individual atoms making up the ethanol molecule

+715.1 kcal mole⁻¹ (energy required to produce separate atoms from reactant molecules)

−771.7 kcal mole⁻¹ (energy given off when ethanol molecules form)

Level of reactant molecules

Heat of formation of ethanol −56.6 kcal mole⁻¹

Level of ethanol product molecules (gas)

We must add to this the heat involved in atomizing solid graphite, and H_2 and O_2 gases:

2 C atoms:	2×171.70 kcal	$= 343.4$ kcal
6 H atoms	6×52.09 kcal	$= 312.5$ kcal
1 O atom:	1×59.16 kcal	$= \underline{\;\;59.2}$ kcal
		715.1 kcal

This sum is the heat of the reaction

$$2C(s) + 3H_2(g) + \tfrac{1}{2}O_2(g) \rightarrow 2C(g) + 6H(g) + O(g)$$

$$\Delta H = +715.1 \text{ kcal}$$

We can get the formation reaction we are seeking by subtracting the first reaction from this one:

$$2C(s) + 3H_2(g) + \tfrac{1}{2}O_2(g) \rightarrow CH_3CH_2OH(g)$$

$$\Delta H = (+715.1) - (+771.7) = -56.6 \text{ kcal per mole of ethanol}$$

Compare this with the value of -56.3 kcal mole^{-1} from the table of measured heats of formation given on Page 274. Accuracy to within one kilocalorie is considered quite good.

We can see what is going on physically by means of the energy-level diagram at the bottom of the opposite page. The isolated C, H, and O atoms are in a state 715.1 kcal higher in energy than graphite crystals and H_2 and O_2 gases, because 715.1 kcal are required to produce the separated atoms. In turn, because the calculation from bond energies showed that 771.7 kcal are required to tear an ethanol molecule apart, the intact molecule must be 771.7 kcal lower in energy than the separated atoms. The observable heat of formation of ethanol molecules from elements (not atoms), unfortunately, is a small difference between two large numbers:

$$\Delta H = +715.1 - 771.7 = -56.6 \text{ kcal mole}^{-1}$$

This is one reason for the relative inaccuracy of bond-energy calculations. A small percent error in a number the size of 700 means a much bigger percent error in the difference of 57.

BENZENE AND RESONANCE

One can calculate heats of formation from bond-energy values for hundreds of molecules, and never be in error more than a kilocalorie or two. However, in those cases where the discrepancy is large, one can learn something new about the nature of chemical bonding. Benzene is a good illustration of this. Let us try to calculate the standard heat of formation of benzene, C_6H_6. As we saw in Chapter 9, benzene is an example of a molecule for which simple single bond and double bond ideas are inadequate, and structures using them, such as the Kekulé structures at the right, are wrong. Benzene has six electrons delocalized around the ring. From a bond-energy viewpoint, how bad is the localized Kekulé model?

BENZENE

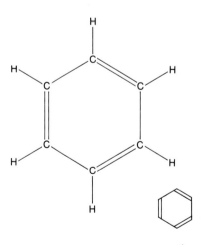

The two Kekulé models of benzene with alternating single and double bonds between carbon atoms. Stylized drawings of these models are shown at the right.

If we provisionally accept the Kekulé structures, then benzene has three C—C single bonds, three C=C double bonds, and six C—H single bonds. The energy involved in taking one mole of benzene molecules apart into atoms is

$$
\begin{array}{llll}
3\ \text{C—C:} & 3 \times & 83.1 = & 249.3\ \text{kcal} \\
3\ \text{C=C:} & 3 \times & 147.0 = & 441.0\ \text{kcal} \\
6\ \text{C—H:} & 6 \times & 98.8 = & \underline{592.8\ \text{kcal}} \\
& & & 1283.1\ \text{kcal}
\end{array}
$$

The energy needed to make the same number of isolated atoms from graphite and H_2 gas is

$$
\begin{array}{llll}
6\ \text{C:} & 6 \times & 171.7 = & 1030.2\ \text{kcal} \\
6\ \text{H:} & 6 \times & 52.1 = & \underline{312.6\ \text{kcal}} \\
& & & 1342.8\ \text{kcal}
\end{array}
$$

The difference between these two numbers should be the heat of formation, as shown below:

$$\Delta H^0 = 1343 - 1283 = +60\ \text{kcal per mole of benzene}$$

By this calculation, heat is absorbed, not emitted, when benzene is formed from its elements.

When benzene is formed from H_2 gas and graphite, heat is *absorbed*. Bond-energy calculations based on one Kekulé model predict that 60 kcal of heat will be absorbed from the surroundings in making a mole of benzene vapor. In fact only 20 kcal are absorbed (far right). The difference arises from the 40 kcal mole^{-1} of extra stability that benzene molecules have because of delocalization of electrons.

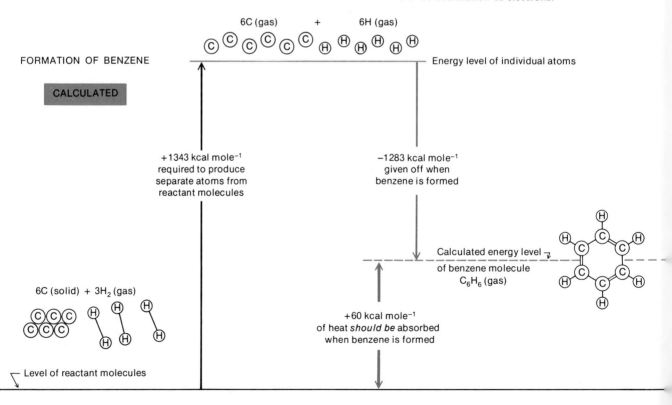

FORMATION OF BENZENE

CALCULATED

6C (gas) + 6H (gas)

Energy level of individual atoms

+1343 kcal mole^{-1} required to produce separate atoms from reactant molecules

−1283 kcal mole^{-1} given off when benzene is formed

Calculated energy level of benzene molecule C_6H_6 (gas)

6C (solid) + 3H_2 (gas)

+60 kcal mole^{-1} of heat *should be* absorbed when benzene is formed

Level of reactant molecules

We encounter trouble as soon as we try to compare this calculated value of +60 kcal mole^{-1} with reality. It is true that heat is absorbed when benzene is made from carbon and hydrogen, but only 20 kcal mole^{-1}, not 60. As the energy-level diagram below shows, the "real" benzene molecule is 40 kcal mole^{-1} more stable than the Kekulé bond model would predict. We saw the reason in terms of bonding in Chapter 9: In the benzene molecule, six electrons are delocalized around the ring (right), and all six C—C bonds are the same length, intermediate between that of a single and double bond. Each bond has a partial double bond character, and the molecule as a whole gains 40 kcal mole^{-1} of added stability.

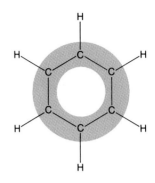

A more realistic model of the benzene molecule than the Kekulé structures shows carbon-to-carbon bonds of equal lengths, intermediate between single and double bonds. Six electrons are delocalized around the entire six-carbon ring.

WHY IS FIRE HOT?—A QUANTITATIVE ANSWER

We can pull everything in this chapter together and bring it to a close by taking a second look at a question that was raised in Chapter 6 and again at the beginning of this chapter: Why is fire hot? The answer given previously was that oxidations give off heat because electrons in the product molecules are shifted toward the electronegative O or F atoms, and the molecules are more stable as a result. Now, with the aid of bond energies, we can stop being qualitative and put numbers to our argument.

The bond-energy values in the table on Page 277 support the assertion that the more the electrons in a bond are shifted toward an electronegative atom, the more stable the bond is. Single-bond ener-

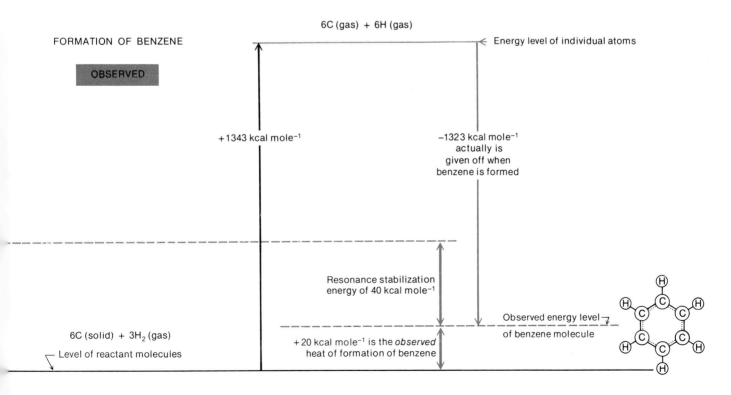

FORMATION OF BENZENE

OBSERVED

6C (gas) + 6H (gas)

Energy level of individual atoms

+1343 kcal mole^{-1}

−1323 kcal mole^{-1}
actually is
given off when
benzene is formed

Resonance stabilization
energy of 40 kcal mole^{-1}

Observed energy level
of benzene molecule

6C (solid) + 3H$_2$ (gas)

+20 kcal mole^{-1} is the *observed*
heat of formation of benzene

Level of reactant molecules

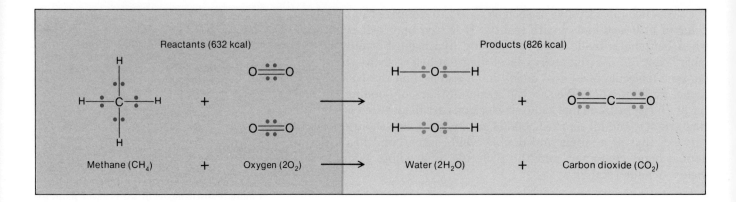

Reactants (632 kcal)

Methane (CH$_4$) + Oxygen (2O$_2$) ⟶

Products (826 kcal)

Water (2H$_2$O) + Carbon dioxide (CO$_2$)

In the combustion of methane, heat is generated because of the greater stability of bonds in product molecules. Colored dots emphasize the relative positions of shared electrons in the bonds.

gies between H and some other elements are

Bond:	H—C	H—O	H—F
Bond type:	nonpolar	intermediate	polar
Bond energy (kcal mole^{-1}):	98.8	110.6	134.6

The same trend appears in bonds between carbon and other atoms:

Bond:	C—C	C—O	C—F
Bond energy (kcal mole^{-1}):	83.1	84.0	105.4

The spring model seems reasonable so far.

A bond-energy calculation of the heat of combustion of methane yields no surprises:

$$CH_4(g) + 2O_2(g) \rightarrow CO_2(g) + 2H_2O(g) \qquad \Delta H = ?$$

A. Bond energies of product molecules:

$$\begin{array}{lll} 2\,C{=}O{:} & 2 \times 192 & = 384 \text{ kcal} \\ 4\,O{-}H{:} & 4 \times 110.6 & = 442 \text{ kcal} \\ \hline & & 826 \text{ kcal} \end{array}$$

B. Bond energies of reactants:

$$\begin{array}{lll} 4\,C{-}H{:} & 4 \times\ 98.8 & = 395 \text{ kcal} \\ 4\,O(g){:} & 4 \times\ 59.2 & = 237 \text{ kcal} \\ \hline & & 632 \text{ kcal} \end{array}$$

C. Net heat of combustion:

$$\Delta H = +632 - 826 = -194 \text{ kcal mole}^{-1}$$

The observed heat of combustion can be calculated from the heats of formation listed on Page 274:

$$\Delta H^0_{obs} = \Delta H^0_{CO_2} + 2\Delta H^0_{H_2O} - \Delta H^0_{CH_4} - 2\Delta H^0_{O_2}$$

$$\text{(products)} \quad - \quad \text{(reactants)}$$

$$\Delta H^0_{obs} = +\ (-94.05) + 2(-57.80) - (-17.89) - 2(0)$$
$$= -191.8 \text{ kcal mole}^{-1}$$

Electronegativities		Bond energies (kcal mole^{-1})
2.1 H———C 2.5		98.8
2.1 H———O 3.5		110.6
2.1 H———F 4.0		134.6

The greater the difference in electronegativities between bonded atoms, the more stable the bond (other factors being the same), and the greater the energy needed to break the bond.

This is as good agreement with experiment as one could hope for when bond-energy values are used.

So far we only have been manipulating numbers. Let us look at these numbers more closely and see what they tell us about shifts of electrons and energy, by comparing bond breaking and remaking in reactant and product molecules.

D. Single bonds:

Break 4 C—H:	+395 kcal (heat absorbed)
Make 4 O—H:	−442 kcal (heat emitted)
Net gain:	−47 kcal given off as heat

E. Double bonds:

Break 2 O=O:	+237 kcal
Make 2 C=O:	−384 kcal
Net gain:	−147 kcal given off as heat

Part of the stability of the C=O bonds in CO_2 arises from resonance stabilization involving bond structures of the type

$$\overset{-}{:}\overset{..}{O}\!-\!C\!\equiv\!O\!:\quad\quad :O\!\equiv\!C\!-\!\overset{..}{\underset{..}{O}}\overset{-}{:}\quad\quad \overset{..}{\underset{..}{O}}\!=\!C\!=\!\overset{..}{\underset{..}{O}}$$

Had there been no resonance or delocalization in CO_2, the C=O bonds would have strengths of 174 kcal mole^{-1}, as they do in other nondelocalized molecules, rather than the 192 kcal mole^{-1} that is observed in CO_2. Without delocalization, the calculation in Part E would have been

F. Double bonds:

Break 2 O=O:	+237 kcal
Make 2 C=O:	−348 kcal
Net gain:	−111 kcal

We now can summarize the three components in the molar heat of combustion of methane:

C—H vs. O—H	More stable single bonds:	−47 kcal
O=O vs. O=C	More stable double bonds:	−111 kcal
CO_2 resonance forms	Resonance stabilization:	−36 kcal
Total heat of combustion:		−194 kcal

Eighty-one percent of the heat of combustion of methane comes from the electronegativity of oxygen, and 19% from the special stability of product CO_2 molecules caused by the delocalization of electrons.

Combustions of all types with oxygen are very exothermic because oxygen is quite electronegative and draws electrons to it (a feature shared with fluorine), and the oxide of carbon is given extra stability by delocalization (not shared by F). The special electronic properties of CO_2 make up, in part, for the scarcity of F in the universe and our having to settle for a second-best oxidant. Voltaire's Dr. Pangloss was right; this is almost the best of all possible worlds!

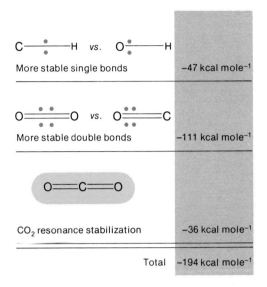

The contribution to the total heat of combustion of methane from three sources: more stable single bonds, more stable double bonds, and an extra stability because of delocalization in a product molecule.

283

QUESTIONS

1. How can potential energy be changed into kinetic energy? Give an example of the reverse process, changing kinetic energy into potential energy.

2. How can work be converted into potential energy? How does a water mill use potential energy, and what does it convert it into? Why does a water mill convert some of this energy into heat, and where does the heat appear?

3. Give an example of the conversion of heat into work, and of work into heat.

4. If the burning process gives off real heat, why do chemists say that the heat of reaction is *negative?*

5. Why are energy, E, and enthalpy, H, different? Which quantity represents the heat of a reaction carried out in a constant-pressure situation such as the open air of a laboratory?

6. How might you carry out an experiment such that the energy, E, rather than H, represented the heat of reaction?

7. What is the standard heat of formation of a substance?

8. Why is the standard heat of formation of a liquid always more negative than that of the corresponding gas? Illustrate with an energy-level diagram.

9. Why does liquid water have an unusually high heat of vaporization and boiling point? Why are these effects less pronounced in H_2Se? Se is two rows below oxygen in Group VIA of the periodic table.

10. What is Hess' law of heat summation, and how does it make our life simpler? How is it related to the first law of thermodynamics?

11. Why are fats a better choice for energy storage in animals than are starches? Why is this a secondary consideration for plants?

12. Why do living organisms on Earth use a second-best oxidant with their foods? What molecule would be better than O_2?

13. Why are molecules in which C and H atoms are combined with O atoms lower in energy than molecules with direct C-to-H bonding? Why does this make combustion exothermic?

14. If we know the heats of formation for all reactant and product molecules in a reaction, how can we calculate the heat of the reaction in question? What principle are we using to do this?

15. What energy factors affect the dissolving of a salt? Which factor would tend to make the salt readily soluble, and which would tend to make it insoluble?

16. If both of the factors of Question 15 are large energy quantities, why is a prediction of solubilities of salts so difficult?

17. What is bond energy? Why is the standard heat of formation of a molecule not the same as the sum of bond energies of all of the bonds in the molecule? What is the missing component?

18. Why does a simple bond-energy calculation fail for benzene?

19. How does your answer to Question 18 also pertain to the heat of combustion of carbon-containing substances?

PROBLEMS

1. The standard heat of formation of liquid water is -68.32 kcal mole^{-1}. (a) Write a balanced equation for this reaction. Is heat absorbed, or given off? (b) What is the heat of combustion of hydrogen gas per mole?

2. The heat of combustion of liquid acetaldehyde, CH_3CHO, to carbon dioxide and liquid water is -278.8 kcal mole^{-1}. (a) Write a balanced equation for the combustion reaction. (b) How much heat is evolved per mole of acetaldehyde burned? Per mole of water vapor produced? Per mole of oxygen used? (c) How much heat is released when a gram of acetaldehyde is burned?

3. When an inch of rain falls on New York City, it results in a rainfall of 19.8×10^9 liters over the city's 300-square-mile area. (a) Assuming a density of liquid water of 1.00 g cm^{-3}, how much heat is released when this quantity of water condenses from vapor in the rain clouds? (Think of condensation as a chemical reaction, $H_2O(g) \rightarrow H_2O(l)$, and use thermodynamic data from Appendix 2.) (b) A ton of TNT releases around 10^6 kcal of energy. How many megatons of TNT (1 megaton $= 10^6$ tons) would be needed for an explosion that releases as much energy as the inch of rain in Part a?

4. The heat of combustion of solid urea, $(NH_2)_2CO$, to CO_2 and liquid water is -151.1 kcal mole^{-1}. (a) Write a balanced equation for the reaction. (b) How much heat is given off per mole of oxygen used? (c) Use the above data plus data for CO_2 and water from Appendix 2 to calculate the standard heat of formation of urea. Compare your figure with the value tabulated in the appendix.

5. Use the following heats of reaction to calculate the heat of formation of NO. Compare your answer with that given in Appendix 2.

$$4NH_3 + 5O_2 \rightarrow 4NO + 6H_2O(l) \qquad \Delta H = -279.4 \text{ kcal}$$
$$4NH_3 + 3O_2 \rightarrow 2N_2 + 6H_2O(l) \qquad \Delta H = -365.8 \text{ kcal}$$

6. From data in Appendix 2, calculate the heat given off when limestone is dissolved by acid:

$$CaCO_3(s) + 2H^+(aq) \rightarrow Ca^{2+}(aq) + CO_2(g) + H_2O(l)$$

7. (a) Write a balanced equation for the combustion of liquid methanol, CH_3OH, in an ample supply of oxygen to produce liquid water. (b) From data in Appendix 2, calculate the heat given off during this reaction.

8. (a) How much heat is released when a mole of gasoline, C_8H_{18}, is burned in the open air? Write a balanced equation for the reaction that produces liquid water. (b) How much heat is obtained if the gasoline is burned with a restricted oxygen supply, so CO is produced instead of CO_2? (c) How much heat results if this CO now is oxidized to CO_2? How do your answers to Parts b and c compare with that to Part a? What principle does this represent?

9. (a) Calculate the heat of combustion of ethanol,

$$CH_3CH_2OH(l) + \tfrac{7}{2}O_2 \rightarrow 2CO_2 + 3H_2O(l)$$

(b) Do the same for glucose, $C_6H_{12}O_6$. (c) How do the heats of

285

combustion of ethanol and glucose compare on a gram of reactant basis? By this calculation, which is a better energy source, gin or candy? (Assume gin to be 45% ethanol by weight.) (d) Many microorganisms, including yeast, obtain their energy by fermenting glucose to ethanol, which they give off as a waste product:

$$C_6H_{12}O_6(s) \rightarrow 2C_2H_5OH(l) + 2CO_2(g)$$

We use the ethanol in wine, and even use the carbon dioxide in champagne and sparkling wines. Calculate the energy that the yeast obtains per mole of glucose. What can you deduce from this and Part b about the advantages of combustion of glucose with O_2, over simple fermentation without O_2?

10. (a) Calculate the heat of formation of liquid hydrazine, N_2H_4, from the data below. (b) Write the balanced equation for the combustion of N_2H_4 in O_2 to N_2 and liquid water. What is the heat of combustion of hydrazine?

$2NH_3 + 3N_2O$	$\rightarrow 4N_2 + 3H_2O(l)$	$\Delta H = -241.35$ kcal
$N_2O + 3H_2$	$\rightarrow N_2H_4(l) + H_2O(l)$	$\Delta H = -75.76$ kcal
$2NH_3 + \frac{1}{2}O_2$	$\rightarrow N_2H_4(l) + H_2O(l)$	$\Delta H = -34.18$ kcal
$H_2 + \frac{1}{2}O_2$	$\rightarrow H_2O(l)$	$\Delta H = -68.32$ kcal

11. (a) In liquid fuel rockets, such as the lunar module of the Apollo moon missions, the fuel is liquid hydrazine, N_2H_4, and the oxidant is N_2O_4. Write a balanced equation for the reaction of these two substances to form liquid water and N_2 gas. (b) How much heat is given off in this reaction per mole of hydrazine? (c) Would more, or less, heat be given off if the oxidant were O_2 instead of dinitrogen tetroxide? How much?

12. In the manufacture of water gas, a commercial heating gas, steam is passed through hot coke, and the following reaction occurs:

$$C + H_2O(g) \rightarrow CO + H_2$$

(a) What is the standard enthalpy of this reaction per mole of carbon in the coke? How much heat is stored per mole of carbon? (b) Write the reactions that occur when water gas is burned in air. How much energy is released when water gas containing a mole each of CO and H_2 is burned to CO_2 and liquid water? (c) How much heat is given off when 100 liters of water gas (measured at 1 atm pressure and $298°K$) are burned?

13. Producer gas is another way of converting coke into a combustible gas, by passing dry air (20% O_2 and 80% N_2 by volume or moles) through hot coke so the following reaction occurs:

$$C + \frac{1}{2}O_2 \rightarrow CO$$

(a) If 100 liters of air are passed through the furnace, how many liters of O_2 are used up? How many liters of CO are formed? How many liters of N_2 go through the furnace unchanged? What volume of producer gas is obtained from 100 liters of air? (b) How much heat is given off when 100 liters of producer gas (1 atm and $298°K$) are burned?

14. The following are some of the gas reactions that take place in our atmosphere. Use bond-energy information to calculate the enthalpy for each reaction.

(a) $N + O_2 \rightarrow NO + O$ (c) $N + N \rightarrow N_2$

(b) $NO_2 + O \rightarrow NO + O_2$ (d) $O + O_3 \rightarrow 2O_2$

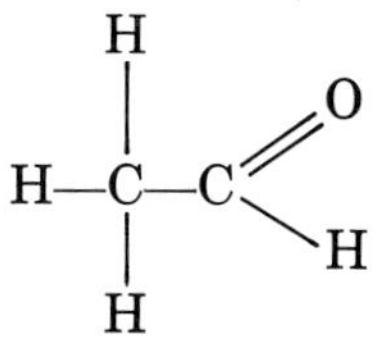

15. The heat of combustion of gaseous dimethyl ether, CH_3—O—CH_3, to carbon dioxide and liquid water is -348 kcal mole^{-1} of ether. Calculate the standard heat of formation of dimethyl ether and compare your value with that tabulated in Appendix 2.

16. (a) From data in Appendix 2, calculate the heat of isomerization of liquid ethanol to dimethyl ether:

$$CH_3—CH_2—OH(l) \rightarrow CH_3—O—CH_3(g)$$

(b) Calculate the corresponding heat of isomerization beginning with ethanol vapor. Explain the difference between this and the answer to Part a. (c) Calculate the heat of the reaction in Part b from data in the bond-energy table in this chapter. How different are the bond-energy and thermodynamic values? (d) Account for the heat of isomerization of ethanol vapor in terms of the bonding in each molecule.

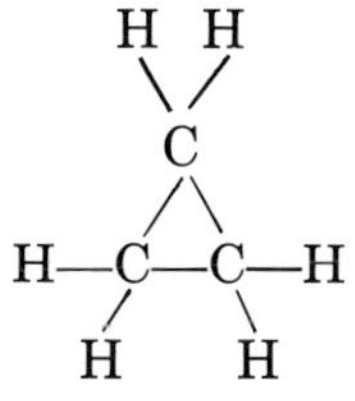

17. Use bond energies to calculate the heat of formation of acetaldehyde vapor, at $25°C$ from graphite, and O_2 and H_2 gases. Illustrate your calculations with an energy-level diagram as was used for ethanol and benzene in this chapter. Compare your answer with the thermodynamic value in Appendix 2. How good is the bond-energy method, according to this?

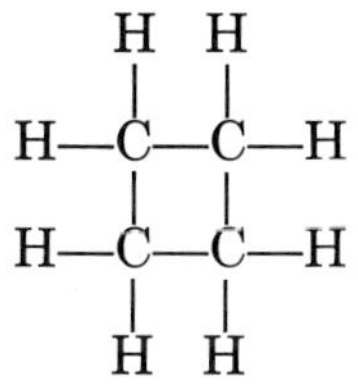

18. (a) Using bond energies, calculate the standard heat of formation of one mole of gaseous cyclopropane from graphite and hydrogen gas. Illustrate your calculation with an energy-level diagram. (b) The experimental value of the heat of formation of cyclopropane is listed in Appendix 2. Add this level to your energy-level diagram. How can you account for the large difference between calculated and observed values?

19. Repeat the calculations of Problem 18 with cyclobutane, cyclopentane, and cyclohexane. Compare these numbers with the observed values in Appendix 2. What trend do you see in agreement between calculated and measured heats of formation, and how do you account for it?

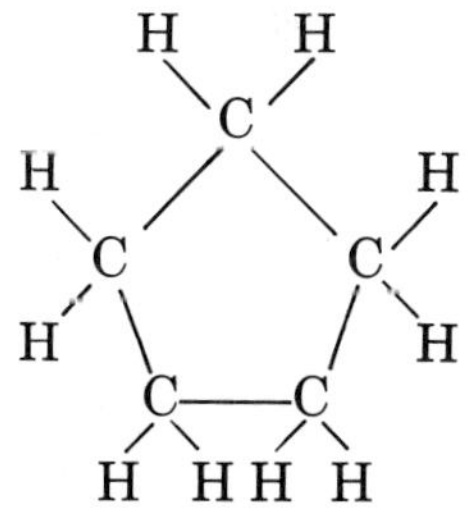

20. (a) Assume that the bond structure of carbon monoxide is C=O, and that of carbon dioxide is O=C=O. Calculate the standard enthalpy of the following reaction from bond-energy data: $CO(g) + \frac{1}{2}O_2(g) \rightarrow CO_2(g)$. Compare this with the observed value. How big is the error, and how good do your assumptions about the bond structure of these two molecules appear to be? (b) Select two other chemical reactions from the data in Appendix 2, one involving CO but not CO_2, and the other the opposite. Calculate the enthalpies of these two reactions from bond energies, compare them with thermodynamic values, and decide which bond assumption of Part a is worse, that of C=O or of O=C=O.

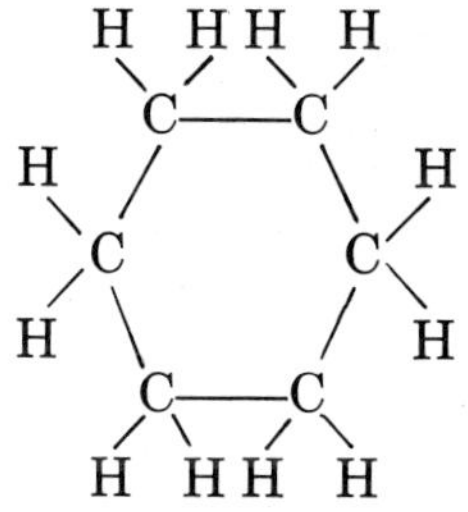

acetaldehyde

cyclopropane

cyclobutane

cyclopentane

cyclohexane

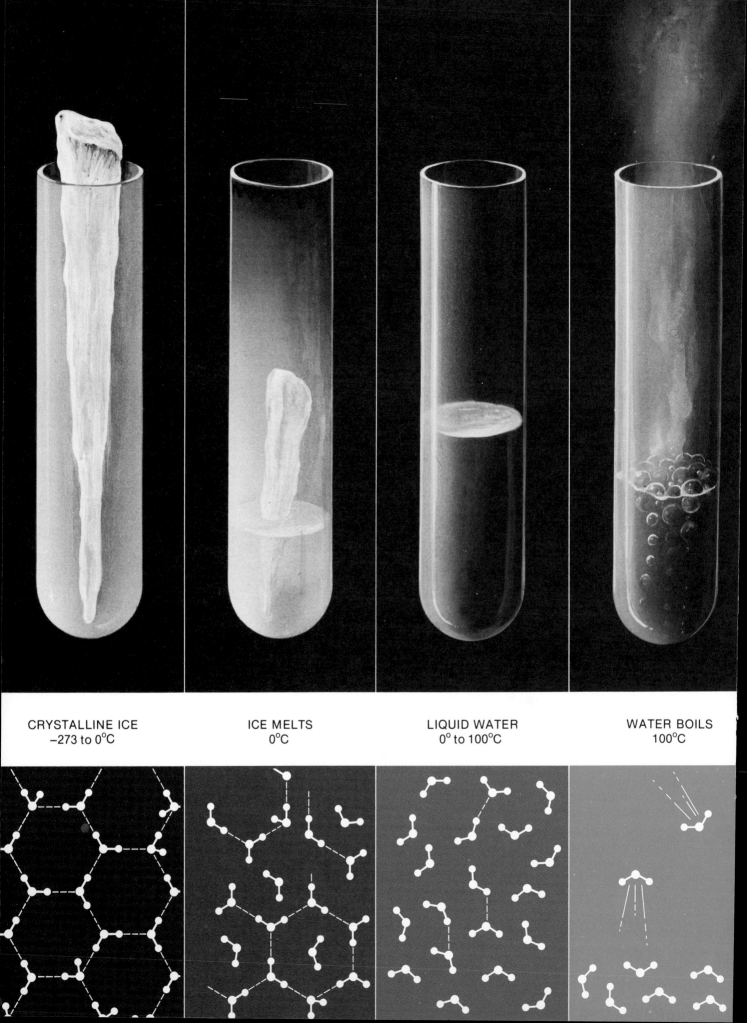

CRYSTALLINE ICE
−273 to 0°C

ICE MELTS
0°C

LIQUID WATER
0° to 100°C

WATER BOILS
100°C

◀ *Molecular disorder increases as ice changes to water, and as water changes to steam*

CHAPTER 13

How to Measure Disorder

The U.S. Army Corps of Engineers had an extravagant slogan during World War II: "The difficult we do at once; the impossible takes a little longer." This time division into the easy, the difficult, and the impossible also applies to chemical reactions. Some chemical reactions are very fast; others will take place eventually if you have the patience to wait. Yet a third class of chemical reactions will never go in a desired direction without outside help, even if you wait forever. If you want a particular reaction to occur, it is obviously of interest to be able to predict into which category the reaction falls. In the next two chapters we will see what governs how *fast* a reaction will go. In this chapter we are concerned with the simpler question of predicting whether a given reaction will *ever* occur by itself, given unlimited time. The key step will be learning how to measure the order or disorder that is produced when molecules interact, or the *entropy* of a reaction.

Whether a reaction ever will proceed by itself depends on two quantities that sometimes cooperate but more often conflict: heat or energy, and disorder or entropy. The central theme of this chapter is that a lowering of energy, and an increase in disorder, both are changes that tend to occur spontaneously. In the melting of the icicle shown on the opposite page, water can lose heat and go to a state of lower energy by freezing, but at a cost of increasing its order in the ice crystal. Conversely, a frozen icicle can go to a more disordered state by melting, but only if enough heat is supplied to break the hydrogen bonds in the ice crystal. The energy factors say "freeze," and the entropy factors say "melt." For reasons that we will explore in this chapter, energy is more important at low temperatures, and entropy, or disorder, dominates at higher temperatures. The temperature at which these two conflicting tendencies balance is the melting point of ice.

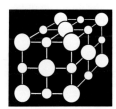

The most orderly object in the universe is a perfect crystal with motionless atoms at absolute zero, or −273°C.

FORMS OF POTENTIAL ENERGY

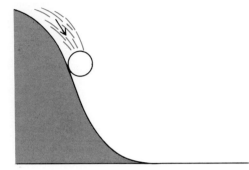

Gravitational

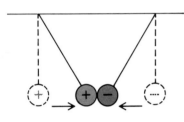

Electrostatic

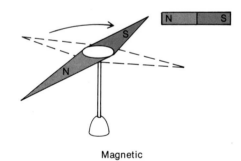

Magnetic

In each of the above spontaneous processes, movement is in the direction of lower energy, or down a potential slope.

SPONTANEOUS REACTIONS

Spontaneous reactions are those that will take place by themselves, given enough time. They do not have to be rapid; speed is not a factor in the definition of spontaneity. Explosions and many other spontaneous reactions are rapid, but other spontaneous processes, such as the precipitation of calcium carbonate in the stalactites of Mammoth Cave, require thousands of years. We recognize the irrelevance of time to the idea of spontaneity when we use the term "spontaneous combustion" for the slow smouldering of paint-soaked rags. The oxidation of newsprint is spontaneous, although we do not worry about our morning paper bursting into flames as we read it. At 25°C, the reaction of newsprint with oxygen is exceedingly slow, but the gradual browning of old newspapers in library files shows us that the process is spontaneous nevertheless. In contrast, the same reaction at the temperature of a lighted match is both spontaneous and rapid. By raising the temperature we have hastened the achievement of a chemical reaction, but the tendency for the reaction to take place was already there, even at room temperature. It is this *tendency* to react that we mean when we talk about spontaneity, and it is this tendency toward reaction that we would like to be able to predict.

One good reason for wanting to predict spontaneity is that, if a reaction is genuinely spontaneous but slow, we may be able to speed it up by changing the experimental conditions. Changing the temperature is one way that is particularly effective for oxidations. Finding a suitable catalyst is another. If a reaction is spontaneous, a catalyst will accelerate it. If the reaction is not spontaneous to begin with, then looking for a catalyst is a waste of time. This chapter is focused on one fundamental question: How can we tell in advance whether a reaction that has not been tried will be spontaneous?

ENERGY AND SPONTANEITY

If we let a ball loose on a slope, it will roll spontaneously downhill (left). If we give one object a positive charge, it will be attracted spontaneously toward a second object with a negative charge. If we bring the north pole of a bar magnet near a compass needle, the needle will rotate to point its south pole toward the magnet. All three of these spontaneous processes are in the direction of lower energy—lower gravitational energy for the ball on a slope, lower electrostatic energy for the two charged objects, and lower magnetic energy for the compass and magnet. Common sense seems to tell us that spontaneous processes are those that lead to a decrease in some form of energy. We would be surprised indeed to see boulders roll up a mountainside by themselves. There is a duck hunter's joke about a hardy breed of bird that always flies past the blind upside down, so that when they are hit, they fall *up*. We find this ridiculous because common sense tells us that things always happen spontaneously in the direction of lower, not higher, energy. But in predicting chemical reactions, common sense often is wrong.

It is true that in most spontaneous chemical reactions, energy or enthalpy falls. The energy that the chemical substances lose during reaction is given off as heat. Another way of expressing the situation is to say that *most* spontaneous chemical processes are exothermic. The combustion of gasoline, like all combustions, liberates heat, because the carbon dioxide and water molecules produced have lower energy than the gasoline and oxygen molecules from which they came. Is it valid to state as a general law that *all* spontaneous reactions go in the direction of lower energy, or that all spontaneous reactions are exothermic?

The difficulty with general laws is that they are so hard to prove but so easy to disprove. If you are testing the proposition that "all Irishmen have red hair," then ten million red-haired Irishmen will not prove the law beyond challenge; they merely will make it more probable. But a single blond Irishman will wipe out the proposition completely. (All is not necessarily lost, however. If you look into the reasons for the yellow hair you may learn something about people.)

The analogy is not facetious. Any number of spontaneous, heat-emitting reactions will not rigorously prove the statement "all spontaneous reactions tend to minimize energy," yet one lone, spontaneous but heat-absorbing process will scuttle it. If we look more closely at why some heat-absorbing reactions are spontaneous, we will discover a new fundamental principle about chemical reactions.

Exceptions to the principle that all spontaneous reactions emit heat are not hard to find. N_2O_5 is the oxide of nitrogen with its highest oxidation number, +5. The solid dissolves in water to form HNO_3:

$$N_2O_5(s) + H_2O(l) \rightarrow 2HNO_3(aq) \qquad \Delta H^0 = -20.5 \text{ kcal per mole of } N_2O_5$$

Crystalline N_2O_5 is unstable and will explode spontaneously:

$$N_2O_5(s) \rightarrow 2NO_2(g) + \tfrac{1}{2}O_2(g) \qquad \Delta H^0 = +26.2 \text{ kcal per mole of } N_2O_5$$

The remarkable aspect is that when N_2O_5 decomposes it *absorbs* 26 kcal of heat per mole. Here is a spontaneous and rapid reaction that clearly goes to a state of *higher* energy.

Another example is the cooling effect when a salt such as ammonium chloride is dissolved in water (right). The reaction

$$NH_4Cl(s) \xrightarrow{\text{H}_2\text{O}} NH_4^+(aq) + Cl^-(aq) \qquad \Delta H^0 = +3.6 \text{ kcal per mole of } NH_4Cl$$

absorbs enough heat to chill its surroundings, yet we do not expect an ammonium chloride solution to separate spontaneously into salt crystals and pure water just because in this direction the reaction gives off heat.

An even simpler example is the vaporization of water. The heat of vaporization at room temperature is $\Delta H^0 = +10.5$ kcal mole^{-1}. Heats of vaporization for all liquids are positive because energy is required to break the attractive forces between molecules in the liquid and create a gas. Yet evaporation frequently is spontaneous. If only heat-yielding processes were spontaneous, then all gases in the universe

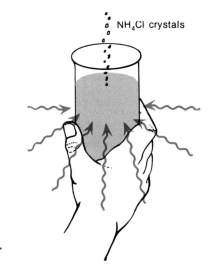

NH$_4$Cl crystals

Ammonium chloride crystals dropped into water *absorb* heat from the surroundings as they dissolve. The tumbler (above) feels cold to the touch.

291

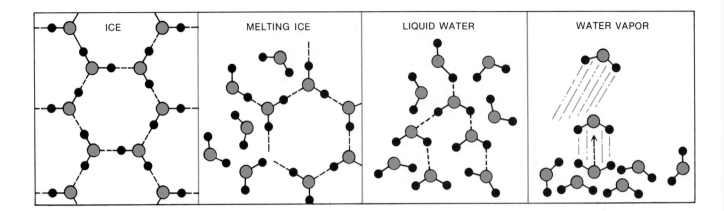

| ICE | MELTING ICE | LIQUID WATER | WATER VAPOR |

Disorder increases from ice to liquid to vapor, as more hydrogen bonds are broken and as water molecules begin to move past one another freely.

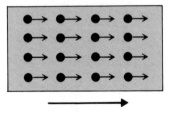

Kinetic energy of a solid is the coordinated motion of all molecules in the same direction.

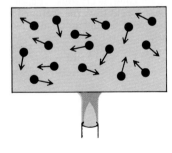

Heat in a solid is the random motion of individual molecules around average positions in the crystal structure.

would condense to liquids, all liquids would freeze to crystalline solids, and the world would be nothing but rock and ice. This obviously is not so, and energy obviously cannot be the only factor in making chemical reactions spontaneous.

What is the missing factor? What do the N_2O_5, NH_4Cl, and evaporation processes have in common with most exothermic reactions that makes them take place spontaneously, even though these reactions are endothermic? The answer is that all of these reactions create disorder. NO_2 and O_2 gas molecules are more disordered than crystals of N_2O_5. Hydrated ammonium and chloride ions in solution are more disordered than the regular array of NH_4Cl ions in a crystal. H_2O molecules moving about freely as water vapor are more disordered than the closely packed molecules of the liquid, or the frozen molecules of the solid (above). Most explosions are destructive precisely because they convert solids or liquids into gases that push out against their surroundings. (The expansion of the gases when they are heated by the reaction is another destructive factor.) A decrease in energy or enthalpy certainly is an important component in determining spontaneity, but the other aspect is the production of disorder.

DISORDER AND SPONTANEITY

How do we measure disorder? The means of doing this came originally from physics, not chemistry. During the middle of the last century, physicists were interested in the nature of heat and its manipulation, an understandable bias in an era of steam power. James Joule, Julius Mayer, and others concluded after careful experimental measurements that heat, work, and energy all were merely different aspects of the same thing.

William Thomson (later Lord Kelvin, of the Kelvin or absolute-temperature scale) and Rudolf Clausius were struck by the fact that the interconversion of heat and work is a one-way street. It is easy to convert the energy of work completely into heat, but the reverse transformation is never complete. Thomson's version of the second law of thermodynamics states that it is impossible by any cyclic, repeatable process to take heat and convert it entirely into work without losing some of this heat to a reservoir at a lower temperature. There can be no steam engines without condensing cylinders, and part of the available heat always is lost to the condenser instead of being converted to useful work. The second law in any of its forms makes heat look like the lowest or most degraded form of energy: easy to obtain but hard to reconvert.

We now know what Thomson and Clausius a century ago did not. On a molecular level, kinetic energy is the coordinated movement of all of the molecules in a solid in the same direction (far left margin). Heat in a solid object is the disunited motion of individual molecules about their equilibrium positions. Kinetic energy is organized, coherent motion and heat is random, incoherent motion. It is easy to change coordinated motion into random motion but impossible to turn uncoordinated vibration completely back into uniform motion. When we heat a can of soup, all of the molecules begin moving faster but in a random manner. What is the probability that, purely by chance, all of the molecules in the soup will begin to move faster *in the same direction*, taking the pan and the kitchen wall with them?

As any good statistical physicist or cook can tell you, the chance of this happening is effectively zero. If every one of n molecules has an equal chance of moving up or down in the soup, or a 50% chance of being found moving upward, the probability that at some instant all n molecules will move upward in unison is given by the expression $(\frac{1}{2})^n$. For the $n = 1.7 \times 10^{25}$ molecules in a half liter of soup, this is an unimaginably small number.

Arthur Eddington expressed these probabilities vividly in 1928 in his book *The Nature of the Physical World*. Speaking of the mathematically identical problem of the probability of finding all of the molecules of a gas in one half of a container at the same time, he said:

> The reason why we ignore this chance may be seen by a rather classical illustration. If I let my fingers wander idly over the keys of a typewriter it *might* happen that my screed made an intelligible sentence. If an army of monkeys were strumming on typewriters they *might* write all the books in the British Museum. The chance of their doing so is decidedly more favourable than the chance of the molecules all moving to one half of the vessel.

With 44 keys, one monkey should average one "d" a minute by chance.

Three monkeys should achieve a "dear" every eleven weeks.

10,000 of them will average one "dear sir" every 500 years. Three million apes working continuously would barely have had time to type one flawless "so long adam" since *Homo sapiens* went his separate way ten million years ago.

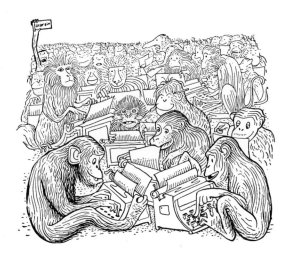

It is true that, given enough time, the most unlikely events could happen by chance. Order could come from molecular disorder spontaneously, and an army of monkeys could type all the books in the British Museum. Neither is worth waiting for in the real world. From *How To Take A Chance* by Darrell Huff. Copyright © 1959 W. W. Norton & Company, Inc.

The scenario above involves a spontaneous creation of disorder, and is intuitively recognized as a possible occurrence. In contrast, the scene below involving spontaneous re-creation of order after a catastrophe, is rejected by common sense and past experience.

We instinctively recognize that the creation of disorder is the natural course of spontaneous events in the real world. In the illustrations above, the motorcyclist, initially moving with a high kinetic energy, hits a brick wall. His kinetic energy of motion is changed into energy needed to break the bricks apart, into a large increase in disorder, and into random molecular motion of the metal parts of the wreckage, which will be warm to the touch. This is the normal, or expected, chain of events. In the drawings below, kinetic energy is changed into work to break down the wall, disorder, and heat to warm the wreckage. In the third panel this work, disorder, and heat have been recombined and reconverted back into the kinetic energy of the now-unharmed motorcyclist, who goes on his way. We instinctively recognize this as ridiculous. Disorder comes spontaneously from order in our universe, but order cannot come spontaneously from disorder. Random motion (heat) tends to stay random unless we make an effort to "unrandomize" it. For this we must pay a price in energy. We can rebuild the brick wall if we make the effort, but the bricks will not fall into place by themselves, as the bottom scenario would have it.

We now have a second factor to consider in spontaneous processes: disorder. Spontaneous reactions tend to occur in the direction of lower energy, but they also tend to occur in the direction of greater disorder. In some cases both trends may reinforce; in others the result may be a trade-off between two opposing tendencies.

MEASURING DISORDER: ENTROPY

One of the consequences of the second law and the studies by people such as Kelvin and Clausius was the invention of a new and useful function, the entropy, S. As originally defined, entropy was strictly a function of heat and temperature. With enough experimental ingenuity and patience, the entropy of any substance at a given temperature can be calculated from calorimetric measurements. Because of the third law of thermodynamics, which states that the entropy of every pure, crystalline substance at absolute zero is zero, these values calculated from calorimetric measurements are called third-law entropies. They are tabulated as S^0_{298} for elements and compounds in their standard states at 298°K, alongside heats of formation, in Appendix 2 (and in any standard chemical handbook).

Thermodynamic entropy has some interesting properties. In any real, spontaneous reaction or process in an isolated system (one in which neither heat, energy, nor matter flow in or out) the total entropy always increases. The act of isolating the system from the remainder of the universe means that there is no energy exchange with the surroundings during reaction. Therefore we can say that, energy considerations aside, spontaneous reactions are those that go in the direction of greater entropy. The entire material universe by definition is an isolated thermodynamic system, so what was just said about a small reacting system also holds for the universe as a whole. Clausius gave us a famous version of the first and second laws of thermodynamics:

> First law—The total energy of the universe is constant.
> Second law—The total entropy of the universe is always
> increasing.

These conclusions from classical thermodynamics are universally valid, and as far as we know never have been contradicted by observation (with the correction for mass–energy conversion, of course). They are not very helpful to us yet because we do not know what entropy really is or what it signifies.

THE STATISTICAL MEANING OF ENTROPY

The man who gave entropy a molecular meaning was Ludwig Boltzmann, a mathematician and physicist who worked during the last half of the nineteenth century. Boltzmann first suggested that entropy was a measure of disorder and gave this suggestion a concrete form. He proposed that entropy, S, was related to the number of different microscopic ways of obtaining a macroscopically definable and observable situation. If the number of ways of constructing a situation is W, then the entropy is proportional to the logarithm of W:

$$S = k \ln W$$

The proportionality constant, k, is the gas constant (discussed in Chapter 2) *per molecule*, or

$$k = \frac{R}{N}$$

in which R is the gas constant and N is Avogadro's number. The con-

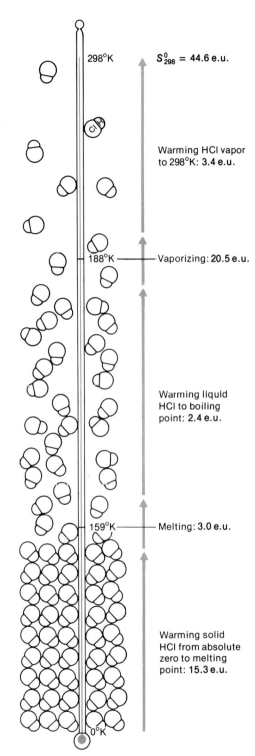

298°K $S^0_{298} = 44.6$ e.u.

Warming HCl vapor to 298°K: 3.4 e.u.

188°K —— Vaporizing: 20.5 e.u.

Warming liquid HCl to boiling point: 2.4 e.u.

159°K —— Melting: 3.0 e.u.

Warming solid HCl from absolute zero to melting point: 15.3 e.u.

0°K

At absolute zero (0°K), solid, crystalline HCl has no disorder and zero entropy. At room temperature (25°C or 298°K), HCl gas has 44.6 entropy units (e.u.) of disorder per mole. This disorder arises from warming the solid from absolute zero to its melting point, melting it, warming the resulting liquid to the boiling point, evaporating it, and warming HCl gas to room temperature.

295

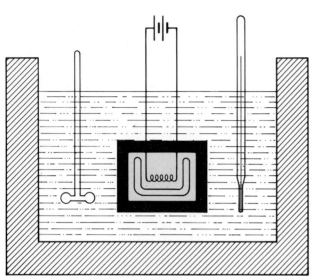

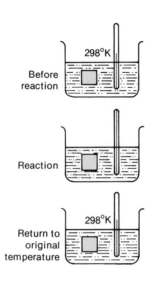

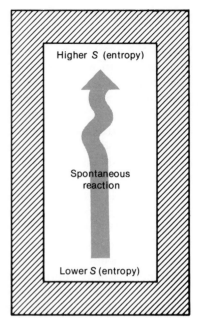

The entropy of a substance at 298°K can be calculated from purely thermodynamic or calorimetric measurements, including the heats of fusion and vaporization of solid and liquid, and heats of warming a substance from one temperature to another, as outlined for HCl on the preceding page. No assumptions about order or disorder are involved in calculating the numerical value for the entropy. A spontaneous process in an isolated system always leads to an increase in entropy.

stant k was chosen by Boltzmann such that his statistical entropy would have the same units, and be on the same scale, as thermodynamic entropy. It is called, appropriately enough, the Boltzmann constant.

The important physical quantity in the equation is the number of ways of obtaining a given state, W. There is only one way of putting together a perfect crystal, provided of course that the molecules are indistinguishable from one another (see far right margin). For a perfect crystal with motionless molecules at absolute zero, $W = 1$ and $S = k \ln 1 = 0$. In contrast, if we were molecular architects we would find that there are many ways of building a liter of gas at a given temperature and pressure, all of which would look identical to the outside world (upper far right). For example, the individual positions of molecules in a gas do not have to be specified, nor do their individual speeds. All that is required is that the total number of molecules of each kind and the total energy per mole be known; all gases that satisfy these conditions will appear alike to a macroscopic observer. The number of ways of constructing a mole of gas is greater than for a crystal; W is large, so $\ln W$ is a positive number, and $S = k \ln W$ is greater than zero.

Boltzmann made the crucial connection between thermodynamic entropy and disorder. Any situation that is so definite that it can be put together only in one or a small number of ways is recognized by our minds as *orderly*. Any situation that could be reproduced in thousands

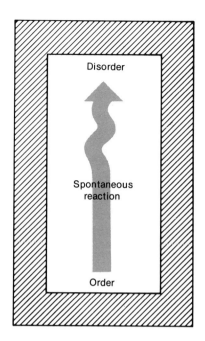

The statistical explanation of entropy equates it with the degree of disorder in a system. A spontaneous process in an isolated system always leads to an increase in disorder.

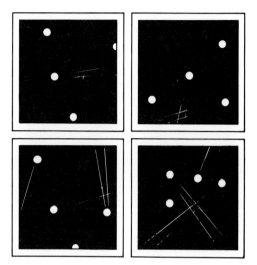

The entropy of a chemical system is related to the number of equivalent ways in which the system can be put together from its molecules. The four "snapshots" of a gas (above) show molecules in different positions; yet all of these would look alike to a macroscopic observer.

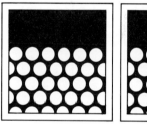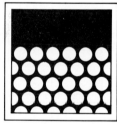

The two "snapshots" of a crystal show no change in structure from one instant to the next. There is only one way to build a perfect crystal at absolute zero, where molecular vibration has stopped.

or millions of different but equivalent ways is *disorderly*. Boltzmann's law tells us that the most perfect, orderly object conceivable in the universe would be a perfect crystal at absolute zero. Anything else—a crystal at any temperature above $0°K$, a liquid, a gas, or a mixture of substances—is more disordered and has a positive entropy. The higher the entropy, the greater the disorder.

When we combine Boltzmann's ideas with thermodynamics, we arrive at one of the most important principles of science: In any real, spontaneous processes, including chemical reactions, the disorder of the universe always increases. In any isolated system, in which the total energy does not change, a spontaneous reaction is one in which entropy (and disorder) increases. Any process that produces order, or lowers the entropy, cannot occur without outside help. If we supply enough energy, we can make a reaction occur even though the entropy decreases in the process. If we do not supply enough energy, a reaction leading to increased order will not take place.

The two ways of looking at entropy—thermodynamic and statistical—are contrasted at the top of these two pages. The thermodynamicist measures heats of processes, and calculates from them a numerical value for the third-law entropy, S^0_{298}, of the substance. The theoretician can compute from the known amount of disorder in a substance what its entropy should be. If his estimate of disorder and his subsequent calculations are valid, he will arrive at a final number that agrees with the value that was measured from heat experiments.

297

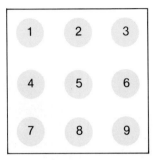

The "Universe"

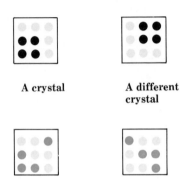

A crystal   A different crystal

Two different arrangements of atoms leading to a gas

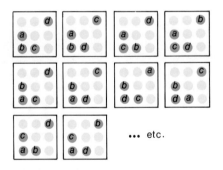

··· etc.

If atoms had labels, all of these and others like them would represent different arrangements of atoms.

Since atoms do not have names or labels, and all look alike, all of the previous pictures correspond to the single atomic arrangement shown above: four atoms at positions 3, 4, 7, and 8.

LIFE IN A NINE-POINT UNIVERSE

What do we mean when we say that entropy, S, can be calculated from the expression $S = k \ln W$, in which W is the number of equivalent ways the molecules can be arranged to give the same observable result? Why should a gas inevitably have a higher entropy than a crystal of the same substance? It is hard to answer these questions in our own universe without getting bogged down in mathematics. But it is much easier in an imaginary universe with only four atoms in it, and only nine places where the atoms can be.

Imagine that the nine places in our mini-universe are arranged in the 3×3 grid shown at the upper left. All four atoms placed in a close-packed square will constitute a "crystal" in our imaginary space, and any other arrangement of the four atoms will be called a "gas." Examples of crystals and gases are given in the margin. If we examine every possible arrangement of four atoms in our nine-point universe, how many of these arrangements will lead to crystals and how many to gases?

First of all, how many total arrangements are there for both gases *and* crystals? The first atom can go to any one of 9 places. The second atom has 8 places left open, the third has 7 places, and the last atom has only 6 unoccupied choices. The total number of ways of placing four atoms on the nine locations is $9 \cdot 8 \cdot 7 \cdot 6 = 3024$ ways.

This is not quite correct, because we have overcounted. The answer of 3024 would be correct if the atoms had names or labels, and if arrangements of the type shown at the lower left really were different. But atoms have no labels. If by some miraculous process we could photograph the atoms at a chosen instant and study them, we could tell the difference between the four arrangements at the upper left because the atoms would occupy different places. However, we could see absolutely no difference in the twelve arrangements at the middle left, because one atom is just like every other atom of the same type. The most that we could say is that atoms were present at Positions 3, 4, 7, and 8 of our mini-universe.

How can we correct for this overcounting? How do we "remove the labels" from the atoms? As a correction factor, how many different label shufflings can be made for each arrangement of four atoms? Label a could be given to any one of the four atoms, label b to any of the remaining three, label c to two, and label d then has to go to the last atom. There are $4 \cdot 3 \cdot 2 \cdot 1 = 24$ meaningless permutations of labels for every really different arrangement of atoms. We have overcounted by a multiplicative factor of 24.

Hence the 3024 ways of arranging atoms must be divided by 24 to remove the labels on the atoms. The number of different ways of arranging four *indistinguishable* atoms among nine locations is

$$W = \frac{9 \cdot 8 \cdot 7 \cdot 6}{4 \cdot 3 \cdot 2 \cdot 1} = \frac{3024}{24} = 126$$

In case you are skeptical about the logic of the derivation just given, all 126 arrangements are shown below. Of the 126 possible arrangements only four are crystals, and the other 122 lead to a gas. Even in such a tiny and restricted universe, a gas is far more likely to result from a random arrangement of atoms than is a crystal. This is true because the specifications for a crystal are so much more restrictive:

Crystal—four adjacent atoms in a square;
Gas—four atoms in any arrangement *except* those that lead to a crystal.

For crystals and gases, $W_c = 4$ and $W_g = 122$; thus a gas is more than 30 times as likely to occur as a crystal.

Out of the 126 possible arrangements of atoms, only the four shown in color are "crystals." The other 122 are "gases."

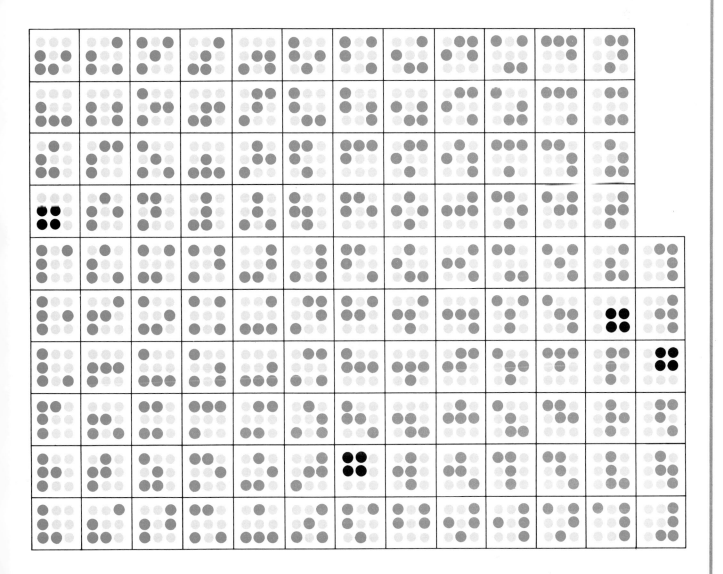

Gas  Crystal

Four atoms in a 16-point universe. Only 9 of the 1820 possible arrangements are "crystals"; the other 1811 are "gases."

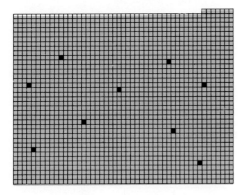

If we were to repeat the experiment with four atoms in a 4×4 "universe" or box, we would find that

$$W = \frac{16 \cdot 15 \cdot 14 \cdot 13}{4 \cdot 3 \cdot 2 \cdot 1} = 1820$$

different arrangements would be possible, of which 9 would be crystals and 1811 would be gases (left). In that universe a gas would be more than 200 times as probable as a crystal. When we jump to the real world, with many times Avogadro's number of atoms and many, many places for atoms to be, W becomes astronomical. It is easier to use a logarithmic representation in which 10, 10,000,000, and 100,000,000,-000,000 (or 10^1, 10^7, and 10^{14}) are reduced to a more manageable 1, 7, and 14. The entropy, S, is simply the number of ways of obtaining a given state of matter, expressed logarithmically instead of linearly:

$$S = k \ln W = 2.303 \, k \log_{10} W$$

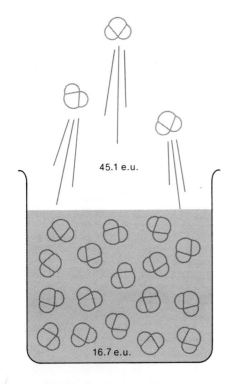

45.1 e.u.

16.7 e.u.

Entropy increases when a liquid or solid is vaporized. Liquid water evaporates at 298°K with an increase in disorder of 28.4 entropy units (e.u.) per mole.

THIRD-LAW ENTROPIES AND COMMON SENSE

As already has been mentioned, the third-law entropies, S^0_{298}, (tabulated alongside heats of formation in Appendix 2) were calculated entirely from calorimetric, or heat, measurements and owe nothing to any theories about entropy and randomness. Nevertheless, it is a tribute to Boltzmann's genius that we can explain these relative entropy values so well using the concept of disorder and what we know about the structures and physical properties of substances. If Boltzmann did not exist, it would be necessary to invent him.

Let us look at matter through Boltzmann's eyes, and interpret measured third-law entropies in terms of order and disorder. We can see several clear-cut trends, and they all become obvious if we replace the word "entropy" with "disorder."

A. The entropy (or disorder) increases whenever a liquid or solid is converted to a gas (left). Sodium metal, liquid bromine, and water provide examples.

Substance:	Na(s)	Br$_2$(l)	H$_2$O(l)
S^0 (solid or liquid):	12.2 e.u.	36.4 e.u.	16.7 e.u.
S^0 (gas phase):	36.7 e.u.	58.6 e.u.	45.1 e.u.

The units of entropy are calories per degree per mole, or entropy units per mole, abbreviated e.u. mole^{-1}. The molar entropies (S^0) of sodium, bromine, and water all increase as the substances are vaporized because the gases are more disordered than the condensed phases.

300

B. The entropy increases when a solid or liquid is dissolved in water (right). This can be illustrated by liquid methanol and crystalline ammonium chloride.

Substance:	$CH_3OH(l)$	$NH_4Cl(s)$
S^0 before solution:	30.3 e.u.	22.6 e.u.
S^0 after solution:	31.6 e.u.	$27.0 + 13.2 = 40.2$ e.u.
		(NH_4^+) (Cl^-)

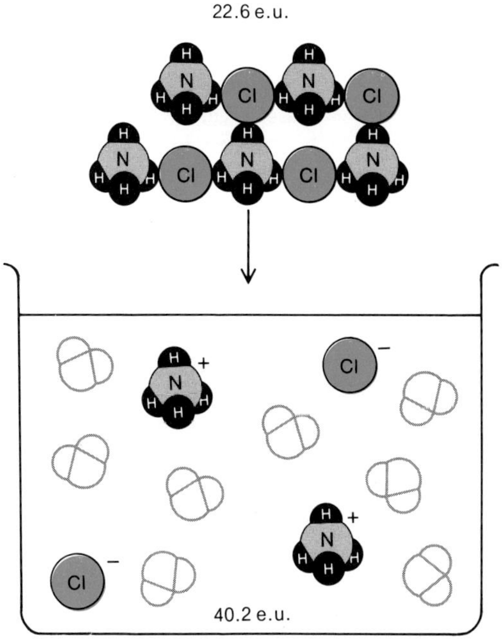

The entropy of ammonium chloride in solution is the sum of the entropies of the hydrated ions; this is based on a convention that assigns an entropy of zero to the hydrated H^+ ion. Notice that the entropy changes that result from dissolving suggest that ammonium chloride solution is much more disordered than crystalline NH_4Cl, whereas the difference in disorder between liquid methanol and methanol in aqueous solution is small. This is explained by the breakup of a regular array of NH_4^+ and Cl^- ions in the crystal lattice when NH_4Cl dissolves, whereas liquid methanol has no such regular structure.

C. Entropy falls when a gas is dissolved in water (below). Methanol and hydrogen chloride gases are nonionizing and ionizing examples, respectively.

Substance:	$CH_3OH(g)$	$HCl(g)$
S^0 before dissolving:	56.8 e.u.	44.6 e.u.
S^0 after dissolving:	31.6 e.u.	$0 + 13.2 = 13.2$ e.u.
		(H^+) (Cl^-)

As before, the entropy of ionized HCl in solution is the sum of the entropies of the individual ions. Compare methanol vapor shown here, with liquid methanol in the preceding example. The molecular mixtures of substances that we call solutions are more disordered than pure crystals or liquids, but are less disordered than gases. Thus when methanol vapor dissolves in water its entropy decreases, almost to the value for pure liquid methanol.

22.6 e.u.

40.2 e.u.

Entropy increases when a liquid or solid is dissolved in another liquid. Disorder increases by 17.6 e.u. per mole when NH_4Cl crystals are dissolved in water.

56.8 e.u.

31.6 e.u.

Entropy decreases when a gas is dissolved in a liquid. When methanol vapor dissolves in water, it becomes more ordered by 25.2 e.u. per mole.

Four molecules with a total of six units of energy

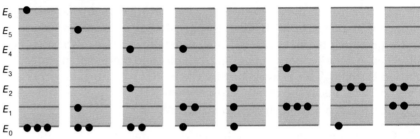

Light molecule; widely spaced energy levels; $W = 2$

Heavier molecule; more closely spaced energy levels; $W = 8$

Entropy increases with mass. A heavier molecule has more closely spaced energy levels, and there are more ways of obtaining a mole of such molecules with a given total energy. In this example, four molecules together have six units of energy, and we can represent the energy of each molecule by locating it on a diagram of the possible energy levels. For the light molecules with widely spaced levels, only two distributions are possible, whereas eight different arrangements exist for the heavier molecules. Hence the heavier molecules have a larger entropy, by $S = k \ln W$.

D. Entropy rises with increasing mass, other things being equal. We can show this by comparing the entropies of the diatomic halogens, in order of increasing mass,

Substance:	$F_2(g)$	$Cl_2(g)$	$Br_2(g)$	$I_2(g)$
S^0 (e.u.):	48.6	53.3	58.6	62.3

or by looking at a series of molecules with increasing numbers of atoms.

Substance:	$K(g)$	$Cl_2(g)$	$P_4(g)$	$As_4(g)$
S^0 (e.u.):	38.3	53.3	66.9	69.0

This is an important principle, but a hard one to account for without quantum mechanics. Simple quantum theory tells us that as the size and mass of an atom or molecule increase, the spacings between its energy levels decrease. We have used this principle constantly in discussing delocalized electrons in molecules. A large and massive object with a certain total energy has more quantum states available to it, so W is larger and $S = k \ln W$ is greater. For the nonquantum mechanically inclined, a bull in a china shop creates more disorder than a mouse.

E. Entropy is lower in covalently bonded solids than in solids with partial metallic character (left).

C (diamond): 0.58 e.u.	Sn (gray, diamond structure): 10.7 e.u.
C (graphite): 1.36 e.u.	Sn (white, close-packed metallic): 12.3 e.u.

The entropy is lower in framework solids such as diamond and gray tin, because the covalent bonds hold the atoms in a more orderly arrangement than do the nondirectional attractions of metals. For the very same reasons, covalent three-dimensional network solids are harder and more resistant to deformation.

DIAMOND — 0.58 e.u.   GRAPHITE — 1.36 e.u.

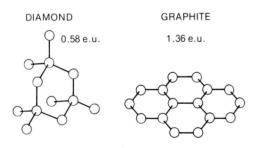

Entropy is lower in a covalently bonded solid than in a sheet structure.

F. Entropy is lower in extended sheet structures than in molecular solids (right).

P (black, semimetallic sheets):   7.0 e.u.

P (white, individual P_4 molecules in the solid):   10.6 e.u.

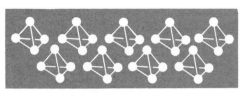

WHITE PHOSPHORUS   10.6 e.u.

Again, the covalently bonded infinite sheets are more ordered than are P_4 molecules, which are held together in the solid only by weak van der Waals forces.

G. In general, entropy rises with increasing softness and weakness of bonds between atoms (bottom illustration).

Substance:	C(s)	Be(s)	SiO$_2$(s)	Pb(s)	Hg(l)	Hg(g)
Form:	dia-mond	hard metal	quartz	soft metal	liquid	vapor
S^0 (e.u.):	0.58	2.3	10.0	15.5	18.5	41.8

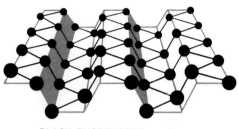

BLACK PHOSPHORUS   7.0 e.u.

Entropy is lower in extended sheets than in isolated molecules.

This actually is a generalization of the more specific principles E and F. The increased disorder (entropy) and softness both are indicators of the same thing, the lack of strong geometrical bonds to hold the atoms together.

H. Entropy increases with chemical complexity. This principle holds for ionic salt crystals with increasing numbers of ions per mole,

	NaCl(s)	MgCl$_2$(s)	AlCl$_3$(s)
S^0 (e.u.):	17.3	21.4	40

for crystals with increasing numbers of water molecules in the crystal,

	CuSO$_4$(s)	CuSO$_4 \cdot$ H$_2$O(s)
S^0 (e.u.):	27.1	35.8

	CuSO$_4 \cdot$ 3H$_2$O(s)	CuSO$_4 \cdot$ 5H$_2$O(s)
S^0 (e.u.):	53.8	73.0

and for organic compounds with larger carbon frameworks.

	CH$_4$(g)	C$_2$H$_6$(g)	C$_3$H$_8$(g)	C$_4$H$_{10}$(g)
S^0 (e.u.):	44.0	54.9	64.5	74.1

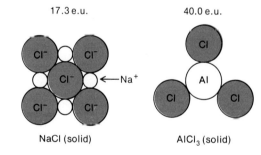

17.3 e.u.   40.0 e.u.

NaCl (solid)   AlCl$_3$ (solid)

Entropy rises with chemical complexity.

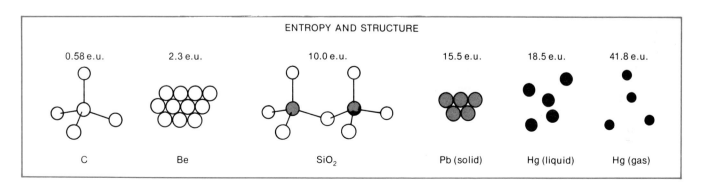

ENTROPY AND STRUCTURE

0.58 e.u.   2.3 e.u.   10.0 e.u.   15.5 e.u.   18.5 e.u.   41.8 e.u.

C   Be   SiO$_2$ Pb (solid)   Hg (liquid)   Hg (gas)

Solid | Gas

| | | | | | | | | 1 H 31.2 | | | 2 He 30.1 |

For structures of solids, see Page 206

3 Li 6.7	4 Be 2.3	5 B 1.6	6 C 0.6 / 1.4	7 N 45.8	8 O 49.0	9 F 48.6	10 Ne 34.5	
11 Na 12.2	12 Mg 7.8	13 Al 6.8	14 Si 4.5	15 P 10.6 / 7.0	16 S 7.7	17 Cl 53.3	18 Ar 37.0	
19 K 15.2	20 Ca 10.0	31 Ga —	32 Ge 10.1	33 As 8.4	34 Se 10.0	35 Br 36.4	36 Kr 39.2	
37 Rb 16.6	38 Sr 13.0	49 In —	50 Sn 10.7 / 12.3	51 Sb 10.5	52 Te 11.9	53 I 27.9	54 Xe 40.5	
55 Cs 19.8	56 Ba 16.0	81 Tl 15.4	82 Pb 15.5	83 Bi 13.6	84 Po —	85 At —	86 Rn 42.1	

Solid | Gas

Typical molar entropy values for common structures of different types. Entropy increases from three-dimensional framework solids on the left, to molecular gases on the right.

Third-law entropies, although they come purely from thermal measurements, tell us something about molecular structure if we know how to interpret them. These trends in entropies are summarized below, and the entropies of the pure elements as they ordinarily are encountered at room temperature are listed on the periodic table above. All of the trends in this table now should be understandable. Although entropy originally began as a rather abstract concept involving heat, it has a definite and visualizable meaning. Entropy is a direct and quantitative measure of disorder.

Increasing entropy ⟶

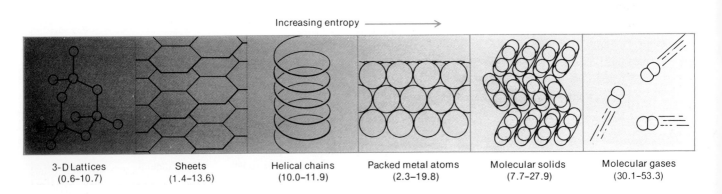

3-D Lattices (0.6–10.7)   Sheets (1.4–13.6)   Helical chains (10.0–11.9)   Packed metal atoms (2.3–19.8)   Molecular solids (7.7–27.9)   Molecular gases (30.1–53.3)

ENTROPY AND CHEMICAL REACTIONS

What does all this discussion of physical properties and entropies have to do with chemistry? Entropy is the missing factor that we needed when we saw that energy, or enthalpy, alone is not enough to determine whether a chemical reaction will be spontaneous. A drop in enthalpy (ΔH negative) will help to make a process spontaneous, but is not enough by itself to guarantee that it will be so. Spontaneity is favored by simultaneously minimizing H and maximizing S, or minimizing H and $-S$. We can define a new function whose minimization combines both of the above requirements. This is the *free energy*, G:

$$G \equiv H - TS$$

The units of H (cal mole^{-1}) and S (cal deg^{-1} mole^{-1}) require that S be multiplied by the absolute temperature, T. For a reaction with the same initial and final temperature, the changes in enthalpy, entropy, and free energy are related by the expression

$$\Delta G = \Delta H - T\Delta S$$

This expression says that, at constant temperature, the change in free energy, ΔG, is the change in enthalpy, ΔH, minus the change in entropy multiplied by the absolute temperature, $T\Delta S$. It is not too difficult to prove that a spontaneous reaction is one in which the *overall free energy* decreases, regardless of what happens to the enthalpy and entropy individually. Spontaneity is a combined effect of both H and S, and the above equation is the proper way of combining them.

This equation is easier to understand with the aid of arrow diagrams, as at the right. An upward pointing arrow represents an increase in free energy, enthalpy, and order, or a positive value for ΔG, ΔH, and $(-T\Delta S)$. This is the nonspontaneous direction. Conversely, an arrow pointing downward symbolizes a decrease in free energy or enthalpy, and an increase in *disorder*. These correspond to negative values for ΔG, ΔH, and $(-T\Delta S)$, and are in the direction of spontaneity. The ΔG arrow is the sum of the ΔH and the $(-T\Delta S)$ arrows, and if the ΔG arrow points downward, the reaction is spontaneous.

In many reactions the contributions of enthalpy and entropy (disorder) reinforce one another, as in the arrow diagram at the upper right. In such a reaction heat is released and disorder is created, both of which favor the spontaneous reaction. We will see examples of such reactions shortly.

In other reactions enthalpy and entropy may work against one another, as at the lower right. In this particular example, heat is given off, thereby favoring the reaction; but order increases (the $-T\Delta S$ arrow points up), thus hindering the reaction. The enthalpy effect dominates in this case and the reaction still is spontaneous, but this need not always be true. The examples we cited at the beginning of the chapter to show the fallacy of deciding spontaneity on the basis of enthalpy alone were in this category.

How do the changes in enthalpy and entropy compare when ammonium chloride dissolves in water? Which effect predominates? Recall from Chapter 12 that heat is absorbed: $\Delta H^0 = +3.62$ kcal mole^{-1}.

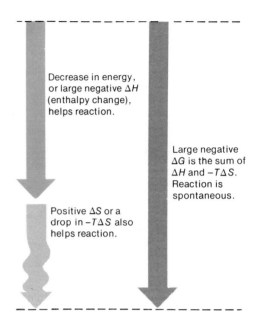

Decrease in energy, or large negative ΔH (enthalpy change), helps reaction.

Large negative ΔG is the sum of ΔH and $-T\Delta S$. Reaction is spontaneous.

Positive ΔS or a drop in $-T\Delta S$ also helps reaction.

A drop in enthalpy and an increase in disorder both favor the reaction.

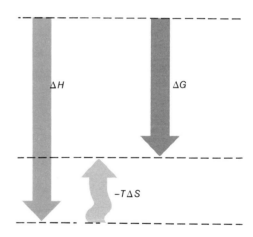

ΔH

ΔG

$-T\Delta S$

A drop in enthalpy (ΔH) may be opposed by an increase in order. The difference between ΔH and $-T\Delta S$ is the "free" energy change, or ΔG. The reaction is spontaneous, but not as much as enthalpy alone would suggest.

305

This by itself works against the dissolving process. But the molar entropy increases from 22.6 e.u. to 40.2 e.u., an increase in disorder per mole of 17.6 e.u., or cal deg^{-1}. If $\Delta S = +17.6$ cal deg^{-1} mole^{-1}, then at room temperature or 298°K:

$$T\Delta S = 298° \ (+17.6 \text{ cal deg}^{-1} \text{ mole}^{-1}) = 5245 \text{ cal mole}^{-1}$$
$$= 5.25 \text{ kcal mole}^{-1}$$

The free energy change per mole then can be calculated:

$$\Delta G = \Delta H - T\Delta S = +3.62 \text{ kcal} - 5.25 \text{ kcal} = -1.63 \text{ kcal}$$

Enthalpy applies 3.62 kcal worth of opposition to the dissolving of ammonium chloride in water, but entropy, or disorder, favors the dissolving process by 5.25 kcal. The net effect is that NH_4Cl dissolves with an overall free energy drive of 1.63 kcal mole^{-1}. The key to chemical spontaneity is not what enthalpy or entropy may do individually, but what happens to the free energy during the process. The results are easier to understand, however, if we realize that two components are involved, H and S.

It obviously is unnecessary to tabulate free energies if heats of formation and third-law entropies are available, but standard free energies of formation of compounds from their elements are so useful that they normally are included in tables of the type given at the left and in Appendix 2. Let us use these tabulated values for some reactions that will illustrate how free energy behaves.

Standard heats (ΔH^0_{298}) and free energies (ΔG^0_{298}) of formation and third-law entropies (S^0_{298})

Substance	ΔH^0_{298} (kcal mole^{-1})	ΔG^0_{298} (kcal mole^{-1})	S^0_{298} (cal deg^{-1} mole^{-1})
$H_2(g)$	0	0	31.21
$CO_2(g)$	−94.05	−94.26	51.06
$C_2H_5OH(l)$	−66.36	−41.77	38.4
$C_6H_{12}O_6(s)$	−301.2	−219.7	69.04
$NO_2(g)$	+8.09	+12.39	57.47
$N_2O_5(s)$	−10.0	+32.0	27.1
$NH_4^+(aq)$	−31.74	−19.00	26.97
$NH_4Cl(s)$	−75.38	−48.73	22.6
$O_2(g)$	0	0	49.00
$H_2O(l)$	−68.32	−56.69	16.72
$Cl_2(g)$	0	0	53.29
$Cl^-(aq)$	−40.02	−31.35	13.2
$HCl(g)$	−22.06	−22.77	44.62

Explosion of H_2 and Cl_2

When working with enthalpies, entropies, and free energies, it is convenient to write the reaction equation first and then tabulate the individual values below each component of the reaction.

Reaction:	$H_2(g)$	+ $Cl_2(g)$	$\rightarrow 2HCl(g)$	Overall
ΔH^0 (kcal):	0	0	2(−22.1)	$\Delta H^0 = -44.2$ kcal
S^0 (cal deg^{-1}):	31.2	53.3	2(+44.6)	$\Delta S^0 = +4.7$ cal deg^{-1}
ΔG^0 (kcal):	0	0	2(−22.8)	$\Delta G^0 = -45.6$ kcal

Note that the standard free energies of formation of elements, like their standard heats of formation, are zero by definition because the elements already are in their standard states. The entropies, in contrast, are not entropies of formation from elements, but are absolute measures of disorder. Hence the elements have molar entropies just as the molecular compounds do. As a check, we can verify that

$$\Delta G^0 = \Delta H^0 - T\Delta S^0 = (-44.2) - 298° \left(\frac{+4.7 \text{ cal deg}^{-1}}{1000 \text{ cal kcal}^{-1}} \right)$$
$$\Delta G^0 = -44.2 - 1.4 = -45.6 \text{ kcal}$$

In the formation of HCl, the enthalpy falls drastically and the entropy, or disorder, rises to a minor extent. Both effects favor reaction, so the explosion is spontaneous. Disordering contributes to reaction, so the

306

free energy of 45.6 kcal, which makes the reaction spontaneous and which *can potentially be harnessed to do useful work*, actually is greater than would be expected from heat-energy arguments alone. This reaction, which liberates only 44.2 kcal of heat, thus can do as much as 45.6 kcal mole^{-1} of useful work.

We can portray the rise and fall of energies and the drive toward reaction in the arrow diagram at the upper right. The long downward-pointing arrow at the left of the diagram represents the release of 44.2 kcal of enthalpy or heat ($\Delta H = -44.2$ kcal); this favors the reaction. The shorter arrow next to it symbolizes the decrease in order, which leads to $(-T\Delta S) = -1.4$ kcal. The long ΔG arrow at the right of the diagram is the sum of these two, and represents the overall drop in free energy of 45.6 kcal ($\Delta G = -45.6$ kcal). In this HCl example, both enthalpy and entropy contribute to making the reaction spontaneous.

Combustion of Ethanol

Now let us look at an example for which enthalpy and entropy affect the reaction differently. Ethanol burns spontaneously in air to form liquid water.

Reaction:	$C_2H_5OH(l)$	$+ 3O_2(g)$	$\rightarrow 2CO_2(g)$	$+ 3H_2O(l)$	Overall
ΔH^0 (kcal):	-66.4	0	$2(-94.1)$	$3(-68.3)$	-326.7
S^0 (cal deg^{-1}):	38.4	$3(49.0)$	$2(51.1)$	$3(16.7)$	-33.1
ΔG^0 (kcal):	-41.8	0	$2(-94.3)$	$3(-56.7)$	-316.9

Again, we can verify that

$$\Delta G^0 = \Delta H^0 - T\Delta S^0$$

$$\Delta G^0 = -326.7 - 298\left(\frac{-33.1}{1000}\right) = -326.7 + 9.9 = -316.8$$

In the combustion of ethanol to liquid water, the products are more ordered than the reactants by 33.1 cal deg^{-1}, so the reaction is impeded by entropy. The reaction is less spontaneous because *order* is generated in the products. Of the 327 kcal of heat given off by the reaction, only 317 kcal are capable of being harnessed to some other useful process. Ten kilocalories of heat are unavailable, the price paid for creating order in the products. This is why G is called "free" energy. It represents the portion of the energy released that is free and available for other purposes. In this reaction the free energy is less than the total heat evolved because of the cost of creating order. In the HCl explosion the free energy drop was even larger than the heat evolved; the added energy came from the production of disorder. Entropy, as well as enthalpy, is a driving force for or against reactions.

The vector diagram for ethanol combustion is shown at the right. ΔH^0 is negative and is represented by a downward arrow. Because ΔS^0 is negative, the quantity $(-T\Delta S^0)$ is positive and is shown by an upward arrow, which works against ΔH^0. The resultant arrow, ΔG^0, is negative, but less so than ΔH^0. However, the reaction remains spontaneous.

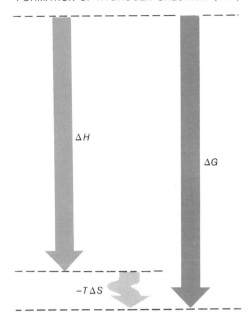

FORMATION OF HYDROGEN CHLORIDE (HCl)

Enthalpy and entropy both favor spontaneous reaction in the formation of HCl from H_2 and Cl_2.

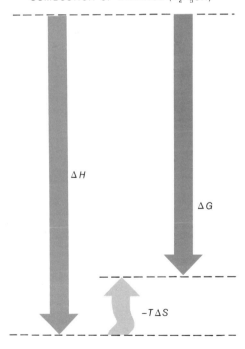

COMBUSTION OF ETHANOL (C_2H_5OH)

Enthalpy favors, but entropy opposes, the combustion of ethanol to form liquid water. If water vapor were the product, an entropy increase would favor the reaction as well.

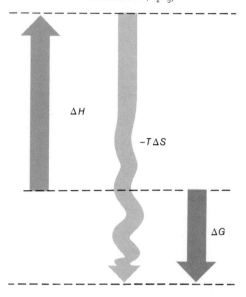

DECOMPOSITION OF DINITROGEN
PENTOXIDE (N_2O_5)

ΔH

$-T\Delta S$

ΔG

The absorption of heat opposes the decomposition of N_2O_5 but the entropy factor, arising from disorder produced, is more than enough to counteract this trend and to make the decomposition spontaneous.

Decomposition of N_2O_5

As a final example, let us examine the exception that showed the flaws in the principle of energy minimization alone.

Reaction:	$N_2O_5(s) \rightarrow$	$2NO_2(g)$	$+ \frac{1}{2}O_2(g)$	Overall
ΔH^0 (kcal):	-10.0	$2(+8.1)$	0	$+26.2$ kcal
S^0 (cal deg^{-1}):	27.1	$2(57.5)$	$\frac{1}{2}(49.0)$	$+112.4$ cal deg^{-1}
ΔG^0 (kcal):	$+32.0$	$2(+12.4)$	0	-7.2 kcal

The enormous entropy increase comes from the breaking up of crystalline N_2O_5 into gases. Heat is absorbed, disfavoring the reaction by 26.2 kcal. The entropy increase favors reaction by the amount

$$-T\Delta S^0 = -298 \left(\frac{+112.4}{1000}\right) = -33.5 \text{ kcal}$$

In this special case entropy overwhelms enthalpy, and the reaction is spontaneous even though it absorbs heat:

$$\Delta G^0 = +26.2 - 33.5 = -7.3 \text{ kcal}$$

The vector diagram for this reaction is shown at the upper left. The enthalpy arrow points up, but the entropy arrow points down and is so long that the sum of these two is a downward-pointing free energy arrow. Disordering is so potent a driving force in this reaction that it carries the reaction along with it to a state of *higher* enthalpy, thereby drawing heat energy from its surroundings and cooling them in the process. The cooling effect of melting ice cubes has the same origin.

FREE ENERGY AND LIVING ORGANISMS

As has been stated, the key to spontaneity in chemical reactions is a decrease in *free* energy, G, and not simply in the total energy or enthalpy, H. This residual free energy is the total thermal energy minus any energy that is required to create order:

$$\underset{\substack{\text{free} \\ \text{energy}}}{\Delta G} = \underset{\substack{\text{heat} \\ \text{energy}}}{\Delta H} - \underset{\substack{\text{energy expended} \\ \text{for order}}}{T\Delta S}$$

In the combustion of ethanol, 327 kcal of energy are given off per mole as heat, but not all 327 kcal can be used for outside work. The equivalent of 10 kcal of heat is the price that must be paid in entropy when one mole of liquid and three of gas are transformed by reaction into three moles of liquid and only two of gas. It is the loss of one mole of gas that is critical from an entropy standpoint. If all of the chemical energy of the ethanol combustion is dissipated as heat, 327 kcal will be given off. If we couple this combustion to another, nonspontaneous reaction and use the driving force of the ethanol reaction to make the second process take place, we can use only 317 of the 327 kcal as this driving force. This is what the "free" in free energy means.

Living organisms depend on coupled reactions. They use energy-producing reactions to synthesize compounds that are high in free energy and to make a great many energetically unfavorable reactions run "uphill." Enzymes are the keys to this coupling. They bind reactant and product molecules selectively to their surface, and ensure that when a "downhill" reaction occurs, the "uphill" reaction accompanies it so that a minimum of energy is wasted as emitted heat.

The main energy-producing reaction in all oxygen-using living organisms is combustion of the sugar glucose:

$$C_6H_{12}O_6(s) + 6O_2(g) \rightarrow 6CO_2(g) + 6H_2O(l)$$

From the table in Appendix 2, you should be able to verify the following for this reaction:

$\Delta H^0 = -673$ kcal

$\Delta S^0 = +43.3$ cal deg^{-1} $-T\Delta S^0 = -13$ kcal

$\Delta G^0 = -686$ kcal

A large quantity of heat, 673 kcal, is given off during the burning of glucose because of the large number of bonds formed between oxygen and other atoms during the reaction. At the same time, one mole of a solid is converted to six moles of a liquid, so the entropy, or disorder effect, is appreciable. (The O_2 and CO_2 gases have similar entropies.) Entropy gives the glucose reaction an extra 13-kcal push.

In a living cell, glucose combustion is connected to the machinery for synthesizing a special energy-storage molecule, adenosine triphosphate, or ATP (right), which we saw in Chapter 10. This coupling occurs via an elaborate set of reactions—fermentation, citric acid cycle, and respiratory pathway—using more than twenty different enzymes in succession. The sole purpose of this complicated metabolic system is to ensure that as much of the 686 kcal of free energy as possible is stored as ATP molecules rather than being dissipated as heat. Each ATP molecule synthesized from ADP and inorganic phosphate (represented by P_i) stores 7.3 kcal mole^{-1} of free energy for later use:

$$ADP + P_i \rightarrow ATP \qquad \Delta G^0 = +7.3 \text{ kcal mole}^{-1}$$

The important feature about ATP is its universality. All energy-producing reactions in living organisms store their energy in ATP, and all energy-requiring reactions obtain this energy from ATP. The ultimate uses and the origins of any particular packet of energy in the organism are thereby separated.

Not all of the free energy liberated by the glucose reaction can be saved. The best that has been achieved in three billion years of evolution of life on this planet is the synthesis of 38 molecules of ATP for every molecule of glucose burned:

$$38ADP + 38P_i \rightarrow 38ATP \qquad \Delta G^0 = 38(+7.3) = +277 \text{ kcal}$$

The overall reaction still liberates enough free energy to be highly spontaneous:

$$C_6H_{12}O_6(s) + 38ADP + 38P_i \rightarrow 6CO_2(g) + 6H_2O(l) + 38ATP$$

$$\Delta G^0 = -686 + 277 = -409 \text{ kcal}$$

ADP
(adenosine diphosphate)

+

P$_i$
(inorganic phosphate)

+ H$^+$

ATP
(adenosine triphosphate)

+

H$_2$O

$$ADP + P_i + H^+ \longrightarrow ATP + H_2O$$

$$\Delta G = 7.3 \text{ kcal mole}^{-1}$$

Conversion of ADP to ATP stores 7.3 kcal of free energy per mole. Hydrolysis of ATP to ADP and inorganic phosphate releases 7.3 kcal per mole.

309

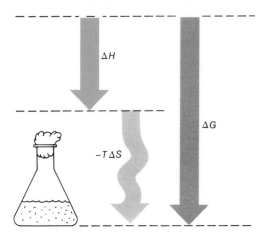

FERMENTATION OF YEAST

Enthalpy and entropy both favor reaction.

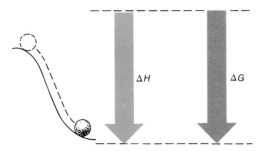

BALL ROLLING DOWN HILL

Entropy, or disorder, is unimportant; spontaneity is decided on the basis of energy (enthalpy) alone.

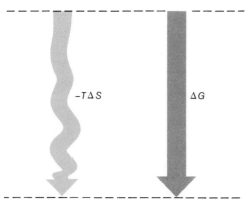

LOST SPACE CAPSULE

No energy exchanged with surroundings; spontaneity is determined by direction of rise in entropy, or disorder.

It may look bad that only 277/686 or 40% of the available free energy of the glucose reaction is saved. However, the 409 kcal of energy that are dissipated are not useless. They make the reaction spontaneous and ensure that it never can proceed the wrong way. The situation is analogous to that of a water-mill operator who is content to take a smaller amount of energy out of a rushing stream to power his mill in return for the guarantee that the stream will never back up.

If yeast is given a plentiful supply of oxygen, it will burn glucose and produce energy by the overall reaction just given. But if oxygen is cut off, yeast can do what we cannot. Yeast can shut down its citric acid cycle and respiratory chain, and continue to produce energy on a smaller scale by fermenting glucose to ethanol:

$$C_6H_{12}O_6(s) \rightarrow 2C_2H_5OH(l) + 2CO_2(g)$$

$$\Delta H^0 = -19.6 \text{ kcal}$$

$$\Delta S^0 = +109.5 \text{ cal deg}^{-1}$$

$$\Delta G^0 = -19.6 - 298(109.5)/1000 = -19.6 - 32.6 = -52.2 \text{ kcal}$$

More free energy drive is provided by the disordering of products (32.6 kcal) than by the liberation of heat (19.6 kcal)! Much less energy is saved in this fermentation; only two molecules of ATP are synthesized instead of 38:

$$2ADP + 2P_i \rightarrow 2ATP \qquad \Delta G^0 = +14.6 \text{ kcal}$$

The ATP synthesis comes close to using more chemical energy than was provided by the heat of reaction. This does not matter; entropy is just as effective as enthalpy in driving other reactions. What does matter is the overall ΔG. The vector energy diagram for glucose fermentation in yeast is shown at the upper left. Enthalpy and entropy arrows both point downward, but the entropy arrow is longer.

We now can go back to the example of gravitational energy—the rock rolling down a hillside (middle left). This is a special case in which the entropy change is negligible. A hill with a rock at the top has the same degree of disorder, or entropy, as a hill with a rock at the bottom. The relationship $\Delta G = \Delta H - T\Delta S$ still holds, but ΔS is zero. In such a situation it is correct to say that spontaneous processes lead to lower energy, but it must be kept in mind that this is only a special case of the general relationship.

Conversely, there are situations in which the enthalpy change is zero and the entropy, expressed as $-T\Delta S$, is all-important. This is true for the universe as a whole, or for any part of it that constitutes an isolated system, which interchanges neither mass nor energy with its surroundings. One meaningful example in recent years is a sealed space capsule (lower left margin). Every operation that the astronauts perform increases the disorder in the capsule, thereby decreasing the overall free energy, or capacity to do still other things: $\Delta G = -T\Delta S$. The space capsule and everything in it literally run down, like the universe, but on a far shorter time scale. If the capsule is not opened and provided with new supplies of free energy, eventually it and all of its contents will degrade to the state of high entropy that conventionally is known as death.

310

ENTROPY AND TIME

Physicists worry about the contrast between the obviously irreversible, one-directional nature of time in the macroscopic world, and the apparent complete reversibility of all of the laws of mechanics. Any molecular collision or reaction can take place equally well in a forward or a reverse direction. If we were able to make molecular-scale "home movies" of any atomic process, we would have no clue from the movie alone as to whether it was being run forward or backward (see bottom of page). If the forward process was a reaction of molecules of H_2 and I_2 to form two HI molecules, the reverse process would be equally possible collision of two HI molecules to form H_2 and I_2. One would have no basis for defining a "positive sense" to the flow of time at the molecular level. This is known as the *principle of microreversibility* in physics and chemistry: On the molecular scale, if a forward reaction is possible, the reverse reaction must be equally possible.

In contrast, the positive direction of time presents no problem at the level of the macroscopic world. Movies run backward are considered hilarious just because they violate common sense so completely. At the top of the next page is a series of frames representing the simple operation of dissolving ink in water. At the bottom of the page are the same frames in reverse order. We have no difficulty in saying that the top order is right and the bottom order is wrong. But what is the basis for this decision? The basis is our deeply ingrained, intuitive realization that order can lead to chaos, but chaos never spontaneously produces order. Beginning students sometimes feel that entropy is an abstruse concept, but we all appreciate what it means even before we put a name to it.

Order and arrangement are not properties of individual particles, but of collections of particles. (Try describing to someone the "arrangement" of just one object.) The total energy of a mole of gas molecules is 6.022×10^{23} times the average energy of one molecule. We

An imaginary molecular "home movie." The movie makes perfectly good chemical sense whether run forward or backward.

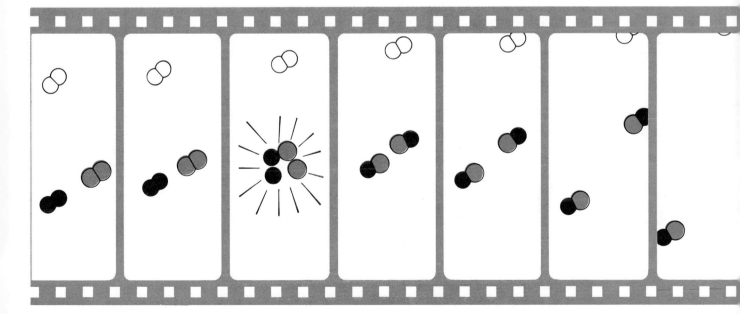

Home movies on a larger scale: Ink dropped into water diffuses and mixes.

can talk about the entropy of a mole of gas molecules, but it is not legitimate to divide this by 6.022×10^{23} to obtain an "average molecular entropy." The entropy depends on more than merely how many molecules are present, multiplied by some intrinsic property of each molecule. Entropy describes how the particles are *arranged* relative to one another. It thus gives a sense to the flow of time. Even though the mechanical motions of each particle are reversible in time, the steady increase in "mixed-upness" of a large collection of particles is not.

The second law of thermodynamics, as we have discussed it, states that, in any isolated region of space, entropy always spontaneously increases with time. The physicist Arthur Eddington turned this statement around and said: "On the microscopic level, all of the laws of physics are completely reversible in time, and positive and negative directions in time are undefined. On the macroscopic level, *positive* time is that sequence of events in which the entropy or disorder within an isolated system increases." By Eddington's statement the second law becomes, not a statement about entropy, but a definition of positive time. This is why Eddington characterized entropy as "Time's Arrow."

Regardless of which way your own philosophical bent leads you to look at the second law, it does make one important connection: In the real universe positive time and increasing entropy always go together.

This movie run in reverse goes against common sense. A drop of pure ink will not separate from a thin water solution of ink and jump back into the dropper. This sequence obviously has been run backwards in time.

ENTROPY AND THE UNIVERSE

Nothing can take place in this universe without a gradient—a difference in some property between one part of the universe and another. All the heat in the world is incapable of conversion to work if the temperature everywhere is uniform; a steam engine requires both a hot box and cold water for a condenser. Mechanical work requires a potential-energy gradient; the heaviest weight imaginable can do no work if there is no place for it to fall. Chemical work requires the presence of high-free-energy compounds that can be broken down into low-free-energy molecules such as CO_2 and water, or else high concentrations of a substance in one location and a scarcity of that substance somewhere else. This structure to the universe—different properties in different places—is a form of order. Every time a real process takes place, some of this order is whittled away. The "mixed-upness," or entropy, of the universe increases.

The universe therefore carries the seeds of its own death. From a free energy standpoint, it continually is running down. The only way for nothing to run down is for nothing to happen. Every time something real does take place, it makes the universe just a little bit less able to cause more things to happen. When a boulder rolls downhill it can be harnessed to a device for saving some of its energy; but the energy saved, if used to hoist the boulder, will not be quite enough to get it to the top of the hill again. These losses are tied up with the inevitable rise of entropy in any real process.

When the last star has burned out and has either shrunk to a white dwarf or exploded into a supernova, when the last heat source has been dissipated, the last energy-rich organic compound has broken down, and the universe is a uniform dispersion of cold dust, then everything will be over. If the laws of thermodynamics as we see them are universally valid, then there appears to be no way of escaping this "entropy death" of the universe. It will be a long time in coming, but is inevitable.

A seeming exception to the dogma that everything eventually runs down is the phenomenon of life. If spontaneous processes always lead to disorder, how can a highly organized living creature survive? There is a deceptive fallacy that maintains that life, by remaining superorganized, violates the second law of thermodynamics and therefore stands outside the purely natural order of things. The fallacy lies in applying a version of the second law, which is applicable only to isolated systems, to a living organism, which is very much an *open* thermodynamic system. In order to survive, all living creatures must have a constant influx of high-free-energy compounds, and must be able to get rid of a steady stream of entropy in the guise of disordered waste products. This continual supply of free energy is mandatory if the high level of organization of a living cell is to be maintained. Turn a living organism into a closed system by sealing it into an airtight steel coffin, and you will see how quickly it runs down.

The presumed paradox can be enlarged by one step. In view of the second law, how could such a highly organized, low-entropy phenomenon as life ever have evolved on Earth? How can we maintain that the Earth is "running down," when the past three billion years have seen a progression from simple chemical compounds to *Homo sapiens*

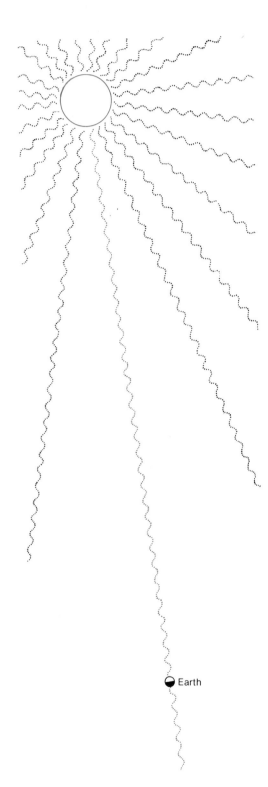

The Earth-Sun thermodynamic system. All of our energy comes from the Sun, but the Earth intercepts only one part in two billion of the Sun's radiant energy. This minute fraction is the thermodynamic mainspring for all activity on Earth.

and his neighbors? The fallacy is the same. The Earth is no more an isolated thermodynamic system than is a single individual. The Earth intercepts only a minute fraction of the energy radiated by the sun (approximately one part in two billion), but this energy is enough to keep the entire terrestrial clockwork running. When the sun dies, the Earth dies with it.

For all chemical and physical processes, the ultimate driving force is the same: free energy, G. For localized mechanical processes ΔS is negligible and ΔH is all-important. For isolated systems, including our entire universe, ΔH must be zero by definition and ΔS is crucial. These, however, are only two extremes of the generally applicable relationship $\Delta G = \Delta H - T\Delta S$.

QUESTIONS

1. In what way do energy (or enthalpy) and entropy considerations affect the melting of ice?

2. What is a spontaneous reaction? Are spontaneous reactions always fast?

3. What effect does a catalyst have on a spontaneous reaction?

4. What is an exothermic reaction? Are spontaneous reactions always exothermic?

5. What are the molecular interpretations of heat and kinetic energy in a solid? In what sense is the conversion of kinetic energy into heat a creation of disorder?

6. Other factors being equal, is a spontaneous reaction favored, or disfavored, by the uptake of heat by the participating molecules?

7. Other factors being equal, is a spontaneous reaction favored, or disfavored, by the creating of order in the products?

8. When both heat and order change during a reaction, what combination of them is the controlling factor in favoring or disfavoring spontaneity?

9. What is the thermodynamic quantity that measures heat in a process carried out at constant overall pressure?

10. What is the thermodynamic quantity that measures the degree of disorder?

11. How is entropy related to the number of different microscopic ways of building a given macroscopically observable situation?

12. Why should there be more microscopic ways of constructing a gas than a solid from the same molecules?

13. How many different ways are there of building a perfect crystal at absolute zero? What does this tell us about the entropy of the solid at absolute zero? Why is the entropy not the same once the solid at absolute zero is warmed a few degrees?

14. How does the entropy change when a solid is melted? Using data in Appendix 2, give an example other than those used in this chapter.

15. How does entropy change when a liquid is vaporized? Give an example other than those used in this chapter.

16. How does entropy change when a solid is dissolved in a liquid? Why is this different from what happens when a gas dissolves in a liquid?

17. Why should a decreased spacing between quantum levels as the mass of a molecule increases lead to a greater entropy?

18. Why should covalently bonded solids have smaller entropy per mole than close-packed metals?

19. In what general way can entropy be correlated with mechanical strength of a solid? Why should this be so? Give an example other than those used in this chapter.

20. Why is the difference between enthalpy change and absolute temperature times the entropy change called a "free" energy? Why would the term "free" not be appropriate for the energy measured by H?

21. In the combustion of ethanol, does enthalpy favor the reaction or not? Does entropy favor the reaction?

22. Does enthalpy favor the breakdown of N_2O_5 to NO_2 and O_2? What contribution does entropy make? Is the reaction spontaneous?

23. When glucose is burned, how does the heat given off compare with the total energy that can be harnessed to do useful work? Why the discrepancy and where does it come from?

24. In what sense is free energy stored in molecules of ATP? How is this stored energy released for use later?

25. How is entropy related to time? What happens to entropy in an isolated system? How could the entropy–time relationship be used to establish a common-sense definition of "positive" time flow?

26. In view of the statements made about increasing disorder in this chapter, how do living organisms maintain a state of high order?

PROBLEMS

1. Which would have the greater entropy:
   (a) a packaged deck of cards or the cards spread on a table?
   (b) an assembled automobile or the unassembled parts needed to make an automobile?
   (c) carbon dioxide, water, and minerals, or the tree that grows from them?

2. In each of the following pairs of states which state has the higher entropy:
   (a) a mole of liquid water or a mole of water vapor at 1 atm pressure and 25°C?
   (b) five pennies on a tabletop showing four heads and a tail, or showing three heads and two tails?
   (c) 100 g of liquid H_2O or 100 g of liquid D_2O?
   (d) 100 g of liquid H_2O and 100 g of liquid D_2O in separate beakers, or the 200 g mixture of the two?
   (e) a mole of gaseous CO_2 or a mole of CO_2 in the form of carbonated water?

3. Predict the sign of the entropy change in the following reactions:
   (a) $2CO(g) + O_2(g) \rightarrow 2CO_2(g)$
   (b) $Mg(s) + Cl_2(g) \rightarrow MgCl_2(s)$
   (c) $Al(s) \rightarrow Al(l)$
   (d) $I_2(s) \rightarrow I_2(g)$
   (e) $CH_4(g) + 2O_2(g) \rightarrow CO_2(g) + 2H_2O(l)$

4. Calculate the entropy changes of the following chemical reactions, all at $298°K$:
   (a) $Ba(s) + \frac{1}{2}O_2(g) \rightarrow BaO(s)$
   (b) $BaCO_3(s) \rightarrow BaO(s) + CO_2(g)$
   (c) $Br_2(g) \rightarrow 2Br(g)$
   (d) $H_2(g) + Br_2(l) \rightarrow 2HBr(g)$
   Explain the sign of each of the entropy changes by qualitatively comparing the freedom of motion, or molecular disorder, that characterize reactants and products.

5. Why would the entropy increase in the reaction $Br_2(l) + Cl_2(g) \rightarrow 2BrCl(g)$?

6. Metal rod A is hot at one end and cold at the other; rod B has the same absolute heat content but has a uniform temperature. Which rod has the greater entropy?

7. Calculate the change in entropy, ΔS^0, for the reaction $S(s) + O_2(g) \rightarrow SO_2(g)$, given $\Delta G^0 = -71.79$ kcal mole^{-1} and data in Appendix 2.

8. Using the data in Appendix 2, calculate ΔS^0 in two different ways for the reaction $\frac{1}{2}H_2(g) + \frac{1}{2}Cl_2(g) \rightarrow HCl(g)$.

9. For the reaction $2Ag(s) + Br_2(l) \rightarrow 2AgBr(s)$ ($25°C$, 1 atm), $\Delta H^0 = -47.6$ kcal mole^{-1} and $\Delta G^0 = -45.8$ kcal mole^{-1}.
   (a) Calculate the entropy change, ΔS^0, in e.u., for the reaction.
   (b) What does this value of ΔS^0 tell you about the relative degree of order in the reactants and products?

10. The reaction $2H_2(g) + O_2(g) \rightarrow 2H_2O(g)$ proceeds spontaneously even though there is an increase in order within the system. How can this be?

11. Calculate the standard free energy change for the reaction

    $Fe_2O_3(s) + 3C(graphite) \rightarrow 2Fe(s) + 3CO(g)$

    Is this reaction spontaneous under standard conditions? What contribution (in kcal mole^{-1}) is made by enthalpy and by entropy? Verify the relationship $\Delta G^0 = \Delta H^0 - T\Delta S^0$.

12. What is the standard free energy change at $25°C$ for the reaction $Cl_2(g) + I_2(g) \rightarrow 2ICl(g)$? What are the relative contributions of enthalpy and entropy to the reaction? Which effect is more important? Is the reaction spontaneous?

13. Calculate ΔG^0 at $25°C$ for the following reactions, using data in Appendix 2.
    (a) $2NaF(s) + Cl_2(g) \rightarrow 2NaCl(s) + F_2(g)$
    (b) $PbO_2(s) + 2Zn(s) \rightarrow Pb(s) + 2ZnO(s)$

14. In view of your answers to Problem 13, comment on (a) the likelihood of obtaining $F_2(g)$ if you treat NaF with Cl_2, and (b) the use of zinc to reduce PbO_2 to the metal.

15. Arrange the following substances in order of increasing entropy: $N_2O_4(g)$, $Na(s)$, $NaCl(s)$, $Br_2(l)$, $Br_2(g)$.

16. Consider the reaction $CH_4(g) + 2O_2(g) \rightarrow CO_2(g) + 2H_2O(l)$.
    (a) According to the calculated ΔG^0, does this reaction tend to occur spontaneously?
    (b) How do you account for the fact that CH_4 and O_2 can exist in contact indefinitely at room temperature without detectable reaction?

17. What is the free energy change for the conversion of diamond into graphite under standard conditions? In view of your answer, why don't the diamonds in diamond rings change into lumps of graphite?

18. Ammonia reacts with HCl at 25°C to produce ammonium chloride. What is the standard free energy change for the reaction? What is the standard enthalpy change? Use these two quantities to calculate the standard entropy change, and compare your answer with the one obtained directly from third-law entropies in Appendix 2. Give a physical explanation for the sign of the entropy change.

19. Calculate the standard free energy for the reaction producing acetylene from hydrogen gas and graphite:

    $$2C(graphite) + H_2(g) \rightarrow HC\!\!=\!\!CH(g)$$

    Is this reaction spontaneous? How might such a reaction be made to occur in spite of the ΔG^0 value?

20. Calculate the change in free energy, enthalpy, and entropy at 25°C for the reaction $2Ag(s) + Hg_2Cl_2(s) \rightarrow 2AgCl(s) + 2Hg(l)$. Verify that $\Delta G^0 = \Delta H^0 - T\Delta S^0$. Is this reaction endothermic? Is it spontaneous? What effects do enthalpy and entropy have on spontaneity in this reaction? Which factor predominates? Explain the entropy effect on molecular grounds.

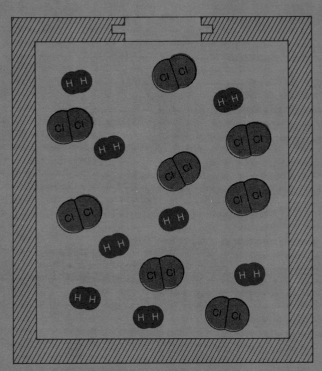

1 Hydrogen gas (H$_2$) and chlorine gas (Cl$_2$) . . .

2 . . . exposed to light will trigger . . .

3 . . . an explosion, after which there will be . . .

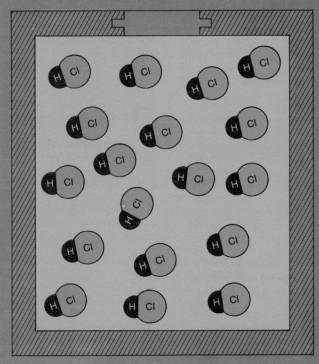

4 . . . only molecules of hydrogen chloride (HCl).

◀ *The explosive reaction of hydrogen and chlorine gases is fast and virtually complete*

CHAPTER 14

Chemical Equilibrium

In Chapter 13 we were concerned with the question: Will a given reaction ever take place spontaneously, even if one waits forever? The answer was that any reaction that leads to a *lower* free energy will occur spontaneously. Any reaction that requires an *increase* in free energy will not; it will be spontaneous in the reverse direction instead. Now we come to a more difficult but very practical question in this and the following chapter: Granted that a given reaction is spontaneous, how far will it go, and will it take place within a reasonable time? What factors determine the *rates* of chemical reactions?

Some chemical reactions appear to go essentially to completion, ending with products and an undetectable or negligible amount of reactants. Some but not all of these reactions also are very fast (e.g., explosions). Other reactions stop short of completion and remain a mixture of reactants and products after all visible chemical change is over. Still other reactions do not appear to take place at all within a reasonable time, even though their calculated free energy change is quite negative.

HCl synthesis is an example of the first kind of reaction: fast, and apparently complete (see facing page). If hydrogen gas and chlorine gas are mixed in a container with a window and kept in the dark, no reaction will occur. But light will trigger an explosion:

$$H_2(g) + Cl_2(g) \rightarrow 2HCl(g)$$
$$\Delta G^0 = -45.54 \text{ kcal per 2 moles of HCl}$$

After the explosion almost no detectable quantities of H_2 and Cl_2 will remain. The large negative free energy change indicates that the reaction should be spontaneous, and the light-triggered explosion shows that this is so. Then why is there no reaction in the dark? The answer is that the reaction in the dark is still spontaneous, but is so *slow* that we do not notice any changes.

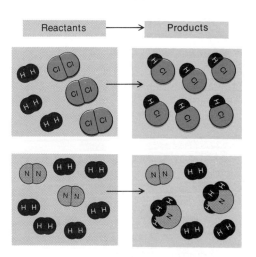

In some reactions, such as HCl formation, virtually all the reactants are changed into products (top). In others, such as the formation of ammonia from H_2 and N_2 at 450°K, the products remain a mixture, in this case of H_2, N_2, and NH_3 gases.

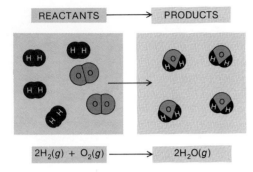

REACTANTS → PRODUCTS

$$2H_2(g) + O_2(g) \longrightarrow 2H_2O(g)$$

When hydrogen and oxygen react, the conversion to H_2O is essentially complete.

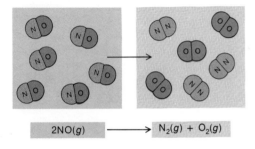

$$2NO(g) \longrightarrow N_2(g) + O_2(g)$$

Nitric oxide decomposes to N_2 and O_2 very slowly.

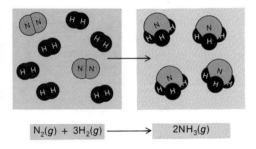

$$N_2(g) + 3H_2(g) \longrightarrow 2NH_3(g)$$

At room temperature ammonia is formed very slowly from N_2 and H_2.

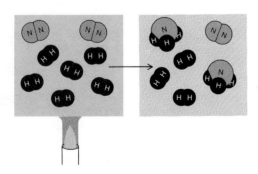

With heat, ammonia is formed faster, but the reaction is less complete at equilibrium, with less NH_3 and more N_2 and H_2 present.

Hydrogen and oxygen gases behave similarly. The reaction

$$2H_2(g) + O_2(g) \rightarrow 2H_2O(g)$$

$$\Delta G^0 = -109.3 \text{ kcal per 2 moles of } H_2O$$

has a large negative free energy change and therefore is highly spontaneous. Yet we can allow a mixture of hydrogen and oxygen to sit for years without seeing an appreciable reaction. We have only to bring a lighted match up to the mixture, however, for a vivid demonstration of how intrinsically spontaneous the reaction is. The same effect can be produced by a catalyst such as platinum black, a finely divided form of metallic platinum that has a large surface area.

One of the villains in automotive smog is nitric oxide, NO. If we calculate the free energy of decomposition of NO,

$$2NO(g) \rightarrow N_2(g) + O_2(g)$$

$$\Delta G^0 = -41.4 \text{ kcal per 2 moles of NO}$$

we arrive at the conclusion that the reaction should be spontaneous. The breakdown of NO to harmless atmospheric gases should be quite complete. Yet any inhabitant of the Los Angeles basin can tell you that this is only wishful thinking. Oxides of nitrogen are among the most difficult components of the smog problem. They do not break down to N_2 and O_2 at an appreciable rate, although breakdown is thermodynamically spontaneous. By analogy with the water reaction, you might expect that a catalyst could be found that would speed up the decomposition of NO, and this is true.

The other factor that we have mentioned that speeds up reaction is temperature. Changing the temperature can do more than just accelerate a reaction; it also can affect the nature of the products. As an example, the synthesis of ammonia is important as a means of fixing atmospheric nitrogen for use in fertilizers and explosives:

$$N_2(g) + 3H_2(g) \rightarrow 2NH_3(g)$$

$$\Delta G^0 = -7.95 \text{ kcal per 2 moles of } NH_3$$

If the reaction is run at room temperature, the final mixture is almost entirely NH_3, with very little N_2 and H_2 left. A disadvantage is that the reaction is extremely slow, but it can be speeded up with an iron–manganese catalyst. Trying to accomplish the same result by raising the temperature leads only to trouble, since at $450°K$, the product is no longer virtually pure NH_3, but is a mixture of N_2, H_2, and NH_3 in roughly equal proportions. The standard free energy change at this temperature is zero. (The standard starting condition of 1 atm partial pressure for each gas is, in fact, the equilibrium condition at $450°K$.) Even worse, at $1000°K$ the standard free energy change is $+29.6$ kcal (compared with -7.95 kcal at $298°K$), and almost no ammonia is formed.

From these examples of HCl, H_2O, NO, and NH_3 reactions, we can make two observations:

1. Not all chemical reactions go to completion. Even after an infinitely long time, some systems remain mixtures of reactants and products.

Preparing for battle PHASE I

2. Some reactions that are highly spontaneous by free energy criteria do not proceed at a measurable rate. Catalysis or heat sometimes can help.

We will explain the reasons for both of these observations in this chapter and the next, which will focus on two main ideas: *chemical equilibrium* and the *rates* of chemical reactions.

CRABAPPLES AND EQUILIBRIUM

Let us introduce the idea of chemical equilibrium by an analogy, seemingly far-fetched at first sight, but actually mathematically correct. Imagine that a crabapple tree sits on the dividing line between two homes, one inhabited by a crotchety old man, and the other by a father who has told his young son to go out and rid the back yard of crabapples. The boy quickly realizes that the easiest way to dispose of the crabapples is to throw them into the neighboring yard. He does so, arousing the ire of the old man. The boy and the man start throwing crabapples back and forth across the fence as fast as they can. Who will win?

The battle is outlined in five phases, as shown on this page and on the next four pages. Assuming that the boy is more energetic and agile

THE GREAT CRABAPPLE WAR between man (M) and boy (B). See text for the complete history of the conflict.

321

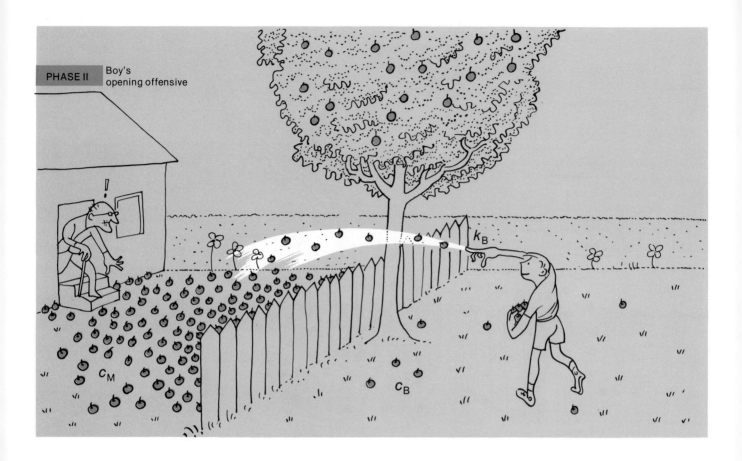

PHASE II Boy's opening offensive

k_B

c_M

c_B

Rate$_B$ is the rate at which the boy throws apples across the fence.

k_B is the speed with which the boy collects apples off the ground.

c_B is the concentration of apples in the boy's yard.

rate$_B$ = $k_B c_B$

than the old man, you might think at first that the conflict would end with all of the apples on the old man's side (Phases I and II). It is true that with equal numbers of crabapples on either side, the boy will throw apples across the fence faster than the old man can return them. But this only means that apples will become more plentiful on the old man's side, and easier to reach. They will become scarcer on the boy's side, and require more running around to locate. Eventually a standoff, or *equilibrium*, will be reached, in which the number of apples crossing the fence is the same in both directions. The old man will throw less quickly but will have less trouble finding apples (Phase III); the boy will throw more rapidly but will waste time scurrying around hunting for the relatively few crabapples on his side (Phase IV). The ratio of apples on the two sides of the fence ultimately will be determined by the relative agility of the two combatants, but all of the apples will *not* end up on one side (Phase V).

We can express the rate at which the old man throws apples by

$$\text{rate}_M = k_M c_M$$

The rate is measured in apples per second across the fence, and c_M is the concentration of apples on the man's side of the fence in apples per square foot of ground. The rate constant, k_M, has units of square feet

322

per second:

$$\text{rate}_\text{M} = k_\text{M} \times c_\text{M}$$

$$\frac{\text{apples}}{\text{second}} = \frac{\text{ft}^2}{\text{second}} \times \frac{\text{apples}}{\text{ft}^2}$$

The value of k_M expresses the agility of the old man, and his speed in covering the territory on his side of the fence.

The rate at which the boy throws apples back across the fence is given by

$$\text{rate}_\text{B} = k_\text{B} c_\text{B}$$

in which c_B is the concentration of apples in the boy's yard, and k_B is the rate constant, or agility constant, which tells how fast the boy gets around on his side of the fence, in square feet per second. Since we have assumed that the boy is livelier than the man, k_B is greater than k_M.

If the boy had cleaned up his yard completely before the old man came out, then as the battle began, rate_M would be greater than rate_B, and there would be a net flow of apples to the boy's side. His agility would do him no good if there were no apples on his side to pick up. Conversely, if the battle had begun with equal concentrations of apples on each side, then rate_B would have been greater than rate_M because

Rate_M is the rate at which the man throws apples across the fence.

k_M is the speed with which the man collects apples off the ground.

c_M is the concentration of apples in the man's yard.

$$\text{rate}_\text{M} = k_\text{M} c_\text{M}$$

At equilibrium, $\text{rate}_\text{M} = \text{rate}_\text{B}$
$$\text{or}$$
$$k_\text{M} c_\text{M} = k_\text{B} c_\text{B}$$

323

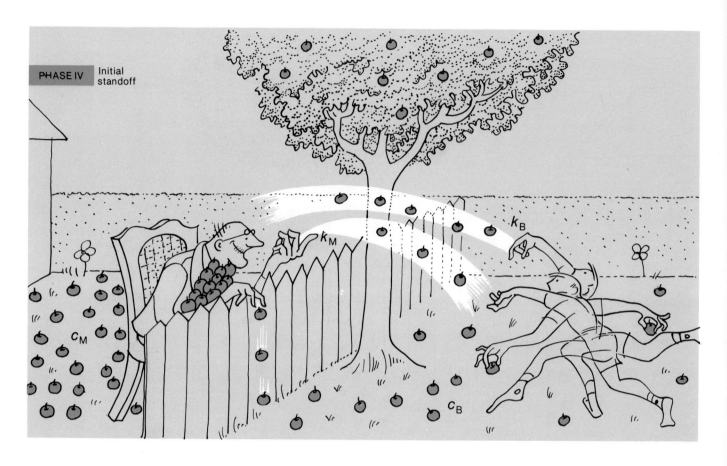

EQUILIBRIUM Phases IV and V

$$k_\text{M} \quad \times \quad c_\text{M} \quad = \quad k_\text{B} \quad \times \quad c_\text{B}$$

small number	large number	large number	small number

$$\underbrace{\qquad\qquad}_{\text{rate}_\text{M}} \qquad \underbrace{\qquad\qquad}_{\text{rate}_\text{B}}$$

or

$$\frac{k_\text{B}}{k_\text{M}} = \frac{c_\text{M}}{c_\text{B}} = K_\text{eq} = \textbf{equilibrium constant}$$

the agility constant k_B is greater than k_M. With the same number of apples at their disposal, the boy always can do better than the old man because he gets around faster. In either case, a neutral observer would have found to his surprise that the battle eventually settled down into a stalemate, or equilibrium in which rate$_\text{M}$ = rate$_\text{B}$, at a point where the extra apples on the old man's side just compensated for the extra agility of the boy. The rates of throwing apples across the fence in both directions then would be the same:

$$\text{rate}_\text{M} = \text{rate}_\text{B}$$

$$k_\text{M}c_\text{M} = k_\text{B}c_\text{B}$$

The ratio of these standoff, or steady-state, concentrations, will tell us the relative agilities of the man and boy:

$$\frac{c_\text{M}}{c_\text{B}} = \frac{k_\text{B}}{k_\text{M}}$$

This ratio of apples in the two yards when the stalemate is reached will be the same no matter what the starting conditions—whether all of the apples began in the boy's or the man's yard, or were shared between them at the beginning. The *ratio* of apples in the two yards at equilibrium also will be the same no matter how many apples were involved—

324

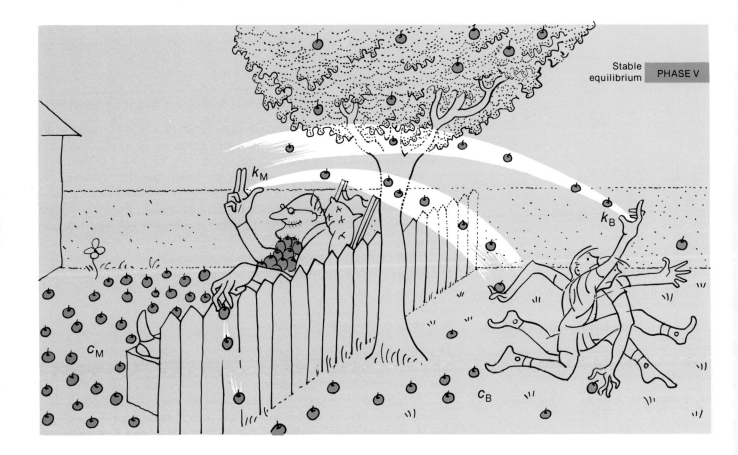

a dozen or a thousand (as long as we can rule out fatigue). Doubling the number of apples in the war doubles the rate at which the boy can find and throw them, but also doubles the rate at which the old man can return them. The two effects cancel out in the ratio.

Such a ratio, which is independent of starting conditions or of absolute numbers, is called the equilibrium constant, K_{eq}:

$$K_{eq} = \frac{k_B}{k_M} = \frac{c_M}{c_B}$$

If we know the value of this equilibrium constant, either from past battles or from knowledge of the agility constants, k_M and k_B, then after a standoff has been reached, we can find out how many apples are on the old man's side merely by counting the apples on the boy's side and doing some simple arithmetic.

Example. The boy is twice as fast at covering territory as the old man. At stalemate, the boy's yard is littered with three apples per square foot. What is the density of apples on the old man's side?

Solution. From the conditions of the problem,

$$K_{eq} = \frac{k_B}{k_M} = 2 \qquad \text{and} \qquad c_B = 3 \text{ apples ft}^{-2}$$

325

Then

$$2 = \frac{c_M}{3}$$

or

$$c_M = 6 \text{ apples ft}^{-2}$$

The old man has six apples per square foot on his side at equilibrium.

The stalemate is an *equilibrium* between two opposing apple-throwing processes. At equilibrium the throwing of apples back and forth obviously has not stopped, yet if we were keeping a tally only of the number of apples on either side, we would see that no more net changes were taking place. This is illustrated by the Phase V stalemate. The concentration of apples on the two sides of the fence will not change any further until one or the other combatant gets tired and begins to slow down.

The crabapple analogy is a mathematically correct treatment of the simple reaction in which one substance changes into another:

$$A \rightleftharpoons B$$

or

$$A \rightarrow B \quad \text{and} \quad B \rightarrow A$$

In terms of the analogy, A and B represent apples on the man's or the boy's side of the fence, and the chemical reaction is the throwing of apples from one side to the other.

Every chemical process is reversible on the molecular level. If A molecules can change into B molecules, then B must be able to change into A, although perhaps at a different rate. If k_f and k_r are the rate constants for the forward and reverse reactions, then as in the crabapple analogy,

forward rate = forward rate constant × concentration of reactants
$$\text{rate}_f = k_f\,[A]$$

reverse rate = reverse rate constant × concentration of products
$$\text{rate}_r = k_r\,[B]$$

$[A]$ and $[B]$ are the concentrations of molecules of A and B. Instead of units of apples per square foot, we measure molecular concentrations in molecules per cubic centimeter, or more conveniently, moles of molecules per liter (1 mole = 6.022×10^{23} molecules and 1 liter = 1000 cm^3). If overall reaction rates are expressed in moles of substance reacting per second, then the rate constants, k_f and k_r, have units of liters per second:

$$\text{rate}_f = k_f \times [A]$$
$$\frac{\text{moles}}{\text{second}} = \frac{\text{liters}}{\text{second}} \times \frac{\text{moles}}{\text{liter}}$$

These rate constants again describe how fast each of the forward and reverse reactions "cover the territory" that the molecules occupy.

After the forward and reverse reactions proceed for a suitable length of time, the concentrations of A and B will settle down to a fixed ratio, which will not depend on the starting conditions or the absolute number of A and B molecules present. This is the condition of equilib-

A → B is the forward reaction converting reactants to products.

B → A is the reverse reaction, re-forming reactants from products.

rate_f = rate of the forward reaction in moles per second.

rate_r = rate of the reverse reaction in moles per second.

k_f = rate constant for the forward reaction from A to B in liters per second

k_r = rate constant for the reverse reaction from B to A in liters per second

$[A]$ = concentration of reactants in moles per liter

$[B]$ = concentration of products in moles per liter

rium, at which forward and reverse rates are exactly in balance:

$$\text{rate}_f = \text{rate}_r$$

$$K_{eq} = \frac{k_f}{k_r} = \frac{[B]}{[A]}$$

Equilibrium does not imply that all chemical activity has stopped, only that forward and reverse reactions are proceeding at the same rate, so no further net change in the amounts of reactants and products occurs.

EQUILIBRIUM AND SECOND-ORDER PROCESSES

Very few chemical reactions are spontaneous decompositions of molecules, with first-order kinetics and equilibrium as in the crabapple war. First-order kinetics are encountered more commonly in radiochemistry and the decay of atomic nuclei. Most chemical reactions occur when two or more molecules or ions collide, so the rates of reaction depend simultaneously on the concentrations of more than one substance. In the hydrogen–iodine reaction,

$$H_2(g) + I_2(g) \rightleftarrows 2HI(g)$$

one molecule of hydrogen gas must interact with one molecule of iodine vapor for chemical reaction to take place. If the interaction were a simple collision of two molecules (we will discuss the actual mechanism in the next chapter), then doubling the concentration of either H_2 or I_2 would double the rate of reaction, and doubling both at the same time would make the collisions, and hence the reaction, occur four times as fast. The rate of forward reaction then would be given by

$$\text{rate}_f = k_f\,[H_2]\,[I_2]$$

This expression says that the rate of forward reaction is proportional to each of the reactant concentrations independently, with a propor-

The rate of reaction depends on the rate of collision between reacting molecules. If the H_2 reactant molecule concentration is doubled and the I_2 concentration is tripled, then formation of HI will take place six times as fast.

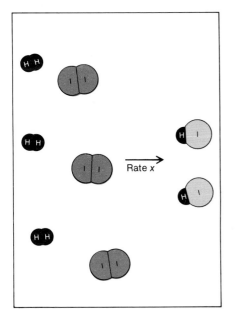

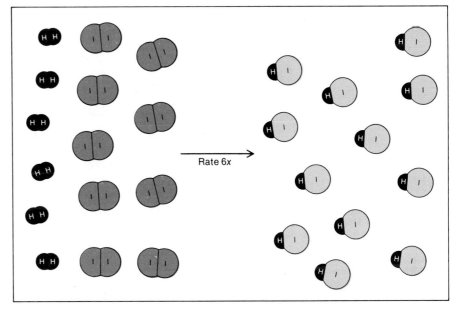

327

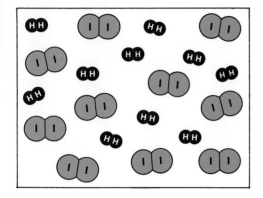

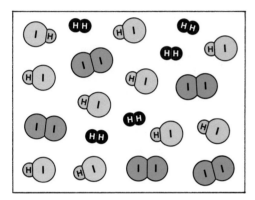

EQUILIBRIUM

Equilibrium between molecules of H_2, I_2, and HI. In the top drawing, 1 mole each of H_2 and I_2 are placed in a 10-liter tank at 448°C. After a few hours half the H_2 and I_2 molecules have formed HI (center) and the reaction is continuing. Equilibrium eventually is reached (bottom) with 0.22 mole of H_2, 0.22 mole of I_2, and 1.56 moles of HI. No further change occurs in the composition of the gas mixture.

tionality constant, k_f. If the rate is measured in moles per second, and concentrations are in moles per liter, then k_f has units of liter² mole⁻¹ sec⁻¹. These rather strange units for k_f mean that as one type of molecule sweeps through the available volume, colliding with other molecules, its rate of sweep can be expressed in liters per second, per unit of concentration (moles per liter) for that type of molecule.

The rate equation for the hydrogen–iodine reaction indicates that if the hydrogen concentration is doubled, and the iodine vapor concentration is trebled, the reaction will proceed $2 \times 3 = 6$ times as fast. If the hydrogen concentration is halved, but the iodine concentration is doubled, the rate will be unchanged. Although only half as many H_2 molecules are available for reaction, collisions of any one of them with I_2 molecules will be twice as frequent, so the effects of the two concentration changes will cancel. Since the overall rate depends on the product of two concentrations, this is a second-order reaction.

It is a little trickier to see why the reverse reaction, decomposition of HI into H_2 and I_2, also should be a second-order process, proportional to the square of the HI concentration:

$$2HI \rightarrow H_2 + I_2$$

$$\text{rate}_r = k_r[HI][HI]$$

$$= k_r[HI]^2$$

An isolated molecule of HI does not split apart spontaneously into H and I atoms, which wait until two more H and I atoms drift by before becoming H_2 and I_2. Far too much energy would be required to pull the HI molecule apart; and once done, the hyper-reactive H and I atoms would promptly recombine. Reaction takes place only when *two* molecules of HI collide with enough energy to change partners and end as H_2 and I_2. The chance that any one HI molecule will react within the next second depends on how many other HI molecules there are to collide with it, or on [HI]. The overall rate of reaction of all HI molecules depends on how many molecules there are, and on the chance that any one will react:

$$\text{rate}_r = \text{(No. of HI to react)} \times \text{(likelihood of reaction per HI)}$$

$$\text{rate}_r = [HI] \times k_r[HI]$$

$$\text{rate}_r = k_r[HI][HI]$$

$$= k_r[HI]^2$$

Doubling the concentration of HI molecules doubles the number of molecules available for collision, and independently doubles the rate at which each one collides with a neighbor. The result is a second-power dependence, and a second-order reaction.

At equilibrium, synthesis and breakdown of HI are exactly in balance. The forward and reverse reaction rates are equal, and

$$k_f[H_2][I_2] = k_r[HI]^2$$

$$K_{eq} = \frac{k_f}{k_r} = \frac{[HI]^2}{[H_2][I_2]}$$

328

This is the equilibrium-constant expression for the HI reaction. It tells us that regardless of whether the absolute concentrations are high or low, at equilibrium the ratio of products to reactants will be the same. If we add more of one component, or remove some of another, either the forward or the reverse reaction will be favored; the separate concentrations will adjust, and when equilibrium is restored after the disturbance, the K_{eq} ratio will be the same as before. K_{eq} varies with temperature, but at a given temperature it is entirely independent of the individual concentrations of reactants and products.

The illustrations in the left and right margins emphasize the fact that the conditions of equilibrium are the same no matter from which side they are approached. Starting from either pure H_2 and I_2 or pure HI, the reaction eventually will reach equilibrium at the same ratio of products to reactants given by K_{eq}.

The proof of the validity of all of the foregoing discussion of collisions and first- and second-order processes, of course, lies in its agreement with actual chemical experiments. The HI reaction was one of the first chemical equilibrium systems to be studied. The table below shows some data collected by Max Bodenstein in 1893. Bodenstein set up a series of experiments with different amounts of reactants and products, permitted the reactions to come to equilibrium, and then measured the concentrations of H_2, I_2, and HI in moles per liter. His results are not particularly accurate by present-day standards, but even so they demonstrate that the product-to-reactant ratio, $[HI]^2/[H_2][I_2]$, is constant, whereas the simpler ratio, $[HI]/[H_2][I_2]$, is far from constant as concentrations are changed.

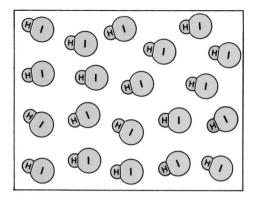

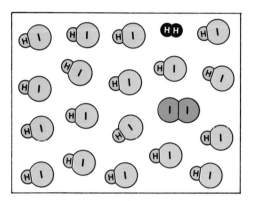

EQUILIBRIUM

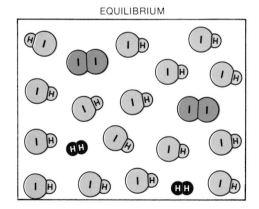

Experimental measurements for the HI reaction,
$H_2(g) + I_2(g) \rightleftarrows 2HI(g)$

Measured concentrations[a]			$\dfrac{[HI]}{[H_2][I_2]}$	$\dfrac{[HI]^2}{[H_2][I_2]} = K_{eq}$	Deviation from average K_{eq}
$[H_2]$	$[I_2]$	$[HI]$			
18.14	0.41	19.38	2.60	50.50	−0.04
10.96	1.89	32.61	1.57	51.34	+0.70
4.57	8.69	46.28	1.16	53.93	+3.39
2.23	23.95	51.30	0.96	49.27	−1.27
0.86	67.90	53.40	0.91	48.83	−1.71
0.65	87.29	52.92	0.93	49.35	−1.19
				6)303.22	6)8.20
				50.54	1.36

Average $K_{eq} = 50.54$ Mean deviation $= \dfrac{1.36}{50.54} \times 100 = 2.7\%$

[a] All measurements were made at 448°C in a sulfur-vapor constant-temperature bath. Concentrations are in moles per liter $\times 10^3$ (e.g., the first H_2 concentration is 18.14×10^{-3} mole per liter).

Equilibrium approached from the other side. In the top picture, the same tank is filled with 2 moles of HI. After a time, measurable quantities of H_2 and I_2 are present (center). When equilibrium is reached and the composition of the tank becomes constant, the same equilibrium concentrations are observed as before, 0.22 mole each of H_2 and I_2, and 1.56 moles of HI. The equilibrium conditions are the same, no matter what the direction of approach.

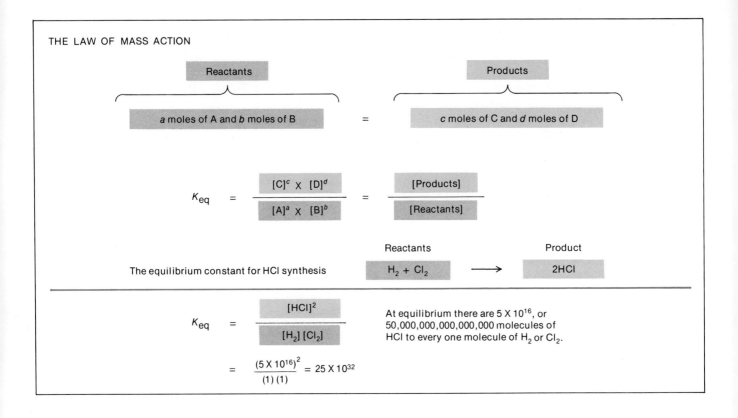

THE LAW OF MASS ACTION

Reactants

Products

a moles of A and b moles of B = c moles of C and d moles of D

$$K_{eq} = \frac{[C]^c \times [D]^d}{[A]^a \times [B]^b} = \frac{[Products]}{[Reactants]}$$

The equilibrium constant for HCl synthesis

Reactants

$H_2 + Cl_2 \longrightarrow$

Product

$2HCl$

$$K_{eq} = \frac{[HCl]^2}{[H_2][Cl_2]}$$

At equilibrium there are 5×10^{16}, or 50,000,000,000,000,000 molecules of HCl to every one molecule of H_2 or Cl_2.

$$= \frac{(5 \times 10^{16})^2}{(1)(1)} = 25 \times 10^{32}$$

THE GENERAL EQUILIBRIUM-CONSTANT EXPRESSION

For a general reaction, in which a moles of substance A and b moles of B react to form c moles of C and d moles of D,

$$aA + bB \rightleftarrows cC + dD$$

the equilibrium-constant expression is

$$K_{eq} = \frac{[C]^c[D]^d}{[A]^a[B]^b}$$

This is the *law of mass action*.

Concentrations can be measured in any terms that express the relative numbers of molecules per unit volume. In solutions, concentrations usually are given in *molarity*, or moles per liter, c_j. This is indicated by a subscript C to the equilibrium constant: K_C. Gases sometimes are measured in moles per liter also, but more often are measured in *mole fractions*, X_j, or in *partial pressures*, p_j. (The subscript j simply refers to any species.) The equilibrium constants using these units are indicated by K_X and K_P.

The mole fraction of the jth component of a gas mixture, X_j, is the number of moles of that particular gas, divided by the total number of moles of all gases present:

$$X_j = \frac{n_j}{n_1 + n_2 + n_3 + n_4 + n_5 + \cdots}$$

Our atmosphere has one molecule of O_2 for every four molecules of N_2;

330

thus the mole fraction of oxygen gas is

$$X_{O_2} = \frac{1}{1+4} = 0.20$$

and that of nitrogen is

$$X_{N_2} = \frac{4}{1+4} = 0.80$$

The sum of mole fractions of all the gases in a mixture, of course, must be exactly one.

Exercise. From the abundance table in Chapter 7, what are the concentrations of H and He atoms in the entire universe, expressed in mole fractions?

Answer. $X_H = 0.928$ $X_{He} = 0.072$

The other common concentration unit for gases is partial pressure, p_j. In a mixture of gases, each gas molecule moves independently, and every gas in the mixture behaves as if it were alone in the same volume. In a mixture of gases, if one molecule out of every three is a Cl_2 molecule, then the chlorine gas acts as if it alone occupied the same volume with the same total number of Cl_2 molecules, or one third the total pressure. If the total pressure is 1 atm, then the partial pressure of Cl_2 gas is one third of an atmosphere. In any gas mixture the partial pressure of each component is its mole fraction times the total pressure from all gases:

$$p_j = X_j \times P_T$$

Thus oxygen gas in our atmosphere has a partial pressure of 0.20 atm and nitrogen gas has a partial pressure of 0.80 atm. The sum of partial pressures of all components in a mixture must add to give the total pressure of the mixture.

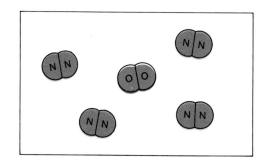

PARTIAL PRESSURE
There are four molecules of N_2 in our atmosphere for each O_2 molecule. Hence the mole fraction of N_2 is 0.80 and that of O_2 is 0.20. Nitrogen gas contributes 0.80 atm partial pressure and oxygen gas contributes 0.20 atm partial pressure to the total pressure of 1 atm.

EXAMPLES OF EQUILIBRIUM CONSTANTS

Equilibrium-constant calculations involving gases quickly become more complicated than the ideas they were intended to illustrate, and we will defer most equilibrium calculations to the discussion of aqueous solutions in Chapter 16. However, it is useful to look briefly at the equilibrium constants for some of the reactions discussed previously in this chapter. Along the way we will encounter some of the fundamental ideas about manipulating equilibrium-constant expressions.

HCl Synthesis

The equilibrium-constant expression for the HCl reaction has the same form as that of HI synthesis:

$$H_2(g) + Cl_2(g) \rightleftharpoons 2HCl(g) \qquad \Delta G^0 = -45.54 \text{ kcal per 2 moles of HCl}$$

$$K_P = \frac{[HCl]^2}{[H_2][Cl_2]}$$

The experimental value of K_{eq} for this reaction is 2.5×10^{33}. Notice that, with equal power of concentration terms in both numerator and denominator, K_{eq} for HCl is a unitless quantity. K_{eq} for this reaction will have the same numerical value whether concentrations are measured in moles per liter, mole fractions, partial pressures, or any other convenient system ($K_{eq} = K_C = K_X = K_P$). This is not always true.

If we begin with equal concentrations of H_2 and Cl_2, then since they react in equal amounts, the concentrations of these two substances always will be equal, $[Cl_2] = [H_2]$, and at equilibrium we can write:

$$\frac{[HCl]^2}{[H_2]^2} = 25 \times 10^{32} \qquad \text{or} \qquad \frac{[HCl]}{[H_2]} = 5.0 \times 10^{16}$$

Equilibrium constant for synthesis of HCl:

$H_2 + Cl_2 \rightleftarrows 2HCl$

$K_P = \dfrac{[HCl]^2}{[H_2][Cl_2]} = 2.5 \times 10^{33}$ **(no units)**

This tells us that equilibrium will not be reached until the ratio of HCl to H_2 (or Cl_2) has risen to 50 million billion to one! It is not surprising that we cannot detect any H_2 or Cl_2 in the products at equilibrium.

So large an equilibrium constant indicates that the reaction starting with equal concentrations of H_2, Cl_2, and HCl should be highly spontaneous, since the reaction has a long way to go before reaching equilibrium. The large negative standard free energy change, $\Delta G^0 = -45.54$ kcal per two moles of HCl, indicates the same thing.

Combustion of H_2

Equilibrium constant for synthesis of H_2O:

$2H_2 + O_2 \rightleftarrows 2H_2O$

$K_P = \dfrac{[H_2O]^2}{[H_2]^2[O_2]} = 1.35 \times 10^{80}$ **atm^{-1}**

The water reaction is even more extreme. The reaction is

$$2H_2(g) + O_2(g) \rightleftarrows 2H_2O(g)$$

$$\Delta G^0 = -109.3 \text{ kcal per 2 moles of } H_2O$$

and the equilibrium-constant expression is

$$K_P = \frac{[H_2O]^2}{[H_2]^2[O_2]} = 1.35 \times 10^{80}$$

Even without putting pencil to paper we can see that there should be infinitesimal amounts of hydrogen and oxygen gases at equilibrium. The equilibrium mixture should be nearly pure water. As the large negative ΔG^0 also indicates, the forward reaction will be very spontaneous.

This equilibrium-constant expression, unlike that for HCl, has different powers of concentration in the numerator and denominator. If concentrations are specified as partial pressures in atmospheres, then K_P will have units of $\text{atm}^2/\text{atm}^3 = \text{atm}^{-1}$. We now must be careful, for the numerical value of K_P given was for these units only:

$$K_P = 1.35 \times 10^{80} \text{ atm}^{-1}$$

If we used this numerical value but expressed concentrations in moles per liter, the results of the calculation would be meaningless.

We could just as well have written the H_2 combustion reaction as

$$H_2(g) + \tfrac{1}{2}O_2(g) \rightleftarrows H_2O(g)$$

$$\Delta G^0 = -54.6 \text{ kcal per mole of } H_2O$$

in which case the equilibrium-constant expression would be

$$K_P = \frac{[H_2O]}{[H_2][O_2]^{\frac{1}{2}}} = 1.16 \times 10^{40} \text{ atm}^{-\frac{1}{2}}$$

If we halve the coefficients of a chemical reaction, we must halve the corresponding free energy change of the reaction, and take the square root of the equilibrium-constant expression (which is the same as halving the exponents). We also must take the square root of the value of the equilibrium constant, K_{eq}. If we double the coefficients of a reaction, we must double the free energy change and square the equilibrium expression and K_{eq}. Whenever you use either equilibrium constants or free energies, you must be careful to be sure that you know the chemical reaction and the concentration units to which the numerical values of K_{eq} apply.

Ammonia Synthesis: Incomplete Reaction

The ammonia synthesis reaction is less extreme than H_2 combustion:

$$3H_2(g) + N_2(g) \rightleftarrows 2NH_3(g)$$

$$\Delta G^0 = -7.95 \text{ kcal per 2 moles of } NH_3$$

The equilibrium constant is not the enormous exponential value that we saw for the HCl and H_2O reactions; it is

$$K_P = \frac{[NH_3]^2}{[H_2]^3[N_2]} = 6.7 \times 10^5 \text{ atm}^{-2} = 670,000 \text{ atm}^{-2}$$

Note how the exponents on each concentration term are related to the number of molecules in the chemical reaction, and how all of the exponents determine the overall units of atm^{-2} for K_P. If concentrations were given in moles per liter instead of atmospheres, the numerical value of the equilibrium constant K would be different.

  The rates of forward and reverse reactions become equal when appreciable amounts of both reactants and products are still present. In our crabapple analogy, the two opponents are more evenly matched in the ammonia reaction, and there is no overwhelming pileup at equilibrium on either side of the fence. The ammonia reaction is not "complete" in the way that the other two reactions are.

Equilibrium constant for synthesis of NH_3:

$$3H_2 + N_2 \rightleftarrows 2NH_3$$

$$K_P = \frac{[NH_3]^2}{[H_2]^3[N_2]} = 670,000 \text{ atm}^{-2} = 6.7 \times 10^5 \text{ atm}^{-2}$$

K_P AND K_C

In the water and ammonia syntheses just discussed, the numbers of molecules of reactants and products in the equation were different, so K_{eq} was not a unitless quantity. The conversion of units from atmospheres to moles per liter is a simple one involving the ideal gas law, $PV = nRT$, which we discussed in Chapter 2. In this expression P is the pressure in atmospheres, V is the volume in liters, n is the number of moles, T is the absolute temperature, and R is the gas constant expressed in units of liter atm per deg per mole:

$$R = 0.08205 \text{ liter atm deg}^{-1} \text{ mole}^{-1}$$

For the jth component in a mixture of gases,

$$p_j V = n_j RT$$

$$p_j = \frac{n_j}{V}RT = c_j RT$$

in which p_j is the partial pressure and c_j is the concentration of the jth gas in moles per liter.

Equilibrium constants with concentrations expressed as partial pressures in atmospheres are designated by K_P, and constants in units of moles per liter are designated by K_C. For the water formation reaction that we have just seen, these constants can be written as

$$K_P = \frac{p_{H_2O}^2}{p_{H_2}^2 \, p_{O_2}} \qquad \text{and} \qquad K_C = \frac{c_{H_2O}^2}{c_{H_2}^2 \, c_{O_2}}$$

To obtain K_C from K_P, one need only substitute $p_j = c_j RT$ for each chemical substance, reactant and product:

$$K_P = \frac{(c_{H_2O} RT)^2}{(c_{H_2} RT)^2 (c_{O_2} RT)} = \frac{c_{H_2O}^2}{c_{H_2}^2 \, c_{O_2}} \times \frac{(RT)^2}{(RT)^2 (RT)}$$

$$= K_C \times \frac{1}{RT}$$

$$K_C = K_P RT = 1.35 \times 10^{80} \text{ atm}^{-1} \times RT \text{ atm (mole/liter)}^{-1}$$

$$K_C = 1.35 \times 10^{80} \times 0.08205 \times 298 \text{ liter mole}^{-1}$$

$$= 3.31 \times 10^{81} \text{ liter mole}^{-1}$$

Exercise. What is K_C for the ammonia reaction, for which $K_P = 670,000$ atm^{-2}?

Answer. $K_C = 402,000,000$ liter^2 mole^{-2}

Only if the number of moles of reactants and products is the same, will K_P and K_C be the same unitless number. In general, if the balanced chemical equation shows an increase of Δn in the number of moles of gas in the products as compared with reactants, then

$$K_P = K_C (RT)^{\Delta n}$$

FACTORS AFFECTING EQUILIBRIUM

Equilibrium represents a balance between opposing reactions. How sensitive is this balance to changes in the conditions of a reaction? What outside perturbations will change the equilibrium state? These are very practical questions if, for example, one is trying to increase the yield of a useful product in a reaction.

The easiest way to perturb a reaction and obtain more products is to remove the products as fast as they are formed. This means that the reaction is kept off-balance and that equilibrium is never achieved. More and more reactants interact in a vain effort to maintain a balance, as products are taken away. For example, NH_3 is quite soluble in water, whereas N_2 and H_2 are only slightly soluble. Therefore washing the ammonia reaction mixture with a spray of water dissolves and removes most of the NH_3, and leaves behind the unused N_2 and H_2 for further reaction. This sort of product removal does not change the actual conditions of equilibrium; it only ensures that more N_2 and H_2 react than

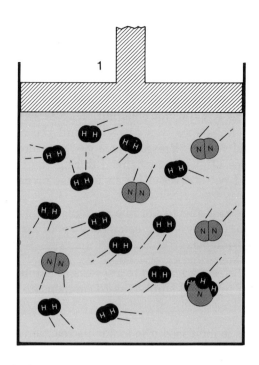

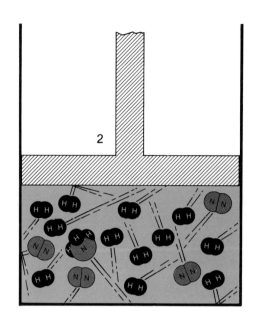

LE CHATELIER'S PRINCIPLE

(1) At initial equilibrium 17 molecules (moles) of gas are present: 12 of H_2, 4 of N_2, and 1 of NH_3.

(2) When the gas is compressed into a smaller volume a stress is created, which is evidenced by a higher pressure.

(3) This stress can be relieved and the pressure reduced if some of the molecules of H_2 and N_2 combine to form more NH_3, since the total number of gas molecules is thereby reduced.

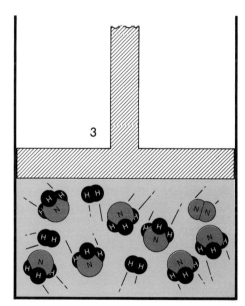

would be the case if N_2, H_2, and NH_3 were allowed to come to equilibrium without interference. The same trick of keeping a reaction off-balance can be used if one of the products is a gas that bubbles out of the reaction mixture, or a solid that precipitates.

Pressure can be used to shift the actual equilibrium conditions of any reaction during which the total number of moles of gas changes. In the ammonia reaction three moles of H_2 and one of N_2 react to form two moles of ammonia. Increasing the pressure shifts the equilibrium in the direction of more ammonia formation, and decreasing the pressure leads to more dissociation of ammonia (see above). The value of the equilibrium constant does not change,

$$K_P = \frac{[NH_3]^2}{[H_2]^3[N_2]} = 670{,}000 \text{ atm}^{-2}$$

but the relative amounts of N_2, H_2, and NH_3 do change. You can understand this by imagining that the total pressure on the reaction vessel is doubled, so that the partial pressures of each of the gases also are doubled. The concentration or pressure ratio

$$\frac{[NH_3]^2}{[H_2]^3[N_2]}$$

would decrease by a factor of $(2)^2/(2)^3(2) = \frac{1}{4}$, and would become smaller than the equilibrium constant, K_P. More N_2 and H_2 would react until the imbalance was corrected and the concentration ratio again was equal to K_P. Pressure changes have no effect if the total number of moles of gas is unchanged during the reaction. The HCl synthesis would be unaffected by an increase or decrease in external pressure.

These pressure effects are one example of an important general principle, which, if understood, can save a lot of mathematics. This is *Le Chatelier's principle:*

> If external stress is applied to a system at equilibrium, the equilibrium conditions will shift so as to compensate for, or counteract, the stress.

If pressure is increased, the ammonia reaction shifts in the direction that decreases the total number of moles of gas and lowers the pressure. If we dilute the reacting mixture by adding an inert gas such as argon, but keep the total pressure constant (which means that the volume must increase), then Le Chatelier's principle predicts that the ammonia equilibrium will shift in the direction that increases the total number of moles of gas. More ammonia will dissociate. We can arrive at the same prediction from the equilibrium-constant expression. Diluting an equilibrium mixture with an equal volume of argon gas at fixed total pressure cuts each of the partial pressures of N_2, H_2, and NH_3 in half—exactly the same effect as halving the pressure or doubling the volume. The concentration ratio increases by a factor of 4,

$$\frac{(\frac{1}{2})^2}{(\frac{1}{2})^3(\frac{1}{2})} = 4$$

and more ammonia dissociates until the concentration ratio again is equal to the equilibrium constant: $K_P = 670,000$ atm^{-2}. Only if reactants and products contain the same number of moles of gas will equilibrium be unaffected by pressure changes or dilution.

TEMPERATURE AND THE EQUILIBRIUM CONSTANT

A particularly important application of Le Chatelier's principle is the prediction of what happens when the temperature is raised or lowered. In this case, unlike the previous example, the actual numerical value of K_{eq} will change. Chemical reactions arise from collisions between molecules, and molecules move faster and collide more often and more effectively at higher temperatures. Both the forward and reverse reactions will be speeded up by a rise in temperature, and slowed by a temperature drop, but not necessarily by the same amounts. In our crabapple analogy, a cold spell may cause both of the combatants to slow down, but may affect the old man more than the boy.

The effect can be predicted without any calculations. If heat is supplied to a chemical reaction to raise the temperature, then Le Chatelier's principle predicts that the equilibrium will be shifted in the direction in which heat is absorbed, since some of the applied heat is thereby removed. Conversely, a heat-emitting, or exothermic reaction, is favored by a drop in temperature, since the external removal of heat will be counteracted partially by heat from the reaction.

The synthesis of ammonia gives off heat:

$$3H_2(g) + N_2(g) \rightarrow 2NH_3(g)$$

$$\Delta H^0_{298} = -22.1 \text{ kcal per 2 moles of } NH_3$$

Ammonia molecules absorb heat when they dissociate. The energy released in forming one $N\equiv N$ and three $H—H$ bonds is not enough to break apart six $N—H$ bonds in the two ammonia molecules. Raising the temperature therefore should favor dissociation, because the extra thermal energy is put to work pulling molecules apart (right). This is borne out by the measured values of K_P for the reaction as written.

Temperature $T(°K)$	ΔG^0_T (kcal per 2 moles NH_3)	K_P (atm^{-2})	Description of the equilibrium mixture
298	−7.95	6.7×10^6	Almost entirely NH_3
457	0	1.00	Mixture of N_2, H_2, and NH_3
1000	+29.6	3.4×10^{-7}	Virtually no NH_3

This is why raising the temperature to make the reaction go faster is counterproductive in the sense that it causes *less* NH_3 to be present at equilibrium. A catalyst can help to speed up the reaction, and we will see how in the next chapter.

FREE ENERGY AND THE EQUILIBRIUM CONSTANT

So far we have treated standard free energies and equilibrium constants as if they were independent, experimentally measured quantities, and entirely separate criteria for looking at a reaction. They actually are not independent; if you know one, you can calculate the other. You may have noticed from the ammonia reaction and other examples in this chapter that as ΔG^0 becomes more negative, indicating greater spontaneity, K_{eq} becomes larger, representing a greater excess of products over reactants at equilibrium. Conversely, when ΔG^0 is zero, K_{eq} is 1.00, and as ΔG^0 becomes more positive, K_{eq} falls below 1.00:

$\Delta G^0 =$ very negative	zero	very positive
$K_{eq} =$ very large positive number	1.00	very small positive number

This suggests a logarithmic relationship.

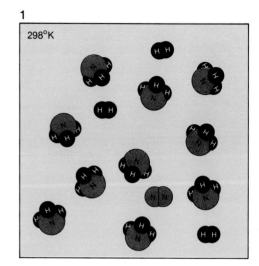

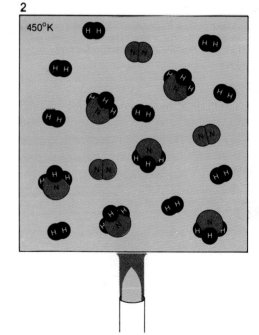

LE CHATELIER'S PRINCIPLE AND TEMPERATURE

(1) Ammonia equilibrium at room temperature.

(2) The temperature rise produced by adding heat is partially counteracted by using some of the heat to dissociate NH_3 molecules and form N_2 and H_2.

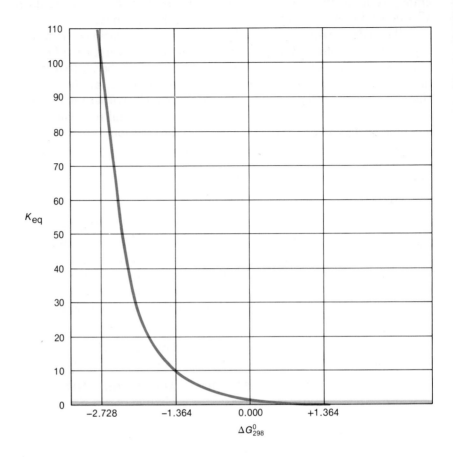

A linear plot of K_{eq} against ΔG^0. The graph is unreadable for K_{eq} values less than 1 (colored area), and rapidly goes off scale for large K_{eq} values.

If we go a little farther in thermodynamics than this book will, it is not hard to prove the logarithmic relationship between ΔG^0 and K_{eq}:

$$\Delta G^0 = -RT \ln K_{eq} \qquad \text{or} \qquad K_{eq} = e^{-\Delta G^0/RT}$$

In the equation above ln is the natural logarithm, not $\log_{10}$, or logarithm to base 10. R is the gas constant discussed in Chapter 2, with a numerical value of 1.987 cal deg^{-1} mole^{-1} or 0.08205 liter atm deg^{-1} mole^{-1}. It also is Avogadro's number times the Boltzmann constant, k, of Chapter 13. The superscript zero on ΔG indicates that the free energy change in this equation is the *standard* free energy change of the reaction—the value at the given temperature when all gases are at one atmosphere partial pressure and all solution components are at concentrations of one mole per liter. In contrast, K_{eq} is the ratio of products to reactants *at equilibrium*, which may be quite different from standard conditions. The equation above compares the strength of the drive toward equilibrium from the standard state, with the ratio of products to reactants once equilibrium is attained. The more that equilibrium is skewed toward an excess of products (large K_{eq}), the greater the initial impetus of movement (large negative ΔG^0) if the reaction is begun from standard concentrations.

338

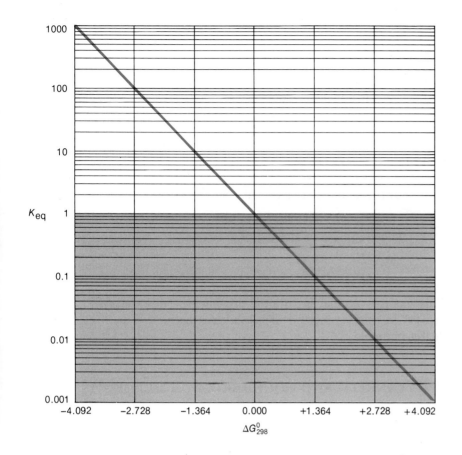

K_{eq} plotted on a logarithmic scale against ΔG^0. The large K_{eq} region of the vertical axis is compressed and the small K_{eq} region is expanded, so both are readable. Compare the colored areas on the two graphs.

For practical calculations, logarithms to base 10 are easier to use than natural logarithms. Since $\ln K_{eq} = 2.303 \log_{10} K_{eq}$,

$$\Delta G^0 = -2.303\, RT \log_{10} K_{eq}$$

and

$$K_{eq} = 10^{-\Delta G^0/2.303\, RT}$$

At $298°K$, $2.303\ RT = 2.303 \times 1.987 \times 298\ \text{cal} = 1364\ \text{cal} = 1.364$ kcal; therefore

$$\Delta G^0_{298} = -1.364 \log_{10} K_{eq}$$

and

$$K_{eq} = 10^{-\Delta G^0/1.364}$$

(Remember that the 1.364 kcal factor is valid *only* at $298°K$.)

This logarithmic relationship between ΔG^0 and K_{eq} is shown in the two graphs at the top of these two pages. At the left, K_{eq} is plotted directly against ΔG^0. The range of variation in K_{eq} is so extreme that the graph is readable only over a limited region. A better representation is given above, with $\log_{10} K_{eq}$ plotted against ΔG^0. As the equations predict, this is a straight line with a negative slope.

You should verify the relationship by checking one of the previous examples. In the HCl reaction $\Delta G^0_{298} = -45.54$ kcal per 2 moles of HCl. Then

$$K_{eq} = 10^{-(-45.540/1.364)} = 10^{+33.4} = 10^{0.4} \times 10^{33} = 2.5 \times 10^{33}$$

This tallies with the value of K_{eq} quoted previously, which is necessarily so since this is how the value was obtained originally. For many reactions with extremely large or small equilibrium constants, it is easier and more accurate to measure the free energy change of the reaction and use the equations given above, than to try to obtain K_{eq} from concentration measurements at equilibrium.

At temperatures other than 298°K, the 1.364 factor cannot be used. For the ammonia reaction at 1000°K:

$$\Delta G^0_{1000} = -2.303\, RT \log_{10} K_{eq}$$
$$+29{,}600 \text{ cal} = (-2.303 \times 1.987 \times 1000 \log_{10} K_{eq}) \text{ cal}$$
$$\log_{10} K_{eq} = -6.47$$
$$K_{eq} = 10^{-6.47} = 10^{+0.53} \times 10^{-7} = 3.4 \times 10^{-7}$$

This was the value of K_{eq} quoted previously. Note that ΔG^0_{1000} was expressed in calories instead of kilocalories because R is in calories per degree per mole.

SPONTANEITY AND EQUILIBRIUM: A SUMMARY

In this chapter we have been looking at two of the most fundamental ideas of chemistry: spontaneity and chemical equilibrium. They are fundamental because they tell us when a reaction has an inherent tendency to occur (which is not to say that it will occur rapidly without help). If the forward and reverse reactions of a chemical process are occurring at the same rate, this condition of balance is *equilibrium*. A reaction that is not at equilibrium but is moving in that direction is *spontaneous*.

The higher the concentrations of reacting substances, the greater will be their tendency to react to form products. Conversely, as the concentration of products increases, the reverse reaction will be favored more and more over the forward process. At equilibrium the ratio of products to reactants has a characteristic numerical value known as the *equilibrium constant*, K_{eq}. For a general chemical reaction,

$$a\text{A} + b\text{B} \rightleftharpoons c\text{C} + d\text{D}$$

the equilibrium-constant expression has the form

$$K_{eq} = \frac{[\text{C}]^c [\text{D}]^d}{[\text{A}]^a [\text{B}]^b}$$

Concentrations usually are expressed in moles per liter for solutions, or in mole fractions or partial pressures for gases. The equilibrium constants expressed in partial pressures and moles per liter often are designated by K_P and K_C, respectively. In general, K_P and K_C will have different numerical values, but one can be calculated from the other using the ideal gas law.

Reactants | Products
$a\text{A} + b\text{B} \rightleftharpoons c\text{C} + d\text{D}$

$$K_{eq} = \frac{[\text{C}]^c [\text{D}]^d}{[\text{A}]^a [\text{B}]^b} = \frac{[\text{Products}]}{[\text{Reactants}]}$$

Le Chatelier's principle is an important shortcut in predicting how a system at equilibrium will behave. It says that if an outside stress is applied to a chemical system at equilibrium, the system will shift in such a way to reduce that stress. If the stress is a pressure increase, the reaction will shift in the direction that decreases the number of moles of reactants and products. If the stress is a dilution, then equilibrium shifts to increase the number of moles in the reaction mixture. These adjustments do not change the numerical value of K_{eq}. If the temperature is raised, however, the reaction will shift in the direction in which heat is absorbed, and K_{eq} will change.

The equilibrium constant gives the ratio of products to reactants at equilibrium. If, for a given set of experimental conditions, the actual ratio

$$\frac{[C]^c[D]^d}{[A]^a[B]^b}$$

is less than K_{eq}, equilibrium has not yet been reached, and will not be reached until A and B have formed more C and D. Conversely, if the concentration ratio is numerically larger than K_{eq}, then the reaction is on the far side of equilibrium. Equilibrium then will be attained only after C and D have broken up spontaneously into more A and B.

In Chapter 10 a negative free energy change was used as a criterion for spontaneity. The standard free energy change, ΔG^0_{298}, is the free energy of the reaction with all substances at 298°K, all gases at partial pressure of 1 atm, and all dissolved substances at concentration of 1 mole per liter. This standard free energy change and the equilibrium constant are related by the expressions

$$\Delta G^0_{298} = -RT \ln K_{eq} \qquad \text{or} \qquad K_{eq} = e^{-\Delta G^0/RT}$$

A large negative standard free energy change for a reaction indicates a large value for K_{eq}, and a large positive standard free energy change means an extremely small value for K_{eq}. If $\Delta G^0 = 0.000$, then $K_{eq} = 1.000$.

In Chapter 13 we answered the question as to *when* a reaction would, or would not, be spontaneous and moving toward equilibrium. This chapter dealt with the matter of just *how far* a reaction would go before it arrived at equilibrium, but still said nothing about the time needed to get there. The next chapter will answer this final question: *How fast* will a chemical reaction go?

POSTSCRIPT: SMOG AND EQUILIBRIUM

The primary offenders in the photochemical smog that blankets the Los Angeles basin and covers an increasing number of other cities on bad days are unburned hydrocarbons and oxides of nitrogen. Even with stringent controls on stationary sources of pollution, as in Los Angeles, the automobile remains a serious polluter.

Smog from oxides of nitrogen begins with nitric oxide, NO, which is formed at high temperatures from O_2 and N_2 in the combustion

Smog begins with nitric oxide (NO) from an automobile tailpipe. NO is oxidized to brown nitrogen dioxide (NO₂).

2NO₂

2NO + O₂ →

chambers of automotive engines:

$$O_2 + N_2 \rightleftarrows 2NO$$

NO is emitted in the exhaust and is oxidized by atmospheric O_2 to brown nitrogen dioxide:

$$NO + \tfrac{1}{2}O_2 \rightleftarrows NO_2$$

NO_2 is brown because its unpaired electron leads to closely spaced electronic energy levels that permit absorption of light in almost the entire visible spectrum. Some of this absorption causes breakdown to NO and atomic oxygen:

$$NO_2 \xrightarrow{\ h\nu\ } NO + O\cdot$$

The NO can be reoxidized to NO_2, and the oxygen atom goes on to do further damage. If you add the two preceding reactions, you will see that the oxides of nitrogen are really only the cyclic machinery for using photons of visible light to tear oxygen molecules apart into atoms:

$$O_2 \xrightarrow{\ h\nu\ } 2O\cdot$$

Free oxygen atoms are damaging because they combine with O_2 to form ozone (O_3):

$$O_2 + O\cdot \rightarrow O_3$$

Ozone is an excellent oxidant that attacks organic matter, including hydrocarbon pollutants, rubber, paint and plastics, and the lining of our lungs.

The peak temperature in an automobile engine is around 2300°K, and the exhaust temperature typically is 900°K. Standard enthalpies, free energies, and equilibrium constants for the breakdown of NO,

$$2NO \rightleftarrows N_2 + O_2$$

are given below for these temperatures and room temperature.

Temperature (°K)	ΔH^0_T	ΔG^0_T	K_{eq}
	(kcal per 2 moles NO)		
298°	−43.16	−41.39	2.20×10^{30}
900°	−43.22	−37.78	1.50×10^{9}
2300°	−43.20	−29.27	605

(Verify for yourself the rather remarkable drop in K_{eq} with decreasing temperature, starting with the ΔG^0_T values.) Notice that the heat of the reaction is quite insensitive to temperature, remaining constant within 0.06 kcal throughout a temperature range of two thousand degrees. This is reasonable, since the heat arises mainly from making and breaking chemical bonds, and it takes just as much energy to break a bond at 2300°K as at 298°K. If you were to use the expression

$$\Delta G^0 = \Delta H^0 - T\Delta S^0$$

to calculate the entropy change during reactions at 298°K, 900°K, and 2300°K, you would find the values $\Delta S^0 = -5.94$, -6.04, and -6.06 cal deg^{-1}, respectively, for the reactions involving two moles of NO. Neither the heat of reaction nor the disorder produced by the reaction are very temperature sensitive, and most of the temperature dependence of the free energy (and therefore K_{eq}) arises from the T term in the preceding equation. The temperature magnifies the importance of the entropy change; a given amount of disorder produced in a reaction is more important in determining free energy and spontaneity at high temperatures than at low.

These values for K_{eq} raise some paradoxical questions. At 2300°K inside the combustion chamber, appreciable amounts of NO will be formed from N_2 and O_2 from the intake of air.

Example. At equilibrium a 1-liter steel tank at 2300°K contains 0.04 mole of N_2, 0.01 mole of O_2, and an unknown amount of NO. How many moles of NO are present, and what is the mole fraction of NO?

Solution. The equilibrium-constant expression for the reaction is:

$$K_{eq} = \frac{[N_2][O_2]}{[NO]^2}$$

$$605 = \frac{(0.04)(0.01)}{[NO]^2}$$

$$[NO] = 0.00081 \text{ mole liter}^{-1}$$

total moles $= 0.04 + 0.01 + 0.0008 = 0.0508$

$$X_{NO} = \frac{0.0008}{0.0508} = 0.016$$

The hot engine gases thus are 1.6% (mole percent) NO, which is an appreciable amount. However, if we repeat the calculations of the preceding example, but at room temperature, we arrive at the paradoxical conclusion that NO should be no problem in air pollution; equilibrium at 298°K lies far on the side of N_2 and O_2:

$$K_{eq} = 2.20 \times 10^{30}$$

$$[NO] = 5.2 \times 10^{-10} \text{ mole liter}^{-1} \text{ within the steel tank}$$

This quantity of NO would be totally undetectable and unimportant.

Where is the flaw in the analysis? The oxide NO obviously *is* a serious problem in photochemical smog. It is produced at high temperatures in internal combustion engines, but why does it not break down spontaneously into N_2 and O_2 as the gases rush out the tailpipe and are cooled down? The problem is one of rates of reaction, and not of equilibrium. True, NO at equilibrium at 298°K should break down into N_2 and O_2, but the gases in our atmosphere are far from equilibrium. The breakdown reaction is a very slow one, and NO remains intact long enough to be oxidized to NO_2 and enter the smog-producing pathway. Rates of reaction are important, and "How fast?" often is a more important question than "How far?". "How fast?" is the question to be considered in the following chapter.

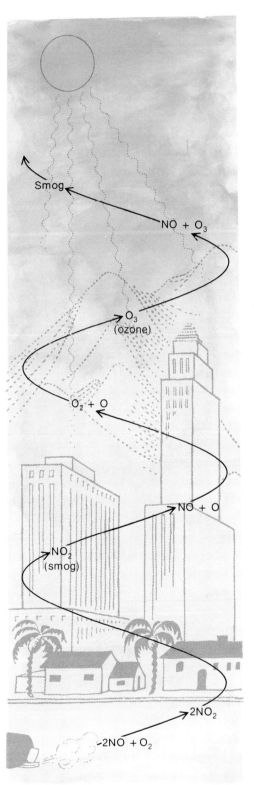

Continuing photochemical chain reactions use light energy to create ozone and more nitrogen dioxide.

QUESTIONS

1. What is the difference between the spontaneity and the rate of a chemical reaction? Give an example of a spontaneous but slow chemical reaction.

2. How can a spontaneous but slow reaction be accelerated?

3. What is the form of the equilibrium-constant expression for the reaction $2NO(g) + O_2(g) \rightleftarrows 2NO_2(g)$? Justify the exponents that you use on the concentration terms.

4. The reaction of Question 3 just as easily could be written $NO(g) + \frac{1}{2}O_2(g) \rightleftarrows NO_2(g)$. What is the equilibrium-constant expression for the reaction written in this way? How are the numerical values of the K_{eq} in this question and Question 3 related?

5. Write the equilibrium-constant expression for the reaction $2NO_2(g) \rightleftarrows 2NO(g) + O_2(g)$. How does the numerical value for this equilibrium constant and that in Question 3 compare?

6. What are the *units* for the equilibrium constants in Questions 3, 4, and 5?

7. Why is it reasonable that the rate constant for the first-order process in the crabapple war should have units of square feet per second, and in what sense is this an "agility constant"? Why should it also be reasonable for the first-order rate constant in molecular processes to have units of liters per second?

8. What principle about the meaning of equilibrium is used to relate the equilibrium constant to the forward and reverse rate constants?

9. Does a state of equilibrium mean that all activity on the molecular level has stopped? If not, then what does equilibrium mean?

10. What is the definition of mole fraction for a mixture of gases? If pure water is decomposed by electrolysis, and the resulting gases are collected as a mixture, what is the mole fraction of each component?

11. Since the formation of water from its elements is highly spontaneous, how is it possible to collect the product gases as described in Question 10? Is the mixture of O_2 and H_2 gases at equilibrium? How can they be made to come to equilibrium again, and what would be the resulting substance?

12. If the gases obtained as described in Question 10 are collected in a tank that then is sealed, and if the tank has a total interior pressure of 0.5 atm, what is the partial pressure of each gas?

13. Which reaction is more spontaneous, starting from standard conditions, the synthesis of HCl, NH_3, or H_2O? In which reaction will more of the starting materials remain unreacted when equilibrium has been reached?

14. What is the difference between K_C, K_P, and K_X? What is the relationship between K_C and K_P for the ammonia synthesis reaction when written as $3H_2 + N_2 \rightleftarrows 2NH_3$?

15. What is the general expression relating K_C and K_P for gases?

16. Dalton's law of partial pressures tells us that partial pressure is related to mole fraction in a gas mixture by the expression $p_j = PX_j$, in which P is the total pressure. What is the general expression relating K_P and K_X for gases?

17. What is Le Chatelier's principle? What would it indicate about the effect on an equilibrium constant of raising the temperature at which the reaction took place?

18. How can Le Chatelier's principle predict the effect on equilibrium concentrations of a change in overall pressure?

19. Does a change in pressure bring about a change in the numerical value of the equilibrium constant, K_P? Does a change in temperature lead to a change in numerical value of K_P?

20. If a reaction has a large negative standard free energy change, is the reaction spontaneous if started from standard conditions? What is meant by standard conditions? Will the equilibrium constant for this reaction be large, or small, and how is it related to the standard free energy change?

21. If an equilibrium constant is very much smaller than 1.0, what does this tell us about the standard free energy change? What does this tell us about the spontaneity of the reaction, when begun from standard conditions?

22. The decomposition of NO to oxygen and nitrogen is a highly exothermic process. Is heat absorbed, or emitted, during the decomposition? If more decomposition products are desired at equilibrium, should this reaction be carried out at high, or low, temperatures? Does the standard free energy change become more positive, or more negative, as the temperature is raised?

23. In view of your answers to Question 22, how can there be appreciable amounts of NO in a polluted atmosphere at room temperature?

PROBLEMS

1. The equilibrium constant for the reaction

$$A_2(g) + B_2(g) \overset{k_f}{\underset{k_r}{\rightleftarrows}} 2AB(g)$$

at a given temperature is $K_P = 2.5 \times 10^{-6}$. The quantities k_f and k_r are the forward and reverse rate constants. If the reverse rate constant has a numerical value of 151 atm^{-1} sec^{-1}, what is the value of k_f?

2. The equilibrium constant for the reaction $N_2 + O_2 \rightleftarrows 2NO$ at 2130°C is 2.5×10^{-3}. What are the units for this equilibrium constant? What is the numerical value for the equilibrium constant for the reaction $NO \rightleftarrows \frac{1}{2}O_2 + \frac{1}{2}N_2$?

3. Does the synthesis of NO as described in Problem 2 occur with the absorption, or emission, of heat? (Use Appendix 2.) For the following conditions, decide whether the gas mixture described is at equilibrium, or whether a net forward or reverse reaction will

take place spontaneously:

    (a) A 1-liter box contains 0.020 mole of NO, 0.010 mole of O_2, and 0.020 mole of N_2 at 2130°C.

    (b) A 20-liter box contains 1×10^{-2} mole of N_2, 1×10^{-3} mole of O_2, and 2×10^{-2} mole of NO at 2130°C.

    (c) A 1-liter box contains 1.00 mole of N_2, 16 moles of O_2, and 0.2 mole of NO at 2500°C.

4. A 1-liter tank is filled with 0.10 mole of HI, 1.5 moles of I_2, and 1.0 mole of H_2 at 448°C. Using information from the table on HI equilibrium in this chapter, calculate the concentrations of HI, I_2, and H_2 in the tank after the components have come to equilibrium.

5. At 25°C and 20 atm pressure, the reaction $N_2(g) + 3H_2(g) \rightleftarrows 2NH_3(g)$ has a standard enthalpy change of -22.1 kcal per mole of N_2.

    (a) If the temperature is raised to 300°C while the pressure is held at 20 atm, will more ammonia be present at equilibrium, or less?

    (b) If the pressure is increased to 30 atm while the temperature remains at 25°C, will more, or less, ammonia be present, compared with initial conditions?

    (c) If half the ammonia is removed and the system is allowed to come to equilibrium again, will the amount of nitrogen gas present increase, or decrease?

    (d) What will be the effect on the original equilibrium mixture if a catalyst for ammonia synthesis is added?

6. A 1-liter tank contains 0.095 mole of ammonia, 1.13 moles of nitrogen gas, and 1.5 moles of hydrogen gas at equilibrium.

    (a) Calculate K_C for the reaction $N_2 + 3H_2 \rightleftarrows 2NH_3$.

    (b) Calculate K_C for the reaction $NH_3 \rightleftarrows \frac{1}{2}N_2 + \frac{3}{2}H_2$.

    (c) How are the K_C's calculated for Parts a and b related?

    (d) Calculate K_P for the reaction as written in Part a.

7. K_C for the reaction $N_2 + 3H_2 \rightleftarrows 2NH_3$ is 0.00237 at 1000°K. If a 10-liter steel tank at this temperature contains 20 moles of N_2 and 30 moles of H_2, how many liters of ammonia will be present?

8. For the reaction of Problem 7, in a 10-liter tank at 1000°K what will be the equilibrium concentration of hydrogen gas, if 6.8 moles of nitrogen and 10.5 moles of ammonia are present? How many moles of hydrogen gas will be present?

9. The equilibrium constant for the reaction $PCl_5(g) \rightleftarrows PCl_3(g) + Cl_2(g)$ is $K_C = 0.0224$ at 500°K.

    (a) What are the proper units for this K_C?

    (b) What is the numerical value for K_P, and what are its units?

    (c) How many moles of Cl_2 will be present at equilibrium in a 100-liter tank at 500°K, if there are 4.3 moles of PCl_5 and 132 moles of PCl_3?

    (d) If the pressure on the contents of the tanks is increased, will more, or less, Cl_2 be present at equilibrium?

    (e) If the temperature of the tank is raised, will more, or less, Cl_2 be present? (Use Appendix 2 data where helpful.)

10. The equilibrium constant for the dissociation of gaseous iodine molecules at $1000°K$ is $K_c = 3.76 \times 10^{-5}$ for the reaction $I_2(g) \rightleftharpoons 2I(g)$. An experiment is begun by placing 1.00 mole of pure I_2 in a 2.00-liter box at $1000°K$. How much atomic iodine will be present after the contents have come to equilibrium?

◀ *A fanciful analogy symbolizing activation barriers and catalytic pathways*

CHAPTER 15

The Rates of Chemical Reactions

In Chapter 14 we answered the question as to why some reactions are not 100% complete, even after an infinite period of time, and why they remain as a mixture of reactants and products after all visible reaction has ceased. A competition exists between forward and reverse reactions, and equilibrium is a condition of balance between these opposing processes. Now we come to the second question: Why do some reactions, which by their free energy values should be spontaneous and far from equilibrium, sit inert and unreactive for years, whereas other reactions go with explosive rapidity? The decomposition of NO to nitrogen and oxygen is thermodynamically spontaneous, so why do we have photochemical smog from oxides of nitrogen? If all combustions with oxygen liberate free energy, and the atmosphere is full of oxygen, then why doesn't everything that is potentially flammable burn at once, including ourselves? The answer is that these decompositions and combustions, although thermodynamically spontaneous, occur at miniscule rates at room temperature. The rates of chemical reactions and the factors that affect them are the subjects of this chapter.

The central theme to be developed in this chapter is that the rate of a chemical reaction depends on its reaction mechanism. Two molecules coming together must collide and rearrange their atoms to make product molecules. The intermediate arrangements of atoms may have a high energy, and if so, the reaction will be slow because not all colliding molecules will have enough energy to rearrange properly. The concept of an "activation-energy" barrier to reaction is illustrated with the mountain analogy on the facing page. The boulder cannot roll off the edge of the mountain without first surmounting the activation barrier crowned by a double dagger symbol (the conventional indication of an activated intermediate state). A catalyst makes a chemical reaction go faster by providing an alternate path with a lower activation-energy barrier. This is symbolized by the winding path down the side of the mountain.

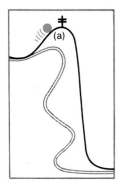

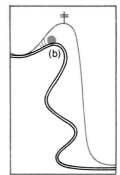

(a) The activation energy is symbolized by a hill that the boulder must surmount before it can roll off the mountain.

(b) A catalyst provides an alternate reaction pathway with a lower activation-energy barrier.

Assume a curve in which x depends upon t:

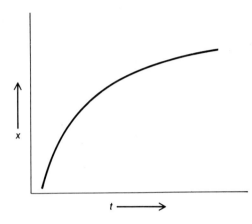

The *average* slope of the curve between Points 1 and 2 is $\frac{x_2 - x_1}{t_2 - t_2} = \frac{\Delta x}{\Delta t}$. This is *not* the same as the slope of the curve at any intermediate point, P.

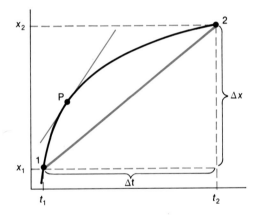

The slope of the curve at Point P is the limit of $\Delta x / \Delta t$ as Points 1 and 2 approach P from either side. This limiting slope *at point P* is designated as dx/dt.

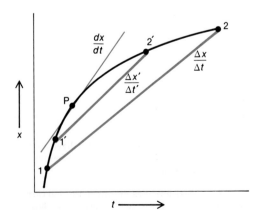

If x represents the position of an object, and t is time, then $\Delta x / \Delta t$ is the *average* speed during the time interval Δt, and dx/dt is the *instantaneous* speed at time t.

EXPERIMENTAL RATE LAWS

A rate law is an equation that relates the rate of disappearance of reactants, or appearance of products, to the reactant concentrations. The simplest type of reaction is the spontaneous decomposition of isolated molecules or atoms, and is encountered most commonly in radioactive decay of unstable nuclei, as we saw in Chapter 11. The rate law for the breakdown of carbon-14 nuclei is

$$\text{rate of decay} = \frac{d[^{14}\text{C}]}{dt} = -k[^{14}\text{C}]$$

The expression

$$\frac{d[^{14}\text{C}]}{dt}$$

should be read as "the rate of change of carbon-14 concentration with time." (For any quantity, x, whose value changes with time, the expression dx/dt means "the rate of change of x with time.")

The rate law just given can be translated as: "The rate of disappearance of carbon-14 atoms is proportional to the number of carbon-14 atoms that are present per liter and available for decay." Since each atom has the same inherent probability of decaying during a specified time interval, and since the probability of one atom's decaying is independent of the presence or absence of other atoms, this is the rate law that would be expected intuitively. As in Chapter 14, $[^{14}\text{C}]$ represents the concentration of carbon-14, and k is the rate constant. Since the carbon-14 concentration decreases with time, $d[^{14}\text{C}]/dt$ is a negative number; thus a minus sign is required on the right side of the equation. It is common to bring the minus sign to the left side, beside the rate term, and to write the rate equation as

$$-\frac{d[^{14}\text{C}]}{dt} = k[^{14}\text{C}]$$

In Chapter 14 we saw that the rate of the hydrogen–iodine reaction depends on the concentrations of H_2 and I_2:

$$H_2 + I_2 \rightarrow 2HI$$

$$\text{rate} = -\frac{d[H_2]}{dt} = -\frac{d[I_2]}{dt}$$

$$= +\frac{1}{2}\frac{d[HI]}{dt} = k[H_2][I_2]$$

The only unfamiliar aspect about this rate equation is the dx/dt style of writing rates. This equation should be translated as: "The rate of disappearance of H_2 and the rate of disappearance of I_2, both are half the rate of appearance of HI (since two HI molecules are produced), and each of these is proportional to the product of H_2 and I_2 concentrations."

ORDER OF A REACTION

The *order* of an experimental rate equation describes how the rate depends on the power of the concentration terms. The rate of breakdown of carbon-14 is proportional to the first power of ^{14}C concentration, so the reaction is *first order*. The hydrogen–iodine reaction rate depends on the product of two concentrations, so the reaction is *second order* in overall concentration. One also can focus on the individual reactants, and say that the HI reaction is separately first order in H_2 and I_2 concentrations, since these each occur in the rate equation with a first-power dependence.

Example. The decomposition of N_2O_5 vapor,

$$2N_2O_5(g) \rightarrow 4NO_2(g) + O_2(g)$$

has been observed experimentally to follow the rate law

$$-\frac{d[N_2O_5]}{dt} = k[N_2O_5]$$

What is the order of this reaction?

Solution. The reaction is a first-order decomposition, because the rate depends on the first power of N_2O_5 concentration.

Notice that the order of a reaction is an experimentally measured quantity, which does not depend on how you write the equation for the reaction. Writing the reaction with a coefficient 2 in front of the N_2O_5 term in the above example does not make the reaction second order, any more than writing the same reaction as

$$N_2O_5(g) \rightarrow 2NO_2(g) + \tfrac{1}{2}O_2(g)$$

would make it first order. To determine the order of a chemical reaction, you must carry out real experiments.

Example. The reduction of NO with H_2,

$$2NO(g) + 2H_2(g) \rightarrow N_2(g) + 2H_2O(g)$$

is observed to depend on the NO and H_2 concentrations in the following way:

$$-\frac{d[NO]}{dt} = k[NO]^2[H_2]$$

with a dependence on the first power of the H_2 concentration rather than $[H_2]^2$ as the balanced equation might suggest. What is the order of the overall reaction, and what is its order with respect to each of the reacting substances?

Solution. The reaction is third order overall, is second order in NO concentration and is first order in H_2 concentration. Observe once again that the simple answer that you might expect from looking at the coefficients of NO and H_2 in the balanced equation does *not* correspond with the experimental facts.

Example. The reaction of chlorine with chloroform to yield carbon tetrachloride and hydrogen chloride is

$$CHCl_3 + Cl_2 \rightarrow CCl_4 + HCl$$

and the observed rate expression for production of HCl is

$$\frac{d[HCl]}{dt} = k[CHCl_3][Cl_2]^{\frac{1}{2}}$$

What is the overall order of reaction, and what is the order with respect to each reactant?

Solution. The reaction is first order in chloroform concentration, half order in chlorine concentration, and $1\frac{1}{2}$ order overall. Note that there is no reason that the order cannot be fractional in one or more concentrations.

The reason that the coefficients in the balanced equation and in the rate law generally do not agree is that the actual chemical reaction mechanism usually is not a simultaneous collision of as many molecules as the coefficients indicate. Instead, the overall mechanism is built up from a series of smaller steps. Four- and five-body simultaneous collisions are very improbable events. A reaction in which four or five molecules interact is much more likely to occur in a series of steps, in which two reactant molecules first collide and form an intermediate substance, this substance collides with the next reactant molecule, and so on. The observed rate law is a summary of all of these steps, and may depend on reactant concentrations in a complicated way. The form of the experimental rate law is the first step on the way toward unscrambling the actual mechanism of reaction, but it does not give us the entire story. Only for simple, one-step reactions will the order of the rate law necessarily agree with the coefficients of the balanced equation. This occurs almost exclusively with first-order decompositions and with those relatively rare second-order collisions that are uncomplicated by further reactions.

In spite of what we have just said, the statements in Chapter 14 about the *equilibrium constant* remain valid. The exponential coefficients in the equilibrium-constant expression do match the coefficients in the balanced chemical equation. The equilibrium-constant expression for the HI reaction is

$$K_{eq} = \frac{[HI]^2}{[H_2][I_2]}$$

and that for the reduction of NO with H_2 is

$$K_{eq} = \frac{[N_2][H_2O]^2}{[NO]^2[H_2]^2}$$

with a second-power dependence on H_2 concentration in the denominator. The reason for the apparent contradiction between this equilibrium-constant expression and the rate law is that any complications of mechanism that affect the forward reaction and its rate law also affect the reverse reaction in the same way. They both cancel out in the overall equilibrium-constant expression. Although the correct rate law for the forward or reverse reaction cannot be deduced from the balanced chemical reaction alone, the equilibrium-constant expression can be.

A classical example of complications in a rate expression is the reaction analogous to HI production, but with bromine instead of iodine:

$$H_2 + Br_2 \rightarrow 2HBr$$

The equilibrium-constant expression is as would have been expected from the preceding chapter:

$$K_{eq} = \frac{[HBr]^2}{[H_2][Br_2]}$$

However, the *rate* of the forward reaction when little or no HBr is present is observed to depend on H_2 and Br_2 concentrations in the following way:

$$\frac{d[HBr]}{dt} = k[H_2][Br_2]^{\frac{1}{2}}$$

The rate of production of HBr with time is proportional to the product of the H_2 concentration and the *square root* of the Br_2 concentration. Under these conditions, the reaction has an overall order of 3/2. After appreciable amounts of HBr have accumulated, the overall rate law is

$$\frac{d[HBr]}{dt} = \frac{k'[H_2][Br_2]^{\frac{1}{2}}}{k'' + \frac{[HBr]}{[Br_2]}}$$

(Notice that this expression reduces to the simpler form when the ratio $[HBr]/[Br_2]$ is close to zero.) When the rate law becomes this complex, the concept of reaction order begins to lose meaning.

Such a complex rate behavior occurs because the actual reaction mechanism is a series of steps, one after the other. We will examine this chain reaction later in the chapter. If the mechanism were simply a collision of H_2 and Br_2 molecules, the rate law would be

$$\frac{d[HBr]}{dt} = k[H_2][Br_2]$$

The fact that this is observed by experiment to be the wrong rate law tells us that the simple reaction mechanism also is wrong.

EXPONENTIAL FIRST-ORDER DECAY

The first-order rate law for the decay of carbon-14 nuclei,

$$-\frac{d[^{14}C]}{dt} = k[^{14}C]$$

is a differential equation. It tells us how the change in concentration with time depends on concentration. It would be desirable to have

After death, the organism ceases to replenish its ^{14}C from the atmosphere, and that which was present at the time of death slowly decays.

The concentration of ^{14}C in our atmosphere is constant, representing a balance between synthesis by cosmic ray neutrons and spontaneous decay:

$$^{14}_{7}N + ^{1}_{0}n \rightarrow ^{14}_{6}C + ^{1}_{1}p \quad \text{(synthesis)}$$

$$^{14}_{6}C \rightarrow ^{14}_{7}N + ^{0}_{-1}e \quad (\beta^- \text{ decay})$$

Living organisms maintain equilibrium between their ^{14}C content and that of the atmosphere, mainly via the CO_2 in photosynthesis and respiration.

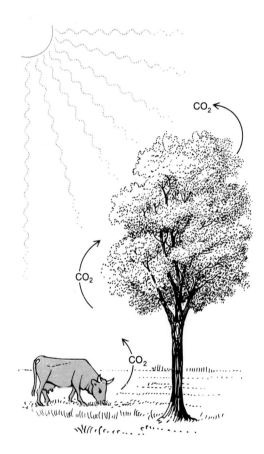

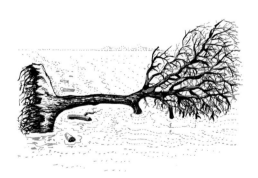

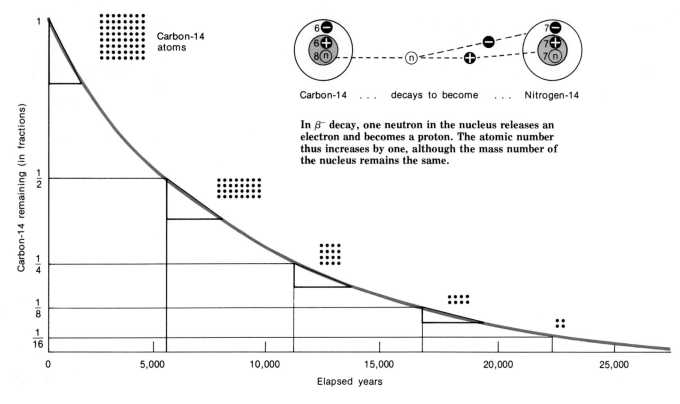

Carbon-14 ... decays to become ... Nitrogen-14

In β^- decay, one neutron in the nucleus releases an electron and becomes a proton. The atomic number thus increases by one, although the mass number of the nucleus remains the same.

Rates of decay of carbon-14. The rate depends on the *concentration* of ^{14}C, and declines as the number of ^{14}C nuclei left for potential decay falls. Half of any given starting quantity will decay in 5570 years. The rate of decay at any time is given by the slope of the curve. Note how this rate gradually decreases as the number of ^{14}C atoms remaining decreases.

another expression that simply told how the concentration varies with time in a first-order decay process:

$$[^{14}C] = \text{some function of } t$$

Elementary calculus shows us how we can derive an expression for concentration versus time from a rate equation, using the process of integration. The general method is beyond the scope of this chapter, but we can give the result for a first-order decay:

$$[^{14}C] = [^{14}C]_0 \, e^{-kt}$$

Starting from an initial concentration at time $t = 0$ of $[^{14}C]_0$, the concentration of carbon-14 at some later time, t, decreases exponentially, as shown above. One property of exponential decay is that, if after a certain time interval the concentration has fallen by half, then after another interval of equal length the concentration will have fallen by half again, or to one quarter its original value. After another equal time interval the concentration will be at an eighth its starting value, then a sixteenth, and so on. The time required for any beginning quantity of material to decay by a first-order process to half its starting con-

354

centration is known as the *half-life* for the decay. The faster the decay the shorter the half-life. For carbon-14 the half-life is 5570 years, which means that if an experiment is begun with one gram of pure carbon-14, only a half gram will be left after 5570 years. In 11,140 years only a quarter gram will remain, and after 16,710 years, one eighth gram will remain. Unstable nuclei vary widely in their decay rates or half-lives: uranium-238 has a half-life of 4,510,000,000 years, whereas the elusive polonium-213 nucleus has a half-life of only 4.2 millionths of a second. Since the half-life, $t_{\frac{1}{2}}$, is the time required for the concentration ratio $[^{14}C]/[^{14}C]_0$ to decrease to 0.5, the half-life and the decay rate constant, k, are related by the expression

$$0.5 = e^{-kt_{\frac{1}{2}}}$$

$$\ln \tfrac{1}{2} = -kt_{\frac{1}{2}}$$

$$\ln 2 = +kt_{\frac{1}{2}}$$

$$k = \frac{\ln 2}{t_{\frac{1}{2}}} = \frac{0.692}{t_{\frac{1}{2}}}$$

If either the rate constant or the half-life is known, the other can be calculated. Half-lives usually are used because they have an immediate physical meaning.

The exponential decay curve on the opposite page can be used to give the rate law a physical meaning. The rate of change of concentration with time, $d[^{14}C]/dt$, is simply the *slope* of the first-order decay curve at any time, t. Because carbon-14 is disappearing, the slope is negative. By drawing a tangent line to the decay curve at several points and examining the slope, you should be able to verify that the slope of the curve at any time t is proportional to the remaining concentration of carbon-14, measured in the vertical direction. This is what the rate law for a first-order process means:

$$-\frac{d[^{14}C]}{dt} = k[^{14}C]$$

REACTION MECHANISMS

Thus far we have established that the rates of chemical reactions depend on the concentrations of reactant species, and that this dependence often has a complicated form that cannot be predicted directly from the coefficients of the balanced chemical equation (as the equilibrium-constant expression can). The reason for these complications is that the actual mechanism of reaction may involve a series of small, one- or two-molecule reactions, with intermediate complexes of atoms that are used up in subsequent steps. The rate equation only summarizes the overall process and does not tell us what is happening in the individual steps. Nevertheless, if we can come up with a series of hypothetical reaction steps that faithfully reproduce the observed rate expression, then we feel confident that our hypothetical mechanism must be close to the actual mechanism.

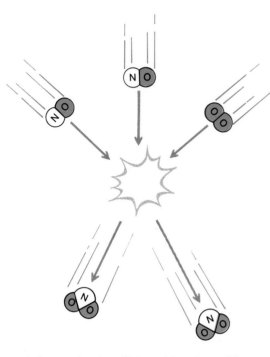

Molecules react when they collide, provided that the collision generates enough energy to tear the atoms apart from one another and rearrange them into new molecules. Bimolecular collisions (between two molecules) are common in gases, but simultaneous trimolecular collisions are a thousand times rarer, and four-molecule simultaneous impacts are so infrequent as to be eliminated from consideration. Then how does the following multimolecular smog reaction take place?

$$2NO(g) + O_2(g) \rightarrow 2NO_2(g)$$

One possible mechanism would be the collision of two NO molecules to form the unstable but perfectly legitimate N_2O_2 molecule, followed either by its decomposition to NO again or its collision with O_2 to form NO_2:

$$2NO \overset{k_1}{\rightarrow} N_2O_2 \qquad (k_1 = \text{rate constant for } N_2O_2 \text{ formation})$$

$$N_2O_2 \overset{k_2}{\rightarrow} 2NO \qquad (k_2 = \text{rate constant for } N_2O_2 \text{ breakdown})$$

$$N_2O_2 + O_2 \overset{k_3}{\rightarrow} 2NO_2 \qquad (k_3 = \text{rate constant for reaction with } O_2)$$

A three-molecule collision, although possible, is less likely to occur than a series of two-molecule collisions leading to the same products (below).

This mechanism is shown at the bottom of the page. If we assume that the buildup and breakdown of N_2O_2 are very fast reactions in comparison with the collision of N_2O_2 and O_2, and that the first two reactions are in equilibrium, then we can describe the association and dissociation reactions involving constants k_1 and k_2 in terms of an equilibrium constant:

$$k_1[NO]^2 = k_2[N_2O_2]$$

$$\frac{k_1}{k_2} = \frac{[N_2O_2]}{[NO]^2} = K_{eq}$$

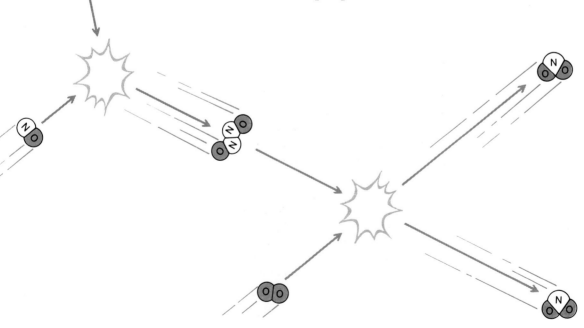

The slower collision of N_2O_2 with O_2 is called the *rate-determining step*, since the overall reaction rate depends on how fast the slowest step occurs. If the reaction takes place by collision of N_2O_2 and O_2, then the rate of production of NO_2 will be proportional to the concentrations of these two molecules:

$$\frac{d[NO_2]}{dt} = k_3[N_2O_2][O_2]$$

It would be difficult or impossible to measure the concentration of N_2O_2 because the molecule is a short-lived reaction intermediate, but fortunately this is unnecessary. The equilibrium-constant expression relates the N_2O_2 concentration with that of the reactant NO concentration:

$$[N_2O_2] = K_{eq}[NO]^2$$

Substituting in the rate equation, we get

$$\frac{d[NO_2]}{dt} = k_3 K_{eq}[NO]^2[O_2]$$

$$= k'[NO]^2[O_2]$$

in which $k' = k_3 K_{eq}$. This is the same rate expression that would have resulted if the reaction had occurred by the simultaneous three-molecule collision of NO, NO, and O_2, but the mechanism just proposed assumes a series of two-molecule collisions instead. One cannot decide the actual mechanism of a reaction from the rate equation alone. For this example, it would be necessary to carry out chemical experiments to determine the presence or absence of reaction intermediates such as N_2O_2. Finding them would support the proposed mechanism; but not finding them might only mean that the chemical detection methods were not sensitive enough. This is why the number of proposed reaction mechanisms in the chemical literature is much greater than the number of well-established mechanisms. We will look at three other examples of reaction mechanisms, and see how they account for the observed rate expressions.

The Hydrogen–Iodine Reaction

An example of a long-standing error in reaction mechanisms is the HI reaction, which we and others have used so often because it apparently is so well-behaved. The reaction is

$$H_2 + I_2 \rightarrow 2HI$$

and the observed rate equation is

$$\frac{d[HI]}{dt} = k[H_2][I_2]$$

For nearly seventy-five years, everyone assumed that the process occurred by the collision of one hydrogen molecule and one iodine molecule, with enough energy to bring about reaction. Only as recently as 1967 was it demonstrated that the actual reaction involves the reversible dissociation of I_2 molecules into atoms, followed by the reaction of

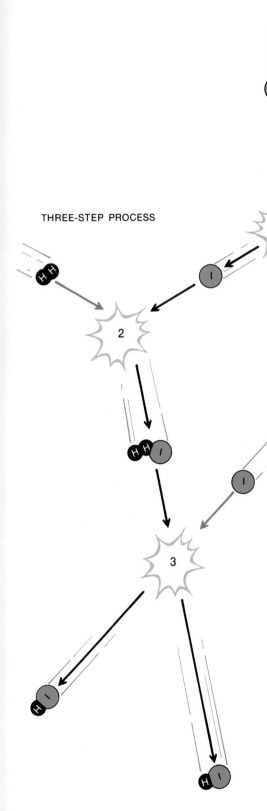

THREE-STEP PROCESS

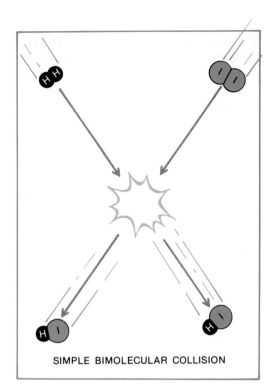

SIMPLE BIMOLECULAR COLLISION

Surprisingly, a three-step process with iodine atoms as intermediates can have the same overall result and the same rate expression as a simple bimolecular collision (upper right).

these I atoms with H_2:

$$I_2 \overset{k_1}{\underset{k_2}{\rightleftarrows}} 2I \qquad \text{(rapid equilibrium)}$$

$$H_2 + 2I \overset{k_3}{\to} 2HI \qquad \text{(slow, rate-determining step)}$$

As with the NO reaction just discussed, one can write an equilibrium constant for the dissociation and reassociation of I_2:

$$K_{eq} = \frac{k_1}{k_2} = \frac{[I]^2}{[I_2]}$$

The rate of reaction is determined by the slowest step, and hence is

$$\frac{d[HI]}{dt} = k_3 [H_2] [I]^2$$

Using the equilibrium expression to eliminate the concentration of the short-lived I atom intermediate, produces a rate expression that is identical with that predicted from simple collision theory:

$$[I]^2 = K_{eq}[I_2]$$

$$\frac{d[HI]}{dt} = k_3 K_{eq} [H_2] [I_2]$$

$$= k'[H_2][I_2]$$

How then can one decide which mechanism is right, bimolecular collision, or dissociation of I_2 and subsequent reaction of I atoms?

358

In 1967, J. H. Sullivan found an ingenious way to decide. At equilibrium at any given temperature, the iodine molecule and atom concentrations always will be linked by the equilibrium expression

$$[I]^2 = K_{eq}[I_2]$$

Sullivan found a way to change the relative concentrations of I_2 and I by using ultraviolet light from a mercury vapor lamp to cause more iodine molecules to dissociate:

$$I_2 \xrightarrow{h\nu} 2I$$

In effect, the photons from the lamp gave this reaction a vigorous kick to the right. Sullivan then could alter the relative amounts of I_2 and I at will, by controlling the amount of ultraviolet light from the lamp. The question became: Is the rate of reaction dependent on the concentration of I_2 molecules, or of I atoms? The answer from the experiments was clear; the rate depends on the concentration of I atoms. The actual rate equation under all conditions is

$$\frac{d[HI]}{dt} = k_3[H_2][I]^2$$

The simpler form, which makes it look as if the rate depends on the first power of the concentration of iodine *molecules*, is valid only because in the absence of UV disturbance, I_2 and I always are in rapid equilibrium.

The Sullivan mechanism for HI was startling because it destroyed what was long believed to be a classical example of true bimolecular collision. The mechanism given above seems to demand a three-body collision between one H_2 molecule and two I atoms, but this, too, can be avoided by assuming a rapid equilibrium between H_2 and another intermediate molecular species, H_2I:

$$I_2 \rightleftarrows 2I \qquad K_A = \frac{[I]^2}{[I_2]}$$

$$H_2 + I \rightleftarrows H_2I \qquad K_B = \frac{[H_2I]}{[H_2][I]}$$

$$H_2I + I \xrightarrow{k} 2HI \qquad \text{(slow, rate-determining step)}$$

This is the mechanism outlined on the opposite page. The rate then is given by

$$\frac{d[HI]}{dt} = k[H_2I][I]$$
$$= kK_B[H_2][I][I]$$
$$= kK_BK_A[H_2][I_2]$$
$$= k'[H_2][I_2]$$

Once again, this is the same expression that would be expected from a simple bimolecular reaction. It emphasizes the truth of the statement that neither the overall chemical equation nor even the correct rate equation is enough by itself to tell you the detailed mechanism of a reaction.

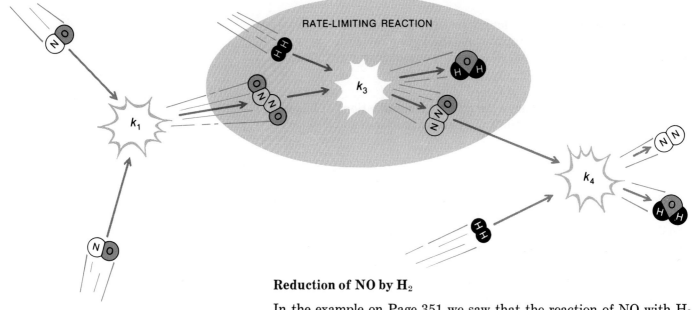

RATE-LIMITING REACTION

k_1 k_3 k_4

Reduction of NO by H_2

In the example on Page 351 we saw that the reaction of NO with H_2 leads to a rate expression that is different from what might be expected from the equation of the reaction alone:

$$2NO + 2H_2 \rightleftarrows 2H_2O + N_2$$

$$\frac{d[N_2]}{dt} = k[NO]^2[H_2]$$

The reaction is first order in H_2 concentration, not second order. One mechanism that will account for this rate behavior is

$$2NO \underset{k_2}{\overset{k_1}{\rightleftarrows}} N_2O_2 \qquad \text{(rapid equilibrium)}$$

$$N_2O_2 + H_2 \overset{k_3}{\rightarrow} N_2O + H_2O \qquad \text{(slow, rate-determining step)}$$

$$N_2O + H_2 \overset{k_4}{\rightarrow} N_2 + H_2O \qquad \text{(rapid reaction)}$$

This mechanism is illustrated above. If all reactions except the k_3 process are quite fast, then the rate equation is

$$\frac{d[N_2O]}{dt} = k_3[N_2O_2][H_2]$$

You should be able to use the first equilibrium condition to eliminate N_2O_2 concentration, and show that the rate equation given previously is the result. The last reaction (k_4) occurs so fast that it scavenges any N_2O as rapidly as it is formed, and has no effect on the overall rate of the process. In effect, N_2 is produced as fast as N_2O appears, so

$$\frac{d[N_2]}{dt} = \frac{d[N_2O]}{dt}$$

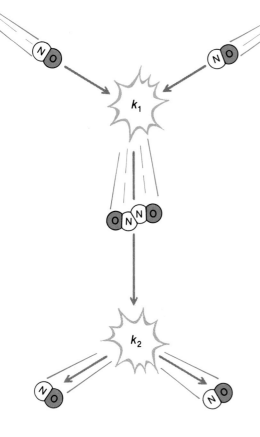

Reaction of NO with H_2. At the top, some of the NO reacts with H_2 in three successive steps to produce N_2 and H_2O. N_2O_2 is a reaction intermediate. Above, other NO combines to N_2O_2, which decomposes again to NO.

In a series of reactions, the slowest one has the greatest influence on reaction rates. To invoke a painful analogy, if it takes ten days to to get a certified letter from Los Angeles to the White House, then rushing to get it into the one o'clock mail instead of the three o'clock will make little difference in the long run.

360

Formation of HBr

The rather horrendous rate law for the HBr reaction,

$$H_2 + Br_2 \rightleftharpoons 2HBr$$

$$\frac{d[HBr]}{dt} = \frac{k'[H_2][Br_2]^{\frac{1}{2}}}{k'' + [HBr]/[Br_2]}$$

arises because the true process is a chain reaction that involves first the dissociation of Br_2 molecules into atoms, then the reaction of atoms with other H_2 and Br_2 molecules:

$Br_2 \rightarrow 2Br$	(chain-initiation step)
$Br + H_2 \rightarrow HBr + H$	(slow, nearly rate-determining step)
$H + Br_2 \rightarrow HBr + Br$	(chain-propagation step)

The latter two equations constitute a chain reaction, each one yielding a molecule of HBr and producing the reactant atom for the other chain step (see margin). There also are reactions that either damp down or reverse the chain process:

$2Br \rightarrow Br_2$	(chain damping)
$H + HBr \rightarrow H_2 + Br$	(chain reversal)

With these reactions and a certain amount of algebra, one can arrive at the observed rate expression in a straightforward though tedious manner. Although the rate equation looks complicated, we can understand it in terms of the HBr mechanism. For example, as [HBr] increases, its presence in the denominator decreases the rate of reaction. This happens because the chain-reversal reaction sends more HBr back to H_2 molecules and Br atoms. At low HBr concentration, for which the ratio $[HBr]/[Br_2]$ is small in comparison with the rate constant k'', the rate law simplifies to the $1\frac{1}{2}$-order expression that we saw previously:

$$\text{rate} = \frac{k'}{k''}[H_2][Br_2]^{\frac{1}{2}}$$

In this chain reaction, a Br atom sets in motion the formation of 8 HBr from 4 H_2 and 4 Br_2. In the last collision shown, the Br atom is regenerated to continue the chain even further.

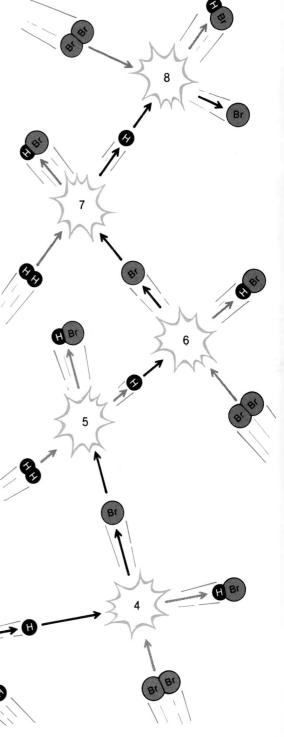

Chain reaction begins here

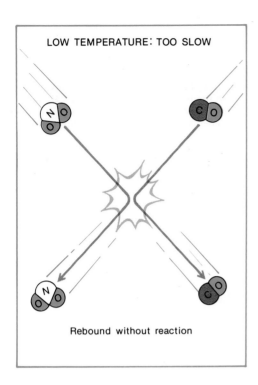

LOW TEMPERATURE: TOO SLOW

Rebound without reaction

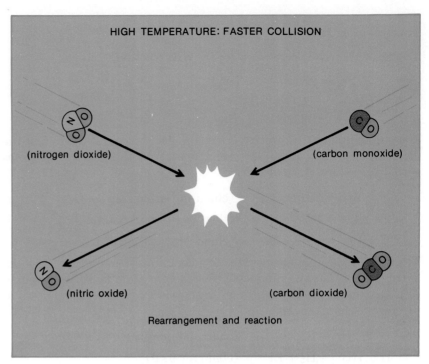

HIGH TEMPERATURE: FASTER COLLISION

(nitrogen dioxide)

(carbon monoxide)

(nitric oxide)

(carbon dioxide)

Rearrangement and reaction

MOLECULAR COLLISIONS AND REACTION

All reactions other than spontaneous decompositions of single particles involve collisions between molecules. As we have just seen, some reactions that look simple from their overall stoichiometric equations actually involve elaborate chain mechanisms, and it is not possible to predict the true mechanism just by looking at the equation for the chemical reaction. Even these more complex processes, however, involve separate steps that usually are simple two-body collisions, and what we derive from bimolecular reactions below can be applied to each of the individual steps. The principles are the same for both simple and complex mechanisms.

A reaction that does appear to proceed by a simple two-body collision is the following:

$$NO_2(g) + CO(g) \rightleftarrows NO(g) + CO_2(g)$$

The rate of the forward reaction, by which NO_2 and CO molecules collide and react, can be written as

$$\text{rate} = k[NO_2][CO]$$

We know that we can increase the rate of the forward reaction by increasing the concentrations of NO_2 and CO. Can we also find some way to increase the rate constant, k?

The most obvious factor that affects k is temperature; k increases as T increases. All reactions go faster at higher temperatures, because

362

the molecules move faster, and collide more often and more effectively. We could *calculate* k from basic principles if we knew the answers to two questions:

1. How frequently do two molecules in a reaction collide?
2. What is the probability that when they do collide, they will react instead of rebounding and going harmlessly on their way?

The collision frequency of gas molecules depends on the number of molecules in a given volume, how large they are, and how fast they are moving. The measurable variables that control these are concentration, molecular weight, and temperature. Molecules move faster as the temperature increases, and for a given temperature (or kinetic energy), lighter molecules move faster than heavier ones. The kinetic theory of gases can give us an exact expression for the collision frequency.

What is the probability that any given collision will lead to chemical reaction rather than to recoil? The simplest possible model of chemical reactivity proposes a threshold energy, E_a, such that if the kinetic energy of two colliding molecules along their line of approach is greater than E_a they will react, but if the collision energy is less than E_a the molecules will rebound without reacting (see left drawing at top of opposite page). This threshold energy, E_a, is called the *energy of activation*. It can be thought of as a barrier that the reaction must surmount before it can go to completion (right).

From the usual random distribution of energy among molecules, the fraction of molecules that have enough kinetic energy to collide with energy E_a or greater is

$$f = e^{-E_a/RT}$$

This fraction increases with temperature. At absolute zero, it has the value:

$$f = e^{-E_a/0} = e^{-\infty} = 0$$

This is reasonable, since if the molecules are motionless at absolute zero, none of them have enough energy to react. As the temperature approaches infinity, the fraction of molecules capable of reacting approaches unity, no matter how large the activation energy, E_a, might be:

$$f = e^{-E_a/\infty} = e^{-0} = 1$$

At any finite temperature, the larger the activation energy, the smaller the fraction of molecules that have enough energy to surmount this barrier and react.

The simple collision theory of chemical reaction states that the rate constant can be represented by

$$k = Ae^{-E_a/RT}$$

in which A is a constant derived from the collision frequency. It depends on the molecular weight, the molecular diameter, and the square

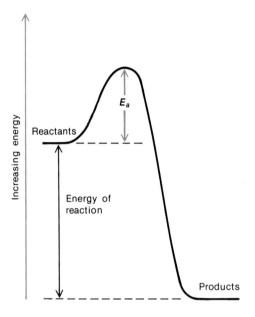

The activation-energy barrier, E_a, which colliding molecules must overcome to react rather than rebounding unchanged, is not directly related to the energy emitted when the overall reaction occurs.

363

root of the temperature. This temperature dependence of collision frequency is almost negligible in comparison with the exponential temperature dependence of the $e^{-E_a/RT}$ term, which gives the fraction of the colliding molecules with energy greater than E_a. The collision theory tells us how the experimental rate constant should vary with temperature: There should be a straight-line relationship between the logarithm of k and the reciprocal temperature, $1/T$, with a negative slope proportional to the activation energy, E_a:

$$\ln k = \ln A - \frac{E_a}{R}\left(\frac{1}{T}\right)$$

$$\text{slope} = -\frac{E_a}{R}$$

If we measure k at several temperatures and plot $\ln k$ against $1/T$, we obtain an Arrhenius plot like that shown below. (This kind of plot is named after the Swedish chemist who first developed the theory.) This is the most direct means of obtaining the activation energy of a reaction, and is convincing evidence for the entire picture of activation-energy barriers.

In order that the reverse reaction occurs, the same energy level for the reaction intermediates must be achieved by the collision of product molecules. If product molecules are more stable than reactants (ΔH^0 negative), then the energy of activation will be greater for the reverse

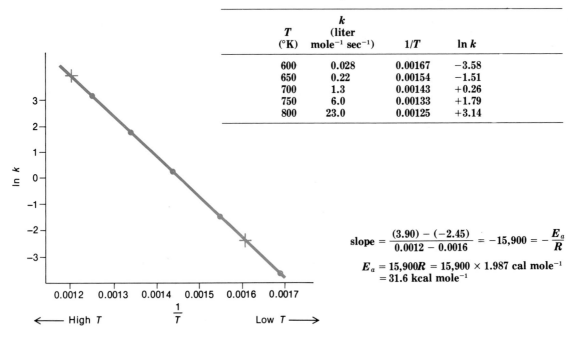

Arrhenius plot and E_a

$$NO_2 + CO \xrightarrow{k} NO + CO_2$$

T (°K)	k (liter mole^{-1} sec^{-1})	$1/T$	$\ln k$
600	0.028	0.00167	−3.58
650	0.22	0.00154	−1.51
700	1.3	0.00143	+0.26
750	6.0	0.00133	+1.79
800	23.0	0.00125	+3.14

$$\text{slope} = \frac{(3.90) - (-2.45)}{0.0012 - 0.0016} = -15,900 = -\frac{E_a}{R}$$

$$E_a = 15,900R = 15,900 \times 1.987 \text{ cal mole}^{-1}$$
$$= 31.6 \text{ kcal mole}^{-1}$$

reaction than for the forward. The relationships between energies of reactants, the activated state, and products are shown in the drawing below for the $NO_2 + CO$ reaction. The activated state, which the molecules must reach before either the forward or the reverse reaction is possible, is 31.6 kcal mole^{-1} higher in energy (enthalpy) than the NO_2 and CO reactants, and 85.7 kcal mole^{-1} higher in energy than the NO and CO_2 products. The difference between the forward and reverse E_a's is the thermodynamic enthalpy of reaction ($\Delta H^0 = -54.1$ kcal mole^{-1}).

In the *collision theory* of reaction, the activation energy is simply a barrier that the colliding molecules must surmount before they can react. The *transition-state theory* proposes that this activated state is an intermediate arrangement that the molecules go through, which has a real physical existence although it cannot be isolated and studied at leisure. In the $NO_2 + CO$ reaction, this transition state, or *activated complex*, would be one in which the O to be transferred has not yet been completely lost by NO, nor completely acquired by CO. If the two molecules approached end-on, the activated complex would be something like

$$O = N \cdots O \cdots C = O$$

The dots indicate attractions between atoms that are longer than normal covalent bonds, and quantum mechanical calculations suggest that they might be some 30% longer. The activated complex will decompose when molecular vibrations rupture either one of these bonds, and it

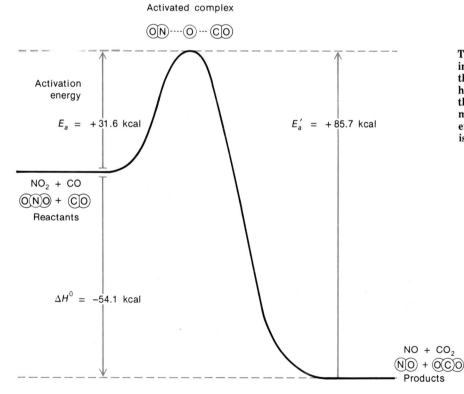

Activated complex

Activation energy

$E_a = +31.6$ kcal

$E_a' = +85.7$ kcal

$NO_2 + CO$

Reactants

$\Delta H^0 = -54.1$ kcal

$NO + CO_2$

Products

The activated complex, or transition state, during the reaction is 31.6 kcal higher in energy than the reactant molecules, and 85.7 kcal higher than the products. This is the barrier that both the forward and the reverse reactions must surmount for them to occur. The difference between these two activation energies is the heat of the reaction, ΔH^0.

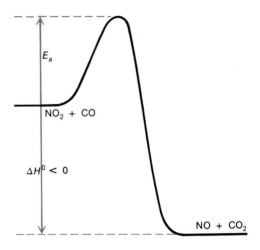

The forward reaction in this example has a negative heat of reaction, ΔH^0, and a smaller activation energy, E_a, than the reverse reaction.

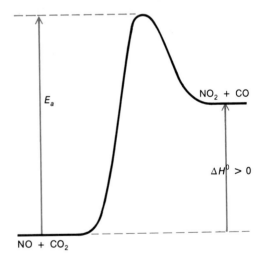

Since the reverse reaction has a larger activation energy, E_a, it goes more slowly than the forward reaction. Equilibrium is achieved only when excess of products over reactants is present.

could just as well result in reactant molecules as product molecules. In the transition-state theory, the rate of forward reaction depends on the concentration of activated complex, and the probability that it will break down to form products and not reactants. We will find the picture of an activated complex as being a reaction intermediate useful, even though we will not go into the mathematics of the transition-state theory. The activated complex is the state at the top of the "mountain" in the drawing on the preceding page.

In the $NO_2 + CO$ reaction, which we have been using as an illustration, the energy of activation of the reverse reaction ($E_a = 85.7$ kcal) is greater than that of the forward reaction ($E_a = 31.6$ kcal), as shown at the left. By the simple collision theory, the rates of the forward and reverse reactions are

$$\text{rate}_f = A_f e^{-31.6/RT}[NO_2][CO]$$

$$\text{rate}_r = A_r e^{-85.7/RT}[NO][CO_2]$$

The factors A_f and A_r are approximately equal, thus most of the difference in the two rate constants lies in the exponentials that contain E_a. If we begin with equal concentrations of reactants and products, the forward reaction will be faster than the reverse because $e^{-31.6/RT}$ is greater than $e^{-85.7/RT}$. More products will accumulate. Equilibrium, defined by $\text{rate}_f = \text{rate}_r$, will not be reached until the excess of products is great enough to compensate for the larger forward rate constant, which is a consequence of the smaller activation energy of the forward reaction. The equilibrium constant, which is the ratio of products to reactants at equilibrium, therefore will be larger than 1.00. If the products are thermodynamically less stable than reactants (positive ΔH^0 of reaction), then the reverse rate constant will be greater than the forward, equilibrium will be attained with an excess of reactants, and K_{eq} will be less than 1.00. Both situations are diagrammed in the left margin.

SPEEDING A REACTION BY CATALYSIS

It is always possible to increase a rate constant and accelerate a reaction by increasing the temperature. For reactions with an activation energy of 12 to 13 kcal, at temperatures around 298°K the rate constant doubles with every 10° rise in temperature. (Can you prove this?) But as we have seen with NH_3, there can be difficulties: The reverse reaction may be accelerated faster than the forward reaction, so that fewer products are obtained. The products or reactants may be unstable at elevated temperatures, or in special applications the surroundings may preclude the use of higher temperatures. For example, one cannot light a match to burn glucose in the human body; this reaction must be carried out at approximately 98.6°F.

It is for such reactions that catalysis becomes useful. In general, catalysts lower the activation barrier for a reaction (E_a), thereby making the rate constants larger and the reactions faster. This is repre-

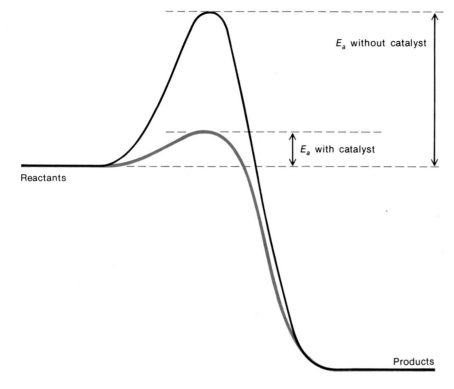

E_a without catalyst

E_a with catalyst

Reactants

Products

A catalyst accelerates an already spontaneous reaction by providing an alternative reaction pathway with a lower activation energy, E_a. With a smaller energy barrier to overcome, a greater fraction of potentially reacting molecules actually have enough energy to react, so the process takes place more rapidly.

sented schematically by the drawing above. Lowering E_a means finding an alternative pathway or mechanism for the reaction, in which the intermediate states (activated complexes) at all times are at a lower energy.

Both the forward and the reverse reactions are speeded up by a catalyst, since lowering the forward E_a necessitates lowering the reverse E_a by the same amount. A catalyst has no effect on K_{eq} or on the ultimate equilibrium conditions for a reaction; it only provides a way in which a spontaneous but slow reaction can arrive at equilibrium faster. If the reaction is not already thermodynamically spontaneous, a catalyst will be of no use. Thermodynamics does not tell a chemist how to find a catalyst for a given reaction, but it does tell him when it is, or is not, worth his time to look for one.

A SIMPLE CATALYTIC MECHANISM

How does a catalyst provide a reaction mechanism with a lower activation energy? Although inorganic and metallic catalysts have been used for decades in the chemical and petroleum industries, we are in the rather odd position of knowing more of the details of catalytic mechanisms for enzymes than for these simpler catalysts, mainly because of recent x-ray crystallographic structure analyses of enzyme molecules. Nevertheless, we can find a simple explanation of why platinum, nickel, or other clean metal surfaces are effective accelerators for reactions involving hydrogenation. (We will return to biological catalysts when we study enzymes in Chapter 24.)

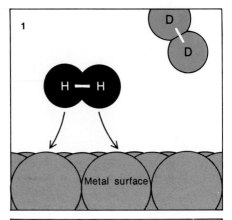

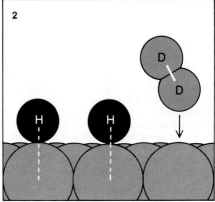

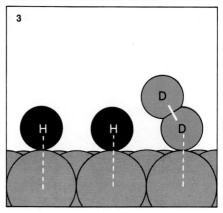

Many hydrogenation reactions, such as the following, are catalyzed by metal surfaces:

$$H_2 + H_2C{=}CH_2 \rightarrow H_3C{-}CH_3$$
$$\text{ethylene} \qquad \text{ethane}$$

$$2H_2 + CO \rightarrow H_3C{-}OH$$
$$\text{methanol}$$

It would be difficult to give these molecules enough kinetic energy in the gas phase to cause them to react upon colliding. The metal surface assists by adsorbing H_2 molecules and pulling them apart into hydrogen atoms, which bind to metal atoms at the surface. These reactive H atoms then combine more rapidly with other molecules that collide with the surface. A particularly simple reaction involving H_2 is isotope exchange with D_2. The probable series of events for the reaction

$$H_2 + D_2 \rightleftarrows 2HD \qquad (D = \text{deuterium, or } {}^2H)$$

is shown in the panels at the left.

In the first panel, an H_2 molecule is pulled apart as it binds to two metal atoms on the catalytic surface. The energy that is required to dissociate the H_2 molecule is gained from the energy of the two H—metal bonds that are formed. In panel two, a D_2 molecule approaches the catalytic surface, and in panel three, one end of the molecule binds to another site on the surface. By forming a weak D—metal bond, the molecule weakens its own internal D—D bond, thereby making it more susceptible to attack by the nearby bound H atom. In panel four the central D atom is shared equally between H and D in a configuration that is analogous to the activated complex in the uncatalyzed reaction. This activated complex could decompose equally well in two ways: on to panels five and six, or back through panels three and two. In about half the cases it will continue on as in panel five, breaking the D—D bond entirely and leading in panel six to a released H—D molecule and a deuterium atom bound to the surface.

The energy released when two H atoms and a D_2 molecule are bound to the catalytic surface is approximately equal to the energy re-

THE "RACK" MECHANISM OF METAL-SURFACE CATALYSIS

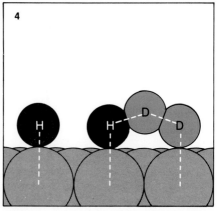

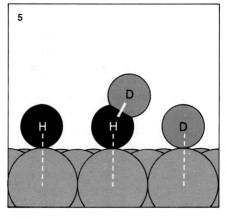

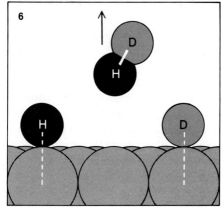

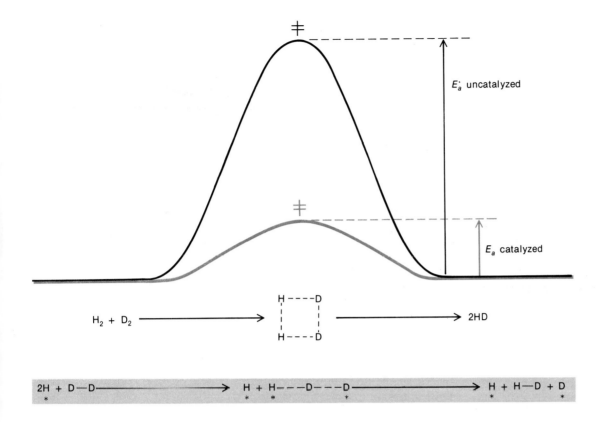

quired to dissociate the H_2 molecule; thus panels one and three represent nearly the same energy states. The contribution of the catalyst arises because the energy of the activated complex in panel four is not nearly as high as that of the intermediate complex in the gas phase:

$$
\begin{array}{ccc}
H & \cdots\cdots & D \\
\vdots & & \vdots \\
\vdots & & \vdots \\
H & \cdots\cdots & D
\end{array}
$$

The metal atoms help to hold the complex in place and stabilize it. The activation barrier therefore is lower, and the reaction takes place faster. Reaction energy profiles for uncatalyzed and catalyzed reactions are shown above.

This particular kind of assistance by a catalyst is known as a "rack" mechanism, because it literally pulls molecules apart and weakens bonds, thereby making them more susceptible to attack. The molecules that bind to a catalytic surface and are acted upon are called *substrate* molecules. A catalytic surface, whether it be a clean surface of a finely divided metal or metal oxide, or the active site of an enzyme molecule, must be structured in such a way that it can bind substrate molecules from the reaction that it catalyzes, enable them to react, and release the products afterward. In the words of Emil Fischer, a turn-of-the-century enzyme chemist, a catalyst and its substrate molecules must fit one another like a lock and key. We shall come back to this topic in Chapter 24, and give some actual examples of what a lock-and-key fitting means in atomic terms.

The initial and final states of the uncatalyzed and catalyzed reactions are identical, but the intermediate or transition state is different. The four-atom cluster, which is the activated complex in the gas-phase reaction, has a high energy, whereas the E_a of the strained atomic complex on the platinum surface is lower.

POSTSCRIPT: CATALYSTS AND THE ENVIRONMENT

One aspect of the current pollution problem is that substances that should be degraded spontaneously by the atmosphere or by microorganisms are not, so they remain in the environment to cause trouble. Much of this trouble is our own fault. In the presynthetic era, most raw materials were natural substances taken from the environment. They blended back into the environment when we were through with them. They decayed, decomposed, and rotted, oxidized by the atmosphere and eaten by bacteria that had evolved with these substances as their natural foods.

With the coming of synthetic compounds, the picture changed because some of the man-made compounds do not blend back into the environment. Polyamino acids (proteins) can be degraded by bacteria; polyethylene and polystyrene cannot. The new materials also are more resistant to spontaneous oxidation. When a manufactured item is in use, this stability is an advantage; as soon as the item is discarded, it becomes a serious liability. What is to be done? Can we teach microorganisms to eat polyethylene and silicone plastics?

One company, Bio-Degradable Plastics, Inc. of Boise, Idaho, has managed to do nearly that. It has developed a disposable polystyrene lid for take-out drink cups that is capable of self-destruction. The plastic of the lid is impregnated with a catalyst that causes ultraviolet light to break up the polystyrene into smaller organic molecules. These smaller molecules then can be metabolized by soil bacteria. After 30 days of exposure to sunlight, a discarded lid begins to break up; after 150 days little visible traces remain. If only we could find a catalyst for all of our litter!

The problem is not quite so simple. A general oxidation catalyst would be a disaster. In a simpler era of chemistry, an intellectual nonproblem in the tradition of the Philosopher's Stone and the Perpetual Motion Machine was the Universal Solvent. (What would you keep it in?) The Universal Catalyst is in the same league. If some way could be found to make all spontaneous reactions rapid, then all organic matter on our planet, including ourselves, would be converted quickly into carbon dioxide, water, and nitrogen. We can exist in an oxygen atmosphere only because of the existence of activation-energy barriers to reaction.

Catalysts do have a limited use in cleaning up the environment. One line of approach to automotive pollution is the use of afterburners for hydrocarbons. To get rid of oxides of nitrogen, catalytic beds are used to accelerate reactions of the type

$$2NO(g) \rightarrow N_2(g) + O_2(g) \qquad \Delta G^0_{298} = -41.4 \text{ kcal per 2 moles NO}$$

Some of the practical difficulties include finding a catalyst that has a long lifetime and is not poisoned easily by lead and other components of commercial gasolines. While we search for the perfect catalyst for nitrogen oxide degradation, it might be well to keep in mind another reaction involving nitrogen:

$$H_2O(g) + N_2(g) + \tfrac{5}{2}O_2(g) \rightarrow 2HNO_3(aq)$$
$$\Delta G^0_{298} = +1.78 \text{ kcal per 2 moles HNO}_3$$

While this reaction under standard conditions (including 1-molar nitric acid as product) is not quite spontaneous, the nitric acid concentration only has to fall to 0.44 mole liter^{-1} to make it spontaneous. Were it not for the high activation energy of this reaction, all of the water vapor, all of the oxygen, and a good part of the nitrogen, would be swept from our atmosphere, and the oceans would become a solution of dilute nitric acid.[1] We had better be sure that the "perfect catalyst" for the smog reaction does not also catalyze nitrogen reactions in general!

QUESTIONS

1. What is a rate expression for a chemical reaction, and in what way does it depend on the concentrations of substances present?

2. If c is the concentration of a substance in moles per liter, what is the meaning of dc/dt? If the substance is a reactant in a chemical process, is dc/dt positive, or negative? If the substance is a product, what is the sign of dc/dt?

3. If P is the air pressure in a tire, what is the meaning of dP/dt, and what is its algebraic sign if the tire is punctured?

4. In spontaneous decay, why is it reasonable for the decay rate to depend on the first power of reactant concentration?

5. What is the overall reaction order, and what are the orders with respect to each of the reactant species, for the following reactions:

	Reaction	Observed rate law
(a)	$N_2O_4 \rightarrow 2NO_2$	rate = $k[N_2O_4]$
(b)	$C_2H_4 + H_2 \rightarrow C_2H_6$	rate = $k[C_2H_4][H_2]$
(c)	$2N_2O_5 \rightarrow 4NO_2 + O_2$	rate = $k[N_2O_5]$
(d)	$2NO + 2H_2 \rightarrow N_2 + 2H_2O$	rate = $k[NO]^2[H_2]$
(e)	$CHCl_3 + Cl_2 \rightarrow CCl_4 + HCl$	rate = $k[CHCl_3][Cl_2]^{\frac{1}{2}}$
(f)	$2NO_2 + F_2 \rightarrow 2NO_2F$	rate = $k[NO_2][F_2]$
(g)	$2NH_3 \xrightarrow[\text{catalyst}]{\text{tungsten}} N_2 + 3H_2$	rate = $k[NH_3]^0$ = constant

6. Why can the equilibrium-constant expression be obtained from a balanced chemical equation, even though the rate expression cannot?

7. What are the equilibrium-constant expressions for the reactions in Question 5?

8. What is the complete rate equation for the HBr reaction discussed in this chapter? Show how it reduces to an expression of order $1\frac{1}{2}$ when the HBr concentration is low.

---

[1] This nitric acid reaction is the way in which nitrate is "fixed" in the atmosphere by lightning discharge. Raindrops in a severe electrical storm are slightly acid because of dissolved nitric acid from this process. Of the nitrate that is fixed every year, a little over half comes from bacteria, a little over one third from industrial processes, and approximately 10% from atmospheric fixation during thunderstorms. Thunderstorms were an even more important means of chemical synthesis in the period before life arose, when there was no competition, conscious or unconscious, from living organisms.

9. How is carbon-14 produced in the upper atmosphere? How is it eliminated from the planet? How is it exchanged with living organisms? Where do animals get the carbon-14 that they have in their tissues? Why does the ratio of carbon-14 to carbon-12 remain constant during the lifetime of a living organism? What happens to this ratio after death?

10. What are the units of a first-order rate constant, if concentrations are measured in mole liter^{-1}? The half-life of ^{14}C is 5570 years. What is its first-order rate constant?

11. How can a series of two-body collisions and a one-step, trimolecular collision yield the identical rate expression? Illustrate with an example from this chapter.

12. What is a "rate-determining step" and why is it important in mechanisms of reactions?

13. How did Sullivan demonstrate that HI synthesis was not a simple bimolecular collision of H_2 and I_2 molecules? Why does it appear to be so from the observed rate expression?

14. How can the rate of the NO reduction reaction depend only on the first power of H_2 concentration, when two H_2 molecules enter into the reaction?

15. According to the rate expression for the formation of HBr, does adding extra HBr to the reacting mixture speed up, or slow down, the reaction? What mechanistic step is assumed to be responsible for this behavior?

16. What is a chain reaction? What are chain-initiating steps, chain-propagating steps, and chain-damping steps? Illustrate with an example from this chapter.

17. In the collision theory of reactions, does every collision between potentially reacting molecules lead to a reaction? What other requirement must be satisfied? How does temperature affect the situation?

18. What is the activation energy of a reaction? How is it calculated from experimental rate constants?

19. If a chemical reaction absorbs heat, will the activation energy of the reverse reaction be greater, or less, than that for the forward reaction? Illustrate with an energy diagram.

20. The frequency with which molecules collide increases with the square root of the temperature, and this dependence is included in the A term of the collision-theory expression for a rate constant:

$$k = Ae^{-E_a/RT}$$

What physical situation does the exponential term represent? What is the most important contribution that a temperature increase makes in leading to a larger rate constant and a faster reaction?

21. What is an activated complex, or a transition state, in a chemical reaction? How does the energy of such a complex affect the rate of reaction? Why should the energy of this complex be lower in the

platinum-catalyzed hydrogen reaction described in this chapter than for the uncatalyzed gas-phase process?

22. What does a catalyst do to E_a when it speeds up a reaction? From energy diagrams show that a catalyst that accelerates the forward reaction but not the reverse would be a logical impossibility.

PROBLEMS

1. The half-life of ^{14}C is 5570 years. (a) Calculate the first-order rate constant, k. (b) How many radioactive disintegrations will occur per minute in a one-gram sample of pure ^{14}C? (c) A fresh sample of wood shows 15.3 disintegrations per minute per gram of carbon. What percent of the carbon is ^{14}C? (d) A sample of wood from an Egyptian mummy case gives 9.4 decay counts per minute per gram of carbon. How old is the mummy case? (e) In the skeleton of a fish caught in the Pacific Ocean in 1960, the ^{14}C disintegration rate was observed to be 17.2 counts per minute per gram of carbon. How can this be? What does this imply for Pacific archaeology?

2. For the reaction $2NO + H_2 \rightarrow N_2O + H_2O$ it was found in a series of experiments that doubling the initial concentration of NO made the initial reaction rate four times as fast, whereas doubling the initial H_2 concentration only made the initial reaction twice as rapid. Write the rate law for this reaction.

3. The method of studying the order of a reaction as outlined in the preceding problem is known as the *initial-rate* method. The reaction $S_2O_8^{2-} + 2I^- \rightarrow 2SO_4^{2-} + I_2$ in aqueous solution was studied by the initial-rate method, with the results for three trial runs given below.

	Initial $[S_2O_8^{2-}]$ (mole liter^{-1})	Initial $[I^-]$ (mole liter^{-1})	Initial rate (mole liter^{-1} min^{-1} of I_2)
Run A:	0.00010	0.010	0.65×10^{-6}
Run B:	0.00020	0.010	1.30×10^{-6}
Run C:	0.00020	0.005	0.65×10^{-6}

What is the rate expression for this reaction? What is the overall order of the reaction?

4. In the gas-phase reaction $2NO + Cl_2 \rightarrow 2NOCl$, the results given below were obtained in three runs of an initial-rate experiment.

	Initial p_{NO} (mm Hg)	Initial p_{Cl_2} (mm Hg)	Initial rate (atm sec^{-1})
Run A:	380	380	0.0051
Run B:	760	760	0.040
Run C:	380	760	0.010

Write the correct rate expression for the reaction. What is the overall order?

5. Isopropyl bromide reacts with water to form isopropyl alcohol and HBr by the overall reaction $(CH_3)_3CBr + H_2O \rightarrow (CH_3)_3COH + HBr$.

   (a) What would be the rate expression if the reaction were a simple bimolecular collision?

   (b) What would the rate expression be if the mechanism were

   $$(CH_3)_3CBr \rightarrow (CH_3)_3C^+ + Br^- \qquad \text{(slow)}$$
   $$(CH_3)_3C^+ + H_2O \rightarrow (CH_3)_3COH + H^+ \qquad \text{(fast)}$$

   (c) Could you distinguish between these two mechanisms, if the reaction takes place in dilute aqueous solution? Why, or why not?

6. The following data were measured for the decomposition of ammonia, $2NH_3 \rightarrow N_2 + 3H_2$.

Time (sec):	0	1	2
$[NH_3]$ (mole liter^{-1}):	2.000	1.993	1.987

   Plot the logarithms of the concentrations against time and show that this is a first-order process. Calculate the rate constant and half-life for ammonia decomposition.

7. The reaction $SO_2Cl_2 \rightarrow SO_2 + Cl_2$ is a first-order process with a rate constant of $k = 2.2 \times 10^{-5}$ sec^{-1} at 320°C. What fraction of the initial SO_2Cl_2 will have decomposed after heating at 320°C for 90 minutes?

8. For the decomposition of N_2O_5 in carbon tetrachloride, a plot of ln $[N_2O_5]$ against time gives a straight line. The rate constant is $k = 6.2 \times 10^{-4}$ sec^{-1} at 45°C. If one begins with 1 mole of N_2O_5 in a 1-liter flask, how long will it take for 20% of the N_2O_5 to decompose? What is the half-life of this decomposition?

9. The following data give the temperature dependence of the rate constant for the decomposition of N_2O_5:

T (°K)	k (sec^{-1})
273	7.87×10^{-7}
298	3.46×10^{-5}
308	1.35×10^{-4}
318	4.98×10^{-4}
328	1.50×10^{-3}
338	4.87×10^{-3}

   Make an Arrhenius plot and calculate the energy of activation for the reaction.

10. For a reaction with an activation energy of 4.0 kcal mole^{-1}, calculate the fraction of molecules with energy E_a or greater, $f = e^{-E_a/RT}$, for 0°K, 100°K, 1000°K, 10,000°K, and 100,000°K. Plot these on a linear graph of f versus T. What does this graph tell you about the influence of temperature on reaction rate?

11. The rate constant for the reaction $H_2 + I_2 \rightarrow 2HI$ was measured at several temperatures, with the following results:

T (°K)	k
556	4.5×10^{-5}
575	1.4×10^{-4}
629	2.5×10^{-3}
666	1.4×10^{-2}
781	1.34

Calculate the energy of activation for the reaction. Why do you not need to know the units of k to solve the problem?

12. Use the E_a for the reaction $H_2 + I_2 \rightarrow 2HI$ calculated in Problem 11, and standard heat of formation data from Appendix 2, to calculate the activation energy for the reverse reaction, $2HI \rightarrow H_2 + I_2$. Illustrate the relationships between these three numbers on an energy plot.

13. It is often said that, near room temperature, the rate of a reaction will double if the temperature is increased by 10°C. Calculate the activation energy of a reaction whose rate exactly doubles between 27°C and 37°C.

14. What is the activation energy for a reaction whose rate is tripled by a temperature increase from 20°C to 30°C?

15. For the decomposition of CH_3I at 285°K, E_a is 43 kcal mole^{-1}. What fraction of the molecules have this energy or greater at 285°K? Assuming that E_a is not a function of temperature (which is nearly so but not quite), calculate the percent *increase* in the fraction of molecules with energy greater than E_a, when the temperature is raised to 300°K.

16. The rate constant for the decomposition of N_2O_5 in carbon tetrachloride is 6.2×10^{-4} sec^{-1} at 45°C. Calculate the rate constant at 200°C, if the activation energy is 24.7 kcal mole^{-1}.

17. Why does it take longer to boil an egg on the top of Mt. Wilson (5710 feet) than in Pasadena (750 feet)? (Smog is not the answer.)

CHAPTER 16

Ions and Equilibrium; Acids and Bases

Acids are familiar to us because of their power as corrosive agents and solvents, bringing into solution compounds that are insoluble in water alone. Strong acids will attack many metals, converting them to soluble ions and liberating bubbles of hydrogen gas in the process. Acids also will dissolve carbonates such as limestone, and certain other minerals and inorganic compounds. The weaker acids that are safe to taste, such as citric acid in lemons and acetic acid in vinegar, have a characteristic mouth-puckering sharp taste that we immediately recognize and designate as "acid."

Bases also are useful for dissolving water-insoluble substances, especially oils, greases, and other organic compounds. Sodium hydroxide, for example, will attack the oils of the skin and turn them into soap, which is why solutions of household lye feel slippery to the touch. We have seen previously that there are many substances, amphoteric oxides among them, that are insoluble in plain water but are dissolved either by an acid or a base, or both.

Besides their usefulness as solvents, acids and bases are important as catalysts. Because of their small size, mobility, and charge, H^+ and OH^- ions from acids and bases can attack compounds in such a way as to make reactions occur more easily and faster. This is the key to their catalytic effectiveness. If a substance provides a faster pathway for reaction but is regenerated again at the end of the process, it is a true catalyst. If catalysts are ions or molecules dissolved in the same solution as the reactants and products, they are known as *homogeneous catalysts*. This is the type of catalysis discussed in the postscript to this chapter. In Chapter 15 we saw examples of *heterogeneous catalysts*, in which the catalyst is a separate phase—a surface to which the gaseous or dissolved reactants diffuse and from which the products separate. In either type of catalysis the principle is the same: *A catalyst is a substance that accelerates a thermodynamically spontaneous reaction by providing an alternate mechanism, without itself being*

HYDRATED IONS

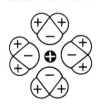

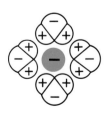

When a positive ion is hydrated, it is surrounded by water molecules with their negatively charged oxygen atoms pointing at it. Around a negative ion, the positively charged water hydrogens are in closest contact.

377

consumed by the overall reaction. It can participate in several steps of the process, as long as it is regenerated at the end. Acids and bases are widely used homogeneous catalysts.

STRONG ACIDS AND BASES

When salts dissolve in water the attractive forces within the ionic lattice are broken, and are replaced by attractive forces between individual ions and the polar water molecules that surround them in a hydration shell. (See illustration at chapter head.) As we saw in Chapter 12, the heat of solution is the difference between hydration energy and crystal-lattice energy. In addition, the salt becomes more disordered when it dissolves, so the entropy increases. If the combination of entropy increase and heat of hydration is enough to overcome the crystal-lattice energy, the salt will dissolve. We can write the overall process as

$$NaCl(s) \rightarrow Na^+(aq) + Cl^-(aq)$$

Salts such as NaCl are 100% ionized in the crystal and in aqueous solution. The symbol (aq) indicates that each ion is hydrated, or surrounded by a shell of polar water molecules in the manner that we saw first in Chapter 5, and in the drawing at the beginning of this chapter. For the sake of brevity, we will not use the (aq) symbol in equations in this chapter, but you should remember that ions in aqueous solution always are hydrated, and that hydration energy is largely responsible for making the salt dissolve. If there were no hydration energy to balance the loss of energy from crystal attractions, then dissolving NaCl would be as difficult as vaporizing it, which can be accomplished only at temperatures above 1400°C.

The behavior of strong acids and bases is similar to that of salts. Strong acids dissociate completely in water (below) with the liberation

Hydrogen chloride (HCl) dissolved in water breaks apart into a positive hydrogen ion (H⁺, represented here by a white plus sign on a black dot) and a negative chloride ion (Cl⁻). These charged ions are surrounded by polar water molecules. Because HCl dissociates completely in water, donating a proton for each HCl molecule, hydrochloric acid is a strong acid.

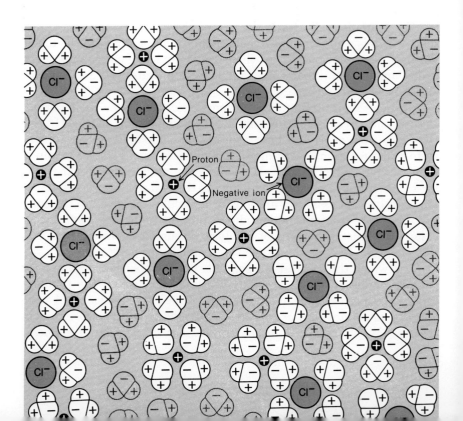

of a proton (hydrogen ion):

$$HCl \rightarrow H^+ + Cl^- \qquad \text{hydrochloric acid}$$

$$HNO_3 \rightarrow H^+ + NO_3^- \qquad \text{nitric acid}$$

$$H_2SO_4 \rightarrow H^+ + HSO_4^- \qquad \text{sulfuric acid}$$

$$HClO_4 \rightarrow H^+ + ClO_4^- \qquad \text{perchloric acid}$$

(Sulfuric acid also releases a second proton, but only incompletely, as a weak acid.) Strong bases in aqueous solution produce hydroxide ions:

$$NaOH \rightarrow Na^+ + OH^- \qquad \text{sodium hydroxide}$$

$$KOH \rightarrow K^+ + OH^- \qquad \text{potassium hydroxide}$$

Since these compounds dissociate completely in water, the concentration of H^+ or OH^- ions produced is the same as the overall concentration of the added acid or base. The concentration of hydrogen ions in a tenth-molar solution of nitric acid is 0.10 mole per liter.

WEAK ACIDS AND BASES

Other acids and bases are only incompletely dissociated into ions in solution, and exist in part as undissociated molecules (below). Dissolved hydrogen fluoride, for example, exists as an equilibrium mixture of HF molecules and hydrated H^+ and F^- ions:

$$HF \rightleftharpoons H^+ + F^-$$

The equilibrium constant for this dissociation usually is written as K_a, for acid dissociation, rather than K_{eq}:

$$K_a = \frac{[H^+][F^-]}{[HF]} = 0.000353 \text{ mole liter}^{-1} = 3.53 \times 10^{-4} \text{ mole liter}^{-1}$$

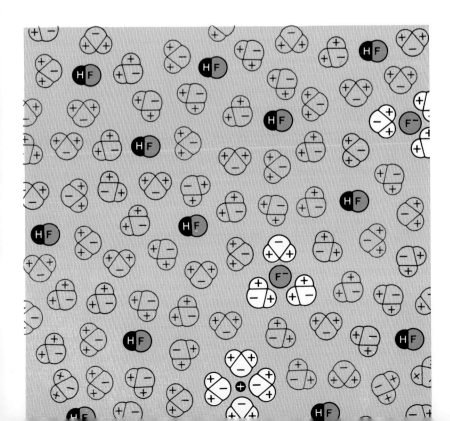

Only a few of the hydrogen fluoride molecules dissoved in water will dissociate into protons (H^+, represented by white plus sign on black dot) and fluoride ions (F^-). Because HF is only partially dissociated, it is a weak acid.

Hydrogen fluoride is an inorganic acid. Acetic acid is an organic acid, but behaves in a similar way:

$$CH_3\!-\!\overset{\displaystyle O}{\overset{\|}{C}}\!-\!OH \rightleftarrows CH_3\!-\!\overset{\displaystyle O}{\overset{\|}{C}}\!-\!O^- + H^+$$

Because acetic acid is so common, it often is given the shorthand representation HOAc, with Ac— symbolizing $CH_3\!-\!\overset{\|}{\underset{O}{C}}\!-\!$. The dissociation then is written

$$HOAc \rightleftarrows H^+ + OAc^-$$

The acid-dissociation equilibrium constant is

$$K_a = \frac{[H^+][OAc^-]}{[HOAc]} = 1.76 \times 10^{-5} \text{ mole liter}^{-1}$$

In such expressions concentrations of ions and molecules in solution always are given in molarity (M), or moles per liter of solution. The units of K_a are unmistakable, and ordinarily are omitted.

Hydrocyanic acid, HCN, is much weaker than any of the acids we have considered thus far. By comparison with HCl, HF, or acetic acid, it dissociates only to a minute extent:

$$HCN \rightleftarrows H^+ + CN^-$$

$$K_a = \frac{[H^+][CN^-]}{[HCN]} = 0.000000000493 = 4.93 \times 10^{-10} \text{ mole liter}^{-1}$$

Ammonia is an example of a weak base that reacts with water to yield ammonium and hydroxide ions, but the reaction is far from complete:

$$NH_3 + H_2O \rightleftarrows NH_4^+ + OH^-$$

$$K_{eq} = \frac{[NH_4^+][OH^-]}{[NH_3][H_2O]}$$

Water is both solvent and reactant in this reaction. For moderately dilute solutions of ammonia, the concentration of water will not change appreciably from that of pure water:

$$\frac{1000 \text{ g liter}^{-1}}{18.0 \text{ g mole}^{-1}} = 55.5 \text{ moles liter}^{-1}$$

For simplicity, the constant H_2O concentration of 55.5 moles liter^{-1} can be brought to the left side of the equation and incorporated into the equilibrium constant:

$$K_b = \text{base-dissociation constant} = 55.5\, K_{eq}$$

$$K_b = \frac{[NH_4^+][OH^-]}{[NH_3]} = 1.76 \times 10^{-5} \text{ mole liter}^{-1}$$

This is the usual practice whenever a water concentration term occurs explicitly in an acid–base equilibrium expression. (The identity of the numerical value of K_b for ammonia with K_a of acetic acid is only coincidence.)

380

CALCULATIONS WITH EQUILIBRIUM CONSTANTS

In half molar nitric acid, the concentrations of H^+ and NO_3^- ions are each 0.5 mole liter^{-1}, since strong acids are completely dissociated. In 0.5-molar acetic acid, dissociation is incomplete, and the ion concentrations are much less than 0.5 mole liter^{-1}. We can find out how much less by using the acetic acid equilibrium expression. Let the original, overall HOAc concentration be c_0 moles liter^{-1} before dissociation takes place, and suppose that when equilibrium is reached, y moles per liter of this acid have dissociated. Then c_0 is specified by the initial conditions of the experiment, and y is the concentration of each ion, because for every dissociated HOAc molecule, one H^+ ion and one OAc^- ion are formed. At equilibrium:

$[HOAc] = c_0 - y$ (initial acid less that which has dissociated)

$[H^+] = [OAc^-] = y$ (products of dissociation)

$$K_a = \frac{[H^+][OAc^-]}{[HOAc]} = \frac{y \times y}{c_0 - y} = \frac{y^2}{c_0 - y} = 1.76 \times 10^{-5}$$

This is a quadratic equation in y, and can be solved exactly using the quadratic formula:

If $ay^2 + by + c = 0$ then $y = \dfrac{-b \pm \sqrt{b^2 - 4ac}}{2a}$

You can avoid the quadratic formula by using a little chemical common sense instead. With a dissociation constant as small as 0.0000176, only a small fraction of the acetic acid present will be dissociated, so y is small. Hence we should be able to neglect y in the denominator, because it is subtracted from the much larger c_0, and solve a simpler equation instead:

$c_0 - y \simeq c_0$

$\dfrac{y^2}{c_0} = 1.76 \times 10^{-5}$ or $y^2 = 1.76 \times 10^{-5}\, c_0$

For half-molar acetic acid, $c_0 = 0.50$, and

$y^2 = 8.8 \times 10^{-6}$ mole^2 liter^{-2}

$y = 2.97 \times 10^{-3}$ mole liter$^{-1} = 0.00297$ mole liter^{-1}

You now can check the validity of the approximation:

$c_0 - y = 0.50 - 0.00297 \simeq 0.50$ (approximation is valid)

If the acid had dissociated enough so that y was a few percent of c_0, this approximation would not have been valid. You then could either have used the quadratic formula, or have used your initial y value to correct c_0 to $c_0 - y$, and performed a second calculation to find a better value for y by a method of successive approximations.

Our calculation tells us that, although the overall acetic acid concentration is 0.50 mole liter^{-1}, such a small amount dissociates that the acetate and hydrogen ions each are present at only 0.00297 mole liter^{-1} concentration. This is why acetic acid is classed as a weak acid.

Dissociation constants of some acids^a at 25°C

Acid	HA	A$^-$	K_a	pK_a
Perchloric	$HClO_4$	ClO_4^-	$\sim 10^{+8}$	~ -8
Permanganic	$HMnO_4$	MnO_4^-	$\sim 10^{+8}$	~ -8
Chloric	$HClO_3$	ClO_3^-	$\sim 10^{+3}$	~ -3
Nitric	HNO_3	NO_3^-		
Hydrobromic	HBr	Br$^-$		
Hydrochloric	HCl	Cl$^-$		
Sulfuric (1)^b	H_2SO_4	HSO_4^-		
Hydrated proton or protonated solvent	$H^+(aq)$	H_2O (solvent)	1.00	0.00
Trichloroacetic	CCl_3COOH	CCl_3COO^-	2×10^{-1}	0.70
Oxalic (1)	HOOC—COOH	HOOC—COO$^-$	5.9×10^{-2}	1.23
Dichloroacetic	$CHCl_2COOH$	$CHCl_2COO^-$	3.32×10^{-2}	1.48
Sulfurous (1)	H_2SO_3	HSO_3^-	1.54×10^{-2}	1.81
Sulfuric (2)	HSO_4^-	SO_4^{2-}	1.20×10^{-2}	1.92
Phosphoric (1)	H_3PO_4	$H_2PO_4^-$	7.52×10^{-3}	2.12
Bromoacetic	$CH_2BrCOOH$	CH_2BrCOO^-	2.05×10^{-3}	2.69
Malonic (1)	HOOC—CH_2—COOH	HOOC—CH_2—COO$^-$	1.49×10^{-3}	2.83
Chloroacetic	$CH_2ClCOOH$	CH_2ClCOO^-	1.40×10^{-3}	2.85
Nitrous	HNO_2	NO_2^-	4.6×10^{-4}	3.34
Hydrofluoric	HF	F$^-$	3.53×10^{-4}	3.45
Formic	HCOOH	HCOO$^-$	1.77×10^{-4}	3.75
Benzoic	C_6H_5COOH	$C_6H_5COO^-$	6.46×10^{-5}	4.19
Oxalic (2)	HOOC—COO$^-$	$^-$OOC—COO$^-$	6.4×10^{-5}	4.19
Acetic	CH_3COOH	CH_3COO^-	1.76×10^{-5}	4.75
Propionic	CH_3CH_2COOH	$CH_3CH_2COO^-$	1.34×10^{-5}	4.87
Malonic (2)	HOOC—CH_2—COO$^-$	$^-$OOC—CH_2—COO$^-$	2.03×10^{-6}	5.69
Carbonic (1)	$CO_2 + H_2O$	HCO_3^-	4.3×10^{-7}	6.37
Sulfurous (2)	HSO_3^-	SO_3^{2-}	1.02×10^{-7}	6.91
Hydrogen sulfide (1)	H_2S	HS$^-$	9.1×10^{-8}	7.04
Phosphoric (2)	$H_2PO_4^-$	HPO_4^{2-}	6.23×10^{-8}	7.21
Ammonium ion	NH_4^+	NH_3	5.6×10^{-10}	9.25
Hydrocyanic	HCN	CN$^-$	4.93×10^{-10}	9.31
Silver ion	$Ag^+ + H_2O$	AgOH	9.1×10^{-11}	10.04
Carbonic (2)	HCO_3^-	CO_3^{2-}	5.61×10^{-11}	10.25
Hydrogen peroxide	H_2O_2	HO_2^-	2.4×10^{-12}	11.62
Hydrogen sulfide (2)	HS$^-$	S^{2-}	1.1×10^{-12}	11.96
Phosphoric (3)	HPO_4^{2-}	PO_4^{3-}	2.2×10^{-13}	12.67
Water^c	H_2O	OH$^-$	1.8×10^{-16}	15.76

^{a} HA is the acid form, with acid strength decreasing down the table. A$^-$ is the conjugate base, with base strength increasing down the table. The equilibrium is $HA \rightleftharpoons H^+(aq) + A^-(aq)$, and the equilibrium-constant expression is

$$K_a = \frac{[H^+][A^-]}{[HA]} \qquad pK_a = -\log_{10} K_a$$

^{b} (1) is a first dissociation or proton-transfer reaction; (2) is a second dissociation; (3) is a third dissociation.
^{c} Note that this K_a value for water explicitly uses $[H_2O] = 55.5$ moles liter^{-1} in the denominator, for the sake of consistency with the other entries in the table, and that $55.5 \times 1.8 \times 10^{-16} = 1.0 \times 10^{-14} = K_w$.

The percent dissociation is

$$\frac{0.00297 \text{ mole liter}^{-1}}{0.50 \text{ mole liter}^{-1}} \times 100 = 0.59\%$$

The table shown at left gives dissociation constants for some of the more common weak acids. They range from the extensively dissociated trichloroacetic acid ($K_a = 0.20$) to the extremely weak third dissociation step of phosphoric acid:

1. $H_3PO_4 \rightleftarrows H_2PO_4^- + H^+$ $K_a = 7.52 \times 10^{-3}$
2. $H_2PO_4^- \rightleftarrows HPO_4^{2-} + H^+$ $K_a = 6.23 \times 10^{-8}$
3. $HPO_4^{2-} \rightleftarrows PO_4^{3-} + H^+$ $K_a = 2.2 \times 10^{-13}$

The acids above trichloroacetic acid in the table are so strong that they are totally dissociated in aqueous solution.

DISSOCIATION OF WATER

Water itself dissociates to a small but significant extent:

$$H_2O \rightleftarrows H^+ + OH^-$$

$$K_{eq} = \frac{[H^+][OH^-]}{[H_2O]}$$

As with ammonia, the constant term, $[H_2O] = 55.5$ moles liter^{-1}, can be incorporated into the equilibrium constant:

$$K_w = 55.5 K_{eq} = [H^+][OH^-]$$

in which K_w is the "ion product" for water. The numerical value of K_w varies with temperature:

At $0°C$, $K_w = 0.12 \times 10^{-14}$
At $25°C$, $K_w = 1.008 \times 10^{-14}$
At $40°C$, $K_w = 2.95 \times 10^{-14}$

(Can you use these data and Le Chatelier's principle to predict whether the dissociation of water is endothermic or exothermic? Check your prediction against ΔH^0 from Appendix 2.) The value of K_w that conventionally is used in calculations is

$$K_w = [H^+][OH^-] = 1.0 \times 10^{-14}$$

Because this ion product is an equilibrium constant, hydroxide and hydrogen ion concentrations can be related in aqueous solution. If we increase the hydrogen ion concentration by adding acid to a solution, we will repress the dissociation of water. Some of the added H^+ will combine with OH^-, and the hydroxide ion concentration will decrease until the ion product again is 10^{-14}. After equilibrium has been reestablished, the hydrogen and hydroxide ion concentrations will be different than before, but their product will be the same. Similarly, if we add hydroxide ions to a solution, they will combine with some of the H^+ originally present, until the ion product once again is 10^{-14}. When an acid and a base are mixed, some of the H^+ and OH^- ions combine to form H_2O. This is called *neutralization*. A solution in which $[H^+]$ and $[OH^-]$ are equal is termed a neutral solution.

$$H_2O \rightleftarrows H^+ + OH^-$$

$$K_{eq} = \frac{[H^+][OH^-]}{[H_2O]}$$

$$[H_2O] = \frac{1000 \text{ g liter}^{-1}}{18 \text{ g mole}^{-1}}$$
$$= 55.5 \text{ moles liter}^{-1}$$

$$K_w = [H_2O]K_{eq}$$
$$= 55.5K_{eq} = [H^+][OH^-]$$

In dilute aqueous solutions, the water concentration is effectively constant at 55.5 moles liter^{-1}. Hence the equilibrium expression can be simplified by incorporating the concentration $[H_2O]$ into the equilibrium constant, to produce the ion-product constant, K_w.

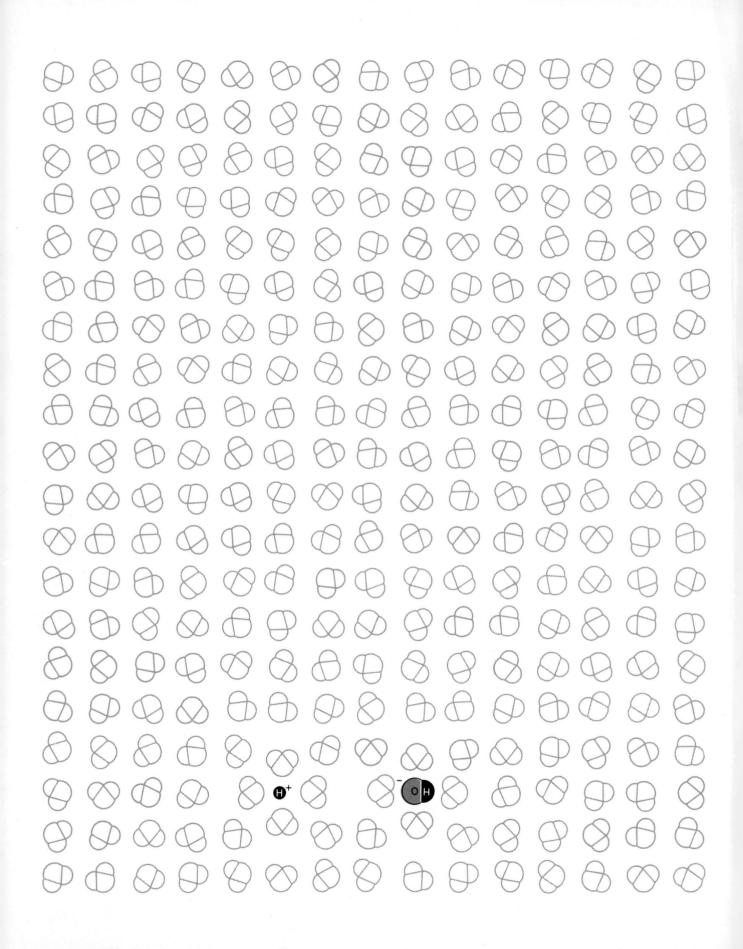

In pure water or any neutral solution, the hydroxide and hydrogen ion concentrations are

$$[H^+] = [OH^-] = 10^{-7} \text{ mole liter}^{-1}$$

A simple calculation can show how small a fraction of water molecules is dissociated. A concentration of 1.0×10^{-7} mole of H^+ per liter of water means that 1.0×10^{-7} mole of H_2O has dissociated per 55.5 moles of water, or one part in

$$\frac{55.5}{1.0 \times 10^{-7}} = 0.56 \times 10^{+9}$$

Approximately two water molecules out of every billion are dissociated into H^+ and OH^- ions. The drawing on the left page shows 300 water molecules, and a 600-page book filled with nothing but such drawings would have 180,000 water molecules. One would have to examine a library of 3000 such books, on the average, before finding *one* dissociated water molecule!

In 0.50-molar hydrochloric acid, which is completely dissociated,

$$[H^+] \quad = 0.50 \text{ mole liter}^{-1}$$

$$[OH^-] = \frac{K_w}{[H^+]} = \frac{10^{-14}}{0.50} = 2.0 \times 10^{-14} \text{ mole liter}^{-1}$$

The HCl has almost completely repressed the hydroxide ion concentration. The indefatigable librarian on this page would have to look through *five million* libraries of 3000 books each, to find one dissociated water molecule!

The situation is less extreme in 0.50-molar acetic acid. From the example that was worked out previously, the hydrogen ion concentration is 2.97×10^{-3} mole liter^{-1}, so the hydroxide ion concentration is

$$[OH^-] = \frac{K_w}{[H^+]} = \frac{10^{-14}}{(2.97 \times 10^{-3})}$$

$$= 3.36 \times 10^{-12} \text{ mole liter}^{-1}$$

The librarian's search would be reduced from 5 million libraries to only 30,000 libraries.

THE pH SCALE

Concentrations involving such extreme powers of ten, extending over 14 orders of magnitude, are clumsy to handle. In the discussion of entropy in Chapter 13 we found it convenient to reduce a wide-ranging quan-

DISSOCIATION OF WATER
In pure water, $[H^+] = [OH^-] = 10^{-7}$ mole liter^{-1}. Only one molecule per 500 million is dissociated into H^+ and OH^- ions. On the opposite page, 300 water molecules are shown, with one of them dissociated. On the average, 3000 books the size of this one, with their pages covered with water molecules, would have to be examined to find one dissociated molecule.

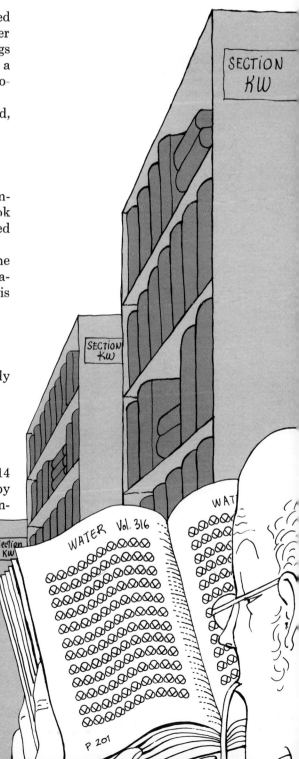

The $10 \times 10 \times 10$ cube contains 1000 blocks. One face contains 1/10 of the entire cube, one edge contains 1/100, and a single block is 1/1000 of the whole.

tity, probability, to more manageable numbers by taking the logarithm:

$$S = k \ln W = 2.303 \, k \log_{10} W$$

In Chapter 14 we saw that standard free energies convey the same information as equilibrium constants, but in a more compact logarithmic form:

$$\Delta G^0 = -RT \ln K_{eq} = -2.303 \, RT \log_{10} K_{eq}$$

The value of logarithmic notation can be illustrated by the $10 \times 10 \times 10$ stack of blocks at the left. The entire stack contains 1000 blocks. One face of the stack has 100 blocks, or 1/10 of the whole. One edge contains 10 blocks, or 1/100 of the stack, and one corner block represents 1/1000 of the entire ensemble. The fractions represented by the full block, face, edge, and corner, can be represented by 1 (or 10^0), 10^{-1}, 10^{-2}, and 10^{-3}. We also can represent these different orders of magnitude by picking out the negative exponents: 0, 1, 2, and 3. We can label these numbers pF values if we define pF as the negative logarithm to base ten of the fraction, F:

$$pF = -\log_{10} F$$

Instead of saying that a corner block is one thousandth of the complete stack, or F = 0.001, we could say that relative to the stack as a whole, a single corner block represents pF = 3.

This is the basis of the pH scale, with ions in solution replacing blocks in a stack. The pH of a solution is defined as the negative logarithm to base 10 of the hydrogen ion concentration:

$$pH = -\log_{10} [H^+]$$

In the same way, pOH is the negative logarithm of the hydroxide ion concentration, $pOH = -\log_{10} [OH^-]$, and pK is the negative logarithm of any equilibrium constant, $pK = -\log_{10} K$. The table on Page 382 gives the value of pK_a as well as K_a.

We can write the water dissociation equilibrium expression as $K_w = [H^+][OH^-] = 10^{-14}$; then $pK_w = pH + pOH = 14.00$. The *product* of the concentrations of H^+ and OH^- ions is a constant, 10^{-14}, and the *sum* of pH and pOH is another constant, 14. Pure water has a pH of 7.00, acids have pH values less than 7, and bases have pH values above 7. The pH of several commonly encountered liquids are given in the table at the top of the next page. In our previous example of 0.50-

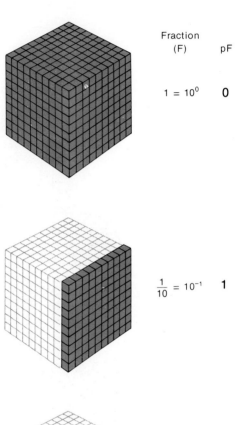

Fraction (F)	pF
$1 = 10^0$	**0**

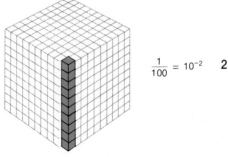

$\frac{1}{10} = 10^{-1}$	**1**

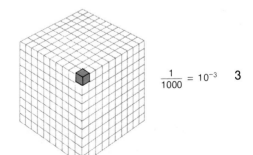

$\frac{1}{100} = 10^{-2}$	**2**

$\frac{1}{1000} = 10^{-3}$ **3**

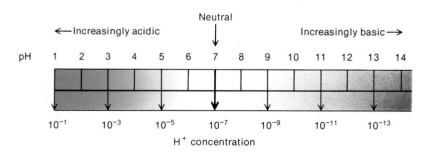

pH values are at the top. At the bottom is H^+ concentration in moles per liter.

Acidity (expressed as pH) of some common solutions

Substance	pH
Commercial concentrated HCl (37% by weight)	∼ −1.1
1-molar HCl solution	0.0
Gastric juice	1.4
Lemon juice	2.1
Orange juice	2.8
Wine	3.5
Tomato juice	4.1
Black coffee	5.0
Urine	6.0
Rainwater	6.5
Milk	6.9
Pure water at 24°C	7.0
Blood	7.4
Baking soda solution	8.5
Borax solution	9.2
Limewater	10.5
Household ammonia	11.9
1-molar NaOH solution	14.0
Saturated NaOH solution	∼15.0

molar acetic acid,

$$[H^+] = 2.97 \times 10^{-3} \text{ mole liter}^{-1} \quad \text{and}$$

$$[OH^-] = 3.36 \times 10^{-12} \text{ mole liter}^{-1}$$

$$\text{pH} = -\log_{10}(2.97 \times 10^{-3}) = 3.00 - \log_{10}(2.97)$$
$$= 3.00 - 0.47 = 2.53$$

$$\text{pOH} = -\log_{10}(3.36 \times 10^{-12}) = 12.00 - \log_{10}(3.36)$$
$$- 12.00 - 0.53 = 11.47$$

Or, more directly: $\text{pOH} = pK_w - \text{pH} = 14.00 - 2.53 = 11.47$.

NEUTRALIZATION

If a strong acid is added to a strong base, the product of hydrogen and hydroxide ion concentrations will be high at first. Some of these ions will recombine to form water until the product of $[H^+]$ and $[OH^-]$ is again brought down to 10^{-14} mole^2 liter^{-2}. This is the process of neutralization:

$$H^+ + Cl^- + Na^+ + OH^- \rightarrow Na^+ + Cl^- + H_2O$$

You can see from this that the neutralization of an acid and a base really involves only the H^+ and OH^- ions, and that other ions, Na^+ and Cl^- ions in this case play only a passive role.

One mole of an acid that liberates one H^+ per molecule, or one mole of a base that produces one OH^- per molecule, are said to possess one *equivalent* of neutralizing power. For H_2SO_4, which can release two protons per molecule, one mole of acid produces *two* acid–base equivalents. When an acid and a base have exactly neutralized one another, the number of equivalents of acid and base must be the same, no matter what the concentrations of the individual solutions.

NEUTRALIZATION

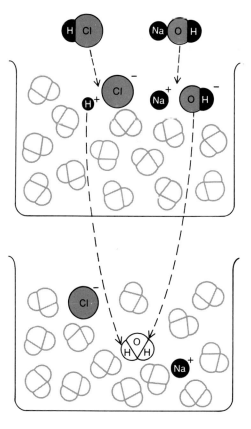

HCl and NaOH, when dissolved in water, dissociate into H^+, Cl^-, Na^+, and OH^- ions. The H^+ and OH^- ions combine to make H_2O in the process of acid–base neutralization. The Cl^- and Na^+ ions take no direct part in this reaction.

387

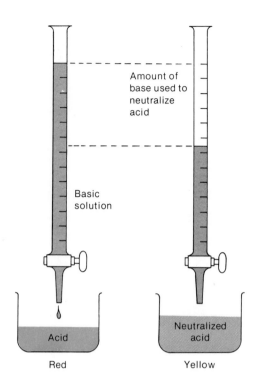

Amount of base used to neutralize acid

Basic solution

Acid

Neutralized acid

Red   Yellow

The acidic solution in the beaker has a red color from a few drops of methyl orange indicator. Basic solution of known strength is added from a graduated burette until the red color of the indicator just changes to yellow, indicating complete neutralization of the acid by the base. From the amount of base used, the concentration of the unknown acid can be calculated.

When a strong acid such as HCl is titrated with a strong base such as NaOH, the curve of pH versus the amount of base added looks like the one at the right. Any acid–base indicator that changes color between pH = 3 and pH = 11 will be usable in this titration.

Example. How many milliliters of a 0.10-molar NaOH solution will be required to neutralize 100 ml of 0.75-molar HCl?

Solution. The amount of HCl present is

$$0.100 \text{ liter} \times 0.75 \text{ mole liter}^{-1} = 0.075 \text{ mole HCl}$$

Since each mole of HCl yields one mole of H^+ upon complete dissociation, this quantity is also equal to 0.075 *equivalent* of HCl. For neutralization, the same number of equivalents of NaOH are required, 0.075. Again, since one mole of NaOH yields one mole of OH^- upon dissociation, 0.075 equivalent of NaOH equals 0.075 mole. The volume of 0.10-molar NaOH required to produce this amount is

$$\frac{0.075 \text{ mole}}{0.10 \text{ mole liter}^{-1}} = 0.75 \text{ liter or } 750 \text{ ml}$$

Just as milliliters are easier to use than liters in most situations because they replace decimal fractions with whole numbers, so millimoles (mmole) and milliequivalents (meq) often are more convenient than moles and equivalents; 1 mole = 1000 millimoles. The previous problem could be solved using millimoles and milliequivalents as follows:

$$100 \text{ ml} \times 0.75 \text{ meq HCl ml}^{-1} = 75 \text{ meq HCl}$$

$$\frac{75 \text{ meq NaOH}}{0.10 \text{ meq ml}^{-1}} = 750 \text{ ml of NaOH solution}$$

The easiest way of measuring how much of an unknown acid or base is present in solution is to neutralize it with just enough base or acid to bring the pH to 7.00, as measured by an acid–base indicator or other means. At neutrality, the number of equivalents of acid and base must be the same. This process of neutralization as a means of measuring the amount of unknown acid or base present is known as *titration*. The sample to be measured and a small amount of acid–base indicator are placed in a beaker, and the titrating base or acid is added from a graduated burette, as shown at the left, until a change of color of the

A TITRATION CURVE

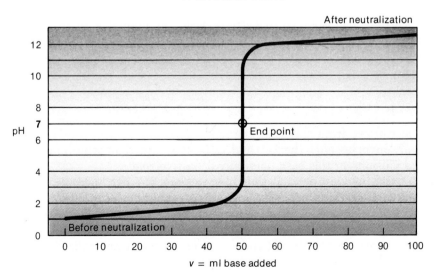

After neutralization

End point

Before neutralization

v = ml base added

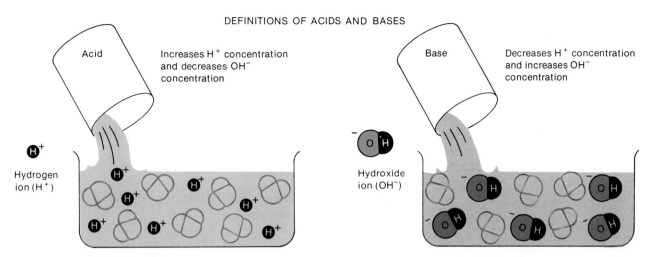

DEFINITIONS OF ACIDS AND BASES

Acid — Increases H$^+$ concentration and decreases OH$^-$ concentration

Base — Decreases H$^+$ concentration and increases OH$^-$ concentration

Hydrogen ion (H$^+$)

Hydroxide ion (OH$^-$)

acid–base indicator in the sample solution shows that neutralization, or the end point, has been reached.

Example. A solution of acetic acid of unknown concentration is titrated against 0.01-molar KOH, and it is found that 83 ml of base are required for complete neutralization of the acid. How many equivalents, and how many grams, of acetic acid were present?

Solution. The base solution contains 0.01 meq ml^{-1}, since KOH yields only one OH$^-$ ion per molecule. The 83 ml of base solution contain

$$83 \text{ ml} \times 0.01 \text{ meq ml}^{-1} = 0.83 \text{ meq of base}$$

This also must be the number of milliequivalents of acid, if neutralization is complete. Because each acetic acid molecule yields one H$^+$, 0.83 meq corresponds to 0.83 mmole or 0.83×10^{-3} mole of HOAc. Since the molecular weight of acetic acid is 60.05 g mole^{-1}, or 60.05 mg mmole^{-1}, the amount of acetic acid in the sample titrated is

$$60.05 \text{ mg mmole}^{-1} \times 0.83 \text{ mmole} = 44.8 \text{ mg of acetic acid}$$

Example. In an analysis of industrial sulfuric acid, a 5.00-ml sample was diluted to one liter, then 20 ml of the diluted acid were titrated with 0.10-molar NaOH. What is the concentration of the original acid, if 15.0 ml of NaOH solution are required to neutralize the acid?

Solution. The number of milliequivalents of NaOH used is

$$15.0 \text{ ml} \times 0.10 \text{ meq ml}^{-1} = 1.50 \text{ meq of NaOH}$$

This much NaOH will neutralize the same number of meq of H$_2$SO$_4$, 1.50 meq; but since each mole of H$_2$SO$_4$ contributes *two* moles of protons, 1.50 meq are obtained from only 0.75 mmole of sulfuric acid. The diluted sample had 0.75 mmole in 20 ml, or

$$\frac{0.75 \text{ mmole}}{20 \text{ ml}} = 0.0375 \text{ mmole ml}^{-1} \text{ or mole liter}^{-1}$$

The original undiluted sample was more concentrated by a factor of 5/1000, and hence had a sulfuric acid concentration of

$$0.0375 \text{ mole liter}^{-1} \times \frac{1000}{5} = 7.5 \text{ moles liter}^{-1}$$

By the most common definition, an acid is any substance that increases the hydrogen ion concentration when added to an aqueous solution, and a base is any substance that decreases the hydrogen ion concentration and increases the hydroxide ion concentration.

THE MEANING OF ACIDS AND BASES

In the view formalized for acids and bases at the turn of the century, an acid was any substance that dissociated to give H^+ ions in aqueous solution, and a base was any substance that dissociated to give OH^- ions. This definition (proposed by Arrhenius) was fine for potassium hydroxide, but where was the hydroxide ion in ammonia, NH_3? Ammonia releases hydroxide ions when it dissolves, but only because the ammonia steals a proton from a water molecule:

$$NH_3 + H_2O \rightleftharpoons NH_4^+ + OH^-$$

One could talk about "ammonium hydroxide," NH_4OH, but there is no evidence that the compound exists.

A better definition of acids and bases in aqueous solutions is: An *acid* is any substance that, when added to an aqueous solution, increases the hydrogen ion concentration; a *base* is any substance that, when added to an aqueous solution, decreases the hydrogen ion concentration and increases the hydroxide ion concentration. Since $[H^+]$ and $[OH^-]$ are linked by the water dissociation equilibrium, when one is increased, the other must decrease. By this definition, both NaOH and NH_3 are bases because they increase the hydroxide ion concentration, $[OH^-]$. In the case of NaOH, the hydroxide ions come from the crystal lattice of the solid, and in the case of NH_3 they come from dissociated water molecules whose protons have combined with NH_3 to form NH_4^+. The overall effect is the same.

The foregoing is the most useful everyday definition of acids and bases, applicable to aqueous solution. The *Brønsted–Lowry* theory goes one step further, and frees us from a dependence on water as a solvent. It also is helpful in explaining the difference between strong and weak acids. According to Brønsted and Lowry, an acid is any substance that releases protons in solution, and a base is any substance that combines with protons and removes them from solution. Thus in the dissociation of HCl, $HCl \rightleftharpoons H^+ + Cl^-$, the molecule of HCl is a B–L (Brønsted–Lowry) acid because it can release a proton, and the Cl^- ion is a B–L base because it can combine with a proton. HCl and Cl^- are called a *conjugate acid–base pair* (see left). In the two-proton dissociation of sulfuric acid,

$$H_2SO_4 \rightleftharpoons H^+ + HSO_4^- \quad \text{and} \quad HSO_4^- \rightleftharpoons H^+ + SO_4^{2-}$$

the bisulfate ion, HSO_4^-, is the conjugate base of the B–L acid H_2SO_4, and at the same time is the conjugate acid of the B–L base SO_4^{2-}. The words "acid" and "base" in the Brønsted–Lowry theory do not describe what a molecule *is*, but rather what it *does*.

For any given conjugate pair, if the acid is strong (marked tendency to lose a proton), the base will be weak (small attraction for a proton), and if the acid is weak (small tendency to lose its proton), the base is strong (great attraction for a proton). All of the B–L conjugate bases of the strong acids—Cl^-, ClO_4^-, NO_3^-, and HSO_4^-—are extremely weak B–L bases with little tendency to draw protons to themselves. We saw why this was true for the oxyacids in Chapters 5 and 6, in terms of a central electronegative atom pulling electrons away from the surface of the ion.

In the theory of Brønsted and Lowry, an acid is any substance that releases protons in solution, and a base is any substance that removes protons by combining with them. HCl is a strong acid because it readily releases H^+ ions. Cl^- is a weak base because it has a small tendency to combine with H^+. HCl and Cl^- are termed a conjugate pair of acid and base.

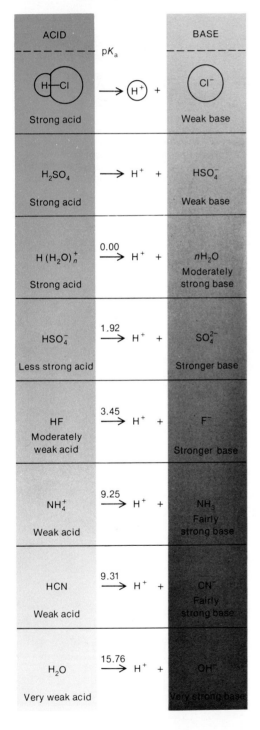

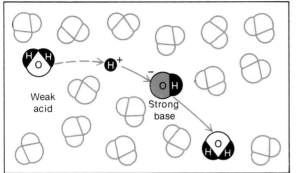 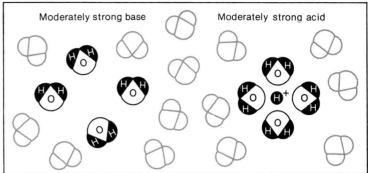

In contrast, the cyanide ion, CN^-, is a strong B–L base. It has a great attraction for protons, and the reaction

$$CN^- + H^+ \rightleftarrows HCN$$

$$K_{eq} = \frac{[HCN]}{[H^+][CN^-]} = \frac{1}{K_a} = 2.02 \times 10^9$$

is heavily shifted to the right. As a result, HCN is a very weak acid.

In the examples discussed so far, the acidic species has been electrically neutral and the basic species charged. This need not always be so. Ammonia is a B–L base, and the ammonium ion is a B–L acid, capable of releasing a proton:

$$NH_4^+ \rightleftarrows H^+ + NH_3$$

We can write an acid-dissociation equilibrium expression in the usual way:

$$K_a = \frac{[H^+][NH_3]}{[NH_4^+]}$$

This is related to the base-dissociation constant seen previously, K_b, by

$$K_b = \frac{[NH_4^+][OH^-]}{[NH_3]} = \frac{[NH_4^+][OH^-][H^+]}{[NH_3][H^+]} = \frac{K_w}{K_a}$$

or

$$K_a = \frac{K_w}{K_b} = \frac{1.00 \times 10^{-14}}{1.76 \times 10^{-5}} = 5.68 \times 10^{-10}$$

This is the value of K_a for the ammonium ion that is given in the table on Page 382. You either can think of NH_3 as a moderately strong base with a K_b of 1.76×10^{-5}, or NH_4^+ as a very weak acid with a K_a of 5.68×10^{-10}. The results of any calculation involving this acid-base equilibrium always will be the same whether you use K_a or K_b, as long as you know what you are doing.

Water can act as both a B–L acid and a B–L base. When water dissociates, it functions as a very weak B–L acid:

$$H_2O \text{ (weak acid)} \rightleftarrows H^+ + OH^- \text{ (strong base)}$$

We can regard the hydrating water molecules around a proton in solution as a weak B–L base:

$$H^+ + H_2O \text{ (weak base)} \rightleftarrows H_3O^+ \text{ (strong acid)}$$

H_2O is a weak acid and OH^- is a strong base, so only one water molecule in 10^{-7} is dissociated in a neutral solution (left). H_2O also is a fairly strong base, taking protons away from HCl or HNO_3 to form hydrated protons or "hydronium ions" (right).

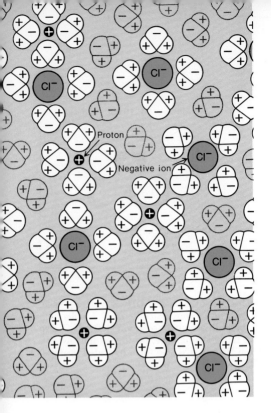

In aqueous solution HCl behaves as a strong acid, dissociating almost completely into hydrated H^+ and Cl^- ions.

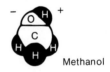

Methanol

In methanol as a solvent, HCl behaves as a weak acid, with only a fraction of the HCl molecules dissociating and giving their proton to solvent molecules.

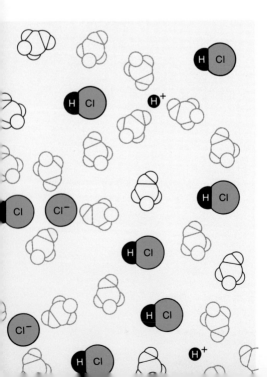

The Brønsted–Lowry theory has so influenced chemistry that two generations of chemists have written H_3O^+ for the hydrated form of H^+, and called it the "hydronium ion," even though the true hydration state of the proton is not known, but is probably more like $H^+(H_2O)_4$ or $H_9O_4^+$.

THE DIFFERENCE BETWEEN STRONG AND WEAK ACIDS

The hydronium ion notation is convenient in explaining why acids are divided into two categories, strong (complete dissociation in water) and weak (incomplete dissociation). Two equilibria compete for the proton when a general acid, HA, dissociates into H^+ and A^-:

$$H^+ + A^- \rightleftarrows HA \qquad \text{(binding of } H^+ \text{ by acid anion)}$$
$$H^+ + H_2O \rightleftarrows H_3O^+ \qquad \text{(binding of } H^+ \text{ by water molecules)}$$

One can regard A^- and H_2O as two B–L bases in competition for the proton, with the H_2O having the unfair advantage of being present in great excess. If the acid anion, A^-, is a stronger B–L base than the water molecule, it will have a greater attraction for protons. It will be able to compete successfully with water moleules for the available protons. Most of the acid then will exist as HA instead of A^-, and we will call HA a weak acid.

In contrast, if H_2O is a stronger B–L base than is A^-, the attraction of water molecules for protons will be greater than that of A^- ions. H_2O will take protons away from HA and form hydronium ions (hydrated H^+). Moreover, the large excess of water molecules present in an aqueous solution will push the equilibrium

$$H_2O + HA \rightleftarrows H_3O^+ + A^-$$

far to the right, in the direction of dissociated acid. For strong acids such as $HClO_4$, HNO_3, HCl, and H_2SO_4 (or weak B–L bases such as ClO_4^-, NO_3^-, Cl^-, and HSO_4^-), the donation of the proton by the acid to H_2O, as shown in the reaction to the left above, is effectively complete. We refer to these as the *strong acids*, in contrast to the weak acids that show only partial dissociation in aqueous solution. Although these strong acids do have different degrees of attraction for their protons, they all appear equally strong when water is the solvent. This is called the *leveling effect* of the solvent. If we want more information about the relative strengths of these acids, we must turn to a different solvent, which exerts less of a pulling power on the acid protons.

Methanol, CH_3OH, has a smaller attraction for protons than water does. HCl behaves as a weak acid in methanol solution, because it is only partially dissociated (lower left). One can measure dissociation constants in methanol or other nonaqueous solvents for compounds that are completely dissociated strong acids in water solution, and thus can make the relative strength ranking shown in the table on Page 382.

Whether an acid will behave as a strong or weak acid thus depends both on the acid and the solvent. Because the fluoride ion, F^-, is small, thus permitting the proton to come close to it and feel a strong electrostatic attraction, it is a moderately strong B–L base. Even though water molecules are present in great excess, the attraction of F^- for

392

protons is great enough that HF is only partially dissociated in aqueous solution. In contrast, the Cl⁻ ion is large, with a diffuse electron density, and does not permit the proton to approach as closely. It attracts protons more weakly, and is a weak B–L base. So many molecules of H_2O surround each Cl⁻ ion that they overwhelm Cl⁻ and compete successfully for the available H^+ ions, thereby pushing the dissociation equilibrium effectively to completion. Hence HCl is classed as a strong acid in water. In methanol, Cl⁻ ions in similar concentration find no difficulty in competing successfully with an excess of CH_3OH molecules for the available H^+, because of the very small attraction of CH_3OH molecules for H^+. Even in methanol, however, perchloric acid is a strong acid because the perchlorate ion, ClO_4^-, has less attraction for protons than methanol molecules do. $HClO_4$ is the strongest of all the common acids because ClO_4^- is the weakest of all the B–L bases.

ACIDS WITH SEVERAL DISSOCIATING PROTONS

Sulfuric acid can lose two protons. The first dissociation is that of a strong acid, and is complete in aqueous solution:

$$H_2SO_4 \xrightleftharpoons{} H^+ + HSO_4^-$$

The bisulfate ion, HSO_4^-, is more reluctant to lose another positive ion, since it already has one negative charge. The sulfate ion is a strong B–L base, and competes successfully with water molecules for the proton. Therefore HSO_4^- is a weak acid with a measurable dissociation constant:

$$HSO_4^- \rightleftharpoons H^+ + SO_4^{2-} \qquad K_{a_2} = 1.20 \times 10^{-2} \qquad pK_{a_2} = 1.92$$

Phosphoric acid has three dissociating protons, of varying degrees of weakness:

$$H_3PO_4 \rightleftharpoons H^+ + H_2PO_4^- \qquad K_{a_1} = 7.52 \times 10^{-3} \qquad pK_{a_1} = 2.12$$
$$H_2PO_4^- \rightleftharpoons H^+ + HPO_4^{2-} \qquad K_{a_2} = 6.23 \times 10^{-8} \qquad pK_{a_2} = 7.21$$
$$HPO_4^{2-} \rightleftharpoons H^+ + PO_4^{3-} \qquad K_{a_3} = 2.2 \times 10^{-13} \qquad pK_{a_3} = 12.67$$

The pK_a values are especially convenient, because the pK_a of a dissociation reaction is just the pH at which the undissociated and dissociated forms are present in equal amounts:

$$HA \rightleftharpoons H^+ + A^-$$

$$K_a = \frac{[H^+][A^-]}{[HA]}$$

$$\log_{10} K_a = \log_{10}[H^+] + \log_{10}\frac{[A^-]}{[HA]}$$

$$\log_{10}\frac{[A^-]}{[HA]} = -\log_{10}[H^+] + \log_{10} K_a$$

$$\log_{10}\frac{[A^-]}{[HA]} = pH - pK_a$$

If the pH exactly equals the pK_a for the acid under consideration, then $\log_{10}\frac{[A^-]}{[HA]} = 0$, $\frac{[A^-]}{[HA]} = 1$, and A^- and HA are present in equal amounts. If the pH falls below pK_a (more acidic), then $\log_{10}[A^-]/$

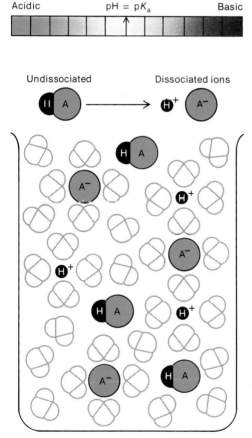

The pH equals the pK_a for dissociation of an acid or base when the concentrations of dissociated and undissociated species are equal.

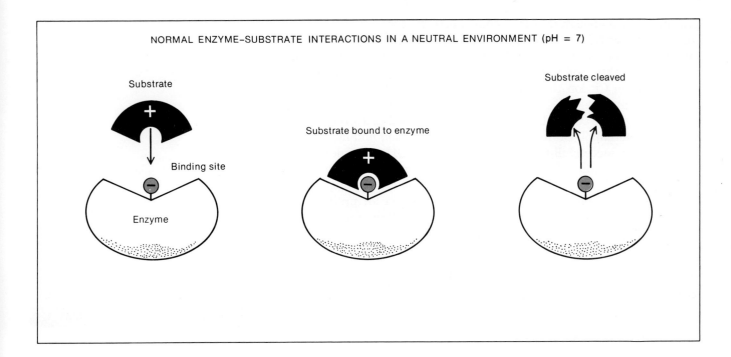

NORMAL ENZYME–SUBSTRATE INTERACTIONS IN A NEUTRAL ENVIRONMENT (pH = 7)

Substrate

Binding site

Enzyme

Substrate bound to enzyme

Substrate cleaved

Enzymes operate by binding a substrate molecule or molecules, helping a chemical reaction to occur more easily, and releasing the products. Binding is facilitated by steric fit between enzyme and substrate, and by hydrogen bonds, hydrophobic interactions, and electrostatic attractions. The enzyme shown here has a negatively charged chemical group at its binding site that attracts a positively charged region on the substrate.

[HA] will be negative, the ratio [A$^-$]/[HA] will be less than 1.00, and the HA form will be favored. In physical terms, if the pH is lowered by the addition of H$^+$, some of the excess H$^+$ combines with A$^-$ to make more of the undissociated acid. The dissociation equilibrium is shifted to the left. In contrast, if the pH is greater than pK_a for the acid, then $\log_{10}$[A$^-$]/[HA] will be positive, [A$^-$]/[HA] will be greater than 1.00, and A$^-$ will be favored over HA. Again, in physical terms, a shortage of H$^+$ ions in a basic solution forces more HA to dissociate and yield A$^-$. The equilibrium shifts to the right. For every unit of difference between pH and pK_a, the ratio of basic [A$^-$] to acidic [HA] forms changes by a factor of 10.

With this in mind, we can look at the pK_a values for the three phosphoric acid dissociations and say that, at physiological pH values of around 7.0 in a living organism, any phosphate present would be found as H$_2$PO$_4^-$ and HPO$_4^{2-}$ in roughly equal amounts. Since there are five pH units between the pK_a of a neutral solution and that of the first H$_3$PO$_4$/H$_2$PO$_4^-$ dissociation (pK_{a_1} = 2.12), the ratio of undissociated H$_3$PO$_4$ to H$_2$PO$_4^-$ ion at pH = 7 will be approximately 10^{-5}, or 1 to 100,000. Similarly, since the third dissociation of phosphoric acid has a pK_{a_3} of more than 12, the ratio of HPO$_4^{2-}$ to PO$_4^{3-}$ at pH = 7 will be more than 100,000 to 1. The approximate relative amounts of the four phosphate species at pH = 7 will be

H$_3$PO$_4$	H$_2$PO$_4^-$	HPO$_4^{2-}$	PO$_4^{3-}$
less than 10^{-5}	1.0	1.0	less than 10^{-5}

This is important physiologically because of the large number of phosphate compounds in living organisms. Adenosine triphosphate (ATP) was discussed as an energy-storage molecule in Chapter 10. It has four dissociable protons. The first three dissociations occur at pK_a values around pH = 2–3, so in neutral solutions these three dissociations

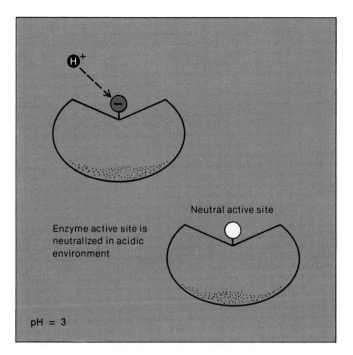

Enzyme active site is neutralized in acidic environment

Neutral active site

pH = 3

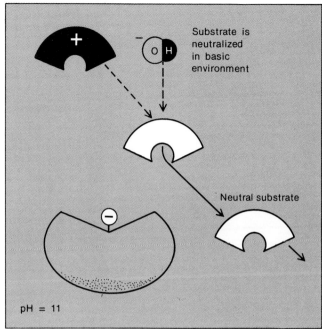

Substrate is neutralized in basic environment

Neutral substrate

pH = 11

are essentially complete. The fourth dissociation has $pK_a = 6.5$, so at pH = 7 the ratio of ATP^{4-} to ATP^{3-} is $10^{0.5} = 3.2$ to 1.

BUFFERS AND pH CONTROL

In many chemical reactions, especially in biological systems, it is important to keep the pH or acidity within defined limits. The bloodstream of humans is kept at pH − 7.4 ± 0.2, and acidosis or alkalosis outside this range can be fatal. (Those of you who read Michael Crichton's novel *The Andromeda Strain* may recall that the plot hinged on the alien life form in the victims' bloodstreams being even more sensitive to pH than the infected humans were.) pH control also is important in controlling enzyme activity. Most enzymes have an optimum pH range in which they function best, with sharply reduced efficiency outside this range. At too high or too low pH, acidic and basic groups on the enzyme or on its substrate molecules may pick up or lose extra protons, thereby altering the charge distribution at the molecular surface and possibly making a mating of enzyme and substrate difficult or impossible (see above). Many industrial processes go most efficiently, or most rapidly, at certain pH values. It is important to have some way of keeping pH changes to a minimum. The answer is the use of acid–base buffers.

A buffer is a mixture of a weak acid and its salt, or a weak base and its salt, such as:

1. acetic acid (HOAc) and sodium acetate (NaOAc);
2. carbonic acid (H_2CO_3) and sodium bicarbonate ($NaHCO_3$);
3. potassium dihydrogen phosphate (KH_2PO_4) and dipotassium hydrogen phosphate (K_2HPO_4);
4. ammonia (NH_3) and ammonium chloride (NH_4Cl).

pH control is important for enzyme activity. In the example begun on the opposite page, too acid conditions will neutralize the negative charge on the enzyme, and too basic conditions will neutralize the positive charge on the substrate. Both lead to diminished binding between enzyme and substrate, and diminished catalytic activity.

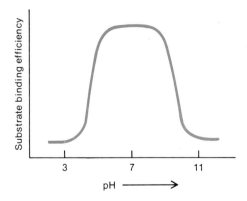

Most enzymes have an optimum pH, often around 7, and become less active at lower or higher pH.

The secret of pH control with acid buffers is that, if a small amount of strong acid is added to the buffer solution, some of the anions from the buffer salt will combine with the added protons to form more undissociated buffer acid. The change in pH is less than if the protons from the added acid had remained uncombined. Similarly, if a small amount of extra base is added, some of the buffer acid reacts with it to form more buffer salt. The reactions are

with added acid:
H^+ (outside source) + A^- (buffer salt) $\rightarrow$ HA

with added base:
OH^- (outside source) + HA (buffer acid) $\rightarrow$ H_2O + A^-

In the example on the opposite page, the buffer mixture is symbolized by five undissociated HA molecules and five A^- ions from NaA salt. As soon as three protons are added to the buffer, they are neutralized by three of the five A^- ions, and the pH of the solution is affected very little:

$$5HA + 5A^- + 3H^+ \rightarrow 8HA + 2A^-$$

Conversely, if three OH^- ions are added to this buffer mixture, as shown at the far right, they steal protons from three of the five undissociated HA molecules and are neutralized to form three more water molecules:

$$5HA + 5A^- + 3OH^- \rightarrow 2HA + 8A^- + 3H_2O$$

Without the buffer, the added H^+ and OH^- ions would have caused a large alteration in pH. Of course, if *six* H^+ ions had been added instead of three, then pH control would have broken down. This is called exceeding the *buffer capacity* of the solution. Buffers are designed to damp down minor perturbations in acidity, and the amount of buffer acid and salt must be greater than the amount of perturbing acid or base encountered.

Before any outside acid or base is added, the pH of a buffer mixture of a weak acid and its salt is given by the same expression that we derived previously from the equilibrium constant:

$$K_a = \frac{[H^+][A^-]}{[HA]}$$

$$\log_{10} K_a = \log_{10} H^+ + \log_{10} \frac{[A^-]}{[HA]}$$

$$pH = pK_a + \log_{10} \frac{[A^-]}{[HA]}$$

The pH of the buffer solution is determined by the pK_a of the acid used and the ratio of basic form (salt, A^-) to the acidic form (acid, HA). To prepare the buffer mixture, $[A^-]$ can be assumed to be equal to the total concentration of the salt, and $[HA]$ equal to the total concentration of the weak acid used. If the ratio of salt to acid is 1:1, then the pH will be the same as the pK_a, but one obviously can obtain any desired pH close to pK_a by altering the salt–acid ratio of the solution as it is made up.

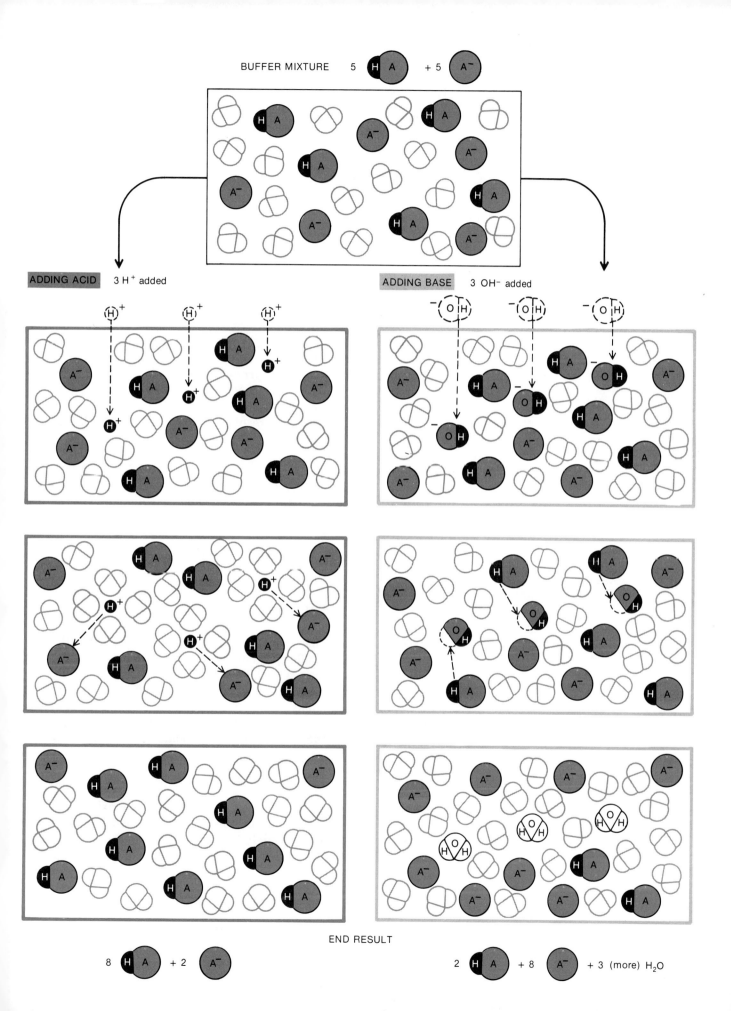

BUFFER MIXTURE   5 [H A] + 5 [A⁻]

ADDING ACID   3 H⁺ added

ADDING BASE   3 OH⁻ added

END RESULT

8 [H A] + 2 [A⁻]

2 [H A] + 8 [A⁻] + 3 (more) H₂O

Example. The second dissociation of phosphoric acid has a pK_a near 7.0:

$$H_2PO_4^- \rightleftharpoons H^+ + HPO_4^{2-} \qquad pK_{a_2} = 7.21$$

What should the ratio of K_2HPO_4 to KH_2PO_4 be to obtain a solution with a pH exactly 7.00?

Solution.

$$pH = pK_a + \log_{10}\frac{[A^-]}{[HA]}$$

$$7.00 = 7.21 + \log_{10}\frac{[HPO_4^{2-}]}{[H_2PO_4^-]}$$

$$\log_{10}\frac{[HPO_4^{2-}]}{[H_2PO_4^-]} = -0.21$$

$$\frac{[K_2HPO_4]}{[KH_2PO_4]} = \frac{[HPO_4^{2-}]}{[H_2PO_4^-]} = 10^{-0.21} = 10^{0.79} \times 10^{-1} = 0.62$$

A phosphate buffer solution at $pH = 7.00$ should be approximately two parts K_2HPO_4 to three parts KH_2PO_4. This is reasonable, because we want the solution to be a little on the acid side of the observed pK_a, and therefore we need a little more of the acid form of the buffer pair, KH_2PO_4.

Suppose now that we begin with a buffer mixture of 1.00 mole liter^{-1} of KH_2PO_4 and 0.62 mole liter^{-1} of K_2HPO_4, and add to this buffer mixture 0.01 mole liter^{-1} of any strong acid. How much will the pH shift? The added acid will react with HPO_4^{2-} and produce more $H_2PO_4^-$, so to a good approximation we can write:

$$[HPO_4^{2-}]_{new} = 0.62 - 0.01 = 0.61 \text{ mole liter}^{-1}$$

$$[H_2PO_4^-]_{new} = 1.00 + 0.01 = 1.01 \text{ mole liter}^{-1}$$

$$pH = 7.21 + \log_{10}\frac{0.61}{1.01} = 7.21 - 0.22 = 6.99$$

The 0.01-molar acid has managed to lower the pH only by 0.01 unit. If there had been no buffer present, addition of 0.01-molar strong acid would have shifted the pH to 2.00, a change in acidity similar to that between water and lemon juice. With a buffer the effect of the addition of strong acid is negligible.

Whenever pH changes are harmful, buffers have obvious applications. The bloodstream is buffered by carbonic acid and bicarbonate ions:

$$H_2CO_3 \rightleftharpoons H^+ + HCO_3^- \qquad pK_{a_1} = 6.37$$

Since the blood is to be maintained approximately one pH unit higher than the pK_a for this equilibrium, the ratio of bicarbonate ion to carbonic acid must be approximately 10:1. The reason a carbonate buffer and not a phosphate buffer is used in the bloodstream, even though the pK_{a_2} of phosphate is closer to 7.4, is apparently because CO_2 is already present as a by-product of respiration. It is available for use in buffering without any special supply system being needed:

$$H_2O + CO_2 \rightleftharpoons H_2CO_3 \rightleftharpoons H^+ + HCO_3^-$$

MEASURING pH: ACID–BASE INDICATORS

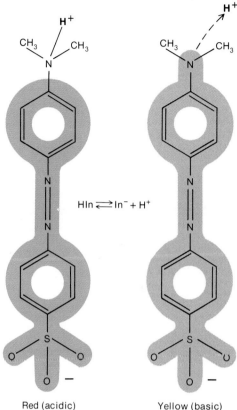

So far we have said nothing about how pH is detected and measured. Acids have a sharp taste, and bases have a bitter taste, but this method is both inexact and dangerous. Bases feel slippery because they saponify, or make soap from the oils of your fingertips, but testing for bases in this way can be dangerous and is strongly not recommended. Elaborate and convenient pH meters using glass electrodes provide the most accurate means of measuring pH. The most common detectors, however, are the color changes of acid–base indicators.

An acid–base indicator is a weak acid (or a weak base) that has different colors in its un-ionized and ionized states. Most indicators are aromatic molecules that have delocalized electrons, and in Chapter 9 we saw the reason for their color changes. The equilibrium

$$HIn \rightleftharpoons H^+ + In^-$$

with HIn representing the acid form of the indicator compound, is shifted to the left by an excess of acid, and to the right by an excess of base. The ratio of basic to acidic form of the indicator is linked to the pH by the now familiar expression

$$\log_{10}\frac{[In^-]}{[HIn]} = pH - pK_a$$

in which pK_a is the acid-dissociation constant for the weak indicator acid, HIn. The eye is sensitive to color changes over approximately a 1:10 to 10:1 concentration ratio, meaning that visible color changes in an indicator occur in a pH range of around 2 units, centered on the indicator's own pK_a. Litmus paper changes from red in acid to blue in base, in the pH range 5–8. Phenolphthalein solution added in minute quantities to the solution being tested or titrated changes from colorless (acid) to red (base) in the range of pH 8–10 because it has a pK_a around 9. Other common indicators, color changes, and useful pH ranges are shown below.

Methyl orange is red in acid and yellow in base. The color tint shows the different extent of delocalization of electrons in the two pH forms of methyl orange. The extent of delocalization affects the wavelengths of light absorbed and the color produced, as described in Chapter 9.

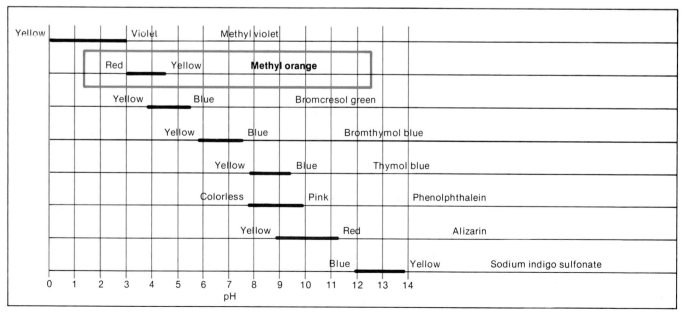

SOLUBILITY EQUILIBRIA

The most familiar salt, sodium chloride, is so soluble that we tend to think that all salts are equally soluble. This is far from true, and many salts are quite insoluble in water. Solubility is the result of competition between the mutual attractions of ions in the crystal, and hydration of individual ions by solvent molecules. Both of these processes involve large energies, and solubility depends on the frequently quite small difference between them. It is difficult to calculate crystal-lattice energies and hydration energies accurately enough to predict whether the difference between them will be positive or negative. Although we understand the forces at work when a salt dissolves, it is not easy to predict whether a given salt will dissolve or not.

There are a few common-sense principles that help in a general way. A crystal is held together by electrostatic forces between oppositely charged ions. Crystals with small ions that can be packed close together generally are harder to pull apart than crystals with large ions. Hence fluorides (F^-) and hydroxides (OH^-) tend to be less soluble than nitrates (NO_3^-) and perchlorates (ClO_4^-) with the same positive ion; chlorides (Cl^-) are intermediate in solubility. This rule is too simple in real situations, since small ions also permit a closer approach by the hydrating water molecules, which favors solution. The crystal-energy factor usually dominates, so salts with small ions are usually (but not aways) relatively insoluble. For similar electrostatic reasons highly charged ions such as phosphates (PO_4^{3-}) and carbonates (CO_3^{2-}) interact strongly with cations in the crystal and therefore are less soluble than are the singly charged nitrates and perchlorates. Silicates, with SiO_4^{4-} and larger frameworks, are notoriously insoluble, which is fortunate for the development of our planet.

Although real salts do seem to separate into the readily soluble and the barely soluble, "soluble" and "insoluble" really are terms for two extremes of an equilibrium between an intact salt and hydrated ions in solution. Silver chloride is an example of a sparingly soluble salt in equilibrium with its solid:

$$AgCl(s) \rightleftarrows Ag^+ + Cl^-$$

The usual equilibrium-constant expression would be written

$$K_{eq} = \frac{[Ag^+][Cl^-]}{[AgCl]}$$

As long as any solid AgCl remains in contact with the solution, it provides an infinite reservoir of more material, so the effective concentration of AgCl is unchanged. This constant term, like the water concentration term in the denominator of the K_w equilibrium expression, might as well be lumped together with the equilibrium constant. The resulting combined constant is known as the solubility-product constant, K_{sp}:

$$K_{sp} = [Ag^+][Cl^-]$$

This tells us that, as long as a solution of Ag^+ and Cl^- ions is in equilibrium with solid AgCl, the product of the two ion concentrations in solution will be constant. If more of either ion is added from the outside, then solid AgCl will precipitate until the product of ion concentrations again equals K_{sp}. If one ion is partially removed by a chemical reaction, or if the solution is diluted so both concentrations decrease, then more AgCl will dissolve until the ion solubility product is reached again. Solubility-product constants, like all equilibrium constants, vary with temperature, but values at 25°C are ordinarily used.

Example. The solubility of AgCl in water is 0.000013 mole liter⁻¹ at 25°C. What is the solubility-product constant, K_{sp}?

Solution. Since one mole of AgCl produces one mole each of Ag^+ and Cl^-, the concentration of each ion in a saturated solution is

$$[Ag^+] = [Cl^-] = 1.3 \times 10^{-5} \text{ mole liter}^{-1}$$

Hence,

$$K_{sp} = [Ag^+][Cl^-] = (1.3 \times 10^{-5})^2 \text{ mole}^2 \text{ liter}^{-2}$$

$$K_{sp} = 1.7 \times 10^{-10} \text{ mole}^2 \text{ liter}^{-2}$$

Example. Would AgCl be more, or less, soluble in 0.01-molar sodium chloride than in pure water? What would its solubility be?

Solution. The solubility-constant expression tells us that the product of concentrations of Ag^+ and Cl^- is fixed, no matter what the source of the ions. Hence, if we let x be the solubility of AgCl under these conditions, there will be 0.01 mole of Cl^- ion per liter from NaCl, and x moles per liter from AgCl. The total ion concentrations will be

$$[Ag^+] = x \text{ moles liter}^{-1}$$

$$[Cl^-] = 0.01 + x \text{ moles liter}^{-1}$$

The solubility-product constant will be the same as in the previous example; thus,

$$K_{sp} = 1.7 \times 10^{-10} = x(0.01 + x)$$

We can guess in advance that adding more chloride ion will make AgCl less soluble, because the product of $[Ag^+]$ and $[Cl^-]$ remains unchanged, or that x will turn out to be less than 1.3×10^{-5} mole liter⁻¹. We then can neglect x in comparison with 0.01 in the sum, and thereby avoid having to solve a quadratic equation. With this simplification,

$$0.01x = 1.7 \times 10^{-10}$$

$$x = 1.7 \times 10^{-8} \text{ mole liter}^{-1}$$

If you compare this result with that of the preceding example, you will find that the solubility of AgCl in 0.01-molar NaCl is only one 76th its solubility in pure water.

This decrease in solubility of a slightly soluble salt in the presence of another salt that shares an ion is known as the *common ion effect*. We could have predicted it from Le Chatelier's principle: When a system at equilibrium is subjected to a stress, the equilibrium shifts in such a way as to partially relieve that stress. Thus if Ag^+ and Cl^- are in balance in pure water, and if more Cl^- is added from another salt, then

Solubility-product constants, K_{sp}, at 25°C

Fluorides		Chromates (continued)		Hydroxides (continued)	
BaF_2	2.4×10^{-5}	$BaCrO_4$	8.5×10^{-11}	$Ni(OH)_2$	1.6×10^{-16}
MgF_2	8×10^{-8}	Ag_2CrO_4	1.9×10^{-12}	$Zn(OH)_2$	4.5×10^{-17}
PbF_2	4×10^{-8}	$PbCrO_4$	2×10^{-16}	$Cu(OH)_2$	1.6×10^{-19}
SrF_2	7.9×10^{-10}			$Hg(OH)_2$	3×10^{-26}
CaF_2	3.9×10^{-11}	Carbonates		$Sn(OH)_2$	3×10^{-27}
		$NiCO_3$	1.4×10^{-7}	$Cr(OH)_3$	6.7×10^{-31}
Chlorides		$CaCO_3$	4.7×10^{-9}	$Al(OH)_3$	5×10^{-33}
$PbCl_2$	1.6×10^{-5}	$BaCO_3$	1.6×10^{-9}	$Fe(OH)_3$	6×10^{-38}
$AgCl$	1.7×10^{-10}	$SrCO_3$	7×10^{-10}	$Co(OH)_3$	2.5×10^{-43}
$Hg_2Cl_2^a$	1.1×10^{-18}	$CuCO_3$	2.5×10^{-10}		
		$ZnCO_3$	2×10^{-10}	Sulfides	
Bromides		$MnCO_3$	8.8×10^{-11}	MnS	7×10^{-16}
$PbBr_2$	4.6×10^{-6}	$FeCO_3$	2.1×10^{-11}	FeS	4×10^{-19}
$AgBr$	5.0×10^{-13}	Ag_2CO_3	8.2×10^{-12}	NiS	3×10^{-21}
$Hg_2Br_2^a$	1.3×10^{-22}	$CdCO_3$	5.2×10^{-12}	CoS	5×10^{-22}
		$PbCO_3$	1.5×10^{-15}	ZnS	2.5×10^{-22}
Iodides		$MgCO_3$	1×10^{-15}	SnS	1×10^{-26}
PbI_2	8.3×10^{-9}	$Hg_2CO_3^a$	9.0×10^{-15}	CdS	1.0×10^{-28}
AgI	8.5×10^{-17}			PbS	7×10^{-29}
$Hg_2I_2^a$	4.5×10^{-29}			CuS	8×10^{-37}
		Hydroxides		Ag_2S	5.5×10^{-51}
Sulfates		$Ba(OH)_2$	5.0×10^{-3}	HgS	1.6×10^{-54}
$CaSO_4$	2.4×10^{-5}	$Sr(OH)_2$	3.2×10^{-4}	Bi_2S_3	1.6×10^{-72}
Ag_2SO_4	1.2×10^{-5}	$Ca(OH)_2$	1.3×10^{-6}		
$SrSO_4$	7.6×10^{-7}	$AgOH$	2.0×10^{-8}		
$PbSO_4$	1.3×10^{-8}	$Mg(OH)_2$	8.9×10^{-12}	Phosphates	
$BaSO_4$	1.5×10^{-9}	$Mn(OH)_2$	2×10^{-13}	Ag_3PO_4	1.8×10^{-18}
		$Cd(OH)_2$	2.0×10^{-14}	$Sr_3(PO_4)_2$	1×10^{-31}
Chromates		$Pb(OH)_2$	4.2×10^{-15}	$Ca_3(PO_4)_2$	1.3×10^{-32}
$SrCrO_4$	3.6×10^{-5}	$Fe(OH)_2$	1.8×10^{-15}	$Ba_3(PO_4)_2$	6×10^{-39}
$Hg_2CrO_4^a$	2×10^{-9}	$Co(OH)_2$	2.5×10^{-16}	$Pb_3(PO_4)_2$	1×10^{-54}

^{a} As Hg_2^{2+} ion. $K_{sp} = [Hg_2^{2+}][X^-]^2$

Ag^+ and Cl^- will combine and precipitate as solid AgCl until the product of $[Ag^+]$ and $[Cl^-]$ once again is as low as K_{sp} for AgCl.

Solubility-constant expressions can be written for all slightly soluble salts. Salts such as NaCl are very soluble, and their K_{sp}'s are effectively infinite, as far as solubility-product calculations are concerned. Soluble and slightly soluble salts resemble strong and weak acids, for although in theory there is no sharp demarcation between the two categories, in practice the division between two kinds of behavior is useful.

Solubility-product constants for various salts are given in the table above. Remember that these come from equilibrium-constant expressions, so if dissociation of a mole of a salt produces n moles of one of the ions, that ion will appear in the K_{sp} expression as the nth power of the concentration. For example,

$$CaF_2 \rightleftharpoons Ca^{2+} + 2F^- \qquad K_{sp} = [Ca^{2+}][F^-]^2$$

$$Ag_3PO_4 \rightleftharpoons 3Ag^+ + PO_4^{3-} \qquad K_{sp} = [Ag^+]^3[PO_4^{3-}]$$

$$Ba_3(PO_4)_2 \rightleftharpoons 3Ba^{2+} + 2PO_4^{3-} \qquad K_{sp} = [Ba^{2+}]^3[PO_4^{3-}]^2$$

Example. The solubility product for aluminum hydroxide, $Al(OH)_3$, is $K_{sp} = 5 \times 10^{-33}$. What is the solubility of aluminum hydroxide in pure water, in moles liter^{-1}?

Solution. Let the solubility be x. The dissociation reaction is

$$Al(OH)_3 \rightleftarrows Al^{3+} + 3OH^-$$

and the solubility-product expression is

$$K_{sp} = [Al^{3+}][OH^-]^3$$

The two ion concentrations will be

$$[Al^{3+}] = x \text{ moles liter}^{-1}$$

and

$$[OH^-] = 3x \text{ moles liter}^{-1}$$

Hence we can write

$$K_{sp} = x(3x)^3 = 5 \times 10^{-33}$$

$$x^4 = 2 \times 10^{-34} = 200 \times 10^{-36}$$

$$x = 4 \times 10^{-9} \text{ mole liter}^{-1}$$

Solubility-product calculations rarely are worth carrying beyond one or two significant figures, because of inaccuracies in K_{sp}. They also are accurate mainly for dilute solutions, since the equilibrium-constant expressions contain hidden assumptions that the ions in solution do not interact with one another, and that their behavior depends only on how many of them there are.

POSTSCRIPT: ACID–BASE CATALYSIS

One of the reasons given at the beginning of this chapter for an interest in acids and bases was their widespread use as catalysts for chemical reactions. We distinguish between *heterogeneous catalysis*, in which the substrate molecules diffuse to a catalytic surface, and *homogeneous catalysis*, in which the catalysts are ions dissolved in the same solution as the reactants. H^+ and OH^- are among the best of the homogeneous catalysts.

When rates of reaction began to be studied carefully at the end of the last century, one of the most-studied reactions was the hydrolysis (literally "cleaving by water") of ethyl acetate into ethanol and acetic acid:

$$\underset{\text{ethyl acetate}}{CH_3-\overset{\overset{\text{O}}{\|}}{C}-O-C_2H_5} + H_2O \rightarrow \underset{\text{acetic acid}}{CH_3-\overset{\overset{\text{O}}{\|}}{C}-OH} + \underset{\text{ethanol}}{HO-C_2H_5}$$

This is typical of many other hydrolysis reactions, including the dissolving of fats in soapmaking, and the digestion of proteins. It received

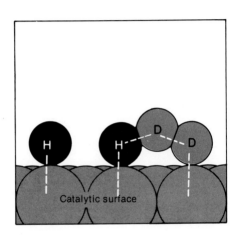

In heterogeneous catalysis substrate molecules are absorbed to the surface of a solid catalyst.

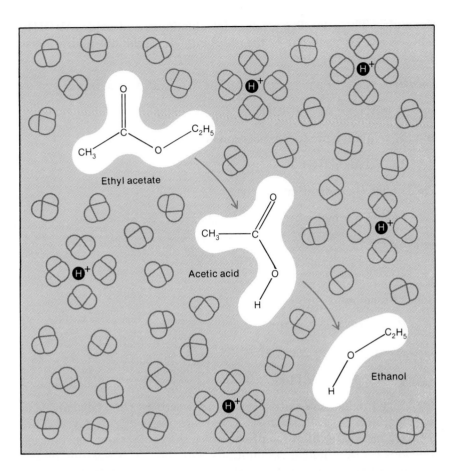

In homogeneous catalysis both the substrate molecules and the catalytic molecules or ions are present in the same phase, usually an aqueous solution. Hydrogen ions, H^+, and hydroxide ions, OH^-, are common catalysts in aqueous solution for many chemical reactions, among them the hydrolysis of an ester molecule, as shown on the opposite page.

a lot of attention because its equilibrium constant is close to 1.00, making the accurate measurement of concentrations of reactants and products at equilibrium easy. Another attraction is the dramatic effect that is produced on this reaction by catalysts.

The reaction is slow in the absence of a catalyst; ethyl acetate is relatively unreactive in water. The addition of a small amount of a strong acid or a strong base has a great effect. The rate of hydrolysis, as expected, is proportional to the concentrations of ethyl acetate and water. But if the catalyst is HCl or a similar strong acid, then the rate is also proportional to the hydrogen ion concentration. The experimental rate expression is

$$\text{rate}_f = k_f [H^+] [CH_3\text{---}CO\text{---}O\text{---}C_2H_5] [H_2O]$$

Doubling the ethyl acetate concentration doubles the speed of reaction, and doubling the hydrogen ion concentration does the same thing. Lowering the pH by one unit (a tenfold increase in $[H^+]$) makes the hydrolysis ten times as fast.

The rate therefore is sensitive to the concentration of a substance that does not appear in the overall reaction and is not represented in

404

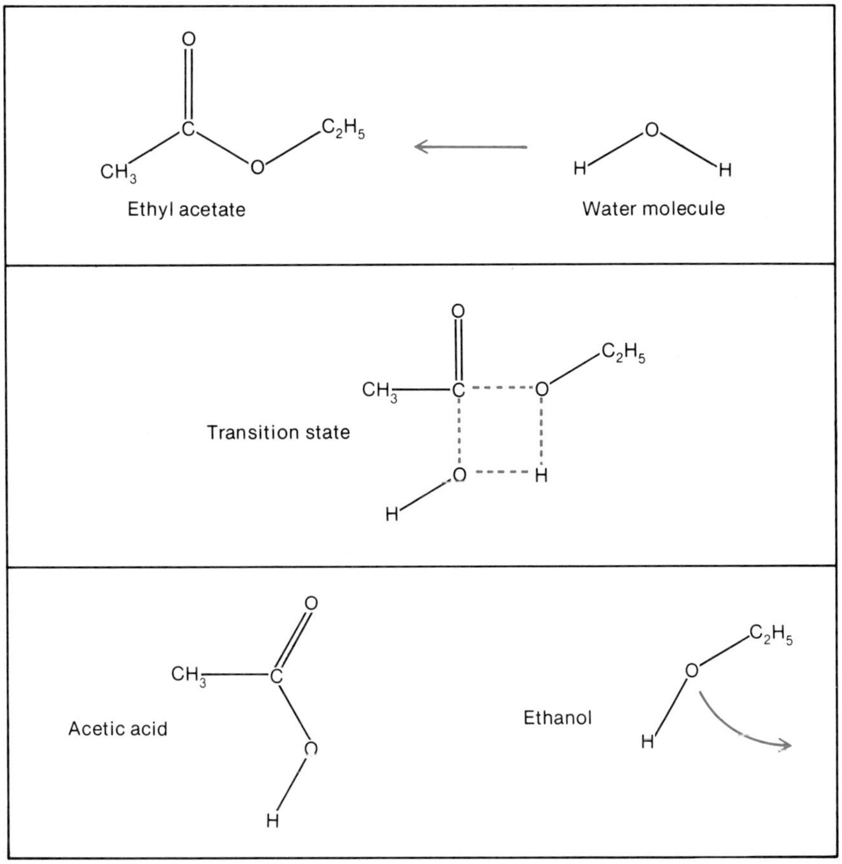

The uncatalyzed hydrolysis of ethyl acetate by a water molecule in neutral solution would involve a transition state (center) of such high energy that the process would be a slow one.

the equilibrium-constant expression:

$$K_{eq} = \frac{[CH_3\!-\!CO\!-\!OH]\,[C_2H_5\!-\!OH]}{[CH_3\!-\!CO\!-\!O\!-\!C_2H_5]\,[H_2O]}$$

This behavior is a clue that catalysis is involved. It occurs because the rate of the reverse reaction, synthesis of ethyl acetate from ethanol and acetic acid, also is proportional to hydrogen ion concentration:

$$rate_r = k_r[H^+]\,[CH_3\!-\!CO\!-\!OH]\,[C_2H_5\!-\!OH]$$

Protons, or hydrogen ions, catalyze both the forward and reverse reactions to the same degree, and proton concentrations cancel from the overall equilibrium expression.

How do protons catalyze this reaction? The overall process requires the pulling apart of a C—O bond in ethyl acetate, and an O—H bond in water, and a rejoining of the pieces in a different way (above). In pure water, we might imagine the reaction to occur via an intermediate activated complex like that at the center above. This activated complex, or transition state, would be a very unstable entity, and the reaction would have a high energy of activation, E_a. Chemical reaction by this mechanism would be extremely slow.

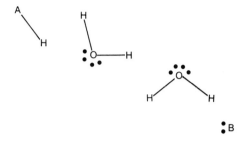

Proton transfer from one substance to another in aqueous solution can be a very fast process because an individual proton does not have to migrate from the donor (A–H) to the recipient (:B).

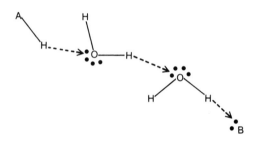

Each molecule need only transfer a proton to an adjacent molecule, in a dominolike cascade of transfers from the donor, through solvent H_2O molecules, to the recipient.

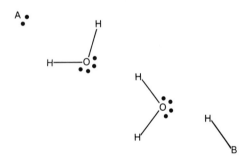

The net effect is the rapid transfer of one proton over a long distance from A to B, although no single proton moved more than a short distance.

The actual proton-catalyzed reaction, as it has been pieced together by chemists after many years of study, is outlined on the opposite page. Any C=O bond is polarized to some extent, because the oxygen atom is more electronegative than the carbon atom and draws electrons from the double bond to itself. (This slight polarization of charge is represented by delta symbols, δ^+ and δ^-, in contrast to + and −, which represent full electron charges.) With its two lone electron pairs and slight excess of negative charge, the carbonyl oxygen has a natural attraction for a proton in acidic solution. A proton is attracted to the O atom (a), and uses one of the oxygen lone pairs to form a covalent O—H bond (b). Since the lone pair thereby is pulled toward the H atom, a small positive charge is created on the oxygen atom. This positive charge exerts an even greater pull on the electrons of the double bond, turning it into a single bond and another O lone pair (c), and transferring the positive charge to the carbon.

The positively charged carbon atom in turn has an attraction for the unpaired electrons of the water molecules surrounding it. One of these can form a bond to the carbon (d), thereby shifting the positive charge to the incoming water oxygen. Step d represents a short-lived intermediate in the reaction, which cannot be isolated for study at leisure, but which is detectable by rapid spectroscopic and magnetic resonance methods. From d the reaction can go in more than one direction. It could reverse itself through Steps c, b, and a, or one of the protons could dissociate and take the positive charge with it. One of the possibilities is a rapid proton transfer from the charged oxygen to the bridge oxygen (e), taking the positive charge with it. Substance e, in turn, could break down in a series of Steps f–h, which are mirror images of Steps c–a, but with HOC_2H_5 playing the role of HOH. Step g involves a protonated acetic acid molecule instead of protonated ethyl acetate as in b, and the proton falls away again in the last step, h. The proton is used at the beginning and regenerated at the end; thus it facilitates the reaction but is not destroyed by it.

Hydrogen ions help to catalyze this reaction in two ways. The binding of a proton in Step a places a positive charge on the molecule and makes it more susceptible to attack by electron pairs of a water molecule (or any other electron-rich or negatively charged entity). The other thing that a proton can do better than other ions in aqueous solution is to move about rapidly from one part of a molecule to another. The fast shift between Steps d and e could not be accomplished by a sodium ion or any other substance. The reason why proton transfer in water solution is so easy and so fast is that protons can cascade dominofashion along a row of hydrogen-bonded water molecules, with each proton moving only from one oxygen atom to its neighbor, and with the proton that comes out at the end of the cascade different from the one that went in. This is illustrated at the left. In Steps d and e of the catalytic mechanism, the same proton does not have to move bodily from one oxygen atom to the other. It can transfer to a nearby water molecule and cause that molecule to donate one of its protons to the bridge oxygen. Proton transfer in aqueous solution is faster and easier than any other kind of atom shift.

Any compound that has lone electron pairs on an electronegative atom can attract a proton in acid solution. This includes almost every

ACID CATALYSIS OF THE HYDROLYSIS OF ETHYL ACETATE

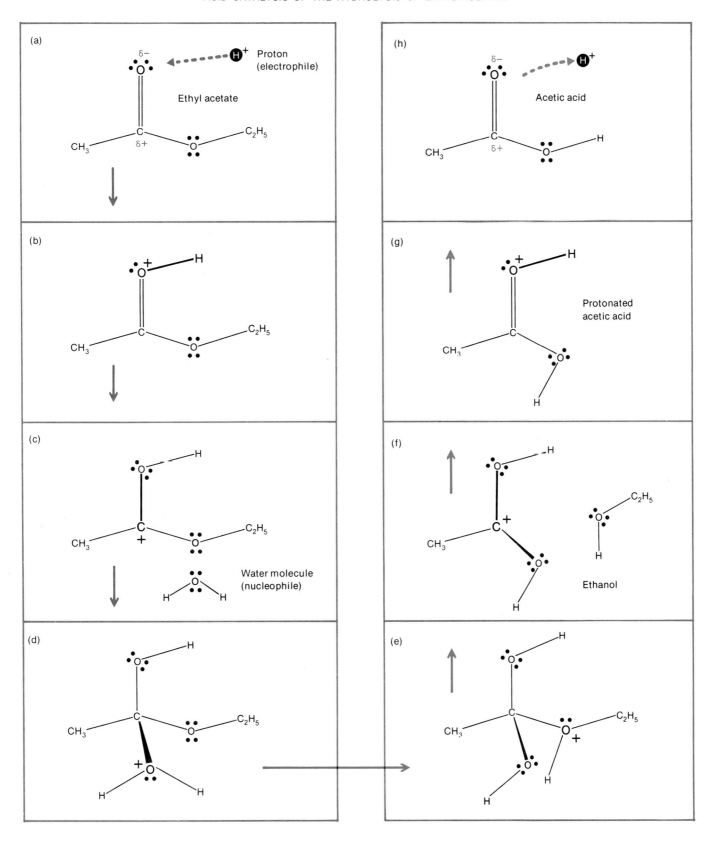

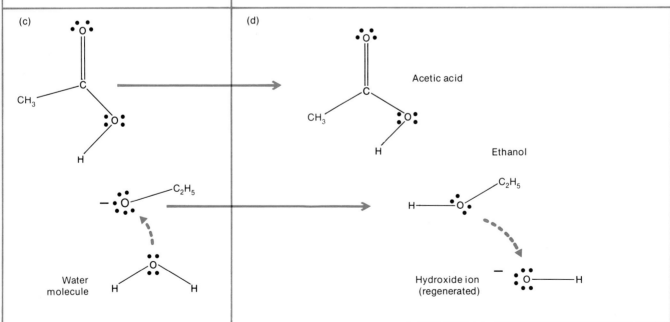

(a)

Ethyl
acetate

Hydroxide ion
(nucleophile)

(b)

Bridge
oxygen

(c)

Water
molecule

(d)

Acetic acid

Ethanol

Hydroxide ion
(regenerated)

type of organic compound. A proton also can be attracted to the electrons of a double bond and catalyze the addition of HBr or some other substance across the bond:

$$CH_3-\underset{\underset{H^+}{\uparrow}}{C}=C-CH_3 \rightarrow CH_3-\underset{H}{\overset{H\ H}{C}}-\underset{+}{\overset{}{C}}-CH_3 \rightarrow CH_3-\overset{H\ H}{C}-\underset{H\ Br}{\overset{}{C}}-CH_3$$

$$Br^-$$

There are few reactions of carbon compounds that acid will not catalyze. This is why we have hydrochloric acid in our stomach, to help enzymes digest and hydrolyze proteins. This is also why acid catalysis is so important in the chemical industry, from synthesis of rubbers and organic dyestuffs to pharmaceutical compounds.

Hydroxide ions also are good catalysts for many organic reactions. The mechanism for base-catalyzed hydrolysis of ethyl acetate is shown at the left. A negatively charged hydroxide ion is attracted to the slight positive charge on the carbon atom of a C=O bond, and a C—O bond is formed with the hydroxyl group. This pushes electrons in the C=O double bond toward the other O atom, thereby giving it a negative charge (b). This excess of electrons can be shifted back either to the hydroxyl oxygen (a) or to the bridge oxygen (c). As electrons in that C—O bridge bond are pushed toward the O, the C_2H_5—O^- group can fall away. The steps from b to c and b to a are identical except that they involve different C—O bonds. Once the C_2H_5—O^- group has departed, it can react with water to regenerate a hydroxide ion:

$$C_2H_5-O^- + H_2O \rightarrow C_2H_5-OH + OH^-$$

As with acid catalysis, the OH^- ion is involved in a lower-energy pathway, but is regenerated intact at the end of the process.

408

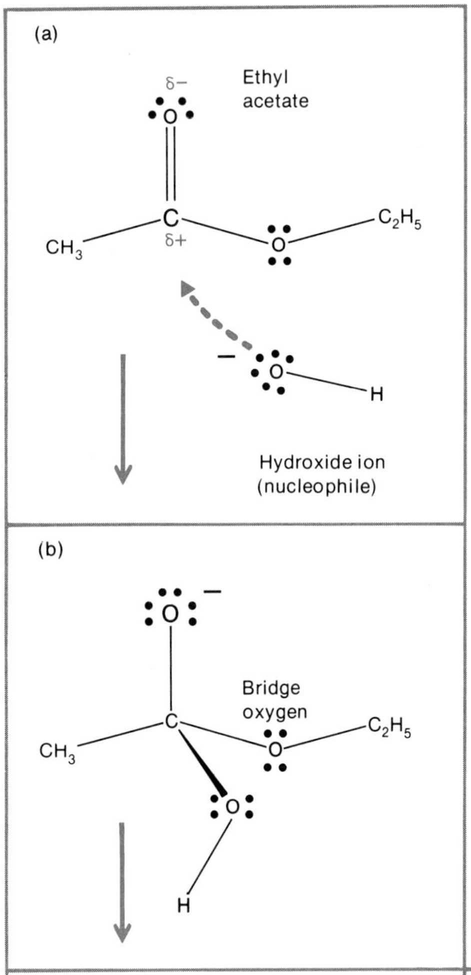

Acids and bases are effective catalysts because they contribute charged ions that can push and pull electrons around in a molecule. We will see in Chapter 24 that some of the catalytic mechanisms used by enzymes are very similar to mechanisms of acid–base catalysis.

QUESTIONS

1. From where does the energy come to overcome the attractions between ions when a salt crystal dissolves?

2. What is the distinction between a strong acid and a weak acid? Give an example of each.

3. Are there also both strong and weak bases? If there are, give examples.

4. For an acid that dissociates to release a single proton, what is the general expression for the dissociation constant, K_a?

5. What is the expression for the base-dissociation constant, K_b, for a weak base?

6. It often is convenient to use an acid-dissociation constant, K_a, for a weak base instead of K_b. For NH_3, what is the acid form and what is the expression for K_a? Show that, in general, $K_a \times K_b = K_w$.

7. What is the method of successive approximations, and when can it be used in solving acid–base equilibrium problems?

8. Why does the equilibrium-constant expression for the dissociation of water ordinarily not have an H_2O concentration term in the denominator? What happened to this concentration term? What is this H_2O-dissociation constant commonly called? How does its numerical value depend on temperature, and what value usually is used?

9. How can Le Chatelier's principle and the observed dependence of the ion-product constant upon temperature be used to decide whether the dissociation of water is exothermic or not? Check your prediction against information in Appendix 2.

10. What is the process of counteracting an acid with a base called? What ions are involved in this process, and how do they interact? What is the product?

11. What are the concentrations of H^+ and OH^- ions in pure water? How do these concentrations change when the solution is made acidic?

12. What is the pH scale, and why is it convenient in expressing hydrogen ion concentration? What is pOH?

13. How are pH and pOH related in aqueous solution? What values, or range of values, do they have in acidic, neutral, and basic solutions?

14. What is an *equivalent* in acid–base neutralization? How many equivalents are there per mole of the following: HCl, KOH, NH_3, H_2CO_3, H_3PO_4, HNO_3?

15. What is a *milliequivalent*? How many milliequivalents are present in a mole of H_2SO_4?

16. What are the Brønsted–Lowry definitions of acids and bases?

17. According to the traditional, or Arrhenius, definition of acid and base, KOH is the base in a potassium hydroxide solution. What is the base in such a solution, according to the Brønsted–Lowry theory? What is the conjugate acid of this B–L base?

18. What is meant by a conjugate acid-base pair in Brønsted–Lowry theory? If the acid is strong, will the conjugate base also be strong? Give an example.

19. Which of the following molecules or ions are Brønsted–Lowry acids and which are bases? In each case, what is the conjugate base or acid? What is the relative strength of each member of a conjugate pair?

NO_3^-, HBr, NH_3, SO_4^{2-}, H_3PO_4, H_2SO_4, HSO_4^-, NH_4^+, H_2O

20. How does the Brønsted–Lowry theory explain the difference between strong and weak acids? In what sense is this a competition theory, and what entities are the competitors? For what do they compete? How does the great excess of H_2O molecules in aqueous solutions affect the situation?

21. Show that when the pH of a solution is the same as the pK_a of a dissociating solute, the concentrations of dissociated and undissociated species are equal.

22. Show that when the pH of a solution containing an acid is one pH unit lower than the pK_a of the acid, the undissociated acid and the acid anion are present in a 10:1 ratio.

23. What is a buffer? How does it help to control or stabilize pH? What substances are combined to form a buffer solution?

24. When acid is added to a buffer solution, what happens to the extra protons? What happens when base is added to a buffer?

25. What is meant by "buffer capacity"? What happens when this buffer capacity is exceeded?

26. What is an acid–base indicator? Why does a change in pH lead to a color change in the solution?

27. What is a solubility-product constant? How is it related to the equilibrium constant for the dissolving of a solid salt?

28. What factors affect the solubility of a salt in water? Why do these factors make predictions of solubilities difficult?

29. If chloride ion (e.g., from NaCl) is added to a saturated silver chloride solution, how will this affect the concentration of silver ions? How is this similar to the ion-product equilibrium for the dissociation of water?

30. How does acid enable the hydrolysis of ethyl acetate to proceed faster than it would occur in neutral solution?

31. In what ways are acid and base catalysis of ethyl acetate different? How are they similar?

32. Why is the transfer of H^+ much faster than that of Na^+ in a solution containing both ions?

PROBLEMS

1. What is the pH of a 0.01-molar NaOH solution?

2. What is the pH of a 10^{-10}-molar HCl solution?

3. If a 0.10-molar acetic acid solution is 1.3% ionized, what is the pH of the solution? What is K_a for acetic acid? Compare your value with that in the table on Page 382.

4. If a 0.10-molar HF solution is 5.75% ionized, what is the pH of the solution? What is K_a for HF? Compare your value with that in the table on Page 382.

5. From the data in the table on Page 382, calculate the base-dissociation constant for ammonium hydroxide. Is undissociated NH_4OH really present in the solution? If not, what is the reaction for the production of ammonium ion and OH^-? What is the pH of a 0.0100-molar solution of ammonia?

6. A detergent box must bear a warning label if its contents will form a solution that has a pH greater than 11 because strong base degrades protein structure. Should a box bear such a label if the H^+ concentration of a solution of its contents is found to be 2.5×10^{-12} mole liter^{-1}?

7. The ionization constant for arsenous acid $(HAsO_2)$ is 6.0×10^{-10}. What is the pH of a 0.10-molar solution of arsenous acid? What is the pH of a 0.10-molar solution of $NaAsO_2$?

8. A solution of ammonia has a hydrogen ion concentration of 8.0×10^{-9} mole liter^{-1}. What is the pOH of this solution?

9. What is the CN^- ion concentration and the pOH in a 1.00-molar aqueous solution of HCN?

10. Pyridine is an organic base that reacts with water as follows:

    $C_5H_5N + H_2O \rightleftharpoons C_5H_5NH^+ + OH^-$

    The base-dissociation constant for this reaction, K_b, is 1.58×10^{-8}. What is the concentration of $C_5H_5NH^+$ ion in a solution that was initially 0.10 molar in pyridine? What is the pH of the solution?

11. What is the equilibrium concentration of NO_2^- ion in a 0.22-molar aqueous solution of nitrous acid? What is the pH? What is the percent ionization of HNO_2?

12. Hydrazine is a weak base that dissociates in water according to the equation

    $N_2H_4 + H_2O \rightleftharpoons N_2H_5^+ + OH^-$

    The equilibrium constant for this dissociation at 25°C is 2.0×10^{-6}. Write the equilibrium-constant expression for this reaction. If the initial hydrazine concentration is 0.010 molar, what is the concentration of hydrazinium ion, $N_2H_5^+$? What is the pH?

13. What is the pH of a 0.18-molar solution of ammonium chloride?

14. What is the pH of a 0.025-molar solution of sodium acetate?

15. What is the pH of a 1.0-molar solution of sodium cyanide?

16. A buffer solution is made with 0.30-molar sodium cyanide and 0.30-molar HCN. What is the pH of the buffer solution?

17. What is the pH of a buffer prepared to be 0.20 molar in NH_3 and 0.40 molar in NH_4Cl?

18. A buffer solution is made from equal volumes of 0.10-molar acetic acid and 0.10-molar sodium acetate. What is the pH of the buffer?

19. What is the pH of a solution made from equal volumes of 0.20-molar propionic acid and 0.20-molar sodium propionate?

20. A solution is 0.10 molar in formic acid and 0.010 molar in sodium formate. What is the pH of the solution?

21. If 0.010 mole of HCl gas is dissolved in one liter of pure water, what is the final pH? If the same amount of HCl is dissolved instead in one liter of the buffer solution of Problem 19, what is the final pH?

22. If 20 ml of a solution of 0.6-molar ammonia are mixed with 10 ml of a 1.8-molar ammonium chloride solution, what is the final pH? If 1 ml of a 1.0-molar HCl solution is added, what will the pH become? If the buffer solution had been prepared from 0.06-molar ammonia and 0.18-molar ammonium chloride, would the same HCl solution change the pH more, or less, than in the first situation? Why?

23. Novocain (Nvc) is a weak organic base that reacts with water as follows:

$$Nvc + H_2O \rightleftarrows NvcH^+ + OH^-$$

The base-equilibrium constant for this reaction is $K_b = 9.0 \times 10^{-6}$. Suppose that a 0.010-molar solution of Novocain is titrated with nitric acid. (a) What is the pH of the Novocain solution at the beginning of titration, before any acid has been added? (b) At the end point of the titration, the solution behaves just like a solution of 0.010-molar $NvcH^+NO_3^-$. What is the pH of this solution? (c) The indicator bromcresol green has a pK_a of 5.0. Is this indicator suitable for the titration?

24. The solubility of silver phosphate, Ag_3PO_4, in water is 0.0065 g liter^{-1} at 20°C. What is the solubility product (K_{sp}) for this salt? What is the solubility of silver phosphate in moles liter^{-1} in a solution that contains a total of 0.10 mole liter^{-1} of Ag^+?

25. If a solution containing 0.16 mole liter^{-1} of Pb^{2+} is made 0.10 molar in chloride ion, 99.0% of the Pb^{2+} is removed as $PbCl_2$. What is K_{sp} for $PbCl_2$?

Data in the table on Page 402 will help you solve the following problems.

26. Calculate the solubility in moles liter^{-1} of MgF_2 in pure water. What is the solubility in 0.050-molar NaF?

27. What is the solubility of CoS in pure water in moles liter^{-1}? What is the solubility of CoS in 0.10-molar sodium sulfide solution?

28. What is the silver ion concentration in a solution of silver chromate in pure water? In 0.10-molar chromate solution?

29. Calculate the calcium ion concentration in a saturated solution of calcium fluoride.

30. A solution is made 0.10 molar in Mg^{2+}, 0.10 molar in NH_3, and 1.0 molar in NH_4Cl. Will $Mg(OH)_2$ precipitate?

31. In the precipitation of metal sulfides, selective precipitation can be achieved by adjusting the hydrogen ion concentration. At what pH does ZnS begin to precipitate from a 0.077-molar solution of H_2S containing 0.08-molar Zn^{2+}? (Necessary data are in the tables of K_a and K_{sp} on Pages 382 and 402.)

32. What is the solubility of AgOH in a buffer at pH $= 13$?

33. In a water solution saturated with H_2S, $[H^+]^2[S^{2-}] = 1.3 \times 10^{-21}$. Calculate the solubility of FeS at pH $= 9$ and at pH $= 2$. Can you see how this behavior might be useful in analytical separations?

34. Calculate the solubility of $Mg(OH)_2$ in aqueous solution at pH $= 2$ and pH $= 12$. How is this behavior useful in chemical separations?

◀ *"Waterfall," lithograph by the famous Dutch artist M. C. Escher, 1961. From the collection of C. V. S. Roosevelt, Washington, D.C.*

CHAPTER 17

The Drive to Make Things Happen: Chemical and Electrical Potential

When we think about the force of gravity, and the spontaneous tendency for a stream to flow or a ball to roll downhill, it is convenient to regard it as a tendency for the water or the ball to go from a region of high to low potential energy. Only when such a drop in potential is possible can useful work be obtained from the process, which is why we immediately recognize the paradox on the opposite page as absurd. The attractive force that the Earth exerts on a ball of mass m is $F = mg$, in which g is the gravitational constant. If we lift the ball to a height h above some starting level, we give it an extra potential energy of $E_P = mgh$. The ball can convert this potential energy to kinetic energy of motion by rolling downhill to the original level, as represented on the next page. Spontaneous motion occurs from a region of high potential to one of low potential.

The same language is useful in studying chemical reactions. In Chapter 13 we saw that a spontaneous chemical reaction at constant overall temperature and pressure is one that leads to a decrease in free energy, G. The combination of hydrogen with oxygen to form water is highly spontaneous, and can be explosively fast:

$$H_2(g) + \tfrac{1}{2}O_2(g) \rightarrow H_2O(g) \qquad \Delta G^0 = -54.64 \text{ kcal per mole of } H_2O$$

We can think of this reaction as a process in which the atoms of hydrogen and oxygen move from a state of high chemical potential (H_2 and O_2 molecules) to a state of lower chemical potential (molecules of water vapor). It is reasonable to think of the free energy per mole of a substance as its *chemical potential*, and to regard a spontaneous chemical reaction as a rolling of atoms down a chemical potential "slope." The free energy given off in a spontaneous process then is just the change in potential (ΔG per mole) times the amount of substance undergoing the change (number of moles).

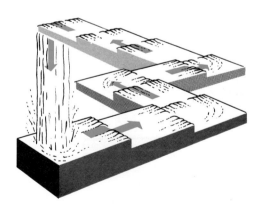

Water that drops from a higher to a lower level can do useful work. In the picture at the left, M. C. Escher has shown us an apparent perpetual motion machine, in which the water tumbles over a waterfall and drives a mill wheel, flows down a canal and then finds itself at the top of the waterfall again, ready to do more work. The mechanics of the illusion are shown above.

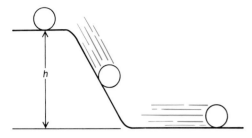

A ball rolling down a hill with a vertical fall of **h**, develops a kinetic energy equal to **E = mgh**, in which **m** is the amount of matter undergoing a potential drop of **gh**. This kinetic energy can be used to do useful work.

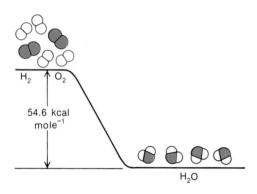

H_2 and O_2 combining to form H_2O develop a free energy equal to 54.6 **n** kilocalories, where **n** is the number of moles of H_2O formed and the free energy drop is 54.6 kcal mole^{-1}. This free energy can be used to do useful work.

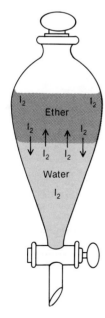

Iodine molecules will partition themselves between the ether and water layers until their molar free energy, or escaping tendency, is the same in each layer.

In equation form the preceding statement can be written

free energy emitted = change in potential × amount of reaction

For the water-vapor reaction, the free energy change per mole of water vapor formed is −54.64 kcal mole^{-1} H_2O. This is the chemical potential drop during the water reaction. If fifty moles of water vapor are produced, then the total free energy given off is

$$\Delta G^0 = (-54.64 \text{ kcal mole}^{-1})\ (50 \text{ moles}) = -2732 \text{ kcal}$$

In the language of gravitation, this amounts to rolling 50 balls down a 54.64 kcal hill (left). The concept of a potential of some kind to explain why spontaneous processes take place is a useful one, which we will see again in this chapter in connection with oxidation–reduction processes and electrochemistry.

FREE ENERGY AND ESCAPING TENDENCY

Free energy also is a measure of escaping tendency, as the experiment at the bottom left illustrates. Ether and water will not mix; they are mutually insoluble because the polar water molecules can form much stronger interactions by separating from the nonpolar ether molecules into their own phase. If we shake water and ether together in a flask, they divide into two layers upon standing.

Iodine crystals are soluble to a limited extent in both ether and water. If we add a small amount of iodine to the ether phase, some of the deep violet color slowly will appear in the water phase as a brown coloration, and if we add iodine to the water, some of it will diffuse into the ether. The free energy per mole, or chemical potential, of a substance in a mixture depends on its concentration. The higher the concentration, the higher the chemical potential. The spontaneous tendency of molecules to diffuse from regions of high concentration to more dilute regions is another example of the tendency to move from high to low potential. In the ether–water experiment, if iodine is added to the ether, its chemical potential in ether initially is higher than in water; hence iodine molecules migrate from ether to water until their chemical potential or free energy per mole is the same in both phases. When this condition is reached, no further change in free energy is produced by moving a molecule of I_2 from one phase to the other, $\Delta G = 0$ for the transfer, and equilibrium exists.

Because chemical potential or molar free energy determines when a substance will move from one chemical region to another, it often is referred to as an *escaping tendency*. When I_2 is concentrated in the ether layer, it has a high free energy per mole, or a high escaping tendency. If the escaping tendency of I_2 in water is lower because the concentration there is low, then iodine will diffuse from ether to water until its escaping tendencies in the two phases are the same. This relationship between free energy and escaping tendency is especially helpful in understanding some of the properties of solutions, and these are the subject of the first part of this chapter.

416

SOLUTIONS AND COLLIGATIVE PROPERTIES

Liquids are held together by van der Waals attractions, dipole forces if the molecules are polar, hydrogen bonds, and electrostatic attractions between ions of a molten salt. We will be concerned mainly with molecular liquids such as water, in which hydrogen bonds and van der Waals and dipole forces are the most important factors.

Not all molecules in a liquid move with the same speed. In general, the higher the temperature, the faster they move; but the molecules in a liquid have a range of speeds rather than one uniform speed. As molecules collide with one another they gain and lose energy, but the liquid as a whole maintains a velocity distribution of the type shown below. Increasing the temperature simply shifts the distribution maximum to higher speeds.

At any temperature, some of the molecules in a liquid will be moving so fast when they encounter the liquid–gas interface that they keep right on going into the gas phase as vapor (right). Most of the molecules of liquid have too little energy, and are pulled back from the interface into the liquid by the attractions of their neighbors. The overall free energy per mole of liquid rises as the temperature increases, and can be thought of as an average escaping tendency of molecules from the liquid.

At the same time, molecules in the vapor above the liquid also have a range of speeds and energies, and the slower-moving among them may be captured when they strike the liquid surface. The likelihood that this will happen increases with the number of gas molecules hitting the liquid surface per second, which in turn depends on the concentration or partial pressure of vapor molecules above the liquid. The higher this partial pressure of vapor, the more frequently the molecules will strike the surface of the liquid, and the greater will be the tendency of vapor molecules to move back into the liquid.

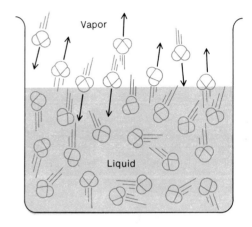

Molecules are in constant motion in both a liquid and the vapor above it. The pressure at which the return of gas molecules to the liquid just balances the escape of molecules from the liquid is the equilibrium vapor pressure of the liquid for a given temperature.

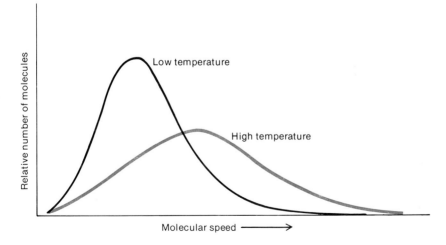

Not all molecules in a gas or liquid have the same energy or speed. At any temperature there is a distribution of speeds, with a maximum that increases as the temperature is raised.

417

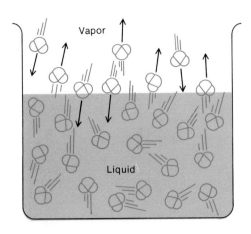

In the absence of solute molecules in the liquid, equilibrium is established between liquid and vapor at a certain vapor pressure.

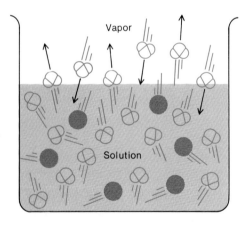

If solute molecules are present (black dots), then the rate of escape of liquid molecules is less, and the vapor pressure is lower at equilibrium.

At any temperature, equilibrium exists when the escaping tendency (or free energy per mole) of molecules in the liquid and vapor is the same. If the temperature is raised, the escaping tendency of liquid increases. More liquid will evaporate until the vapor pressure rises to the point at which the escaping tendency of vapor molecules back into the liquid matches the tendency of the liquid molecules to evaporate. This equilibrium partial pressure of vapor above a liquid is known as the equilibrium *vapor pressure* of the substance.

The vapor pressure of water at room temperature (25°C) is 0.0313 atm, or 23.8 mm of mercury (760 mm Hg = 1 atm). This means that if a still body of air over a lake is saturated with moisture at 25°C, there will be 0.0313 atm of water vapor in the air, and 0.969 atm of O_2, N_2, and other gases. The way in which equilibrium vapor pressure changes with temperature is shown in the graph at the far right. At 0°C the molecules of liquid water move slowly, their escaping tendency is small, and the equilibrium vapor pressure above the liquid is only 4.6 mm Hg. At 50°C it increases to 92.5 mm Hg, and at 100°C it equals 760 mm Hg or 1 atm pressure. This is the definition of the boiling point of a liquid—the temperature at which its vapor pressure equals the external pressure. Below the boiling point, atmospheric pressure on the liquid surface is greater than the pressure that bubbles of vapor can develop in the liquid, so these bubbles are prevented from forming. Evaporation takes place only at the liquid–gas interface. But at the boiling point, the vapor pressure becomes as great as the total pressure on the liquid surface. Bubbles of vapor begin to form inside the liquid as well as at its surface, which leads to the rapid agitation that we call boiling.

What would happen to the equilibrium vapor pressure of a liquid if some nonvolatile solute molecules or ions were added? The effect can be understood from the diagrams at the left. In the pure liquid water, every molecule that approaches the surface has a certain chance of escaping into the vapor phase, depending on its kinetic energy. If a nonvolatile material such as sugar is added so that one molecule in ten is sugar and not water, then only 90% of the molecules that formerly were potential escapees have a possibility of getting out of the liquid. The average escaping tendency of water molecules from a given amount of solution is reduced, but the rate of condensation is unaffected, since no sugar molecules are present in the vapor. Condensation gets ahead of vaporization, so more vapor condenses. When vapor–liquid equilibrium is established once more, we find that the equilibrium vapor pressure is only 90% as great as it was originally.

The mole fraction of a substance in a mixture is the number of moles of that substance divided by the total number of moles of all substances present:

$$X_j = \frac{n_j}{n_1 + n_2 + n_3 + \cdots} = \text{mole fraction of component } j$$

If a nonvolatile solute, A, is added to a pure solvent, B, until the mole fraction of the original solvent has decreased from one to X_B, then the vapor pressure will be only X_B times the vapor pressure of the pure liquid, p_B^0:

$$p_B = X_B p_B^0$$

418

This is Raoult's law. The *lowering* of vapor pressure of B will be proportional to the mole fraction of the added solute, A:

$$\Delta p_B = X_A p_B^0$$

You should be able to show that this follows from the previous expression, with the added fact that the sum of mole fractions is unity:

$$X_A + X_B = 1$$

The actual identity of the solute molecules is unimportant to the lowering of vapor pressure. Since theirs is a "spoiling" role in decreasing the frequency with which solvent molecules approach the surface, only their numbers matter. If a substance such as a salt dissociates into two particles or ions in solution, then it is doubly effective. One mole of NaCl lowers the vapor pressure of water by twice as much as a mole of glucose, because it yields twice the number of particles in an aqueous solution.

Example. At $35°C$ the vapor pressure of water is 42.2 mm Hg. What is the vapor pressure of an aqueous solution of glucose that has one glucose molecule for every 100 water molecules?

Solution. The mole fractions of water and glucose are

$$X_{glu} = \frac{1}{101} = 0.00990 \qquad X_{H_2O} = \frac{100}{101} - 0.990$$

The vapor pressure of water above the solution is

$$p_{H_2O} = X_{H_2O} p_{H_2O}^0 = 0.990(42.2) = 41.8 \text{ mm Hg}$$

For such dilute solutions it is more accurate to calculate the vapor pressure lowering instead:

$$\Delta p_{H_2O} = X_{glu} p_{H_2O}^0 = 0.0099(42.2) = 0.42 \text{ mm Hg}$$

Example. The elemental abundance table in Chapter 8 shows that ocean water can be considered as a solution with 330 NaCl "molecules" for every 33,000 water molecules. The vapor pressure of pure water on a hot summer day $(35°C)$ is 42.2 mm Hg. What is the vapor pressure of water in the middle of the ocean at that temperature?

Solution. We must be careful in calculating mole fractions now, since three species are present in solution: water molecules, and Na^+ and Cl^- ions. On the basis of one NaCl per 100 water molecules, the relative number of moles in each case is

$$n_{Na^+} = 1 \qquad n_{Cl^-} = 1 \qquad n_{H_2O} = 100 \qquad n_{total} = 102 \text{ (not 101)}$$

The mole fractions are

$$X_{Na^+} = \frac{1}{102} = 0.0098$$

$$X_{Cl^-} = \frac{1}{102} = 0.0098$$

$$X_{H_2O} = \frac{100}{102} = 0.980$$

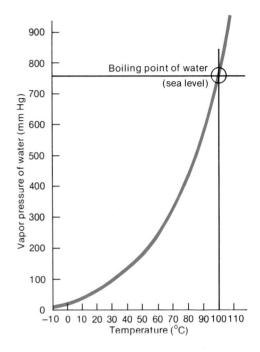

The equilibrium vapor pressure of water rises sharply with temperature, reaching 760 mm Hg at 100°C. This is the normal boiling point of water at sea level.

The vapor pressure of sea water then is

$$p_{H_2O} = 0.980(42.2) = 41.4 \text{ mm Hg}$$

The total vapor pressure lowering produced by the combination of Na^+ and Cl^- ions is

$$\Delta p_{H_2O} = (0.0098 + 0.0098)42.2 = 0.83 \text{ mm Hg}$$

Lowering of the equilibrium vapor pressure of a liquid by ions or molecules of a solute is known as a *colligative property* (meaning "collective" or "joint") because the size of the effect depends only on the total number of solute molecules or ions, and not on their identity. There are three other common colligative properties of solutions: boiling point elevation, freezing point lowering, and osmotic pressure. In all four cases, adding solute molecules or ions decreases the escaping tendency of solvent molecules from the liquid. Therefore some adjustment in temperature or pressure must be made to restore equilibrium between the liquid and the other phase.

BOILING POINT ELEVATION

Since the boiling point is defined as that temperature at which the vapor pressure equals the atmospheric pressure, anything that lowers the vapor pressure obviously will raise the boiling point. In terms of molar free energies or escaping tendencies, adding sugar molecules to boiling water at $100°C$ dilutes the H_2O molecules, lowers their escaping tendency, and causes the boiling to cease. To make the solution boil again, we must raise the temperature until the escaping tendency of the remaining H_2O molecules is as great as before. We can set up a free-energy expression that tells how the escaping tendency depends on concentration and temperature, and look for conditions under which these two effects cancel. The result for dilute solutions, in which interactions between solute molecules or ions can be neglected, is that the increase in boiling point, ΔT_b, is proportional to the solute concentration expressed as *molality*, or number of moles of solute particles per kilogram of pure solvent:

$$m_A = \text{molality of } A$$

$$= \text{moles of } A \text{ per kilogram of pure solvent } B$$

$$\Delta T_b = k_b m_A$$

The proportionality constant, k_b, varies from one solvent to another but is completely independent of the nature of the solute particles, A. The solute exerts its effect only by virtue of the number of molecules or ions present. As with vapor pressure, salts that produce several ions per molecule are more effective than molecules that do not dissociate.

Example. The molal boiling point elevation constant for water is $k_b = 0.512$. What is the boiling point (T_b) of a solution of 0.10 mole of glucose in 1000 g of water?

420

Solution.

$$m = \frac{0.10 \text{ mole}}{1 \text{ kg}} = 0.10 \text{ molal}$$

$$\Delta T_b = 0.512(0.10) = 0.051°C$$

$$T_b = 100 + 0.051 = 100.051°C$$

The boiling point is raised, but only by a twentieth of a degree.

Example. What is the boiling point of a 0.10-molal solution of NaCl?

Solution. Since each mole of NaCl produces two moles of ions, the effective molality is 0.20 mole of ions per 1000 g of water. The increase in boiling point is twice as great as it was for 0.10-molal glucose solution, or 0.10°C, and the boiling point of the solution is 100.10°C.

The meaning of a boiling point and the effect of salts can be illustrated by two cooking phenomena. Boiling water is a simple way of attaining a reproducible (constant) high temperature, which at sea level (1 atm pressure) is 100°C. The situation is slightly different at high altitude. At 8000 feet in Aspen, Colorado, atmospheric pressure is 560 mm Hg rather than 760 mm. (The U. S. Weather Bureau rule of thumb for change of atmospheric pressure with altitude is "an inch of mercury per thousand feet.") Water needs to be heated only to 92°C before its vapor pressure equals 560 mm, as shown below, and the turbulent bubbling away of vapor that we call boiling begins. Indeed, 92°C is as hot as an open pan of water can be heated in Aspen. If more heat is supplied, the temperature remains at 92°C, and the liquid simply boils away faster. Among the practical consequences of this are cold coffee,

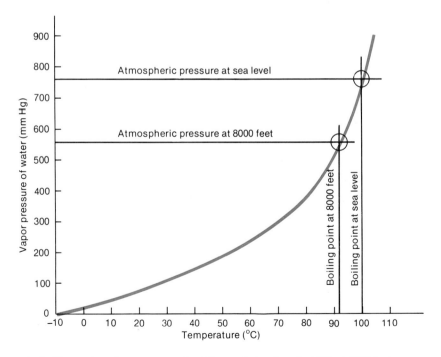

The boiling point of water at sea level is 100°C, but is only 92°C at 8000 feet.

and hard-boiled eggs that take forever to cook. At the other extreme, in a sealed pressure cooker that can take an overpressure of 3 atm (or total pressure of 4 atm), one can raise the temperature to 134°C, thereby making cooking much faster.

The second cooking phenomenon illustrates the influence of salts on boiling point. If a pot of water is brought to a boil, and salt is added, boiling immediately stops. The added ions lower the escaping tendency of water molecules. Only at a higher temperature will the vapor pressure again reach atmospheric pressure, and boiling recommence.

FREEZING POINT DEPRESSION

Addition of solute molecules also depresses the freezing point of a liquid, for reasons that can be seen at the left. The freezing point is the temperature at which freezing and thawing are in equilibrium. If solute ions or molecules are added until only 90% of the particles in the liquid are the original solvent molecules, then only 90% of the collisions of solvent particles with a crystal have a chance of adhering to the solid. Hence the temperature must be lowered, to decrease the tendency for molecules to break loose from the solid and escape into the solution, before freezing and thawing again are in balance.

For dilute solutions, the lowering of freezing point is proportional to the *molality* of the solute:

$$\Delta T_f = -k_f m_A$$

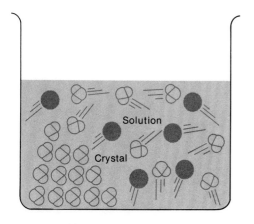

Solute molecules interfere with the crystallization of molecules of liquid, but not with the melting of the crystal. Hence solutes lower the temperature at which these opposing processes are in equilibrium, or the freezing point of the solution.

Example. The molal freezing point depression constant for water is $k_f = 1.86$. What is the freezing point of a solution of 0.10 mole of glucose in 1000 g of water?

Solution.

$$m = \frac{0.10 \text{ mole}}{1 \text{ kg}} = 0.10 \text{ molal}$$
$$\Delta T_f = -1.86(0.10) = -0.19°C$$

Because the freezing point of water is 0°C, the freezing point of the solution is −0.19°C.

Example. What is the freezing point of the ocean water described previously in this chapter?

Solution. Ocean water was described as containing approximately one NaCl per 100 water molecules, or one mole of NaCl per 100 moles of H_2O. Since the molecular weight of water is 18.0, this is equivalent to one mole of NaCl for every 1800 g of water, or $1.0/1.8 = 0.556$ mole of NaCl per kilogram of water. Because each mole of NaCl yields two moles of ions, the effective molality of all ions is twice this, or 1.11 molal, and the freezing point depression is

$$\Delta T_f = -1.86(1.11) = -2.06°C$$

Sea water freezes at two degrees below zero.

Colligative properties were the basis for one of the original proofs that salts really did dissociate, and for determining how many ions were produced. For example, one could imagine that the compound potassium ferricyanide, $K_3Fe(CN)_6$, dissociates in solution as follows:

$$\overset{?}{K_3Fe(CN)_6 \rightarrow 3K^+ + Fe^{3+} + 6CN^-}$$

Is this true? A freezing-point experiment can settle the matter.

Example. When 300 mg of potassium ferricyanide are dissolved in 10 ml of water, the freezing point falls to $-0.68°C$. How many ions are produced by one $K_3Fe(CN)_6$ formula unit?

Solution. Since 1 ml of water weighs 1 g, the solution was prepared at a strength of 30 g salt per kilogram of water. The molecular weight of potassium ferricyanide is 329 g mole^{-1}, so the molality is

$$m_A = \frac{30 \text{ g kg}^{-1}}{329 \text{ g mole}^{-1}} = 0.0912 \text{ mole kg}^{-1}$$

The expected freezing point lowering of water if no dissociation takes place would be

$$\Delta T_f = -1.86(0.0912) = -0.170°C$$

The observed depression is four times this, so potassium ferricyanide must dissociate into four ions in aqueous solution. We know from other evidence that the answer is

$$K_3Fe(CN)_6 \rightarrow 3K^+ + Fe(CN)_6^{3-}$$

The potassium ions dissociate, but the ferricyanide complex remains intact as a unit. (What would the freezing point of the solution have been, had potassium ferricyanide dissociated completely in the way proposed prior to the exercise?)

When we add ethylene glycol to automobile radiators as an antifreeze, we are taking advantage of the freezing point lowering of the radiator water. Ethylene glycol evaporates too readily in the summer months, but with other less volatile "year-round" antifreezes, we also make use of the raising of the boiling point of the radiator water to prevent boilover in hot weather. When we scatter salt on icy sidewalks, Na^+ and Cl^- ions lower the freezing point of water and cause the ice to melt into a concentrated brine. Similarly, home ice cream makers use rock salt and ice to produce a slush at a lower temperature than can be achieved with pure water and ice. All of these are applications of the colligative properties of molecules and ions dissolved in water.

Another important application of colligative properties is in determining molecular weights. A freezing point depression measurement can tell us how many moles of a solute are present, and if we already know the number of grams, it is easy to calculate the molecular weight.

Example. A saturated solution of glutamic acid (an amino acid) in water has 1.50 g of glutamic acid per 100 g of water. The observed freezing point of the solution is $-0.189°C$. What is the molecular weight of glutamic acid?

Freezing point and boiling point constants for common solvents[a]

Solvent	T_f, °K	k_f^b	T_b, °K	k_b^b	M, g
Water (H_2O)	273.16	1.86	373.0	+0.52	18.0
Carbon tetrachloride (CCl_4)	250.5	~30.00	350.0	5.03	154.0
Chloroform ($CHCl_3$)	209.6	4.70	334.4	3.63	119.5
Benzene (C_6H_6)	278.6	5.12	353.3	2.53	78.0
Carbon disulfide (CS_2)	164.2	3.83	319.4	2.34	76.0
Ether ($C_4H_{10}O$)	156.9	1.79	307.8	2.02	74.0
Camphor ($C_{10}H_{16}O$)	453.0	40.0			152.2

[a] T_f is the normal freezing point; k_f, the molal freezing point lowering constant; T_b, the normal boiling point; k_b, the molal boiling point elevation constant; M, the molecular weight of the substance.
[b] In units of degrees per mole per kilogram.

Solution.

$$\Delta T_f = -k_f m_A$$

$$-0.189 = -1.86 m_A$$

$$m_A = 0.102 \text{ mole kg}^{-1}$$

The solution was prepared with 15.0 g of glutamic acid in 1 kg of water, so 15.0 g is equivalent to 0.102 mole. Hence the molecular weight of glutamic acid is

$$m_A = \frac{15.0 \text{ g kg}^{-1}}{0.102 \text{ mole}} = 147 \text{ g mole}^{-1} \text{ kg}^{-1}$$

Check this value against the actual molecular structure of glutamic acid, which is shown at the left.

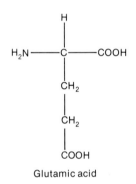

Glutamic acid

Unfortunately, freezing point depression measurements are of little use with large molecules, because the temperature changes are too small, even in saturated solutions.

Example. A 200-mg sample of cytochrome c (a protein) is dissolved in 10 ml of water. The molecular weight of cytochrome c is 12,400. What is the expected freezing point depression?

Solution. The 200 mg per 10 ml (or 10 g) equals 20 g of protein in 1 kg of water. Since the molecular weight is 12,400, this is 20/12,400 = 0.0016 mole per kilogram of solvent. Then,

$$\Delta T_f = -1.86(0.0016) = -0.003°C$$

This change in temperature is too small for an accurate determination of molecular weight of an unknown protein molecule.

The sensitivity of molecular weight measurements can be increased somewhat by choosing solvents with larger k_f or k_b, and some alternatives are given in the table above. Camphor, an organic compound, often is used because it has a k_f of 40.0. Using molten camphor as a solvent increases the sensitivity by more than twenty times, but this is practical only if the molecule whose molecular weight is to be found is both soluble in camphor and stable at the camphor melting point of 180°C.

OSMOTIC PRESSURE

The fourth colligative property is osmotic pressure, and it is useful in molecular-weight determinations when freezing point depressions are not. Many membranes have pores large enough to let some molecules pass through, but too small to pass others. These are known as *semipermeable membranes*. Some will permit water to pass, but not ions or salts. Others, with larger pores, will be permeable to water, salts, and small molecules, but not to protein molecules with molecular weights in the thousands. This selective passage of ions and small molecules but not proteins is called *dialysis*, and is a common biochemical method of separation and purification. Our kidneys essentially are fine networks of dialysis tubing, excreting liquids, salts, and small waste molecules, but at the same time preventing the loss of proteins from body fluids. Artificial kidney machines simulate this blood-purification process with man-made dialysis tubing, in which the blood from the patient flows across one side of semipermeable membranes, and wash fluid flows across the other.

Osmotic pressure is particularly easy to understand on the basis of escaping tendencies. It is illustrated by the diagram in the margin, which shows a single glass tube with one end covered by a semipermeable membrane, and immersed in a beaker of water. With pure water on both sides of the membrane, the escaping tendency of molecules through the membrane from either side is the same. Now if molecules of some solute that cannot pass through the membrane are added to the tube, but not to the beaker, the escaping tendency of water molecules from the tube is decreased, as shown in the second drawing at the right. Although the rate of flow of water molecules through the membrane into the tube is unimpeded, the reverse flow from tube to beaker is hindered, since not every molecule that approaches the membrane from the inside surface will be a water molecule. If only 90% of the molecules in the tube are H_2O, then the flow of water out to the beaker will be only 90% as great. More water will flow in than out, and the water level will rise in the tube, as shown in the third drawing at the right.

An increase in pressure inside the tube increases the escaping tendency of water molecules from within the tube, since their escape through the membrane lowers the pressure. Water initially flows into the tube because the escaping tendency of H_2O molecules of the solution inside is less than that of pure water outside. This inflow of water builds up a hydrostatic head of pressure in the tube, which in turn raises the escaping tendency of H_2O molecules within the tube. When the pressure is high enough, inward flow is matched by outward flow, and a new equilibrium results. This equilibrium pressure is known as *osmotic pressure*. The more solute molecules or ions in solution, the higher the osmotic pressure must be to block the inward flow of water molecules.

As before, the proper approach to the problem is to set up expressions for the way in which molar free energy or escaping tendency of water molecules depends on concentration and pressure in a solution, and find the conditions under which these two opposing effects exactly cancel. The result for dilute solutions is that the osmotic pressure neces-

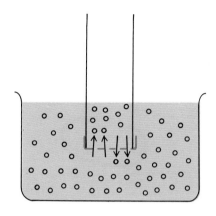

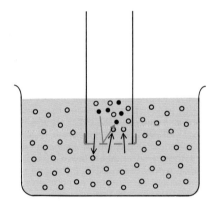

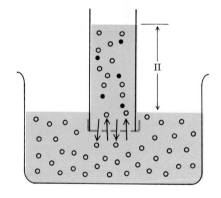

Key

o Solvent

• Solute

- - - Membrane permeable to solvent but not to solute

Solute molecules interfere with the exit of liquid from the tube through the membrane, but not with the flow into the tube. Equilibrium is restored and net inward flow of liquid is halted only when an osmotic pressure of II has developed inside the tube.

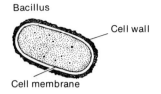
Bacillus
Cell wall
Cell membrane

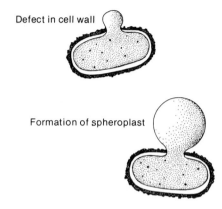
Defect in cell wall
Formation of spheroplast

Living cells are subject to stresses from osmotic pressure. Plants and bacteria protect themselves with rigid cell walls around their outer membranes. A defect in the cell wall of a bacillus (above) allows the cell membrane to assume a spherical shape, called a spheroplast. In a hypotonic environment (below) this spheroplast would not survive, but would swell and burst under the strain of osmotic pressure produced by the inward flow of water molecules. Reprinted by permission from *Agents of Bacterial Disease* by Albert S. Klainer, M.D., and Irving Geis. Copyright © 1973 by Harper and Row, Hagerstown, Maryland.

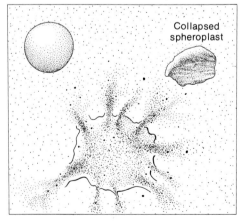
Collapsed spheroplast
Hypotonic environment

sary to balance flow across a membrane is related to the molarity of the solute particles on the side of the membrane to which pressure must be applied:

$$c_A = \text{molarity of } A = \text{moles of } A \text{ per liter of solution}$$

$$\Pi = c_A RT = \text{osmotic pressure}$$

The molarity of a solution is the number of moles of solute *per liter of solution*, in contrast to molality, which is the number of moles of solute *per kilogram of pure solvent*. With water as the solvent (which has a density of 1 kg per liter) and with dilute solutions, in which the change in volume of solvent upon adding solute is small, the difference between molarity and molality also is small. In the above expression, if the osmotic pressure (Π) is measured in atmospheres, concentration (c_A) is in moles per liter, and T is the absolute temperature in degrees Kelvin, then R is the gas constant encountered first in Chapter 2: $R = 0.0821$ liter atm deg^{-1} mole^{-1}. (Notice the similarity between the osmotic pressure law for ideal dilute solutions and the gas law for ideal gases.) Osmotic pressure is more sensitive to concentration than is freezing point depression, and therefore is more useful for molecular-weight determinations of large molecules.

Example. A 200-mg sample of cytochrome c is dissolved in 10 ml of water. The molecular weight of cytochrome c is 12,400. What will be the osmotic pressure in the solution when diffusion equilibrium is restored?

Solution. In such a dilute aqueous solution, molarity and molality are virtually the same. Hence,

$$\Pi = c_A RT = (0.0016)(0.0821)(298) = 0.039 \text{ atm} = 30 \text{ mm Hg}$$

It is easy to measure a pressure change of 30 mm Hg accurately, so a good molecular-weight determination is possible.

Osmotic pressure is important in living cells, because they are surrounded by a semipermeable cell membrane through which they communicate with the outside world. Cells are designed to function with a certain internal salt concentration. If they are put in a concentrated brine solution they lose water through the membrane and shrivel; conversely, if they are placed in distilled water they take up more water and swell (left). If the osmotic pressure inside becomes too great for the membrane strength the cell ruptures. Plant cells have rigid cell walls of cellulose around them to protect them from such osmotic shock.

The fundamental idea behind all four colligative properties is that the molar free energy, chemical potential, or escaping tendency of solvent molecules must be the same in two phases if equilibrium is to exist between them. When foreign molecules or ions are added to a liquid phase, the chemical potential of the liquid decreases in that phase. There is less tendency to migrate into a nearby vapor phase, solid phase, or to the other side of a membrane. To redress the balance and reestablish equilibrium, the temperature or the pressure of the solution must be adjusted.

REDOX REACTIONS AND ELECTROCHEMICAL POTENTIAL

Oxidations and reductions involve the escape of electrons from molecules or ions of one substance and their capture by other chemical substances. As with the movement of entire molecules discussed in previous sections, free energy is the key to understanding this escaping tendency. Oxidation–reduction (redox) reactions are important because they are the principal sources of energy on this planet, both natural (or biological) and artificial. For reasons discussed in Chapter 12, oxidation of molecules by removal of hydrogen or combination with oxygen normally liberates large quantities of energy. The synthesis of reduced organic molecules (sugars) by photosynthetic green plants is the main device for trapping and storing solar energy on this planet.

Oxidation either can involve the outright loss of electrons:

$$Cu \rightarrow Cu^{2+} + 2e^-$$

or the shifting away of bonding electrons toward a more electronegative atom:

$$2H_2 + O_2 \rightarrow 2H_2O$$

In the first example, electrons are physically removed from copper atoms to produce positively charged copper ions. In the second example, electrons on hydrogen that originally were shared equally with another hydrogen atom are partially lost by being shared unequally with oxygen atoms. Since electrons are never created or destroyed in chemical reactions, whenever one atom is oxidized, another atom must be reduced. When hydrogen is oxidized by the process above, oxygen is reduced. The copper reaction is incomplete, since some unspecified substance must become reduced by taking up the two electrons indicated on the right side of the equation.

In the water reaction written above, hydrogen is oxidized and oxygen is reduced. Free energy is given off because oxygen is a strong oxidizing agent (meaning that it has a strong attraction for electrons) and hydrogen is a good reducing agent (meaning that it lets go of its electrons easily to something else). The standard free energy change during this reaction is $\Delta G^0 = -54.6$ kcal mole^{-1} of water vapor (right). In general, the oxidation of a substance with a tenuous hold on its electrons, by a strong oxidant with a powerful pull for electrons, is accompanied by the release of free energy. It is a spontaneous process.

Oxidation does not necessarily require the outright removal of electrons, as we have said. Yet oxidation–reduction reactions in which electrons actually are moved from one substance to another are especially useful, since if the donor and recipient can be isolated, and the electrons made to flow through an external wire or circuit, some of the free energy of the oxidation–reduction process can be harnessed to do useful work. As an example, zinc metal has less of an affinity for its outer electrons than metallic copper does. In a competition between Cu^{2+} and Zn^{2+} ions for electrons, copper ions will win. The reaction

$$Zn + Cu^{2+} \rightarrow Zn^{2+} + Cu \qquad \Delta G^0 = -50.7 \text{ kcal mole}^{-1}$$

is highly spontaneous, with a standard free energy change of -50.7 kcal

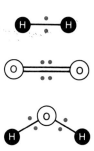

When H_2 and O_2 react to form water, electrons undergo a net shift toward the more electronegative oxygen atoms. Hence H is oxidized, and O is reduced.

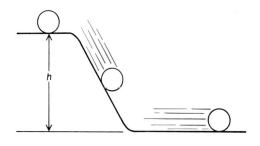

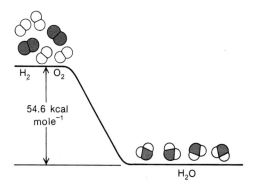

The act of permitting electrons to move toward a more electronegative atom that attracts them more strongly releases energy. The water reaction is a "downhill" process.

per mole. If we dip a zinc strip into a copper sulfate solution, as shown below, the zinc will be eaten away, a spongy layer of metallic copper will plate out on the zinc strip, and the deep blue color of copper sulfate will gradually fade. (Zinc sulfate, which is formed, is colorless.) In contrast, if we immerse a copper strip in a zinc sulfate solution, no reaction will occur because the reverse reaction is highly nonspontaneous, with a +50.7 kcal per mole free energy barrier to surmount.

This spontaneous transfer of electrons from zinc to copper is not useful because the free energy released is dissipated as heat. It is analogous to burning a spoonful of sugar with a match instead of eating it and converting the free energy of oxidation into useful muscle work. If some means could be found to separate the removal of electrons from zinc (oxidation) from the donation of electrons to copper ions (reduction), then the electrons might be made to do something useful along the way.

One answer is the simple electrochemical cell shown at the far right. On the left side, a piece of metallic zinc is immersed in zinc sulfate solution, and on the right, copper is immersed in copper sulfate. The two pieces of metal are connected by a wire, and the two solutions are connected by a porous barrier that allows the migration of ions but

When a zinc rod is immersed in a copper sulfate solution, the spontaneous reaction

$$Zn + Cu^{2+} \rightarrow Zn^{2+} + Cu$$

causes the zinc rod to be eroded away, and metallic copper atoms to be deposited in place of the zinc.

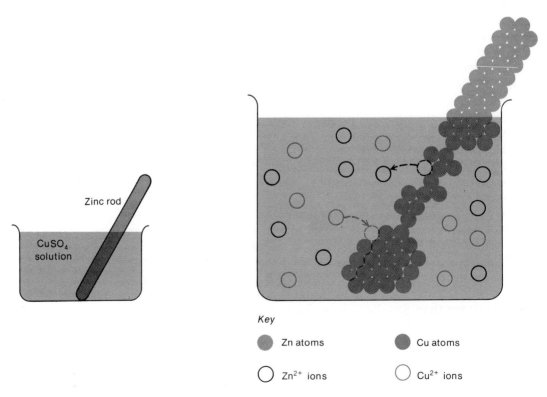

Zinc rod

CuSO₄ solution

Key

● Zn atoms   ● Cu atoms

○ Zn²⁺ ions   ○ Cu²⁺ ions

prevents the bulk mixing of the two solutions. At the left metal rod, called an *electrode*, zinc atoms give up electrons and enter the solution as zinc ions. This electrode is slowly eaten away. At the copper electrode on the right, copper ions from solution combine with electrons and plate out on the electrode as metallic copper. This electrode slowly increases in bulk as the reaction progresses. The electrons needed to reduce the copper ions at the right come from oxidation of zinc atoms at the left, but to do so they must travel through the external wire circuit. In the two solutions, as zinc ions enter the left compartment and copper ions are removed from the right, negative sulfate ions must migrate slowly through the porous barrier from right to left, and positive zinc ions from left to right, to preserve electrical neutrality in the two solutions. The two electrodes, connecting wire, and porous barrier form a closed circuit, with negative electrons moving from left to right through the wire, and positive and negative ions moving through the porous barrier. The main purpose of the barrier is to keep Cu^{2+} ions away from direct contact with the Zn electrode. The positive Cu^{2+} ions have no tendency to migrate by electrostatic forces from right to left, but they could be brought up to the zinc metal by stirring or agitation. This is what the barrier prevents.

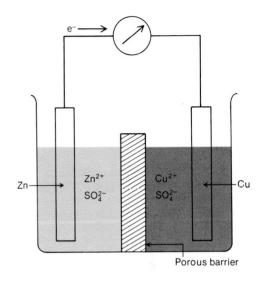

If the oxidation and reduction steps in the zinc–copper reaction can be carried out in different compartments of a cell and the electrons made to flow through an external circuit, then useful work can be obtained from the free energy of the oxidation–reduction reaction. The two compartments are separated here by a porous barrier that prevents solution mixing but permits ion flow.

The electrode at which oxidation takes place always is called the *anode*, and the reducing electrode, the *cathode*. In the Zn–Cu cell, the zinc electrode is the anode, and the copper is the cathode. Negative ions are called *anions* because they flow toward the anode in an electrochemical cell, and positive ions are *cations* because they migrate toward the cathode. Negatively charged sulfate anions, for example, migrate from the copper sulfate compartment, through the porous barrier, and into the zinc sulfate compartment where the anode is found. The logic in naming the anode arises because it is the electrode from which electrons flow up and out of the cell (Greek: *ana*, meaning up), and the cathode is the pole at which electrons flow back into the cell (Greek: *cata*, meaning down). This is as hard to remember as the terms themselves. The best memory device is to recall that *A*node and *O*xidation begin with vowels, *C*athode and *R*eduction with consonants, or that *A*node precedes *C*athode in the alphabet, and *O*xidation precedes *R*eduction. (It may not be elegant, but it works.)

Although the zinc rod in copper sulfate and the two-solution cell just described are physically different, the same chemical reaction takes place in both:

$$Zn + Cu^{2+} \rightarrow Zn^{2+} + Cu \qquad \Delta G^0 = -50.7 \text{ kcal mole}^{-1}$$

In the cell, however, the 51 kcal of free energy released by the reaction can be used for other purposes. Every time a mole of the above reaction occurs in the cell, two moles of electrons flow from the zinc anode, through the external circuit, to the copper cathode. As we saw previously, in chemical reactions and phase changes it is useful to define a chemical potential as the free energy change *per mole of a specific reactant*, as the equation is written. This chemical potential is the intrinsic capacity of the reaction to do work; and the actual work done, or free energy released, is the product of this potential times the number of moles of a substance undergoing chemical change.

In exactly the same way, we can define the electrochemical potential of a cell using oxidation–reduction reactions as the free energy change *per mole of electrons transferred*. If one mole of reaction occurs with the transfer of n moles of electrons ($n = 2$ in the Zn–Cu cell), and if $\mathscr{F}$ is the charge on one mole of electrons, then the electrochemical potential, $\mathscr{E}$, is given by

$$\Delta G^0 = -n\mathscr{F}\mathscr{E}^0$$

The superscript 0 on the potential, $\mathscr{E}^0$, has the same meaning as for free energy. It signifies the value when reactants and products all are in standard states of 1-molar concentrations, or 1-atm partial pressures for gases. It usually also refers to a temperature of 25°C. The charge on a mole of electrons, $\mathscr{F}$, is known as *Faraday's constant*. It has various numerical values, depending on the units involved, but if free energy is in kcal mole^{-1}, n has units of electrons, and potential is expressed in volts, then $\mathscr{F} = 23.056$ kilocalories per mole per electron volt (eV), or 23.056 kcal mole^{-1} eV^{-1}.

Example. What is the standard electrochemical potential of the Zn–Cu cell?

Solution. Since two electrons are transferred per unit of reaction, $n = 2$. Thus,

$$-50.7 = -2(23.06)\mathscr{E}^0$$

$$\mathscr{E}^0 = \frac{+50.7}{2(23.06)} = +1.10 \text{ volts}$$

The voltage of an electrochemical cell or battery is a familiar concept. It measures the *potential* for doing useful work with the cell. The actual amount of work done is the product of this potential times the amount of chemical reaction carried out through the cell; just as the amount of work that can be harnessed from a waterfall depends on the height of the waterfall (analogous to potential, $\mathscr{E}$), and the amount of water that flows over the falls (analogous to electrons, $n\mathscr{F}$). For both waterfalls and electrochemical cells, the product of potential drop and quantity of matter reacted is the free energy released in the process, ΔG.

The porous barrier between the two solutions can be eliminated in the particularly simple version of the Zn–Cu cell shown at the left, the Daniell gravity cell. In this cell the lighter zinc sulfate solution is carefully layered on top of a denser copper sulfate solution, and the electrodes are gently lowered into place, with the copper electrode insulated where it passes through the zinc sulfate layer. The Daniell cell delivers a dependable 1.10 volts, and at one time was used widely as a stationary power source for telegraph lines and doorbells. It obviously would be useless in a moving vehicle, for agitation would mix the two solutions. Metallic zinc then could transfer its electrons directly to copper ions in solution, and the electrons would not have to pass through the external wire. The cell would be ruined by an internal short-circuit, and the free energy released would be wasted as heat. As was pointed out previously, the purpose of the salt bridge, or porous barrier, is to permit the migration of counter ions to maintain charge neutrality, while avoiding mixing the solutions and thereby short-circuiting the cell.

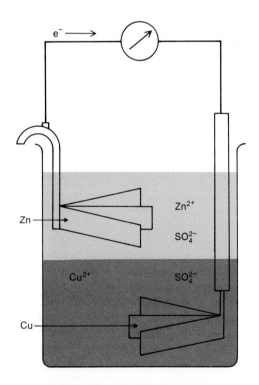

The porous barrier is unnecessary in the Daniell version of the zinc–copper cell because density differences keep the ZnSO₄ and CuSO₄ solutions separated in two layers.

430

ADDITION OF CELL REACTIONS

Nickel also is a good electron donor to copper, although not as good as zinc. In a competition between Ni^{2+} and Cu^{2+} for electrons, Cu^{2+} will win, but in a contest between Zn^{2+} and Ni^{2+}, the nickel ions will take the electrons. The following reaction is spontaneous and has the indicated free energy change:

$$Ni + Cu^{2+} \rightarrow Ni^{2+} + Cu \qquad \Delta G^0 = -26.63 \text{ kcal mole}^{-1}$$

If an electrochemical cell were made up with a nickel electrode immersed in nickel sulfate, and a copper electrode in copper sulfate, as shown at the right, nickel would be oxidized to Ni^{2+} ions, copper ions would be reduced to metallic copper, and electrons would flow through the external circuit from the Ni anode to the Cu cathode. The cell would have an electrochemical potential of

$$\mathscr{E}^0 = \frac{-\Delta G^0}{n\mathscr{F}} = \frac{26.63}{2(23.06)} = +0.58 \text{ volt}$$

Compared with the Daniell cell, this cell would have approximately half as intense an "electron pressure" between the two electrodes, available for doing work.

Free energies of balanced chemical reactions always are additive. Using only the information that we have so far about Zn–Cu and Ni–Cu cells, we can predict what would happen if we built a Zn–Ni cell. The reaction of this Zn–Ni cell can be obtained by subtracting the Ni–Cu reaction from the Zn–Cu reaction. (Remember that subtracting a reaction is the same as adding the reverse reaction, with the opposite sign for the free energy.)

$Zn \quad + Cu^{2+} \rightarrow Zn^{2+} + Cu$	$\Delta G^0 = -50.7 \text{ kcal mole}^{-1}$
$Ni^{2+} + Cu \quad \rightarrow Ni \quad + Cu^{2+}$	$\Delta G^0 = +26.6 \text{ kcal mole}^{-1}$
$Zn \quad + Ni^{2+} \rightarrow Zn^{2+} + Ni$	$\Delta G^0 = -24.1 \text{ kcal mole}^{-1}$

The negative free energy of the Zn–Ni reaction means that it is spontaneous in the direction written. The potential of the Zn–Ni cell can be calculated from $\Delta G^0 = -n\mathscr{F}\mathscr{E}^0$:

$$\mathscr{E}^0 = \frac{-(-24.1)}{2(23.06)} = +0.52 \text{ volt}$$

The positive cell potential means the same thing as the negative free energy change: The cell reaction in the direction written is spontaneous.

From this example it appears that cell voltages are additive, as are free energies. Just as we can write for free energies of a reaction, 24.1 kcal + 26.6 kcal = 50.7 kcal, we can write for cell voltages, 0.52 volt + 0.58 volt = 1.10 volts. This case is especially simple because the number of electrons transferred is the same for all reactions, $n = 2$. But remember that cell potential or voltage does *not* represent a quantity of energy. It is a tendency to react, or an electron "pressure." The quantity of energy, which by the principles of thermodynamics always is additive when reactions are added, is the free energy, $\Delta G = -n\mathscr{F}\mathscr{E}$. Whenever there is the slightest question as to whether voltages are additive in a given situation, go back and work with free energies instead.

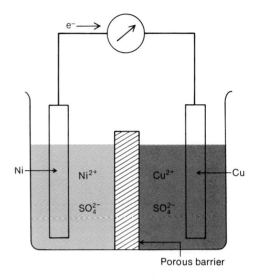

The same design of cell can be used to obtain a smaller quantity of free energy from the nickel–copper reaction:

$$Ni + Cu^{2+} \rightarrow Ni^{2+} + Cu$$

HALF-REACTIONS AND REDUCTION POTENTIALS

In Chapters 12 and 13 we saw that it was both inefficient and unnecessary to tabulate the heat or free energy for every single chemical reaction that could occur. Since heats and free energies of reactions are additive, it is sufficient to tabulate only the heat and free energy of reaction of each compound as made from its elements. The heats and free energies of all reactions between these compounds then can be found by combining their heats of formation, with the contributions from the elements canceling out.

In a similar way, it is not necessary to measure and tabulate the free energies and cell potentials of all conceivable oxidation–reduction cells. If there were a hundred different substances capable of oxidation and reduction, then these might be combined into as many as $100 \times 99 = 9900$ different electrochemical cells, each with its own free energy drop and voltage. However, one need only select one substance as a reference standard, and tabulate the free energies or voltages for reactions of all other substances with this standard. The free energy of a cell not involving the standard substance then can be found by subtracting one of these reactions from another, and subtracting free energies in the same way. The contribution of the "standard" reaction cancels out. If there were 100 different oxidation–reduction substances, we would need to tabulate only 99 different values of free energy and cell voltage rather than 9900. The saving is obvious.

The standard half-reaction that has been chosen is the oxidation of hydrogen gas to hydrogen ions in solution:

$$H_2(g) \rightarrow 2H^+ + 2e^-$$

Pairing the zinc, nickel, and copper half-reactions separately with this half-reaction leads to the following tabulation:

	ΔG^0 (kcal mole^{-1})	$\mathscr{E}^0$ (volts)
$Zn^{2+} + H_2 \rightarrow Zn + 2H^+$	+35.2	−0.76
$Ni^{2+} + H_2 \rightarrow Ni + 2H^+$	+11.1	−0.23
$Cu^{2+} + H_2 \rightarrow Cu + 2H^+$	−15.5	+0.34

The positive signs for free energy of the zinc and nickel reactions, and the negative signs of their cell potentials, indicate that the reactions are *not* spontaneous in the direction written. Zinc ions will not be reduced spontaneously by hydrogen gas. Quite the contrary, if metallic zinc is dropped into acid, in which H^+ ions are plentiful, zinc will be dissolved into Zn^{2+} ions, and hydrogen gas will be evolved:

$$Zn + 2H^+ \rightarrow Zn^{2+} + H_2 \qquad \Delta G^0 = -35.2 \text{ kcal mole}^{-1}$$

Similarly, Ni^{2+} ions will not oxidize H_2 to H^+ spontaneously, but metallic nickel will dissolve in acid with the release of hydrogen gas, although not as readily as does zinc. Copper is not attacked by acid as zinc and nickel are, because the following reaction is spontaneous:

$$Cu^{2+} + H_2 \rightarrow Cu + 2H^+ \qquad \Delta G^0 = -15.5 \text{ kcal mole}^{-1}$$

432

One cannot make a solid electrode out of hydrogen gas, of course, but the same effect can be achieved by bubbling a stream of hydrogen gas over an inert conductor such as a platinum electrode, as shown at the bottom of the page. The H_2 molecules can dissociate at the surface of the platinum, give up their electrons to the external circuit through the metal electrode, and go into solution as H^+ ions. Similar electrodes can be made with other gases.

In thinking about standard cell reactions, it is customary to forget that they are paired with the hydrogen half-reaction, and to speak of them as if they were isolated reactions of one half of the cell. We can talk about half-reactions, and their free energies and half-cell potentials, as though the following had physical reality:

	ΔG^0 (kcal mole^{-1})	$\mathscr{E}^0$ (volts)
$Zn^{2+} + 2e^- \rightarrow Zn$	$+35.2$	-0.76
$Ni^{2+} + 2e^- \rightarrow Ni$	$+11.1$	-0.23
$2H^+ + 2e^- \rightarrow H_2$	0.0	0.0
$Cu^{2+} + 2e^- \rightarrow Cu$	-15.5	$+0.34$

The potentials as written above are *reduction potentials*, positive if the ion is easier to reduce than H^+ ions, and negative if harder to reduce than H^+. A large positive reduction potential for a half-reaction is a sign that the reduced form of the substance is strongly favored, as with copper in the above examples.

A hydrogen electrode using the reaction

$$H_2 \rightleftarrows 2H^+ + 2e^-$$

can be obtained by bubbling a stream of hydrogen gas over a platinum electrode covered with finely divided platinum black, which catalyzes the dissociation and reassociation of H_2 molecules.

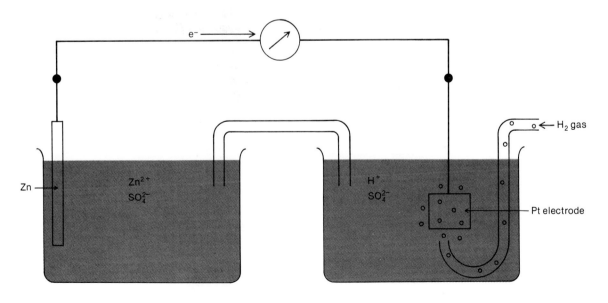

Standard reduction potentials in acid solution at 298°K

Half-reaction	$\mathscr{E}^0$ (volts)
$F_2 + 2e^- \rightarrow 2F^-$	2.87
$Ag^{2+} + e^- \rightarrow Ag^+$	1.99
$H_2O_2 + 2H^+ + 2e^- \rightarrow 2H_2O$	1.78
$MnO_4^- + 4H^+ + 3e^- \rightarrow MnO_2 + 2H_2O$	1.68
$PbO_2 + 4H^+ + SO_4^{2-} + 2e^- \rightarrow PbSO_4 + 2H_2O$	1.69
$MnO_4^- + 8H^+ + 5e^- \rightarrow Mn^{2+} + 4H_2O$	1.49
$PbO_2 + 4H^+ + 2e^- \rightarrow Pb^{2+} + 2H_2O$	1.46
$Cl_2 + 2e^- \rightarrow 2Cl^-$	1.36
$Cr_2O_7^{2-} + 14H^+ + 6e^- \rightarrow 2Cr^{3+} + 7H_2O$	1.33
$MnO_2 + 4H^+ + 2e^- \rightarrow Mn^{2+} + 2H_2O$	1.21
$O_2 + 4H^+ + 4e^- \rightarrow 2H_2O$	1.23
$Br_2(l) + 2e^- \rightarrow 2Br^-$	1.06
$AuCl_4^- + 3e^- \rightarrow Au + 4Cl^-$	0.99
$NO_3^- + 4H^+ + 3e^- \rightarrow NO + 2H_2O$	0.96
$2Hg^{2+} + 2e^- \rightarrow Hg_2^{2+}$	0.90
$Ag^+ + e^- \rightarrow Ag$	0.80
$Hg_2^{2+} + 2e^- \rightarrow 2Hg$	0.80
$Fe^{3+} + e^- \rightarrow Fe^{2+}$	0.77
$O_2 + 2H^+ + 2e^- \rightarrow H_2O_2$	0.68
$MnO_4^- + e^- \rightarrow MnO_4^{2-}$	0.56
$I_2 + 2e^- \rightarrow 2I^-$	0.54
$Cu^+ + e^- \rightarrow Cu$	0.52
$Cu^{2+} + 2e^- \rightarrow Cu$	0.34
$Hg_2Cl_2 + 2e^- \rightarrow 2Hg + 2Cl^-$	0.27
$AgCl + e^- \rightarrow Ag + Cl^-$	0.22
$SO_4^{2-} + 4H^+ + 2e^- \rightarrow H_2SO_3 + H_2O$	0.20
$Cu^{2+} + e^- \rightarrow Cu^+$	0.16
$2H^+ + 2e^- \rightarrow H_2$	0.00
$Pb^{2+} + 2e^- \rightarrow Pb$	−0.13
$Sn^{2+} + 2e^- \rightarrow Sn$	−0.14
$Ni^{2+} + 2e^- \rightarrow Ni$	−0.23
$PbSO_4 + 2e^- \rightarrow Pb + SO_4^{2-}$	−0.36
$Cd^{2+} + 2e^- \rightarrow Cd$	−0.40
$Cr^{3+} + e^- \rightarrow Cr^{2+}$	−0.41
$Fe^{2+} + 2e^- \rightarrow Fe$	−0.41
$Zn^{2+} + 2e^- \rightarrow Zn$	−0.76
$Mn^{2+} + 2e^- \rightarrow Mn$	−1.03
$Al^{3+} + 3e^- \rightarrow Al$	−1.66
$H_2 + 2e^- \rightarrow 2H^-$	−2.23
$Mg^{2+} + 2e^- \rightarrow Mg$	−2.37
$La^{3+} + 3e^- \rightarrow La$	−2.37
$Na^+ + e^- \rightarrow Na$	−2.71
$Ca^{2+} + 2e^- \rightarrow Ca$	−2.76
$Ba^{2+} + 2e^- \rightarrow Ba$	−2.90
$K^+ + e^- \rightarrow K$	−2.92
$Li^+ + e^- \rightarrow Li$	−3.05

Standard reduction potentials in basic solution[a] at 298°K

Half-reaction	$\mathscr{E}^0$ (volts)
$HO_2^- + H_2O + 2e^- \rightleftarrows 3OH^-$	0.88
$MnO_4^{2-} + 2H_2O + 2e^- \rightleftarrows MnO_2 + 4OH^-$	0.60
$O_2 + 4e^- + 2H_2O \rightleftarrows 4OH^-$	0.40
$Co(NH_3)_6^{3+} + e^- \rightleftarrows Co(NH_3)_6^{2+}$	0.10
$HgO + H_2O + 2e^- \rightleftarrows Hg + 2OH^-$	0.10
$MnO_2 + H_2O + 2e^- \rightleftarrows Mn(OH)_2 + 2OH^-$	−0.05
$O_2 + H_2O + 2e^- \rightleftarrows HO_2^- + OH^-$	−0.08
$Cu(NH_3)_2^+ + e^- \rightleftarrows Cu + 2NH_3$	−0.12
$Ag(CN)_2^- + e^- \rightleftarrows Ag + 2CN^-$	−0.31
$Hg(CN)_4^{2-} + 2e^- \rightleftarrows Hg + 4CN^-$	−0.37
$S + 2e^- \rightleftarrows S^{2-}$	−0.48
$Pb(OH)_3^- + 2e^- \rightleftarrows Pb + 3OH^-$	−0.54
$Fe(OH)_3 + e^- \rightleftarrows Fe(OH)_2 + OH^-$	−0.56
$Cd(OH)_2 + 2e^- \rightleftarrows Cd + 2OH^-$	−0.81
$SO_4^{2-} + H_2O + 2e^- \rightleftarrows SO_3^{2-} + 2OH^-$	−0.93
$Zn(NH_3)_4^{2+} + 2e^- \rightleftarrows Zn + 4NH_3$	−1.03
$Zn(OH)_4^{2-} + 2e^- \rightleftarrows Zn + 4OH^-$	−1.22
$Mn(OH)_2 + 2e^- \rightleftarrows Mn + 2OH^-$	−1.55
$Mg(OH)_2 + 2e^- \rightleftarrows Mg + 2OH^-$	−2.69
$Ca(OH)_2 + 2e^- \rightleftarrows Ca + 2OH^-$	−3.03

[a] *Note:* Half-reactions involving ions not affected by changing pH (such as $Na^+|Na$) have the same potential in acid or base.

Standard reduction potentials for various half-reactions under acidic and basic conditions are given in the tables on the facing page. Remember that these potentials really are for cells in which the electrons required on the left side of the given half-reaction are provided by oxidizing H_2 to H^+ ions, but that whenever we use two of these half-reactions to calculate the potential of a real cell, the hydrogen contributions cancel. Also remember that a potential is a "pressure" on a *per electron* basis, no matter how many electrons appear in the half-reaction. The free energy for that half-reaction coupled in a cell with the hydrogen half-reaction can be found by multiplying the reduction potential by -23.06 kcal times the number of electrons involved in the half-reaction.

Example. What are the cell voltage and free energy change in a cell with the reaction

$$Al^{3+} + \tfrac{3}{2}H_2 \rightarrow Al + 3H^+$$

Which way will the reaction go spontaneously?

Solution. The reduction potential for the half-reaction

$$Al^{3+} + 3e^- \rightarrow Al$$

is listed as -1.66 volts, and this is the voltage of the cell specified in the problem. The free energy of the reaction as written is

$$\Delta G^0 = -n\mathscr{F}\mathscr{E}^0 = -3(23.06)(-1.66) = +114.8 \text{ kcal mole}^{-1}$$

Reduction of Al^{3+} ions by hydrogen is a highly nonspontaneous reaction with a large positive standard free energy. The reverse reaction, attack of metallic aluminum by acid, is highly spontaneous:

$$Al + 3H^+ \rightarrow Al^{3+} + \tfrac{3}{2}H_2 \qquad \Delta G^0 = -114.8 \text{ kcal mole}^{-1}$$

From a free energy standpoint, aluminum is a highly reactive metal, and the only reason it ordinarily appears relatively inert is that it is protected by a tightly adhering coat of aluminum oxide.

BUILDING CELLS FROM HALF-REACTIONS

The half-cell potentials in the tables can be used to calculate the voltage of any cell that can be put together by combining two of these half-reactions. The procedure is straightforward:

1. Write the half-reactions that occur at each electrode, writing both as reductions.
2. Choose one of the two half-reactions to be a reduction at the cathode, and the other as an oxidation at the anode. Reverse the anode half-reaction, and change the sign of its potential. (You may have to guess to begin with, but if you guess wrong the method will correct itself in Step 5.)
3. Determine the overall cell reaction by adding the cathode reaction and the reverse anode reaction, after multiplying if necessary to

make the number of electrons in both half-reactions the same. (If this is done properly, free electrons will not appear in the final cell reaction.)

4. Obtain the overall cell voltage by adding the cathode potential and the reversed anode potential (with a change of sign). Since half-cell potentials already are on a one-electron basis, you will *not* have to multiply them by the number of electrons as you did the half-reactions in Step 3.

5. If the cell voltage is positive, you made the right choice of anode and cathode reactions. If it is negative, the anode and cathode reactions must have been reversed. Rewrite the cell equation the other way, and change the sign of the cell voltage to positive.

Example. Use half-cell potentials to find the voltage of the Zn–Cu cell, and the direction of spontaneous reaction.

Solution. The half-reactions written as reductions, and the corresponding reduction potentials from the table, are

$$Zn^{2+} + 2e^- \rightarrow Zn \qquad\qquad \mathscr{E}^0 = -0.76 \text{ volt}$$

$$Cu^{2+} + 2e^- \rightarrow Cu \qquad\qquad \mathscr{E}^0 = +0.34 \text{ volt}$$

Let us deliberately make the wrong choice at this point, by assuming that the copper half-reaction is the anode oxidation:

$$Cu \rightarrow Cu^{2+} + 2e^- \qquad\qquad \mathscr{E}^0 = -0.34 \text{ volt}$$

Adding this to the zinc cathode reaction yields

$$Zn^{2+} + Cu \rightarrow Zn + Cu^{2+} \qquad \mathscr{E}^0 = -1.10 \text{ volt}$$

The negative $\mathscr{E}^0$ tells us at once that the reaction actually runs spontaneously in the reverse direction, with zinc at the anode and copper at the cathode. Thus the correct cell equation is

$$Zn + Cu^{2+} \rightarrow Zn^{2+} + Cu \qquad \mathscr{E}^0 = +1.10 \text{ volt}$$

There is a convenient shorthand method of representing a cell as a linear diagram, by writing from left to right the anode material, anode solution ions, cathode solution ions, and cathode material. A single vertical line separates an electrode from its solution, and a double line represents a porous barrier or interface between two solutions. The linear diagram of a Zn–Cu cell is

$$Zn|Zn^{2+}||Cu^{2+}|Cu$$

The ion concentrations (usually molarities, M) can be shown if desired; for example,

$$Zn|Zn^{2+}(0.5M)||Cu^{2+}(0.4M)|Cu$$

The cell built from a zinc electrode and a standard hydrogen electrode can be diagrammed as

$$Zn|Zn^{2+}||H^+|H_2,Pt$$

Sulfate ions or other similar anions are omitted from these cell descriptions because they play no direct role in the oxidation–reduction process, being only carriers of ionic current. The Pt is a reminder of the actual electrode material in a gas electrode. The cell made by combining the hydrogen and copper half-cells would be written:

$$Pt,H_2|H^+||Cu^{2+}|Cu$$

The hydrogen half-cell is on the left in this cell, since it now is the anode, where oxidation occurs.

Example. Find the direction of spontaneous reaction, and the cell voltage, for the cell made with a $Ag|Ag^+$ electrode and a $Cu|Cu^{2+}$ electrode. Write out the diagram of the cell.

Solution. The two electrode reactions, written as reductions, are

$$Ag^+ + e^- \rightarrow Ag \qquad \mathscr{E}^0 = +0.80 \text{ volt}$$
$$Cu^{2+} + 2e^- \rightarrow Cu \qquad \mathscr{E}^0 = +0.34 \text{ volt}$$

Obviously, if a positive overall cell voltage is desired, the copper half-reaction must be reversed, not the one for silver. Hence copper is the anode of the cell. Reversing its half-reaction, we get

$$Cu \rightarrow Cu^{2+} + 2e^- \qquad \mathscr{E}^0 = -0.34 \text{ volt}$$

The silver and copper half-reactions cannot be added as they stand, because the silver reaction involves only one electron, whereas the copper reaction provides two. We must multiply the silver half-reaction by two before adding:

$$
\begin{array}{ll}
2Ag^+ + 2e^- \rightarrow 2Ag & \mathscr{E}^0 = +0.80 \text{ volt} \\
\underline{Cu \qquad\qquad \rightarrow Cu^{2+} + 2e^-} & \underline{\mathscr{E}^0 = -0.34 \text{ volt}} \\
2Ag^+ + Cu \rightarrow 2Ag + Cu^{2+} & \mathscr{E}^0 = +0.46 \text{ volt}
\end{array}
$$

The half-cell potential of the silver reaction is *not* multiplied by two, since potentials, by definition, are on a one-electron basis. The overall cell potential is the sum of the two half-cell potentials, after reversing the sign of the anode potential. Since $\mathscr{E}^0$ came out positive, we made the correct choice of anode and cathode. The cell diagram is

$$Cu|Cu^{2+}||Ag^+|Ag$$

We can show the legitimacy of this procedure of adding or subtracting half-cell potentials without taking the number of electrons involved into account, by working through the Ag–Cu example again, but using free energies instead. The free energies of the half-reactions are found by multiplying each potential by $-n\mathscr{F}$, where $n = 1$ for silver and $n = 2$ for copper:

$$Ag^+ + e^- \rightarrow Ag \qquad \begin{aligned}\Delta G^0 &= -1(23.06)(+0.80) \\ &= -18.4 \text{ kcal mole}^{-1}\end{aligned}$$

$$Cu \rightarrow Cu^{2+} + 2e^- \qquad \begin{aligned}\Delta G^0 &= -2(23.06)(-0.34) \\ &= +15.7 \text{ kcal mole}^{-1}\end{aligned}$$

The silver half-reaction must be multiplied by two before it can be combined with the copper half-reaction. The free energy also must be multiplied by two because it is a quantity rather than a "pressure," and thus is doubled when the chemical equation is doubled. The proper way of combining these two half-reactions and free energies is

$$2Ag^+ + 2e^- \rightarrow 2Ag \qquad \Delta G^0 = 2(-18.4) = -36.8 \text{ kcal}$$

$$\underline{Cu \qquad\qquad \rightarrow Cu^{2+} + 2e^- \qquad \Delta G^0 = \qquad\qquad +15.7 \text{ kcal}}$$

$$2Ag^+ + Cu \rightarrow 2Ag + Cu^{2+} \qquad \Delta G^0 = \qquad\qquad -21.1 \text{ kcal}$$

The negative free energy change tells us that this is the spontaneous direction of the cell. With two electrons involved per unit of reaction as written, the cell voltage is

$$\mathscr{E}^0 = \frac{-(-21.1)}{2(23.06)} = +0.46 \text{ volt}$$

This is exactly the answer that we obtained by combining half-cell potentials directly. Having worked through one example using free energies, we can combine half-cell potentials as oxidations and reductions from now on to obtain an overall cell reaction, and can feel confident that we will not go astray.

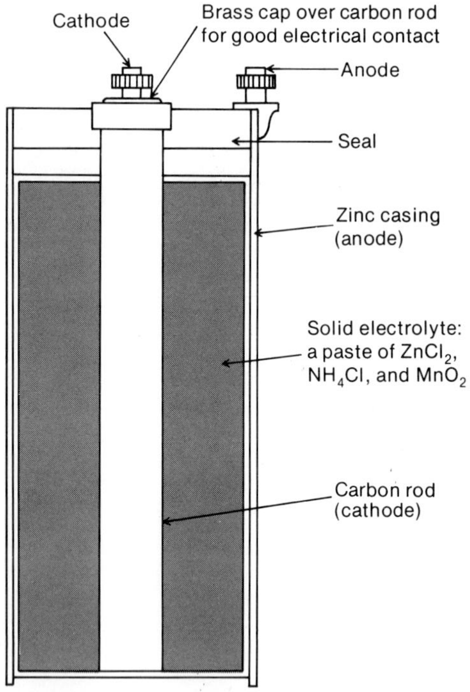

The familiar dry cell delivers a dependable 1.5 volts and contains no liquids to splash about, but the cell is not rechargeable once it is depleted.

THE DRY CELL

In the cells considered so far, it has been implied that the electrodes were in contact with ions in solution. The dry cell, shown at the left, is especially convenient because the solutions are replaced by a moist paste in a sealed container. The zinc casing is the anode, with the half-reaction

$$Zn \rightarrow Zn^{2+} + 2e^-$$

$$\mathscr{E}^0 = +0.76 \text{ volt}$$

The cathode is a central carbon rod surrounded by a paste of manganese dioxide (MnO_2), ammonium chloride (NH_4Cl), and water. The paste and the zinc casing are separated only by a porous paper barrier. The cathode reaction is a complex one, but can be represented as

$$2MnO_2 + 4NH_4^+ + 2e^- \rightarrow 2Mn^{3+} + 4NH_3 + 4OH^-$$

$$\mathscr{E}^0 \simeq +0.75 \text{ volt}$$

A dry cell delivers about 1.5 volts (0.76V + 0.75V). If the cell is used continuously, the current slowly decreases as ammonia gas builds up around the carbon rod and insulates it. If the cell is allowed to rest, this ammonia diffuses toward the anode and combines with zinc ions to form a complex ion, $Zn(NH_3)_4^{2+}$. The cell then is able to deliver a stronger current again. This is why flashlight batteries appear to run down with steady use, but to recover after standing idle for a time.

438

THE LEAD STORAGE BATTERY

The dry cell, useful as it is, cannot be recharged and used again. This is because the products of the electrode reactions diffuse away, and the reactions cannot be reversed simply by passing an external charging current through the cell. The lead storage battery, shown at the right, has the great advantage that the products of each electrode reaction adhere to the electrode. When a reverse current is passed through the storage battery, the products are reconverted to reactants, energy is stored, and the battery is ready to deliver electrical energy again.

The anode is a spongy lead screen, and the cathode is a screen impregnated with lead dioxide. Both are immersed in the same sulfuric acid solution. Lead is oxidized to Pb^{2+} ions at the anode, and these ions immediately form insoluble lead sulfate, which sticks to the anode:

$$Pb + SO_4^{2-} \rightarrow PbSO_4 + 2e^- \qquad \mathscr{E}^0 = +0.36 \text{ volt}$$

At the cathode, lead oxide with Pb in the +4 oxidation state is reduced to more Pb^{2+} ions, which also stick to the cathode as $PbSO_4$:

$$PbO_2 + 4H^+ + SO_4^{2-} + 2e^- \rightarrow PbSO_4 + 2H_2O \qquad \mathscr{E}^0 = +1.69 \text{ volts}$$

The overall cell reaction therefore is

$$Pb + PbO_2 + 2H_2SO_4 \rightarrow 2PbSO_4 + 2H_2O \qquad \mathscr{E}^0 = +2.05 \text{ volts}$$

Six-volt and twelve-volt automobile batteries are obtained by connecting three or six of these cells in series.

When the lead storage battery has run down, most of the lead and lead oxide is in the form of lead sulfate, and the battery fluid is depleted of sulfuric acid. The fluid then is less dense, which is the reason that the specific gravity (or density) of the battery fluid can be used by a service station attendant as a measure of the state of charge of the battery. If a direct current is passed through a run-down battery so electrons flow into the anode (originally Pb) and out the cathode (originally PbO_2), the half-reactions are reversed. Lead sulfate is reconverted to Pb and PbO_2, the battery fluid becomes a more concentrated (and denser) sulfuric acid solution, and electrochemical energy is stored in the cell, ready for later use.

ELECTROLYSIS CELLS

When the lead storage battery is being used as a power source, oxidation-reduction reactions generate electricity. When a depleted battery is being recharged, electricity from an outside source causes oxidation–reduction reactions to go against the natural free energy gradient. This same principle of using electric current to bring about energetically unfavorable chemical changes is used widely in electrolytic cells. Many metals can be obtained from their ores (usually oxides or sulfides) by reducing them with carbon, but the alkali metals, such as sodium, are too reactive for this. They must be obtained by electrolysis, as in the cell shown on the next page.

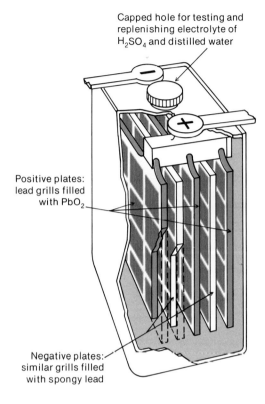

Capped hole for testing and replenishing electrolyte of H_2SO_4 and distilled water

Positive plates: lead grills filled with PbO_2

Negative plates: similar grills filled with spongy lead

Because the products of oxidation and reduction remain in place, the lead storage battery is rechargeable after it has run down. Metallic Pb is converted to insoluble $PbSO_4$ at the anode, and solid PbO_2 also is converted to $PbSO_4$ at the cathode. Running an external current in reverse through the cell regenerates Pb and PbO_2 from $PbSO_4$, and recharges the battery.

In the electrolysis of molten sodium chloride, the reduction that cannot be accomplished chemically is carried out electrochemically. Current is passed through two electrodes immersed in NaCl heated above its melting point of 801°C. At one electrode, Cl⁻ ions are oxidized to Cl_2 gas, and it therefore is the anode. At the cathode, Na^+ ions are reduced to sodium metal. The Cl_2 gas is collected and piped away, and the sodium, which is a liquid at this temperature and lighter than the fused salt, floats to the surface and is recovered. The half-reactions are

Anode: $2Cl^- \rightarrow Cl_2 + 2e^-$ $\mathscr{E}^0 = -1.36$ volts

Cathode: $2Na^+ + 2e^- \rightarrow 2Na$ $\mathscr{E}^0 = -2.71$ volts

$2Na^+ + 2Cl^- \rightarrow 2Na + Cl_2$ $\mathscr{E}^0 = -4.07$ volts

The electrode potentials used here are only approximate because they are for dilute aqueous solutions, not for a fused salt. They do indicate that a large potential must be applied across the electrodes of the cell before electrolysis and decomposition of the salt will begin.

Electrolysis is the only practical process for obtaining aluminum metal from its ores, primarily Al_2O_3. Many other metals are either obtained or purified by electrolytic cells. For example, if a current is passed through two copper electrodes immersed in a copper sulfate solution, copper will be oxidized to Cu^{2+} ions at the anode, and Cu^{2+} ions will be reduced and will plate as metallic copper on the cathode (far right margin). If an ingot of impure copper is used as the anode, then pure copper will build up on the cathode, and impurities will settle to the bottom of the electrolysis tank. In a similar way, electrolysis can be used to plate metal on any object that can be made to conduct electricity and hence can be used as the cathode in an electrolysis cell.

Metallic sodium and chlorine gas are made commercially by electrolysis of molten NaCl.

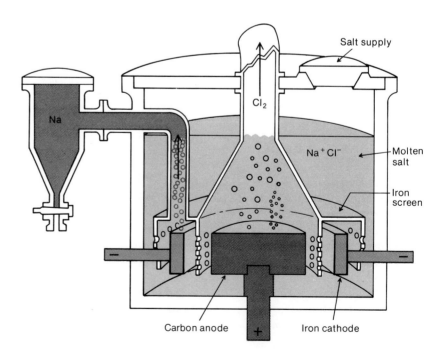

FARADAY'S LAWS OF ELECTROLYSIS

One of the most important single steps in establishing the electrical nature of the forces between atoms was the electrolysis experiments in 1833 by Michael Faraday. He carried out a series of experiments to study the chemical changes produced when electric currents were passed through solutions and mixtures of chemical substances. He observed that chemical changes occurred of the type that we have been examining in the preceding section. He made two quantitative observations, now called Faraday's laws:

1. The weight of chemical substance produced in an anode or cathode reaction in an electrolysis cell is proportional to the quantity of electricity passed through the cell.

2. The weights of two different substances produced by the same quantity of electricity are proportional to the equivalent weights of the substances in reactions between them or with other substances.

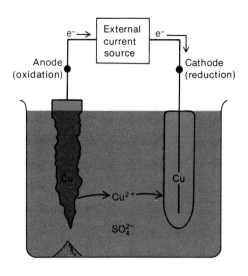

Copper can be refined electrolytically by oxidizing copper from an impure ingot at the anode, and plating out pure copper metal at the cathode.

As an example, if a given amount of electricity releases 5 g of H_2 gas when passed through an electrolysis cell for the decomposition of water, then twice as much electricity will produce 10 g of hydrogen gas. Furthermore, if enough electricity is passed through the cell to yield 2 g of H_2 gas at the cathode, then 16 g of O_2 gas will be released at the anode. These numbers are easily recognizable as representing 1 mole of H_2 and $\frac{1}{2}$ mole of O_2, which are the relative proportions in which these gases combine to form H_2O. In Faraday's time, his experiments were a remarkable set of observations that helped to establish the principles of chemical combination. Today they are self-evident consequences of the theory that electrons form chemical bonds.

We have referred to Faraday's constant previously as representing one mole of electrons, and have used it in the form

$$\mathscr{F} = 23.056 \text{ kcal mole}^{-1} \text{ eV}^{-1}$$

It is more convenient in electrolysis experiments to express $\mathscr{F}$ in coulombs, the customary unit of electrical charge. As you can see from Appendix 1, the charge on an electron is 1.6021×10^{-19} coulomb, so one mole of electrons will have a total charge of

$$1.6021 \times 10^{-19} \text{ coulomb} \times 6.022 \times 10^{23} \text{ mole}^{-1} =$$
$$96{,}487 \text{ coulombs mole}^{-1}$$

Passing 96,487 coulombs of electricity through a cell means sending one mole of electrons from one electrode to the other, with the corresponding chemical changes.

Example. When 96,487 coulombs of electricity are passed through an electrolysis cell containing molten NaCl, how many moles, and how many grams, of Na and Cl_2 are produced?

Solution. Since one faraday, or 96,487 coulombs, represents one mole of electrons, and since each Na^+ ion requires one electron for reduction, one mole of sodium metal will be produced. This amounts to 23 g of sodium. Since each mole of Cl^- ions requires one mole of electrons to yield one half mole of Cl_2 gas, this experiment will liberate one half mole of Cl_2 gas, or 35.5 g.

Example. Exactly 200,000 coulombs of electricity are passed through an electrolysis cell containing a copper sulfate solution that is designed to purify copper electrolytically. How much copper will plate on the cathode?

Solution. The number of faradays, or moles of electrons, is

$$\frac{200,000 \text{ coulombs}}{96,487 \text{ coulombs mole}^{-1}} = 2.07 \text{ moles of electrons (or faradays)}$$

The reduction of copper ions in solution occurs with the uptake of two electrons per ion, $Cu^{2+} + 2e^- \rightarrow Cu$, so every mole of electrons causes the deposition of half a mole of metallic copper. Hence the amount of copper deposited by 200,000 coulombs is

$$\frac{2.07 \text{ moles}}{2} = 1.035 \text{ moles of copper}$$

$$1.035 \text{ moles} \times 63.54 \text{ g mole}^{-1} = 65.8 \text{ g of copper}$$

In acid–base neutralizations (Chapter 16), the amount of substance that would release or take up one mole of protons was referred to as one *equivalent* of acid or base. Hence one equivalent of acid–base neutralizing ability is supplied by one mole of HCl or NaOH, one half mole of H_2SO_4, or one third mole of H_3PO_4. In a similar manner, we can define one *redox equivalent* of a substance being reduced or oxidized as that amount of substance that takes up or releases one mole of electrons, or one faraday. Hence in the first example of this section, one mole of sodium metal and one half mole of Cl_2 gas each represent one redox equivalent. In the second example, one mole of copper represents two redox equivalents in the reduction of Cu^{2+} to Cu, since two moles of electrons, or faradays, of electricity are needed.

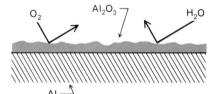

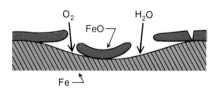

The surface of aluminum is protected against corrosion by a tightly adhering Al_2O_3 coating. Iron oxide does not adhere as well to iron, and the surface of the metal is constantly exposed to attack by oxygen and water.

REDOX CHEMISTRY GONE ASTRAY: CORROSION

The corrosion of metals is an oxidation process. Iron can be oxidized either by oxygen or by acid, if enough moisture is present to allow ionic reactions to proceed at an appreciable rate:

Oxidation: $Fe \rightarrow Fe^{2+} + 2e^-$ $\mathscr{E}^0 = +0.41$ volt

Reduction: $\begin{cases} \frac{1}{2}O_2 + H_2O + 2e^- \rightarrow 2OH^- & \mathscr{E}^0 = +0.40 \text{ volt} \\ 2H^+ + 2e^- \rightarrow H_2 & \mathscr{E}^0 = 0.00 \text{ volt} \end{cases}$

When iron rusts, metallic iron is oxidized first to the +2 state and deposited as flakes of $Fe(OH)_2$ and FeO, later being oxidized even further to Fe(III). Aluminum corrodes even more vigorously,

$Al \rightarrow Al^{3+} + 3e^-$ $\mathscr{E}^0 = +1.66$ volts

but the Al_2O_3 oxide coating, having a crystal structure similar to the metal, adheres tightly to the metal surface and prevents further corrosion (left margin). In contrast, the crystal structures of metallic iron

442

and iron oxide are not similar, and the two do not adhere. The oxide flakes away as it forms, exposing fresh metal for attack by oxygen or acid. A good layer of paint adheres better than FeO, but still is not permanent.

It happens that there is an electrochemical solution to this electrochemical problem. Iron will not rust or oxidize if it is plated with a more reactive metal—one with a more negative reduction potential. Aluminum is a possible candidate. If iron and aluminum are in contact, iron will behave as the cathode and aluminum as the anode, as their reduction potentials indicate:

$$Fe^{2+} + 2e^- \rightarrow Fe \qquad \mathscr{E}^0 = -0.41 \text{ volt}$$

$$Al^{3+} + 3e^- \rightarrow Al \qquad \mathscr{E}^0 = -1.66 \text{ volts}$$

A coating of aluminum will prevent iron from being oxidized, and its own oxide will protect the aluminum from continual destructive corrosion.

But if you are going to aluminum-plate iron, you might as well make the objects out of aluminum to begin with, and gain the advantage of lightness. Unfortunately, aluminum is expensive. A cheaper alternative is to galvanize the iron by giving it a thin coating of zinc. You can see from the half-cell potential of zinc that the principle is the same. A galvanized steel bucket is corrosion-free, not merely because zinc shields the iron as paint would, but because zinc electrochemically prevents iron from being reduced (right). Scratch a galvanized pail and the pail will not corrode; the zinc will be oxidized instead. In principle the iron object does not even have to be covered completely for protection to occur. The zinc itself is relatively well protected because when some of it is oxidized, it absorbs CO_2 from the air and forms a tightly adhering zinc oxide–carbonate coating.

A "tin can" is a different story. Tin has a higher reduction potential than iron, and a greater tendency to remain reduced as the metal. A tin can is tin-plated iron, and if the surface is scratched, the iron will oxidize preferentially instead of the tin. Nothing electrochemical is gained by plating the can with tin; it is only a super-tight protective coating like paint. When the coating is breached, corrosion is rapid.

FREE ENERGY, ESCAPING TENDENCY, AND POTENTIAL

The theme of this chapter has been the use of free energy and potential as a measure of the drive toward chemical change. The free energy change per mole of molecules or electrons is the "pressure" on these molecules or electrons to move: from one solid, liquid, or gas phase to another for molecules; or from one atom, ion, or molecule to another for electrons.

An important concept adapted from gravitation is the idea that the free energy involved in a chemical change can be described as the product of a *potential* for change times the amount of substance that undergoes the change. The kinetic energy that a ball gains in rolling down a hill of height h is $E = mgh$. This is the product of the mass of the ball, m, and the gravitational potential, gh. The total free energy released by a chemical reaction is the energy change per mole times the

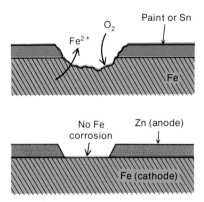

A tin coating protects iron only in the way that paint does, by providing a barrier against O_2 and H_2O. Once the barrier is broken, corrosion occurs. A zinc coating provides electrochemical protection as well. Because iron has a higher reduction potential, it tends to remain reduced while the zinc coating corrodes instead.

443

number of moles of reaction that occur. The free energy released during the transfer of electrons in an oxidation–reduction process is the free energy change per mole of electrons times the number of moles of electrons transferred.

As long as a higher potential exists for a starting state than for a final state, the shift from the initial state to the other is spontaneous, and the energy released can be harnessed to drive some other process. Water running downhill can turn a mill wheel or generate electricity. Burning gasoline can push a piston or heat a room. And electrons moving from zinc to silver can send a telegraph message or lay down a track of silver on a printed circuit board for a computer. When a potential gradient has "run down," and no difference in potential exists between two states, then the system is at equilibrium. No more drive toward change exists, and no more useful energy or work can be obtained from the system. This is the situation when all of the water has run to the bottom of the hill, a solution is in equilibrium with solid or vapor, or a battery has run down.

QUESTIONS

1. What is meant by gravitational potential? Chemical potential? Electrical potential? How do each of these influence the way that things occur spontaneously?

2. How are free energy, escaping tendency, and chemical potential interrelated?

3. The temperature of a gas is related to the speed with which the gas molecules are moving. At a given temperature, do all the molecules in a gas have the same speed?

4. How does the addition of nonvolatile solute molecules to a liquid disturb the liquid–vapor equilibrium? What happens to the vapor pressure?

5. What is meant by the boiling point of a liquid? Below the boiling point, can any of the liquid molecules exist as vapor in equilibrium with the liquid? What is the physical basis for the phenomenon that we describe as boiling, and why does it occur at a particular temperature?

6. Why does adding nonvolatile solute to a liquid raise the boiling point of the liquid? (Explain in terms of escaping tendency, and how it is affected by temperature and by solute molecules.)

7. Why does NaCl cause twice as great an elevation of the boiling point of water as the same number of moles of methanol?

8. What is Raoult's law, and how is it relevant to boiling point elevation?

9. What is the molecular basis for the phenomenon of freezing point depression? How is escaping tendency involved? Why does a temperature change have an effect on the equilibrium?

10. How can molecular weights of small molecules be determined by a measurement of freezing point depression or boiling point elevation? Why are these methods not so useful for macromolecules?

11. What is osmotic pressure? What is the molecular basis for this phenomenon? How is escaping tendency involved in your explanation?

12. How can osmotic pressure measurements be used to determine the molecular weights of large molecules?

13. What is the difference between molarity and molality as concentration units? Why are they approximately the same in dilute solution? Why are they not the same in more concentrated solutions? Why are they not the same even in quite dilute solutions, if a liquid other than water is the solvent?

14. Does oxidation necessarily require the removal of electrons? Give an example if this is not so.

15. Why is the type of oxidation where electrons actually are removed particularly important in electrochemistry?

16. What is the source of the free energy produced by a simple zinc–copper electrochemical cell? Why is it necessary to keep the zinc reaction and the copper reaction physically separated? What happens if this is not done?

17. In the zinc–copper cell, which electrode is the anode and which is the cathode? What are the individual electrode half-reactions, and at which electrode does oxidation occur?

18. How does a salt bridge or a porous barrier help to prevent an internal short-circuit of a cell? Why is no such barrier necessary in the Daniell cell?

19. What is the free energy change in the Daniell cell? What is meant by the standard electrochemical potential of a cell, and how is it related to the free energy change? What is the standard potential of the Daniell cell?

20. What is Faraday's constant? How is it related to a quantity of electrons? What is its numerical value in coulombs of electricity? What other units are especially convenient when working with potential and energy?

21. How can cell reactions be added, and when is it also proper to add their potentials to obtain the potential of another cell reaction?

22. What is a half-reaction? How are half-reactions combined to form a complete cell reaction? How are the corresponding half-cell potentials combined? How does the sign of the overall cell potential indicate spontaneity or lack of spontaneity?

23. What is a linear diagram of a cell? Write the linear diagram for the Daniell cell. How are concentrations indicated? How is a porous barrier symbolized?

24. Why is a dry cell inherently not rechargeable after it is used up? What is it about the electrode reactions of a lead storage battery that makes it rechargeable?

25. Why does a service station attendant measure the extent of charge of a storage battery by using a hydrometer to measure the density of the battery fluid? What chemical reactions of the cell cause this density to vary during the battery life?

26. What is electrolysis? How does the amount of electricity passed through an electrolytic cell affect the amount of chemical reaction that takes place?

27. What are Faraday's laws of electrolysis? Explain them in terms of electrons and chemical reactions.

28. Why doesn't aluminum "rust" in the way that iron does?

29. In what way is a thin layer of zinc over an iron object a better protection than either a tin layer or a coat of paint? How is electrochemistry used here?

PROBLEMS

1. The vapor pressure of pure benzene (C_6H_6) at 20°C is 75 mm Hg, whereas that for toluene (C_7H_8) is 22 mm Hg. Calculate the vapor pressure of a solution consisting of 10 g of benzene and 10 g of toluene. Calculate the mole fraction of each component in the vapor.

2. Which of the following substances would you expect to give a 0.1-molal aqueous solution with the lowest freezing point: HNO_3, NaCl, glucose, $CuSO_4$, $BaCl_2$?

3. Which will have a greater effect on the colligative properties of an aqueous solution, 20 g of NaCl or 10 g of $MgCl_2$? Assume complete solubility in each case.

4. Calculate the freezing point of a solution made by dissolving 1 g of NaCl in 10 g of water. Repeat your calculation by using 1 g of $CaCl_2$ instead. Which of these salts is more effective as an antifreeze on a weight basis?

5. If 35.5 g of solid chlorine (Cl_2) are dissolved in 32 g of liquid methane (CH_4) at the boiling point of methane, by how much will the vapor pressure of methane be lowered?

6. A solution is prepared by mixing 20 g of a nonvolatile solute, having a molecular weight of 100, with 500 g of solvent, having a molecular weight of 75. The boiling point of the solvent rises from 84.00°C to 85.00°C. Calculate the molal boiling point elevation constant for this solvent.

7. How many grams of methanol must be added to 10.0 kg of water to lower the freezing point of the solution to 263°K? What is the normal boiling point of this solution?

8. A solution is prepared by dissolving 0.40 g of an unknown hydrocarbon in 25.0 g of acetic acid. The freezing point of the solution falls from 16.60°C for pure acetic acid to 16.15°C. The molal freezing point depression constant for acetic acid is 3.60 deg mole^{-1}. What is the molecular weight of the hydrocarbon? Analysis of this compound shows that it contains 93.75% carbon by weight and 6.25% hydrogen. What is its molecular formula?

9. Benzoic acid is 68.9% carbon, 26.2% oxygen, and 4.96% hydrogen. One gram of the acid in 20 g of water freezes at 272.38°K, whereas 1 g in 20 g of benzene freezes at 277.56°K. What is the apparent molecular formula for benzoic acid in each solvent? Can you explain your results?

10. An important hormone that controls the rate of metabolism in the body, thyroxine, can be isolated from the thyroid gland. If 0.455 g of thyroxine is dissolved in 10.0 g of benzene, the freezing point of the solution is 5.144°C. Pure benzene freezes at 5.444°C. What is the molecular weight of thyroxine?

11. Calculate the osmotic pressure at 17°C of a solution containing 17.5 g of sucrose ($C_{12}H_{22}O_{11}$) in 150 ml of solution.

12. Considering that a plant cell wall is an osmotic membrane, explain why a lettuce salad containing salt and vinegar becomes limp in a few hours.

13. An aqueous solution of amygdalin (a sugarlike substance obtained from almonds) containing 96 g of solute per liter has an osmotic pressure of 4.74 atm at 0°C. What is the molecular weight of the solute?

14. A 3% aqueous solution of gum arabic (simplest formula $C_{12}H_{22}O_{11}$) has an osmotic pressure of 0.0272 atm at 25°C. What are the average molecular weight and degree of polymerization of the solute?

15. Why do red blood cells burst when placed in distilled water?

16. The osmotic pressure of human blood versus water varies from about 7.2 atm, which it may be early in the morning, to about 8.0 atm, to which it may rise after a big meal. These values are for a blood temperature of 37°C. Using an average value for osmotic pressure, calculate the mole fraction of the solutes and the number of moles of solutes per 1000 g of water.

17. A normal saline solution contains 9 g of NaCl per liter of water. Estimate its osmotic pressure at 37°C and compare with the osmotic pressures of blood given in Problem 16.

18. The process of *reverse osmosis* for preparing fresh water from salt water (seawater for example) depends on applying a pressure greater than the osmotic pressure to the solution. In this way the solvent is driven to flow from the solution to the pure solvent. The concentrations in moles per kilogram of seawater of the principal solutes of seawater are Cl^-, 0.546; Na^+, 0.456; Mg^{2+}, 0.053; SO_4^{2-}, 0.028; and Ca^{2+}, 0.010. What pressure on a seawater sample confined by a membrane permeable to water would have to be exceeded to produce reverse osmosis?

19. Determine the amount of useful work done when a mole of zinc powder is allowed to react with a 1.00-molar solution of $Cu(NO_3)_2$ in a constant-temperature calorimeter. If the reaction were carried out reversibly, how much useful work could be accomplished? ΔH_{298}^0 for the reaction is -51.40 kcal. Calculate the heat liberated when the reaction is carried out reversibly.

20. Which of the following reactions will be spontaneous under standard conditions:

(a) $Zn + Mg^{2+} \rightarrow Zn^{2+} + Mg$

(b) $Fe + Cl_2 \rightarrow Fe^{2+} + 2Cl^-$

(c) $4Ag + O_2 + 4H^+ \rightarrow 4Ag^+ + 2H_2O$

(d) $2AgCl \rightarrow 2Ag + Cl_2$

21. What is the standard potential, $\mathscr{E}^0$, for each of the following half-cells:

(a) $S^{2-}|CuS(s)|Cu(s)$

(b) $NH_3(aq), Zn(NH_3)_4^{2+}|Zn(s)$

22. The following two reactions have the $\mathscr{E}^0$ values given:

$2Ag + Pt^{2+} \rightarrow 2Ag^+ + Pt \qquad \mathscr{E}^0 = +0.40$ V

$2Ag + F_2 \rightarrow 2Ag^+ + 2F^- \qquad \mathscr{E}^0 = +2.07$ V

If the potential for the reaction $Pt \rightarrow Pt^{2+} + 2e^-$ is assigned a value of zero, calculate the potentials for the following half-reactions:

(a) $Ag \rightarrow Ag^+ + e^-$ (b) $F^- \rightarrow \frac{1}{2}F_2 + e^-$

23. Use the linear cell diagram notation to represent a cell that involves the following half-reactions:

$PbO_2 + 4H^+ + 2e^- \rightarrow Pb^{2+} + 2H_2O$

$PbSO_4 + 2e^- \rightarrow Pb + SO_4^{2-}$

(a) Which is the reaction at the cathode of the cell? Which way do electrons flow in an external circuit?

(b) What is $\mathscr{E}^0$ for this cell?

24. Show that hydrogen peroxide is thermodynamically unstable and should disproportionate to water and oxygen.

25. Find the missing standard reduction potentials for the following half-reactions from data in tables in this chapter.

	$\mathscr{E}^0$(V)
$MnO_4^- + 8H^+ + 5e^- \rightarrow Mn^{2+} + 4H_2O$	+1.49
$Au^{3+} + 3e^- \rightarrow Au(s)$	+1.42
$Cl_2 + 2e^- \rightarrow 2Cl^-$	?
$AuCl_4^- + 3e^- \rightarrow Au(s) + 4Cl^-$	?
$4H^+ + NO_3^- + 3e^- \rightarrow NO + 2H_2O$	?

If we assume that all reactants and products are at the same concentration:

(a) Which substance in the half-reactions above is the best oxidizing agent? Which is the best reducing agent? (b) Will permanganate oxidize metallic gold? (c) Will metallic gold reduce nitric acid? (d) Will nitric acid oxidize metallic gold in the presence of Cl^- ion? (e) Will metallic gold reduce pure Cl_2 gas in the presence of water? (f) Will chlorine oxidize metallic gold if Cl^- ion is present? (g) Will permanganate oxidize chloride ion?

26. For an electrochemical cell in which the spontaneous reaction is $3Cu^{2+} + 2Al \rightarrow 2Al^{3+} + 3Cu$, what will be the qualitative effect on the cell potential if we add ethylenediamine, a ligand that coordinates strongly with Cu^{2+} but not with Al^{3+}?

27. Find the standard reduction potentials for the following half-reactions:

$MnO_4^- + 8H^+ + 5e^- \rightarrow Mn^{2+} + 4H_2O$

$Al^{3+} + 3e^- \rightarrow Al$

$Cl_2 + 2e^- \rightarrow 2Cl^-$

$Mg^{2+} + 2e^- \rightarrow Mg$

(a) Which is the strongest reducing agent? Which is the strongest oxidizing agent? (b) Write the overall reaction for a successful cell made from the Mg and Cl_2 couples. (c) Write the line notation for this cell. (d) Which is the anode of the cell, and which is the cathode? (e) What is $\mathscr{E}^0$ for the cell? (f) What is the equilibrium-constant expression for this cell reaction? Calculate the numerical value of the equilibrium constant at 25°C.

28. Find the standard reduction potentials for the following half-reactions:

$SO_4^{2-} + 4H^+ + 2e^- \rightarrow H_2SO_3 + H_2O$

$Ag^+ + e^- \rightarrow Ag$

(a) Write the balanced overall reaction for a successful cell made from these two half-reactions. (b) Write the line notation for the cell. (c) What is $\mathscr{E}^0$ for the cell? (d) What is the equilibrium constant for the cell reaction at 25°C?

29. Find the standard reduction potentials for the following half-reactions:

$Hg_2^{2+} + 2e^- \rightarrow 2Hg$

$Cu^{2+} + 2e^- \rightarrow Cu$

(a) Write the overall reaction for a successful cell made from these two half-reactions. (b) Write the line notation for the cell. Which material, Hg or Cu, is the anode? (c) What is $\mathscr{E}^0$ for the cell? (d) What is the equilibrium constant for the cell?

30. Using half-reactions, show that Ag^+ and I^- spontaneously form $AgI(s)$ when mixed directly at standard concentrations. Show that K_{sp} for AgI is 10^{-16}.

31. Chrome-plated automobile trim contains an iron core coated by a thick layer of nickel that is coated by a layer of chromium. Arrange these metals in order of ease of oxidation. What is the purpose of the chromium layer? Of the nickel layer?

CHAPTER 18

From Outer Space to Inner Space: Scale in the Universe

The first chapter of this book was entitled "The View from a Distant Universe." In the chapters that followed, we moved in our mind's eye from galaxies and stars down to atoms and subatomic particles. We saw how atoms are synthesized at very high temperatures in stellar interiors, and how at much lower temperatures these atoms associate into molecules and condense into liquids and solids. We saw how atoms are constructed from electrons, neutrons, and protons, and the way in which the structure of atoms brings about a broad range of chemical properties and behavior, culminating in the periodic table. Especially in the preceding seven chapters we have seen how these atoms and molecules react with one another, by breaking chemical bonds and forming new ones, and absorbing or releasing energy.

Nowhere in this chemical landscape have we yet seen ourselves or the most remarkable of all chemical phenomena, *life*. Life is a special kind of chemical system that arose in our corner of the universe (and probably elsewhere, though we have no evidence yet) in a restricted size and temperature range, using a relatively small number of the possible kinds of atoms. "Man is the measure of the universe" is an often-quoted epigram. In reality the universe stretches for many orders of magnitude to either side of the range that man can comprehend easily. One of the purposes of this chapter is to place man and other living organisms in their proper setting.

Although we occupy a relatively restricted corner of the universe, it is an important corner, because here we encounter a new dimension of matter: complex organization. Stars are believed to be basically simple in construction. Temperature gradients and layering of material undoubtedly exist, with different thermonuclear reactions of the type encountered in Chapter 8 occurring at different depths. There also may be convection cells and magnetic field structures within one layer, but even the largest star has none of the organized complexity

Man is midway in size between the sun and a protein molecule.

that we find in a germinating seed. At the other extreme, imperfect as our knowledge of subatomic structure may be today, we still must conclude that atoms, by the criterion of the germinating seed, are relatively simple objects also. Molecules, and especially molecules built with carbon-atom skeletons, seem to be required to build up a sufficiently complex set of chemical reactions to create a living organism. The next eight chapters will be devoted to an examination of carbon compounds: the variety that they can have, the many different properties that they can exhibit, and the way in which they serve as the raw material for life. But before entering the jungle of organic and biochemistry, it may be well to step back and look at our starting point again, the universe.

SCALE IN THE UNIVERSE

The smallest objects on Earth that we can see with the unaided eye differ from the Earth itself by twelve orders of magnitude: twelve tenfold increases in linear size, or a factor of 1,000,000,000,000. This is close to the limit of what we can imagine, because it is the limit of our first-hand experience.

The universe is not limited by our imagination. It stretches for a dozen more orders of magnitude in either direction, toward the immense as well as toward the infinitesimal. Even to record such a range of size requires us to fall back on exponential or power-of-ten notation, in which 1,000,000,000 or one billion becomes 10^9, and one-billionth or 0.000000001 becomes $1/10^9$ or 10^{-9}. The diameter of the Earth is 1,300,000,000 centimeters, or 1.3×10^9 cm, and the diameter of the observable universe has been estimated to be 1.7×10^{28} cm. The Earth fits into this universe like a single small bacterium fits into the entire solar system. At the other extreme, the diameter of an atomic nucleus is only 0.0000000000001 cm, or 10^{-13} cm. Such vast size ranges are nearly beyond our comprehension.

The following two-page spread shows a gallery of objects of different sizes: one typical object for each order of magnitude or ten-fold change in length, from 10^{+28} cm (the universe) down to 10^{-13} cm (an atomic nucleus). These are the boundaries of reality as we know it. Each object is ten times the length of the object just below it, and 100 times the length of the object two places below. The first eleven orders of magnitude, from 10^{28} cm to 10^{18} cm, describe astronomical bodies outside our solar system: stars, galaxies, and galactic clusters. A gap of four orders of magnitude then ensues between the nearest star and the most distant planet, similar to the difference in size between a football stadium and the coin flipped to start the game. Nothing that we know of fills this size gap, although there must be such objects somewhere in our galaxy.

The next twelve orders of magnitude, from 10^{14} cm to 100 cm, bring us from the orbit of Pluto and the edge of the solar system down to human dimensions. Nearly the same relative size ratio, from 100 cm to 10^{-9} cm, bridges the span from the size of man down to the size of an atom. At this point another gap of four orders of magnitude appears, which separates atoms from atomic nuclei. With nuclei of 10^{-13} cm diameter, the lower limit of our known universe is met. We might suppose subatomic particles to be smaller yet, but have no way of establishing their size. At the lower limit, as at the upper, scale in the universe becomes lost in theory.

Our immediately familiar and touchable world ranges from 10^{10} cm to 10^{-2} cm, from the moon to microorganisms. Larger objects such as stars and galaxies are seen but not always fully comprehended; smaller objects from the world of molecules and atoms are comprehended intellectually but seldom seen. We live and work in a midrange of size between these far extremes. A small protein molecule in a cell has the same size relationship to us that we have to the sun, and that the entire solar system has to our galaxy.

ENERGY IN THE UNIVERSE

We live in a midrange of energy as well as size. A living organism must have enough energy to drive it, but not enough to destroy it. Nuclear fission and fusion reactions are useless to a living cell because they create so much energy that the molecules and arrangements of molecules that the cell needs to function would be completely shattered. The main problem today in commercial adaptation of controlled nuclear fusion as an energy source is that we know of no material that can withstand the temperatures developed by fusion, and that can be used to make a container for the reaction. For stars this problem is solved by simple physical separation in space.

Living chemical systems tap a milder energy source, the energy involved in the making and breaking of chemical bonds between atoms, rather than the energy involved in altering atomic nuclei. Such chemical reactions have nothing to do with nuclear forces, but involve only the shifting about of electrons outside the nucleus. Energies involved in covalent bonds are typically one ten-millionth the energies of nuclear reactions, yet these relatively weak interatomic bonds are strong enough to tie atoms together, and to build structures of a complexity unmatched at the stellar or nuclear levels. When we turn our backs on the harsh conditions of stellar interiors and nuclear reactions, we enter the world of the molecule. Large and complex molecules are not common in our universe, but they are essential for the occurrence of life.

TEMPERATURE

The universe beyond our Earth is a study in contrasts of temperature. The center of our sun reaches 40 million degrees, and the fusion reactions in larger stars, discussed in Chapter 8, can reach 2 billion degrees or more. At the other end of the scale, temperature has little meaning in nearly empty space. If we define temperature in terms of the average kinetic energy of molecules, what does temperature mean in a region of outer space that has only one or two atoms per cubic centimeter? Temperature in a vacuum also can be defined in terms of the radiation pass-

1.8 cm

The entire known universe can be encompassed in 42 order-of-magnitude changes. As a standard, the bee (1.8×10^0 cm) is shown here actual size. This ancient Greek coin from Ephesos is also reproduced actual size. From *Ancient Greek Coins* by G. K. Jenkins. G. P. Putnam, 1972.

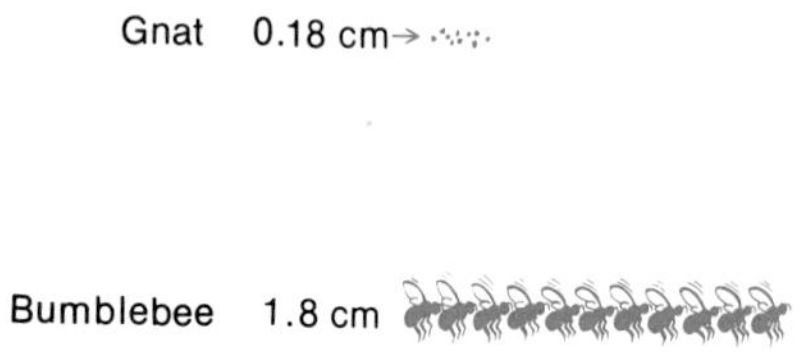

FROM THE UNIVERSE TO THE NUCLEUS IN 42 STEPS OF TEN

n	Object with linear dimensions of 10^n centimeters
28	Diameter of universe = 17 billion light years (LY) = 1.6×10^{28} cm
27	Distance to Radio Galaxy 3C–295 = 6 billion LY = 5.7×10^{27} cm
26	Distance to Radio Galaxy Cygnus A = 600 million LY = 5.7×10^{26} cm
25	Distance to center of nearest neighbor galactic cluster, in Virgo = 40 million LY = 3.8×10^{25} cm
24	Distance to the Great Nebula (Galaxy) of Andromeda in our own galactic cluster = 1.8 million LY = 1.7×10^{24} cm
23	Diameter of our galaxy = 100,000 LY = 10^{23} cm
22	Distance from our sun to center of galaxy = 33,000 LY = 3.1×10^{22} cm
21	Thickness of our galaxy = 1500 LY = 1.4×10^{21} cm
20	Probable average distance between technological civilizations in our galaxy (von Hoerner, quoted by Shklovskii and Sagan[1]) = 100–1000 LY = 10^{20}–10^{21} cm
19	Distance of sun above galactic plane = 30 LY = 2.8×10^{19} cm
18	Distance to nearest star, Alpha Centauri = 4 LY = 3.8×10^{18} cm
17	....
16	....
15	....
14	Radius of orbit of Pluto = 3.67 billion miles = 5.9×10^{14} cm

Gnat   0.18 cm→

Bumblebee   1.8 cm

An order-of-magnitude change means a tenfold change, or a shift of one place of the decimal point. A bumble bee is as long as ten gnats; ten bees are required to equal the length of a small rabbit, and a man is ten times the length of a rabbit.

Rabbit   18 cm

Man   180 cm

13	Radius of orbit of Earth $= 93$ million miles $= 1.5 \times 10^{13}$ cm
12	Radius of orbit of Mercury $= 36$ million miles $= 5.8 \times 10^{12}$ cm
11	Diameter of our Sun $= 864{,}000$ miles $= 1.4 \times 10^{11}$ cm
10	Distance from Earth to Moon $= 240{,}000$ miles $= 3.9 \times 10^{10}$ cm
9	Diameter of Earth $= 7927$ miles $= 1.3 \times 10^{9}$ cm
8	Length of Great Britain $= 1000$ km $= 10^{8}$ cm
7	Width of Lake Michigan $= 130$ km $= 1.3 \times 10^{7}$ cm
6	Cruising altitude of a commercial jet $= 33{,}000$ feet $= 10^{6}$ cm
5	Distance from U.S. Capitol Building to Washington Monument $= 1.5$ miles $= 2.4 \times 10^{5}$ cm
4	Length of football stadium $= 150$ yards $= 1.4 \times 10^{4}$ cm
3	Length of a blue whale $= \sim 100$ feet $= 3 \times 10^{3}$ cm
2	Height of a man $= 6$ feet $= 183$ cm
1	Small rabbit $= 18$ cm
0	Bumblebee $= 1.8$ cm
-1	Gnat $= 0.18$ cm $= 1.8 \times 10^{-1}$ cm
-2	Length of a paramecium $= 2.0 \times 10^{-2}$ cm
-3	Length of a segment of blue-green algae $= 3.7 \times 10^{-3}$ cm
-4	Length of an *E. coli* bacterium $= 2.0 \times 10^{-4}$ cm
-5	Dimensions of a tobacco mosaic virus rod $= (3.0 \times 0.18) \times 10^{-5}$ cm
-6	Diameter of a polio virus sphere $= 3 \times 10^{-6}$ cm
-7	Diameter of a small enzyme molecule $= 30$ Å $= 3 \times 10^{-7}$ cm
-8	Diameter of a carbon atom $= 3$ Å $= 3 \times 10^{-8}$ cm
-9	Radius of electron orbit in hydrogen atom $= 0.53$ Å $= 5.3 \times 10^{-9}$ cm
-10	....
-11	....
-12	....
-13	Diameter of an atomic nucleus $= 10^{-13}$ cm

Key

1 light year (LY) $= 0.946 \times 10^{18}$ cm

1 mile $= 1.61$ km $= 1.61 \times 10^{5}$ cm

1 angstrom unit (Å) $= 10^{-8}$ cm

[1] I. S. Shklovskii and Carl Sagan, *Intelligent Life in the Universe,* Holden-Day, San Francisco, 1966.

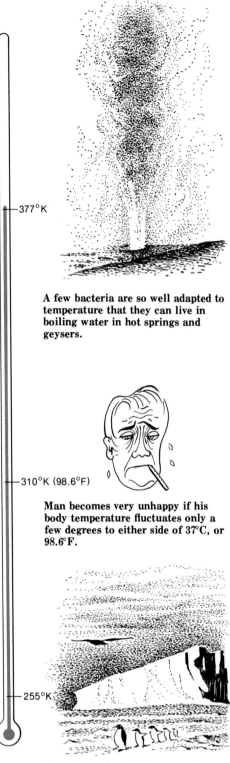

377°K

A few bacteria are so well adapted to temperature that they can live in boiling water in hot springs and geysers.

310°K (98.6°F)

Man becomes very unhappy if his body temperature fluctuates only a few degrees to either side of 37°C, or 98.6°F.

255°K

Some bacteria can live at 18°C below the freezing point of water, but this seems to represent the lower limit for life.

ing through it, compared with the radiation from a perfectly nonreflective black body of measurable temperature. Interstellar space is filled with microwave radiation in the millimeter wavelength range, corresponding to a black-body temperature of only 3°K by this definition. Theoreticians have proposed that this radiation is the last remnant of the primeval "big bang" fireball with which the universe began 15 billion years ago.

The chemistry that we know on Earth is confined to a minute span within this broad range of temperature. At sufficiently high temperatures, electrons are stripped from atoms, and matter exists only as an ionized plasma of electrons and nuclei. In gases the temperature is high enough to overcome the attractions between molecules. In plasmas the temperature is so high that even the attractions between nuclei and electrons are overcome, and neutral atoms no longer exist. Plasmas have been described as a fourth state of matter, along with gases, liquids, and solids at lower temperatures. Electrons and nuclei from a plasma only combine to form atoms at temperatures below 100,000 degrees. Atoms in turn do not associate into molecules, nor do molecules condense into liquids and solids, until temperatures fall below a few thousand degrees. The delicate carbon compounds that we shall be examining in the following chapters break down a few dozen degrees above "normal" or room temperature, which can be assumed to be around 300°K. In contrast, most familiar chemical reactions effectively come to a halt 100°C below room temperature. We saw in Chapter 15 that the rates of chemical reactions depend on energies of activation. A reaction with a modest activation energy of 11 kcal mole^{-1} proceeds 10,000 times faster at 300°K than at 200°K, even assuming that it remains a gas-collision process at the lower temperature. If the reactants and products condense to liquids or solids, then the process at 200°K is even slower. Just as the familiar physical world is encountered between 10^{-2} cm and 10^{10} cm, so the familiar chemical world occurs primarily between 200°K and 2000°K. Life for some simple bacteria can go on as low as 255°K or as high as 377°K, but for the most advanced organism, man, the chemistry of life breaks down a short distance to either side of 310°K or 37°C. The more complex the machinery, the more restricted are its operating conditions.

ORGANIZATION AND COMPLEXITY

We began this book with the viewpoint of a newcomer to the universe. What would he see, and how would he interpret it? The stars would be seen to consist mostly of hydrogen and helium, and the heavier elements would be most apparent in the colder planets that surround some stars. As our visitor approached closer and closer, he would discover first the lightest two elements, and then the rest of the inorganic elements. But if he came close enough to Earth (and probably to some other planets here and there around the galaxy), he would encounter a new kind of chemical organization. In the midrange of size, and under mild conditions of temperature and pressure, there exists a diverse and varied chemistry based on carbon atoms. These atoms can form strong

456

C—C bonds in chains of apparently limitless length. Rather than ions and electrons in a plasma, or single and paired atoms in a gas, or ions in crystalline arrays, our observer would find connected groupings of large numbers of atoms into stable units: *molecules*.

In the midst of this molecular carbon chemistry, and arising from it, highly organized collections of chemical reactions would be detected, which are isolated from the general environment by semipermeable barriers. These *living* entities show a degree of order and organization not yet encountered elsewhere in the universe, and a state of unusually low entropy. Entropy, as we saw in Chapter 13, is a measure of the degree of disorder. Maintenance of this state of order, or of low entropy, requires the production of specific molecules whose synthesis is not thermodynamically spontaneous. Most of the complex carbon compounds that exist on Earth were produced by such organized, living chemical systems. The free energy necessary to drive these nonspontaneous reactions "uphill" is obtained from other carbon-based molecules in the environment. Most of this energy results from the destruction of carbon-containing molecules and the combination of their atoms with oxygen. These organized entities maintain low entropy within their own boundaries by creating even more entropy outside.

The ultimate source of free energy to drive all these chemical systems is the sun. Living chemical systems use a minute fraction of the solar radiation (less than one part in a billion is intercepted by the Earth) to maintain a temporary state of high order in localized regions of space on the surfaces of our planet. The activities necessary for these systems to maintain themselves, to obtain free energy, and to avoid destruction, all have the appearance of being purposeful. Some of these localized chemical units seem more purposeful and more adaptive to changing conditions than others. No matter what the chemistry of our hypothetical outside observer might be, he would undoubtedly recognize such carbon-based chemical systems as being *alive*.

To turn matters around and observe the observer, could such an alien visitor exist with a chemistry based on other than carbon atoms? The answer probably is no. We cannot give a meaningful answer to this question until we know more about the behavior of carbon compounds and of living systems. These are the subjects of the next chapters, but we can make a few general observations about the suitability of possible raw materials now.

Besides size and energy (temperature), another important yardstick exists for measuring the universe, *complexity*. Complexity is accompanied by organization between components, by structure, orderliness, and low entropy. As we construct more and more intricate machines, we find that certain capabilities are a function of the level of complexity of the machine, more than of the particular components from which it is constructed. One can build a clock, or an elementary calculating machine, out of wood, metal, or plastic. The capabilities of the calculator are limited not so much by the materials themselves as by their organization. Such a simple machine cannot alter its preset operations, or make choices based on the state of the machine at any given moment. From more elaborate hardware one can build a digital computer. This machine now can do everything that the primitive calculating machine can do, and much more. It can accept and emit data, can recall, and can calculate in ways not only not preprogrammed in the hardware, *but not even anticipated by the builders*. It can make choices or decisions for future actions based on the current state of its information, and can "learn" to make better decisions from the outcome of previous trials.

The very same computer in a functional sense can be built from quite different raw materials. It can use vacuum tubes or transistors. Its physical memory storage may involve solenoid switches, mercury delay lines, cathode-ray tubes, or magnetic tapes, drums, or core. The user of the computer need never know what is inside. Two computers can show identical behavior, but contain entirely different physical parts. A common technique in the computer industry is to simulate on an existing computer the logical behavior of a new machine that has yet to be built, possibly using radically different constructional principles. The user of a computer sees it, not as a collection of electronic components, but as a logical network to be manipulated by him. The useful properties of the network arise not so much from the components themselves as from the way that they are arranged and interconnected. This is what we mean by complexity, and in a sense this is what entropy measures.

Our experience with computers in the past three decades has led to the realization of an extremely significant principle: *The behavior and properties of any organized system arise not only from its parts, but also from the manner in which they are arranged.* The whole is greater than the sum of the parts. A simple but by no means trivial example is the collection of 200 black, white, and gray blocks shown on the opposite page. In a random pile they have no meaning, but the same 200 physical objects, arranged as at the top of the page, have meaning and convey information. The more complex a system becomes, the more its behavior depends primarily on its state of organization. A computer can be thought of as a childishly simple and primitive model of a living organism—not because the computer is "alive" in any sense, but because it illustrates at a low level the importance of integration and organization in determining the behavior of any complex system.

ORGANIZATION, CARBON, AND LIFE

We can assume that any living creature must be built from atoms with the capability of forming highly organized systems. Despite previous comments about the subordination of material to arrangement, some materials are simply inappropriate. We cannot build a digital computer from wood, or even from metal using the crude shaped-metal technology of a century ago. Charles Babbage, mentioned in Chapter 5, understood and outlined the principles of a punched-card-controlled digital computer with a stored and modifiable program in 1833, but the technology of his time was inadequate to construct one. Similarly, we cannot conceive of a living organism as being built mainly from ionic compounds. Nondirectional forces between ions do not permit the necessary degree of complexity. The main reason why we can claim "no

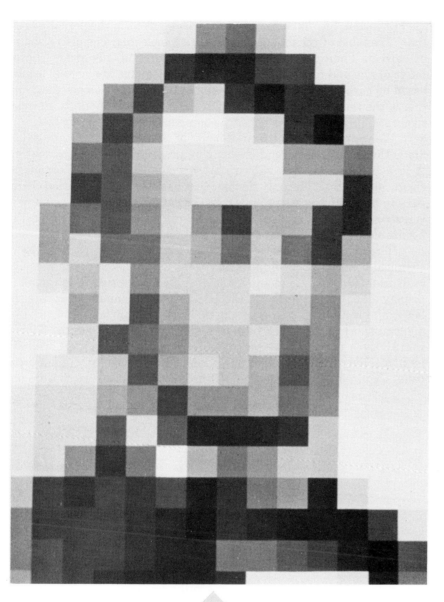

The arrangement of objects often is more important in carrying meaning and information than the nature of the objects themselves. This particular arrangement of 200 black, white, and gray squares carries the impression of a recognizable portrait. (If you can't see it, hold the book away from you a few feet.) The same blocks, arranged differently below, carry no message. The whole in this case obviously is greater than the sum of its parts! Courtesy of Leon A. Harmon and Bell Laboratories.

life but carbon life" is that we see no other element in the periodic table that is capable of the extensive and varied molecular chemistry shown by carbon. There are good reasons why life is found only in a restricted range of size and temperature: This is the size range of macromolecules based on carbon, and of larger assemblies of such macromolecules; and this is the temperature range within which these compounds are relatively stable, yet reactions between compounds are reasonably fast.

We can summarize the arguments of this chapter by stating that life is the most exciting and challenging property exhibited by matter. It is a behavior pattern shown only by complex and well organized chemical systems. The only element that has a sufficiently varied chemistry to build such systems appears to be carbon, and life as we know it is restricted to conditions under which large carbon compounds exist in a suitable balance between stability and reactivity.

The size of living organisms ultimately is tied to the lengths of chemical bonds, and the dimensions of the logical networks that can be built from molecules. Organisms smaller than bacteria are too small to display all of the properties of life. Organisms of planetary size are too large, and would suffer from severe problems of transfer of information and transport of molecules, both internally and to and from the outside world. Even in our primitive computer technology of today, we have built machines in which the limitations on computation time are the times required for electrons to flow through connecting wires from one component to another. We have evaded this difficulty by micro-miniaturization, but we still are far from achieving the level of compactness represented by the human brain. That paragon of miniaturization has 12 billion cells, each connected to at least 100 others, all within one cubic foot of folded cerebral cortex.

The study of the most complex of all chemical phenomena, living organisms, must begin with the study of the compounds of carbon. This is the subject of the next three chapters.

QUESTIONS

1. In what sense do we occupy a midrange of size in the universe? A midrange of temperature?

2. Why would life be difficult to imagine at 10,000°K? At 100°K?

3. Why would it be difficult to imagine a living organism 100 Å in diameter? What disadvantages might there be to a living organism 100 miles in diameter?

4. Why is complexity an important aspect of living organisms? In what sense is the whole greater than the sum of the parts in a living cell?

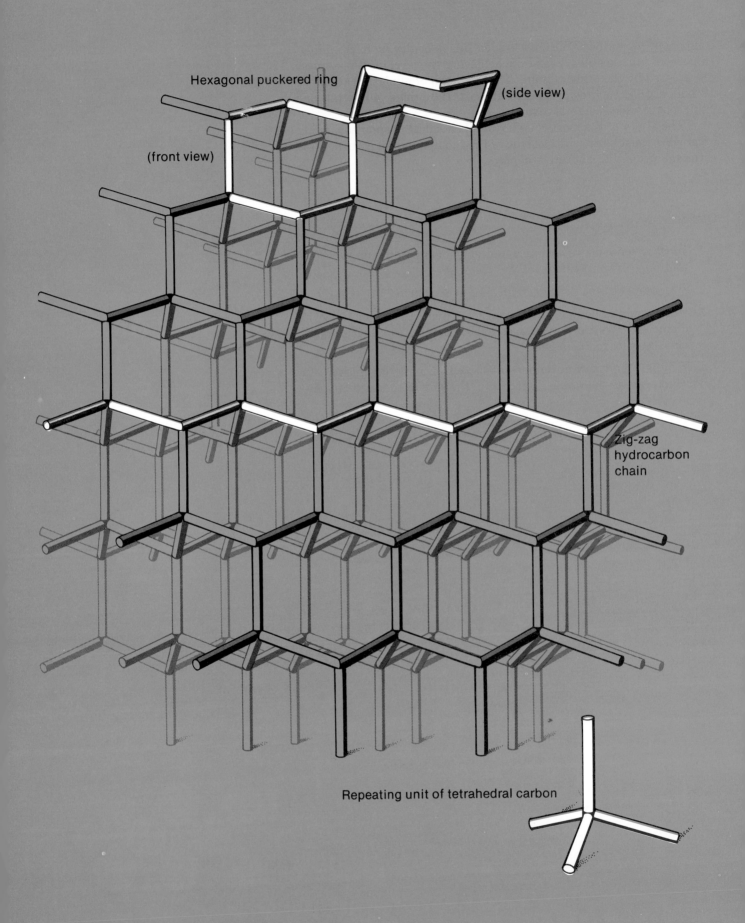

Hexagonal puckered ring

(side view)

(front view)

Zig-zag
hydrocarbon
chain

Repeating unit of tetrahedral carbon

◀ *The tetrahedral geometry of diamond is the framework for all organic molecules with carbon-carbon single bonds*

CHAPTER 19

The Simple Compounds of Carbon

The many organic compounds found in living organisms—proteins and amino acids, sugars, organic acids and bases, fats, and hormones—are possible only because of the many different kinds of atoms and groups of atoms that can be attached to carbon backbones. In the next chapter we shall see what several of these compounds are like. Before we do, however, we must look at the carbon backbones themselves. This chapter is devoted to hydrocarbons—compounds of carbon and hydrogen. Many of the ideas that we will develop about hydrocarbons will carry over directly to more complicated compounds.

The special properties of carbon that make it appropriate for construction of living organisms arise from its central position in the periodic table. In the previous chapter we mentioned that life occupies the midranges of size and temperature in the universe. Carbon occupies the midposition in Row 2 of the periodic table, and has exactly half as many electrons as are needed to fill its outer shell. It neither loses nor gains electrons in chemical reactions, so its compounds are not ionic. This is critical for its role, since the nondirectional electrostatic forces between ions are inadequate for building elaborate molecules (right). Carbon *shares* its four electrons in four covalent bonds with other electron-sharing atoms. Because these four bonding electron pairs still are bound to the atoms from which they came, they hold the atoms together in a molecule. When carbon is bonded to four other atoms, the four electron pairs around the central carbon atom repel one another, thereby causing the four bound atoms to occupy the corners of a tetrahedron in sp^3 hybridization. This gives a geometric shape to the molecule (right). The ultimate in carbon tetrahedra is the crystal lattice of diamond, shown on the opposite page, in which the tetrahedral array of carbon atoms goes on forever, and there are no hydrogen atoms present at all. Hydrocarbons that have only single bonds between carbon atoms can be thought of as fragments of this three-dimensional diamond lattice.

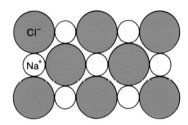

Ionic bonds are nondirectional, so the structural basis for salt crystals is the packing of spherical ions.

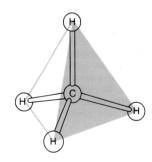

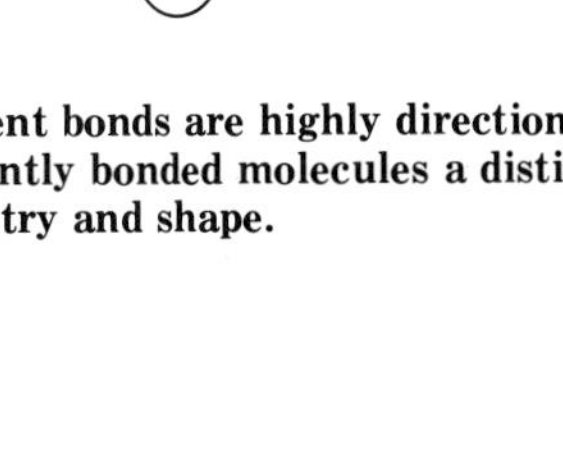

Covalent bonds are highly directional, giving covalently bonded molecules a distinctive geometry and shape.

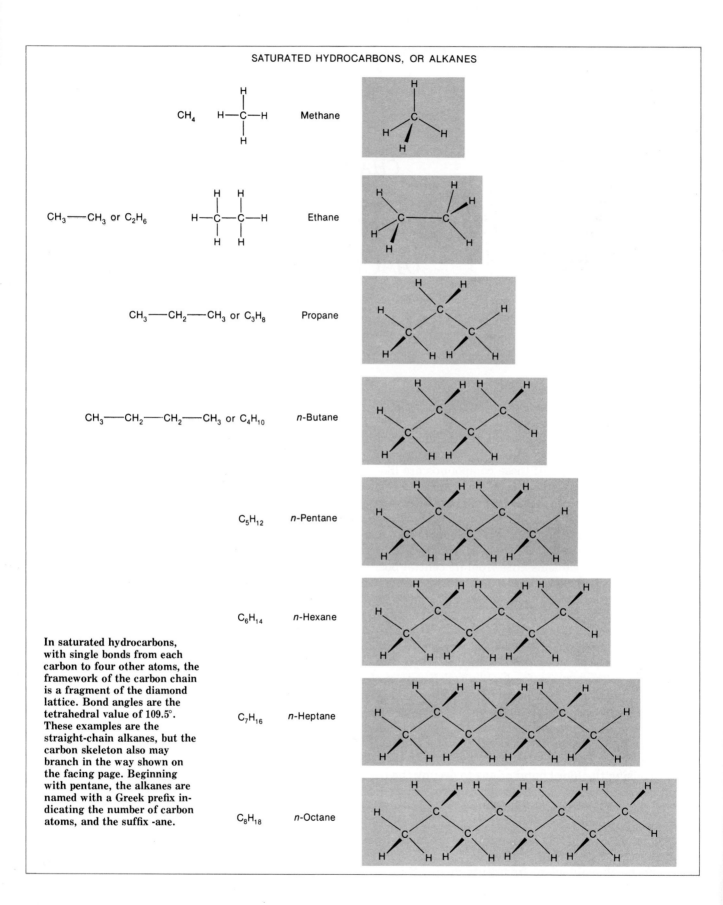

CH_4 Methane

CH_3——CH_3 or C_2H_6 Ethane

CH_3——CH_2——CH_3 or C_3H_8 Propane

CH_3——CH_2——CH_2——CH_3 or C_4H_{10} n-Butane

C_5H_{12} n-Pentane

C_6H_{14} n-Hexane

C_7H_{16} n-Heptane

C_8H_{18} n-Octane

In saturated hydrocarbons, with single bonds from each carbon to four other atoms, the framework of the carbon chain is a fragment of the diamond lattice. Bond angles are the tetrahedral value of 109.5°. These examples are the straight-chain alkanes, but the carbon skeleton also may branch in the way shown on the facing page. Beginning with pentane, the alkanes are named with a Greek prefix indicating the number of carbon atoms, and the suffix -ane.

THE SIMPLEST ORGANIC MOLECULES: HYDROCARBONS

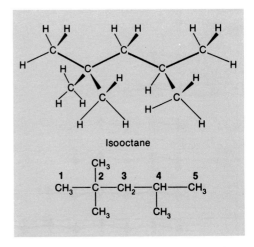

Isooctane

Organic compounds in general are in a reduced state, and therefore are storehouses of energy for the reasons discussed in Chapter 12. Hydrocarbons are the most reduced compounds of all, with nothing but C and H atoms. Hydrocarbons with single C—C bonds, known as *saturated hydrocarbons* or *alkanes*, can be thought of as being built by the snapping together of carbon tetrahedra, with unused carbon bonding positions filled by hydrogen atoms. There are as many different saturated hydrocarbons as there are ways of connecting tetrahedra. The simplest are the straight-chain alkanes (designated "*n-*" for "normal"), which are shown on the opposite page. Methane, ethane, propane, and butane are traditional names for these compounds, but from pentane and hexane onward, the name is derived from the Greek or Latin word for the number of carbons, plus the suffix "-ane" to indicate a saturated hydrocarbon.

The straight-chain *n*-octane molecule at the bottom of the opposite page is not the only way of constructing a C_8H_{18} molecule. Another possible structure is isooctane, shown at the upper right. These two are *structural isomers* of octane, because they have the same number of each kind of atom, but are arranged in different ways. Isooctane is familiar from the "octane rating" of gasoline. Straight-chain gasolines burn suddenly with an audible bang against the cylinder walls of an engine, which we hear as engine knock. Branched-chain molecules burn more slowly and quietly. The octane rating of any gasoline is the percent isooctane in a mixture with *n*-heptane that has the same knock behavior.

Pentane has three structural isomers, all of which are shown in the right margin. Their common names are *n*-pentane, isopentane, and neopentane, but these molecules can be used to illustrate the systematic way of naming organic compounds. "Normal," "iso-" (meaning an isomer), and "neo-" (meaning new) may suffice for a pentane, but for the 75 different structural isomers of decane a more orderly method of choosing names is required.

In systematic nomenclature, the longest continuous carbon backbone that can be traced through the molecule is chosen as the "parent" compound, and prefixes are added to describe groups branching off from this backbone. The carbon atoms along the backbone are numbered from one end. As an example, the longest chain that can be traced through the isopentane molecule contains four carbon atoms, so in systematic nomenclature this molecule is a butane. A methyl group (CH_3—) branches off from the second carbon along the chain, so isopentane is called 2-methylbutane. One also could call it 3-methylbutane by beginning the backbone numbering from the other end, but there is no logical reason for using this name. The numbering is begun at the end that leads to the simplest name with the smallest numbers. Notice that there is no 1-methylbutane or 4-methylbutane; these molecules simply would be the straight-chain pentane.

In systematic nomenclature, neopentane is classed as a propane because the longest carbon chain contains three atoms. Since two methyl groups branch off from the second carbon of the chain, the molecule is called 2,2-dimethylpropane.

Isooctane differs from *n*-octane, shown on the opposite page, only in the way that its atoms are oriented.

Pentane has three structural isomers.

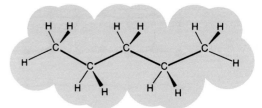

n-Pentane   m.p. −130°C   b.p. 36°C

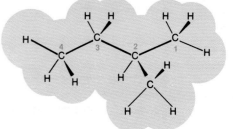

Isopentane   m.p. −160°C   b.p. 28°C

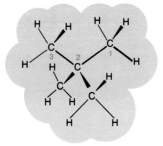

Neopentane   m.p. −17°C   b.p. 10°C

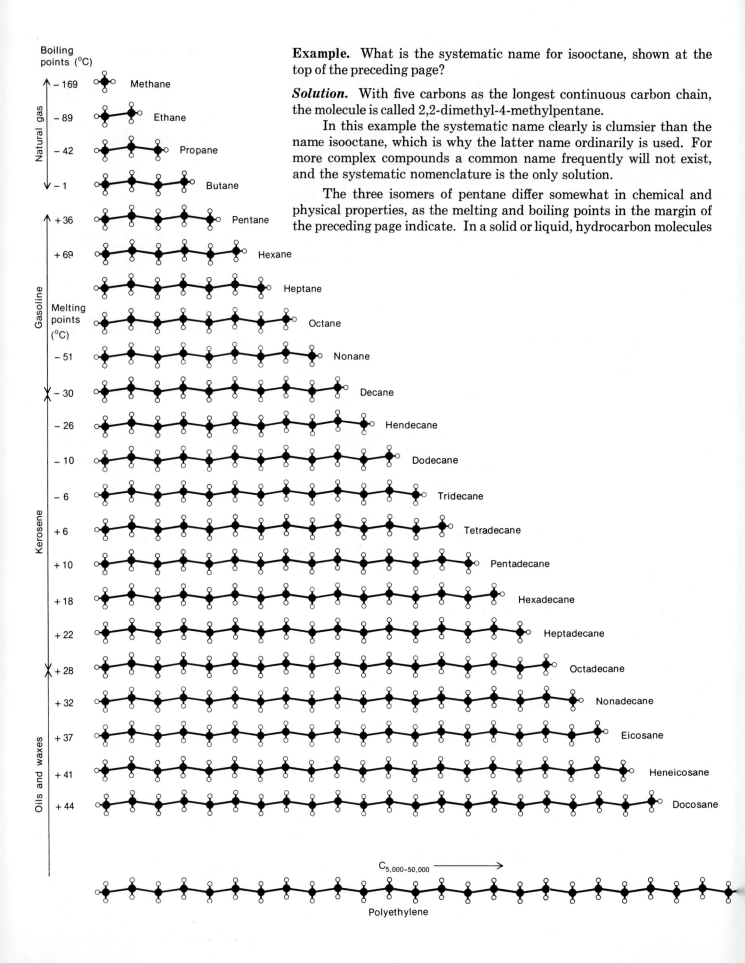

Boiling points (°C)

Natural gas

- −169 Methane
- −89 Ethane
- −42 Propane
- −1 Butane

Gasoline

- +36 Pentane
- +69 Hexane

Melting points (°C)

- −51 Nonane
- −30 Decane

Kerosene

- −26 Hendecane
- −10 Dodecane
- −6 Tridecane
- +6 Tetradecane
- +10 Pentadecane
- +18 Hexadecane
- +22 Heptadecane
- +28 Octadecane
- +32 Nonadecane

Oils and waxes

- +37 Eicosane
- +41 Heneicosane
- +44 Docosane

Heptane

Octane

$C_{5,000-50,000}$ ⟶

Polyethylene

Example. What is the systematic name for isooctane, shown at the top of the preceding page?

Solution. With five carbons as the longest continuous carbon chain, the molecule is called 2,2-dimethyl-4-methylpentane.

In this example the systematic name clearly is clumsier than the name isooctane, which is why the latter name ordinarily is used. For more complex compounds a common name frequently will not exist, and the systematic nomenclature is the only solution.

The three isomers of pentane differ somewhat in chemical and physical properties, as the melting and boiling points in the margin of the preceding page indicate. In a solid or liquid, hydrocarbon molecules are attracted to one another by weak van der Waals forces, which vary with the size and shape of the molecule. Notice that *n*-pentane is roughly sausage-shaped, whereas neopentane is a spherical ball. Neopentane molecules pack better into a crystalline lattice, so more energy is required to melt the solid; thus its melting point is the highest of the three isomers. In contrast, in a liquid the long *n*-pentane sausages lie in closer contact with one another than the neopentane spheres do, so intermolecular van der Waals forces are stronger, and the boiling point of *n*-pentane is highest of all. Isopentane is intermediate in behavior. The number of ways of connecting atoms, and hence the number of isomers, increases astronomically with the number of carbon atoms. There are 2 butane isomers, 3 isomers of pentane, 5 hexanes, 9 heptanes, 18 octanes, 35 nonanes, 75 decanes, and 366,319 different structural isomers of eicosane, $C_{20}H_{42}$.

The smallest of the hydrocarbons, methane (CH_4) through butane (C_4H_{10}), are gases, which are familiar as industrial, cooking, and heating fuels. Methane also is known as marsh gas because some bacteria in swamps can oxidize hydrogen (produced from decomposing matter by other bacteria), using CO_2 rather than O_2, to yield methane and water:

$$4H_2 + CO_2 \rightarrow CH_4 + 2H_2O$$

The flickering fire of ignited marsh gas in a swamp has been the origin of any number of good tales of ghosts and the supernatural.

The larger the hydrocarbon molecule, the stronger are the van der Waals forces between molecules, and the higher the temperature needed to melt the solid or vaporize the liquid. Pentane (C_5H_{12}) through heptadecane ($C_{17}H_{36}$) are liquids at room temperature, and octadecane ($C_{18}H_{38}$) and larger molecules are waxy solids (facing page.) Polyethylene plastic, which is familiar as a tough, inert but flexible material for laboratory and kitchenware, is a straight-chain hydrocarbon with 5000 to 50,000 carbon atoms per chain. Polyethylene is tough because the long molecules are entwined around one another and are difficult to unwind and separate.

We use vast quantities of simple hydrocarbons as fuels and lubricants. Natural gas is 85% methane. Crude petroleum is a mixture of hydrocarbons, which usually are separated by distillation. The fraction with 5 to 10 carbons is sold as gasoline, and kerosene has 10 to 18 carbons. Fuel oils typically have 18 to 22 carbons per molecule, and paraffin waxes have 20 or more. Crude oil contains all of these compounds, plus various ring hydrocarbons. Much of the natural petroleum originally came from the decomposition of organic matter from once-living organisms, under conditions of high temperature and pressure beneath the surface of the Earth. Petroleum thus is a "fossil fuel" like coal is, and the prospect of soon running out of the supply of fossil fuels is currently a distressing one for our energy-devouring economy. What has taken hundreds of millions of years to deposit, we are in danger of depleting in less than two centuries.

Saturated hydrocarbons, or alkanes, can form rings as well as straight and branched chains (right). Open-chain alkanes, straight or branched, have the general formula C_nH_{2n+2}, in which *n* is the number

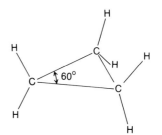

Cyclopropane, C_3H_6; strained ring

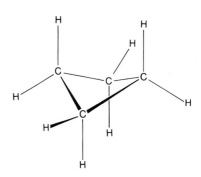

Cyclobutane, C_4H_8; less ring strain

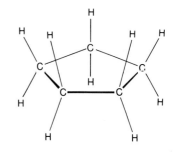

Cyclopentane, C_5H_{10}; almost no strain

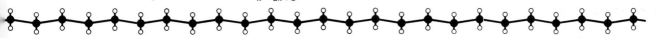

CONFIGURATIONS OF CYCLOHEXANE, C_6H_{12}

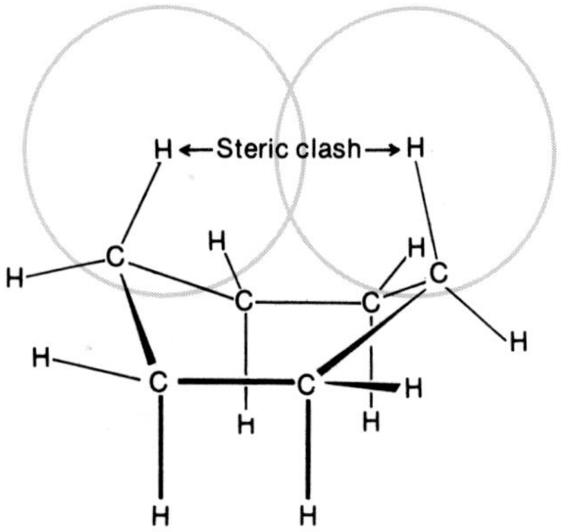

H* = axial hydrogen
H = equatorial hydrogen

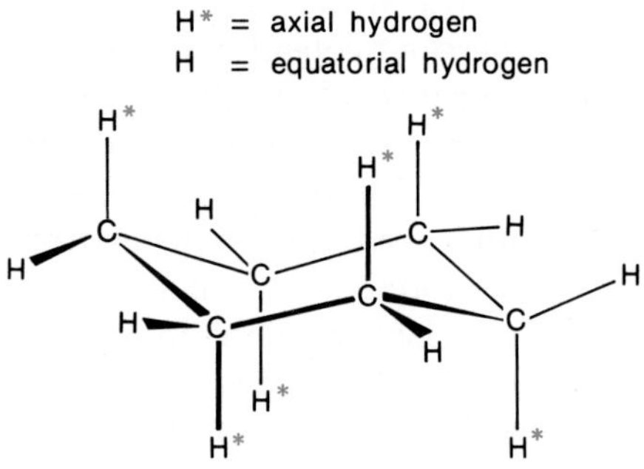

Chair configuration. No ring strain and no steric hindrance.

H ←Steric clash→ H

Boat configuration. Steric clash between hydrogen atoms at bow and stern of boat.

of carbon atoms. In ring alkanes the chain bends back to connect with itself again, and the overall formula is C_nH_{2n}. The smallest of these, cyclopropane (C_3H_6), is strained because the C—C—C angle is 60°, which is far less than the optimum of 109.5° for tetrahedral bonding. The overlap of sp^3 orbitals on adjacent carbon atoms is poor, hence the bonds are weak. Cyclobutane (C_4H_8) and cyclopentane (C_5H_{10}) are less strained, and the cyclohexane ring (C_6H_{12}) has no strain at all. Cyclohexane can adopt either the "chair" or the "boat" configurations shown above, with the "chair" being favored because it keeps the ends of the molecule farther apart. The chair form of cyclohexane is the prototype of the six-membered ring found in glucose and similar sugar molecules, which we shall see in Chapter 21.

ISOMERS OF C_4H_8 (in addition to cyclobutane)

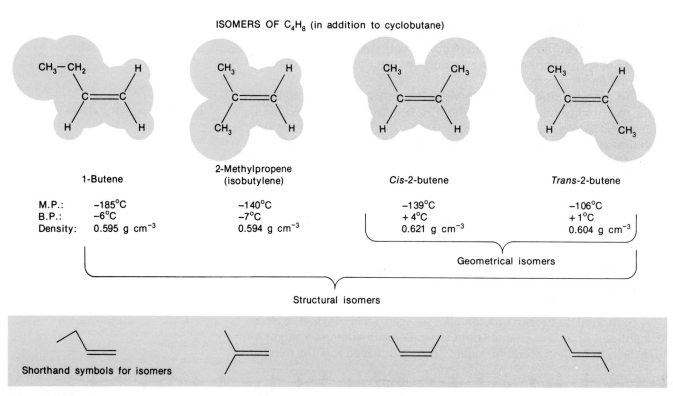

	1-Butene	2-Methylpropene (isobutylene)	Cis-2-butene	Trans-2-butene
M.P.:	−185°C	−140°C	−139°C	−106°C
B.P.:	−6°C	−7°C	+4°C	+1°C
Density:	0.595 g cm⁻³	0.594 g cm⁻³	0.621 g cm⁻³	0.604 g cm⁻³

Geometrical isomers

Structural isomers

Shorthand symbols for isomers

UNSATURATED HYDROCARBONS

Hydrocarbons that have double or triple bonds between carbon atoms are called *unsaturated hydrocarbons;* they are unsaturated in the sense that more hydrogen atoms can be added when H_2 reacts across the double or triple bonds:

$$H_2C{=}CH_2 + H_2 \rightarrow H_3C{-}CH_3$$

ethylene   ethane
(unsaturated)   (saturated)

Virtually free rotation exists about a carbon–carbon single bond. A methyl group ($CH_3{-}$) can spin like a top about the single bond joining it to another atom. In contrast, a molecule such as ethylene cannot be twisted about one of its double bonds without breaking the second bond of the double bond, as we saw in Chapter 9. Double bonds are important in defining the geometry of many biologically important molecules, and in helping to make them rigid.

As was mentioned previously, saturated hydrocarbons are called *alkanes,* and identified by the suffix "ane" in the series methane, ethane, propane, butane, pentane, and hexane, which have one through six carbon atoms, respectively. Unsaturated hydrocarbons, which have double bonds, are called *alkenes* and have similar names ending with the suffix "-ene", as in ethene (C_2H_4), propene (C_3H_6), butene, pentene, and hexene. Ethene, propene, and butene are commonly known as ethylene, propylene, and butylene. Unsaturated hydrocarbons with triple bonds are called *alkynes.* In systematic nomenclature, C_2H_2 would be ethyne, although a more common name for it is acetylene. The simplest alkenes and alkynes are shown in the margin, with the geometry that results from their carbon–carbon bonds.

A new kind of isomerism appears with butene, C_4H_8. Butene has three different structural isomers, depending on whether the four carbons are in a straight or branched chain, and where the double bond is located. These structural isomers are 1-butene, 2-butene (with the number describing the position of the double bond), and isobutylene. (The systematic name for isobutylene is 1-methylpropene.) 1-Butene, 2-butene, and isobutylene are genuine structural isomers because their atoms are connected to one another in different ways.

2-Butene has one methyl group on each double-bonded carbon, but these methyl groups can be placed in two different ways relative to the double bond: on the same side of the molecule, or diagonally across the bond. These two possibilities result in two *geometrical isomers, cis*-2-butene and *trans*-2-butene, which are shown on the facing page. These are geometrical rather than structural isomers because they have the same connections between atoms. All that would be needed to change *cis*-2-butene to *trans*-2-butene is to break the double bond momentarily, twist the molecule around, then reconnect the *same* bond. One cannot go from 2-butene to either of the other structural isomers by breaking, twisting, and then re-forming the same bond. Cis-trans isomerism is possible whenever two different groups are connected to each end of a double bond ("cis-" means "on the same side," and "trans-" means "across from").

All of the isomers of butene have similar chemical and physical properties, and the distinction between geometrical and structural

Ethane. Single bond, free rotation.

Ethene (ethylene). Double bond, no rotation.

Propene (propylene). No rotation.

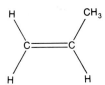

Ethyne (acetylene). Linear molecule.

469

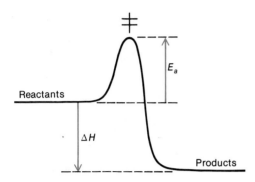

Even though an overall chemical reaction may be a downhill process from an energy standpoint, a reaction barrier can exist in the form of a high-energy intermediate state that the reactants must pass through. This is the activation energy, E_a. The higher E_a is, the slower the reaction.

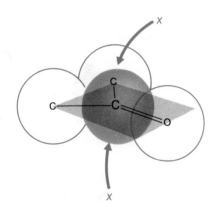

Doubly bonded carbon in a planar group is exposed to attack from either side by an outside group, with little steric hindrance.

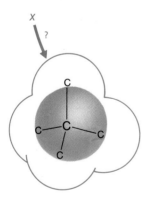

Singly bonded carbon is tetrahedrally surrounded by neighboring atoms and shielded from outside attack. E_a for reaction must include the energy to displace neighbors, so reaction is relatively slow.

isomers is less significant to their properties than is the actual shape of the molecule. 1-Butene has a "swivel" about the bond from the CH_3CH_2- to the $C=C$, and is a flexible molecule. It therefore packs clumsily into a solid crystalline lattice, and melts at a low $-185°C$. All of the other three isomers are rigid. *Trans*-2-butene is a lumpy rod that packs well with its neighbors in the solid and hence does not melt until $-106°C$. The other two isomers are more irregular, but are similar in shape and melt at an intermediate temperature within 1°C of each other. Shape is less important in affecting boiling points because the molecules in a liquid already move freely past one another, so all four isomers boil within a 11°C range.

REACTIONS OF HYDROCARBONS

Many oxidations and other useful chemical reactions are spontaneous (accompanied by a decrease in free energy) and exothermic (accompanied by a decrease in enthalpy) and hence are useful as energy sources; yet the reactions often are extremely slow. As was pointed out in Chapters 13 through 15, we must distinguish between spontaneity and rapidity in chemical reactions. Spontaneous reactions eventually will take place without outside help, but they may take from a microsecond to a billion years to occur. At room temperature hydrocarbons are spontaneously oxidizable with O_2, but are inert. Heat is required to trigger a reaction. If an initial heat supply is provided to start the process, then the heat given off by oxidation is enough to keep the reaction going. Once ignited, combustion is self-sustaining thereafter. A high temperature is needed to overcome the high activation energy (E_a) of the reaction (upper left).

Alkanes are relatively unreactive; the term "paraffins" often applied to them means "little affinity." Why should reactions of saturated hydrocarbons have such high activation energies? What is the barrier to reaction? The answer is that a carbon atom is well-shielded from any attacking group by the four atoms tetrahedrally placed around it. There are no "open sides" exposed to attack (left). In addition, carbon and hydrogen are of approximately equal electronegativity. The C—H bond is nonpolar, so there is no excess or deficiency of charge on either type of atom. Most organic reactions take place by electrophilic or nucleophilic attack (see box on next page). A slight positive charge on an atom encourages attack by a nucleophile (e.g., OH^-, Cl^-, NH_3) and a slight negative charge invites electrophilic attack (e.g., by H^+). In hydrocarbons, carbon has neither charge, hence it is little affected by these attacking groups. This property, plus the tetrahedral shielding around the carbon atom, means that although saturated hydrocarbons may be thermodynamically able to react, they have no convenient mechanism for doing so, and will react only slowly.

The main reactions that saturated hydrocarbons do undergo are dehydrogenation and cracking, combustion (with F_2 or O_2), and halogenation (especially with Cl and Br). If the temperature is raised high enough to surmount the activation barrier, or if catalysts are used to bypass it with an alternative mechanism, then hydrogen atoms may be removed to form unsaturated compounds (dehydrogenation), or a long molecule may be broken into smaller pieces (cracking).

Dehydrogenation:

$$CH_3CH_2CH_2CH_3 \xrightarrow[\text{catalyst}]{\text{heat}} CH_3CH_2CH=CH_2 + H_2$$

n-butane   1-butene

Cracking:

$$CH_3CH_2CH_2CH_3 \xrightarrow[\text{catalyst}]{\text{heat}} CH_3CH=CH_2 + CH_4$$

n-butane   propene   methane

These processes are important in the petroleum industry as a means of converting oils and kerosenes into the more salable gasolines. Dehydrogenation and cracking usually are rather nonspecific processes that lead to a mixture of products. The selection of the right catalyst (often finely divided metals or metal oxides) and right temperature and pressure to maximize the yield of the desired product is one of the black arts of the petroleum chemist.

Combustion or oxidation by O_2 or F_2 is a destructive attack by very electronegative atoms, which results in the complete fragmentation of the molecule:

$$CH_3CH_2CH_2CH_3 + 6\tfrac{1}{2}O_2 \rightarrow 4CO_2 + 5H_2O$$
$$\Delta H^0 = -688 \text{ kcal mole}^{-1} \text{ of butane}$$

$$CH_3CH_2CH_2CH_3 + 13F_2 \rightarrow 4CF_4 + 10HF$$
$$\Delta H^0 = -1262 \text{ kcal mole}^{-1} \text{ of butane}$$

Although these reactions are slow at room temperature, they are self-sustaining once triggered because of the large amount of heat they give off.

With a less electronegative element such as chlorine, the reaction that occurs is a simple displacement of one or more hydrogens, instead

ELECTROPHILES AND NUCLEOPHILES

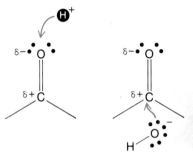

Attack by an electrophile, H^+ Attack by a nucleophile, OH^-

ELECTROPHILES AND NUCLEOPHILES

Most chemical reactions involve the pushing or pulling of electrons, and the most potent attacking groups are those that can take electrons from, or donate them to, the molecule being attacked. Protons (H^+) and other groups that are deficient in electrons, are called *electrophiles* ("electron lovers"). An electrophile is especially attracted to an atom that has a slight negative charge or lone electron pairs, or to the electrons of a double bond. In the example of acid catalysis of the cleavage of an ester linkage in Chapter 16, the electrophilic proton attacked the carbonyl oxygen and placed a small net positive charge on the carbonyl carbon, which then reacted with the lone electron pair of a water molecule to bring about cleavage.

Substances with an excess of nonbonding electrons are *nucleophiles* ("nucleus lovers"). The water molecule in the ester example was a weak nucleophile. The basic hydroxide ion in cleavage of the ester was an even stronger nucleophile—strong enough that it did not need the priming by the proton to attack the carbonyl carbon. Cl^- and NH_3 also are good nucleophiles.

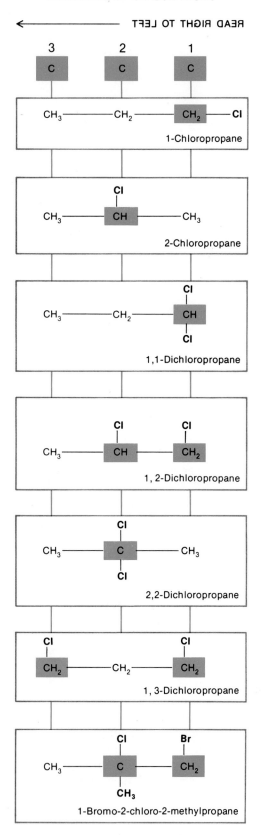

of destruction of the chain:

$$CH_4 + nCl_2 \xrightarrow[\text{light}]{\text{heat or}} \begin{cases} CH_3Cl \text{ (chloromethane)} \\ CH_2Cl_2 \text{ (dichloromethane)} \\ CHCl_3 \text{ (chloroform)} \\ CCl_4 \text{ (carbon tetrachloride)} \end{cases} + nHCl$$

Chlorination, too, usually results in a mixture of products with varying degrees of substitution. The different mono- and dichloropropanes that can result from chlorinating propane are shown at the left. Trichloropropanes and higher chloro-substitutions also are formed.

The dichloropropanes illustrate again the systematic way of naming organic compounds. Carbon atoms are numbered consecutively in the longest straight chain that can be traced through the molecule, then side chains and substituents are identified according to the carbon to which they are attached. The "monster" at the bottom left has the perfectly good systematic name of 1-bromo-2-chloro-2-methylpropane.

Saturated hydrocarbons undergo few other reactions. The halogen derivatives are not important for their own sake, but because they are a bridge to other, more useful compounds. Once formed, halogen compounds can react to form alcohols, acids, amine bases, and other types of molecules to be discussed in Chapter 20.

Unsaturated hydrocarbons are considerably more reactive than alkanes; their reactions take place at moderate temperatures with the help of catalysts. The Achilles' heel of alkanes is the double bond, and the main alkene reaction is the addition across this bond of a variety of reagents.

Hydrogenation:

$$\underset{\text{1-butene}}{CH_3CH_2CH{=}CH_2} + H_2 \xrightarrow[\text{catalyst}]{Pd} \underset{n\text{-butane}}{CH_3CH_2CH_2CH_3}$$

Halogenation:

$$\underset{\text{1-butene}}{CH_3CH_2CH{=}CH_2} + Cl_2 \xrightarrow[\text{solvent}]{CCl_4} \underset{\text{1,2-dichlorobutane}}{CH_3CH_2\overset{Cl}{\underset{|}{C}}H{-}\overset{Cl}{\underset{|}{C}}H_2}$$

Hydration:

$$\underset{\text{propene}}{CH_3CH{=}CH_2} + H_2O \xrightarrow[\text{catalyst}]{H_2SO_4} \underset{\substack{\text{2-propanol}\\ \text{(isopropyl alcohol)}}}{CH_3\overset{OH}{\underset{|}{C}}H{-}CH_3}$$

Hydrohalogenation:

$$\underset{\text{propene}}{CH_3CH{=}CH_2} + HCl \longrightarrow \underset{\text{2-chloropropane}}{CH_3{-}\overset{Cl}{\underset{|}{C}}H{-}CH_3}$$

472

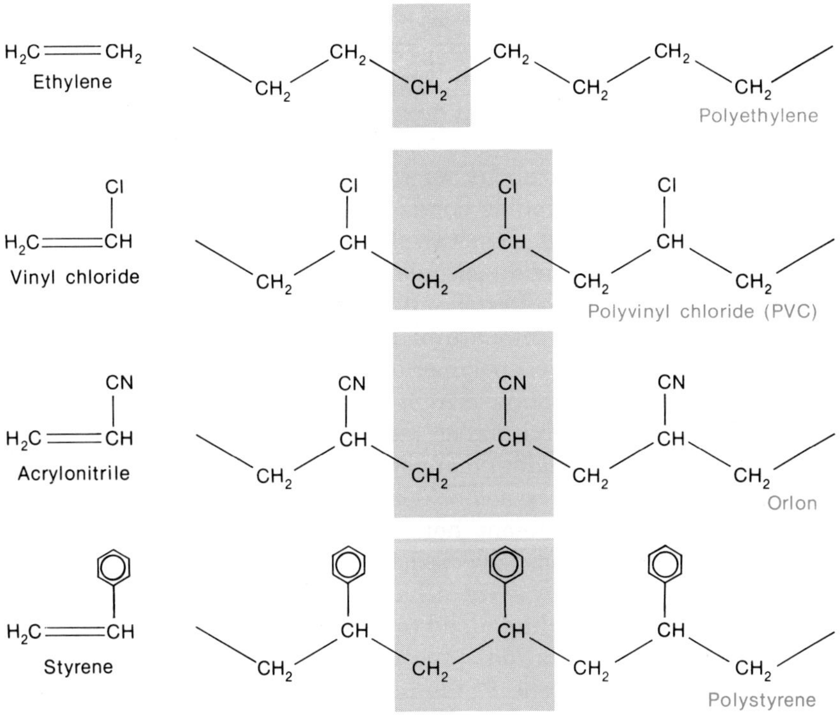

$H_2C{=}CH_2$
Ethylene

$-CH_2-CH_2-\underset{\text{(Polyethylene)}}{CH_2}-CH_2-CH_2-$

Polyethylene

$H_2C{=}\underset{Cl}{CH}$
Vinyl chloride

$-\underset{Cl}{CH}-CH_2-\underset{Cl}{CH}-CH_2-\underset{Cl}{CH}-CH_2-\underset{Cl}{CH}-CH_2-$

Polyvinyl chloride (PVC)

$H_2C{=}\underset{CN}{CH}$
Acrylonitrile

$-\underset{CN}{CH}-CH_2-\underset{CN}{CH}-CH_2-\underset{CN}{CH}-CH_2-\underset{CN}{CH}-CH_2-$

Orlon

$H_2C{=}CH$ (with phenyl)
Styrene

$-CH-CH_2-CH-CH_2-CH-CH_2-CH-CH_2-$ (with phenyl groups)

Polystyrene

Many useful plastics are polymers of the ethylene molecule with one characteristic side chain per ethylene unit. In other plastics, these long chains are cross-linked for greater strength or rigidity in the product.

Notice that only one product is formed when an asymmetric reagent such as HCl or H₂O is used. 2-Chloropropane is formed to the exclusion of 1-chloropropane. This is known as Markovnikov's rule: When a substance HX adds across a double bond, the H always goes to the carbon that already has the greater number of H atoms. For many years organic chemists used Markovnikov's rule without understanding why; now we know that it arises because of the mechanism of reaction, which involves intermediates known as carbonium ions. We shall only note that the rule works, without going into the details of the mechanism.

Alkenes also link together or polymerize into long chains—a reaction that is of great importance in plastics and rubbers. When ethylene polymerizes, the double bond opens up to join monomer units into a continuous, saturated hydrocarbon chain, as shown above. Most plastics must have at least 1000 repeating monomer units in each chain before they begin to show familiar "plastic" properties. Chain lengths usually are not uniform, but the range of lengths can be controlled by the conditions of polymerization. Polyethylene for use in laboratory ware has 5000 to 50,000 carbons per chain.

Changing the substituents on the polyethylene chains gives polymers with a variety of properties. Polyvinyl chloride chains, which have as many as 25,000 units, are used for phonograph records and plastic pipe, and with the addition of a plasticiser, as artificial leather. If all of the hydrogens of polyethylene are replaced by fluorines, the re-

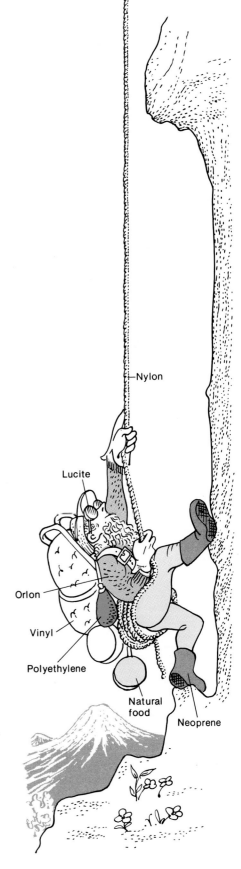

BACK TO NATURE

473

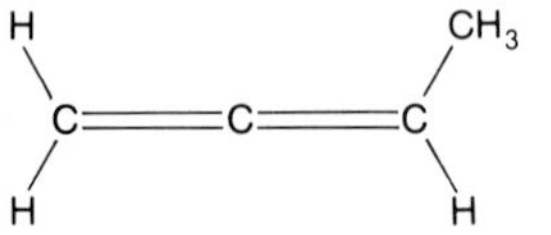

1,2-Butadiene

1,2-Butadiene (above) is a rigid molecule of little practical value. In contrast, 1,3-butadiene with various side groups (below) is the basic unit of natural and synthetic rubbers.

sult is Teflon, a tough and unreactive material widely used for laboratory tubing. Orlon is a well-known artificial fiber, and polystyrene is a hard and clear plastic that even can be used for furniture and walls. Man was once heavily dependent on natural polymers—cellulose, wool, and rubber. It now is possible to be fully equipped to meet the world with no natural polymers about one except one's own skin.

Alkenes with two double bonds per molecule are termed *dienes*, and the smallest, butadiene, has two structural isomers, as shown at the left. 1,2-Butadiene is a rigid molecule of relatively little use. 1,3-Butadiene can be polymerized to polybutadiene, which is the parent compound for a large class of natural and synthetic rubbers (below). Natural rubber is the all-cis polymer of isoprene, a methyl derivative of 1,3-butadiene. As first obtained from the latex of rubber trees it is soft and elastic, with the polyisoprene molecules tangled and coiled back upon themselves in a random manner. When rubber is stretched, the molecules straighten out to a considerable extent and become oriented more nearly parallel to one another. The entropy of the molecules decreases. When the tension is released, the long chains relax back to their disordered, higher-entropy state. Charles Goodyear discovered in 1839 that a small amount of sulfur added to hot rubber makes it stronger and harder. In this "vulcanization" process, the sulfur atoms cross-link between adjacent polyisoprene chains and hold them more nearly stationary, opposing any outside stretch or deformation. Soft rubbers contain 1–2% sulfur; hard rubbers may have as much as 35%. Cross-linking of polymer chains is a standard method today of producing a hard, mechanically strong plastic or resin.

1,3-Butadiene

Isoprene

Chloroprene

Trans-polybutadiene

Trans-polyisoprene (gutta percha)

Cis-polyisoprene (natural rubber) 1000–5000 units

Neoprene rubber

474

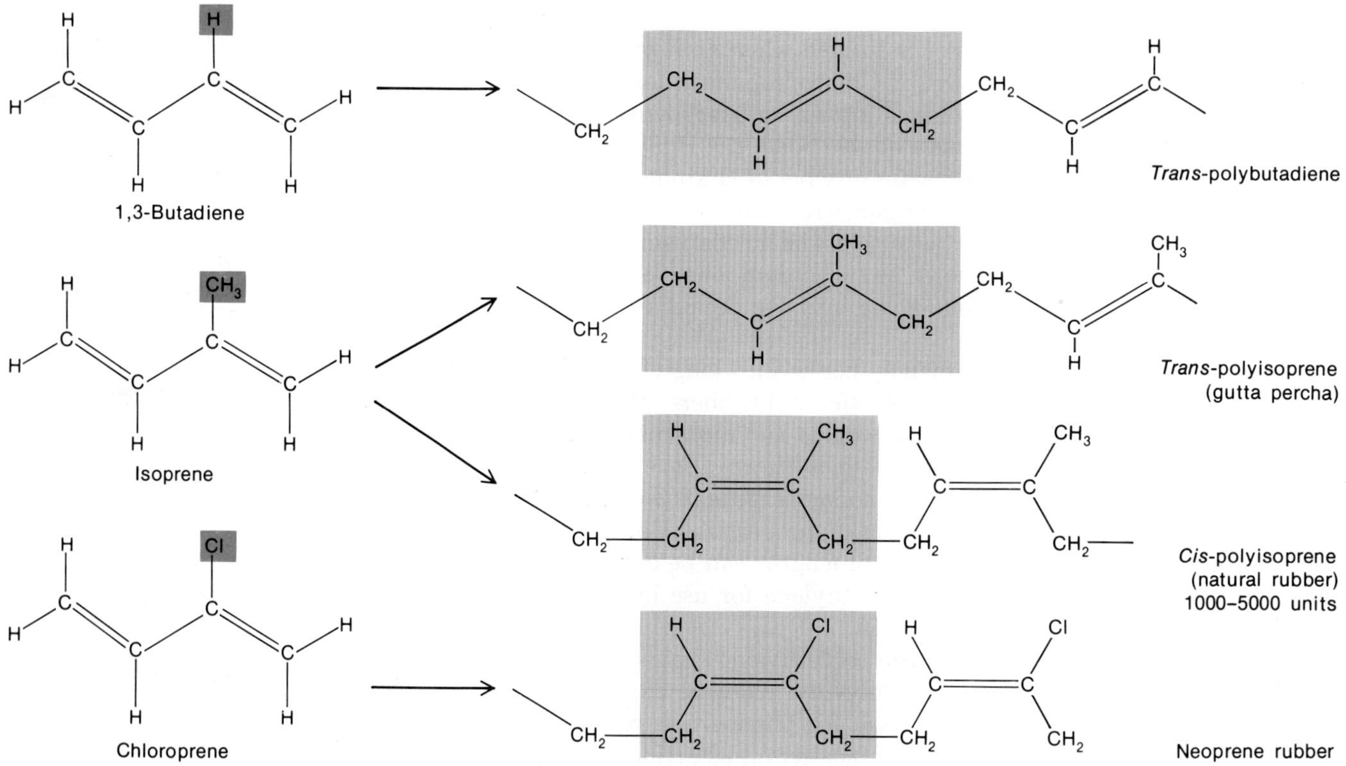

Some plants synthesize the all-trans isomer of polyisoprene, known as *guttapercha*. Guttapercha is hard and horny rather than rubbery, because the orderly *trans*-polyisoprene chains can pack next to one another easily in crystalline regions within the polymer. *Trans*-polyisoprene in guttapercha is hard and semicrystalline, but *cis*-polyisoprene in natural rubber is soft and amorphous. The biggest single hurdle in making usable synthetic rubbers was finding a way of putting together a pure cis polymer. Simple polymerization of isoprene in the laboratory yields a mixture of cis and trans bonds. More subtle methods of polymerization had to be perfected before a dependable method of making a pure cis polymer was developed in 1955.

CONJUGATION, AROMATICITY, AND COLOR

As we saw first in Chapter 9, 1,3-butadiene is a planar molecule because its double bonds are delocalized along the entire four-carbon chain (right). Although the conventional representation shows double bonds between the end pairs of carbon atoms, resonance structures can be drawn in which the central two carbons are double-bonded, and the electron pair of the other double bond is either given to one of the two outside carbon atoms or divided between them. Twisting about the central carbon–carbon bond is as restricted as twisting about either of the outer carbon–carbon bonds, so all ten atoms of the 1,3-butadiene molecule are constrained to lie in one plane. Just as three electron pairs are delocalized around six carbon atoms in a benzene ring, so two electron pairs are delocalized along the four-carbon chain of butadiene.

Delocalization can occur whenever single and double bonds alternate along a chain of atoms, so that after all single bonds are formed, each atom along the chain has an unused *p* orbital and one unused electron. Such molecules are termed *conjugated*. The polybutadiene chains of natural and synthetic rubbers on the opposite page are not conjugated, because more than one single bond intervenes between double bonds. The carbon atoms that are surrounded on both sides by single bonds have all of their electrons and orbitals tied up in sigma bonds, and act as "insulators," thereby preventing the double-bond electrons from combining into one delocalized pool. Many biologically important molecules have these conjugated carbon chains, among them the carotenes shown on the next page. Carotenes are light-absorbing pigments used in photosynthesis by bacteria and green plants. β-Carotene has 11 double bonds in one long conjugated chain, and hence contributes 11 electron pairs, or 22 electrons, to a delocalized electron system. The delocalized region is shaded in color in the drawing of β-carotene on the next page. Spirilloxanthin from purple bacteria has 13 double bonds and 26 delocalized electrons, and isorenieratene from green bacteria has the largest delocalized system of the three: 15 double bonds and 30 delocalized electrons.

These molecules are useful in photosynthesis because they help the plant or bacterium to absorb and harvest light energy. The relationship between the extent of delocalization and wavelength of light absorbed, which we first saw in Chapter 9, applies here. β-Carotene,

The true electronic structure of butadiene can be considered as a hybrid of the various resonance structures shown above. Contributions from the lower three structures give the central carbon–carbon bond a partial double-bond character.

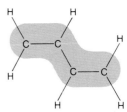

The electronic structure of butadiene also can be explained in terms of delocalization of electrons in molecular orbitals that extend over the entire carbon skeleton, as in benzene. This is termed conjugation. The butadiene molecule is more stable than would be expected if delocalization did not occur.

LIGHT-ABSORBING CAROTENE PIGMENTS

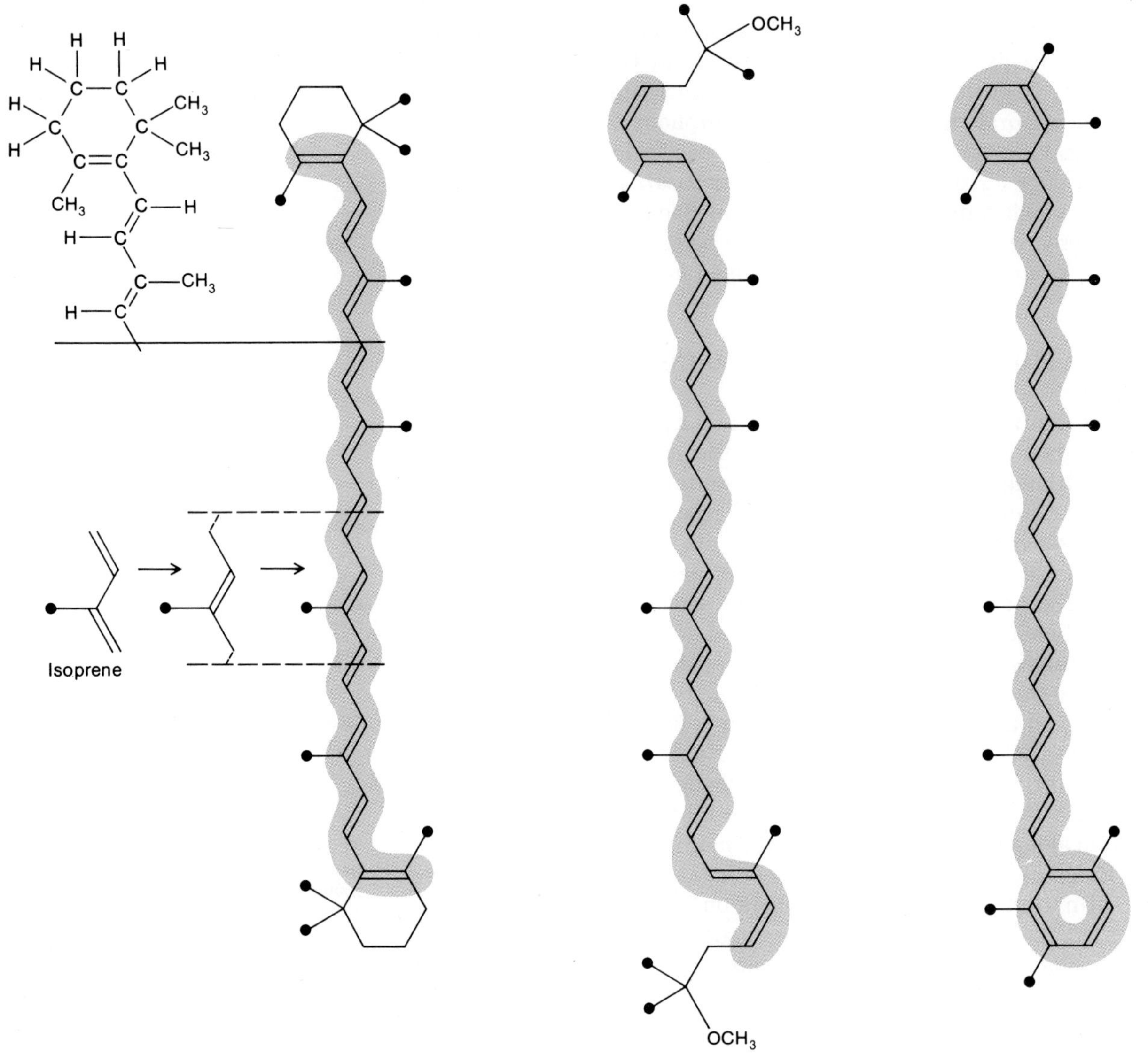

Isoprene

OCH₃

OCH₃

Molecule:	β-Carotene	Spirilloxanthin	Isorenieratene
Conjugation:	11 C══C	13 C══C	15 C══C
Color absorbed:	blue	yellow-green	red
Remaining color seen:	yellow-orange	purple	green
Occurrence:	algae, plants	purple bacteria	green bacteria

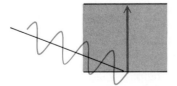
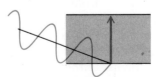

Carotenes with larger delocalized electronic systems have more closely spaced energy levels. They absorb light at longer wavelengths. In this way, green and purple bacteria avoid direct competition with one another and with algae.

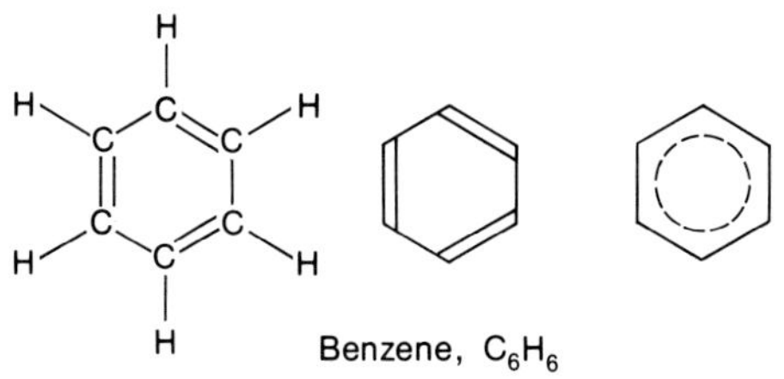

Benzene, C_6H_6

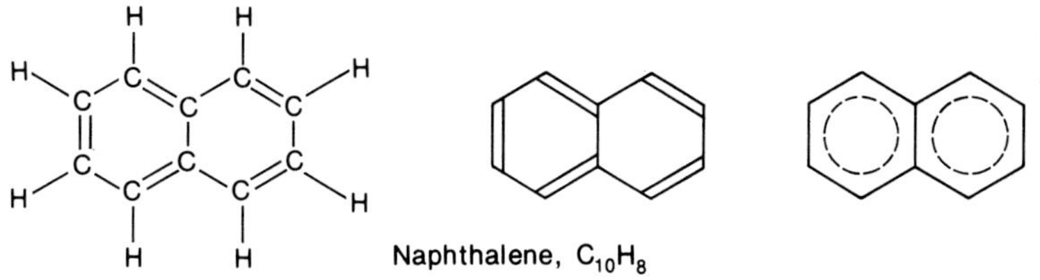

Naphthalene, $C_{10}H_8$

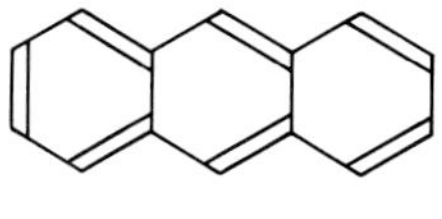

Anthracene, $C_{14}H_{10}$

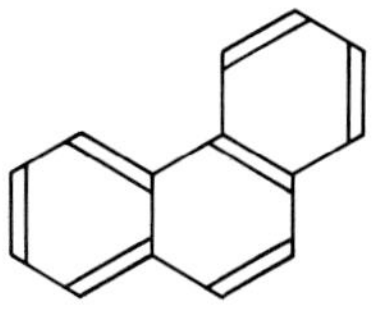

Phenanthrene, $C_{14}H_{10}$

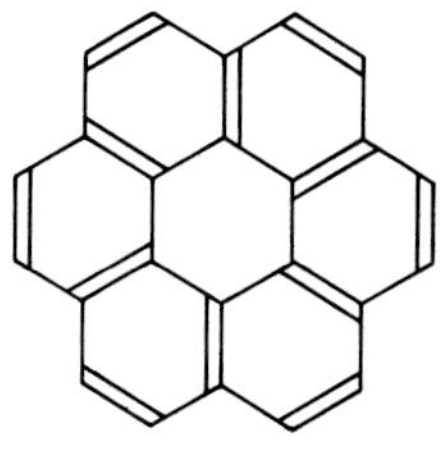

Coronene, $C_{24}H_{12}$

spirilloxanthin, and isorenieratene have successively larger delocalized systems, 11, 13, and 15 electron pairs, respectively. Their electronic energy-level spacings therefore become progressively smaller, as diagrammed at the bottom of the facing page. The three molecules absorb in the blue-violet, the green, and the purple-red regions of the visible spectrum, respectively, so the molecules are colored yellow-orange, purple, and green by the unabsorbed wavelengths. β-Carotene occurs in all green plants (usually masked by the green of chlorophyll), and is responsible for the yellow color of carrots, tomatoes, and autumn leaves. Spirilloxanthin and isorenieratene give purple and green photosynthetic bacteria their characteristic colors. As we shall see in Chapter 23, the carotenes are assistants to chlorophyll in photosynthesis. They absorb light of wavelengths that chlorophyll does not, and transfer the energy in the form of excited electronic states to chlorophyll molecules. They are called *antenna molecules*, and the different numbers of electrons in their delocalized systems represent a "tuning" of the antenna.

Conjugated double bonds and delocalization also are found in cyclic molecules, of which benzene is a familiar example. Naphthalene has two fused six-member rings (above), anthracene and phenanthrene are structural isomers with different arrangements of three rings, coronene has seven rings, and the limit is one sheet of graphite, which is an infinite array of carbon hexagons. In all of these molecules, the double-bond electrons are delocalized over the entire set of carbon atoms (over the entire sheet for graphite). Delocalization sometimes is represented by dotted circles within the rings, as shown above for benzene and naphthalene. The Kekulé-like structures with localized double bonds are easier to draw, however, and cause no confusion as long as one remembers that the double-bond electrons really are delocalized.

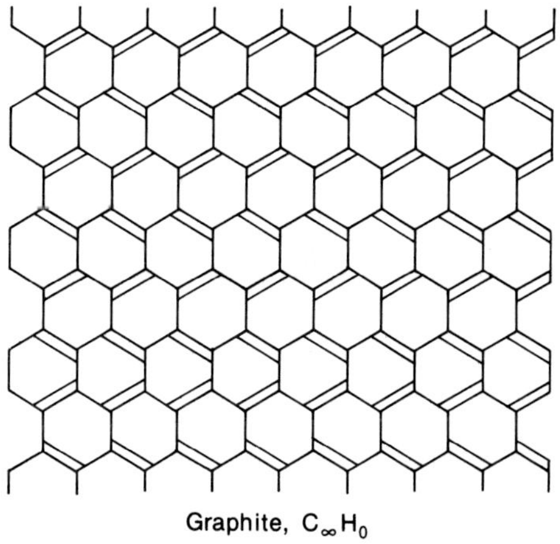

Graphite, $C_\infty H_0$

Cyclic conjugated rings such as benzene are termed *aromatic*. Many rings can be fused to produce larger delocalized molecules, with graphite sheets as the ultimate limit of size. Because of the light-absorbing properties of delocalized aromatic rings, such molecules are the basis of coal-tar dyes.

477

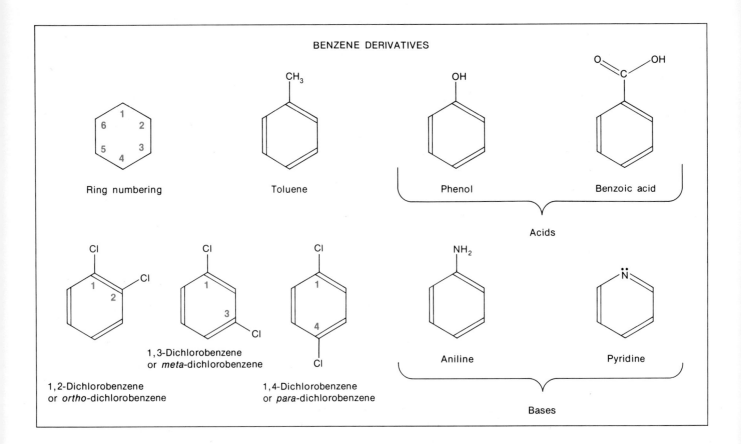

BENZENE DERIVATIVES

Ring numbering

Toluene

Phenol

Benzoic acid

Acids

1,2-Dichlorobenzene
or *ortho*-dichlorobenzene

1,3-Dichlorobenzene
or *meta*-dichlorobenzene

1,4-Dichlorobenzene
or *para*-dichlorobenzene

Aniline

Pyridine

Bases

Aromatic molecules have systematic names based on substitutions at numbered positions around the ring. The simplest of these substituted benzenes, such as methyl benzene (toluene), have common names that always are used. The *ortho-*, *meta-*, and *para-* notation is a convenient way of describing the relative separation of two side groups around the ring. Substituted derivatives of benzene can be neutral and nonpolar (toluene), acidic (phenol), or basic (aniline).

We shall meet many of the derivatives of these aromatic compounds in later chapters, but a few of the more common ones are shown above. Toluene, phenol, aniline, and benzoic acid are derivatives in which different chemical groups are substituted onto the benzene ring. Pyridine is a variant in which a nitrogen atom replaces a C—H in the ring without destroying delocalization. As we saw in Chapter 10, pyridine is a base because it can use its nitrogen lone pair to bind a proton. Ring compounds with more extensive nitrogen substitution are important components of DNA and other nucleic acids. The large porphyrin ring at the far right is the parent compound of chlorophyll and heme. The entire 24-atom ring is one large delocalized system, which makes the molecule a good absorber of light energy. Porphyrin has the same number of delocalized double bonds as β-carotene does, eleven, but is a cyclic rather than a linear molecule.

Ring compounds with delocalized electrons originally were called *aromatic* molecules because many of them have a pronounced odor. The term long since has been stretched beyond its original meaning, and now includes all ring molecules similar to benzene that have delocalized electrons and low chemical reactivity. Nonaromatic hydrocarbons are called *aliphatic* hydrocarbons, a term that originally meant "fatty."

The primary chemical reactions of aromatic molecules are substitutions at the edges of the rings, and not addition across double bonds.

Simple aliphatic molecules with unconjugated double bonds react quickly with bromine or chlorine to form saturated, dihalogenated molecules:

$$CH_3—CH{=}CH_2 + Br_2 \rightarrow \underset{\text{1,2-dibromopropane}}{CH_3—\underset{|}{\overset{Br}{CH}}—\underset{|}{\overset{Br}{CH_2}}}$$
$$\underset{\text{propene}}{}$$

If the Kekulé structure for benzene were correct, one would expect the same rapid halogenation reaction:

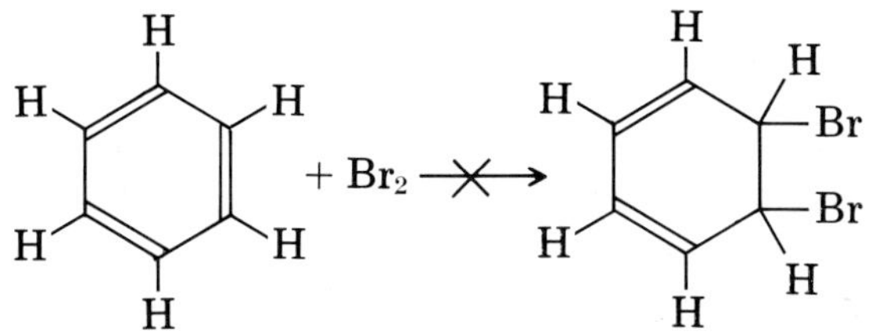

This is not what happens at all. The reaction is slow, and only results in the *substitution* of first one and then two bromine atoms for hydrogens around the ring, with the delocalized ring structure remaining intact:

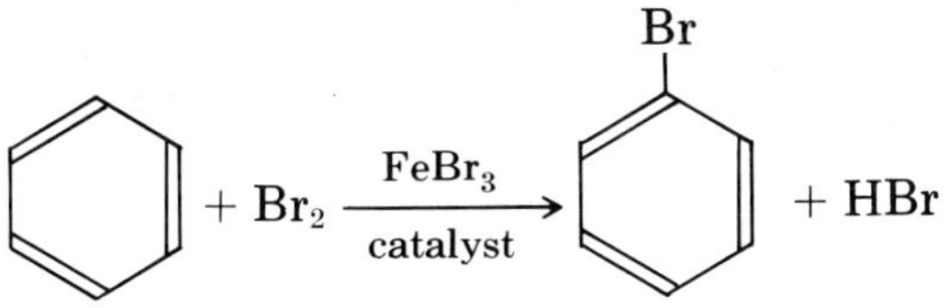

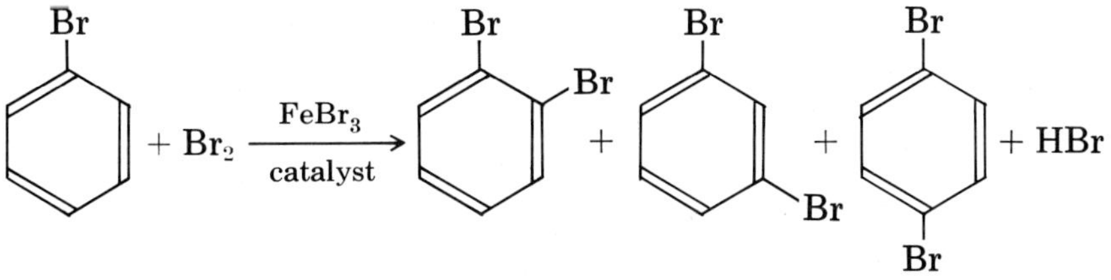

o-dibromo-
benzene

m-dibromo-
benzene

p-dibromo-
benzene

(*Ortho-*, *meta-*, and *para-*dibromobenzene, with the substituted bromine atoms adjacent, separated by one carbon, and diametrically across the ring, are structural isomers of one another.)

The reason why the ring delocalization is not affected, of course, is that delocalization confers 40 kcal mole^{-1} of extra stability on the molecule. Part or all of this 40 kcal mole^{-1} would have to be supplied from an outside source to eliminate some of the delocalization in a chemical reaction. Hence aromatic molecules have a slowness to react that is more like the behavior of alkanes than alkenes.

As with the straight-chain hydrocarbons, so with aromatic molecules: The easiest chemical derivatives to prepare are the chlorides and bromides. These are the gateways to the great variety of organic compounds that are the subject of the next chapter.

THE PORPHYRIN RING IS THE PARENT MOLECULE OF CHLOROPHYLL AND HEME

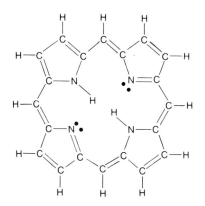

The complete porphyrin ring with all of the single and double bonds in one resonance structure drawn in

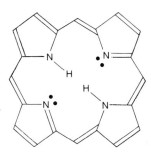

A shorthand representation of the same resonance structure, showing the placement of single and double bonds. In reality the electrons of these double bonds are delocalized over the entire porphyrin ring. This delocalization is important in the light-trapping properties of chlorophyll, and the electron-shifting properties of heme in hemoglobin and cytochrome.

479

QUESTIONS

1. Why are ionic bonds not suitable for the construction of complex molecules? Why are covalent bonds better for this purpose?

2. What are alkanes? What is the fundamental geometry around carbon atoms in alkane molecules?

3. What is meant by "normal" alkanes? What other kinds are there?

4. How are derivatives of normal alkanes named? How is the framework for naming a branched-chain alkane selected? How is the branching specified in the name?

5. Show with diagrams that there are only nine structural isomers of heptane.

6. What is the most common use for alkanes? What makes alkanes relatively unreactive? In the use that you just described, how is this unreactivity overcome?

7. What determines whether an alkane will be a gas, liquid, or solid at room temperature? Where are the boundary lines between these states, in terms of the number of carbon atoms?

8. Why are cyclopropane and cyclobutane termed strained molecules? Sketch the molecular-orbital picture of cyclopropane and account for the strain.

9. Why is the chair conformation of cyclohexane more stable than the boat form?

10. What is an alkene? An alkyne?

11. How are alkene molecules constrained, in a way that alkanes are not?

12. What is the systematic name for isobutylene? What do the numbers in 1-butene and 2-butene signify? Why is there no 3-butene?

13. What is the distinction between structural and geometric isomers? Are 1-butene and 2-butene structural, or geometric, isomers?

14. Draw the structures of *cis*- and *trans*-2-butene. Are they structural, or geometric, isomers?

15. How do the structures of the isomers of C_4H_{10} affect their physical properties?

16. What types of chemical reaction do alkanes most commonly undergo? What are the principal reactions of alkenes?

17. Why is the E_a for alkane reactions inherently higher than for alkenes?

18. What are electrophiles and nucleophiles? In the base-catalyzed hydrolysis of ethyl acetate, is the attacking group an electrophile, or a nucleophile? What determines which end of the carbonyl C=O bond this group attacks?

19. What is Markovnikov's rule, and what does it tell us about the products formed in alkene reactions?

20. How is ethylene the basis for a large family of plastics? What is the corresponding parent molecule for rubbers?

21. What effect does cross-linking have on the physical properties of plastics and rubbers?

22. What are the cis and trans isomers of polybutadiene called? How does their molecular structure account for their differences in physical properties?

23. How does entropy contribute to the elasticity of rubber?

24. What is conjugation in molecules? What does it do to electronic energy levels?

25. What is aromaticity and how is it related to conjugation? What is the most common small aromatic molecule?

26. Why does the extent of delocalization in conjugated and aromatic molecules affect the light-absorbing properties of the molecule? How is this property put to use in living organisms? Name a linear conjugated molecule and a ring compound that are used as light-gathering molecules by green plants.

27. How does a change in the size of the delocalized system change the wavelength of light absorbed in green and purple bacteria? How does this absorption contribute to the names of these classes of bacteria?

28. Why is addition of a molecule across a double bond of the ring an unfavorable reaction for benzene, compared with substitution around the edge of the ring?

PROBLEMS

1. Which of the following compounds are identical?

(a)
$$\begin{array}{cccc} H & H & H & H \\ | & | & | & | \\ H-C-C-C-C-H \\ | & | & | & | \\ H & H & H & Cl \end{array}$$

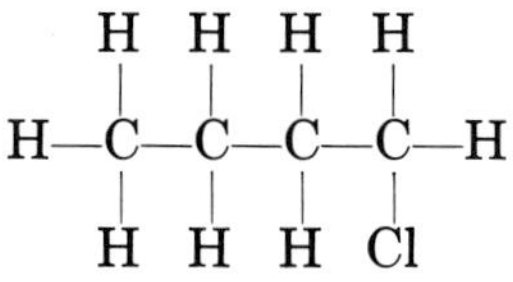

(b)
$$\begin{array}{cccc} H & H & Cl & H \\ | & | & | & | \\ H-C-C-C-C-H \\ | & | & | & | \\ H & H & H & H \end{array}$$

(c)
$$\begin{array}{ccc} H & H & H \\ | & | & | \\ H-C-C-C-H \\ | & | & | \\ H & & Cl \\ & | \\ & H-C-H \\ & | \\ & H \end{array}$$

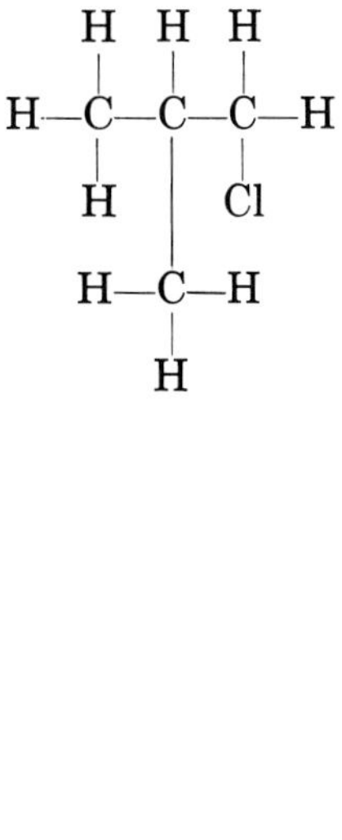

(d)
$$\begin{array}{cccc} H & H & H & Cl \\ | & | & | & | \\ H-C-C-C-C-H \\ | & | & | & | \\ H & H & H & H \end{array}$$

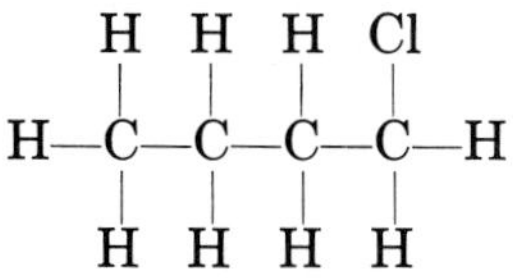

(e)
$$\begin{array}{cccc} H & H & H & H \\ | & | & | & | \\ Cl-C-C-C-C-H \\ | & | & | & | \\ H & H & H & H \end{array}$$

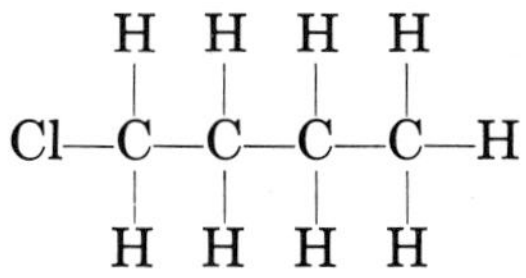

(f)
$$\begin{array}{cccc} H & H & H & H \\ | & | & | & | \\ H-C-C-C-C-H \\ | & | & | & | \\ H & Cl & H & H \end{array}$$

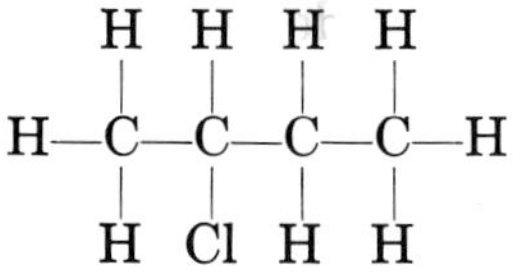

(g)
$$\begin{array}{ccccc} H & H & H & H & H \\ | & | & | & | & | \\ H-C-C-C-C-C-Cl \\ | & | & | & | & | \\ H & H & H & H & H \end{array}$$

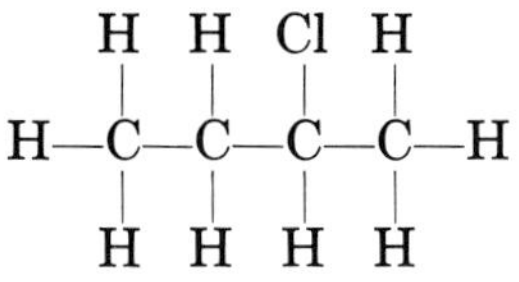

481

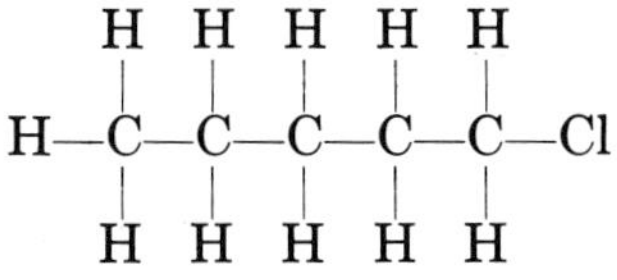

2. Consider the following six molecules:

(a)

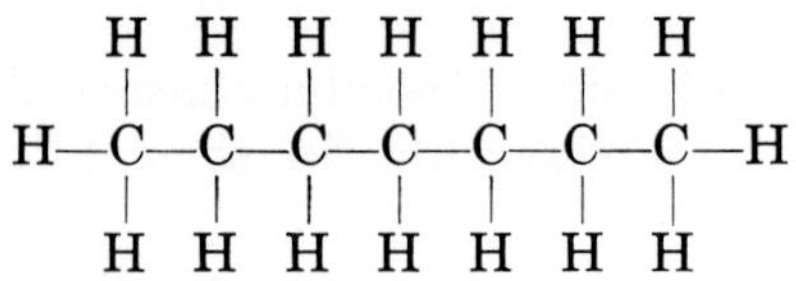

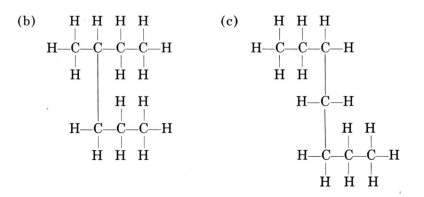

(d)

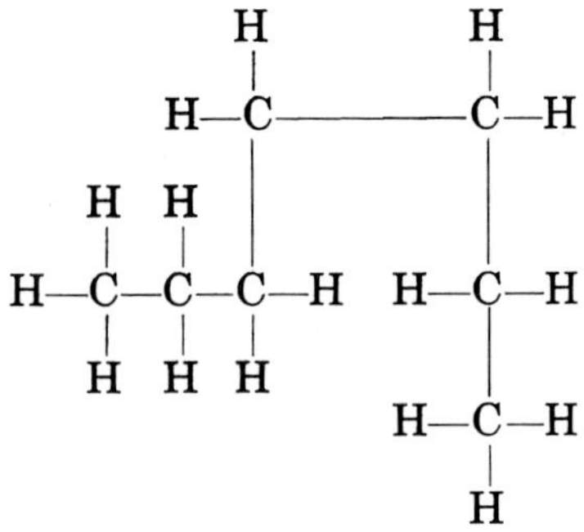

(e)

(f)

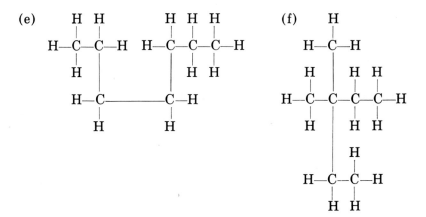

Which of these are identical with *n*-heptane (Molecule a)? What are the systematic names for all of the molecules that are not identical with a?

3. Draw all the possible structures for compounds having the following molecular formulas. Give their systematic names.
   (a) C_3H_8 (b) C_3H_4 (c) C_4H_8 (d) C_3H_5Cl

4. Which of the following compounds are isomers of one another?
   (a) $CH_3CH_2CH_2OH$ (d)   O
   (b) $CH_3CHClCH_3$ ‖
   (c) $CH_3CH_2CH_3$ $CH_3CCH_2CH_3$
                                          (e) $CH_3CH_2CH_2Cl$

5. Sketch the structure of each of the following molecules and indicate the hybridization around each carbon atom.
   (a) C_2Cl_4 (b) CBr_4 (c) C_2Cl_2 (d) CH_2Cl_2 (e) C_2F_6

6. What is the systematic name of each of the following compounds?
   (a) $CH_3CH_2CH{=}CH_2$
   (b) $CH_3CH_2C{\equiv}CH$
   (c) $CH_2{=}CF_2$
   (d) $(CH_3)_2C{=}CHCH_3$
   (e) $CH_3CH{=}CCl_2$
   (f) $CH_2{=}CHCH_2CH_2CH{=}CH_2$
   (g)
   (h) $CH_2{=}CH{-}CBr{=}CH{-}CH_3$
   (i) $(CH_3)_2C{=}CHCH_2CH(CH_3)_2$
   (j) $CH_3CHClC{\equiv}CCH_3$
   (k)

7. Draw the structural formula for each of the following compounds:
   (a) *trans*-2-hexene
   (b) *cis*-2,3-dichloro-2-butene
   (c) 1-methylcyclopentene
   (d) *trans*-1,2-dibromocyclohexane
   (e) 4-ethyl-1-octene
   (f) 3-hexyne
   (g) *cis*-diiodoethylene
   (h) 2-methyl-2-butene
   (i) 2-bromo-1,3-butadiene

8. Draw all the possible structural isomers of C_5H_{10}. Give the systematic name for each isomer.

9. Which isomer in Problem 8
   (a) contains no geometric isomers?
   (b) has no double bonds?
   (c) has the highest boiling point?
   (d) contains geometric isomers, but no double bonds?

10. Write the structural formulas of
    (a) five different, simple alkanes;
    (b) five different, simple alkenes (only *one* double bond);
    (c) five different, simple alkynes (only *one* triple bond);
    (d) five different, simple cycloalkanes (only *one* ring).
    Show that they conform to the general formulas C_nH_{2n+2}, C_nH_{2n}, C_nH_{2n-2}, and C_nH_{2n}, respectively.

11. A compound, A, has the formula C_5H_8. (a) What is the maximum number of rings it could contain? (b) What is the maximum number of double bonds it could contain? (c) What is the maximum number of triple bonds it could contain?
    On treatment with an excess of hydrogen over a nickel catalyst, one mole of A absorbs one mole of hydrogen gas. (d) What is the formula of the product of this hydrogenation reaction? (e) How many rings does A contain? (f) How many double bonds does A contain? (g) How many triple bonds does A contain?

12. A hydrocarbon has a molecular weight of approximately 60 and contains 17.2% hydrogen. What is the molecular formula of the hydrocarbon? Write all of the structural isomers that have this formula.

13. A hydrocarbon has a molecular weight of 56.0 and contains 85.7% carbon. What is its molecular formula? What structural and geometric isomers could it have?

14. Write equations for the reactions of 1-pentene with each of the following reagents:
    (a) Br_2 (b) H_2SO_4 (c) HI   (d) HOCl   (e) H_2 and Ni
    In each case, show the structure of the product organic molecule.

◀ *Many of the pleasant natural odors are esters of carboxylic acids, whose odors are not so pleasant. See Page 497 for details*

CHAPTER 20

The Variety of Organic Compounds

If the chemistry of carbon were limited to the hydrocarbons discussed in Chapter 19, it would be of relatively minor interest. What we have been examining, however, is only the framework upon which all of the interesting chemistry can be hung. Hydrocarbons by themselves are notably unreactive. But once the halogen derivatives have been made, these then can enter into a great variety of chemical reactions that lead to compounds with almost any desired properties. This chapter is an introduction to the most important of these compounds.

Even though the halides are reactive, the hydrocarbon portions of the molecules still retain their identity. When the —Cl of ethyl chloride (CH_3CH_2—Cl) is replaced by an —OH, the molecule becomes ethyl alcohol (CH_3CH_2—OH), which has properties similar to other alcohols. With —COOH the molecule becomes an organic acid, and with —NH_2, a base. Because groups such as —Cl, —OH, —COOH, and —NH_2 determine the gross chemical properties of the molecule, they are known as *functional groups.*

The hydrocarbon chains attached to the functional groups modify the properties of the functional groups while maintaining their essential chemical character. Methyl alcohol, CH_3OH, is water-soluble, whereas dodecyl alcohol, $CH_3CH_2CH_2CH_2CH_2CH_2CH_2CH_2CH_2CH_2$-$CH_2CH_2$—OH, is not; but they both show the chemical properties of an alcohol. The hydrocarbons attached to functional groups are called *radicals* (from "radix," meaning root); CH_3— is the methyl radical, CH_3CH_2— is the ethyl radical, and so on. This distinction between radicals and functional groups is an old one in organic chemistry, but a useful one. A radical often is represented simply by R—, as in R—OH, a general expression for an alcohol. In this chapter we shall look at several important functional groups, seeing first what chemical properties these groups give to a molecule, and then how these properties are modified by the hydrocarbon radical to which they are attached.

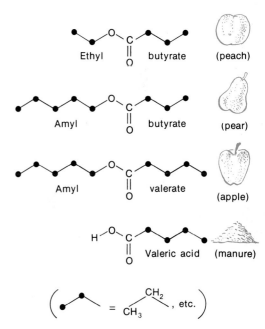

Many esters have fruit or floral odors. Amyl valerate smells like apples, but valeric acid has the odor of manure. Although the prediction of odors from molecular structures is not yet a science, it is believed that the difference in odor in this case comes mainly from the charged —COO⁻ group from the carboxylic acid.

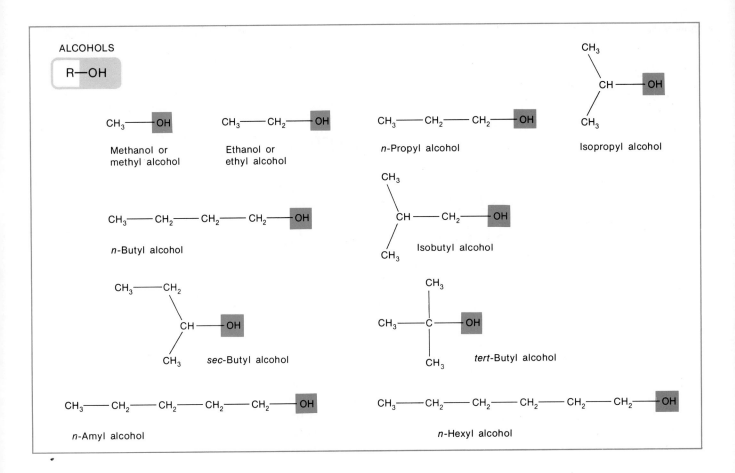

ALCOHOLS

R—OH

Methanol or
methyl alcohol

Ethanol or
ethyl alcohol

n-Propyl alcohol

Isopropyl alcohol

n-Butyl alcohol

Isobutyl alcohol

sec-Butyl alcohol

tert-Butyl alcohol

n-Amyl alcohol

n-Hexyl alcohol

ALCOHOLS, R—OH

Some of the most common alcohols are represented above. The traditional names methyl, ethyl, propyl, and butyl alcohols are familiar, but "amyl" alcohol instead of "pentyl" for the five-carbon alcohol is an historical oddity. From hexyl alcohol on, the Greek numerical prefixes are used. In the systematic nomenclature, alcohols are identified by a single name ending in "-ol," beginning with methanol, ethanol, propanol, butanol, pentanol, hexanol, and continuing with the Greek prefix for the number of atoms in the longest carbon chain that can be traced through the molecule. The position of the —OH group is identified by the number of the carbon atom to which it is attached. Thus n propyl alcohol (above) is 1 propanol in the systematic naming, and isopropyl alcohol is 2-propanol because the —OH group is attached to the second carbon atom in the chain. n-Butyl alcohol becomes 1-butanol and sec-butyl alcohol is 2-butanol, but for isobutyl and tert-butyl alcohols a shorter carbon skeleton than four atoms must be used. Isobutyl alcohol has the systematic name of 2-methyl-1-propanol, or 2-methyl propanol, and tert-butyl alcohol is 1,1-dimethyl ethanol. Common names usually are employed for these small molecules because they are simpler to write. But with more than four or five carbon atoms, the systematic name becomes easier to remember, or to work out from the molecular structure.

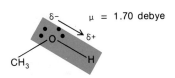

Alcohol	Dipole moment
Methyl	1.70 D
Ethyl	1.69 D
n-Propyl	1.68 D
Isopropyl	1.66 D
n-Butyl	1.66 D

Alcohol molecules, like water molecules, have dipole moments because of their polar —OH bonds. As the proportion of hydrocarbon to —OH in the molecule increases, the molecular dipole moment decreases.

486

Alcohols are classified as primary, secondary, or tertiary, depending on whether the carbon atom bearing the —OH group is connected to one, two, or three other carbons. Of the alcohols illustrated on the opposite page, all are primary except isopropyl alcohol and *sec*-butyl alcohol, which are secondary, and *tert*-butyl alcohol, which is tertiary.

Alcohols can be prepared synthetically by the hydrolysis of chlorides and bromides of hydrocarbons:

$$R—Cl + H_2O \rightarrow R—OH + HCl$$

Since this reaction liberates HCl, it proceeds best in basic solution where the acid can be neutralized as fast as it is made. Many of the lower-molecular-weight alcohols are produced by yeasts, bacteria, and other microorganisms as by-products in their energy-extracting metabolism. Yeasts burn sugars to CO_2 and water (as we do) if given enough oxygen, but under anaerobic conditions they stop halfway and give off ethyl alcohol as a waste product. The ancient art of brewing has given ethyl alcohol (ethanol) the name of "grain alcohol" because of its easiest and cheapest source. The Egyptians were great brewers and wine makers. The Sumerians in Mesopotamia 4000 years ago left records of eight different types of beer from barley, eight from wheat, and three from mixed grains—more variety than this country can muster today. Brewing ranks with tanning and dyeing among the oldest branches of the chemical arts. Methyl alcohol, or methanol, is known as "wood alcohol" because it can be prepared by heating wood in the absence of air. A more practical commercial synthesis is

$$CO + 2H_2 \xrightarrow[\text{400°C; 300 atm}]{\text{ZnO, Cr}_2\text{O}_3} CH_3OH$$

The most useful properties of alcohols arise because they are polar but not ionized. The electronegative oxygen atom in methanol has a slight excess of negative charge and the less electronegative hydrogen has a small positive charge, which leads to a dipole moment of 1.70 debye (far left). For comparison, the water molecule has a dipole moment of 1.87 D, and methane has zero dipole moment. This polarity of alcohols means that the smaller ones, at least, are soluble in water.

Winemaking in ancient Egypt, from a wall painting more than 3000 years old. Courtesy of The Metropolitan Museum of Art, New York City. Photograph by Egyptian Expedition.

Brewing beer in ancient Egypt. This sculpture, about 2400 B.C., shows the brewer working the mash through a strainer. Brewing and baking were done at the same time, using the same starting materials—grain and yeast. Courtesy of The Metropolitan Museum of Art, Rogers Fund, 1920.

487

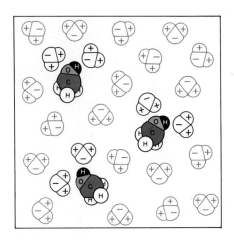

In spite of their hydrocarbon —CH₃ groups, methanol molecules dissolve in water because of polar interactions between their —OH groups and the water molecules.

Their hydrocarbon radicals make them good solvents for organic compounds, and their polar —OH groups tend to make them miscible with water (left). Hence they can bring into aqueous solution organic molecules that will not dissolve in pure water by themselves. They are used extensively as solvents and cleaners, because greases and oils are dissolved by the hydrocarbon radicals, and the alcohol and grease solution then can be washed away with water.

The lower-molecular-weight alcohols are water-soluble, but above approximately 10 carbons, alcohols no longer will mix with water. Their hydrocarbon tails then are large enough to dominate the —OH group. Alcohols with longer hydrocarbon chains form a surface monolayer film at an air–water interface, as shown at lower left. This property of making films with long-chain molecules, half in and half out of solution, will be important later with fatty acids and biological membranes.

The alcohol functional group, —OH, looks misleadingly like the hydroxide group of a base, which might suggest that it dissociates from the rest of the molecule. It cannot be emphasized too strongly that this is not so; an alcohol is held firmly together by covalent bonds and does not dissociate. This is because the oxygen atom and the carbon to which it is bonded in the hydrocarbon radical are of approximately the same electronegativity. *If* the carbon were much less electronegative than the oxygen, then the oxygen of the —OH would pull the bonding electrons to itself and the molecule would ionize as a base does:

$$H_3C—O—H \rightarrow H_3C^+ + :O—H^-$$

This happens with NaOH, but not with CH₃OH. In contrast, *if* the carbon were much more electronegative, then the alcohol would pull electrons away from the O—H bond and release a proton, as an acid does:

$$H_3C—O—H \rightarrow H_3C—O:^- + H^+$$

This occurs with O₂N—O—H (nitric acid, HNO₃), but not with H₃C—O—H (methanol).

PHENOLS, AROMATIC ALCOHOLS

Phenols are aromatic compounds that have an —OH attached directly to the aromatic ring. They are acids and not alcohols because the proton dissociates from the —OH group. The parent compound, phenol or carbolic acid, dissociates to produce the phenolate, or phenoxide ion:

$$\text{⬡—OH} \rightleftharpoons \text{⬡—O}^- + H^+ \qquad pK_a = 9.89$$

As its dissociation constant, or pK_a, indicates, phenol is a weak acid, comparable with HCN, but it is acidic nonetheless. Why should aromatic —OH compounds behave like acids, whereas aliphatic or open chain —OH compounds are alcohols instead?

The answer is essentially the same as for nitric and sulfuric acids, which were discussed in Chapters 5 and 6. Electrons in the negative ion are more delocalized than in the undissociated acid molecule,

Air

Water

Long-chain alcohol molecules form a monolayer at an air–water interface, with their —OH groups immersed in the water and their hydrocarbon tails removed from the water. This same structure is found in soap films, and a similar structure occurs in biological membranes.

488

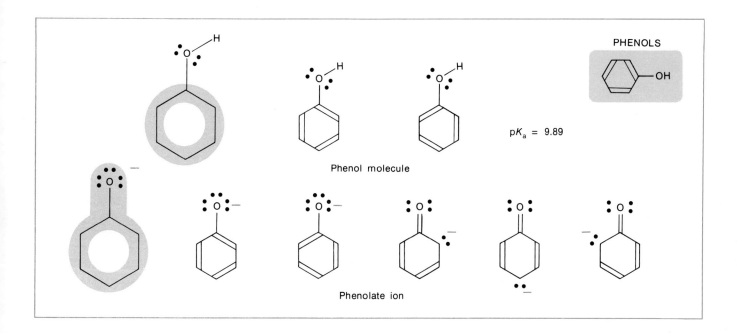

PHENOLS

Phenol molecule

$pK_a = 9.89$

Phenolate ion

thereby making the ion more stable than it would be without delocalization. This encourages dissociation and makes the molecule a stronger acid than it would be otherwise. In Chapter 9 we saw that the extent of delocalization in an aromatic molecule could be determined by writing all possible resonance bond structures for the molecule, and noting the atoms that were connected by double bonds in at least one resonance form. This approach treats each resonance model as a partial or incomplete picture of the actual delocalized-electron bond structure.

Only two resonance structures can be drawn for the undissociated phenol molecule, corresponding to the two Kekulé structures for benzene (above). The oxygen atom has two lone electron pairs and a bond each to H and to C. None of its electrons participate in the ring delocalization. In contrast, once the electrons of the O—H bond are liberated by dissociation of H^+, they can be shifted into a double bond to the ring carbon atom. In addition to the two Kekulé-like resonance structures with the negative charge on the oxygen, other structures can be drawn with a C=O double bond, and with the negative charge transferred to the ring. Three more resonance-bond models can be drawn for the phenolate ion than for phenol. A good practical rule of thumb is that the more resonance structures that can be drawn for a molecule or ion, the greater its delocalization, and the more stable it is. The delocalized system in the phenolate ion is enlarged by one oxygen atom and by two more electrons than in undissociated phenol. The equilibrium between phenol and its ion thus is shifted enough in favor of the ion to make phenol an acid instead of an alcohol.

Some other simple phenolic compounds are shown at the right and on the next page, together with their pK_a values. The ortho, meta, and para isomers of cresol, which differ only in the relative positions of substituents around the aromatic ring, all have roughly the same weak acidity. The —OH group is only acidic when it is attached directly to an aromatic ring. Benzyl alcohol is not an acid; it is an alcohol similar

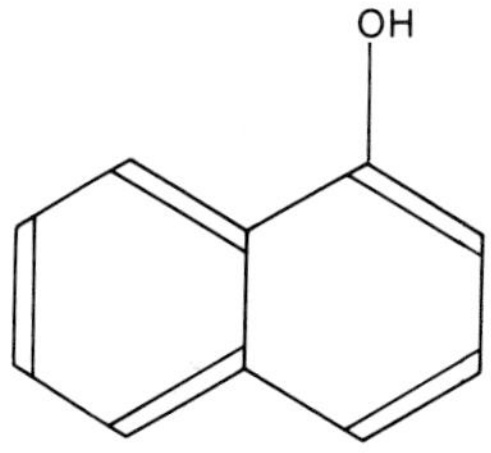

Phenol has six atoms in its delocalized system, and can be regarded as intermediate between two resonance structures. In the phenolate ion a seventh atom participates in delocalization, and five different contributing resonance structures can be drawn. The resulting extra stability of the ion makes phenol an acidic molecule.

α-Naphthol $pK_a = 9.34$

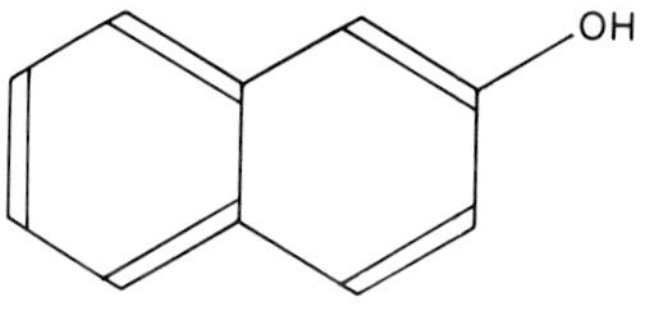

β-Naphthol $pK_a = 9.51$

489

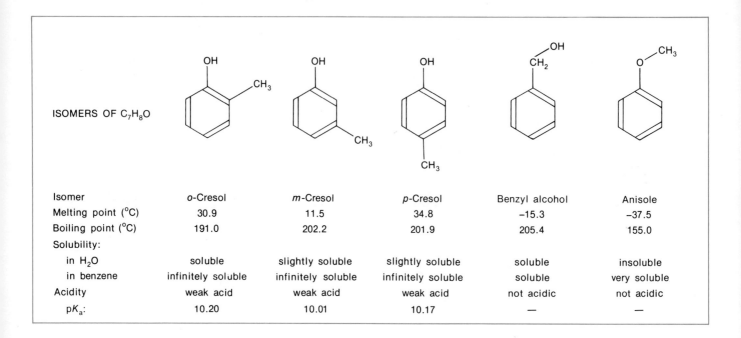

Isomer	o-Cresol	m-Cresol	p-Cresol	Benzyl alcohol	Anisole
Melting point (°C)	30.9	11.5	34.8	−15.3	−37.5
Boiling point (°C)	191.0	202.2	201.9	205.4	155.0
Solubility:					
in H₂O	soluble	slightly soluble	slightly soluble	soluble	insoluble
in benzene	infinitely soluble	infinitely soluble	infinitely soluble	soluble	very soluble
Acidity	weak acid	weak acid	weak acid	not acidic	not acidic
pK_a:	10.20	10.01	10.17	—	—

The five different C₇H₈O molecules above are termed structural isomers, because they contain the same number and kind of atoms but are connected in different ways. These connections have a profound effect on the chemical behavior of the molecules, as the data indicate.

ETHERS

R—O—R

"Roadsign" for an ether molecule. Just as alcohols in general can be represented by R—OH, so the general formula for an ether is R—O—R, with the two R's being hydrocarbon groups that are not necessarily identical. Methyl ethyl ether is CH₃—O—CH₂—CH₃.

to ethanol. The —CH₂— group effectively insulates the —OH from the ring and prevents it from joining the delocalized electron system.

Benzyl alcohol is a structural isomer of the three cresols, since they all have the same overall formula, C₇H₈O. So, for that matter, does anisole, or methyl phenyl ether (above). Their properties are very different: The cresols are acids, the benzyl compound is an alcohol, and anisole is an ether. The way in which atoms are connected to form a molecule is critically important to the chemical properties of the molecule. The properties of these five isomers are listed below their structures above. All of the molecules except anisole are polar because a hydrogen atom is bonded to a much more electronegative oxygen atom. Intermolecular hydrogen bonding is possible between a positively charged hydrogen on one molecule and a negatively charged oxygen on a neighboring molecule. This increases both the boiling and melting points for these compounds in comparison with anisole, which has only van der Waals forces between molecules. The benzene ring makes all of these isomers soluble in benzene, but nonpolar anisole differs from the others in being insoluble in water. As the pK_a values indicate, the cresols ionize in aqueous solution, the other isomers do not.

ETHERS, ALDEHYDES, AND KETONES

Two molecules of an alcohol can be condensed, with the removal of water, to form an *ether*:

$$2CH_3—OH \xrightarrow[\text{heat}]{H_2SO_4} CH_3—O—CH_3 + H_2O$$

methanol   dimethyl ether

Ethers are named according to the radicals on either side of the central oxygen. CH₃—O—C₂H₅ is methyl ethyl ether (left) and anisole (above) is methyl phenyl ether. Ethers are chemically unreactive, yet

490

are good solvents for hydrocarbons, which makes them useful as inert media for organic reactions. Ethers and water generally show opposite trends in dissolving other molecules. Because ethers and water are immiscible, they are useful in two-layer separation schemes in organic chemistry. Ethers are volatile and low-boiling because of the absence of hydrogen bonds in the liquid, and this volatility makes them flammable and dangerous. Diethyl ether, C_2H_5—O—C_2H_5, is a common anaesthetic, but one with a serious spark hazard.

If alcohols are oxidized rather than dehydrated, the results are *aldehydes* and *ketones*. Primary alcohols lead to aldehydes:

"Roadsign" for an aldehyde molecule. R— represents a hydrocarbon group.

$$CH_3CH_2CH_2CH_2OH + [O] \rightarrow CH_3CH_2CH_2-\overset{\overset{\displaystyle O}{\|}}{C}-H + H_2O$$

| *n*-butyl alcohol | *n*-butyraldehyde |
| (butanol) | (butanal) |

$$\begin{matrix} CH_3 \\ \\ CH_3 \end{matrix}\!\!\diagdown\!\!\diagup CH-CH_2-OH + [O] \rightarrow \begin{matrix} CH_3 \\ \\ CH_3 \end{matrix}\!\!\diagdown\!\!\diagup CH-\overset{\overset{\displaystyle O}{\|}}{C}-H + H_2O$$

| isobutyl alcohol | isobutyraldehyde |
| (2-methyl-1-propanol) | (2-methyl propanal) |

The [O] represents oxidizing equivalents from oxidants such as potassium permanganate, $KMnO_4$, or potassium dichromate, $K_2Cr_2O_7$. The aldehyde group, $-\overset{\overset{\displaystyle O}{\|}}{C}-H$, often is written as —CHO, and a general aldehyde is symbolized by R—CHO. Some of the simpler aldehydes and the alcohols from which they are obtained are

methyl alcohol, CH_3—OH   → formaldehyde, H—CHO
   (methanol)   (methanal)

ethyl alcohol, CH_3CH_2—OH   → acetaldehyde, CH_3—CHO
   (ethanol)   (ethanal)

n-propyl alcohol, $CH_3CH_2CH_2$—OH   → propionaldehyde, CH_3CH_2—CHO
   (propanol)   (propanal)

benzyl alcohol, ⬡—CH_2—OH   → benzaldehyde, ⬡—CHO

In the examples above, the common name is given first and the systematic name appears in parentheses. The systematic name is identical to that of the corresponding alcohol, with the ending changed from "-ol" to "-al." The common names for the higher alcohols are totally unsystematic and are derived from the names of the corresponding carboxylic acids, which themselves arose from the historic source of the acid. For example, hexanal ($CH_3CH_2CH_2CH_2CH_2CHO$) is called caproaldehyde because caproic acid ($CH_3CH_2CH_2CH_2CH_2COOH$) has the overripe smell of goats (as in Capricorn).

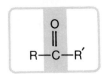

"Roadsign" for a ketone. R— and R'— represent hydrocarbon groups.

Secondary alcohols are oxidized to ketones rather than aldehydes:

$$\underset{\text{isopropyl alcohol}}{CH_3—\underset{\underset{OH}{|}}{CH}—CH_3} + [O] \rightarrow \underset{\text{dimethyl ketone (acetone)}}{CH_3—\underset{\underset{O}{\|}}{C}—CH_3}$$

$$\underset{\textit{sec}\text{-butyl alcohol}}{CH_3—\underset{\underset{OH}{|}}{CH}—C_2H_5} + [O] \rightarrow \underset{\text{methyl ethyl ketone}}{CH_3—\underset{\underset{O}{\|}}{C}—C_2H_5}$$

Tertiary alcohols have no hydrogens on the carbon bearing the —OH group, and therefore undergo no reaction unless oxidizing conditions are vigorous enough to destroy the molecule completely:

$$\underset{\textit{tert}\text{-butyl alcohol}}{CH_3—\underset{\underset{CH_3}{|}}{\overset{\overset{CH_3}{|}}{C}}—OH} + [O] \rightarrow \text{no reaction short of destruction}$$

Aldehydes and ketones are similar in properties, neutral but polar. Like ethers, they are good solvents for organic compounds; but unlike ethers, they are at least partially miscible in water. They resemble ethers in being low-boiling and volatile because of the absence of hydrogen bonds in the liquid, but differ from ethers in being chemically reactive. The polar and exposed $—\overset{\overset{O}{\|}}{C}—H$ and $—\overset{\overset{O}{\|}}{C}—$ groups have a slightly negative oxygen and a slightly positive carbon connected by a double bond and, as mentioned in Chapter 19, are wide open to attack either by electrophiles or nucleophiles (left). Aldehydes and ketones are the starting materials for many organic syntheses.

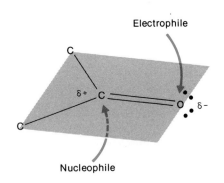

Electrophile

Nucleophile

A C=O bond of an aldehyde or ketone is exposed to attack from two sides by an electrophile (a substance such as H⁺, which is attracted to electrons) or a nucleophile (a substance such as OH⁻ or Cl⁻, which is attracted to regions of local electron deficiency). Hence aldehydes and ketones are useful starting materials for chemical syntheses.

CARBOXYLIC ACIDS, $R—\overset{\overset{O}{\|}}{C}—OH$

Continued oxidation of aldehydes leads to carboxylic acids:

$$\underset{n\text{-butyraldehyde}}{CH_3CH_2CH_2—\overset{\overset{O}{\|}}{C}—H} + [O] \rightarrow \underset{n\text{-butyric acid}}{CH_3CH_2CH_2—\overset{\overset{O}{\|}}{C}—OH}$$

Complete oxidation of alcohols to acids is easy and almost inevitable, unless the volatile aldehyde intermediates are vaporized as fast as they form. Carboxylic acids are extensively hydrogen bonded in the liquid, and therefore have higher boiling points than aldehydes. The acid group, $—\overset{\overset{O}{\|}}{C}—OH$, often is written —COOH, and R—COOH represents a general carboxylic acid.

492

The smaller carboxylic acids are named in a straightforward way, like the related aldehydes:

formaldehyde, H—CHO   → formic acid, H—COOH
                                  (methanoic acid)

acetaldehyde, CH_3—CHO   → acetic acid, CH_3—COOH
                                  (ethanoic acid)

propionaldehyde, C_2H_5—CHO   → propionic acid, C_2H_5—COOH
                                  (propanoic acid)

n-butyraldehyde, C_3H_7—CHO   → n-butyric acid, C_3H_7—COOH
                                  (butanoic acid)

isobutyraldehyde, $(CH_3)_2CH$—CHO → isobutyric acid, $(CH_3)_2CH$—COOH
                                  (1-methyl propanoic acid)

(In each case the systematic name is given in parentheses.) For the longer-chain acids the common name is historical and usually derived from the original source of the compound, but the systematic name continues to be based on the size of the carbon skeleton.

Formula	Common name	Systematic name
C_4H_9COOH	valeric acid	pentanoic acid
$C_5H_{11}COOH$	caproic acid	hexanoic acid
$C_6H_{13}COOH$	heptanoic acid	heptanoic acid
$C_7H_{15}COOH$	caprylic acid	octanoic acid
$C_{11}H_{23}COOH$	lauric acid	dodecanoic acid
$C_{15}H_{31}COOH$	palmitic acid	hexadecanoic acid
$C_{17}H_{35}COOH$	stearic acid	octadecanoic acid

Formic acid is one of the main irritants in ant and bee stings, and acetic acid is familiar from vinegar. Propionic acid, which is produced by certain strains of bacteria, is responsible for the characteristic odor and taste of Swiss cheese, and butyric acid causes the smell of rancid butter. Caproic acid has a ripe goat smell. Valeric acid has the odor that we associate with Limburger cheese and manure, although it first was extracted from the root of the valerian or heliotrope plant. It once was considered medicinally valuable as a sedative, but it is not clear whether its value was physiological or psychological, in terms of the threat of a second dose.

Because one hydrogen atom in a carboxylic acid is attached to the more electronegative oxygen atom rather than to a carbon, these acids are polar and capable of forming extensive hydrogen-bonded networks. They are acids because this same proton dissociates in aqueous solution (right). The explanation for the ready dissociation is similar to that for carbonic acid and phenol. In undissociated acid the proton is bound to one oxygen, and a double bond extends from the carbon to the other oxygen. In the carboxyl ion the electrons of that double bond and the formerly bonding electron pair of the departed proton all are delocalized throughout the entire O—C—O group. This delocalization stabilizes the ion and shifts the equilibrium in favor of dissociation.

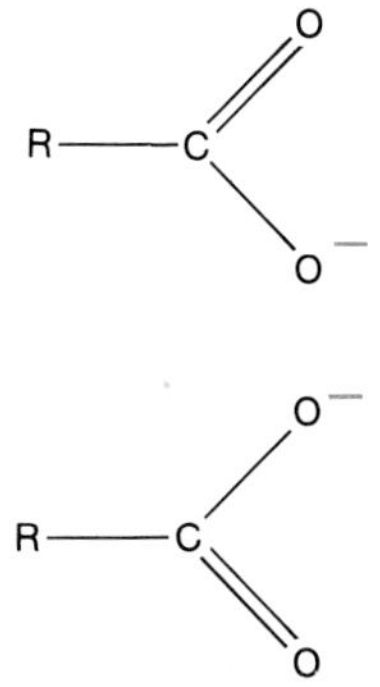

Two resonance structures can be drawn for the carboxylate ion, which differ only in the location of bonding electrons and negative charge. The actual carboxylate ion has a bond structure intermediate between the two extreme forms shown here.

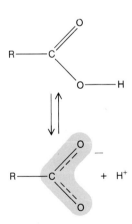

When a carboxylic acid ionizes, both C—O bonds in the ion acquire a partial double-bond character, and the negative charge is delocalized over the entire carboxylate group. The extra stability conferred on the ion by delocalization makes carboxylic acids stronger than they would be otherwise.

493

FATTY ACIDS

Stearic acid $C_{17}H_{35}COOH$

Linoleic acid $C_{17}H_{31}COOH$

Palmitoleic acid $C_{15}H_{29}COOH$

Oleic acid $C_{17}H_{33}COOH$

Palmitic acid $C_{15}H_{31}COOH$

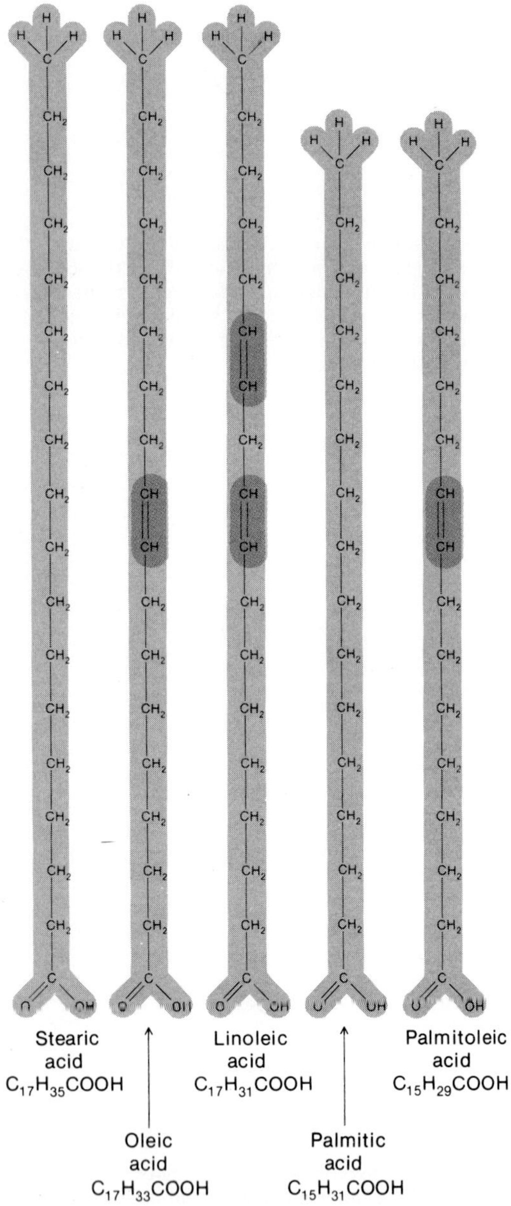

Fatty acids are long-chain carboxylic acids with 10 to 20 carbon atoms. They may contain one or more double bonds in their hydrocarbon tails.

Long-chain carboxylic acids, with 10 to 20 carbons, are called *fatty acids* because they are obtained from fats. They all are insoluble in water and form monolayers at air–water interfaces, as do high-molecular-weight alcohols, with their carboxyl groups in the water and their hydrocarbon tails exposed to air. Five of the most important fatty acids in living organisms are shown at the left. Saturated fatty acids, such as palmitic and stearic, have no double bonds in their hydrocarbon chains; unsaturated fatty acids, such as oleic and palmitoleic, have one double bond; polyunsaturated acids have two or more double bonds.

Carboxylic acids are neutralized by bases, and form salts with them just as inorganic acids do:

$$CH_3-\overset{\overset{\textstyle O}{\|}}{C}-OH + NaOH \rightarrow CH_3-\overset{\overset{\textstyle O}{\|}}{C}-O^- Na^+ + H_2O$$

acetic acid   sodium acetate

Sodium acetate is a water-soluble, ionic solid that dissociates completely into ions in aqueous solution. Since acetic acid is a weak acid, a solution of sodium acetate in water is slightly basic. Some of the acetate ions recombine with H^+ ions from water and leave an excess of OH^- ions:

$$CH_3-COO^- + H_2O \rightarrow CH_3-COOH + OH^-$$

The salts of the long-chain fatty acids are more soluble than the acids themselves are. *Soaps* are salts of fatty acids in the 12- to 18-carbon range, which usually are obtained from animal fats. Sodium stearate, $C_{17}H_{35}COO^- Na^+$, is a common soap. In aqueous solution, stearate ions form monolayers at the air–water interface like fatty acids and long-chain alcohols do, with their polar heads in the water and their hydrocarbon chains in the air. When air is blown through a soap solution, soap bubbles are formed from a double layer of soap molecules, with hydrocarbon tails exposed to the air on either side, and charged heads meeting in a layer of water at the center of the film. The structures of both surface films and bubbles are shown on the opposite page. The water in the center of the soap bubble film still is connected with the bulk water below it. As this water in the center of the "sandwich" gradually drains back down and the film thins, the iridescent interference colors that we associate with soap bubbles are produced. When too much water has drained back, electrostatic repulsion between heads of molecules on the two sides of the bilayer breaks the film, and the bubble bursts.

The effectiveness of soaps as cleaning agents lies in their dual hydrophobic–polar structure. In the bulk of the liquid, soap molecules remove their hydrocarbon tails from water by forming spherical droplets or micelles, with hydrocarbon chains pointing to the interior and negatively charged heads on the surface (see opposite page). Particles of grease, oil, and other hydrocarbons can be picked up and incorporated into the interior of the soap micelles, where the particles are isolated from the water environment. The grease-laden soap micelles then can be flushed away with water, with their negative surface charges helping to keep them apart.

494

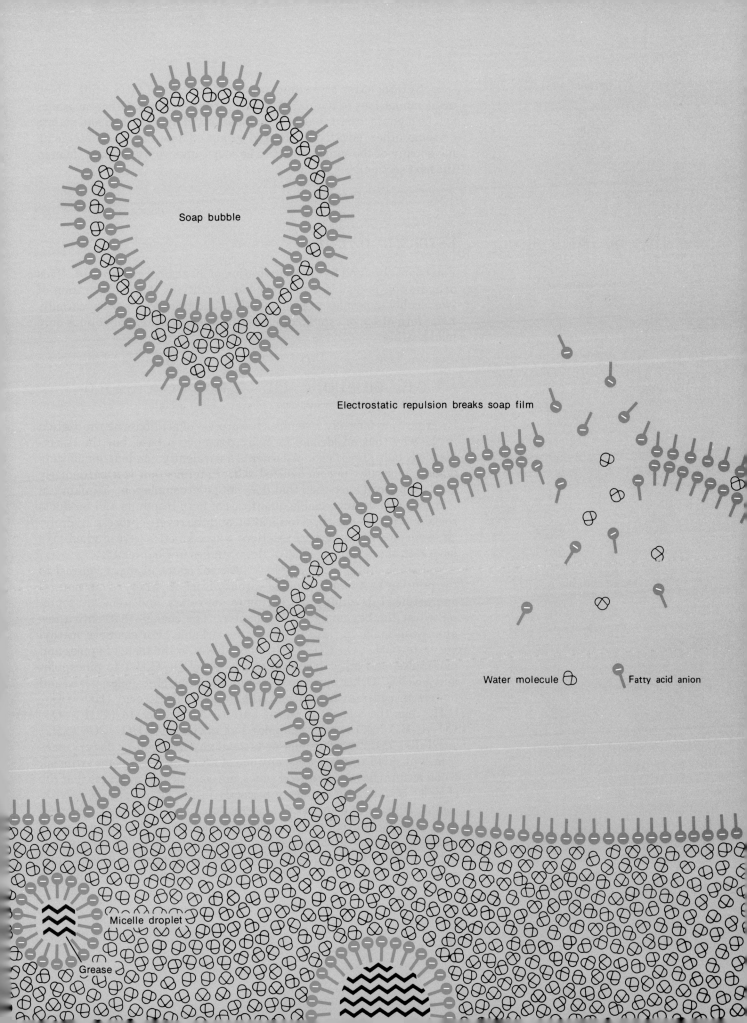

Soap bubble

Electrostatic repulsion breaks soap film

Water molecule ⊕   Fatty acid anion

Micelle droplet

Grease

Benzyl acetate
(jasmine)

Ethyl benzoate
(berry)

Methyl salicylate
(wintergreen)

Amyl salicylate
(clover)

Benzyl benzoate
(musk)

Natural soaps are sodium or potassium salts of fatty acids, which are combinations of hydrocarbon and carboxyl groups. Other molecules can be manufactured that are combinations of hydrocarbon and sulfate or some other negatively charged group. These artificial detergents have many of the same properties as soaps, and we will discuss them in the next section.

ESTERS, $R\!-\!O\!-\!\overset{\overset{\textstyle O}{\|}}{C}\!-\!R$

Esters are obtained by the dehydration of an alcohol and an acid. This dehydration takes place under milder conditions than dehydration of two alcohol molecules to form an ether, and thus occurs preferentially. Ester formation, or *esterification*, is catalyzed by acid and requires only mild heating:

$$C_2H_5\!-\!OH + HO\!-\!\overset{\overset{\textstyle O}{\|}}{C}\!-\!CH_3 \rightarrow C_2H_5\!-\!O\!-\!\overset{\overset{\textstyle O}{\|}}{C}\!-\!CH_3 + H_2O$$

ethyl alcohol   acetic acid   ethyl acetate

Esterification formally resembles the process of acid-base neutralization in the way that an alcohol formally resembles a base, but the resemblance is only superficial. An ester is a covalently bonded, nonionizing organic molecule, not an ionized salt. Esterification is a particularly good example of a reaction that does not go to completion. Equilibrium is reached while appreciable quantities of both reactants and products remain. For this reason, esterification and the reverse process, hydrolysis, were among the earliest reactions whose kinetics were studied. We have seen the results of some of these studies in Chapter 15.

Esters almost uniformly have pleasant odors, in sharp contrast to the pungent and rancid odors of carboxylic acids. Many of our natural and artificial flavorings and perfumes are esters, and some are represented at the beginning of the chapter. The change that only a few atoms can make in taste or odor is remarkable. For example, methyl butyrate ($CH_3\!-\!O\!-\!CO\!-\!C_3H_7$) contributes to the taste of apples and pineapples, and ethyl butyrate ($C_2H_5\!-\!O\!-\!CO\!-\!C_3H_7$) to pineapples and peaches. Other butyric acid esters smell like pineapples, pears, and flowers in general. In contrast, the parent butyric acid ($HO\!-\!CO\!-\!C_3H_7$) has the stench of rancid butter. Amyl valerate ($C_5H_{11}\!-\!O\!-\!CO\!-\!C_4H_9$) has the odor of apples, but valeric acid ($HO\!-\!CO\!-\!C_4H_9$) smells like manure. The odor or taste of any real fruit or flower comes from a blend of several esters, any one of which by itself seems artificial. Good natural flavors, like good wines, are complicated mixtures that the chemist is unable to duplicate perfectly in the laboratory. Esters resemble ketones in being polar, water-soluble, but uncharged. They are used widely as solvents for organic molecules, and as lacquer and paint thinners. Ethyl acetate is the base for fingernail polish removers, and butyl acetate ($C_4H_9\!-\!O\!-\!CO\!-\!CH_3$) for model airplane glues. Amyl acetate ($C_5H_{11}\!-\!O\!-\!CO\!-\!CH_3$), or banana oil, is a widely used lacquer base.

Esters also can be formed from alcohols and inorganic acids:

$$C_2H_5OH + HONO_2 \xrightarrow{H^+, \text{ heat}} C_2H_5-O-NO_2 + H_2O$$

ethyl alcohol   nitric acid   ethyl nitrate

$$C_{12}H_{25}OH + H_2SO_4 \rightarrow C_{12}H_{25}-O-\overset{\displaystyle O}{\underset{\displaystyle O}{\overset{\|}{\underset{\|}{S}}}}-OH + H_2O$$

lauryl alcohol   sulfuric acid   lauryl sulfate

$$\begin{array}{c} H_2C-OH \\ | \\ HC-OH \\ | \\ H_2C-OH \end{array} + 3HNO_3 \rightarrow \begin{array}{c} H_2C-O-NO_2 \\ | \\ HC-O-NO_2 \\ | \\ H_2C-O-NO_2 \end{array} + 3H_2O$$

glycerol, or   glycerol trinitrate,
glycerine   or nitroglycerine

Fats are triesters of fatty acids and glycerol:

$$3\,C_{17}H_{35}-\overset{\displaystyle O}{\overset{\|}{C}}-OH + \begin{array}{c} HO-CH_2 \\ | \\ HO-CH \\ | \\ HO-CH_2 \end{array} \rightarrow \begin{array}{c} C_{17}H_{35}-CO-O-CH_2 \\ | \\ C_{17}H_{35}-CO-O-CH \\ | \\ C_{17}H_{35}-CO-O-CH_2 \end{array} + 3H_2O$$

stearic acid   glycerol   glycerol tristearate,
                                          or tristearin

Tristearin is the most common animal fat, used for energy storage, protection against physical damage, and heat insulation. We will discuss tristearin and other fats and related compounds again in Chapter 21.

The reverse of esterification is *hydrolysis*. Hydrolysis of an ester was used as an example of an acid- or base-catalyzed reaction in Chapter 16. Without the help of an acid or base, the reaction is slow because no easy path for hydrolysis exists. The reaction liberates acid,

$$CH_3-O-\overset{\displaystyle O}{\overset{\|}{C}}-CH_3 + H_2O \rightarrow CH_3-OH + HO-\overset{\displaystyle O}{\overset{\|}{C}}-CH_3$$

methyl acetate   methyl alcohol   acetic acid

and therefore is pushed toward completion by a base, which neutralizes and removes the acid as fast as it is formed. Hydrolysis of natural fats with a base (usually NaOH or KOH) is called *saponification*—literally, "soap making":

$$\begin{array}{c} C_{17}H_{35}-CO-O-CH_2 \\ | \\ C_{17}H_{35}-CO-O-CH \\ | \\ C_{17}H_{35}-CO-O-CH_2 \end{array} + 3NaOH \rightarrow 3\,C_{17}H_{35}COO^- \, Na^+ + \begin{array}{c} HO-CH_2 \\ | \\ HO-CH \\ | \\ HO-CH_2 \end{array}$$

tristearin   sodium stearate   glycerol

One difficulty with natural soaps is that their calcium and magnesium salts are insoluble. If soap is added to hard water containing Ca^{2+} and Mg^{2+}, a greasy soap scum of calcium and magnesium stearate results. One solution to the problem is to use so much soap that all of the divalent cations are precipitated as scum, and more soap is left for

The flavors of the chapter opening photograph

Carboxylic acids

$$HO-\overset{\displaystyle O}{\overset{\|}{C}}-CH_2-CH_3$$
Propionic acid (Swiss cheese)

$$HO-\overset{\displaystyle O}{\overset{\|}{C}}-CH_2-CH_2-CH_3$$
Butyric acid (rancid butter)

$$HO-\overset{\displaystyle O}{\overset{\|}{C}}-CH_2-CH_2-CH_2-CH_3$$
Valeric acid (manure)

$$HO-\overset{\displaystyle O}{\overset{\|}{C}}-CH_2-CH_2-CH_2-CH_2-CH_3$$
Caproic acid (goats)

Esters

$$CH_3-O-\overset{\displaystyle O}{\overset{\|}{C}}-CH_2-CH_2-CH_3$$
Methyl butyrate (pineapples)

$$CH_3-CH_2-O-\overset{\displaystyle O}{\overset{\|}{C}}-CH_2-CH_2-CH_3$$
Ethyl butyrate (peaches)

$$CH_3-CH_2-CH_2-CH_2-CH_2-O-\overset{\displaystyle O}{\overset{\|}{C}}-CH_2-CH_2-CH_3$$
Amyl butyrate (pears)

$$\text{(benzene ring)}-CH_2-O-\overset{\displaystyle O}{\overset{\|}{C}}-CH_2-CH_2-CH_3$$
Benzyl butyrate (flowers)

$$CH_3-CH_2-CH_2-CH_2-CH_2-O-\overset{\displaystyle O}{\overset{\|}{C}}-CH_3$$
Amyl acetate (bananas)

$$CH_3-CH_2-CH_2-CH_2-O-\overset{\displaystyle O}{\overset{\|}{C}}-CH_2-CH_3$$
Butyl propionate (rum)

$$CH_3-CH_2-CH_2-CH_2-CH_2-O-\overset{\displaystyle O}{\overset{\|}{C}}-CH_2-CH_2-CH_2-CH_3$$
Amyl valerate (apples)

AMINES

$$R-NH_2$$

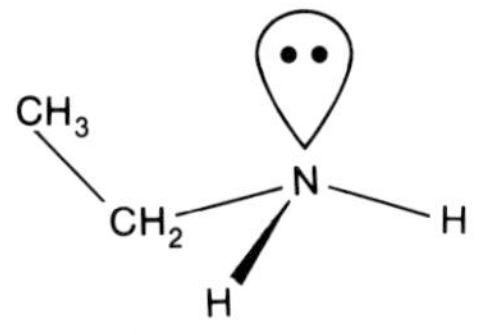

Ethyl amine

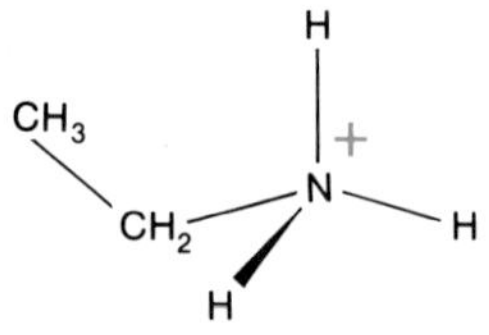

Ethylammonium ion

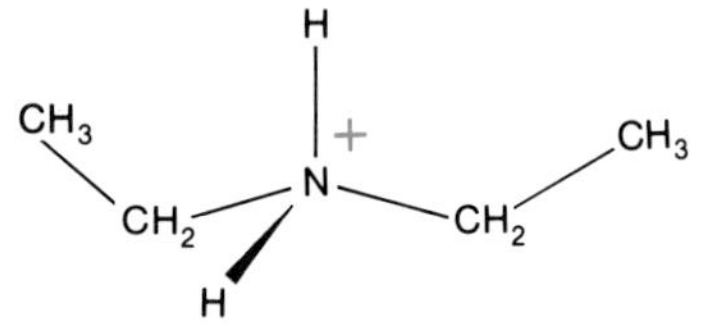

Diethylammonium ion

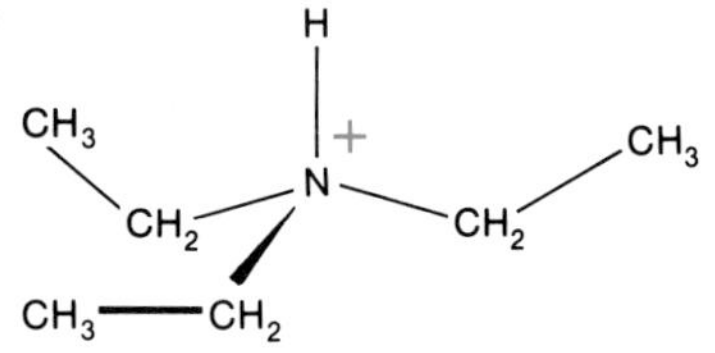

Triethylammonium ion

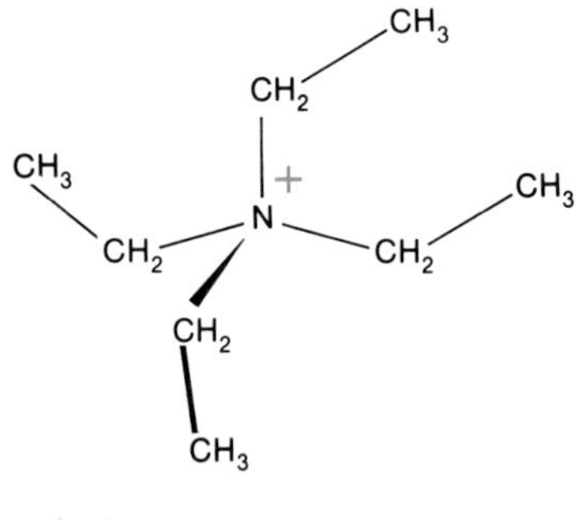

Tetraethylammonium ion

cleaning purposes. This is messy and wasteful. Another solution is to remove the divalent cations ahead of time, and to replace them by Na^+ via an ion-exchange resin in a water-softener. A third possibility is to use artificial detergents whose calcium and magnesium salts are soluble. Sodium lauryl sulfate is one such detergent:

$$C_{12}H_{25}-SO_4^- \ Na^+ \qquad or \qquad C_{12}H_{25}-O-\overset{\displaystyle O}{\underset{\displaystyle O}{\overset{\displaystyle \|}{\underset{\displaystyle \|}{S}}}}-O^- \ Na^+$$

The trouble with many of these compounds is that they are not biodegradable, and eventually will pollute water supplies. The carboxylic acids are "natural" in the sense that they can be used as food by a host of bacteria, and are broken down eventually to CO_2 and H_2O, to blend into the environment. Never having been faced with hydrocarbon sulfates prior to the coming of man, bacteria have not evolved the machinery to use such compounds. They remain untouched in water and soil, occasionally leading to such monstrosities as rivers covered with detergent foam. Biodegradable detergents have been developed recently, which are not precipitated by calcium and magnesium ions, yet which can be eaten by bacteria.

AMINES AND OTHER ORGANIC BASES

Amines and other nitrogen compounds are the bases of the organic world. The amines are prepared by reacting chlorides of hydrocarbons with ammonia, and replacing one or more of the ammonia protons with a hydrocarbon group:

$$C_2H_5Cl + NH_3 \rightarrow \underset{\substack{\text{ethylammonium} \\ \text{ion}}}{C_2H_5NH_3^+} + Cl^- \xrightarrow{\text{NaOH}}$$
$$\underset{\substack{\text{ethyl} \\ \text{chloride}}}{}$$

$$\underset{\substack{\text{ethyl} \\ \text{amine}}}{C_2H_5NH_2} + H_2O + Na^+ + Cl^-$$

$$C_2H_5Cl + C_2H_5NH_2 \rightarrow \underset{\substack{\text{diethylammonium} \\ \text{ion}}}{(C_2H_5)_2NH_2^+} + Cl^- \xrightarrow{\text{NaOH}}$$

$$\underset{\substack{\text{diethyl} \\ \text{amine}}}{(C_2H_5)_2NH} + H_2O + Na^+ + Cl^-$$

$$C_2H_5Cl + (C_2H_5)_2NH \rightarrow \underset{\substack{\text{triethylammonium} \\ \text{ion}}}{(C_2H_5)_3NH^+} + Cl^- \xrightarrow{\text{NaOH}}$$

$$\underset{\substack{\text{triethyl} \\ \text{amine}}}{(C_2H_5)_3N} + H_2O + Na^+ + Cl^-$$

$$C_2H_5Cl + (C_2H_5)_3N \rightarrow \underset{\substack{\text{tetraethylammonium} \\ \text{ion}}}{(C_2H_5)_4N^+} + Cl^-$$

498

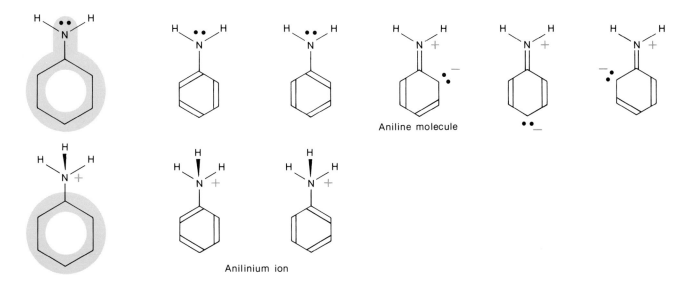

Aniline molecule

Anilinium ion

The aniline molecule resembles the phenolate ion in having seven atoms in its de-localized system and five resonance structures, three of which bring negative charges onto the aromatic ring. The aniline molecule is stabilized relative to the anilinium ion which, like phenol, has only six atoms in the delocalized system and two reso-nance forms. Hence aniline is reluctant to accept a proton, and is a weak base.

Amines are classed as primary, secondary, or tertiary, according to the number of nonhydrogen substituents they have on the nitrogen. Tetra-ethylammonium ion is a quaternary ammonium ion, but there obviously can be no quaternary amine molecules. All of these amines can add a proton to form a substituted ammonium ion, and all are about as strong bases as ammonia, with a $pK_a \sim 10$. The secondary and tertiary amines are toxic, with a nauseating fishy stench.

Aromatic —OH compounds are more acidic than aliphatic R—OH alcohols because of the influence of the delocalized ring electrons. By the same token, aromatic amines are weaker bases than the aliphatic amines that we have just discussed. Methyl amine, CH_3—NH_2, is sim-ilar in strength to ammonia; phenyl amine or aniline, C_6H_5—NH_2, is a weak base with a pK_a of only 4.63. The reason is outlined above. In terms of the resonance structures that can be drawn, the unprotonated aniline molecule resembles the phenolate ion, and the protonated ani-linium ion is like the phenol molecule. All four electron pairs around the nitrogen in the anilinium ion are tied up in sigma bonds to hydro-gen or carbon, and none are free for delocalization into the aromatic ring system. The loss of a proton in the anilinium molecule leaves a lone pair on the nitrogen atom that can be shared with the aromatic ring. As in the phenolate ion, the delocalized system is expanded from six atoms and six electrons to seven atoms and eight electrons. In both phenol and aniline, increased delocalization favors the *unprotonated* species, which are the phenolate ion and the neutral aniline molecule. Phenol loses a proton easily to form the phenolate ion, and therefore is a reasonably strong acid. Aniline only reluctantly accepts a proton to form the anilinium ion, and hence is a weak base. When an —NH_2

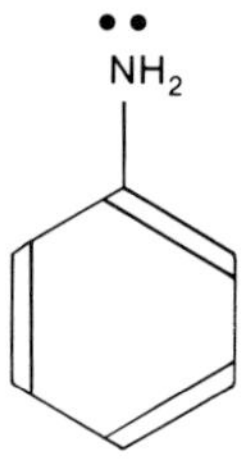

Aniline
$pK_a = 4.63$

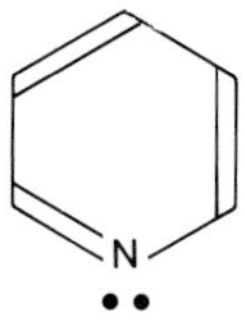

Pyridine
$pK_a = 5.25$

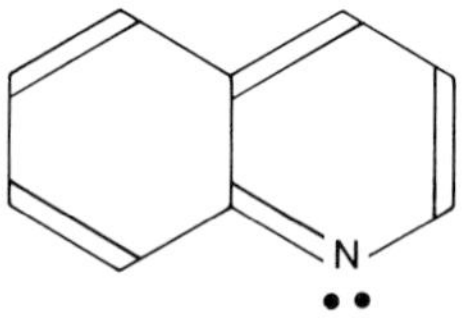

Quinoline
$pK_a = 4.90$

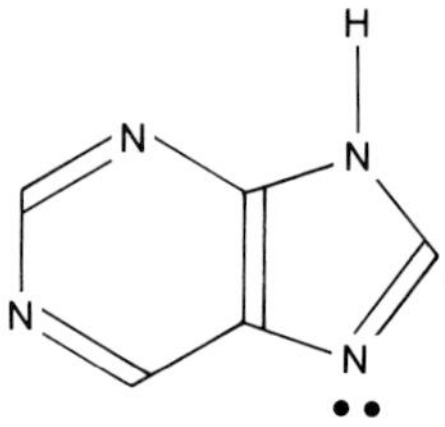

Purine
$pK_a = 8.96$

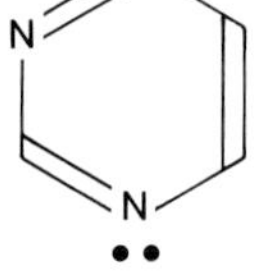

Pyrimidine
$pK_a \simeq 9$

A nitrogen atom in an organic base can be a part of an aromatic ring as well as an open chain. Typical examples and their pK_a's are shown here.

group is attached to an aliphatic radical it receives no comparable de-localization stabilization. It is less reluctant to accept a proton on its nitrogen lone pair, and hence aliphatic amines are stronger bases.

Many other organic nitrogen bases have nitrogen atoms incor-porated within an aromatic ring. A nitrogen atom easily can replace a carbon in an aromatic ring, with a nitrogen lone electron pair taking the place of the fourth C—H bond. This lone pair then is the binding point for a proton when the molecule functions as a base. Four such organic bases are shown at the left. Purine and pyrimidine are the parent com-pounds of a family of bases of great importance in biochemistry, espe-cially in DNA and other nucleic acids.

AMINO ACIDS, $H_2N—\overset{\overset{\displaystyle R}{|}}{C}H—COOH$

One of the main goals of this chapter has been to bring us gradually to amino acids, and thus prepare the way for the discussion of proteins in Chapter 22. Amino acids are bifunctional, with an —NH_2 amine group at one end of the molecule and a —COOH acid group at the other. The general expression for an amino acid is

$$H_2N—\overset{\overset{\displaystyle R}{|}}{\underset{\underset{\displaystyle H}{|}}{C}}—COOH$$

in which R— can be one of many side groups with widely different chemical character. The pK_a of the amine group is around 9.5 and that of the carboxyl is approximately 2.2, so at a neutral pH of 7, both ends of the molecule are charged:

$$^+H_3N—\overset{\overset{\displaystyle R}{|}}{\underset{\underset{\displaystyle H}{|}}{C}}—COO^-$$

This is known as a *zwitterion* (German: "hybrid ion").

Amino acids can be polymerized with the loss of H_2O to form a polypeptide chain, as shown on the opposite page. This chain is the backbone of all protein molecules. We will see in Chapter 22 the ways in which a polypeptide chain can fold into a three-dimensional protein molecule. The order of side groups, here symbolized by R—, determines what protein the chain will form, and how it will fold. Twenty different side chains are coded in the genetic machinery of living organisms; the order or sequence of these side chains in the protein-to-be is specified by the order in which purine and pyrimidine bases appear along the chain sequence in DNA. Among these 20 genetically coded amino acids are: glycine, which has only a hydrogen atom for a side group; valine, which has a hydrocarbon side chain; phenylalanine, which has an aro-matic ring; polar but uncharged serine; negatively charged aspartic

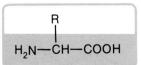

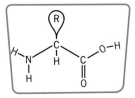

UN-IONIZED AMINO ACID

ZWITTERION

Amino acids exist in solution as doubly charged zwitterions.

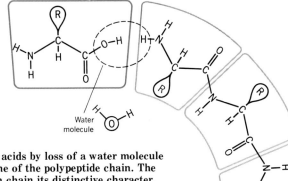

THE AMINO ACID MONOMER

Water molecule

The peptide bond formed between amino acids by loss of a water molecule joins identical units to make the backbone of the polypeptide chain. The variable side chains (R) give each protein chain its distinctive character. The folding of the chain in three dimensions is considered in Chapter 22. Copyright © 1969 Dickerson and Geis; from R. E. Dickerson and I. Geis, *The Structure and Action of Proteins,* W. A. Benjamin, Inc.

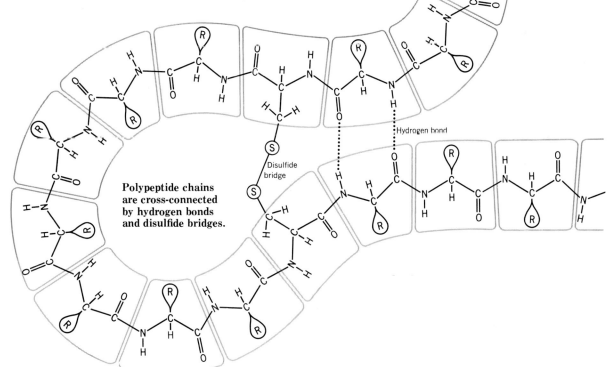

Hydrogen bond

Disulfide bridge

Polypeptide chains are cross-connected by hydrogen bonds and disulfide bridges.

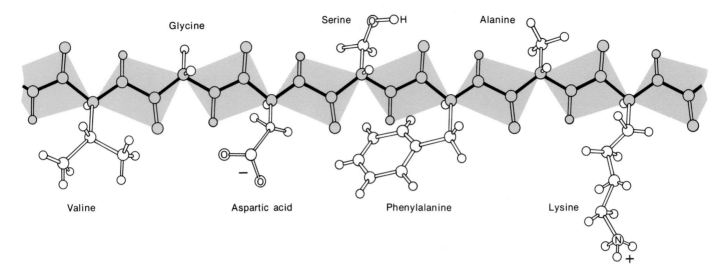

Glycine

Serine

Alanine

Valine

Aspartic acid

Phenylalanine

Lysine

The different kinds of side chains at the links in the polypeptide chain contain the information for the folding of the chain into a three-dimensional protein molecule. These groups can be acidic, basic, polar, or nonpolar.

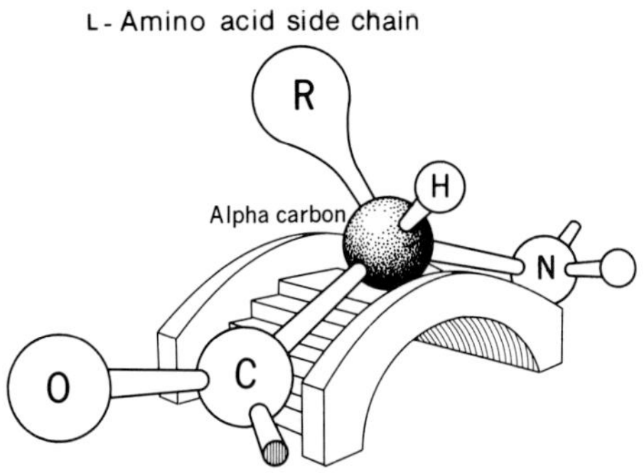

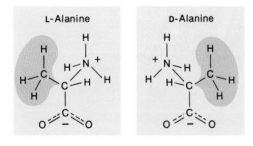

L-Amino acid side chain

R

H

Alpha carbon

N

O

C

L-Alanine

D-Alanine

(Top) A memory device for distinguishing L- from D-amino acids. As one walks over the hump-backed bridge from CO to C_α to NH, the side chain in an L-amino acid is at the left, and that of a D-amino acid is at the right. (Bottom) L-alanine and D-alanine structures. Copyright © 1969 Dickerson and Geis; from R. E. Dickerson and I. Geis, *The Structure and Action of Proteins*, W. A. Benjamin, Inc.

acid; and basic lysine, which has a positive charge. These side chains, —R, are:

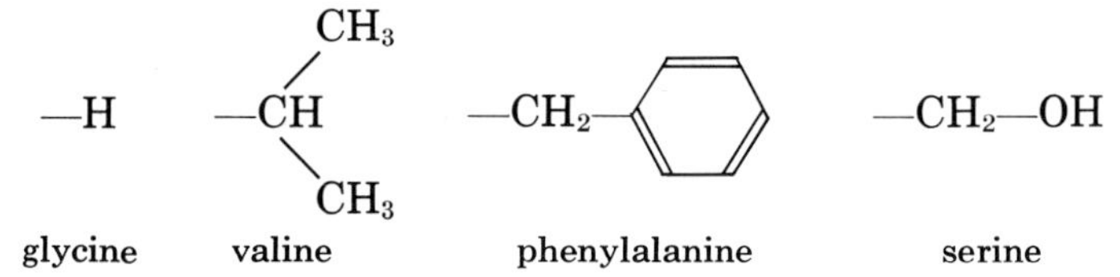

$$-H \qquad -CH\begin{smallmatrix}CH_3\\\\CH_3\end{smallmatrix} \qquad -CH_2-\text{(phenyl)} \qquad -CH_2-OH$$

glycine   valine   phenylalanine   serine

$$-CH_2-COO^- \qquad -CH_2CH_2CH_2CH_2NH_3^+$$

aspartic acid   lysine

These samples of the repertory of amino acids are illustrated in the polypeptide chain shown above. We will see later how important the side chains can be to the chemical behavior of a protein.

Because four different groups are attached to the central carbon of an amino acid, it is called an *asymmetric carbon*, identified as the α-carbon or C_α. Two mirror-isomers, or enantiomorphs, are possible, as with L-alanine and D-alanine, compared at bottom left. The L- originally meant "levo-" or left, and D- meant "dextro-" or right, which refers to the rotation of polarized light by a solution of the molecules. This nomenclature has only a formal meaning today, since a molecule synthesized from an L-molecule also is called an L-form, even though the new molecule might rotate polarized light in the opposite direction. Only L-amino acids are found in living organisms, with the exception of a few cell-wall components in some bacteria. This seemingly arbitrary asymmetry of molecules in living organisms puzzled Pasteur and early biochemists, and we will return to this question later. The drawing at the left is a convenient memory device to fix the structure of L-amino acids in your mind. Imagine that the amino acid is transformed into a hump-backed bridge, and that you are crossing it from the O to the N atom (remember it as "ONward"). Then at the crest of the bridge, the side chain of an L-amino acid will be on your left ("levo") and that of a D-amino acid will be on your right ("dextro").

How proteins fold will be one of the main topics of Chapter 22, but the general idea is outlined in the drawings below. In hemoglobin in blood, and in the closely related oxygen-storage protein myoglobin, several regions along the polypeptide chain fold spontaneously into a helical structure known as an α helix (left, below). These rodlike α helices then fold against one another, with "hinges" at nonhelical parts of the chain between them, to build a three-dimensional molecule. The correct folding together of α helices is guided by having hydrocarbon side chains spaced along the main chain so one side of each cylindrical helix is covered with hydrocarbon groups, and the opposite side is polar and charged. When the helices spontaneously fold against one another in such a way as to bury the hydrocarbon side chains away from the aqueous surroundings, the proper three-dimensional structure is formed.

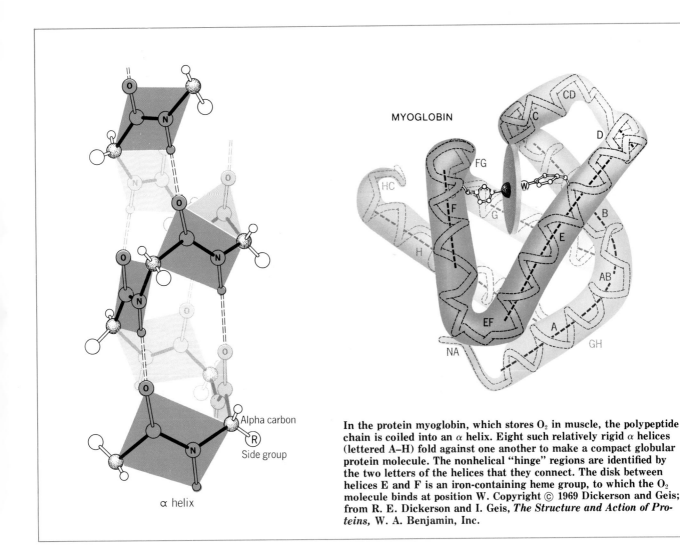

In the protein myoglobin, which stores O_2 in muscle, the polypeptide chain is coiled into an α helix. Eight such relatively rigid α helices (lettered A–H) fold against one another to make a compact globular protein molecule. The nonhelical "hinge" regions are identified by the two letters of the helices that they connect. The disk between helices E and F is an iron-containing heme group, to which the O_2 molecule binds at position W. Copyright © 1969 Dickerson and Geis; from R. E. Dickerson and I. Geis, *The Structure and Action of Proteins*, W. A. Benjamin, Inc.

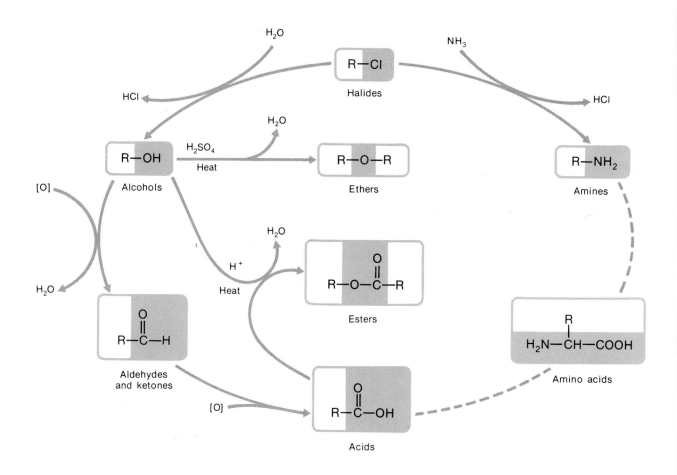

Flow diagram between the classes of organic molecules considered in this chapter. Once the halogenated hydrocarbons are made, they are the gateway to many other compounds.

A ROAD MAP THROUGH ORGANIC CHEMISTRY

This chapter has been a brief introduction to organic chemistry, with many new types of molecules. You should not be overwhelmed with them, because they are interconnected by very simple reactions; and if you can see the connections, then it will be easier to remember the compounds. The diagram above is a "road map" showing in outline how one type of compound can be obtained from another. Only the simplest reactions are shown from among the many possible transformations. The purpose is not to set down every reaction a molecule is capable of, but rather to show in general terms how the different classes of compounds are related.

The starting point is a hydrocarbon halide such as ethyl chloride or butyl bromide. Treatment with water under suitable conditions leads to primary, secondary, and tertiary alcohols, and reactions with ammonia lead to primary, secondary, or tertiary amines. Any of the alcohols can be dehydrated to ethers. Primary alcohols can be oxidized to aldehydes, and secondary alcohols to ketones, but tertiary alcohols are immune to further oxidation short of destruction. Aldehydes, but not ketones, can be oxidized further to carboxylic acids, which in turn can be condensed with alcohols to form esters. Amino acids, although not directly synthesized from carboxylic acids and amines, in a sense are hybrids of these two molecules: amines at one end and acids at the other. When polymerized, these amino acids lead to proteins, which are the topic of Chapter 22.

QUESTIONS

1. What are functional groups in organic molecules? In what ways do they determine the chemical behavior of the molecules?

2. How does the nature of the hydrocarbon radical influence the chemical behavior of a molecule?

3. How does the length of hydrocarbon chain affect the solubility of an alcohol?

4. Why are alcohols useful as solvents?

5. What are primary, secondary, and tertiary alcohols? What happens when each of these is oxidized?

6. How are alcohols prepared from halogenated hydrocarbons? How else can alcohols be obtained?

7. Why does the dipole moment of an alcohol molecule decrease with increasing molecular weight?

8. Of the three compounds with —OH groups, $NaOH$, CH_3OH, and C_6H_5OH, one is an acid, one is a base, and one is neither. Explain in terms of molecular structure and bonding.

9. What are structural isomers? Why do the isomers of C_7H_8O, which were mentioned in this chapter, have such different chemical and physical properties?

10. What is an ether, and how is it made from alcohols? Why is the ether that is made from polar alcohol molecules nonpolar? How does this affect the solvent properties of ethers?

11. How are aldehydes made from alcohols? How are ketones made?

12. Why are aldehydes and ketones polar, whereas ethers are not? Why are aldehydes and ketones susceptible to chemical attack?

13. What compounds are produced when aldehydes are oxidized? Can ketones be oxidized under similar conditions?

14. Why is CH_3—CO—OH an acid, whereas CH_3—CH_2—OH is not? How does the —CO— group contribute to making the molecule acidic?

15. How does delocalization help to make a carboxylic acid more acidic?

16. Where is the negative charge after a carboxylic acid has dissociated?

17. What is a fatty acid? Are fatty acids water-soluble? Why, or why not? What happens when a fatty acid is mixed with water?

18. What are the salts of fatty acids and alkali metal cations called? How do such salts work, and what makes them useful to us?

19. In what sense is a fatty acid anion a more exaggerated version of a long-chain alcohol molecule?

20. What is the structure of the bilayer in a soap film? What produces the colors in a soap bubble? Why does the bubble thicken at the bottom, and eventually burst? Does the initial rupture of the film occur at the bottom, or the top, of the bubble?

21. How do soaps operate as cleaning agents?

22. What is esterification? What is the reverse reaction called?

23. If you had to work in a laboratory filled with carboxylic acids or with their esters, which would you prefer? Why?

24. How are fats related to fatty acids? What is saponification and what chemical substances result from it?

25. What are primary, secondary, and tertiary amines? Is each class acidic, basic, both, or neither?

26. Why can there be primary, secondary, tertiary, and quaternary ammonium ions, but no quaternary amines?

27. In what way is aniline similar to the phenolate ion, and phenol similar to the anilinium ion?

28. What is an amino acid? In what sense is it an acid? A base?

29. Is an amino acid in aqueous solution charged? If so, where are the charges?

30. What is meant by an asymmetric carbon atom in an amino acid? What symmetry of amino acids is encountered in most proteins of living organisms? Why is the other symmetry form not found? Could life on another planet have begun using the other symmetry form of amino acids?

31. How do the side chains of amino acids affect their behavior? What kinds of chemical behavior can the side chains of the 20 naturally occurring amino acids exhibit?

32. How are amino acids combined to form a protein molecule? What molecule is released during this combining process? What is the reverse of this combining process called?

33. How is the order, or sequence, of amino acids along a protein chain determined before the protein is made?

PROBLEMS

1. Write all the structural formulas of the isomeric alcohols with molecular composition $C_6H_{13}OH$. Give each its proper systematic name. Classify them as primary, secondary, or tertiary.

2. Outline a scheme for synthesizing a butanol from 1-butene. What intermediate compound might be formed? Would the product be 1-butanol or 2-butanol, and what is the principle that tells you which?

3. How many structural isomers are there of $C_6H_{14}O$ that are ethers? What are their systematic names? What other kinds of compounds in addition to ethers can be structural isomers of $C_6H_{14}O$?

4. Ethanol and dimethyl ether are isomers of C_2H_6O. From their molecular structures, explain the differences between the two mol-

ecules in melting point, boiling point, vapor pressure at room temperature, and solubility in water.

5. What compounds are obtained by subjecting 1-propanol to moderate (i.e., nondestructive) oxidizing conditions? The intermediate and the final product in this reaction have quite different vapor pressures at room temperature. Explain this in terms of molecular structure. How could this help you to design experimental conditions to maximize the yield of either intermediate or final product?

6. Give the systematic names of the following substances:
   (a) $CH_3CH_2CH_2COOCH_3$ (c) $CH_3CH_2CH_2OCH_2CH_3$
   (b) $CH_3CHOHCH_2CH_2CH_2CH_2CH_3$ (d) $CH_3COCH(CH_3)_2$

7. What is the Brønsted–Lowry conjugate base of phenol? Is aniline a B–L acid or base, and what is its conjugate base or acid?

8. What is the conjugate base of propionic acid? The pK_a of propionic acid is 4.87. (a) Calculate the pH of a 0.1M solution of propionic acid. (b) Calculate the pH of a solution 0.1M in propionic acid and 0.1M in sodium propionate. (Refer to Chapter 16 if necessary.)

9. Write balanced chemical equations for the following: (a) the hydrolysis of isopropyl acetate; (b) the reaction of acetic acid and 2-butanol in the presence of sulfuric acid; and (c) the reaction of methyl chloride with ammonia (more than one product will be formed).

10. Arrange the following substances in order of increasing acidity:
    (a) CH_3CH_2OH (d) CH_3COOH
    (b) C_6H_5OH (e) CH_3CH_3
    (c) HOH

11. Arrange the following compounds in order of increasing solubility in water:
    (a) CH_3CH_2OH (c) $CH_3(CH_2)_6CH_3$
    (b) $CH_3(CH_2)_6CH_2OH$ (d) $HOCH_2CH_2OH$ (1,2-ethanediol, or ethylene glycol)

12. Name the following substances. What kind of chemical compound are they? Are c and d isomers?
    (a) $C_6H_5OC_2H_5$ (c) $CH_3OCH_2CH_2CH_3$
    (b) $(CH_3)_2CHOCH(CH_3)_2$ (d) $CH_3CH_2CH_2OCH_3$

13. Name the following substances. What kind of chemical compound are they? Are c and d isomers?
    (a) $C_6H_5COOC_2H_5$ (c) $CH_3COOCH_2CH_2CH_3$
    (b) $C_2H_5COOC_6H_5$ (d) $CH_3CH_2CH_2COOCH_3$

14. Draw the structural formula for each of the following:
    (a) sodium propionate   (h) benzyl amine
    (b) m-bromobenzoic acid   (i) m-bromoaniline
    (c) ethyl benzoate   (j) tetraethylammonium hydroxide
    (d) isobutyryl chloride   (k) alanine
    (e) methyl formate   (l) aspartic acid
    (f) diethylamine   (m) lysine
    (g) tri-n-propyl amine

β-D-GLUCOSE

In the β-D-glucose unit the —H at Position 1 points downward, perpendicular to the plane of the six-membered ring. The —OH group points out roughly in the plane of the ring.

CELLULOSE

β-D-glucose units are connected to make a chain of cellulose. The chain is nearly straight if alternate units are flipped over.

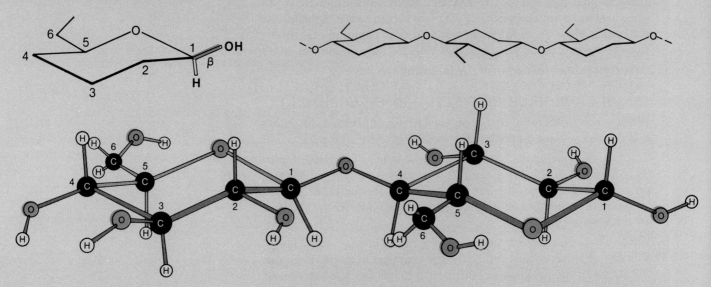

STARCH

α-D-glucose units make a curved chain characteristic of starch. The α connection, at right angles to the glucose ring, prevents the formation of a straight chain like cellulose.

α-D-GLUCOSE

In the α-D-glucose unit the —OH at Position 1 points downward, perpendicular to the ring plane, and —H extends out in the plane of the ring.

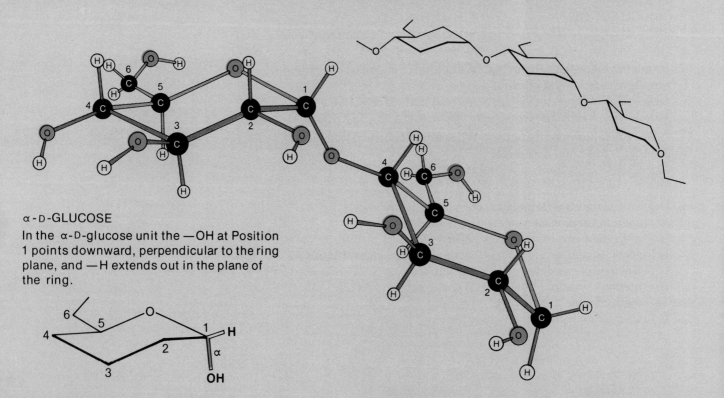

◀ *Glucose molecules can be connected in two different ways to build either cellulose or starch*

CHAPTER 21

Lipids and Carbohydrates

The preceding two chapters emphasized the variety and diversity of carbon compounds. It may seem paradoxical, therefore, to say that over half of the organic carbon on our planet is found in only *one* compound: cellulose. The runner-up, with a clear lead over any third substance, is starch. Both starch and cellulose are polymers of a simple six-carbon sugar, *glucose* ($C_6H_{12}O_6$); thus glucose by long odds must be considered the most outstandingly successful organic molecule on the face of the planet. As we shall see in Chapter 23, the central energy-extraction and energy-storage mechanisms common to all life also are based on this molecule. Life on Earth revolves around glucose.

Cellulose is plentiful because it is the universal building material for cell walls of plants of all kinds, from green algae to California redwoods. The scaffolding of plants is polymerized glucose. Plants also store energy in glucose polymers of a slightly different kind: starch. With the same molecule used for both support and energy storage, a plant is faced with the dilemma of Hansel and Gretel—how to tell the food from the furniture. The answer is an ingenious bit of chemical trickery, the α versus β connections shown on the facing page, which will be discussed later in the chapter.

Animals, too, use the same class of molecules for structure as for energy storage. An animal stores its excess energy in the form of fats. The closely related lipids are one of the two components of all types of biological membranes, in both plant and animal cells. The fatty-acid soap films discussed in Chapter 20 are a surprisingly good model for simple membranes, although turned inside out.

In this chapter we shall look at two large families of carbon compounds: *lipids*, which include membrane materials, fats, and other organic hydrocarbons; and *carbohydrates*, which include starches, cellulose, and the simple sugars that are found in living organisms.

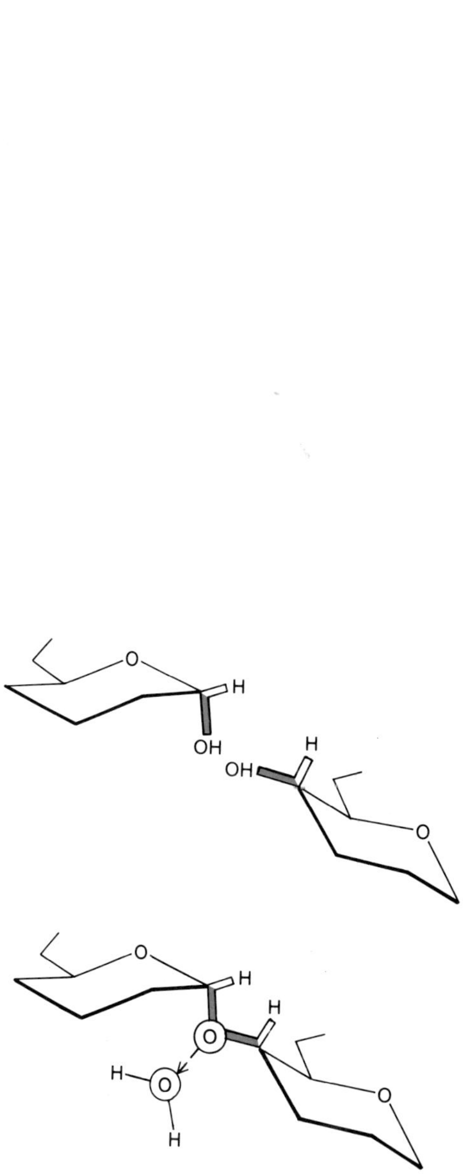

Glucose molecules in cellulose and starch are connected by an oxygen bridge between their carbon Positions 1 and 4. A water molecule is lost during the connecting reaction.

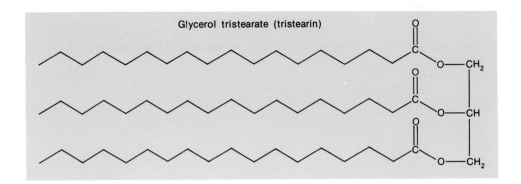

Glycerol tristearate (tristearin)

FATS AND LIPIDS

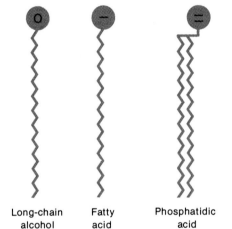

Long-chain alcohol   Fatty acid   Phosphatidic acid

"Lipid" is the general term for any water-insoluble organic molecules that can be extracted from cells by ethers, benzene, or other nonpolar solvents. The most important lipids for our purposes are fats and the fat-derived molecules of membranes. Other types include steroids, terpenes, and various small hydrocarbon derivatives, which serve as membrane components, detergents, some hormones, regulators, and light-gathering antennae. The carotenoids, whose light-absorbing talents we have seen already, fall into this class.

As we saw in Chapter 20, fats are esters of glycerol, with long-chain fatty acids having 10 to 20 carbon atoms in their chains. Tristearin, the most common animal fat, is shown above. The three chains on one glycerol molecule do not have to be identical; mixed fats are possible. Vegetable fats from plants generally have short chains that are unsaturated (with C=C double bonds) or polyunsaturated (with several C=C bonds). The double bonds, which almost invariably are in the cis configuration, introduce kinks into the chains. Because these short, bent chains do not pack together well in a solid, vegetable fats tend to be oily liquids. In contrast, animal fats have longer, saturated fatty-acid chains that pack efficiently to form waxy solids such as lard and tallow. Oily vegetable fats can be "hardened" by hydrogenation, that is, by adding H_2 across the double bonds with a catalyst, thereby producing saturated chains with the kinks straightened out.

It was mentioned in Chapter 20 that an alcohol can be esterified with an inorganic acid just as well as with a carboxylic acid. If glycerol is esterified with two fatty-acid molecules and one molecule of phosphoric acid, the result is phosphatidic acid (below), the simplest *phospholipid*. This can be thought of as a "super fatty acid." Long-chain

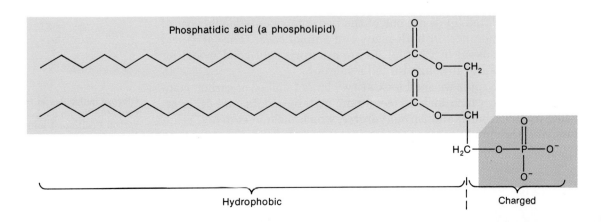

Phosphatidic acid (a phospholipid)

Hydrophobic   Charged

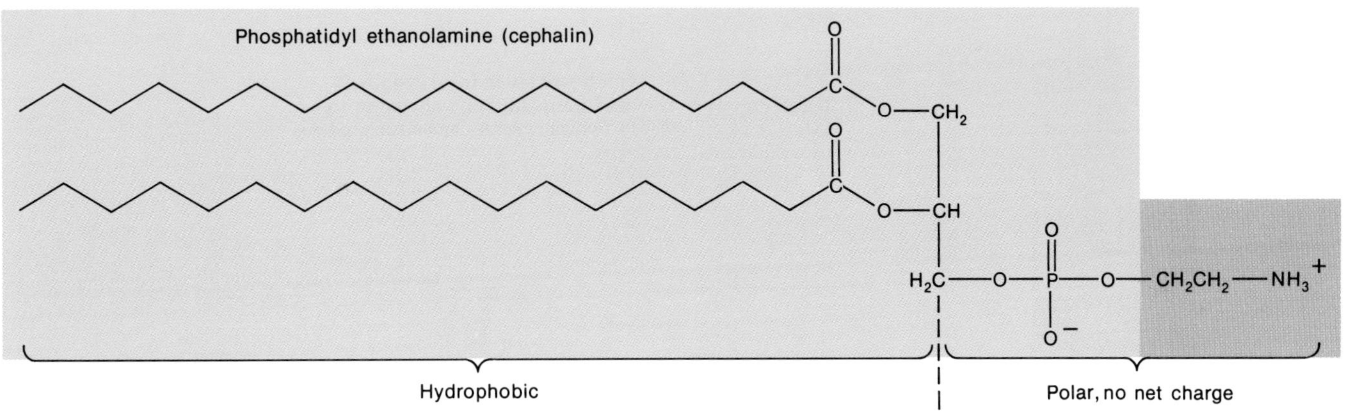

Phosphatidyl ethanolamine (cephalin)

$$H_2C-O-\overset{\overset{\displaystyle O}{\|}}{P}-O-CH_2CH_2-NH_3^+$$
$$\underset{O^-}{}$$

Hydrophobic | Polar, no net charge

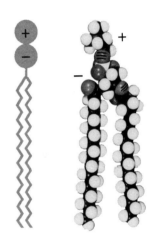

alcohols are partly hydrophobic and partly polar but uncharged (far left), fatty acids are half hydrophobic and half negatively charged, and phosphatidic acid has twice the hydrocarbon chains and twice the negative charge per molecule. These phospholipids are the raw materials of membrane structures.

One disadvantage of phosphatidic acid is that it is a negative ion (anion), and needs nearby positive ions (cations) to neutralize its negative charge. This problem can be avoided, while preserving the charged polar character of the head of the molecule, if the phosphate group is esterified again with an alcohol that carries its own positive charge. Such a molecule is ethanolamine, $HO—CH_2CH_2—NH_2$, which at neutral pH exists in the ionized form: $HO—CH_2CH_2—NH_3^+$. This second esterification produces phosphatidyl ethanolamine, or cephalin (shown above). The cephalin molecule is half hydrophobic and half charged polar, yet electrostatically neutral because it carries its counter ion with it.

Cephalin has one flaw. As a primary amine, it can lose a proton and its positive charge under basic conditions and revert to a negatively charged molecule, such as phosphatidic acid. The ingenious solution that actually is used in membranes is to substitute for ethanolamine a quaternary ammonium ion that cannot deprotonate and lose its positive charge. The main lipid component in biological membranes is phosphatidyl choline, or lecithin (below). In lecithin the phosphate group is esterified with the quaternary ammonium compound choline,

$HO—CH_2CH_2—\overset{+}{N}(CH_3)_3$, which is identical to ethanolamine except for the three methyl groups on the nitrogen. Lecithin cannot lose its positive charge and therefore must remain a neutral molecule overall. The actual shape of a lecithin molecule is indicated by the space-filling model in the right margin.

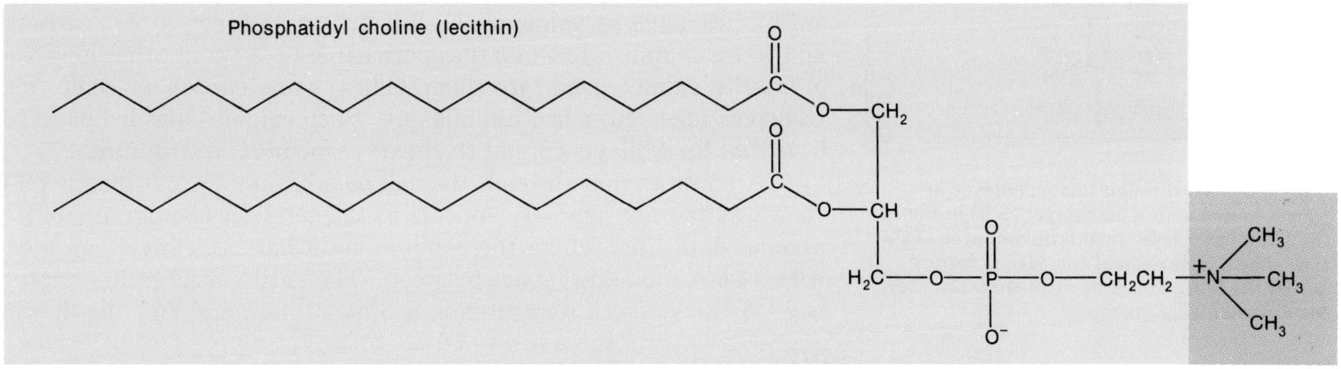

Phosphatidyl choline (lecithin)

$$H_2C-O-\overset{\overset{\displaystyle O}{\|}}{P}-O-CH_2CH_2-\overset{+}{N}\begin{smallmatrix}CH_3\\CH_3\\CH_3\end{smallmatrix}$$
$$\underset{O^-}{}$$

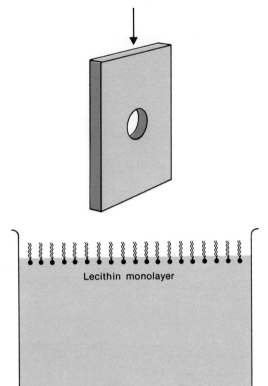

Lecithin, when added to water, forms a monolayer on the surface, with polar head groups in the water and nonpolar tails exposed to the air.

A bilayer of lipids, which has polar head groups exposed on either side and nonpolar tails buried in the interior in an ordered manner, is the basis for models of membrane structures.

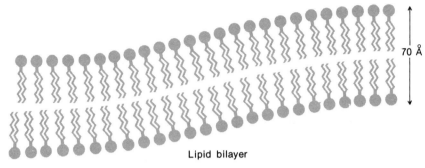

Lipid bilayer

70 Å

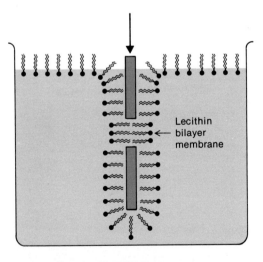

Lecithin bilayer membrane

A plate pushed through this monolayer becomes coated with a monolayer lecithin film. If the plate has a hole, then a lipid bilayer of the type shown at the top of the page is formed across the hole. This bilayer then can be used for diffusion experiments.

MEMBRANE STRUCTURE

If lecithin is suspended in hot water, it forms a monolayer on the surface that is similar to that found with soaps and long-chain alcohols. If a loop of wire or a thin metal plate with a hole is pushed down through this film, a lipid bilayer will be formed within the loop or hole, as diagrammed at the left. In the original surface film, the polar heads of the molecules were underneath, in contact with water. The hydrocarbon tails were above, exposed to the air. The lecithin bilayer formed at the opening in the plate will have the structure shown above, with polar heads exposed on either face of the bilayer and hydrophobic chains meeting at the center. Such a bilayer made with chains the length of stearic acid will be 70 Å thick, similar to biological membranes. Lecithin bilayers are like soap films turned inside out. Both are bilayers of half hydrophobic and half polar molecules. Soap films, in contact with air on either side, have their hydrophobic chains exposed and their polar heads immersed in a layer of water in the center of the film. Lipid bilayers in aqueous solution have their molecules in the reversed position—hydrophobic portion in the center and polar heads out.

There are even more similarities between lecithin bilayers and biological membranes. Bilayers show many membranelike properties. They are easily permeable to water molecules, but not to ions such as Na^+, K^+, and Cl^-. They have a high electrical resistance across the membrane because of the insulating layer of hydrocarbon. Several small antibiotics, such as valinomycin, are known to function as "carriers" and to make natural membranes permeable to K^+ and other ions that ordinarily cannot penetrate them. These same carrier molecules also transport ions across lecithin bilayers. Such evidence has led us to believe that lipid bilayers are at the heart of membrane structure.

A cross section through the cell membrane of a red blood cell is shown at the far right. It appears in the electron micrograph as two parallel dark lines where the osmium stain has been taken up most, with a 25-Å unstained space between. The entire membrane structure is 90 Å thick. Such a membrane is 60% protein and 40% lipid, with

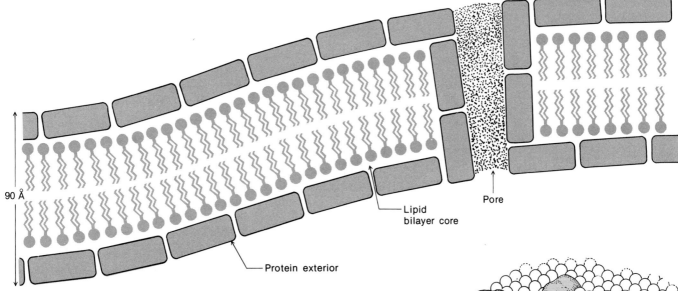

90 Å

Lipid bilayer core

Pore

Protein exterior

The unit-membrane model of a biological membrane: a lipid bilayer covered on both sides with proteins. This simple model must be modified, by assuming pores, to account for observed permeability of membranes to some ions and small molecules.

the lipid part being half cholesterol (see Page 516) and half lecithin, cephalin, and similar molecules.

H. Davson and J. Danielli, in 1935, proposed a membrane structure that was refined by Robertson into the "unit-membrane" model, which has served as the basis for membrane structure theories for many years. The unit-membrane model is diagrammed above: a lipid bilayer core coated on either side with proteins. The inside of the membrane in this model is strongly hydrophobic and the outside is polar. Lipid molecules are held together only by hydrophobic interactions, and lipid and protein molecules are held by hydrophobic forces, plus possible charge attractions between lipid heads and side groups on the proteins. No covalent bonds are assumed to exist between molecules, since membranes can be taken apart gently by solvents and then reconstituted in an apparently intact form. The dimensions of the Davson–Danielli unit membrane correspond to those observed in electron micrographs.

The unit-membrane model still is accepted as a starting point, but now is considered oversimplified. Enough of the proteins must extend all the way through the lipid bilayer to hold the membranes together, since all of the lipids can be extracted from a membrane with ether and still leave the bilayer structure intact, as can be seen in electron micrographs. Conversely, the membrane surface cannot be covered entirely with proteins, since the membrane can be attacked by the enzyme phospholipase, which acts only on lipids. Other evidence suggests that biological membranes have pores, which allow the passage of small neutral molecules, and other molecular machinery, for moving ions and molecules from one side to the other. A better picture of a probable membrane structure than the simple protein-coated lipid bilayer is the "potato" model at the right. Still, the simple unit-membrane model is the best beginning approximation for thinking about actual membrane structures. The unit-membrane model is like a child's drawing of an automobile. It is not an accurate representation of all autos, or even of any one car, but is recognizably symbolic of the type. Perhaps as we grow up chemically, we shall do better with our picture of membranes, too.

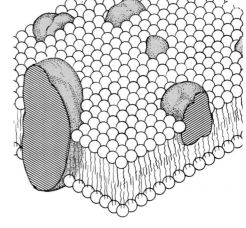

The fluid mosaic-membrane (or "potato") model proposed by Singer and Nicolson, showing a lipid bilayer as the membrane core, but with protein molecules embedded in the bilayer and free to diffuse to a certain extent from one region of the membrane to another. Some parts of the lipid surface are exposed, and some proteins extend all the way through the bilayer. From S. J. Singer and G. L. Nicolson, *Science* 175, 723 (1972).

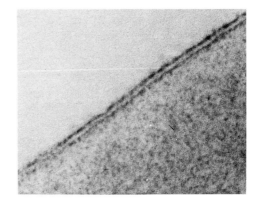

Electron micrograph showing a cross section through the membrane of a red blood cell. The double-layer structure of the membrane is apparent. Courtesy J. David Robertson.

OTHER LIPIDS

Waxes are esters of very long fatty acids (26 to 34 carbons) and mono-hydroxy alcohols. They serve as waterproof protective coatings on the outsides of leaves and fruit, and on skin, fur, and feathers of animals. They are classed as lipids because their long hydrocarbon tails make them insoluble in water, but soluble in organic solvents such as benzene.

Fatty acid derivatives are not the only kind of lipids. Terpenes are volatile oils in plants that can be thought of as being built from units of isoprene, C_5H_8 (below, left). Terpenes extracted from geranium, citronella, bay, lemon, mint, pine, and many other sources, are highly aromatic in the true meaning of the word, but are not necessarily "aromatic" in the special way that chemists have appropriated the term to indicate delocalized ring compounds. A few typical terpenes are shown below, with dashed lines to show how each molecule can be divided into isoprene-sized units. The β-carotene molecule, and the phytol tail on the chlorophyll molecule, are long-chain terpenes.

Vitamin A is a terpene and an alcohol, of which the corresponding aldehyde is *retinal*, the trigger for light reception in our eyes (bottom of next page). Before a photon of light strikes it, retinal, which has a cis conformation about the double bond at Position 11, is attached to the protein opsin to form a molecule of *rhodopsin*. When light hits the visual photoreceptors, the energy of the photon flips the cis double bond in retinal over to the trans form. This is the trigger which, in a way that is not entirely clear, initiates a nerve impulse from eye to brain. Rhodopsin with *trans*-retinal is unstable and falls apart into opsin and

Terpenes are organic molecules that can be considered as being built from units of isoprene, C_5H_8, which are separated below by dashed colored lines. These include the phytol tail of chlorophyll, several light-sensitive pigments, and natural oils and flavorings. The shorthand symbolism used for such organic molecules is shown beside isoprene.

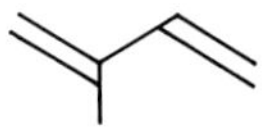

Isoprene, C_5H_8

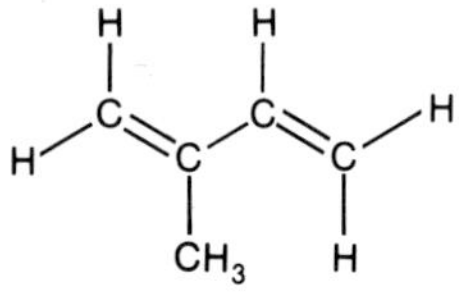

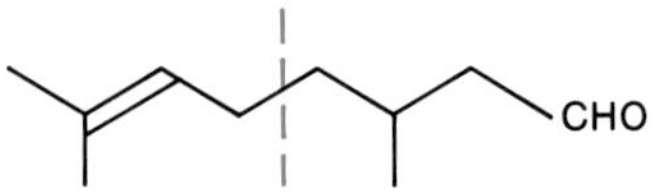

Citronella oil

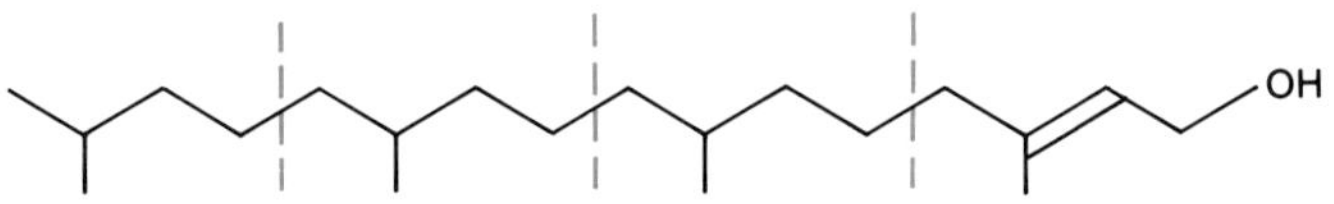

TERPENES

Phytol (tail on chlorophyll)

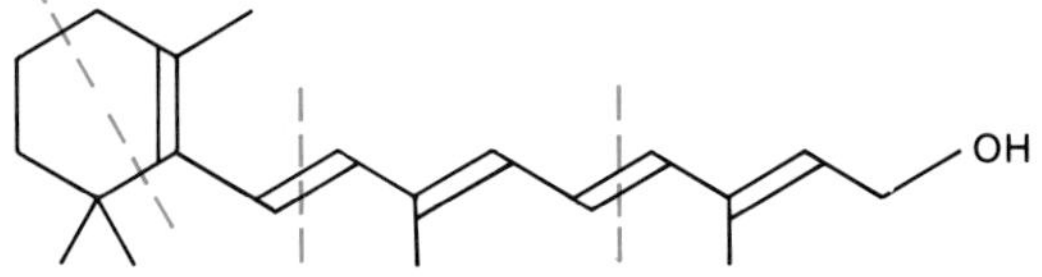

Vitamin A

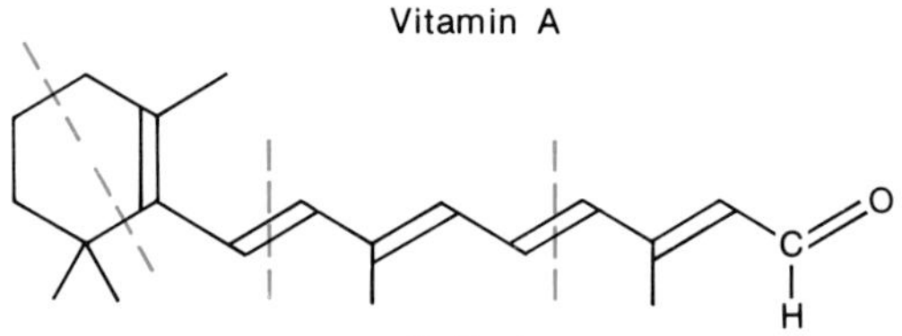

Retinal

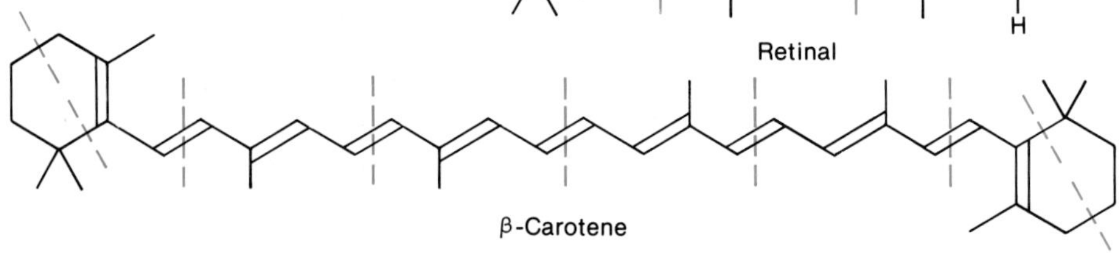

β-Carotene

retinal. *Trans*-retinal is reconverted biochemically to the cis isomer, reconnected to a molecule of opsin, and the trap is set for another photon of light.

Image-forming eyes with lenses and visual pigments have evolved independently three times in the history of life: in insects, in octopi and molluscs, and in vertebrates. Together these eyes provide a remarkable example of parallel evolution. Not only are the general optical principles of these eyes similar, they have identical chemical compounds—opsin and retinal—at their photoreceptors. It may be difficult to explain why the particular retinal molecule was adopted three different times as the trigger for light, but it is not hard to see why a visible-light receptor should involve cis–trans isomerization about a double bond: The energy required to carry out this isomerization falls squarely in the visible spectrum. In Chapter 12 we saw that the energy of a $C=C$ double bond is 147 kcal mole^{-1}, and that of a single bond is 83 kcal mole^{-1}. Twisting a cis double bond over into a trans configuration requires enough energy to go through a temporary single-bond state, or $147 - 83 = 64$ kcal mole^{-1}. This energy corresponds to a wavelength of light in the blue region of the spectrum. It would not take much strain in the *cis*-retinal molecule, as it was bound to the opsin protein, to reduce the isomerization energy to 40 kcal mole^{-1} and make the transformation possible with all visible wavelengths down to the edge of the infrared. Our eyes are designed to detect electromagnetic radiation with a little less than the energy needed to break covalent bonds, from 40 kcal mole^{-1} (dark red) to 70 kcal mole^{-1} (violet). A cis–trans isomerization is a safe means of detecting light because no bonds are permanently broken, only rearranged. In contrast, ultraviolet light is harmful because it breaks carbon–carbon single bonds, and infrared radiation goes undetected because it has too little energy to set off the retinal trigger.

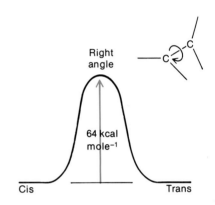

The energy barrier to cis–trans isomerization about a double bond (64 kcal mole^{-1}) corresponds to photons of visible light. Hence this isomerization around a double bond in *cis*-retinal (below) can be used as a light-sensing mechanism in the eye.

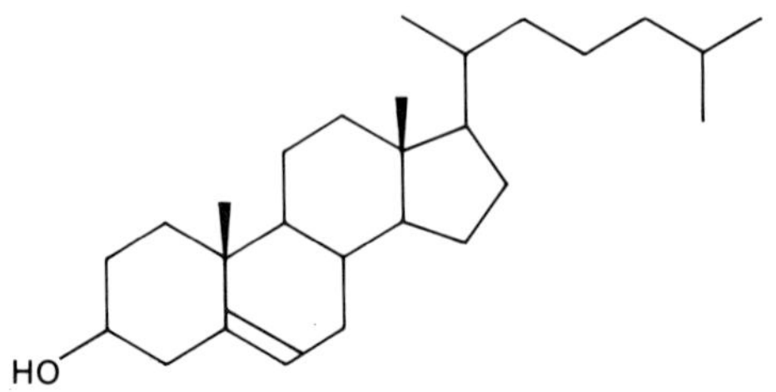

Cholesterol
(membrane lipid)

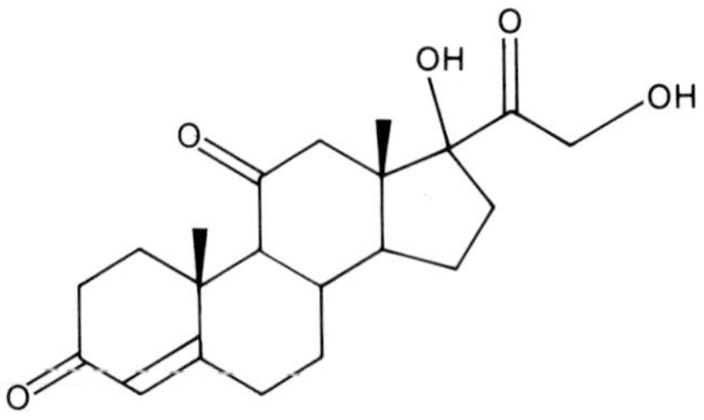

Cortisone
(adrenal hormone)

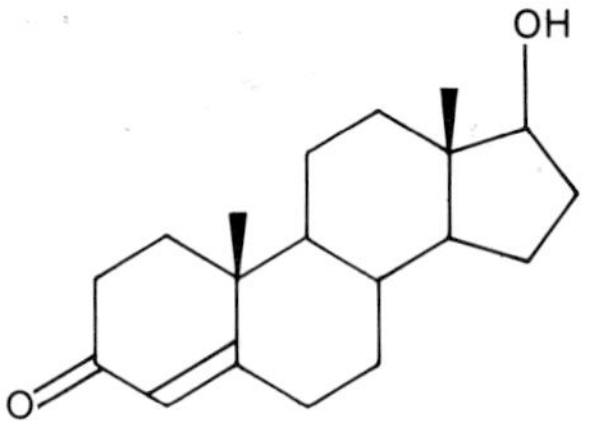

Testosterone
(male sex hormone)

Steroids are based on the fused-ring structure shown in the examples above. Cholesterol is a major lipid component in some membranes, and other steroids are chemical signals and messengers in the body.

A suitable terpene chain can be condensed into a four-ring framework that is typical of another class of lipids: *steroids*. Cholesterol (left) is a steroid molecule that is an important part of many membranes, but which can cause trouble when it occurs as a fatty deposit in blood vessels and chokes off blood flow. Cortisone, testosterone, and other steroids are hormones—chemical messengers that are released in minute amounts at one location in the body, and have profound regulatory effects at a number of other distant locations. Cortisone's main function is to adjust the level of glucose in the blood by conversion of liver glycogen (see Page 522) to glucose. Testosterone is a male sex hormone; and other steroid hormones control the levels of Na^+, Cl^-, and water in the body, influence sexual development, and control inflammation and allergic response. Steroid and polypeptide (protein) hormones seem to be the regulatory messengers in all plants and animals above the one-celled level, carrying information about the state of one group of cells to another group of cells that are capable of taking appropriate action.

CARBOHYDRATES

Carbohydrates are sugars and sugar derivatives. They have the overall formula $C_x(H_2O)_y$, in which x and y are integers. This composition led to the original erroneous impression that they in some sense were "hydrates of carbon," which gave them their name. Simple sugars, or monosaccharides, have the composition $(CH_2O)_n$, in which n can be three to six or more.

Ribose is a pentose, or a sugar with $n = 5$, and a derivative of ribose is an important part of the backbone of the DNA chain, which will be encountered in the next chapter. The ribose molecule is shown on the opposite page in both its open-chain and closed-ring forms. (Asymmetric carbon atoms are marked by asterisks.) These forms are in equilibrium in aqueous solution, with the closed-ring form predominating. The ring can close in one of two ways, leading to different positions of the —OH group on carbon atom one, to produce α-D-ribose or β-D-ribose, as shown. If one were to begin with a pure sample of either type, equilibrium in solution quickly would lead to a 50-50 mixture of the α and β isomers.

The most common sugar of all, glucose, is a hexose with $n = 6$, and with the molecular formula $C_6H_{12}O_6$. Glucose also equilibrates between a closed-ring form and an open chain in aqueous solution. The ring form is shown on the facing page. Glucose has the chair structure of the cyclohexane ring seen in Chapter 19, with all of its —OH groups extending out from the perimeter of the ring (the "equatorial" positions) where they are farthest from one another, and hence most stable. Each of two other common hexoses, mannose and galactose, has a single —OH group moved from the equatorial position to an axial position, extending up or down from the average plane of the puckered six-membered ring.

The same atoms that are present in these hexoses also can combine into a five-membered ring, still with the molecular formula $C_6H_{12}O_6$. This is fructose (fruit sugar), which has a ring structure similar to ribose (right) although it is a hexose and not a pentose.

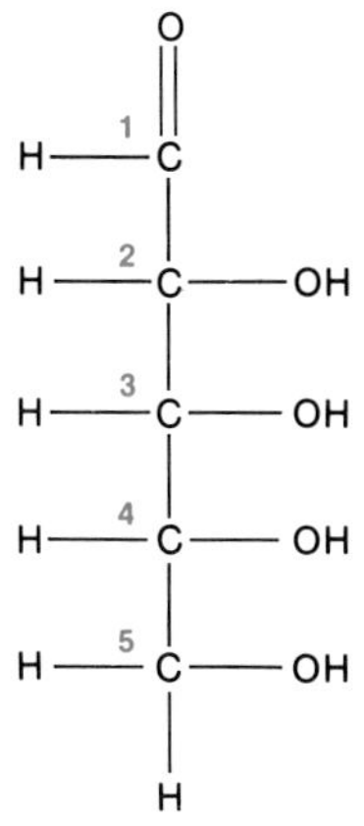

D-ribose
(open chain form)

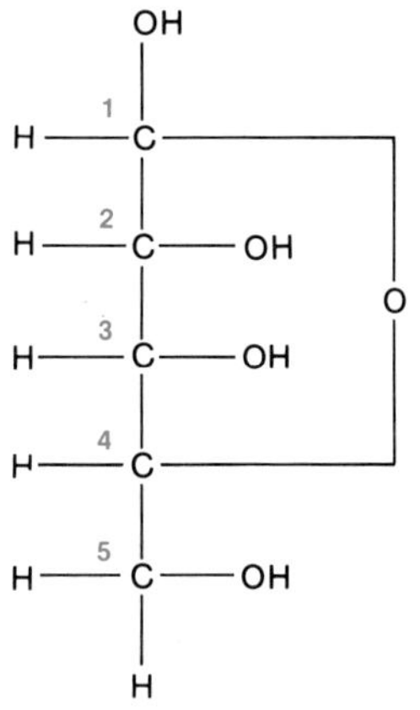

D-ribose
(cyclic form in aqueous solution)

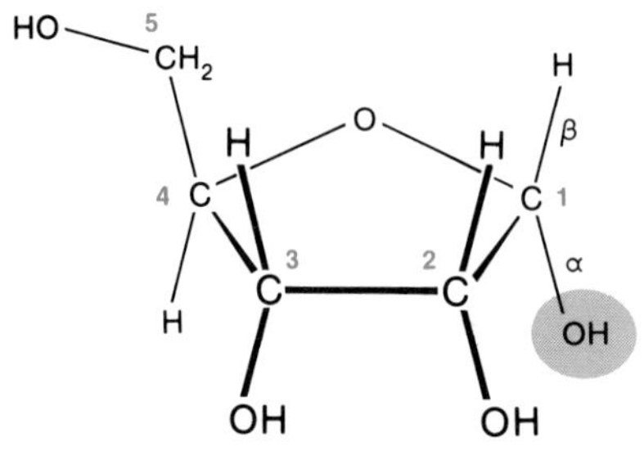

α-D-ribose

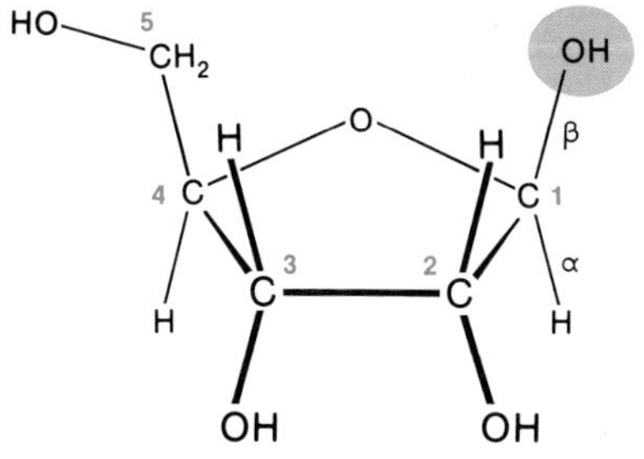

β-D-ribose

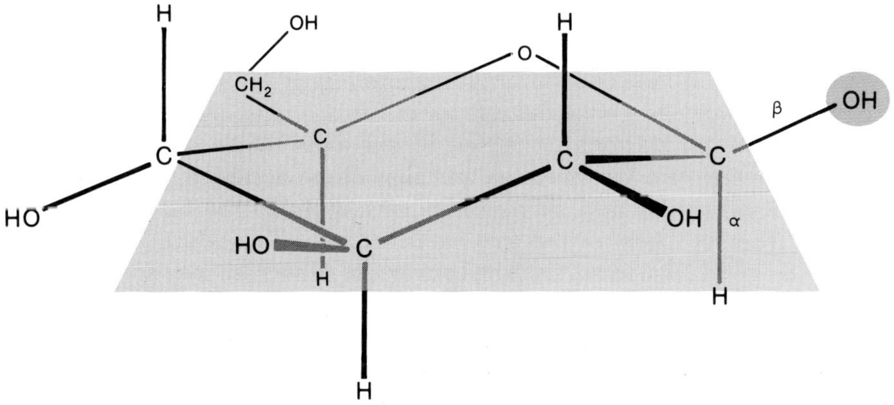

β-D-glucose (all —OH equatorial)

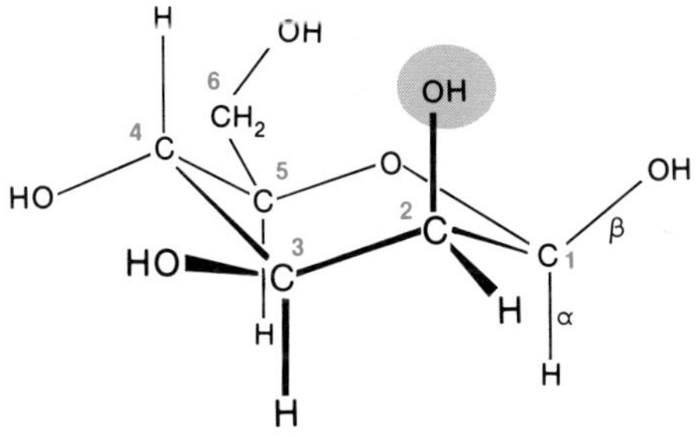

β-D-mannose (C$_2$ —OH axial)

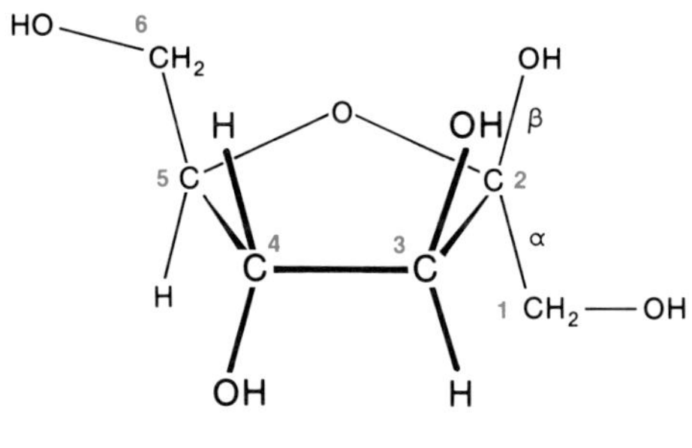

β-D-fructose

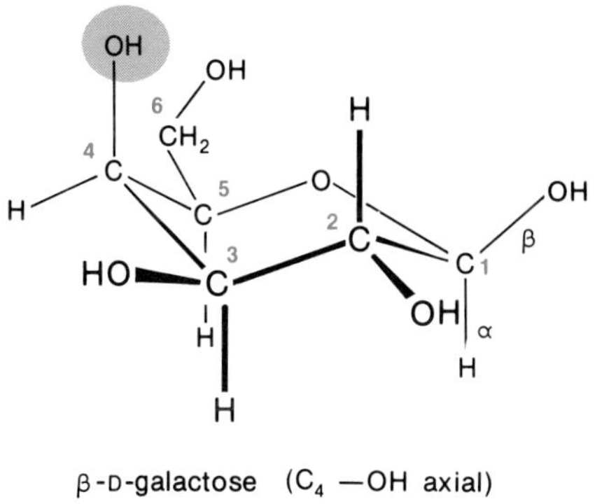

β-D-galactose (C$_4$ —OH axial)

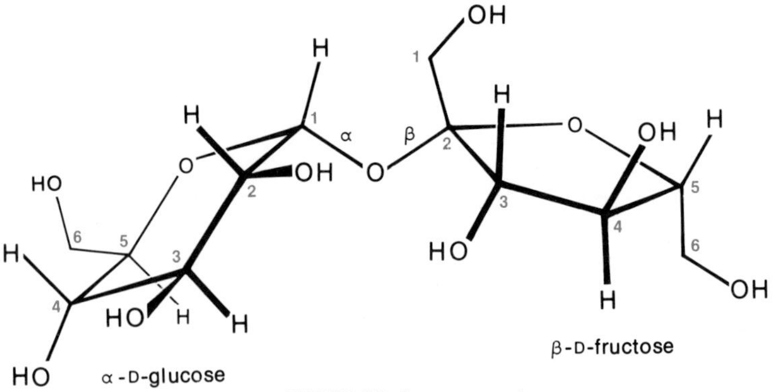

OH

H $\quad$ 1

H α β H

HO $\quad$ O $\quad$ 2 $\quad$ 2 $\quad$ O $\quad$ OH $\quad$ H

OH $\quad$ O $\quad$ 3 $\quad$ 5

H $\quad$ 6 $\quad$ 5 $\quad$ 3 $\quad$ HO $\quad$ 4 $\quad$ 6

4 $\quad$ H $\quad$ OH

HO $\quad$ H $\quad$ H $\quad$ H

HO $\quad$ α-D-glucose $\quad$ β-D-fructose

SUCROSE (cane sugar)

The four drawings on this double spread demonstrate the design similarities between sucrose, lactose, maltose, and cellobiose—all combinations of two sugar monomers. Sucrose is a dimer of glucose (with a six-membered ring) and fructose (with a five-membered ring). Lactose, or milk sugar (below), is a dimer of galactose and glucose, both with six-membered rings.

Because grapes are a rich source of glucose, they have given glucose the name "grape sugar." Honey contains a mixture of glucose and fructose, and was the standard sweetener for mankind for millennia before the advent of sugar cane. Sugar cane and sugar beets contain sucrose, a disaccharide made of glucose and fructose linked together as shown above. Sugar cane appeared in India from Southeast Asia some time around the fifth century B.C. According to the Greek geographer Strabo, one of Alexander the Great's admirals reported seeing Indian "reeds that produce honey, although there are no bees," but sugar did not spread into the Western world until the time of the Arab conquests in the seventh century A.D. At about the same time, the Chinese were importing "stone honey" from India as a luxury. Sucrose did not really replace honey as a cheap sweetener in Europe until the era of the great sugar cane plantations in the New World in the 1600's.

One reason why sucrose was slow to be accepted, aside from its scarcity, may be that sucrose is not as sweet to the taste as glucose and fructose. Acid or the enzyme invertase will catalyze the cleavage of the bond in sucrose, and the conversion of sucrose into an equimolar mixture of the two monomers. This becomes important in the confectionary industry, which has developed a special jargon of its own. Because the mixture of glucose and fructose in solution rotates polarized light in the opposite direction to sucrose, cleavage of sucrose is termed "inversion," the enzyme is named "invertase," and the mixture of

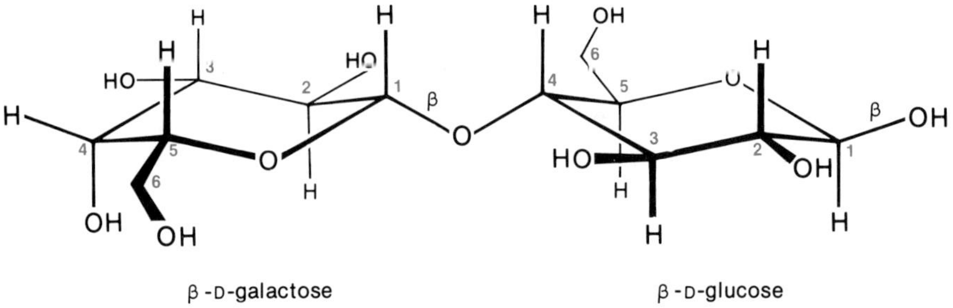

β-D-galactose $\quad$ β-D-glucose

LACTOSE (milk sugar)

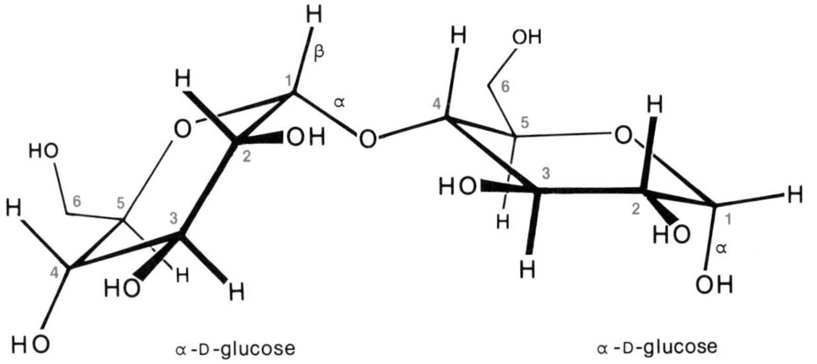

MALTOSE (α-1,4 linkage)

products is "invert sugar." Glucose and fructose are called "dextrose" and "levulose" in the sugar industry because of the way they individually rotate polarized light. What sugar chemists do with special effort, bees do naturally. Honey is already an "invert sugar" mixture of greater than average sweetness because the bees supply their own invertase enzyme along with the honey.

Among other common disaccharides, lactose from milk is a dimer of galactose and glucose (bottom far left). Maltose comes from partially digested starch (above), and cellobiose from partially degraded cellulose (below). These two disaccharides illustrate the key difference between starch and cellulose, which helps the plant to keep them separated. Both maltose and cellobiose are dimers of D-glucose, and both are formed by condensing the monomers at their C1 and C4 positions and removing H_2O. The difference is that maltose is connected through the α-position of the C1 carbon, and cellobiose through the β-position. Maltose therefore is an α-1,4 dimer, and cellobiose a β-1,4 dimer. This may seem like a small difference, but these glucose monomers are put together by enzymes tailored for a precise geometry. An enzyme designed to make or break an α-1,4 bond cannot affect a β-1,4 bond, and vice versa. They are like two locks, each with its own key. All of the 1,4 bonds in starch are α-, and all such bonds in cellulose are β-. To the metabolic machinery in plants keyed to starch and α-1,4 bonds, cellulose is just as alien and unusable a substance as polyethylene.

The dimers of glucose, maltose (above) and cellobiose (below), are the same molecules as those that are used in the chapter opening to illustrate the difference between starch and cellulose. Turn back to Page 508 and review the subtle geometry that makes these structures different. Maltose is a degradation product of starch with its characteristic α-1,4 linkage. Cellobiose, which is prepared by the degradation of cellulose, has the β-1,4 linkage typical of that compound. Notice that cellobiose has been flipped over relative to the chapter-opening drawing.

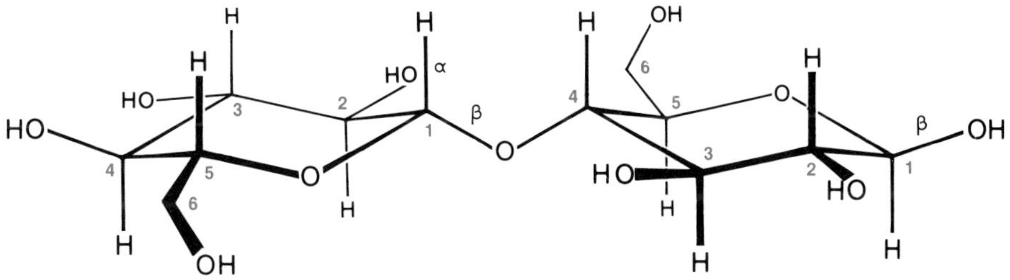

CELLOBIOSE (β-1,4 linkage)

Cellulose   Starch

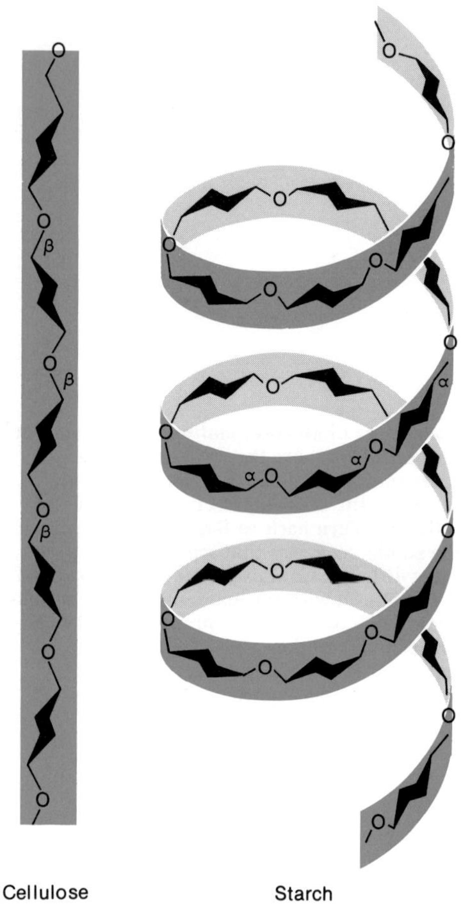

Cellulose has straight chains with β-1,4 linkages. The α-1,4 linkages in starch force the chains into a curved configuration. In the unbranched form of starch, amylose, the curved chain is twisted into a helical coil.

POLYSACCHARIDES: CELLULOSE AND STARCH

Cellulose is the most plentiful organic compound on our planet. The purest natural form of cellulose is cotton, which is 90% cellulose. The woody parts of trees are cellulose, as are the supporting materials in plant stalks and leaves. All algae, except blue-green algae, have cell walls of cellulose. (The name cellulose means "cell sugar.") Although bacteria and animals generally do not depend on cellulose for structural support, two kinds of bacteria and a few marine invertebrates have a celluloselike polymer as an outer protection.

Cellulose is a simple, straight-chain, β-1,4 polymer of glucose, with 300 to 3000 glucose units per molecule, and a molecular weight of 50,000 to 500,000. The structure of one strand of cellulose is shown at the left. These strands then are bundled into fibrils and cross-linked by hydrogen bonds for strength. The fibrils are twisted into bundles, and the bundles into strong fibers that can be used for support. As ropemakers realize, fragile threads can gain great strength if they are twisted into strands, the strands are twisted separately into ropes, ropes into cables, and cables into hawsers. Nature anticipated the human ropemaker by several hundred million years.

If we could digest the β-1,4 glucose bond of cellulose, then almost limitless new food supplies would become available to us. (The dark side of this new food supply is that we probably would permit the population of Earth to grow unchecked until we had stripped the planet bare like locusts. *H. sapiens* has not yet been known for his self-control.) However, our digestive enzymes cannot break the cellulose bond. Aside from some bacteria and protozoa, the only organisms that can digest cellulose are termites, a few species of cockroaches, and ruminant mammals such as cows, sheep, goats, and camels. These cellulose-eating insects and mammals can function only because they have populations of bacteria and protozoa in their digestive tracts that chew up the β-1,4 bonds with the enzyme cellulase, thereby providing their hosts with digestible materials. In cattle the microorganisms are housed in the rumen, the first of four stomachs. Here bacteria convert plant fibers into acetic, propionic, and butyric acids. These acids are absorbed by the cow as nutrients through the walls of the rumen, and generate 60 to 80 liters of CO_2 and methane gas per day, which must be eliminated by continual belching. Bacteria and protozoa thrive in the warm culture vat of the rumen, and the excess population spills over into the lower stomachs of the cow, where they are digested as another rich food source. A cow is an admirably efficient chemical factory. We can duplicate the digestive talents of a cow in the laboratory with acid or cellulase, but the method so far is not a practical proposition. The results cannot yet stand up in either economic or aesthetic competition with prime rib or sirloin. Cows are still cheaper than chemists.

For all except a few bacteria and protozoa and their hosts, starch is the normal source of glucose. Amylose, the simplest form of starch, is an unbranched α-1,4 polymer of 250–300 glucose units per molecule (left). The more common amylopectin has around 1000 such units in a branched chain, as shown on the opposite page. Branching occurs by connecting the α-position of a C1 carbon with the C6 —OH of another

520

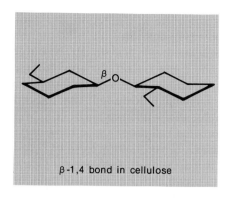

β-1,4 bond in cellulose

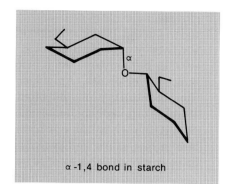

α-1,4 bond in starch

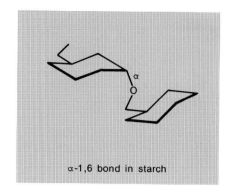

α-1,6 bond in starch

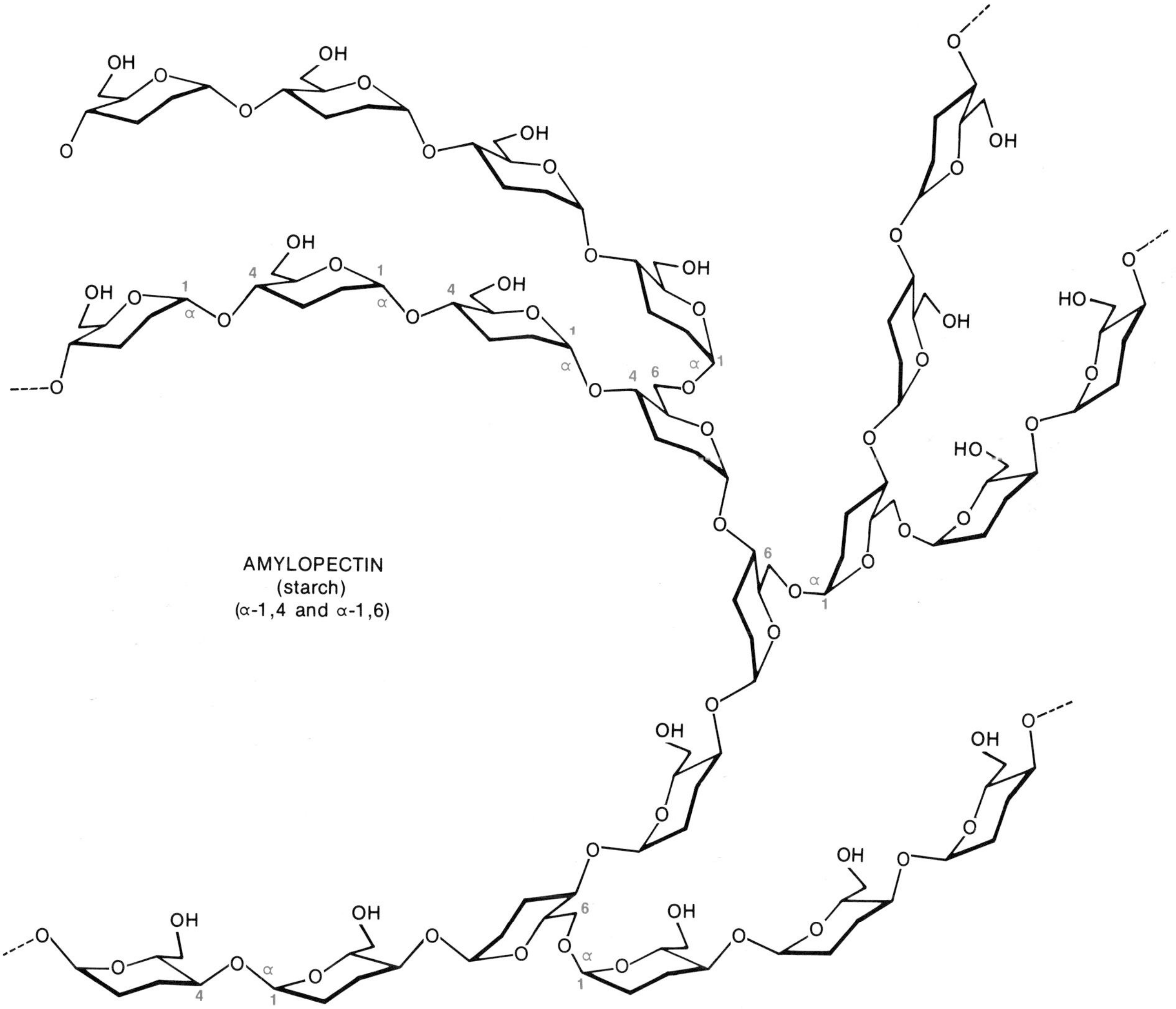

AMYLOPECTIN
(starch)
(α-1,4 and α-1,6)

521

glucose molecule in an α-1,6 bond. This is a one-way junction that leads to the curved, branched trees shown. Amylopectin has one α-1,6 branch per twenty or so glucose units. The smaller amylose is somewhat water soluble, but amylopectin is insoluble and hence is a safer energy-storage molecule for plants. Amylopectin as we obtain it from plant sources in the laboratory probably already is somewhat degraded; the natural starches originally had molecular weights in the millions.

Although we do not have the enzyme cellulase, we do have amylase in our saliva and pancreatic juices. If you hold a piece of bread in your mouth for a minute or two, it will begin to taste sweet. Amylase breaks down the starch from the bread into a mixture of maltose and glucose, which can be sensed by the taste buds on your tongue. The job of cleavage is finished by hydrochloric acid in the stomach, and glucose is absorbed into the bloodstream to be carried off for eventual oxidation.

The attractive feature of starch as an energy storehouse is the utter simplicity of the input and output mechanisms. Only one chemical step is required to combine glucose molecules together to make starch, and with the breaking of only one kind of bond, starch is reconverted to glucose for instant use. In contrast, the synthesis of fats requires half a dozen metabolic steps, and the breakdown of fats into usable small molecules again is equally complicated. The great disadvantage of carbohydrates (starch) as energy-storage molecules is their low energy-to-weight ratio. The table at the left is a summary of an earlier table from Chapter 11, giving the heat per gram for burning several fuels. Hydrogen gas is the best fuel of all, but the hydrocarbons are second-best. Stearic acid is nearly as efficient, and this combustion value can be taken as representative of fats generally. Alanine, which represents protein fuels, is less than half as good, and glucose and its polymers are worse yet.

Animals, which must carry their energy reserves with them, universally have developed the involved chemistry of fats and fatty acids, for the sake of the weight reduction, in using a nearly gasolinelike fuel. Stationary plants, for which portability and a high energy-to-mass ratio are of no advantage, have opted instead for the simplicity of carbohydrate chemistry. However, animals do make one use of carbohydrates as an energy reservoir. They synthesize glycogen (animal starch), which is a more highly branched version of amylopectin, with branching every 8–10 glucose units. Glycogen in the liver and muscle tissues serves as a special rapid-access energy store—a buffer between the immediate needs of the animal and the long-term energy supply in fats.

Thus animals have the best of both worlds, and a good analogy exists between this energy-storage strategy and currency. Paper money in Europe was developed in the 1600's to combat the danger and inconvenience of carrying large amounts of gold and silver coin from place to place. The Italians developed the Girobanks ("circulation banks") to assist the transfer of credit from one city to another, and these Girobank notes gradually became accepted as substitutes for the money they represented. Paper currency was easier to carry than metal, but sometimes was difficult to use. Persuasion and discounts would be needed to get currency accepted as payment in out-of-the-way places. A sedentary businessman could keep all of his wealth in gold and silver. The traveler would transfer his bulk accounts in bank notes (starch)

Heat per gram for combustion of various potential fuels (summary of table from Chapter 11)

Fuel	Heat of combustion (kcal gram^{-1})
Hydrogen, $H_2(g)$	34.0
Methane, $CH_4(g)$	13.3
Octane (gasoline), $C_8H_{18}(l)$	11.5
Stearic acid, $C_{17}H_{35}COOH(s)$	9.5
Alanine, H_2N—$CH(CH_3)$—$COOH(s)$	4.4
Glucose, $C_6H_{12}O_6(s)$	3.7

for the sake of efficiency, but would be careful to keep small amounts in coin for immediate use. Glycogen is the metal coinage of animal energy needs.

STRUCTURE, ENERGY, AND INFORMATION

The two classes of organic compounds that we have been examining in this chapter—lipids and carbohydrates—play similar roles in living organisms. Both classes have some members that serve as important components of structure: cellulose in plants, and membrane lipids in both plants and animals. Both classes also are used in energy storage: starch and glycogen in plants and animals, and fats in animals. The high energy-to-weight ratio in fats is offset by the involved procedures required to get the energy in and out of storage. Fats are insoluble in water, so prior to digestion they must be brought into suspension with bile detergents such as cholic acid. They then are cleaved to glycerol and fatty acids with the enzyme lipase, and finally are broken down into two-carbon acetate units, which can be fed into the energy-extracting machinery. In contrast, digestion of starch is a simple process requiring only one enzyme and acid. This is why glycogen is used for quick-access energy storage in animals even though fats are the primary energy reservoir.

So far we have been talking about molecules that are a part of living organisms, yet are not "vital" in the way that we sense enzymes and nucleic acids to be. For all their useful properties, carbohydrates and lipids still are conventional organic molecules, and seem to belong to the test tube as much as to the cell. They do not have that aura of specialness that envelops DNA. No one has ever suggested seriously that sugars and fats are "alive," but this property has been claimed (naively) at times for both proteins and nucleic acids.

The difference that we instinctively recognize between carbohydrates, lipids, and other organic molecules on the one hand, and proteins and nucleic acids on the other, is that the latter carry *information* in their structure, in a sense that is not true for any other molecules. This concept of information creates a qualitative difference between proteins and nucleic acids, and all other molecules, and makes them suitable as the basis for a chemistry of life. What this information is and how it is stored and used is the subject of the next chapters.

QUESTIONS

1. What properties of molecules cause them to be classed as lipids?
2. What biologically important class of lipids was encountered in Chapter 20?
3. How does the molecular structure of vegetable fats cause them to have lower melting points than animal fats of similar molecular weights? How can such vegetable fats be "hardened"?
4. How are phospholipids related to fats? How are they different? In what way do phospholipids resemble simple fatty acids?

5. Why is ethanolamine better suited for construction of membranes than is phosphatidic acid? Why is phosphatidyl choline even better? Draw their structures to show the differences.

6. Why are the hydrophobic tails of molecules in a lecithin bilayer turned to the inside of the bilayer, whereas in a soap-film bilayer the hydrophobic tails are on the outside? What does this tell you about the importance of the environment in determining biological structure?

7. What is the unit-membrane model of a membrane? In this model, where are the lipids and where are the proteins?

8. How is the fluid-mosaic membrane model of a membrane different from the unit-membrane model? What is different about the arrangement of protein molecules?

9. What evidence is there that some protein molecules penetrate all the way through the membrane, and what evidence suggests that the lipid is exposed on part of the membrane surface?

10. Draw a diagram of the citronella oil molecule, and show how it can be constructed from two molecules of isoprene.

11. How many isoprene molecules would be needed to build a molecule of vitamin A? With a molecular diagram show how the isoprene units are bent and connected to make vitamin A.

12. The retinal light-sensing mechanism of the eye acts by using light photons to break a double bond (converting it briefly to a single bond). We could see in the ultraviolet if the photon receptors used somewhat more energetic photons to break single bonds with 80–100 kcal mole^{-1} of energy. Why would this be a dangerous and impractical kind of photoreceptor? Why is it unlikely that living organisms would evolve ultraviolet-seeing eyes?

13. How are steroids related to terpenes? What are steroids used for in living organisms?

14. Glucose is a hexose (six-carbon sugar) with a six-membered ring. How can fructose be a hexose if it has a five-membered ring like ribose (a pentose)?

15. What is the difference between equatorial and axial positions for groups attached to carbon atoms in glucose? In which positions are the —OH groups in glucose? Does this make the glucose molecule more, or less, stable?

16. Mannose and galactose both have one —OH group in an atypical position relative to glucose. Which glucose —OH group is changed to make each of the other hexoses? Notice that in both mannose and galactose the changed —OH group extends out on the same side of the molecule. Allose, the hexose with a single axial —OH group extending out the other side of the molecule (from C3), is not found in nature, but has been synthesized. Can you think of any reason why mannose and galactose might be found naturally, but not allose? (Think about enzymes and how they operate.)

17. What is the difference in geometry between α-D-ribose and β-D-ribose? Between α-D-glucose and β-D-glucose?

18. What is invert sugar? What are the more common scientific names for dextrose and levulose? Why were dextrose and levulose so named?

19. Why is honey sweeter than sugar?

20. What is the difference between the glucose monomer connections in starch and in cellulose? Why can we digest one but not the other?

21. Why is the starch chain naturally kinked rather than straight like cellulose? How are chain branches formed in starch? What kind of connection is used in branching?

22. What enzyme do we use to break down starch? What organisms have an enzyme for digesting cellulose? How do cows and other ruminants digest cellulose?

23. What advantages does starch have as an energy-storage molecule? What disadvantages does it have in comparison with fats?

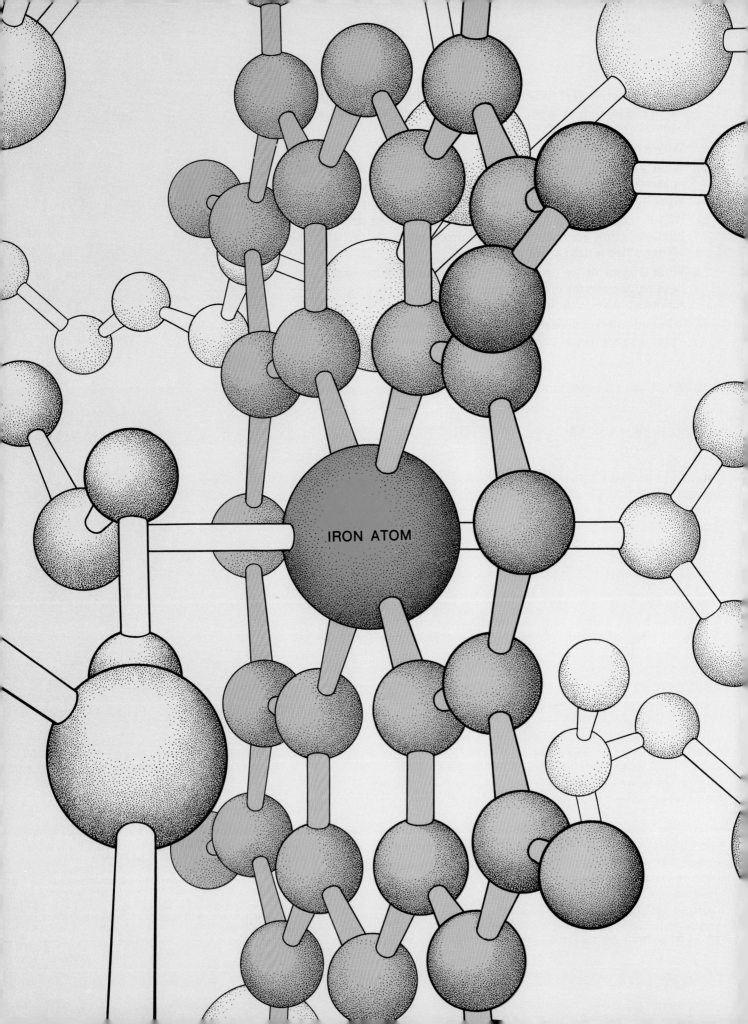

CHAPTER 22

Proteins and Nucleic Acids: Information Carriers

One of the perennial stories that keeps appearing in "Believe-it-or-Not" columns and newspaper fillers is that all of the elements in the human body are worth only $1.25, $1.98, or $3.50, depending on the current state of the chemical market. This is an old cliché, which misses the essential point that makes diamonds more valuable than charcoal. In any collection of atoms, it is the *arrangement* of atoms that is as important, or more important, than the atoms themselves. The arrangement of iron and carbon atoms in the heme group in a protein, shown on the opposite page, bears little resemblance to iron carbide, an inorganic compound that contains the same elements.

Another frequently heard generalization is that a mammal is 65% water, and that this water is a dilute salt solution resembling sea water. In this view, a mammal is a walking bit of oceanic environment. This attitude is less of a cliché because it has a grain of truth in it. As we shall see in Chapter 26, the truth in this theory comes from the way in which life originally evolved in the oceans. Again, however, to say that a living creature is "only enclosed sea water" is to overlook the crucial importance of the nature of the enclosure.

In these final five chapters we shall turn to the most complex and most intricately interwoven collection of chemical reactions to be found on our planet: a living organism. We can talk of "a living organism" as representing all forms of life because, to a remarkable extent, every living thing on this planet is composed of the same set of chemical substances and stays alive by carrying out the same kinds of chemical reactions. We differ in details, but we all are fundamentally alike. This similarity may have arisen partly because only certain substances and reactions are suitable as the basis for life, but another factor is the great probability that all forms of life on this planet evolved from one or a small number of primitive ancestors that carried out these particularly suitable reactions. In this chapter we will be concerned with two of the most fundamental chemical substances of all forms of life: proteins and nucleic acids.

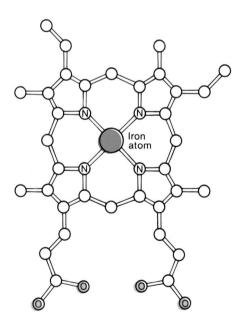

Front view of the heme group, shown in side view on the opposite page. A similar heme group is found in the oxygen-carrying protein hemoglobin. Copyright © 1969 Dickerson and Geis; from R. E. Dickerson and I. Geis, *The Structure and Action of Proteins*, W. A. Benjamin, Inc.

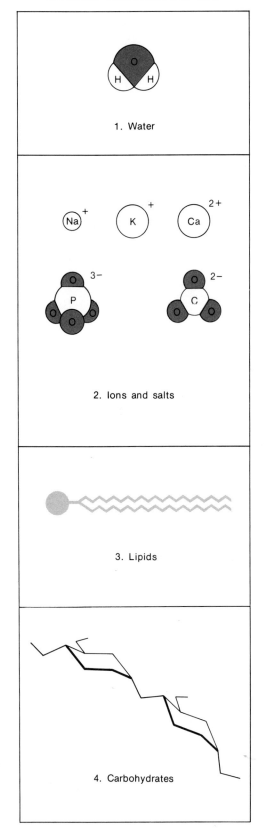

1. Water

2. Ions and salts

3. Lipids

4. Carbohydrates

THE CHEMISTRY OF LIVING ORGANISMS

The primary chemical building blocks of living creatures, wherever they are found on this planet, are

1. water
2. calcium phosphates and carbonates, and other dissolved salts
3. lipids: esters of glycerol with organic and inorganic acids, and terpenes and steroids
4. carbohydrates: polymers of simple sugars such as glucose
5. proteins: polymers of amino acids
6. nucleic acids: alternating sugar–phosphate polymers with side chains composed of organic nitrogen bases.

To this list should be added several small organic molecules, needed in minute amounts and often obtained from outside the organism in the form of vitamins.

Each of these major components has one or more well-defined roles. Water is the solvent medium for all chemical reactions. Calcium sulfates and phosphates are the rigid framework materials of bone, teeth, and shells. Proteins and lipids provide the more dynamic framework materials for membranes, connecting fibers, tendons, and muscle. Fats contribute mechanical protection and thermal insulation. Proteins and fats each have a second role: Fats are the main energy reservoirs in animals, and globular proteins serve as enzymes (catalysts), regulators, carriers, and recognition and protective molecules. Carbohydrates are the structural materials in plants; they also are the rapid-access energy-storage molecules in animals, and the only energy reservoirs in plants. Nucleic acids have a very special role: the storage and transmission of genetic information. Deoxyribonucleic acids (DNA) are the permanent repository of information in the nucleus of a cell, and ribonucleic acids (RNA) are involved in the transcription and translation machinery that interprets that information and uses it to synthesize proteins. A small cousin of nucleic acids, ATP, is the central short-term energy-storage molecule for all life processes.

The small organic molecules act mainly as carriers of energy (ATP), electrons or reducing power (NADH), chemical groups (other ATP-like molecules), or information (hormones). Most vitamins, such as vitamin A, the precursor of retinal and β-carotene, are essentially synthetic precursors of these molecules that we no longer can make metabolically for ourselves. Of the many inorganic ions and metals in living organisms, K^+ is the principal cation within a cell and Na^+ in the extracellular fluids. Calcium has been mentioned for its role in bones, teeth, and shells. Other metal atoms, such as Mg, Mn, Fe, Co, Cu, Zn, and Mo, are essential for the functioning of enzymes, with which they act in electron rearrangement during catalysis, electron transfer, and the binding of O_2 and other small molecules.

All of these chemical components are only the trees, when what we really want to see is the forest. If we say that a mammal is nothing but water, salts, proteins, lipids, carbohydrates, nucleic acids, and small organic molecules, we are only perpetuating a more involved version of the cliché that a man is made of nothing but $1.98 worth of chemical elements. What must be added to these chemical components, or how must they be arranged, to produce a living organism? This is what the last five chapters of this book are really about.

WHAT ARE THE CRITERIA FOR LIFE?

The fundamental viewpoint of the next five chapters can be stated simply: *Life is a behavior pattern that chemical systems exhibit when they reach a certain kind and level of complexity.*

What is this behavior pattern, and what is its chemical basis? This is a difficult question, and is less of an outline for five chapters on biochemistry than a blueprint for the future of chemistry. We cannot yet provide the answers, but we can outline the areas in which these answers some day will be found. This viewpoint is helpful in seeing what, in the broad field of life, is relevant to the chemist and is susceptible to explanation by chemical methods.

Although we have little trouble distinguishing between the living and the nonliving, it is difficult to set down a hard and fast list of criteria for life. Most living things move, react to stimuli, breathe, eat and excrete, grow, propagate, and eventually die. Unfortunately, we can find apparent exceptions to all of these criteria. Most plants do not move, except between generations in the form of seed dispersal. Some lower plants do not react overtly to common stimuli, although most plants exhibit phototropism and geotropism—growth responses to light and gravity. Gangrene bacteria and many other anaerobic microorganisms not only do not breathe, they are killed by the mere presence of oxygen. Viruses neither breathe, nor eat, nor excrete, nor grow. They do little else except blunder into host cells and induce them to make more viruses. Amoebae and other budding or fissioning organisms do not die of old age in the true sense of the word. However, one feature is universal: All living systems propagate.

To add to the confusion, some of the properties on our list also are shared by nonliving things. Sand dunes, supersaturated clay soils, and undermined seashore palisades react to mechanical stimuli and move, often abruptly. A crystal in solution grows by taking up molecules or ions from its surroundings. If chipped at a corner, it will add more molecules selectively to that corner and "heal" itself. Stars are born out of matter from older stars; they grow and develop through predictable stages, and finally die. In spite of these phenomena, no one would claim that sand dunes, crystals, and stars are alive. We must be more critical in our definition of life.

One tentative definition of life is the following: *Living organisms are complex, organized chemical systems that propagate, grow, metabolize, use their environment and protect themselves from it, and evolve and change in response to long-term changes in the environment.* Each of these properties is worth examination to see how our definition of life stands up.

Propagation

This is the universal and essential thing that a living creature does, because it is the means by which life continues. Higher organisms undergo a cycle of birth, sexual reproduction, and death. Many lower

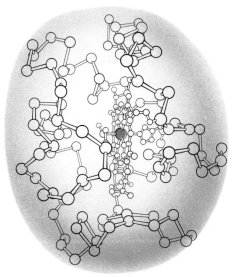

5. Proteins

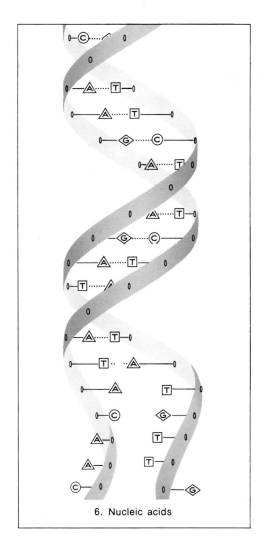

6. Nucleic acids

The peppered moth is a case study in evolution. The moth exists in light and dark forms. Each form has stored within its DNA the instructions for the kind and distribution of wing pigmentation. On a lichen-covered tree the light form is nearly invisible. In the absence of pollution, this form has a better chance for survival. Courtesy Dr. H. B. D. Kettlewell.

organisms propagate by fissioning, budding, or subdividing in some way, and experience individual death only by accident. Viruses reproduce, but only with the aid of other kinds of organisms. All living things propagate in some way, and life goes on.

This continuation of life in the family of organisms or in the individual is different from a static enduring. Rocks and minerals endure, and the material within them remains unchanged. A living creature, in contrast, maintains the same form amid a continuous exchange of molecules with its surroundings. Its individual molecules come and go, but its structure and organization persist. It maintains its identity in the midst of a constant flow-through of matter.

Growth

Living creatures generally increase in size and complexity with the passage of time. They go through a controlled, predictable life cycle or pattern. This pattern of development is not a product only of simple physical forces (as is the "healing" of a broken crystal), but of programmed, prestored information contained in DNA molecules. The proper analogy is not with a bubbling pot or a growing crystal, but with a programmed digital computer, although the computer analogy is grossly insulting to even the simplest bacterium.

Metabolism

Living organisms take chemical substances and free energy from their environment and modify both for their own particular needs. These processes involve chemical transformations: both spontaneous breakdowns that release free energy, and nonspontaneous syntheses that must be driven by some other free-energy source. For the analogy between cell growth and crystal growth to be valid, one would have to propose that a crystal of calcium carbonate (limestone), if dropped into a calcium chloride solution, could grow by ignoring the chloride ions around it and taking CO_2 from the atmosphere to make carbonate ions.

Use of the Environment and Protection From It

Every organism plays an offensive and a defensive role: It tries to get what it needs, and at the same time to protect itself against dangers, often generated by its neighbors trying to get what *they* need. A continual competition exists between buildup and breakdown, or anabolism and catabolism. An unprotected life form would be destroyed quickly and its materials absorbed into its neighbors. The most elementary protective measure is a barrier membrane, and there is no life form above the level of viruses that does not have one. The membrane demarcates the boundary between organism and surroundings, and regulates the flow of materials in and out. Other static safeguards have been invented by living organisms, among them cell walls, bacterial slime capsules, exoskeletons, shells, spines, barbed-wire fences, and concrete blockhouses. Simple fecundity, or production of vast numbers of offspring, is another type of static safeguard. It does not matter if stickleback are a relatively defenseless fish when young, as long as so many are produced at one time that some are sure to survive.

There are more active forms of protection from the environment: avoidance and flight, and active defense. These measures require the ability to detect danger (sensory mechanisms), and to take appropriate action (motor mechanisms). It takes a little reflection to see that growing a shell, overbreeding, running away, and fighting all are comparable responses to the same challenge: defense against a hostile environment and maintenance of the species, if not the individual.

These same sensory and motor mechanisms, once developed, are useful in seeking needed chemicals or environments. Plants grow toward the light, and extend roots toward moisture and food. Animals detect food supplies and move to collect them. All of these sensory and motor systems are *chemical*. They can be simple: the detection of chemical gradients by bacteria, and movement in response to the gradient. They also can be quite elaborate, as in the rhodopsin trigger for light detection and the subsequent nerve impulse to an information processor such as the brain. Whether active or passive, all life forms use their surroundings, and all life forms by one means or another try to make sure that their surroundings do not use them.

Evolution and Change

This is probably the most subtle life process of all, and the most powerful in ensuring the continuance of life in one form or another. Adaptation to rapid changes in the environment, which are short in comparison with the lifetime of any one individual, falls under the heading of stimulus and response, just discussed. But there is another way of adapting to more extensive changes, which take place over long time periods compared with the lifetime of an individual: *evolution*. Without this mechanism, the planet still would be populated only by small localized bits of ordered chemical reactions, and higher life (a self-congratulatory terminology) would not exist. Propagation takes place by copying, and growth by using, the information stored in DNA molecules. This copying of information from one generation to the next is not quite perfect, and a few mistakes, or *mutations*, occur. These mistakes are the raw materials of evolution.

Populations evolve, not individuals. Within a population of individual organisms at any given time, the majority usually are well adapted to existing conditions. A certain minority will vary genetically, and will be somewhat maladapted in one or more tolerable ways. If conditions change, this variability is sufficient to allow some minor and previously maladapted fraction of the original population to become better adapted than the majority. Over several generations the population will change, and the favored few will become the new majority. A small amount of maladaptation and variability is the insurance premium that is paid by the population against the threat of altered conditions. If the entire population were identical, and all were equally well adapted to the original conditions, then they all would be equally badly adapted to any new environmental changes, a possible lethal uniformity.

The soot-blackened bark of trees of the industrial midlands of England give the dark form of the peppered moth a better chance of survival. Even in prepollution populations of the peppered moth there were some of the dark variety, because the copying of DNA from one generation to another is imperfect, and variations creep in. The dark variety came into its own when man changed the moth's natural environment. This slightly imperfect reproduction, followed by selection, is an important characteristic of living organisms. Courtesy Dr. H. B. D. Kettlewell.

The key to maintaining this necessary degree of flexibility is *slightly imperfect* reproduction, followed by testing against the environment. Variability plus natural selection generates the process of evolution. This topic has been developed at length here because it represents probably the most important single criterion of life. No nonliving chemical system, no matter what its complexity, has this ability to respond to long-term challenge and to evolve. The development of an *imperfect* hereditary machinery probably was the most important single step in the evolution of life.

In summary, we can find five hallmarks of living systems that set them apart from all other chemical systems. One need invoke no special properties other than an unusually high level of chemical and spatial organization. *There are no vital principles, only chemical principles.* A living creature is an elaborate chemical system, which has special properties that arise from its complexity. In this chapter and those that follow we shall be concerned with the most challenging question in chemistry today: What are the chemical bases for these essential activities of living systems? Or in brief: What is the molecular basis of life?

INFORMATION-CARRYING MOLECULES

A protein is a folded polymer of amino acids in specific sequence, sometimes accompanied by metal atoms and small organic molecules. The opening illustration in this chapter showed the association of an iron atom and an organic ring in the heme group of cytochrome *c*, a small electron-carrying protein. Every protein, in every species of living creatures, has its own unique amino acid sequence, originally coded in a sequence of organic bases in DNA, as a part of the genetic "library" of the organism. In principle, given the amino acid sequence of a protein, one not only can identify the protein, but can determine from what species it came. It is in this sense that we describe proteins and nucleic acids as "information carriers."

Nucleic acids are the information carriers *par excellence*. From one generation to the next, DNA is the source of the information on how to synthesize proteins, and hence on how to build a living creature. Lipids, carbohydrates, and all the other molecules that we previously have examined are not information carriers in this sense. Some cases are known in which one kind of molecule is used in vertebrates for a given purpose, and a different molecule in invertebrates; or one molecule may be peculiar to a given class of plants. But this is a far cry from being able to say from inspection of the molecule: This protein came from the digestive machinery of a dog, this one from the respiratory system of a horse, and that one from the same respiratory system in bread mold.

The "central dogma" of molecular biochemistry, so labeled tongue-in-cheek by the men who proposed it, is "DNA makes RNA makes protein." This is a concise way of saying that the information contained in a protein molecule came from messenger RNA, and that the ultimate source of the information in RNA was analogous sequences of bases in DNA. Information flows from left to right in the illustration on the opposite page. Some exceptions are known to this simple one-way

DNA MAKES .... RNA MAKES .... PROTEIN

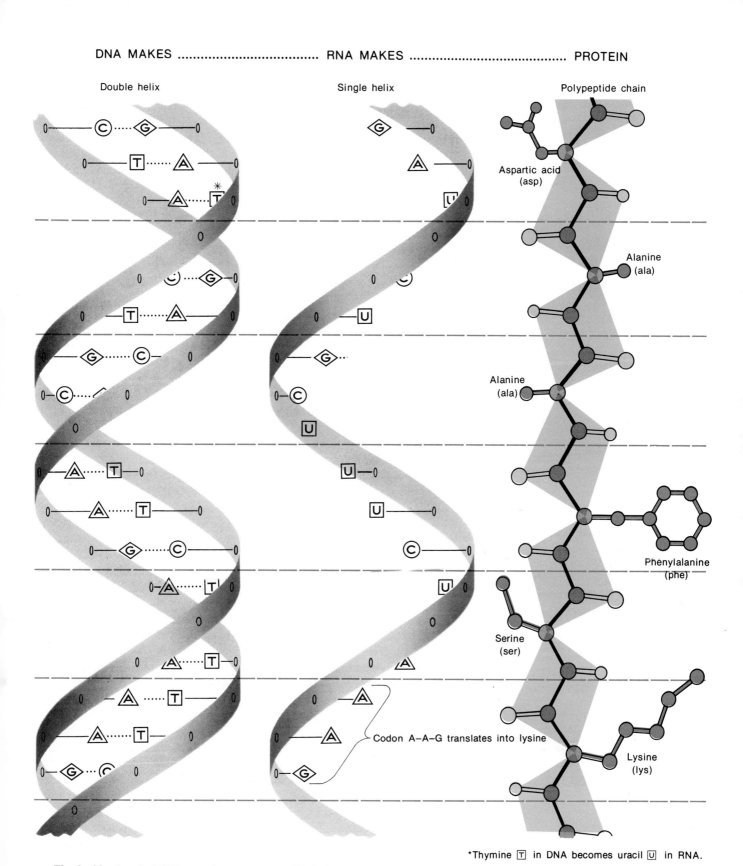

Double helix

Single helix

Polypeptide chain

Aspartic acid (asp)

Alanine (ala)

Alanine (ala)

Phenylalanine (phe)

Serine (ser)

Codon A–A–G translates into lysine

Lysine (lys)

*Thymine Ⓣ in DNA becomes uracil Ⓤ in RNA.

The double strand of DNA contains information on amino acid sequences coded into the sequence of its base pairs.

This information is copied out onto strands of messenger RNA.

The information on the messenger ultimately is translated (by codons consisting of three letters each) into amino acid sequences of proteins.

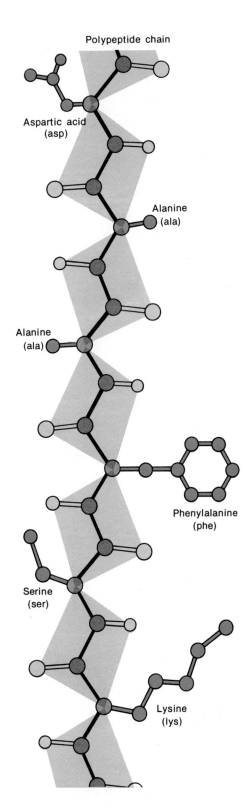

Polypeptide chain

Aspartic acid
(asp)

Alanine
(ala)

Alanine
(ala)

Phenylalanine
(phe)

Serine
(ser)

Lysine
(lys)

Polypeptide backbone and side groups in a protein. With the help of Chapter 20, identify the noncarbon atoms (H, N, O) and indicate one amino acid residue. (Only amide hydrogens are drawn.)

flow of information, but at least we can say "Nucleic acid makes protein," and add "and protein makes everything else." All of the chemical processes of living things are under the control of enzymes, which are protein molecules. Lipids, carbohydrates, and all the small molecules of the cell are products of enzymatic syntheses. They are "second-hand" molecules, in a different category with regard to information. Carbohydrates and lipids are the props and scenery in the living drama; proteins and nucleic acids are the actors.

PROTEINS

If any one class of molecules were to be considered the fundamental building blocks of living organisms, it certainly would be proteins. They are the most versatile of all molecules. In some proteins the strands of polypeptide chains that we encountered in Chapter 20 are twisted about one another into larger cables and fibers, which are used for connections, support, and structure. These are the *fibrous proteins*, found in hair, skin, claws, muscle, tendons, and insect fibers. In a second class of proteins, which have entirely different molecular architecture, the polypeptide chains are coiled back and forth on themselves to make compact, ellipsoidal molecules, 25 Å to 200 Å in diameter. These are the *globular proteins*, which are chemical agents whose job is to act with, or on, other molecules and macromolecules. The catalytic enzymes are the most familiar of the globular proteins, but others serve as oxygen carriers (hemoglobin), electron carriers (cytochromes), and protective antibodies (gamma globulins).

The backbone of a protein is a polypeptide chain made up by linking amino acids together with the removal of water, as we saw in Chapter 20. In globular proteins these chains typically are 60 to 600 amino acids long, and several chains may be present in one molecule. Polypeptides smaller than 60 amino acids seem to be too small to show the versatility that a globular protein demands, and chains larger than 600 amino acids are too costly in terms of coding of sequence information in DNA. It is easier instead to build up larger protein molecules from more than one subunit. Some large protein complexes have several different kinds of subunits and molecular weights of more than a million, but most of the familiar globular proteins have molecular weights of 10,000 to 200,000.

The exact sequence of 20 different amino acids at each position along a protein chain is coded originally in DNA (in the way that we will see at the end of this chapter), and a few of these amino acids then are modified chemically in some proteins after they are built into the polypeptide chain. But this sequence of amino acids is *all* that is coded by the DNA. The way that the protein chain folds in three dimensions, the molecular structure that results, and all of the chemical properties of the folded protein must be contained in the amino acid sequence alone. There are no magic templates for a new polypeptide chain, and nothing else to tell the new protein how to construct itself in three dimensions.

A polypeptide chain of a protein contains important internal constraints on its own geometry. The carbon atom from which an amino acid side chain branches off is called the *alpha carbon* (C_α), and the connection between alpha carbons along the chain is the *peptide group* or *amide group:*

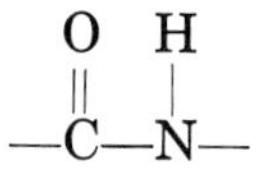

$$\begin{array}{cc} O & H \\ \| & | \\ -C- & N- \end{array}$$

An important feature in the structure of proteins is the fact that all four of the atoms in an amide group, and the two alpha carbons that they connect, must lie in the same plane. This is necessary because the amide bond connecting a C from one amino acid to the N of the next is a partial double bond. The reasons are illustrated at the right. The top drawing shows a conventional bond diagram of an amide group, which has a single C—N bond and a double bond between C and O. The nitrogen atom has an unused lone electron pair, and the carbonyl oxygen has two more. However, this is only one possible resonance structure for the amide group. The middle drawing shows another equally valid bond arrangement, in which the nitrogen lone electron pair has been donated to the C—N bond to make it a double bond, and one of the C=O double bond electron pairs in turn has been pushed onto the oxygen atom. The nitrogen atom has a net positive charge because of the sharing of its lone electron pair, and the oxygen atom is negative because it now has three lone electron pairs. The bond lengths that would be expected for the C=N and C—O bonds in each of these two resonance structures are shown.

As with other resonance bond structures seen in previous chapters, the actual structure is somewhere in between. The measured bond lengths from protein chains are shown on the bottom drawing of the three. The C—O distance is close to that expected for a double bond, but the C—N distance is between the single and double bond values, skewed somewhat toward a double bond. The sharing of the nitrogen lone pair with carbon evidently is incomplete, as is the pushing away of the second electron pair from the C=O bond onto the oxygen atom. Oxygen then acquires a slight excess of electrons and a partial negative charge. The electron deficiency created at nitrogen pulls the N—H bonding pair toward N, so the partial positive charge ends up on the hydrogen atom, as shown. From a delocalization viewpoint, the second electron pair of the C=O double bond and the nitrogen lone pair both have been delocalized over the entire O—C—N region (lower right). This delocalization gives the amide group an extra 21 kcal mole^{-1} of stability, which means that one cannot twist the group about the C—N bond without supplying the 21 kcal mole^{-1} necessary to break the partial double bond.

There are two important structural consequences of this bonding. The planar amide group may be considered as a rigid structural unit whose only degrees of freedom are swivels about the connections to the alpha carbons, and the O and H of the amide plane have slight negative and positive charges that aid in the formation of the hydrogen bonds that hold different chains together. The amide plane as drawn earlier has the two alpha carbons in the trans conformation, at opposite corners of the rectangle. The cis form, with the alpha carbons on the same side of the rectangle, is almost never found in proteins, probably because it introduces a sharp bend in the chain and brings side groups close enough to clash.

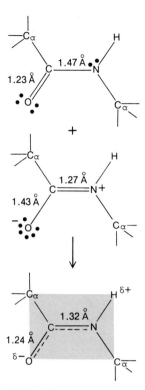

Two possible bonding arrangements in the amide plane in proteins, with the double bond from C to O (top) or from C to N (center). The actual bonding is intermediate (bottom), as the measured bond lengths suggest.

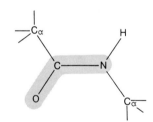

A delocalized molecular-orbital picture of bonding in the amide plane, with four electrons delocalized over all three O, C, and N atoms.

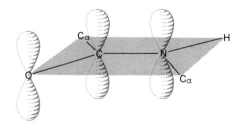

Oblique view of the amide plane, showing the three $2p_z$ atomic orbitals that participate in delocalized bonding.

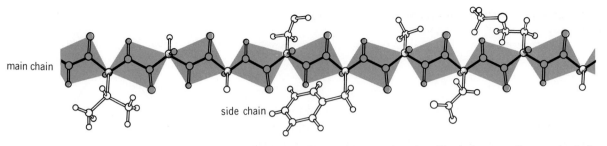

The amide link (—CO—NH—) is the repeating unit of the main chain in proteins; the side chains vary. In an extended chain such as is shown here, side chains project alternately to one side and the other. (All illustrations on this page and the next are from R. E. Dickerson and I. Geis, *The Structure and Action of Proteins*, W. A. Benjamin, Inc. Copyright © 1969 Dickerson and Geis.)

POLAR RESIDUES

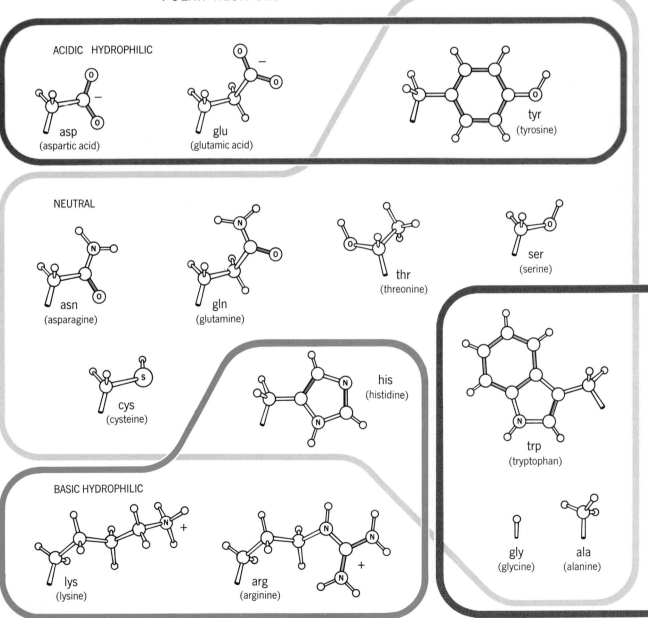

The twenty different amino acid side chains that are coded by DNA are shown on these two pages, grouped according to chemical behavior. The polypeptide main chain with side groupings branching from it appears as a frieze across the top of the opposite page. It is not so important that you remember all of these different side chains as it is that you appreciate the varied chemical properties that they can show. The groups on the opposite page are more or less polar, and tend to be found on the outside of proteins, in contact with water. Aspartic and glutamic acids have carboxylic acid groups (—COOH) on their side chains. These are ionized at pH 7, so aspartic and glutamic acids are means of introducing negative charges onto the surface of a protein molecule. As shown at the bottom of the opposite page, lysine and arginine side chains are bases, which pick up a proton and hence carry a positive charge at neutral pH. The other side chains on the opposite page generally are polar but uncharged. They prefer an aqueous environment for the same reason that methanol molecules do. They help to determine the way a protein chain will fold by tending to keep their parts of the chain on the outside of the molecule.

The side chains drawn within the rectangle below are hydrophobic and tend to force their parts of the protein chain to fold within the non-aqueous interior of the protein molecule. These amino acids range in size from the small and barely hydrophobic alanine, which has only a methyl group for a side chain, to phenylalanine, which has a bulky benzene ring. These variously shaped hydrocarbon side chains can be thought of as the three-dimensional jigsaw puzzle pieces from which the core of the protein molecule is built. When they are fitted together in the completely folded protein, little or no empty space is left between them.

NONPOLAR RESIDUES

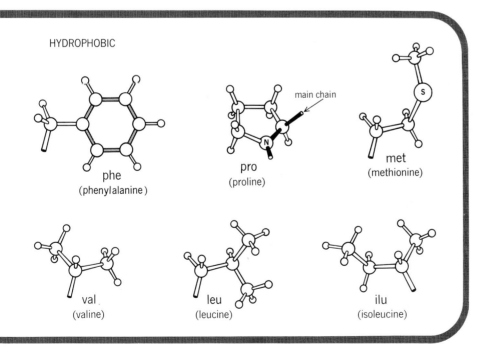

HYDROPHOBIC

phe
(phenylalanine)

pro
(proline)

main chain

met
(methionine)

val
(valine)

leu
(leucine)

ilu
(isoleucine)

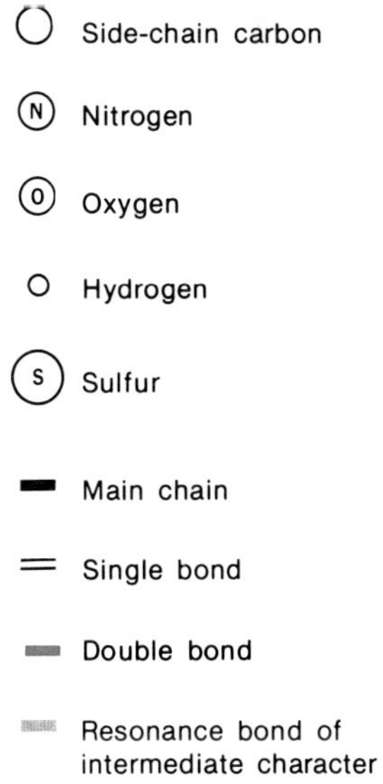

○ Side-chain carbon

Ⓝ Nitrogen

Ⓞ Oxygen

○ Hydrogen

Ⓢ Sulfur

▬ Main chain

═ Single bond

▬ Double bond

▬ Resonance bond of intermediate character

Polar side chains usually found on the surface of a protein molecule are shown on the opposite page. At the immediate left are the side chains (nonpolar) usually found in the interior.

537

In silk and other insect fibers, antiparallel extended chains of protein are cross-linked into sheets by hydrogen bonds. These sheets then are packed into a three-dimensional structure. (This illustration and those on the next page are from R. E. Dickerson and I. Geis, *The Structure and Action of Proteins*, W. A. Benjamin, Inc. Copyright © 1969 Dickerson and Geis.)

CHAIN FOLDING; THE FIBROUS PROTEINS

The slight negative charge on the carbonyl (—CO—) oxygen atoms, and the slight positive charge on the amide (—NH—) hydrogen, are important in determining how a protein chain will fold, since a hydrogen bond can form between the O and the H in the way described for water molecules in Chapter 4. If two protein chains run parallel to one another in opposite directions, a large number of hydrogen bonds can be formed between them like rungs in a ladder (left). This is the way that protein chains are held together in silk, a fibrous protein. Many protein chains are packed next to one another in a sheet, with neighboring chains running in opposite directions and held together by hydrogen bonds. These sheets then are stacked together to build up a three-dimensional structure. Three different kinds of chemical forces are present in the three-dimensional silk structure. Along the protein chains (which also is the direction of the silk fibers) atoms are linked by covalent bonds. At right angles to these chains, within one sheet, the chains are held together by hydrogen bonds. These are weaker than covalent bonds (~6 kcal mole^{-1} compared to 80–100 kcal mole^{-1}), but are important because there are so many of them. In the third dimension, the stacked sheets are held together by weak van der Waals forces between side chains, most of which are glycine and alanine in silk.

This arrangement of bonds gives silk its familiar mechanical properties. Since stretching a silk fiber involves pulling against the covalent bonds of the protein chains, silk fibers are not very elastic or stretchable. However, they are quite bendable or supple, since bending a fiber involves only sliding sheets past one another, as when a ream of typing paper or a telephone book is bent. Silk fibers are flexible, but not extensible.

Wool or hair has a different kind of fibrous protein structure, in which each protein chain is coiled into a right-handed helix known as an α helix (alpha helix). Each —NH— group is hydrogen bonded to a —CO— group one helical turn away in the *same* chain, like vertical supports in a spiral staircase. The α helix is shown at top left on the opposite page. Because of the way the hydrogen bonds must be connected, there are 3.6 amino acids per turn of the helix. The result is a reasonably rigid cylindrical structure, with side chains pointing out from the axis of the cylinder.

The α helix is the basic structural unit for the class of fibrous proteins known as α keratins. Besides hair and wool, they include skin, beaks, nails, claws, and most of the external protective layers possessed by vertebrates. In accordance with good ropemaking principles, the fibers in a human hair go through seven layers of organization from protein chain to complete hair. This organization is shown on the opposite page. The protein chain is twisted into a right-handed α helix that is held together by hydrogen bonds. Three such α helices then are given a gentle left-hand twist to group them into a triple-chain coil called a protofibril. Nine of these protofibrils are bundled into a cylinder surrounding two others to build a 9 + 2 microfibril; and several hundred microfibrils are embedded in a protein matrix to form a macrofibril bundle. The macrofibrils are packed tightly inside the keratin-producing

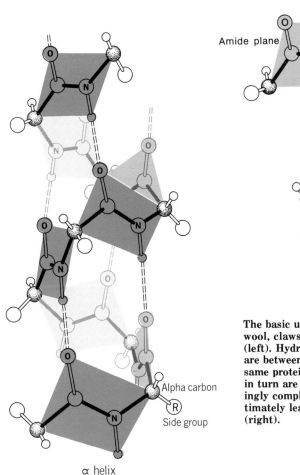

Amide plane

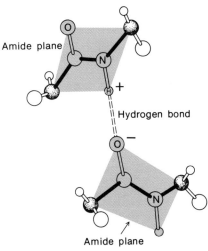

Hydrogen bond

Amide plane

Alpha carbon

(R)

Side group

α helix

The basic unit of the protein in hair, wool, claws, and skin is an α helix (left). Hydrogen bonds in the α helix are between adjacent turns of the same protein chain. These α helices in turn are organized into increasingly complex structures, which ultimately lead to the intact hair fiber (right).

α helix

Protofibril

Microfibril

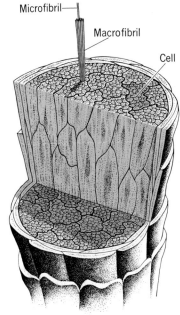

Microfibril

Macrofibril

Cell

cells of the hair, and in the final level of organization these cells make up the hair fiber itself, surrounded by protective scales.

Wool is stretchable in a way that silk is not, because pulling on an α helix stretches only the relatively weak hydrogen bonds, and not covalent bonds. There is a limit to the stretch of wool fibers—when the α helices are pulled into fully extended chains. But if this limit is not exceeded, the fiber will snap back into its original length when the tension is released, with re-formation of the hydrogen bonds. Hence wool is not only stretchable, it is elastic. A good wool cloth has an elastic, springy feel that silk cloth lacks. The explanation lies in the way that the two fibrous proteins are constructed.

The α helix and β sheet (the sheet structure found in silk) are two of the most common structures found in fibrous proteins. There are other structures, but the basic pattern is the same: essentially endless chains of proteins held together by hydrogen bonds that extend either to different chains, or to adjacent helical turns of the same chain. These same basic structures, α helix and β sheet, also are found in the more compact globular proteins, of which enzymes are the most common examples.

539

The polypeptide chain in myoglobin is folded into eight α helices, which then are packed into a compact molecule. Numbered spheres are the α carbon atoms and the —CO—NH— amide bonds connecting them are represented by straight lines. Each α carbon atom has a side chain branching from it, although only a few key ones are shown here. The heme group sits in a pocket between the E and F helices.

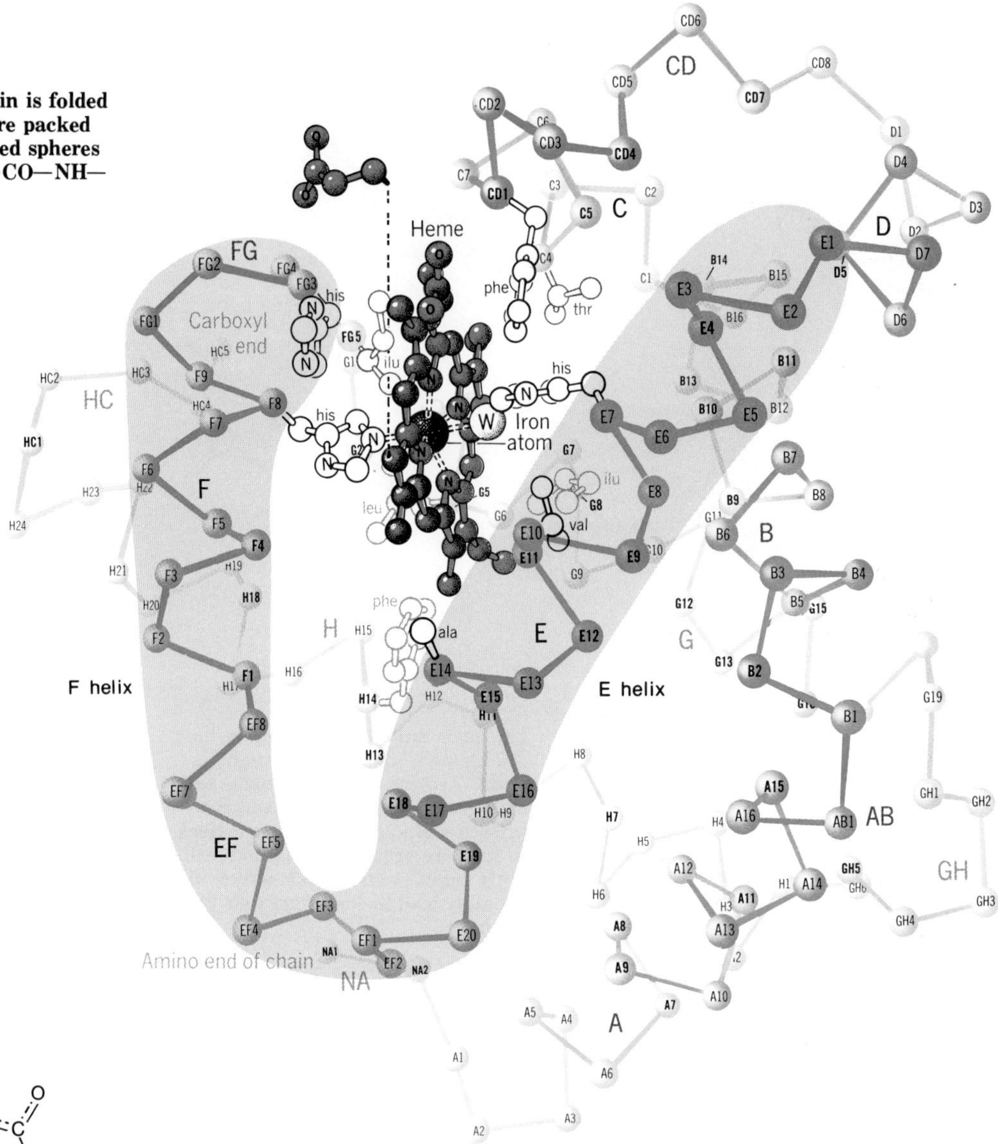

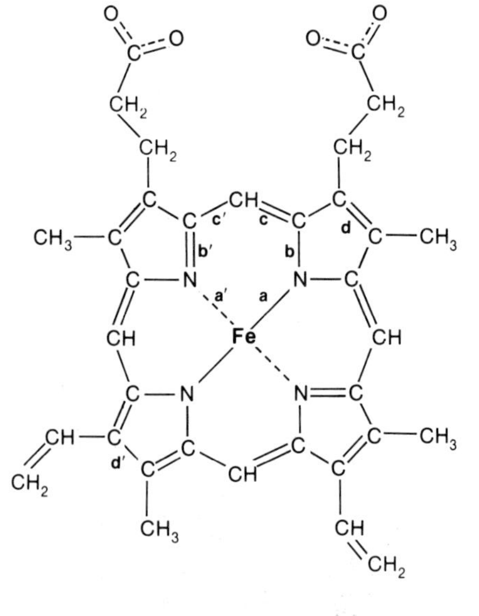

The heme group consists of an iron atom surrounded by a flat porphyrin ring. The O_2 molecule stored by myoglobin binds to the iron in the position marked by W in the upper drawing.

GLOBULAR PROTEINS: MYOGLOBIN AND HEMOGLOBIN

Enzymes and catalysts are the subject of Chapter 24, so at this point we shall introduce globular proteins by means of two molecules that perform other functions: hemoglobin, which carries O_2 in the bloodstream from the lungs to the tissues; and myoglobin, which stores O_2 in muscle cells until it is needed. Both myoglobin and hemoglobin are hemoproteins, with the protein chain enclosing a flat, planar iron–porphyrin ring complex called a heme group, shown at the left. The iron atom and the porphyrin ring together make up one large delocalized-electron system similar to the magnesium–porphyrin system in chlorophyll. Because of the delocalized electrons, both chlorophyll and the heme group absorb light in the visible spectrum, and are brightly colored. Chlorophyll is green because it absorbs strongly in the red end of the spectrum; hemoglobin and myoglobin absorb in the yellow-green and therefore have the red color familiar in blood and beefsteak.

The way in which the protein chain is folded in the myoglobin molecule is shown above. Myoglobin has 153 amino acids in one continuous chain, and a molecular weight of 17,000. It is a relatively small

540

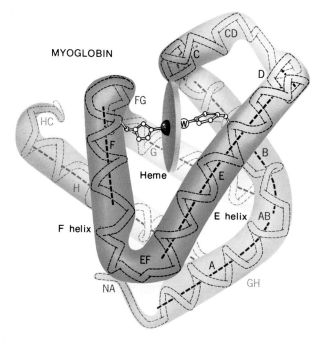

MYOGLOBIN

This representation of the myoglobin molecule emphasizes the α-helical framework and the positioning of the heme in a pocket. Histidine side chains, which have five-membered rings, extend from the E and F helices and interact with the heme iron and the O_2 molecule. (The myoglobin illustrations of this and the opposite pages are from R. E. Dickerson and I. Geis, *The Structure and Action of Proteins*, W. A. Benjamin, Inc. Copyright © 1969 Dickerson and Geis.)

protein. For simplicity, only the alpha carbons of the main chain are shown, and the —CO—NH— amide groups connecting them are represented by a straight line. The chain is coiled into eight segments of cylindrical α helix, identified by the letters A through H. A more schematic diagram of the myoglobin molecule is shown above. The corners or bends between helices are given the two letters of the helices that they connect—corner AB between helices A and B, and so on. Only by such abrupt elbow bends can an essentially linear fibrous structure— the α helix—be fitted into a globular protein of finite dimensions. The α helix occurs in myoglobin and many other globular proteins because it is an efficient way to fold a protein chain, but the price that must be paid is irregular bends every so often along the chain.

Helices E and F form a V-shaped pocket lined with hydrophobic amino acid side chains, into which the heme group (far left) is fitted like a silver dollar in a cupped hand. Iron normally prefers octahedral coordination, that is, to have six ligands, or coordinating atoms, arranged around it at the corners of an octahedron. In the heme group four of these six coordinating groups are provided by nitrogen atoms of the porphyrin ring, but the positions above and below the plane of the ring are unoccupied. In myoglobin the fifth position is filled by the nitrogen atom of a histidine side chain, at position F8 on the F helix, as seen at the left of the heme in the molecular drawing. The sixth octahedral position is open, and it is here that the O_2 molecule binds when myoglobin stores oxygen. The oxygen-binding position is marked by the sphere with "W" in the myoglobin drawings. Another five-membered ring of a histidine side chain extends out from position E7 of the E helix, close enough to interact with the bound O_2 molecule, but not close enough to become a ligand directly to the heme iron.

One of the remarkable aspects of the myoglobin molecule is the way that the properties of the side chains along each α helix help the helices to fold together properly to build the molecule. The inner surfaces of the α helices, where they are to pack against one another, are covered with hydrophobic side chains such as valine, leucine, and phenylalanine. In contrast, the sides of the helices that are to be exposed to the aqueous surroundings in the completely folded molecule

β_2 β_1

α_2 α_1

The four chains of the hemoglobin molecule each are folded like that of myoglobin, and then are packed together into a compact unit. The four heme pockets are exposed on the outside of the molecule where they are available for binding four O_2 molecules. From R. E. Dickerson and I. Geis, *The Structure and Action of Proteins*, W. A. Benjamin, Inc. Copyright © 1969 Dickerson and Geis.

have polar side chains, either charged as in lysine and aspartic acid, or merely polar as in asparagine and serine. If we look at the amino acid sequence of myoglobin, we see that hydrophobic side chains tend to recur every three or four positions along the main chain. Since the α helix has 3.6 residues per turn, this means that these hydrophobic side chains occur on the same side of the helix. This is one example of how the linear amino acid sequence of a protein can contain the instructions for folding in three dimensions.

The hemoglobin molecule, shown above, is essentially four myoglobin molecules put together. Each hemoglobin molecule has four separate protein chains: two α chains and two β chains. Each of these chains is folded in the same way as the myoglobin molecule, and the four chains then are nested against one another as four subunits of a compact molecule. When the hemoglobin molecule picks up four O_2 molecules at the lungs, the subunits shift slightly so the two β units are a little closer together. When the O_2 molecules are turned over to myoglobin at the tissues for storage, the four hemoglobin subunits shift back to their original arrangement. In effect, the hemoglobin molecule is a machine that closes and opens when it binds and releases oxygen. Interactions between subunits also make binding of oxygen to hemoglobin an all-or-nothing proposition. Once an O_2 molecule has bound to one of the four heme groups, a subunit shift makes it much easier to add the other three O_2 molecules. Conversely, once one O_2 molecule has been released at the tissues, the other three fall away more easily.[1] This makes the hemoglobin molecule easy to load with O_2 at the lungs and easy to strip of its cargo at the tissue, properties desirable in an oxygen carrier.

---

[1] One of the men who shared the Nobel Prize in 1961 for the pioneering x-ray crystal structure analyses of myoglobin and hemoglobin, M. F. Perutz of Cambridge, has characterized this as the *Matthew effect:* "For to every one who hath, will more be given, and he will have abundance; but from him who hath not, even that which he hath will be taken away." (Matthew 25:29)

These two globular protein molecules are nearly all α-helical. In other such proteins, the chain is folded in a less regular manner, and several nearly parallel extended chains can be cross-linked by hydrogen bonds to form a sheet resembling a small region of silk. Such a silklike sheet often acts as the central core of a globular protein, with α helices packed against it on either side to form a compact molecule. We will discuss protein structures again in Chapter 24 and see three enzymes that have very little α-helical structure.

NUCLEOTIDES AND NUCLEIC ACIDS

The best known role of nucleic acids is that of carriers of genetic information in DNA, but they have other functions. We have seen that adenosine triphosphate (ATP) is a carrier of chemical energy. Similar small nucleotides carry energy, reducing power, and chemical groups during synthesis.

Five organic nitrogen bases are at the heart of small nucleotides and nucleic acids, and these are shown at the right. Adenine and guanine are derivatives of the double-ring base purine, and cytosine, thymine, and uracil are derivatives of pyrimidine. They are so important that they often are identified only by the letters A, G, C, T, and U. When bonded to the C1′ position of β-D-ribose, as shown on Page 545, they form *nucleosides:* adenosine, guanosine, cytidine, thymidine (with an —H for the —OH at position C2′), and uridine. (Position numbers in the sugar usually are primed to avoid confusion with positions around the rings of the nitrogen bases.) These nucleosides in turn can form esters with phosphate at any of the three —OH positions on the ribose ring: C2′, C3′, or C5′. A nucleoside esterified with phosphate is called a nucleotide. Esters at the 5′ position are the most common. As shown on Page 545, the nucleoside adenosine is esterified with phosphate at the 5′ position to form the nucleotide adenosine-5′-monophosphate (AMP), and to this two more phosphate groups are attached to form adenosine-5′-diphosphate (ADP), and adenosine-5′-triphosphate (ATP).

As was first mentioned in Chapter 10, the free energy of hydrolysis of ATP into ADP and inorganic phosphate is unusually high for organic phosphate compounds, around 7.3 kcal mole^{-1}. This is the energy that must be supplied to produce ATP and water from ADP and phosphate, and this is the free energy that is released again when ATP is hydrolyzed. The further hydrolysis of ADP to AMP and phosphate releases a similar amount of energy, but the free energy of hydrolysis of AMP to adenosine and phosphate is only 3.4 kcal mole^{-1}, which is similar to that of other organic phosphate compounds. The unusually large hydrolysis energies, which arise partly from delocalization of electrons and partly from repulsions between negative charges on the polyphosphate groups, make ATP a useful means of storing chemical energy in living systems. No matter how a particular organism obtains its chemical energy, or what compounds it employs for long-term energy storage, every living organism first converts chemical energy into ATP molecules, and then uses this ATP for its subsequent purposes. It is tempting to think that life began as a scavenger of ATP from the primordial seas, and that all the other energy-gathering processes devel-

BASES OF DNA AND RNA

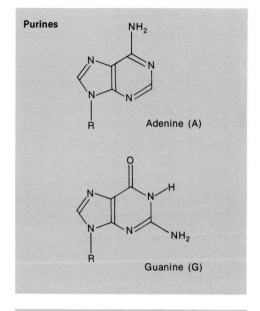

Purines

Adenine (A)

Guanine (G)

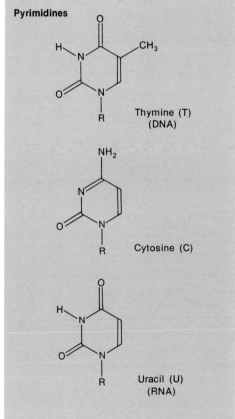

Pyrimidines

Thymine (T)
(DNA)

Cytosine (C)

Uracil (U)
(RNA)

Four organic bases carry the genetic information in DNA. Two purines, adenine and guanine, have double rings; and two pyrimidines, cytosine and thymine, have single rings. In RNA, thymine is replaced by uracil, which does not have the thymine methyl group.

543

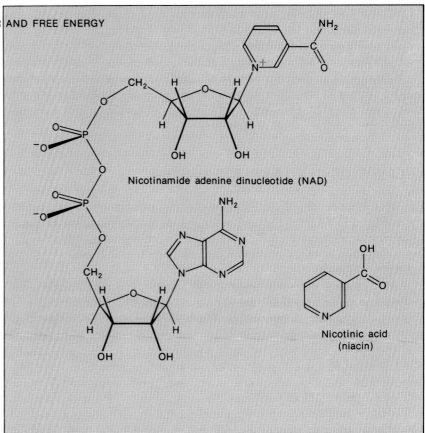

Nicotinamide adenine dinucleotide (NAD)

Nicotinic acid
(niacin)

Flavin adenine dinucleotide (FAD)

Riboflavin
(a vitamin)

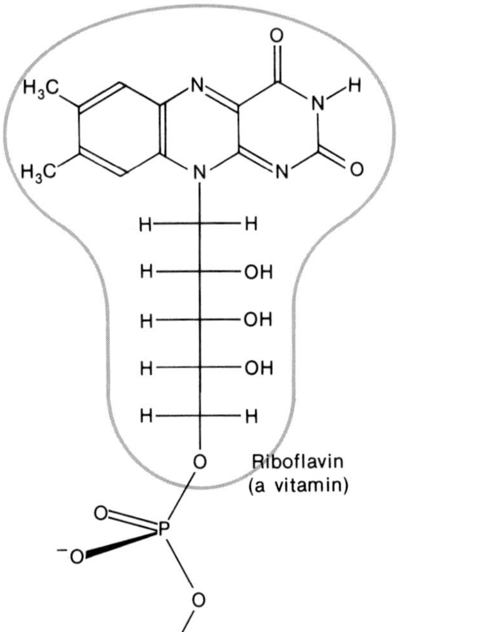

FAD also is built from two organic base–ribose–phosphate units. One base is adenine and the other is riboflavin, or vitamin B₂.

NAD is built from two organic base–ribose–phosphate units connected by their phosphates. One organic base is adenine and the other is derived from nicotinic acid, or niacin.

oped only as alternative ways of making artificial ATP when the natural supply ran out.

The unusually high hydrolysis energy that makes ATP useful as an energy-storage molecule also is found in simple polyphosphates, without the ribose ring and adenine. Some bacteria store energy in the form of polyphosphates. Then why bother with the complication of the adenosine "handle" on the triphosphate? The most probable answer is that these reactions are controlled by being carried out at the surface of enzyme molecules, and the adenosine is indeed a handle by which the enzyme molecule recognizes and binds an ATP molecule so it can undergo reaction.

Nucleoside diphosphates also are important carriers of chemical free energy in the form of reducing power in oxidation–reduction reactions, as we shall see in the next chapter. The standard pattern is a combination of a nucleoside diphosphate with a molecule capable of being oxidized and reduced. In nicotinamide adenine dinucleotide, NAD⁺ (above), the reducible group is an amide of nicotinic acid; and in flavin adenine dinucleotide, FAD (left), it is a molecule of riboflavin. These shuttle molecules are needed only in minute amounts because they are reduced at one place and reoxidized elsewhere. They need replenishing only to the extent that they are accidentally lost or degraded. We have lost what ability we once had to synthesize nicotinic

544

Adenine combined with ribose yields a nucleoside, in this case adenosine. Adenosine esterified with one phosphate produces the mononucleotide adenosine monophosphate (AMP). Subsequent esterifications with more phosphate groups as shown lead to adenosine dinucleotide (ADP) and adenosine trinucleotide (ATP).

Adenine

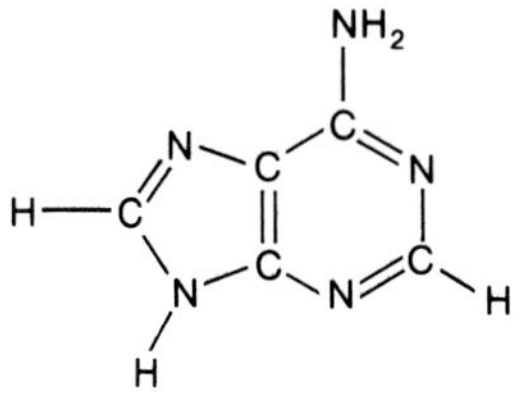

Adenosine

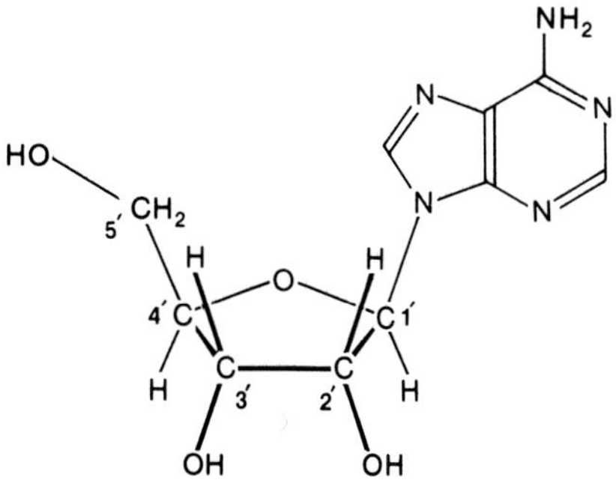

Adenosine monophosphate (AMP)

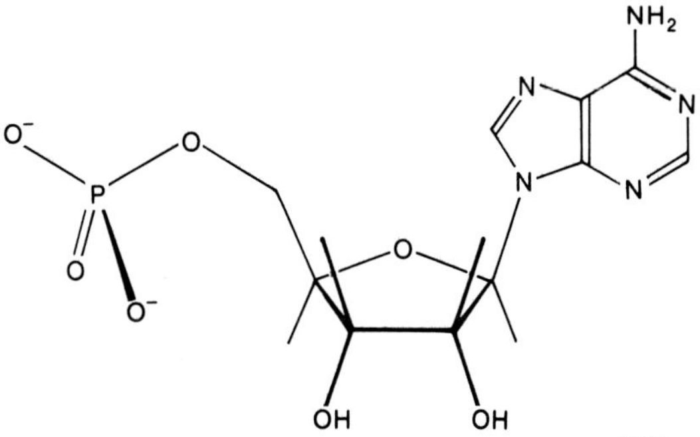

Adenosine diphosphate (ADP)

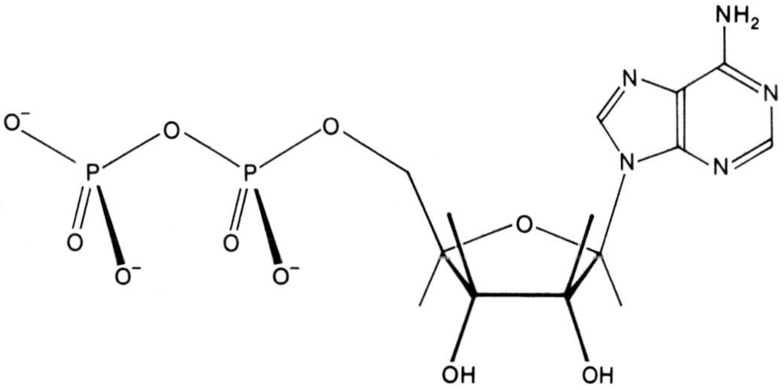

Adenosine triphosphate (ATP)

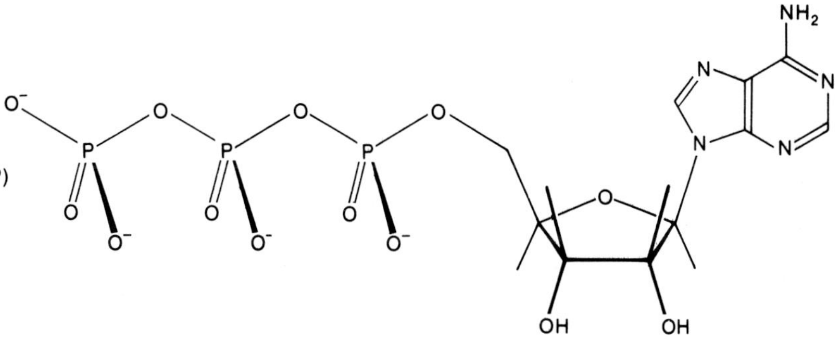

$$NAD^+ + 2[H] \longrightarrow NADH + H^+$$

$$FAD + 2[H] \longrightarrow FADH_2$$

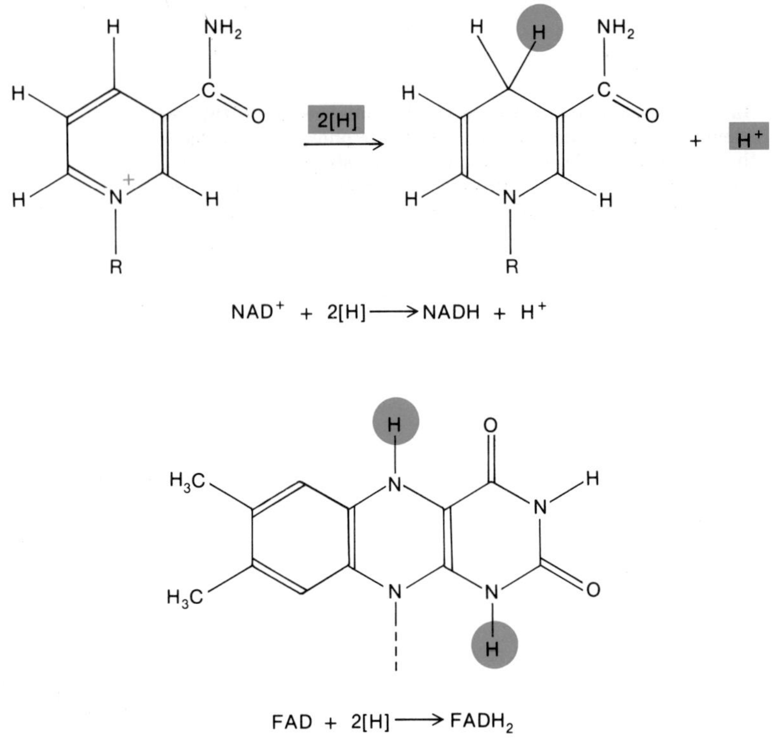

An oxidized NAD^+ molecule is reduced by two hydrogen atoms by binding one of them to the nicotinamide ring and incorporating the electron of the other one into its delocalized electron system. A proton is released into solution. When FAD is reduced, both hydrogen atoms are added to the triple ring, thereby eliminating one of the double bonds.

acid and riboflavin biologically, and are forced to obtain the raw materials for NAD^+ and FAD from our diet. Substances such as these, which are needed only in minute quantities but nevertheless are absolutely essential in these quantities, are termed vitamins. Vitamin A, the precursor of retinal, is one example. Riboflavin is vitamin B_2, and nicotinic acid is niacin. Niacin deficiency in humans causes pellagra, a disease once common in the American rural South but which now has been largely eradicated.

When NAD^+ is reduced, one H binds to the ring, the electron from the second H cancels the positive charge, and the proton goes into solution, as shown above. When FAD is reduced, two hydrogen atoms are attached to the flavin ring at two points, as at the left. Energy is stored in both of these reduced molecules, to be released again when the carrier molecule is reoxidized. Just as the amount of energy obtained in an oxidation depends on what is used as the oxidizing agent, so the energy that we can think of as stored in reduced NADH or $FADH_2$ varies with the substances used to reoxidize them. In normal O_2 respiration, reoxidization of NADH takes place with a liberation of 52.7 kcal mole^{-1} of free energy:

$$NADH + H^+ + \tfrac{1}{2}O_2 \rightarrow NAD^+ + H_2O \qquad \Delta G' = -52.7 \text{ kcal mole}^{-1}$$

(The prime indicates a free energy change under the physiological conditions of pH 7, or $[H^+] = 10^{-7}$ mole liter^{-1}, rather than 1 mole liter^{-1}.) Under these conditions we can think of each mole of NADH as "carrying" 52.7 kcal of free energy from the place where it was reduced to the place where it will be reoxidized. A mole of $FADH_2$ carries somewhat less energy:

$$FADH_2 + \tfrac{1}{2}O_2 \rightarrow FAD + H_2O \qquad \Delta G' = -36.2 \text{ kcal mole}^{-1}$$

546

The dinucleotides NAD$^+$ and FAD, and the nucleotide ATP, co-operate as "big buckets" and "little buckets" for energy in the energy-extracting processes of living cells. When foodstuffs are broken down, 53-kcal quantities of energy are stored by reducing NAD$^+$ to NADH, or smaller amounts by reducing FAD to FADH$_2$. These reduced dinucleotides, no matter what their source, then can funnel into a common respiratory machinery that reoxidizes them and transfers their energy in smaller packages to ATP: three ATP per NADH molecule reoxidized, or two ATP per FADH$_2$. In the banking analogy for energy storage in Chapter 21, NADH molecules are the nickels of the energy coinage and ATP molecules are the pennies.

INFORMATION STORAGE: DNA AND RNA

DNA is the most important of the nucleic acids because it is the ultimate repository of all genetic information. It is a long-chain polymer of D-deoxyribose (right), which differs from D-ribose in having its —OH group at the 2' position replaced by —H. The polymer connection is made by esterifying a phosphate group with the 5' hydroxyl of one sugar molecule and the 3' hydroxyl of the next. The resulting polymer chain has a "sense" or a direction, with a 5' end and a 3' end as shown by the arrow at right. Ribonucleic acid is derived from a similar polymer, but uses D-ribose instead of D-deoxyribose.

In both DNA and RNA, the 1' carbon of each sugar ring is covalently bonded to one of four purine or pyrimidine bases: A, C, G, or T for DNA, and A, C, G, or U for RNA. (T differs from U only by an extra methyl group on the six-membered ring.) Genetic information is coded by the sequence of bases along a strand of DNA or RNA, with three consecutive bases containing the code for one amino acid. The three-base sequence for one amino acid is called a triplet *codon*. With a choice of four different bases at each of three positions, $4^3 = 64$ different codons are possible. Because only 20 amino acids are coded, there obviously must be redundancy within the system, with the same amino acid represented by more than one codon. This redundancy is inevitable, since a two-base codon scheme would have permitted only $4^2 = 16$ different amino acids to be coded. Three of the 64 codons are used for "punctuation," to tell the polypeptide chain when to stop, and the other 61 represent individual amino acids.

One danger in any information-storage system is that the information will become faulty or garbled. Some of this danger is lessened in DNA by having the "message" protected by a second strand running in the opposite direction, with the bases on the two strands paired in a complementary manner. Each purine on one strand is paired with a pyrimidine on the complementary strand in a highly specific way: A only with T, and G only with C. The result is a ladder molecule, as shown on the next page, with the 5'-to-3' direction different in the two uprights of the ladder, and with purine–pyrimidine rungs. Because of the specific A–T and G–C base pairing, each strand has exactly the same information, although in a slightly different language. This is what is meant by saying that the two strands are complementary. This duplication of information is a protective device, since mismatchings caused by chemical mutation or radiation can be recognized by repair

The backbone of DNA is a long polymer of alternating phosphates and deoxyribose molecules esterified at the 3' and 5' positions of the sugar.

547

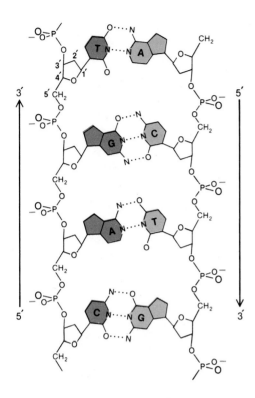

The four bases of DNA, paired as at right, are the four letters in the alphabet of the genetic code. The paired bases are the rungs of a DNA ladder (above), with the 5'-to-3' chain arrangement of the two sides of the ladder running in opposite directions.

enzymes and corrected. Either strand is sufficient to make an intact duplicate of the original DNA again. (In some primitive societies, accounts are kept by notches on sticks, which then are split down the middle with one half going to the debtor, the other to the creditor. Tampering with the records is instantly recognizable by matching the halves of the stick. This is not a bad analogy for the double-stranded information storage in DNA.)

The basis for the specificity of the A–T and G–C base pairing, and the coiling of DNA into a double-stranded helix, are shown on these two pages. Adenine and thymine pair by sharing two hydrogen bonds (below), with each base being a hydrogen donor in one bond and an acceptor in the other. The donor-acceptor roles in these two bonds are reversed in guanine and cytosine, and a third hydrogen bond is added. This role reversal insures that adenine cannot bond with cytosine, or thymine with guanine. Two purines (A and G) are too large to fit as a rung in the DNA double-stranded ladder, shown at the left, and two pyrimidines (C and T) are too small. Hence the only possible pairings on the two strands are A with T, and C with G.

One further protection is given the genetic message. The double-stranded DNA ladder is coiled into a double helix, with the sugar–phosphate backbone on the outside and the base pairs inside, like treads in

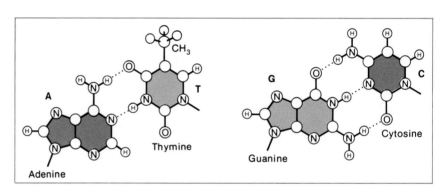

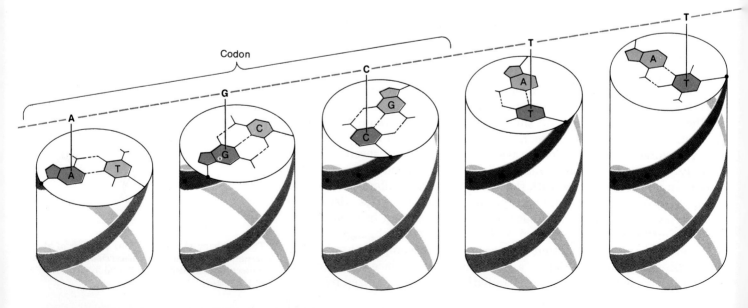

A three-dimensional illustration of base-pair stacking. Complementary base pairs (A–T and G–C) connect two helical strands of deoxyribose. The ten base pairs shown above complete one helical turn.

a spiral staircase. The buildup of the DNA helix is shown across the bottom of these two pages, and the finished helix in space-filling atomic models appears in the right margin. The double helix is a cylinder 22 Å in diameter, with a wide groove and a narrow groove spiraling up the outside. Base pairs in adjacent steps of the staircase are 3 Å apart. There are ten steps, or base pairs, in a complete turn of the helix, so one repeating unit of the helical framework is 30 Å long.

The genetic message in DNA is coded in the bases, grouped in threes. The sequence A–G–C (bottom far left) tells the protein-synthesizing machinery to add a serine to the growing chain. The T–T–G that follows is a triplet code, or codon, for leucine; and G–A–C is the codon for aspartic acid. In this way the amino acid sequence of every protein in a living organism is stored in its DNA.

This base pairing provides a means of duplicating the DNA during cell division. Each strand of the parent DNA molecule unwinds, and different nucleoside triphosphates (deoxyadenosine triphosphate, dATP; deoxycytidine triphosphate, dCTP; etc.) are paired with the exposed bases on each strand. The free energy of the triphosphate is used to connect these paired nucleotides into a 5′–3′ polymer, so that each of the parent DNA strands now is paired with a new strand identical to the one from which it separated. This *replication* process is

Three-dimensional model of DNA. Because the base-pair connections to the backbone are not exactly 180° apart, the two grooves up the outside of the helix are of unequal width.

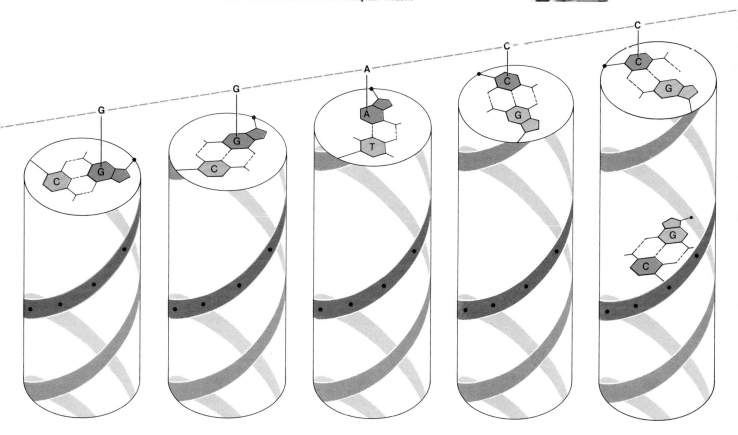

In the last drawing (right), a sample base-pair has been repeated (C–G) to demonstrate how the two helical strands are held together. In one helical strand the sequential bases are in dark color; in the other they are a tint of color.

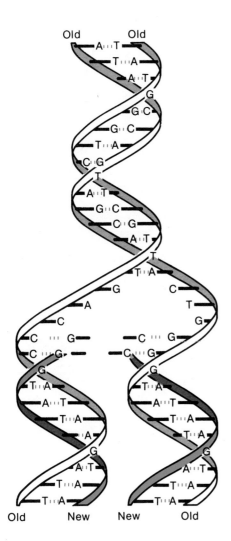

Old   Old

Old   New   New   Old

DNA is replicated by unwinding the two strands and building a new complementary strand to each. The daughter molecules are exact copies of the parent, each with one of the parent strands. From James D. Watson, *Molecular Biology of the Gene,* Second Edition, W. A. Benjamin, Inc. Copyright © 1970 J. D. Watson.

shown schematically at the left. The result is two daughter helices, each identical with the parent in base sequence and pairing, and each containing one of the parent strands and one newly polymerized strand. The double helix is not only a protection, it is the basis for reproduction.

DNA of all organisms above the level of bacteria and blue-green algae is retained as "archive material" within the nucleus of the cell, whereas protein synthesis takes place outside the nucleus in the cytoplasm, or cell fluid. Information is carried from DNA to the site of protein synthesis by appropriately named messenger RNA (mRNA). Messenger RNA contains a copy of the base sequence from one strand of DNA, with the minor change of a substitution of thymine for uracil. The copying of genetic information from DNA to RNA is called *transcription,* and the subsequent use of messenger RNA base sequences to synthesize specific protein chains is called *translation.* The transcription and translation processes are diagrammed on the opposite page.

During transcription, a local unwinding of the double-helical DNA occurs, thereby giving access to the strand to be copied. An RNA polymerase enzyme travels along the DNA strand, adding complementary nucleoside triphosphates to build a messenger RNA strand that is the complement of the original DNA. The completed mRNA strand falls away from the DNA and diffuses out of the nucleus to ribosomes, where translation into a polypeptide chain takes place. The nucleus resembles a rare book room of a library, in which the books themselves cannot be checked out, but photocopies of selected parts may be made for use and eventual discard outside the library.

Ribosomes are RNA-protein complexes, 200 Å in diameter with an overall molecular weight of 3,600,000. Their role is to read the codon information on mRNA and use it to make the corresponding polypeptide chain. With an electron microscope we can see several ribosomes spaced down the same length of mRNA like locomotives down a track, puffing their protein chain behind them. Ribosomes have one problem that the RNA polymerase enzyme does not: translating from one language (nucleic acid sequence) into another (amino acid sequence), with the symbols in the two languages in a 3 to 1 ratio. The translating units are small molecules of transfer RNA (tRNA). Each amino acid has one or more kinds of tRNA. On one end of the tRNA molecule is an anticodon of three bases that is complementary to the codon for an amino acid, and at the other end is a binding site for that particular amino acid. The tRNA molecule is therefore a coupler, making sure that the right amino acid is matched with the right triplet codon. Each tRNA molecule has its own "charging enzyme" that mates tRNA and amino acid before the charged complex migrates to the ribosome and is fed into the growing chain.

At the ribosome, the appropriately charged tRNA is paired with a triplet codon on the messenger. The amino acid is polymerized with the growing chain, and the ribosome moves down the messenger by three bases to repeat the process with the next codon. When one of the three "stop" codons is read, the completed polypeptide chain falls away from the ribosome and completes its folding into a functioning protein molecule.

This in broad outline is the machinery by which linear information in a polynucleic acid is translated into three-dimensional information in

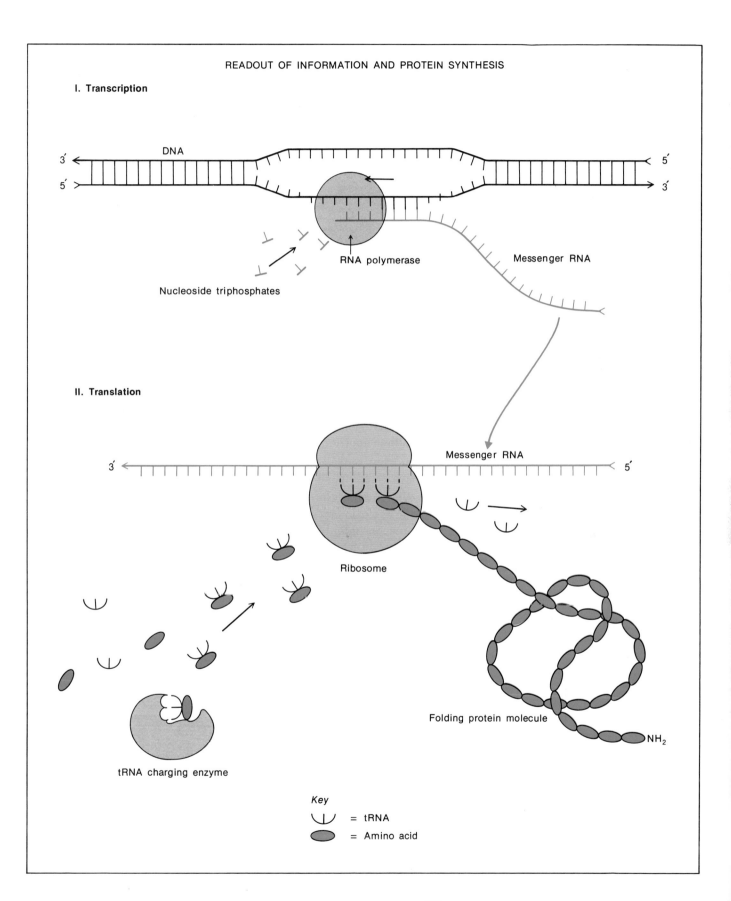

READOUT OF INFORMATION AND PROTEIN SYNTHESIS

I. Transcription

DNA

$3'$ ← → $5'$

$5'$ → → $3'$

RNA polymerase

Nucleoside triphosphates

Messenger RNA

II. Translation

Messenger RNA

$3'$ ← → $5'$

Ribosome

Folding protein molecule

NH$_2$

tRNA charging enzyme

Key

= tRNA

= Amino acid

an enzyme molecule. More details would take us into molecular biology rather than chemistry, and soon would take us to the limits of our present-day knowledge. The information in DNA is sometimes compared with music on a magnetic tape. In principle the music is all there on the isolated tape, but it is inaccessible without a player. The mRNA, tRNA, ribosomes, and various charging and polymerizing enzymes are like the stereo playback set, without which the information is only useless fluctuations along a chain.

QUESTIONS

1. In what sense is the arrangement of atoms of special importance in living organisms? How is this related to entropy?

2. How are lipids used in living organisms? How are proteins used? Where are nucleic acids found in a cell?

3. What is a vitamin? Is the same chemical compound necessarily a vitamin for all living organisms? If not, why would it be a vitamin for one organism and not for another? What use was made of the vitamins that were mentioned in this chapter?

4. Why is growth, by itself, an insufficient criterion for life? What is the difference between the growth of an amoeba and a copper sulfate crystal?

5. In what sense are putting on a coat, and migrating from one latitude to another, comparable adaptations?

6. In what sense are running away, attacking an enemy, and excessive breeding, all comparable adaptations?

7. Why are both imperfect reproduction, and selection, necessary for the evolutionary process? What advantages does the evolutionary process confer on a line of living organisms, which faithful copying from one generation to the next could not offer? In what sense is a slight maladaptation of a part of a population beneficial?

8. How is genetic information stored in a living organism? What type of molecule is used?

9. How is this information used by the creature that carries it?

10. What kinds of instructions are carried by these genetic "archives"? How is the information read out?

11. What is the difference between fibrous and globular proteins? Which are used for structural purposes? What use is made of the other class of proteins?

12. How can globular proteins be constructed from long polypeptide chains?

13. Why are there several different kinds of amino acid side chains in proteins? What different chemical capabilities do these side chains have? Why are some of them found more often on the interior of proteins, and others on the outside?

14. How does the bond structure of the polypeptide link in proteins affect the way that proteins are folded?

15. How does the amide bond structure assist in the formation of hydrogen bonds?

16. How do hydrogen bonds contribute to the three-dimensional structure of proteins?

17. What is the basic structural unit in silk? What is the fundamental unit in wool? Is this structural unit ever found in globular proteins? If so, give an example.

18. What is the physiological role of hemoglobin? Of myoglobin? In what way are these two molecules similar in structure?

19. What is the heme group? How does the iron atom of heme interact with the organic framework?

20. How is the heme group held in the myoglobin molecule? What is the importance of heme to myoglobin's physiological role?

21. How does the amino acid sequence of myoglobin help the molecule to fold properly in three dimensions?

22. How does subunit interaction in hemoglobin affect the way that oxygen molecules bind to it?

23. What is a purine base? A pyrimidine base? Which purines and pyrimidines are used in DNA? What changes occur when DNA changes to RNA?

24. What is a nucleoside? A nucleotide? Give examples, when the base involved is adenine.

25. What structural elements are shared by AMP, NAD^+, and FAD? What structural features distinguish NAD^+ and FAD from one another, and from ATP?

26. Why is NAD^+ written with a $+$ sign, whereas FAD is not? What happens to the hydrogen atoms when each of these dinucleotides is reduced? What is the standard abbreviation for the reduced form of each?

27. If molecular O_2 is the final oxidant, how much free energy is carried by each mole of reduced NAD^+? Of reduced FAD? Of ATP? What advantage is there in having several energy carriers with different capacities?

28. If NAD^+ is needed every time energy is extracted from foods, why do we require only minute quantities of niacin (a precursor of NAD^+), instead of amounts comparable with our other foods?

29. What is riboflavin, and how is it related to energy-carrying molecules?

30. How is information stored in DNA? How many bases in DNA correspond to every amino acid in a protein?

31. In what sense are the two strands in DNA complementary to one another? How is this complementation achieved? What structural features in the side groups of the two DNA strands make incorrect matching difficult (although not impossible)?

32. What is the three-dimensional structure of DNA? How does this structure follow from the complementarity of the strands? How does this structure protect the genetic information?

33. In what sense is DNA the "archival material" of a cell? To what molecule is the information in the DNA initially transcribed? What is done with this information thereafter?

CHAPTER 23

Energy Transformations: Respiration and Photosynthesis

To this point we have been looking at static objects, the various large and small molecules that are the raw materials of life. Now we turn to a more fundamental study, the examination of *patterns*. One of the most characteristic and sustaining aspects of life is the pattern of continual energy flow. The molecules that a living organism ingests, more often than not, are valued more for the energy that they contain than for their atoms. Whenever this energy flow is interrupted, life ceases. We shall be concerned with the two most important patterns of energy flow: the breakdown of glucose to yield useful energy (respiration), and the tapping of solar radiation to synthesize glucose for future needs (photosynthesis). These are the dual mainsprings of life on our planet.

Both plants and animals burn their foods with oxygen to produce stored energy, carbon dioxide, and water. Only plants can use energy from the sun to combine carbon dioxide and water into sugars, releasing oxygen in the process. Thus animals are dependent on plants as primary sources of food and as restorers of oxygen to the atmosphere. The relationship in a way is parasitic; we cannot get along without plants but they can get along without us. Joseph Priestley, the discoverer of oxygen, was one of the first to recognize this interdependence of plants and animals, around the time of the American revolution, and some of his equipment is shown on the facing page.

This chapter inevitably will appear complicated, because the machinery that has developed for efficient energy management during the past 3.5 billion years is complicated, with many moving parts. The important thing, however, is to see patterns and understand principles rather than to memorize molecules. The goal is not to learn the structure of pyruvic acid, for example, but to understand how energy is managed.

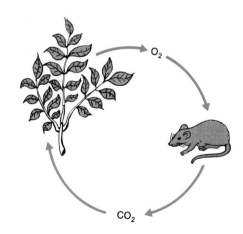

Animals and plants burn glucose with O_2 to give off CO_2 and H_2O. Plants also combine CO_2 with H_2O to synthesize new glucose and to release free oxygen gas into the atmosphere.

Solar energy

Glucose + O_2

Photosynthesis

Respiration

$CO_2 + H_2O$

ATP

Photosynthesis in green plants, and respiration in plants and animals, form a cycle in which C, H, and O atoms are recombined into different molecules that carry energy with them. The driving force for this energy cycle is the sun, which provides the energy for the photosynthesis of glucose.

THE COMMON METABOLIC HERITAGE OF LIFE

We and all other living creatures require a continuous source of chemical free energy to remain alive. This is the reason for eating: We take in highly ordered molecules that have low entropy, high energy, and high free energy, and eject disordered molecules with high entropy, low energy, and low free energy. The ultimate free-energy source for all activity on Earth is the sun (left), and the mechanism for trapping free energy by synthesizing glucose is plant photosynthesis.

All of plant nutrition, and half that of animals, is based on one molecule, glucose ($C_6H_{12}O_6$). Even more remarkable, all life on Earth uses the same metabolic machinery to extract free energy from glucose—not just the same overall reactions, but the same steps, the same intermediates, and the same controlling enzymes. Not every organism uses the entire scheme. Some have lost parts of the machinery, and others never evolved them. Nevertheless, there is a common irreducible metabolic core to all life. We, slime molds, redwoods, and bacteria all share a common chemistry. This is the strongest evidence that life evolved once on this planet, and that all of its inhabitants are related.

We shall look first in this chapter at the metabolism of glucose: its breakdown without oxygen into smaller molecules, the added improvement of combustion with oxygen (respiration), and then the resynthesis of glucose when energy is not needed. We then shall turn to photosynthesis: the light-trapping reactions that make energy-rich ATP and NADPH molecules, and the "dark reactions" that use these molecules to synthesize glucose. Both of these glucose-making pathways have common features, which suggest a common origin, and these clues will be followed up in Chapter 26.

It cannot be emphasized too strongly that this chapter is not intended to be an exercise in memorization. What we are looking for are the pathways of energy flow that living organisms use to stay alive. It is far less important that you remember how to write the conversion of one molecule into another, than that when you look at the two molecules, you understand what happened between one and the other to liberate energy. If any series of chemical reactions can be said to have a strategy, this is what we are after. *Don't memorize the molecules, study the patterns.* It is better to appreciate something you can't remember, than to remember something you don't understand.

PROCARYOTES AND EUCARYOTES

To most people, the fundamental division between living organisms is that between plants and animals. However, there is a far older and more fundamental separation in the history of life, compared to which plants versus animals becomes only a difference in life styles. This is the division between *procaryotes* and *eucaryotes*, that is, between cells without nuclei and those with nuclei (far right). The procaryotes (pre-nuclei) include bacteria and blue-green algae. Their DNA is clustered in the cell fluid without any surrounding boundary or membrane. The metabolic machinery is similarly spread out in the cell: glucose breakdown and energy extraction, photosynthesis if present, and all other processes. There is little that could be called internal structure in a bacterial cell.

The eucaryotes (good nuclei) include green algae, fungi, protozoa, and all other plants and animals. In these organisms the DNA is organized into chromosomes and is confined within a *nucleus* except during cell division. The initial breakdown of glucose to pyruvic acid takes place in the cell fluid, or *cytoplasm*, but respiration (combustion with O_2) occurs in special organelles within the cell called *mitochondria*. Similarly, if photosynthesis is present, it takes place in other cell organelles known as *chloroplasts* (right margin). Eucaryotes represent a more recent and more developed organization for living cells.

For reasons that will be outlined in Chapter 26, we believe that procaryotic life evolved on Earth around 3.5 billion years ago. The "invention" of the more efficient and more versatile eucaryotes took place 2 billion to 1.5 billion years ago; so the first half of life on Earth was procaryotic. Most of the life that we see around us is eucaryotic, and there is a tendency to accept this pattern of life as the norm. This chapter deals mainly with the chemistry of eucaryotes. Bacterial chemistry is much more varied, and one has the feeling that eucaryotes settled upon only one among many possible metabolic choices. Bacterial chemistry can become an exercise in chemical archaeology; many of the fascinating alternative ways of doing things that eucaryotes have uniformly abandoned have been retained in one species of bacteria or another. Some of these alternative chemical schemes are very important and will be discussed in Chapter 26.

We cannot talk meaningfully about these bacterial exceptions before we understand the chemistry of the mainstream, which means the eucaryotes. Two questions will be asked in this chapter:

1. How do eucaryotes break down glucose and other high-free-energy molecules and store the energy for their own use?
2. How do photosynthetic eucaryotes tap solar radiation as a source for synthesizing high-free-energy compounds?

GLUCOSE METABOLISM: OVERALL PLAN

For every mole of glucose that we burn we obtain 673 kcal of heat:

$$C_6H_{12}O_6 + 6O_2 \rightarrow 6CO_2 + 6H_2O(l) \qquad \Delta H^0 = -673 \text{ kcal mole}^{-1}$$

The products are more disordered than the reactants, so we get an extra 13 kcal mole^{-1} of free energy "push" from the increase in entropy: $-T\Delta S^0 = -13$ kcal mole^{-1}. The total free energy of the reaction is

$$\Delta G^0 = \Delta H^0 - T\Delta S^0 = -673 - 13 = -686 \text{ kcal mole}^{-1}$$

This free energy is the potential driving force for other chemical reactions.

If combustion were a one-step process, it would be hopelessly wasteful. There is no efficient way to lock up 686 kcal of chemical energy at one time, in a way that will be useful later. The free energy must be stored in smaller pieces. This is the reason that glucose is

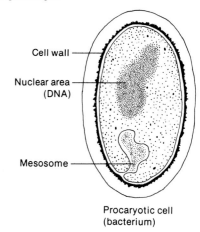

PROCARYOTES

Bacteria
Blue-green algae

Cell wall

Nuclear area
(DNA)

Mesosome

Procaryotic cell
(bacterium)

EUCARYOTES

Green and other algae
Protozoa
Yeasts and fungi
Green plants
Insects
Vertebrates
All animals

Cell wall

Nucleus

Chloroplast

Vacuole

Mitochondrion

Eucaryotic cell
(green plant)

There are only two fundamental kinds of living cells: procaryotes and eucaryotes. Eucaryotes evolved later and are more complex in structure, with different biochemical processes taking place in different compartments, or organelles.

processed through a complex set of biochemical reactions instead of merely touching a match to it.

Part of the process is to break glucose down in a series of small steps, thereby releasing less free energy at any one step. Another trick is to carry out the coupling in two stages—to remove free energy in larger units than the 7.3 kcal mole^{-1} associated with ATP, and to use these units to make several ATP molecules in a separate series of reactions. NAD$^+$ and FAD, which were discussed in Chapter 22, are the means of removal of these larger blocks of energy. If oxygen is the oxidizing agent, then one mole of NADH can be thought of as carrying 52.7 kcal of free energy, and one mole of FADH$_2$, 36.2 kcal. These are the amounts of free energy that are released when the reduced carriers are reoxidized:

$$NADH + H^+ + \tfrac{1}{2}O_2 \rightarrow NAD^+ + H_2O \qquad \Delta G' = -52.7 \text{ kcal mole}^{-1}$$

$$FADH_2 + \tfrac{1}{2}O_2 \rightarrow FAD + H_2O \qquad \Delta G' = -36.2 \text{ kcal mole}^{-1}$$

Every reoxidation of NADH leads to the formation of 3 moles of ATP, with the storage of 3×7.3 kcal $= 21.9$ kcal of free energy. Saving 21.9 kcal out of a total of 52.7 kcal represents a 42% efficiency of energy conversion, which is reasonably typical for biological processes. The reoxidation of FADH$_2$ leads to the synthesis of two ATP molecules and the saving of $2 \times 7.3 = 14.6$ kcal of energy, which is a 40% energy conversion.

The overall scheme of energy extraction in higher organisms is shown on the next page. In the first step, glucose is degraded to pyruvic acid (CH_3—CO—$COOH$), or pyruvate, with the production of relatively little ATP. (Since these organic acids are partially dissociated into anions, it is common to call them interchangeably by the name of the acid or the ion. "Pyruvate" is easier to say than "pyruvic acid," and "lactate" is simpler than "lactic acid." We shall use both forms.) If the NADH produced is reused to convert pyruvate to molecules such as lactate (CH_3—$CHOH$—$COOH$) or ethanol (CH_3—CH_2—OH), then the process can stop at this point. No oxygen is required, but relatively little energy is obtained. This inefficient first step in the energy-extracting process is called *anaerobic* (non-oxygen-using) *fermentation*, or *glycolysis*. It is what yeasts do when they are not given an adequate supply of oxygen, a process that the winemaker turns to his advantage. Our version of this same anaerobic process in muscles yields lactic acid instead of ethanol, and this lactic acid causes muscle cramps, or charley horse, when muscles are exerted too suddenly with inadequate oxygen. When oxygen is brought in to eliminate the lactic acid, the cramps disappear.

The second step in the machinery is much more efficient in extracting energy. Instead of being reduced to lactate or ethanol, pyruvate enters the *citric acid cycle*, where it is broken down to CO_2, with hydrogen atoms being used to reduce NAD$^+$ and FAD to NADH and FADH$_2$. Some additional ATP also is made along the way. The NADH and FADH$_2$ from the citric acid cycle, plus the NADH from fermentation, which now is not needed to convert pyruvate into something else, all flow into the third process, the *respiratory chain*. Here they are reoxidized to NAD$^+$ and FAD and are recycled. The hydrogen atoms ultimately are added to O_2 to make water, and the free energy

$$NADH + H^+ + \tfrac{1}{2}O_2 \rightarrow NAD^+ + H_2O$$

$$\Delta G' = -52.7 \text{ kcal mole}^{-1}$$

$$FADH_2 + \tfrac{1}{2}O_2 \rightarrow FAD + H_2O$$

$$\Delta G' = -36.2 \text{ kcal mole}^{-1}$$

Nicotine adenine dinucleotide and flavin adenine dinucleotide are carrier molecules that can take up free energy when they are reduced, and release this energy when they are reoxidized with oxygen.

558

GLUCOSE METABOLISM
(the nearly universal mechanism for energy extraction)

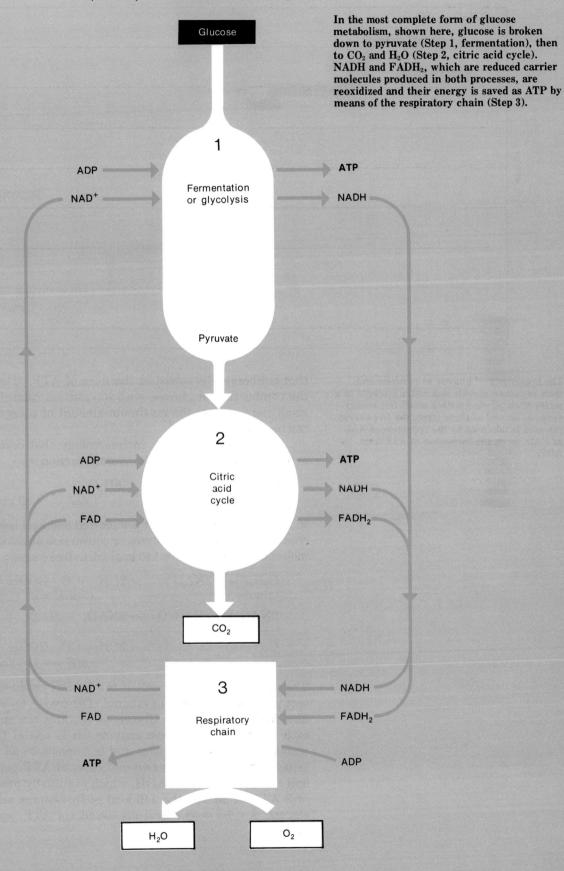

In the most complete form of glucose metabolism, shown here, glucose is broken down to pyruvate (Step 1, fermentation), then to CO_2 and H_2O (Step 2, citric acid cycle). NADH and $FADH_2$, which are reduced carrier molecules produced in both processes, are reoxidized and their energy is saved as ATP by means of the respiratory chain (Step 3).

Glucose

1
Fermentation or glycolysis

ADP → ATP
NAD^+ → NADH

Pyruvate

2
Citric acid cycle

ADP → ATP
NAD^+ → NADH
FAD → $FADH_2$

CO_2

3
Respiratory chain

NAD^+ ← NADH
FAD ← $FADH_2$
ATP ← ADP

H_2O O_2

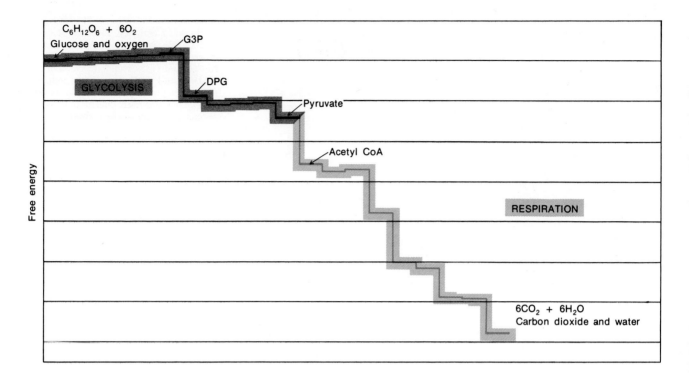

The diagram shows free energy on the vertical axis:

C$_6$H$_{12}$O$_6$ + 6O$_2$
Glucose and oxygen

G3P

GLYCOLYSIS

DPG

Pyruvate

Acetyl CoA

RESPIRATION

6CO$_2$ + 6H$_2$O
Carbon dioxide and water

The breakdown of glucose to pyruvate and then to carbon dioxide and water proceeds in a series of steps, each with a small free energy drop. At several of these steps, the free energy released is taken up by the reduction of NAD$^+$ or FAD, or by the formation of ATP from ADP.

that is liberated is stored in the form of ATP. The overall process—the combustion of glucose with oxygen—is carried out in a series of small steps so that the maximum amount of energy from the reaction can be saved.

The successive drops in free energy that occur during these reactions are shown above. The overall reaction is

$$C_6H_{12}O_6 + 6O_2 \rightarrow 6CO_2 + 6H_2O$$
$$\Delta G' = -686 \text{ kcal mole}^{-1} \text{ of glucose}$$

so carbon dioxide and water are plotted 686 kcal below the level of glucose. The process of glycolysis, or conversion of glucose to two pyruvate molecules, only leads to a 140 kcal fall in free energy:

$$\underset{\text{glucose}}{C_6H_{12}O_6} + 2NAD^+ \rightarrow \underset{\text{pyruvic acid}}{2CH_3-CO-COOH} + 2NADH + 2H^+$$

$$2NADH + 2H^+ + O_2 \rightarrow 2NAD^+ + 2H_2O$$

$$C_6H_{12}O_6 + O_2 \rightarrow 2CH_3-CO-COOH + 2H_2O$$
$$\Delta G' = -140 \text{ kcal mole}^{-1} \text{ of glucose}$$

The process is anaerobic only if the NADH produced is reused to convert pyruvate to lactate or ethanol. Otherwise, O$_2$ is required to reoxidize NADH to NAD$^+$. Glycolysis requires ten successive reactions, each controlled by its own enzyme. It is one of the oldest series of reactions in living organisms and is common to all forms of life. The series of reactions yields two molecules of ATP per glucose molecule, and two molecules of NADH, which eventually produce 6 more ATP, or 8 ATP in all. Of the 140 kcal of free energy released per mole of glucose, $8 \times 7.3 = 58.4$ kcal are saved via ATP, again a 42% energy conversion.

More energy can be obtained from pyruvate by degrading it all the way to CO_2 in the citric acid cycle:

$$2CH_3\text{—}CO\text{—}COOH + 5O_2 \rightarrow 6CO_2 + 4H_2O \qquad \Delta G' = -546 \text{ kcal}$$

The citric acid cycle, which consists of roughly as many successive reactions as glycolysis, is a more recent metabolic invention, found only in organisms that respire and oxidize their foods to completion. It also is physically segregated from the earlier steps: Glycolysis is carried out in the cell cytoplasm, but the steps of the citric acid cycle take place inside the mitochondria. Much more energy is saved in this process: 30 ATP are formed, storing 30×7.3 kcal $= 219$ kcal of free energy per mole of glucose.

If the oxygen supply is ample, then the process just outlined takes place. Glucose is degraded to pyruvate during glycolysis, and pyruvate is broken down to CO_2 in the citric acid cycle, with a yield of 38 molecules of ATP per molecule of glucose. However, if oxygen is in short supply, then in human muscle the pyruvate is reduced to lactate, using up all of the NADH from glycolysis:

$$\underset{\text{pyruvic acid}}{2CH_3\overset{\overset{\textstyle O}{\|}}{\text{—}C}\text{—}COOH} + 2NADH + 2H^+ \rightarrow \underset{\text{lactic acid}}{2CH_3\overset{\overset{\textstyle OH}{|}}{\text{—}CH}\text{—}COOH} + 2NAD^+$$

The overall reaction of converting one glucose molecule to two of lactate is not an oxidation at all, but only a rearrangement and cleavage:

$$C_6H_{12}O_6 \rightarrow 2CH_3\text{—}CH(OH)\text{—}COOH$$
$$\Delta G' = -47 \text{ kcal mole}^{-1} \text{ of glucose}$$

As the diagram at the right indicates, all that is obtained from the conversion of glucose to lactate is *two* molecules of ATP, which makes anaerobic glycolysis a very inefficient process. Yeasts in wine can get nineteen times as much energy per mole of glucose by oxidizing it all the way to CO_2 and H_2O, than by fermenting it anaerobically to ethanol. The winemaker uses this fact to encourage rapid growth of the yeast culture early in the wine-making process by bubbling air through the crushed grapes. No ethanol is produced under these circumstances, but the yeasts multiply rapidly in the presence of a large energy supply. After the yeast colony is large, aeration is halted and the grape juice in the vat is covered with a layer of carbon dioxide to keep out oxygen. The yeasts stop multiplying, turn off their citric acid cycle, and settle down to the anaerobic conversion of glucose to ethanol—less rewarding for the yeast, but more rewarding for the winemaker.

Bacteria have a much richer chemistry. All bacteria begin with fermentation, and for some this is the end of the process. They degrade glucose (and a few other molecules) anaerobically to a number of different waste products; ethanol, or lactic, formic, acetic, propionic, or butyric acids. Other bacteria respire using O_2, giving off H_2O as eucaryotes do. Still others can use sulfate or nitrate as their oxidizing agents. Oxidation with nitrate (yielding N_2) appears to be a recent special adaptation in some bacteria that always prefer O_2 if available. But sulfate respiration (yielding H_2S) may be an independent and very old line of metabolic evolution.

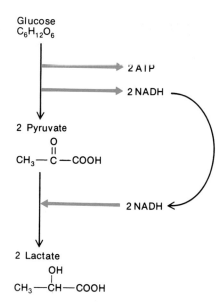

If no oxygen is available to reoxidize NADH via the respiratory chain, the NADH that was produced in glycolysis must be eliminated by using it to re-reduce pyruvate to lactate. Less energy is obtained if this is the case, but at least the organism thereby avoids using NAD⁺ as a fuel. If some other way exists for reoxidizing and recycling NADH, more free energy can be obtained.

561

GLYCOLYSIS: THE OLDEST MACHINERY

With the general strategy of glucose metabolism in mind, we now can look more closely at the first and oldest part of the process, glycolysis. Ten steps are involved in the breakdown of glucose to pyruvate, as outlined on the opposite page, and each step is controlled by its own enzyme. This process takes place in solution in the cytoplasm, or fluid, of the cell.

The first five steps are only pump-priming operations designed to convert one molecule of glucose into two molecules of glyceraldehyde-3-phosphate (G3P):

$$C_6H_{12}O_6 + 2ATP^{4-} \rightarrow 2 \text{ } ^-O\text{--}\underset{\underset{O}{\|}}{\overset{\overset{O^-}{|}}{P}}\text{--}O\text{--}CH_2\text{--}\overset{\overset{OH}{|}}{CH}\text{--}\overset{\overset{O}{\|}}{C}\text{--}H + 2ADP^{3-} + 2H^+$$

glucose

glyceraldehyde-3-phosphate

The free energy that is brought to this reaction by ATP is stored in the phosphate bonds of G3P. These two molecules of G3P produced from a glucose molecule stand poised at the top of the energy hill in the graph on Page 560, ready to tumble down to the level of pyruvate and ultimately to CO_2 and H_2O, releasing energy in the process. To make G3P from glucose, the glucose first is phosphorylated with ATP and rearranged to fructose-6-phosphate, and a second phosphate group is added from another ATP. This molecule then is broken into two fragments, and one fragment is rearranged so that both of them end as G3P.

In the next five steps, from G3P to pyruvate, the energy in the G3P molecule is "cashed in" by using it to make ATP from ADP, and NADH from NAD^+:

$$2 \text{ } ^-O\text{--}\underset{\underset{O}{\|}}{\overset{\overset{O^-}{|}}{P}}\text{--}O\text{--}CH_2\text{--}\overset{\overset{OH}{|}}{CH}\text{--}\overset{\overset{O}{\|}}{C}\text{--}H + 2NAD^+ + 2ADP^{3-} \rightarrow$$

G3P

$$2CH_3\text{--}\overset{\overset{O}{\|}}{C}\text{--}\overset{\overset{O}{\|}}{C}\text{--}OH + 2NADH + 2ATP^{4-}$$

pyruvic acid

The largest single free energy drop occurs between G3P and diphosphoglycerate (DPG), with the storage of energy in NADH. The large free energy yield occurs because this really is a disguised oxidation step, converting an aldehyde into a phosphate ester on the same oxidation level as a carboxylic acid. (Can you see this from the molecular diagrams on the opposite page?) Four smaller free energy steps then take DPG to pyruvate, with the production of four molecules of ATP. Two of these ATP make up for the two that were used to get the process started, and the other two remain as energy "profit" from the reactions. The entire process from glucose to pyruvate shows a net gain of two ATP and two NADH, which eventually will yield six more ATP, for a total of eight moles of ATP per mole of glucose consumed. Pyruvate is not the end of the energy road by any means, as the free energy graph on Page 560 indicates, but the yield obtained from glycolysis is respectable.

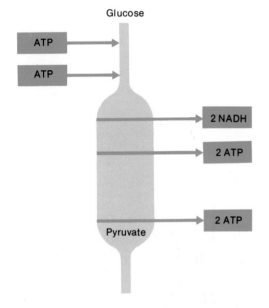

Glucose

ATP

ATP

2 NADH

2 ATP

2 ATP

Pyruvate

Glycolysis requires two moles of ATP per mole of glucose as an energy "primer." At later steps, these and two more moles of ATP are recovered, plus two moles of reduced NADH.

562

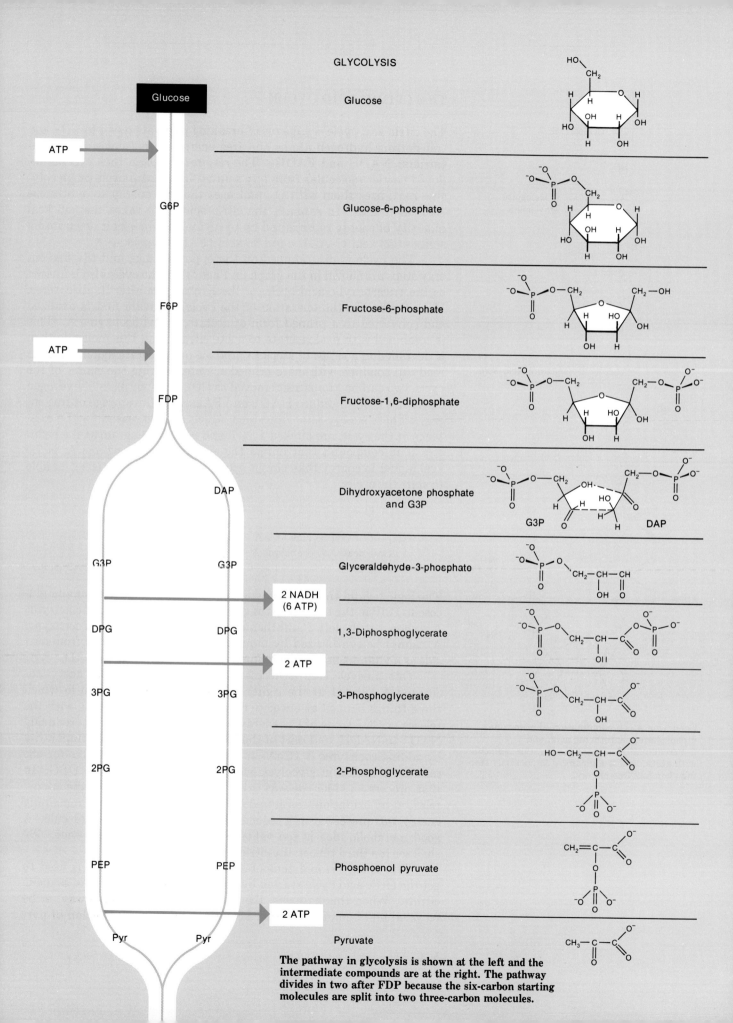

GLYCOLYSIS

Glucose

Glucose-6-phosphate

Fructose-6-phosphate

Fructose-1,6-diphosphate

Dihydroxyacetone phosphate and G3P

Glyceraldehyde-3-phosphate

1,3-Diphosphoglycerate

3-Phosphoglycerate

2-Phosphoglycerate

Phosphoenol pyruvate

Pyruvate

The pathway in glycolysis is shown at the left and the intermediate compounds are at the right. The pathway divides in two after FDP because the six-carbon starting molecules are split into two three-carbon molecules.

THE CITRIC ACID CYCLE

COENZYME A

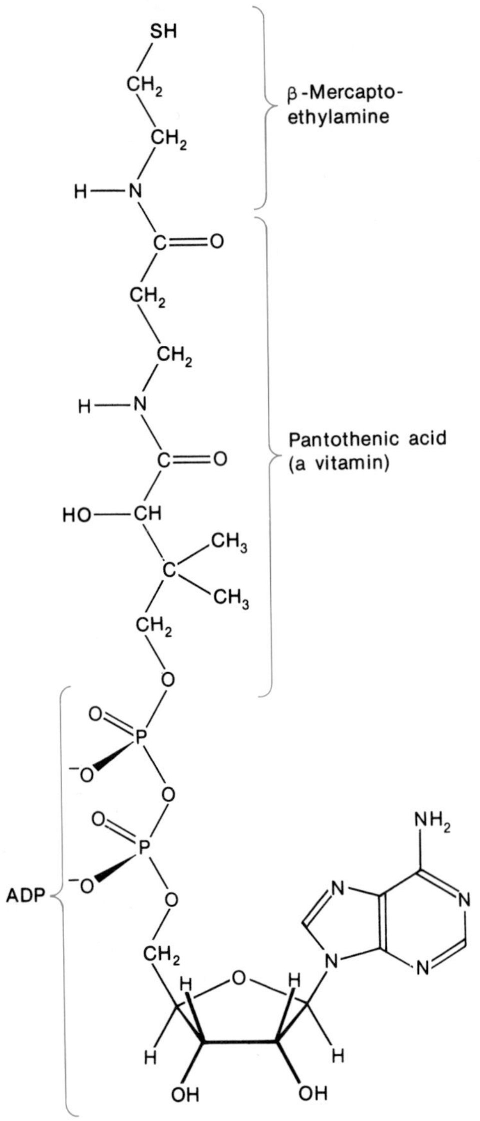

$$SH$$
$$|$$
$$CH_2$$
$$|$$
$$CH_2$$

} β-Mercapto-
ethylamine

$$H—N$$
$$|$$
$$C=O$$
$$|$$
$$CH_2$$
$$|$$
$$CH_2$$
$$|$$
$$H—N$$
$$|$$
$$C=O$$
$$|$$
$$HO—CH \quad CH_3$$
$$\quad\quad C$$
$$\quad\quad CH_3$$
$$|$$
$$CH_2$$
$$|$$
$$O$$

} Pantothenic acid
(a vitamin)

ADP

Coenzyme A is a combination of adenosine diphosphate, pantothenic acid, and β-mercaptoethylamine. Coupling this molecule with acetic acid is a means of temporarily storing chemical free energy.

The citric acid cycle is a means of breaking pyruvate down to CO_2, and transferring hydrogen atoms and free energy to molecules of reduced carriers: NADH and $FADH_2$. The *respiratory chain* then accepts reduced carrier molecules from any source—citric acid cycle or glycolysis—reoxidizes them with O_2, and uses the free energy to synthesize ATP molecules. In essence, the citric acid cycle takes the 546 kcal quantity of energy represented by pyruvate, and breaks it down into a series of 53 kcal (NADH) and 36 kcal ($FADH_2$) packages.

The cycle is diagrammed on the opposite page, and the free energy steps are shown in the graph on Page 567. The cycle also is known as the tricarboxylic acid cycle, or the Krebs cycle after its discoverer, Hans Krebs. In the operation of the cycle, pyruvate first is oxidized and converted to a primed form of acetate, acetyl coenzyme A. This is combined with oxaloacetate to make citrate, and this molecule then is degraded in a series of steps to produce oxaloacetate again, which is ready to combine with more primed acetate. During the course of the cycle, two carbon atoms are removed as CO_2, and four pairs of hydrogen atoms are used to reduce NAD^+ and FAD, with the storage of free energy. These energy-removing steps, which are the reason for the existence of the cycle, are labeled 4, 5, 7, and 9 in the diagram at the right.

The compound that enters the cycle, acetyl coenzyme A, is 7.5 kcal higher in energy than simple acetic acid is, and hence is better able to start the cycle:

$$CH_3—\overset{\overset{\displaystyle O}{\|}}{C}—OH + HS—CoA \rightarrow CH_3—\overset{\overset{\displaystyle O}{\|}}{C}—S—CoA + H_2O$$

acetic acid   coenzyme A   acetyl coenzyme A

$$\Delta G' = +7.5 \text{ kcal mole}^{-1}$$

The logic behind this priming step is the same as that for priming glucose to G3P in the early steps of glycolysis. The structure of coenzyme A is shown at the left. Pantothenic acid, in the working tail of coenzyme A, cannot be synthesized by humans, and must be obtained from outside as a vitamin, as are niacin for NAD^+ and riboflavin for FAD.

One precycle step is necessary to turn pyruvate into acetyl coenzyme A (Step 1 at the right). This is an oxidation step in which three things happen at once: pyruvate is oxidized to acetate with the release of CO_2, some of the energy from oxidation is saved by reducing NAD^+ to NADH, and part of the leftover energy is stored temporarily by adding coenzyme A (CoA) to the acetate. The same three-for-one reaction occurred in glycolysis when G3P was converted to DPG. In that process an aldehyde was oxidized to an ester, some of the energy released by oxidation was stored in NADH, and some of the remaining energy was preserved in a second phosphate bond in the molecule. A good metabolic idea is too valuable not to use more than once. We shall see it a third time in the citric acid cycle.

The energy stored temporarily in acetyl coenzyme A is used to get the citric acid cycle started by a reaction with oxaloacetate to make citrate. When this happens, the coenzyme molecule falls away, to be recycled and bound to another acetate. The overall oxidation of pyr-

THE CITRIC ACID CYCLE

This is the primary energy-extracting machinery of living organisms. It is a cyclic means for converting acetyl coenzyme A into carbon dioxide, which is given off as a waste product, and hydrogen atoms, which are used to reduce NAD^+ and FAD energy-carrier molecules.

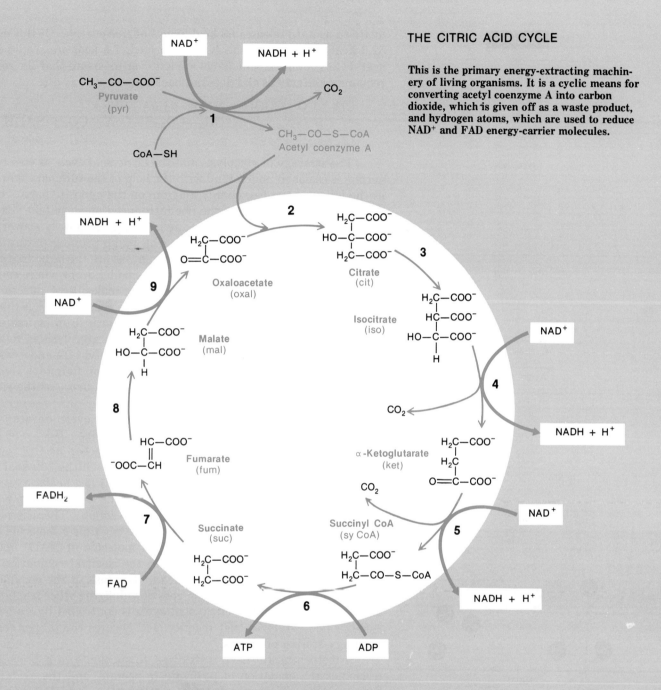

STEPS IN THE CITRIC ACID CYCLE

1. Pyruvate is oxidized to acetate, which is given extra energy by combining it with coenzyme A. Energy is saved as NADH.
2. Acetyl coenzyme A is combined with oxaloacetate from the cycle to make citrate and release coenzyme A for recycling.
3. Citrate is rearranged into isocitrate in preparation for subsequent reactions.

4. Isocitrate is oxidized to α-ketoglutarate, with the release of CO_2 and the saving of energy in the form of NADH.
5. α-Ketoglutarate is oxidized to succinate with release of CO_2; some of the energy is saved as NADH and some is stored temporarily by combining succinate with coenzyme A.
6. Succinyl coenzyme A loses its

coenzyme, and the energy released is ultimately stored as ATP.
7. Succinate is oxidized to fumarate, with the storage of energy in $FADH_2$.
8. Fumarate is rearranged to malate.
9. Malate is oxidized to oxaloacetate with the saving of energy as NADH. Oxaloacetate then is ready to participate in another turn of the cycle.

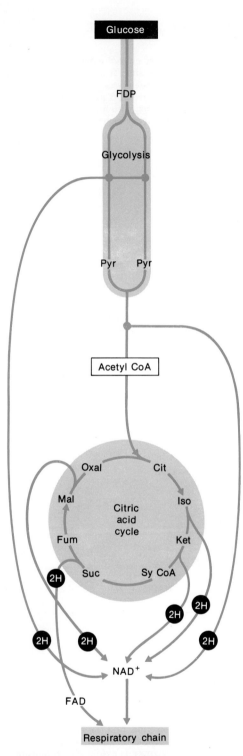

Glucose

FDP

Glycolysis

Pyr   Pyr

Acetyl CoA

Oxal   Cit

Mal   Iso

Citric
acid
cycle

Fum   Ket

2H   Suc   Sy CoA

2H   2H

2H   2H   2H

NAD⁺

FAD

Respiratory chain

FADH₂ from the citric acid cycle, and NADH from the cycle and also from glycolysis, all flow into the respiratory chain to deliver their energy to ATP and be reoxidized and recycled.

uvate to acetate releases 68 kcal mole⁻¹ of free energy. Of this energy, 52.5 kcal are saved in the NADH formed, 7.5 kcal are stored in the acetyl CoA complex, and 8 kcal are left over to ensure that the reaction remains spontaneous and does not back up:

$$CH_3—CO—COOH + NAD^+ + CoA—SH \rightarrow$$
$$CH_3—CO—S—CoA + CO_2 + NADH + H^+$$
$$\Delta G' = -8 \text{ kcal mole}^{-1}$$

The strategy of glycolysis and the citric acid cycle as energy converters is easier to understand with the help of the summary flow chart at the left, and the free energy diagram on the opposite page, which is a more complete version of the one introduced on Page 560. Each intermediate in glycolysis and the citric acid cycle now is shown at its proper energy level below glucose. The pump-priming nature of the steps from glucose to G3P now is apparent, as are the large free energy drop where NADH is made and the two smaller drops where energy is stored as ATP during glycolysis. Since one molecule of glucose yields two molecules of pyruvate, everything to the right of FDP is drawn in terms of two molecules at a time. The 140 kcal drop in free energy from glucose (Glu) to pyruvate (Pyr) during glycolysis is relatively small compared with the much larger drop to acetyl CoA and eventually to oxaloacetate. The numbers on the individual stairsteps represent the free energies of those molecules relative to glucose as the starting point.

In the course of one turn of the citric acid cycle, citrate is rearranged to isocitrate with little free energy change. Isocitrate is oxidized to α-ketoglutarate with the loss of one carbon as CO_2, and the energy from the oxidation is stored as NADH. Of the 109 kcal of energy released (per two isocitrates), $2 \times 52.7 = 105.4$ kcal are saved, an example of remarkably efficient coupling. This coupling is one of the main jobs of the enzyme controlling the reaction. There is nothing intrinsic in the chemistry to dictate that every time a molecule of isocitrate is oxidized to α-ketoglutarate, a molecule of NAD^+ must be reduced to NADH. The free energy of the isocitrate oxidation could just as well be wasted as heat instead. The task of the enzyme is to make sure that when one reaction goes downhill, the other reaction goes uphill. Each step in the citric acid cycle is controlled by its own enzyme, which catalyzes that reaction and ensures the proper coupling to energy-storing processes.

α-Ketoglutarate next is oxidized to succinate in a process that resembles the oxidation of pyruvate to acetate, and the oxidation of G3P to DPG. The same pattern is followed: α-ketoglutarate is oxidized to succinate, part of the energy is stored in NADH, and part is saved temporarily by making a coenzyme A complex with the product. Succinyl coenzyme A then is broken down in the following step, with the formation of ATP. (Guanosine triphosphate, or GTP, actually is formed first, and then is used to make ATP.)

With the formation of succinate, the two big energy-releasing and CO_2-producing steps of the cycle are over, and the original six-carbon citrate has been degraded to a four-carbon molecule. However, more energy is still available. Succinate is oxidized to fumarate with the storage of energy in FADH₂, fumarate is rearranged to malate, and

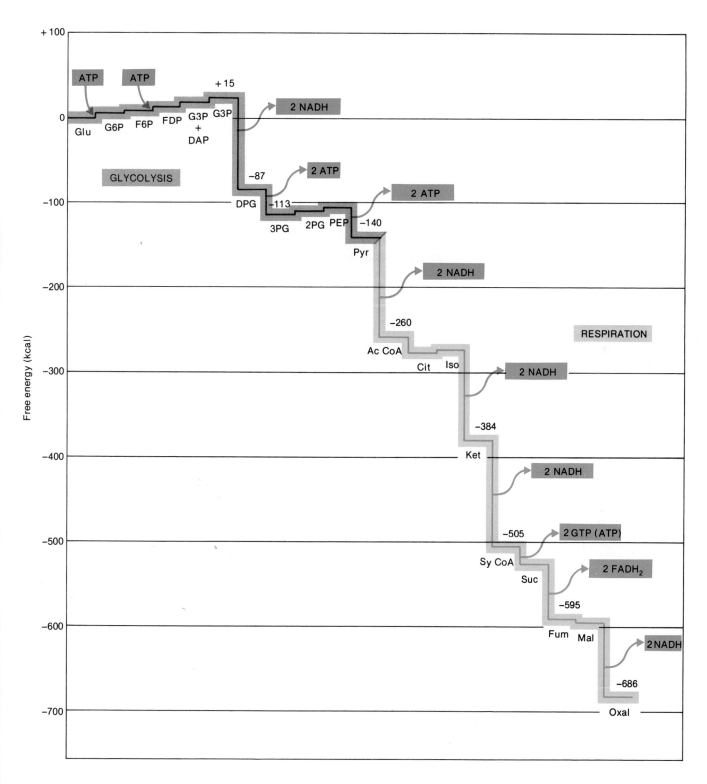

The free energy of each intermediate compound in glycolysis and the citric acid cycle, measured from the starting glucose as a baseline. Places where energy is added via ATP, or removed via ATP or reduced dinucleotides, are marked. These energy removals via NADH and FADH$_2$ all occur at steps that involve large decreases in free energy. Only in such a deliberate, stepwise manner can such a large quantity of energy (686 kcal) be broken up into smaller units and processed efficiently.

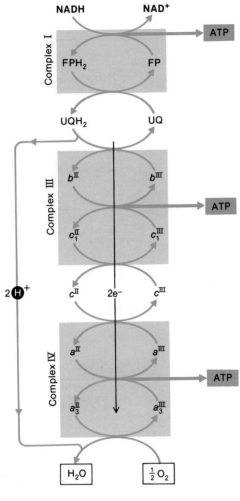

THE RESPIRATORY CHAIN

Key
FP = Flavoprotein
UQ = Ubiquinone
b,c,a = Cytochromes
II = Fe(II); III = Fe(III)

Each member of the respiratory chain is reduced by the compound before it in the chain, and reoxidized by the substance following it. The initial compound to be oxidized is NADH, and the final oxidizing substance is molecular O_2. In the early steps of the chain, reduction occurs by transfer of H atoms, but beyond ubiquinone (UQ), reduction entails the transfer only of electrons from one iron-containing protein to the next.

malate finally is oxidized to oxaloacetate with the simultaneous reduction of NAD^+. The cycle is completed when oxaloacetate combines with acetyl CoA and another turn of the wheel begins.

The unfinished business is the machinery for reoxidizing NADH and $FADH_2$ and making use of their energy. This is the topic of the next section. At this point we can stop and draw a balance sheet of the entire energy situation, from glycolysis through the citric acid cycle.

Aerobic glycolysis:	2 ATP + 2 NADH + 0 $FADH_2$
2 Pyr to 2 acetyl-CoA:	0 ATP + 2 NADH + 0 $FADH_2$
2 Turns of cycle:	2 ATP + 6 NADH + 2 $FADH_2$
Total:	4 ATP + 10 NADH + 2 $FADH_2$

This is equivalent to a total of $(4 \times 1) + (10 \times 3) + (2 \times 2) = 38$ ATP molecules per molecule of glucose. Of the total 686 kcal released per mole of glucose, $38 \times 7.3 = 277$ kcal are saved, a 40% overall efficiency. The other 409 kcal are not entirely useless. They ensure the thermodynamic spontaneity of the reaction, and provide body heat:

$$C_6H_{12}O_6 + 6O_2 + 38ADP + 38P_i \rightarrow 6CO_2 + 6H_2O + 38ATP$$
$$\Delta G' = -409 \text{ kcal}$$

Several energy-producing pathways besides glycolysis funnel together and enter the citric acid cycle to produce energy. When fats are used as an energy source, the fatty acids are broken down into two-carbon acetate and fed into the cycle. During the metabolism of proteins, some amino acids are converted into pyruvate or acetate and then enter the cycle. Thus the biochemical machinery that probably evolved to make maximum use of the products of glycolysis now is used with many other processes. Any molecule that can be broken down to acetate can enter the citric acid cycle and yield energy.

RESPIRATION: REOXIDIZING THE CARRIERS

Respiration completes the process begun by glycolysis and the citric acid cycle, because it provides a way of reoxidizing the carrier molecules, NADH and $FADH_2$. So far there has been no reason to call the reactions that we have discussed "aerobic" because no oxygen has been involved. The oxidative steps have involved only the transfer of H atoms from the molecule being oxidized to a carrier molecule. The respiratory chain provides the means of finally linking these reactions to the use of oxygen.

We again are faced with the dilemma of having the energy available (52.7 kcal per NADH) larger than the amount that can be received and stored in one step (7.3 kcal per ATP). The answer, as before, is a series of smaller free energy steps, at three of which ATP is synthesized. The steps are the successive reduction and reoxidation of the members of the respiratory chain, shown at the left. Incoming NADH is oxidized to NAD^+ in the process of reducing a flavoprotein, an enzyme that has attached to it a flavin group similar to that found in FAD. This flavoprotein is reoxidized as it reduces a small organic molecule, ubiquinone, shown in the far right margin. (The name means

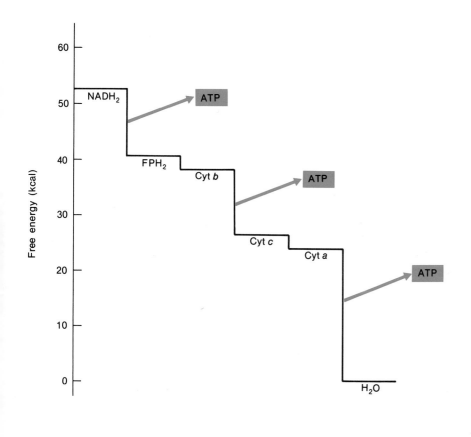

The successive oxidation–reduction reactions in the respiratory chain involve small, stepwise decreases in free energy. At the largest of these steps, three molecules of ATP are synthesized.

UBIQUINONE

6 to 10 isoprene units in chain

"everywhere-quinone," and was chosen by its discoverer because the molecule is found universally in all eucaryotic cells.) Ubiquinone then reduces cytochrome *b*, which is the first of a series of related proteins that contain iron in a heme group, as do myoglobin and hemoglobin, discussed in the preceding chapter. In the subsequent ladder of cytochromes, *b* reduces cytochrome c_1, c_1 reduces cytochrome *c*, *c* reduces cytochrome *a*, *a* reduces cytochrome a_3, and the respiratory chain comes to an end when cytochrome a_3 reduces oxygen to H_2O.

Ubiquinone is a small carrier molecule with a long isoprene-derived tail related to the phytol tail of chlorophyll, to β-carotene, and to the other terpene derivatives discussed in Chapter 20. The working head of ubiquinone is a quinone ring that can accept two hydrogen atoms at the para positions and give them up again. From NADH to ubiquinone, reduction involves the transfer of hydrogen atoms. Beyond ubiquinone, the reducing hydrogens are split into protons, which are released into the solution, and electrons, which travel through the cytochromes from one heme iron atom to the next. Each cytochrome molecule is reduced to the Fe (II) state by the one before it, and then reoxidized to Fe(III).

All of the foregoing respiratory reactions take place inside mitochondria within the cell. The components of the respiratory chain are embedded in the inner mitochondrial membrane, and are organized into four complexes. Complex I contains a flavoprotein (a nonheme iron protein of uncertain function) and phospholipid, and has a molecular

Glucose

$ATP \longrightarrow$ $\longrightarrow P_i$

G6P

F6P

$ATP \longrightarrow$ $\longrightarrow P_i$

FDP

2 G3P

2 NADH $\longleftarrow$ $\longleftarrow$ 2 NADH

2 DPG

2 ATP $\longleftarrow$ $\longleftarrow$ 2 ATP

2 3PG

2 2PG

2 CO$_2$

2 PEP

$\longleftarrow$ 2 ATP

2 Oxaloacetate

(2 Malate)

Cell fluid

(2 Malate)

2 Oxaloacetate

2 ATP

2 CO$_2$ $\qquad$ 2 ATP

2 Pyruvate

Mitochondrion

2 Pyruvate

Gluconeogenesis, the conversion of excess pyruvate to glucose for storage (upward arrows), is almost the reverse of the machinery of glycolysis (downward arrows). Wherever glycolysis yields energy in the form of NADH or ATP, gluconeogenesis requires the same quantities of energy to drive the reaction uphill. Wherever glycolysis requires ATP as an energy primer, gluconeogenesis wastes the equivalent amount of energy by releasing inorganic phosphate, P_i. The crucial energy-adding step from pyruvate to oxaloacetate in gluconeogenesis must be carried out inside the mitochondrion, since this is where the necessary enzymes are. Oxaloacetate must be converted temporarily to malate to pass through the mitochondrial membrane. All of the enzymes of the citric acid cycle are inside the mitochondrion, and the components of the respiratory chain are embedded in the inner mitochondrial membrane.

weight of around 600,000. Complex III (270,000 molecular weight) contains cytochromes c and c_1, more nonheme iron protein, and phospholipids. Complex IV (cytochrome oxidase) has a weight of 200,000 and contains cytochromes a and a_3, copper atoms, and phospholipids. Each pair of complexes is connected by a mobile shuttle, ubiquinone between complexes I and III, and the small cytochrome c molecule between III and IV.

A slightly simplified free energy diagram of the respiratory chain is shown on the preceding page. Each of the three complexes is the site of a major free energy drop, which is coupled to the synthesis of one ATP molecule. The overall action of the chain is to reoxidize NADH with O_2, and to use the released energy to produce three ATP.

Succinate makes only two ATP molecules because it comes into the chain late. The FAD, mentioned in the discussion of the citric acid cycle as being reduced by succinate to FADH$_2$, actually is bound to an enzyme in the form of another flavoprotein on the inner mitochondrial membrane. This flavoprotein and some phospholipid make up Complex II. The FADH$_2$ reduces ubiquinone directly without making any ATP, and the respiratory chain continues past ubiquinone as before, yielding only two ATP per FADH$_2$ oxidized.

This is the master plan by which living organisms convert organic compounds into energy. Carbohydrates are broken into glucose monomers and sent along the glycolytic pathway and citric acid cycle. Fats and proteins are chopped into two-carbon acetate units and fed directly into the cycle. The metabolite molecules are oxidized by removing hydrogens and transferring them to NAD$^+$ and FAD. These molecules then carry the hydrogens to oxygen and use the released oxidation energy to synthesize ATP.

So far we have been looking at the machinery for degradation of glucose to pyruvate and ultimately to CO_2 and water. Whenever there is an excess of pyruvate, and energy is not needed immediately, pyruvate can be reconverted to glucose for storage as glycogen in the liver. (Recall from Chapter 21 that glycogen is a branched-chain starchlike molecule.) This reverse process is *gluconeogenesis*, which simply means "new glucose generation" (left margin). It is almost equivalent to glycolysis in reverse since, except for three controlling steps, it uses the same intermediate compounds, the same reactions in reverse, and even the same enzymes.

It is logical from the standpoint of economy that glucose buildup should use some of the same intermediates and enzymes as glucose degradation. What is surprising is that it also appears that a part of this gluconeogenesis scheme has been picked up bodily and adapted for use in the dark reactions of photosynthesis, even though the starting point for glucose manufacture in photosynthesis is CO_2 instead of pyruvate. We will see evidence later in this chapter that respiration may have evolved from photosynthesis. It also appears that photosynthesis may have taken over some of the chemistry of glycolysis and gluconeogenesis. These borrowings illustrate the idea that nothing is ever really new in evolution. Just as hands and feet came from fins, and lungs from gills, so respiration borrowed from photosynthesis, and photosynthesis from glucose metabolism.

PHOTOSYNTHESIS: THE GRAND STRATEGY

Photosynthesis is a mechanism for using light energy to synthesize glucose from carbon dioxide and water. It is not the only way in which a cell can synthesize glucose, but it is crucial because it opens the way to the use of a virtually unlimited source of free energy, the sun.

The overall reaction is the reverse of glucose oxidation:

$$6CO_2 + 6H_2O \xrightarrow{h\nu} C_6H_{12}O_6 + 6O_2 \qquad \Delta G' = +686 \text{ kcal mole}^{-1} \text{ of glucose}$$

A photosynthesizing plant needs a source of carbon atoms (from CO_2) and a source of reducing hydrogen atoms (from H_2O). The reaction above is the one followed by all photosynthetic eucaryotes and blue-green algae. Some photosynthetic bacteria use CO_2 as their carbon source, but obtain reducing hydrogens from H_2S, H_2, or organic molecules. Other bacteria can use organic matter as both C and H sources. No bacteria use water and release O_2 in the way that blue-green algae and higher plants do. Bacterial photosynthesis will be discussed later, but for the moment we shall focus on the O_2-releasing process of photosynthesis.

The photosynthetic machinery can be divided into two stages, which are connected by ATP and NADPH (not NADH) but otherwise seem to operate quite independently of one another. NADPH, or reduced nicotinamide adenine dinucleotide phosphate, is a carrier molecule identical to NADH except for another phosphate group esterified with the 2' hydroxyl of the adenosine ribose ring (right). The extra phosphate group may function as a label, to say, in effect, "This reduced nucleotide belongs to photosynthesis. Do not use for respiration." The first of the two stages of photosynthesis, the "dark reactions," involve the synthesis of glucose from CO_2 and a reducing agent, or the "fixation" of CO_2. These reactions can take place perfectly well in the absence of light, as long as supplies of NADPH as the reducing agent and ATP for driving energy are available. ATP and the reducing agent are produced by the "light reactions," which involve the trapping of light energy by chlorophyll molecules, and which can operate only in the presence of light. Although the light reactions are what we ordinarily think of as photosynthesis, they appear to be a later addition to the older synthetic machinery of the dark reactions.

The dark reactions resemble parts of the glycolytic and gluconeogenesis pathways, sharing with them some of the same intermediates and enzymes. Confusion is avoided by a physical separation, since glycolysis and gluconeogenesis take place in the cytoplasm, whereas the dark reactions are located inside the chloroplasts of a plant cell. The ability to "fix" CO_2 in organic molecules is one of the oldest and most universal biochemical talents of life. These three glucose pathways appear to be descendants of an extremely ancient carbon biochemistry.

NADP+ (nicotinamide adenine dinucleotide phosphate) differs from NAD+ in having an additional phosphate group at the 2' position of the ribose ring. Eucaryotes use NAD+ for respiration and NADP+ in photosynthesis, whereas bacteria use NAD+ for both purposes.

The dark reactions can be summarized as follows:

$$6CO_2 + 6H_2O \rightarrow C_6H_{12}O_6 + 6O_2 \qquad \Delta G' = +686 \text{ kcal mole}^{-1}$$
$$12NADPH + 12H^+ + 6O_2 \rightarrow 12NADP^+ + 12H_2O \qquad \Delta G' = -632 \text{ kcal mole}^{-1}$$
$$18ATP \rightarrow 18ADP + 18P_i \qquad \Delta G' = -130 \text{ kcal mole}^{-1}$$

$$6CO_2 + 12NADPH + 12H^+ + 18ATP \rightarrow \qquad \Delta G' = -76 \text{ kcal mole}^{-1}$$
$$C_6H_{12}O_6 + 12NADP^+ + 18ADP + 18P_i + 6H_2O \qquad \text{of glucose}$$

The reaction of CO_2 with NADPH by itself would lack 54 kcal of being spontaneous, but the addition of 18 ATP as an energy source makes the overall process spontaneous by 76 kcal of free energy.

The light reactions are not really connected with glucose synthesis except as a continuous source of ATP and NADPH. In the light reactions, light energy trapped by chlorophyll or by various carotenoids is funneled to chlorophyll and then used as a free energy source to synthesize ATP and to reduce $NADP^+$. These molecules then are used to power the dark reactions.

Chemosynthetic bacteria have developed ways of obtaining ATP and NADPH by oxidizing inorganic substances. With these sources they then can use the dark reactions to synthesize glucose without any dependence upon light. Some of the inorganic oxidation reactions are given below.

Energy-producing oxidation reaction	Type of bacteria
$2H_2 + O_2 \rightarrow 2H_2O$	Hydrogen bacteria
$H_2S \rightarrow S \rightarrow S_2O_3^{2-} \rightarrow SO_4^{2-}$	Colorless sulfur bacteria
$Fe^{2+} \rightarrow Fe^{3+}$	Iron bacteria
$NH_3 \rightarrow NO_2^- \rightarrow NO_3^-$	Nitrate, nitrite bacteria

As far as we can determine, chemosynthesis is not in any sense an ancestor of photosynthesis, but is a late, special adaptation used by a few bacteria to exploit special energy-rich environments. However, chemosynthesis in bacteria does emphasize how tenuous the connection is between the light reactions and the dark reactions of photosynthesis, and how well the latter can function if given some other source of energy (ATP) and reducing power (NADH or NADPH).

THE DARK REACTIONS: CARBOHYDRATE SYNTHESIS

The reactions leading to the synthesis of glucose from CO_2 are shown on the next page. The most remarkable feature about this scheme is that the steps from 3PG (3-phosphoglycerate) to glucose have been lifted bodily from the gluconeogenesis pathway (Page 570), with the same intermediates, same enzymes, and same input of carrier molecules and ejection of phosphate. A pre-existing set of reactions and enzymes has been "borrowed" and put to use at another place (inside chloroplasts) for another purpose.

The object of gluconeogenesis is only to make glucose from pyruvate, whereas photosynthesis must begin with a much less reduced com-

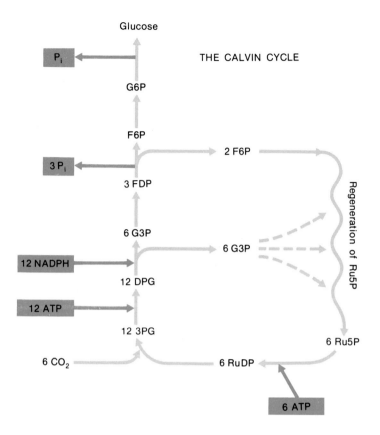

Glucose

THE CALVIN CYCLE

P_i

G6P

F6P

2 F6P

3 P_i

3 FDP

6 G3P

6 G3P

12 NADPH

12 DPG

12 ATP

12 3PG

6 CO_2

6 RuDP

6 Ru5P

6 ATP

Regeneration of Ru5P

The Calvin cycle is the means by which CO_2 is converted into glucose during photosynthesis. It turns what essentially is a reversed glycolysis pathway into a cycle by using a five-carbon sugar (RuDP) as a working substance.

pound, CO_2. How can a set of reactions designed to commence with a three-carbon molecule be adapted to work with a one-carbon molecule? The answer is simple and elegant: Combine the CO_2 with a five-carbon sugar, then cleave the product in half to obtain two three-carbon starting molecules. This plan will work forever if some of the intermediates are shunted off the glucose-synthesis track and used to make enough five-carbon sugar to start the process over again with more CO_2.

This is exactly what has been done in the dark reactions. A portion of a linear process has been turned into one leg of a cycle, known as the Calvin cycle after its discoverer, Melvin Calvin. The five-carbon sugar that keeps the cycle turning is ribulose-1',5'-diphosphate (RuDP). Adding CO_2 and H_2O to RuDP and cleaving the result in half leads to two molecules of 3PG, an intermediate in gluconeogenesis.

The relative numbers of the molecules involved are indicated on the flow diagram above. To make *one* glucose molecule, six CO_2 are combined with six RuDP to produce twelve molecules of 3PG. These in principle could be used to make six glucose molecules, but then the process would not be cyclic, and would grind to a halt as soon as all the RuDP was used up. Instead, only two of the molecules of 3PG are destined to end as glucose, while the other ten, which contain a total of thirty carbon atoms, continue around the Calvin cycle and eventually are converted into six molecules of five-carbon RuDP, ready for reuse.

The Calvin cycle as an adaptation of gluconeogenesis is a beautiful example of the subtlety that trial-and-error and three billion years of

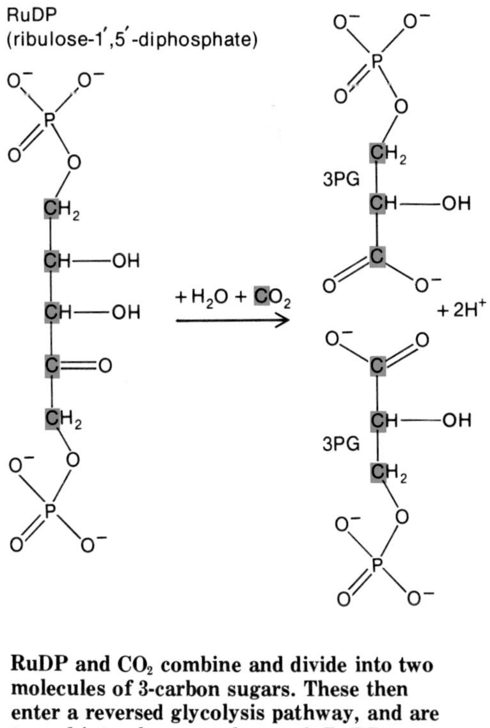

RuDP and CO_2 combine and divide into two molecules of 3-carbon sugars. These then enter a reversed glycolysis pathway, and are turned into glucose and enough RuDP to repeat the cycle.

573

Absorption spectrum in the visible region for several light-absorbing pigments involved in photosynthesis (right). Wavelengths are in nanometers, nm (1 nm = 10 Å). Delocalized electron systems for two pigments are indicated by a color tint (below).

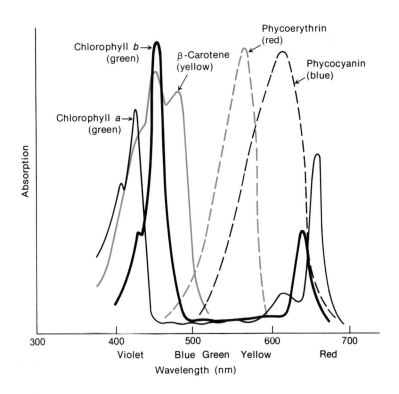

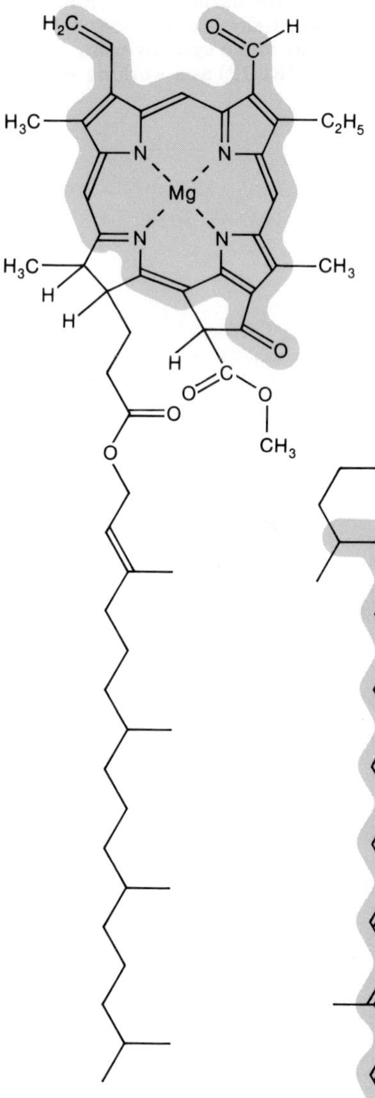

Chlorophyll *b*

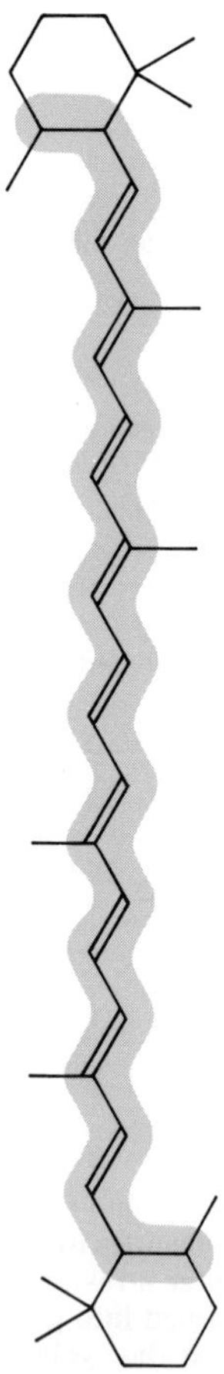

β -Carotene

evolution are capable of. The breakdown of glucose to CO_2 requires all of the complex chemistry of the citric acid cycle. The synthesis of glucose from CO_2 avoids the necessity of running a citric acid cycle in reverse by the trick of using RuDP as a working molecule, and turning a linear gluconeogenesis pathway into a cycle. If our current ideas about the order in which various steps in metabolism evolved on Earth are correct, then at the time that gluconeogenesis was adapted for the purposes of the dark reactions of photosynthesis, life was still anaerobic and the citric acid cycle did not yet exist.

THE LIGHT REACTIONS: TRAPPING SOLAR ENERGY

The heart of the light-trapping apparatus is a collection of molecules that have delocalized electrons: chlorophylls and β-carotene (left) in green plants, and phycoerythrin and phycocyanin in red and blue-green algae. The absorption spectra of these pigments are shown above. The colors of each are understandable in terms of the wavelengths of light that are *not* absorbed. Chlorophyll *a* differs from *b* in having a —CH_3 instead of a —CHO at the upper right corner of the ring, as it is drawn in the margin. This diminishes the extent of delocalization by two atoms, increases the energy-level separations, and shifts the main absorption from the blue toward the violet (see spectra). The carotenes, phycoerythrin, and phycocyanin are "antenna molecules" that trap light at wavelengths at which the chlorophylls are inefficient, and pass their electronic excitation on to chlorophyll.

574

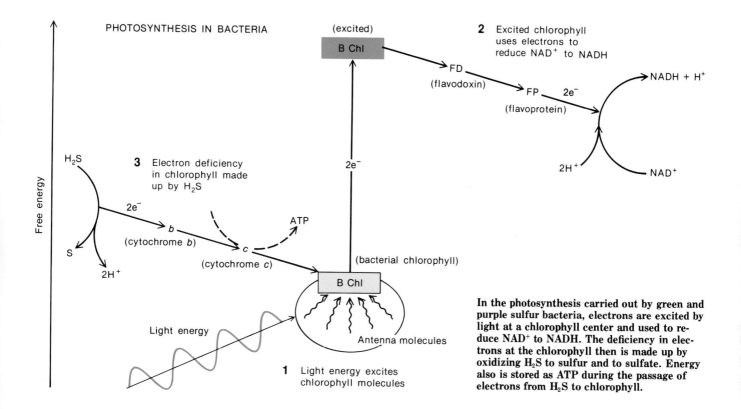

PHOTOSYNTHESIS IN BACTERIA

(excited)
B Chl

2 Excited chlorophyll
uses electrons to
reduce NAD$^+$ to NADH

FD
(flavodoxin)

FP
(flavoprotein)

2e$^-$

NADH + H$^+$

2H$^+$

NAD$^+$

H$_2$S

3 Electron deficiency
in chlorophyll made
up by H$_2$S

2e$^-$

Free energy

b
(cytochrome b)

ATP

c
(cytochrome c)

S

2H$^+$

2e$^-$

(bacterial chlorophyll)

B Chl

Light energy

Antenna molecules

1 Light energy excites
chlorophyll molecules

In the photosynthesis carried out by green and
purple sulfur bacteria, electrons are excited by
light at a chlorophyll center and used to reduce NAD$^+$ to NADH. The deficiency in electrons at the chlorophyll then is made up by
oxidizing H$_2$S to sulfur and to sulfate. Energy
also is stored as ATP during the passage of
electrons from H$_2$S to chlorophyll.

Photosynthesis is simplest in bacteria, and the process in green
and purple sulfur bacteria is diagrammed above. Light energy is absorbed by various antenna molecules and is passed on to a bacterio-
chlorophyll molecule (BChl above) in the form of electronic excitation.
The chlorophyll molecule uses these excited electrons to reduce NAD$^+$
to NADH, passing them first to a flavodoxin (FD, a nonheme iron protein) and then to a flavoprotein (FP). (Bacteria use NADH, even in
photosynthesis.) The chlorophyll molecule then is deficient in electrons, but the shortage is compensated for by an external reducing
agent such as H$_2$S. The H$_2$S is oxidized first to elemental sulfur and ultimately to sulfate. Protons are released into solution, and electrons are
fed into an electron-transport chain that leads to the bacteriochloro-
phyll molecule. This chain contains cytochromes b and c, and other
components such as quinones. It resembles the electron-transport
chain of respiration in this and in another key property: Some of the
energy that is released when electrons run down the free energy scale
from H$_2$S to chlorophyll is captured and used to synthesize ATP. Thus
photosynthetic bacteria obtain two benefits: energy stored as ATP,
and energy and reducing power combined in NADH.

These photosynthetic bacteria have no respiratory machinery for
converting extra NADH into ATP. However, they can control the relative amount of ATP and NADH they make by a kind of "short circuit"
of photosynthesis. The process diagrammed above is called *noncyclic
photophosphorylation*, since ADP is phosphorylated to ATP by light
energy, without recycling electrons. Reducing power is continually
used in making NADH, so an external source of reducing power is con-

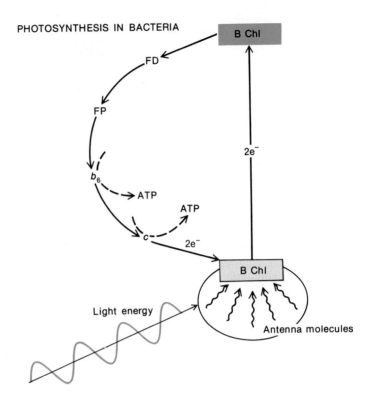

PHOTOSYNTHESIS IN BACTERIA

In purple, nonsulfur bacterial photosynthesis, electrons are excited at the chlorophyll center and then allowed to run through a cyclic chain of protein molecules and to return to the chlorophyll center. Along the way, some of the energy of excitation of the electron is used to synthesize ATP.

stantly needed. The bacteria also can send their electrons back around the circuit, passing them to cytochrome b_6, and from there to some member of the original electron-transport chain. This process is termed *cyclic photophosphorylation* (above), and requires no H_2S but consequently produces no NADH. It appears to have an extra site of ATP synthesis to take advantage of the larger free energy drop between excited and unexcited chlorophyll. The mix between the noncyclic and the cyclic processes depends on the bacterium's relative need at the time for simple energy, or for reducing power for synthesis.

The other class of photosynthetic bacteria is the purple nonsulfur bacteria. These bacteria do not use H_2S as a source of reducing power, and manage quite well with cyclic photophosphorylation. This may be possible because they have made a marvelous invention: They have a citric acid cycle and respiratory machinery, and can function quite well as oxygen respirers if they are kept in the dark, although they much prefer to obtain their ATP energy from photosynthesis. When operating photosynthetically, they apparently use NADH from the citric acid cycle as one source of reducing power for synthesis.

The blue-green algae made another great invention that released them completely from the need for H_2S as a reducing agent in photosynthesis. They evolved a method to turn a very poor reducing agent, H_2O, into a usable one by activating it with light. Although H_2O is a bad reducing agent, it is available everywhere. Any organism that found a way to take electrons away from water obviously would have a great advantage over its more pedestrian cousins. The key was the development of *two* photocenters, one to excite electrons for reduction of NAD^+ (actually, $NADP^+$) in the usual way, the other to provide the

576

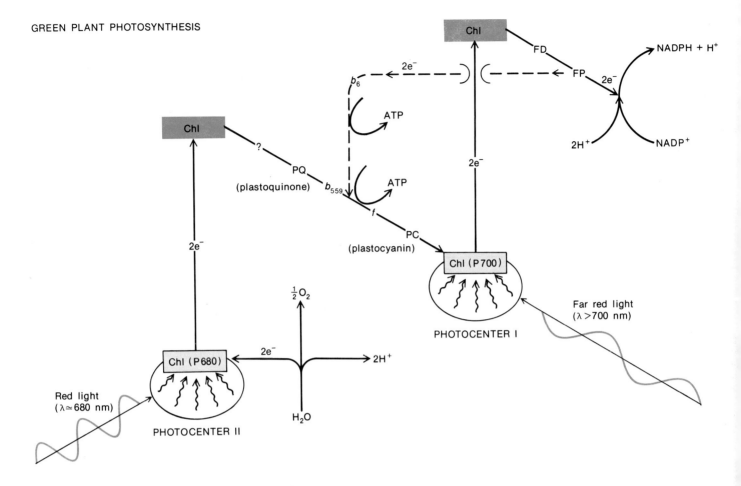

energy required to strip electrons away from water molecules to leave O_2 gas and hydrogen ions:

$$H_2O \xrightarrow[\text{energy}]{\text{light}} \tfrac{1}{2}O_2 + 2H^+ + 2e^-$$

These are Photocenters I and II, diagrammed above. Photocenter I, which is analogous to the photocenter in bacteria, absorbs light in the far-red region at wavelengths of 700 nanometers (7000 Å) and longer. Its chlorophyll is designated as P700 for "700-nm pigment." Photocenter II absorbs slightly shorter wavelengths, with a maximum absorption around 680 nm. This energy is used to excite electrons on that chlorophyll, send them cascading down an electron-transport chain to Photocenter I, and remove electrons from water to make up the deficit.

This is the two-photocenter, water-using, oxygen-liberating form of photosynthesis that has been adopted by all green plants. It is more versatile because it enables the organism to use two photons of light to make a good reducing agent out of a bad one, rather than forcing the organism to seek out a better reducing agent such as H_2S. We know more about the electron-transport chain that bridges the photocenters than we do about the corresponding chain in bacteria, and its resemblance to the respiratory chain is striking. The molecule that accepts electrons from excited Photocenter II may be a flavoprotein analogous to the flavoprotein that accepts electrons from NADH in respiration.

In green-plant photosynthesis, the deficiency of electrons in Photocenter I, after excitation of electrons and synthesis of NADPH, is made up by excited electrons from Photocenter II, which, in turn, receives electrons from the cleavage of water molecules into H^+, e^-, and O_2.

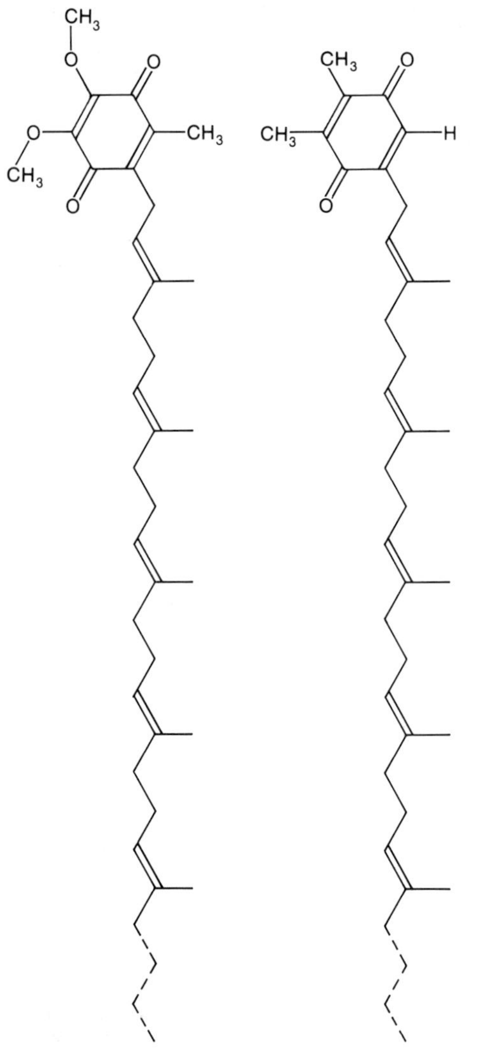

Ubiquinone
(respiration)

Plastoquinone
(photosynthesis)

In both respiration and photosynthesis, one of the intermediates in the electron-transport chain is a quinone molecule, with a characteristic quinone ring and a long hydrocarbon tail. The oxidized forms are shown here. The quinone can accept one hydrogen atom to become a semiquinone, and a second H to become a hydroquinone; thus the two double-bonded O atoms on the ring have been reduced to —OH groups.

This molecule, whatever it is, passes electrons to plastoquinone, which is closely related to the ubiquinone of respiration. From there the electrons go to b- and c-type cytochromes, to a copper protein (plastocyanin), and finally to Photocenter I. (The cytochrome f of photosynthesis actually is a c-type protein. It was labeled f for the Latin "frons," or leaf.) As before, ATP is generated during the passage of electrons down the chain, although how much ATP is not known with certainty. Like the sulfur bacteria, green plants also can carry out part of their photosynthetic process cyclically, passing electrons from the flavoprotein near the end of the chain, back to the middle of the electron-transport chain, and making ATP but not NADPH.

Bacteria that photosynthesize do not also respire (with the exception of the purple nonsulfur bacteria), so there is no confusion as to the use of NADH. Green plants carry out both photosynthesis and respiration, and there might be the possibility that the reduced dinucleotides produced by photosynthesis would be used immediately as fuel for the respiratory chain, even though these reactions are carried out in two different organelles within the cell—chloroplasts and mitochondria. It may be that this is why green-plant photosynthesis has come to operate with a dinucleotide labeled with an extra phosphate group, $NADP^+$ (nicotine adenine dinucleotide phosphate), instead of NAD^+.

METABOLIC ARCHAEOLOGY

One of the most striking aspects of the energy-extracting and -storing machinery of living creatures is its universality. Some processes are shared by all forms of life, and we can assume that this is because they are very old components of a common metabolic heritage of related organisms. Other reactions and processes are possessed only by one branch or another of the living family, and by peeling these layers of metabolism back and looking for similarities to other reactions, we may be able to decide how the chemical machinery that we see today first evolved.

The first living organisms probably were ATP-using, judging from the universality that ATP holds as a short-term energy-storage molecule. We can imagine primitive one-celled creatures evolving glycolysis to make more ATP when competition had depleted the natural supply. This may or may not be true, but it is plausible. In any event, glycolysis as a means of extracting energy from glucose proved so beneficial that it, too, became fixed in the chemistry of life. Some bacteria, such as the strictly anaerobic *Clostridia*, never progressed beyond this stage, and are found today fermenting in anaerobic pockets of our world, away from the oxygen gas that is deadly to them, although it is the breath of life to most organisms.

Photosynthesis broke the dependence on the environment for high-free-energy molecules. Bacteria that could absorb light energy and use it to make their own glucose henceforth were freed from the constraints of a scavenging existence. They trapped light with chlorophyll and took hydrogen from H_2S to make NADH and ATP, and used these products of the light reactions to drive a dark-reaction synthesis of glucose, with the aid of a set of reactions that look very much like glycolysis in reverse. But by turning gluconeogenesis into a cyclic pro-

578

cess involving a five-carbon sugar as a "carrier" molecule, these bacteria found a way to begin the synthesis at the one-carbon CO_2 stage, instead of the three-carbon pyruvate stage that was the starting point of the older mechanism.

The blue-green algae changed the light reactions of photosynthesis from a one-photocenter process that uses a good but scarce hydrogen donor, H_2S, into a two-photocenter process that uses a poor but exceedingly common donor, water. This increased by many times the amount of life this planet could support. The oxygen that this kind of photosynthesis released is believed to have permanently changed the character of the atmosphere of the planet. We will come back to this important point in Chapter 26 when we discuss the origin of life on Earth.

With an ample supply of free oxygen in the atmosphere, the last great energy-managing invention appeared: oxygen-using respiration. The citric acid cycle developed to produce NADH (whether originally for energy or for reducing power), and the respiratory chain evolved to use these molecules to make ATP. This led to the modern system of photosynthesis of glucose and oxygen from carbon dioxide and water, seen in green plants, and the complementary combustion of glucose and oxygen back to carbon dioxide and water, found in both plants and animals. One can think of the planet as a giant chemical machine, with cogs and gears made of glucose, oxygen, carbon dioxide, and water, absorbing energy from the sun and storing it in molecules of ATP to provide a continuing fuel source for that most unusual set of chemical reactions: Life.

QUESTIONS

1. How do plants use oxygen? How do animals use oxygen? How do plants release oxygen, and what is made in the process?

2. How do plants benefit animals biochemically, other than as a source of high-free-energy foods?

3. What probably would happen to the Earth and animal life on it, if all plants were to disappear?

4. Where do plants get the energy required to synthesize glucose? What do they do with the glucose?

5. What is the structural distinction between procaryotes and eucaryotes? Which life form developed earlier? Which are we?

6. Where are respiration and photosynthesis carried out in procaryotes and eucaryotes?

7. When a mole of glucose is burned, how can the free energy available for driving other processes be 686 kcal, when only 673 kcal of heat are produced? Where do the extra 13 kcal come from?

8. Why do living organisms break glucose down in small steps rather than extracting all 686 kcal at once?

9. Of the 686 kcal of free energy available from a mole of glucose, how many kilocalories are saved by an oxygen-breathing organism? How are they saved? How many kilocalories per mole of glucose are saved by a yeast cell living under anaerobic conditions?

10. What are the intermediate molecules to which energy is transferred prior to the synthesis of ATP? What happens to these intermediate molecules? Why are they not used up and constantly in need of replacement? What are the compounds that we need from outside to make these energy carriers called? Why do we need them only in small amounts?

11. What are the three main phases of glucose breakdown in aerobic organisms? What is the end-product for the first of these phases? How is it used to start the second phase, and what are the end-products of this phase? To what molecules is energy transferred in these two phases? Which one provides more stored energy? What is the third phase in glucose metabolism, and what substances from the earlier steps are regenerated? What happens to the energy that is saved in this last phase?

12. What does the prime, instead of a superscript zero, signify in $\Delta G'$?

13. What happens to the pyruvate produced by glycolysis, if the organism is aerobic and a plentiful supply of O_2 is available? What happens to the pyruvate in yeast when it is denied oxygen? In which mode of operation does glycolysis produce more net energy?

14. What is the purpose of the first five steps in glycolysis? Why is ATP necessary? Are the products of these five steps more, or less, stable than the starting glucose?

15. What happens in the second half of glycolysis to produce energy? What is the important oxidation step that yields the largest quantity of free energy? How is this free energy saved?

16. What happens to pyruvate in human muscles if an insufficient supply of O_2 is present? How does this create distress, and how is the distress alleviated?

17. What is the purpose of the citric acid cycle? How do the products of glycolysis enter the cycle?

18. What elements of strategy or of chemical "logic" are common to the following three reactions: (a) the conversion of G3P to DPG during glycolysis, (b) the conversion of pyruvate to acetyl coenzyme A, and (c) the conversion of α-ketoglutarate to succinyl coenzyme A?

19. What ultimately happens to the CO_2 that is liberated during the citric acid cycle?

20. How many equivalents of ATP are produced from a mole of glucose in the entire respiratory process, from glycolysis through the reaction with O_2?

21. What purpose does the respiratory chain play in energy extraction? Why is it called a "chain"? What are flavoproteins, quinones, and cytochromes, and what part do they play in the respiratory chain? Where, and how often, is ATP synthesized as electrons flow down the chain? Where do the electrons eventually go? What happens to the NAD^+ and FAD that are produced by the chain?

22. Where are the enzymes of the citric acid cycle and the components of the respiratory chain located in a eucaryotic cell?

23. What is gluconeogenesis? How is it related to glycolysis? Why is it useful to have the biochemical capabilities conferred by gluconeogenesis? Why is it likely that gluconeogenesis and glycolysis are evolutionarily related?

24. What are the light and dark reactions of photosynthesis? In what sense is the "photo-" term inapplicable to the dark reactions, and "-synthesis" inapplicable to the light reactions?

25. Which set of reactions, light or dark, is evolutionarily related to gluconeogenesis? Which is believed to be older?

26. How has the straight chain of successive reactions found in gluconeogenesis and glycolysis been turned into a cyclic process in the Calvin cycle? What does the Calvin cycle accomplish?

27. How do the chemosynthetic bacteria find ways of replacing the light reactions of photosynthesis?

28. What is meant by cyclic and noncyclic photophosphorylation? Which is more characteristic of purple sulfur bacteria? How do purple sulfur bacteria obtain NADH? How do they obtain ATP?

29. How do purple nonsulfur bacteria obtain ATP? Which kind of photophosphorylation do they use? How do they obtain NADH?

30. Why might eucaryotes have developed both NADH and NADPH? Why go to the trouble of having both kinds of energy carriers?

31. What improvement in photosynthesis is found in green plants, but not in bacteria? What do green plants use as their source of reducing power? Is this substance normally a good reducing agent? What do green plants do to make it so?

32. Where did the free O_2 come from that is found in the atmosphere of the Earth today?

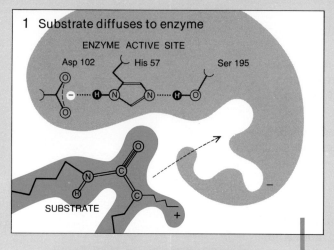

1 Substrate diffuses to enzyme

ENZYME ACTIVE SITE

Asp 102   His 57   Ser 195

SUBSTRATE

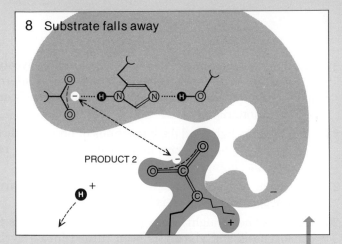

8 Substrate falls away

PRODUCT 2

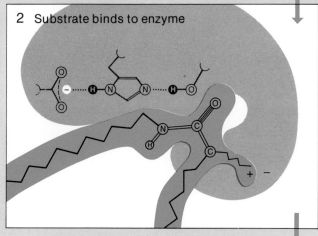

2 Substrate binds to enzyme

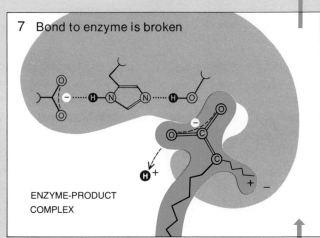

7 Bond to enzyme is broken

ENZYME-PRODUCT
COMPLEX

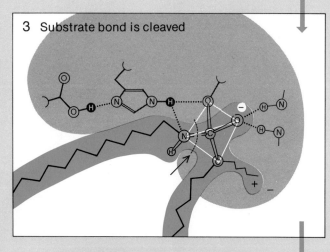

3 Substrate bond is cleaved

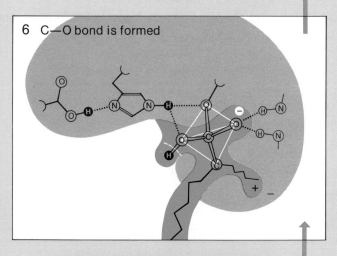

6 C—O bond is formed

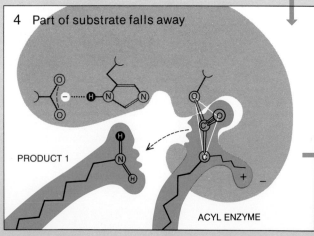

4 Part of substrate falls away

PRODUCT 1

ACYL ENZYME

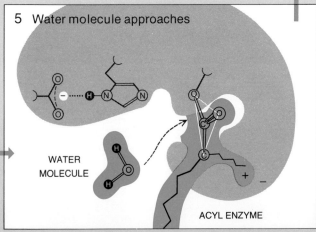

5 Water molecule approaches

WATER
MOLECULE

ACYL ENZYME

CHAPTER 24

Enzymes and Catalysis

Enzymes are protein molecules that act as biological catalysts. As we saw in Chapter 15, catalysts are substances that provide an easier pathway for a chemical reaction, and turn an already spontaneous but slow reaction into a faster one. They will not cause anything to happen that would not happen anyway, given enough time. They do not change the final conditions of equilibrium, only the rate of getting there. In the H_2 reactions at a metal surface (Chapter 15), the platinum catalyst helped H_2 to react with other molecules because the H_2 molecule became strained when it bound to the metal surface, and hence became more reactive. In the ethyl acetate hydrolysis catalyzed by protons (Chapter 16), the proton made the ethyl acetate molecule more susceptible to attack by the lone electron pair of a water molecule by binding to the carbonyl oxygen atom and giving the carbonyl carbon a slight positive charge.

The enzyme trypsin cuts protein chains into pieces, as part of the digestive process in the intestines. The mechanism for doing this, shown on the opposite page, will be discussed in detail later in this chapter as an example of how enzymes function. In this reaction, as in the catalysis of hydrogenation and of ethyl acetate hydrolysis, the original reaction is slow because it requires going through high-energy intermediate complexes. This higher energy is called the activation energy, E_a, and is diagrammed as an energy barrier at the right. Even though this energy is released again when products are formed, the need for energy of at least E_a for reaction to take place means that the overall reaction is slow. The catalyst leads the reactants through one or a series of steps, none of which has as high an activation energy as the original process; hence the catalyzed reaction is faster. In this chapter we will be concerned primarily with how an enzyme accelerates a reaction, using trypsin as an example, but we shall look briefly at larger enzymes and multisubunit enzymes at the end of the chapter.

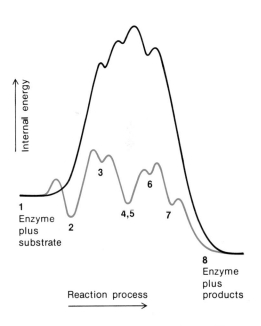

An enzyme accelerates a reaction by providing an alternate, lower-energy pathway. The black curve symbolizes the energy of intermediate states in the uncatalyzed cleavage of a protein chain, by pulling the chain apart and adding H— and HO— across the ends. The colored curve represents the catalyzed mechanism, with numbers corresponding to the various steps on the opposite page. The acyl enzyme is relatively stable. The two tetrahedral intermediates are local energy minima at higher energy, but still less than that involved in the uncatalyzed process.

ACID CATALYSIS

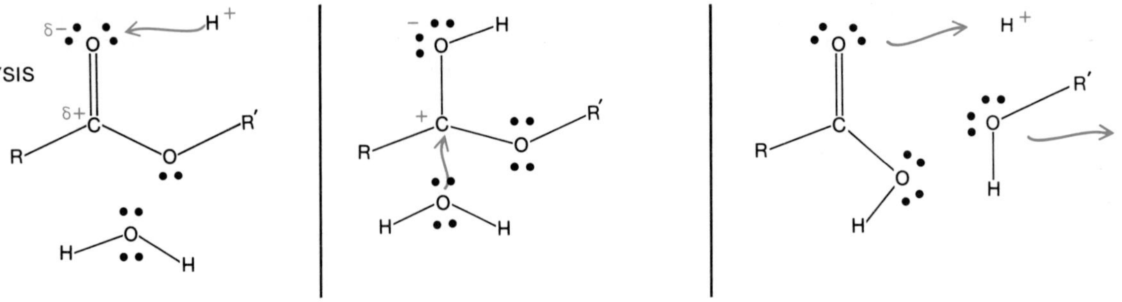

HYDROXIDE CATALYSIS

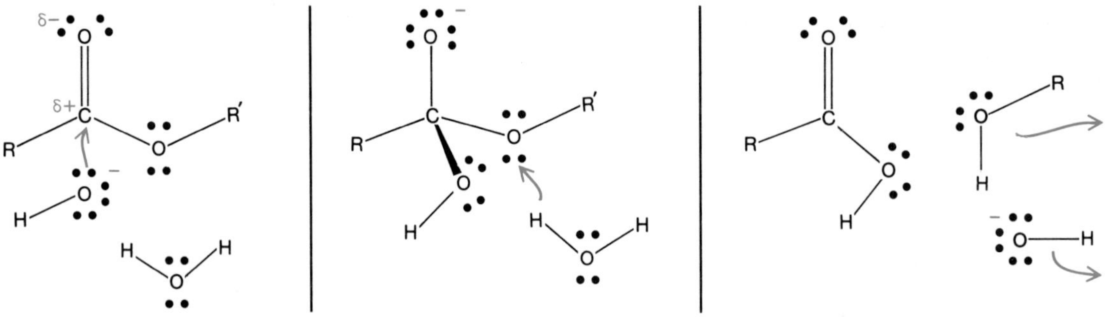

GENERAL ACID CATALYSIS

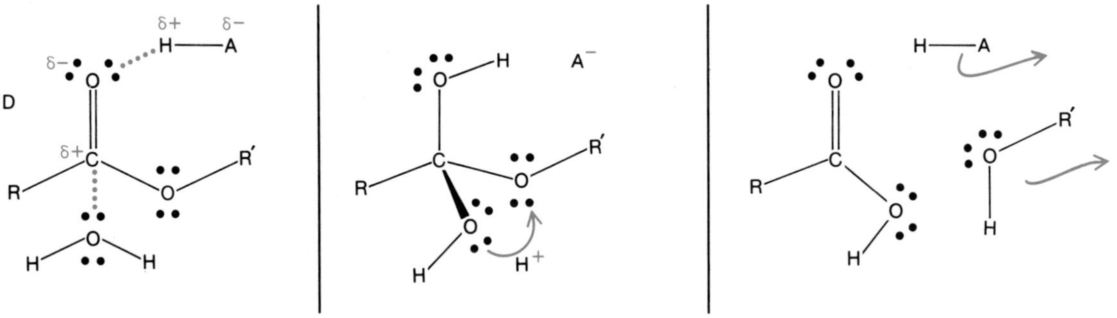

GENERAL BASE CATALYSIS

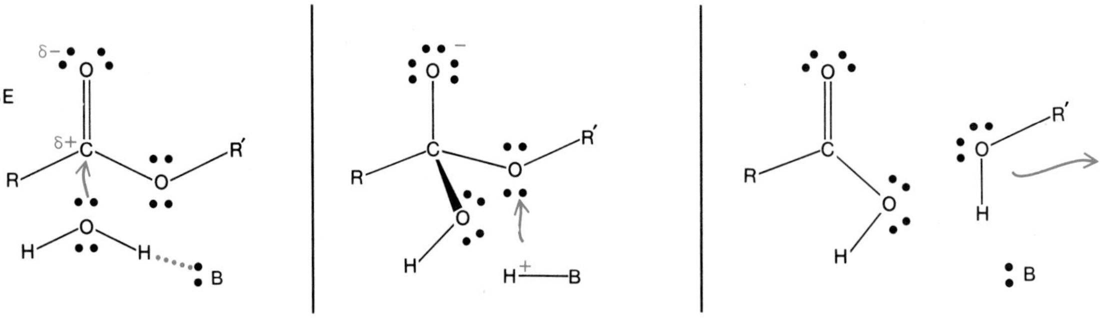

NUCLEOPHILIC ATTACK

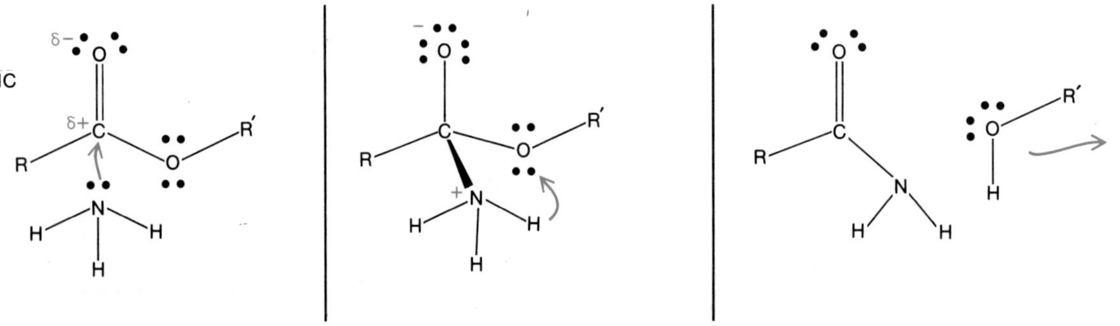

THE ROLE OF ENZYMES

The main role of a catalyst is to provide an alternative mechanism for a reaction—an easier pathway with a lower activation energy. Both directions of a reaction are catalyzed equally, and no change is made in the final equilibrium point. The catalyst only ensures that equilibrium conditions, whatever they are, are reached faster than in an uncatalyzed reaction. Enzymes are catalysts, but because they also are large molecules with appreciable surface area, they can do more than simple acid–base catalysis. They can help to orient the participants in a reaction so they will be more likely to react; they can discriminate between one possible reactant molecule and another; and they can provide a coupling mechanism that ensures that one reaction always is accompanied by another reaction. Before looking at a specific family of enzymes, we shall examine each of these abilities.

Enzymes Provide an Easier Mechanism

Since bonds are formed by electrons, the manipulation of bonds in molecules involves pushing or pulling of electrons. The general principle in all such processes is that electron-deficient substances (electrophiles) are attracted to local negative charges, or excesses of electrons, and electron-rich substances (nucleophiles) are attracted to local positive charges, or deficiencies in electrons. All of the mechanisms found in enzymes are familiar from solution chemistry, and the five most common types of catalytic attack are outlined on the opposite page: proton catalysis, hydroxide catalysis, general acid and base catalysis, and nucleophilic attack. For comparative purposes, the examples all involve cleavage of an ester bond. An ester $C=O$ group is an especially good example, because the electronegative oxygen atom draws electrons to itself and has a local electron excess and negative charge, while the carbon atom has an electron deficiency and a positive charge. These local, fractional excesses and deficiencies of charge are represented by δ^- and δ^+ to distinguish them from full electron charges.

In acid (proton) catalysis, discussed in Chapter 16, the proton is attracted to the carbonyl oxygen atom and draws charge away from the carbonyl carbon. This makes the carbon susceptible to attack by a water molecule, which is too weak a nucleophile to attack it without this added polarization. The H^+, which is an electrophile, thus primes the carbon atom for nucleophilic attack by H_2O. (The abbreviated mechanism on the opposite page should be compared with the more complete mechanism shown in Chapter 16.) In hydroxide catalysis (second row on the opposite page), the OH^- ion is such a strong nucleophile that it can attack the carbonyl carbon atom without outside help.

General acid catalysis (third row) resembles proton catalysis, except that the attacking group is not a dissociated proton from a strong acid, but is a dissociable proton from a weak acid. The effect is much the same; reaction and attack by a water molecule are facilitated, and at the end of the reaction the proton falls away again to rejoin the weak acid anion.

General base catalysis and direct nucleophilic attack are variations on the same theme. Both involve a strong nucleophile. In general base

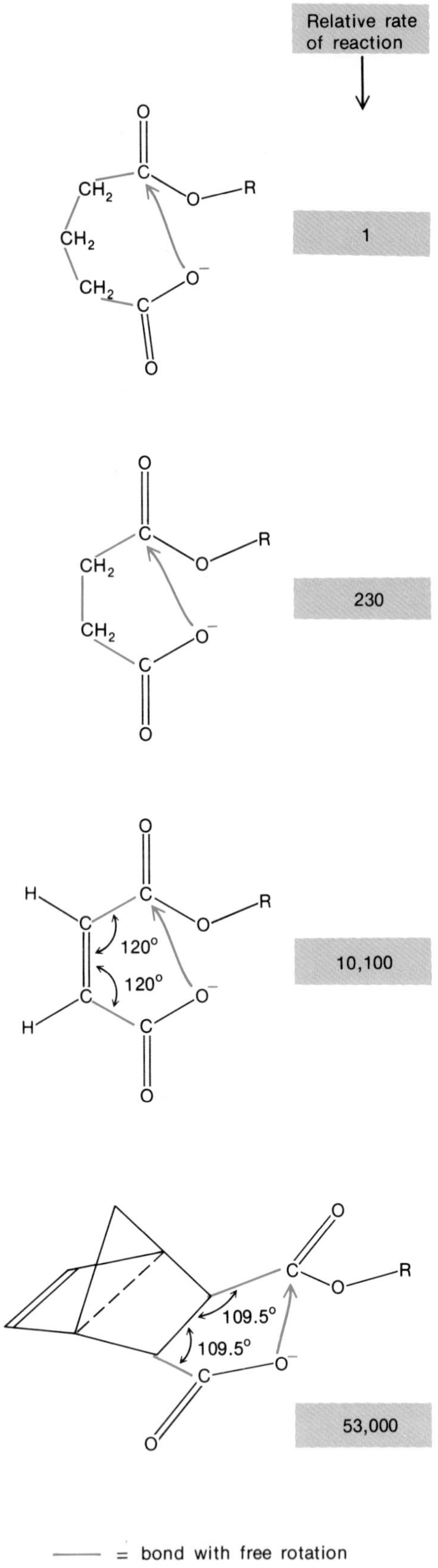

(structure, glutaric acid monoester)	1
(structure)	230
(structure, 120° 120°)	10,100
(bicyclic structure, 109.5° 109.5°)	53,000

—— = bond with free rotation

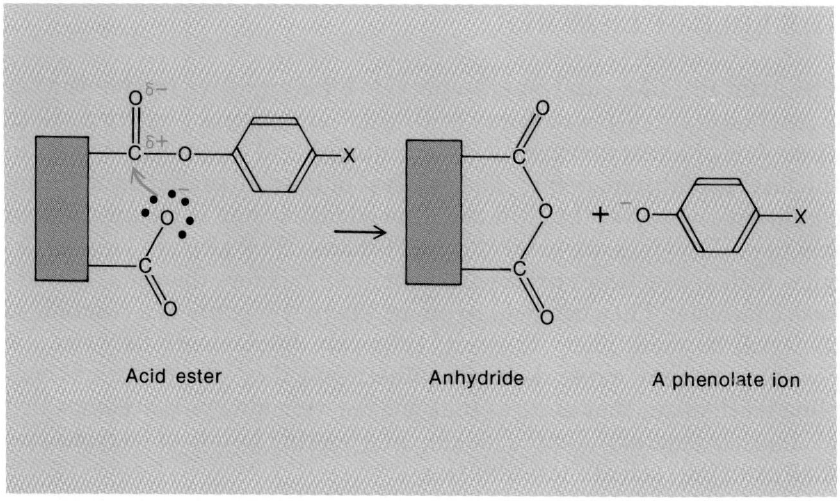

The influence of orientation on the rate of reaction

Acid ester   Anhydride   A phenolate ion

catalysis the nucleophile pulls a proton from a water molecule, polarizes the molecule, and helps it to attack the electron-deficient carbon in the way that the hydroxide ion did by itself in hydroxide catalysis. In short, the base turns an H_2O molecule into the more reactive OH^- ion. In nucleophilic attack, the base interacts directly with the carbon atom, and the solvent plays no role. It sometimes is difficult to tell which of these two mechanisms is used, since the kinetics may be identical. However, if the reaction goes two or three times slower in D_2O than in H_2O, general base catalysis is involved; if the solvent change makes no difference, then the mechanism must be direct nucleophilic attack. We will see some of these mechanisms at work with enzymes, and they illustrate the first role of enzymes, that of providing alternate and easier mechanisms for chemical reaction.

Enzymes Provide Orientation

When two reactants come together in solution, the odds usually are high that they will not collide in a way that favors reaction. They may not be oriented properly for the reacting groups or bonds to come close together, and therefore may rebound with no changes. If some way could be found to hold the two molecules and to bring them together in the most favorable way, then the percentage of collisions that were productive (reactive) would be increased greatly, and the overall rate of reaction would be larger. This is what an enzyme does.

D. E. Koshland, at the University of California at Berkeley, has carried out experiments involving the reaction of an acid with an ester to form an anhydride, in which the acid and the ester are both attached to the same carrier molecule in a series of different sterically constrained ways. He has found a direct correlation between the way in which the two reacting groups are constrained, and the rate at which they react. The specific reaction is shown above, and four test molecules appear in the left margin. The first molecule, a monoester of glutaric acid, has four single-bond "swivels" between the two reacting groups, which permit a variety of orientations of the acid and ester. If the same ester is

586

Cyclohexaamylose, a model for enzyme catalysis and specificity

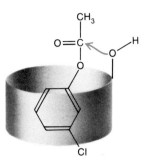

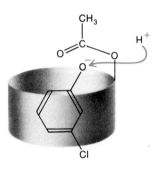

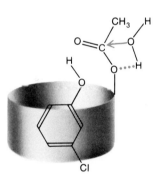

made with succinic acid, which has only three swivels and hence more constraints on the freedom of the two groups, the reaction occurs 230 times faster. Adding a double bond and cutting the number of free bond rotations down to two, leads to another 44-fold increase in reaction rate. The rather subtle change of bringing the two reacting groups slightly closer together by making the bond angles in the carrier molecule 109.5° (tetrahedral) instead of 120° makes the reaction five times faster, or 53,000 times faster than the original glutaric ester reaction! These experiments illustrate the great gain obtained from the ability to point the reacting molecules toward one another in the right way. This positioning and pointing is an important part of enzyme activity.

Another example of the importance of holding and positioning is the "pseudo enzyme" cyclohexaamylose, which is a cyclic hexamer of glucose. As you can see from the photograph of the space-filling molecular model above, cyclohexaamylose is a barrel with a central cavity 5 Å in diameter, which is large enough to surround a benzene ring or a phenyl group. Around both rims of the barrel are several —OH groups from the glucose units.

Cyclohexaamylose is a good catalyst for the hydrolysis of the ester *meta*-chlorophenyl acetate (right margin). The *m*-chlorophenyl group is hydrophobic and is just the right size to fit snugly into the hexaglucose barrel. Even more important for reactivity, no matter how it slips into the molecule, one or another of the glucose —OH groups will be close to the ester bond. Cleavage then occurs as shown at the right. A glucose —OH group acts as a nucleophile and attacks the carbonyl carbon, thereby weakening the bond to the phenyl group. The acetate is transferred from the phenyl to the hydroxyl, to form an *acylated* cyclohexaamylose molecule. Then the same drama is played again, with a water molecule attacking the carbonyl carbon, removing the acyl group as acetic acid, and restoring the glucose —OH to its original state. When the *m*-chlorophenol molecule diffuses away from cyclohexaamylose, catalysis is complete.

This is exactly the mechanism that we shall see for the enzymes trypsin and chymotrypsin, even to the acylation of the enzyme and the

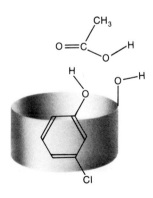

The binding of a substrate molecule in a specificity pocket, and cleavage of a bond by attack by an —OH group, resemble the catalytic mechanism of trypsin shown at the beginning of the chapter.

587

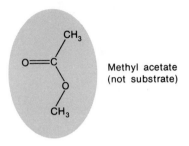

Methyl acetate
(not substrate)

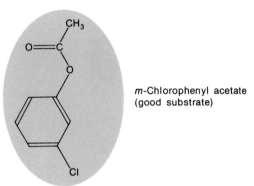

m-Chlorophenyl acetate
(good substrate)

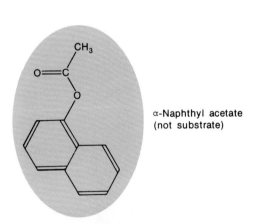

α-Naphthyl acetate
(not substrate)

Cyclohexaamylose demonstrates enzymelike substrate specificity. If the substrate is too small (top) or too large (bottom), it will not fit into the specificity pocket well, and will not bind to the cyclohexaamylose molecule long enough to be cleaved.

binding of a side chain in a "pocket" in the enzyme surface. Chymotrypsin is only a more refined and more efficient version of cyclohexaamylose.

Catalysis by cyclohexaamylose would not have been possible, had the insertion of the chlorophenyl ring inside the molecular cavity not brought the ester bond next to an hydroxyl group on the "enzyme." The proper orientation of reacting groups is vital, whether both are on different reacting molecules, or one is on the "enzyme" itself.

Enzymes Provide Specificity

Specificity, or selectivity among the many possible molecules that an enzyme could cause to react, is so much a property of an enzyme that it is hard to find nonenzymatic examples. Free H^+ ions in solution will catalyze indiscriminately all reactions that they are capable of. An electrophile bound to a properly constructed enzyme surface can catalyze certain reactions and ignore other molecules completely, depending on whether the reactant molecules can bind to the surface of the enzyme properly. A molecule that is acted upon by an enzyme is referred to as that enzyme's *substrate*. The presence or absence of a single atom, or a single charge, may decide whether a molecule is a good substrate or is rejected by the enzyme.

Cyclohexaamylose shows an enzymelike specificity in its choice of acceptable substrates. *m*-Chlorophenyl acetate is a good substrate (left) because the chlorophenyl group is the right size to fit into the cavity in the molecule. The methyl group of methyl acetate is too small, so the molecule does not bind to cyclohexaamylose long enough to be cleaved. The α-napthyl acetate molecule has too large a ring system, and cannot enter the central cavity at all. We will see this idea of a "specificity pocket" again in trypsin and chymotrypsin. Cyclohexaamylose is a good analog of the enzyme chymotrypsin both in its catalytic mechanism and its discrimination among possible substrates.

Enzymes Provide Coupling Between Reactions

Coupling of reactions is an absolutely essential function of enzymes in living organisms, because without it no energy could be stored, and free energy from spontaneous reactions could not be used to drive nonspontaneous processes. The free energy that is liberated by a spontaneous reaction would be dissipated uselessly as heat.

As an example, consider the transformation of one amino acid to another, glutamic acid (Glu) to glutamine (Gln):

$$^+H_3N-\overset{\overset{\displaystyle COO^-}{|}}{C}H-CH_2-CH_2-COO^- + NH_4^+ \rightarrow$$

glutamic acid

$$^+H_3N-\overset{\overset{\displaystyle COO^-}{|}}{C}H-CH_2-CH_2-CO-NH_2 + H_2O$$

glutamine

588

(For simplicity, let us represent the glutamic acid backbone, ^+H_3N—CH(COO$^-$)—CH$_2$—CH$_2$—, by R—.) This is a nonspontaneous reaction with a standard free energy change of $\Delta G' = +3.5$ kcal mole^{-1}. (See energy-level diagram at right.) How can it be made to occur?

The synthesis of glutamine is driven by the simultaneous breakdown of ATP, which acts as "fuel" for the process:

R—COO$^-$ + NH$_4^+$ → R—CO—NH$_2$ + H$_2$O $\Delta G' = +3.5$ kcal mole^{-1}
glutamic acid   glutamine

ATP   → ADP + P$_i$ $\Delta G' = -7.3$ kcal mole^{-1}

R—COO$^-$ + NH$_4^+$ + ATP → R—CO—NH$_2$ + H$_2$O + ADP + P$_i$ $\Delta G' = -3.8$ kcal mole^{-1}
glutamic acid   glutamine

(P$_i$ is a conventional biochemical shorthand for inorganic phosphate, HPO$_4^{2-}$ or H$_2$PO$_4^-$.) The combined reaction is spontaneous by 3.8 kcal mole^{-1}. But how can we be sure that the free energy from ATP is used by the other reaction? Why should a molecule of ATP break down every time a molecule of glutamic acid reacts to form glutamine? What connects, or couples, the two processes?

The coupling is carried out by the enzyme *glutamine synthetase*. It has binding positions on its surface for glutamic acid, ammonium ion, and ATP, and couples the reactions by transferring a phosphate group. The first step is the transfer of phosphate *and free energy* from ATP to glutamic acid:

R—COO$^-$ + ATP → R—CO—O—PO$_3^{2-}$ + ADP
glutamic acid   glutamyl phosphate

The glutamyl phosphate is energetically primed in the way that we have seen several times in Chapter 23, with a higher free energy than an ordinary glutamic acid molecule (right). It remains bound to the enzyme next to the ammonium ion. This energized form of glutamic acid then reacts with ammonium ion, losing the phosphate and replacing it with an amine group:

R—CO—O—PO$_3^{2-}$ + NH$_4^+$ → R—CO—NH$_2$ + H$_2$PO$_4^-$
glutamyl phosphate   glutamine

The substance that links the gain and loss of free energy is the phosphate group, and proper transfer is ensured by binding all reactants to the enzyme surface. In the absence of glutamine synthetase, glutamic acid would have remained unchanged, ATP would have been hydrolyzed to ADP and phosphate, and the temperature of the solution would have risen by a small amount from the energy released by ATP.

These are the four most important roles of enzymes in biological systems—providing an appropriate *mechanism*, efficient *orientation* of substrates and enzymatic groups, *selectivity* among possible substrates, and *coupling* of energy-releasing and energy-requiring reactions. All but the last role will be illustrated by the trypsin family of digestive enzymes.

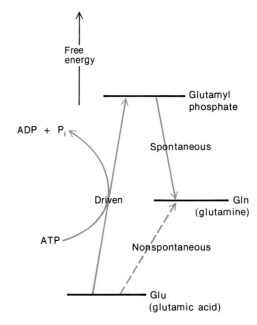

A nonspontaneous reaction, the conversion of glutamic acid to glutamine, can be induced to occur with the aid of free energy from ATP. The enzyme glutamine synthetase transfers free energy along with the phosphate group to glutamic acid, and then holds glutamyl phosphate in the proper orientation for the addition of ammonium ion.

PROTEIN-CUTTING ENZYMES

Chymotrypsin, trypsin, and elastase each cut a polypeptide chain adjacent to a different type of amino acid side chain. Chymotrypsin prefers aromatic rings, trypsin favors positively charged groups, and elastase cuts best next to small, nonpolar side chains. Carboxypeptidase cleaves one amino acid at a time from the carboxy terminal end of the chain.

AN EXAMPLE: THE TRYPSIN FAMILY

Trypsin, chymotrypsin, and elastase are a family of digestive enzymes whose role is to cut polypeptide chains. They are synthesized in the pancreas as inactive zymogens, or pre-enzymes, and then are secreted into the digestive tract and activated just before use. They cut the polypeptide chains of food proteins in the middle of the chain, while other enzymes cleave away one amino acid at a time from the carboxyl end. Together they reduce food proteins to amino acids, which then are absorbed through the walls of the intestines.

The three trypsin family enzymes work as a team: each cleaves a protein chain next to a different type of amino acid side group. The three kinds of cleavage points are indicated in the peptide chain at the left. Trypsin cuts a chain just past the carbonyl group of a basic amino acid, which has a positively charged side chain: lysine or arginine. Chymotrypsin cuts a polypeptide chain next to a bulky aromatic amino acid. Elastase is less discriminating in its choice of cleavage point, but tends to cut preferentially near small, uncharged side chains. These have been one of the most intensively studied families of enzymes because they are small (approximately 250 amino acids or 26,000 molecular weight), easily obtainable in quantity, and relatively stable. They are found in the digestive tracts of all mammals, and the most accessible source has been cows and pigs. Chymotrypsin has been the subject of more chemical studies than trypsin because it is less likely to digest itself in the test tube. Protein-digesting enzymes, being proteins themselves, have a tendency toward suicide. Chymotrypsin is reasonably safe from self-destruction because the large aromatic groups that it favors usually are tucked safely inside the molecule, whereas the positively charged groups that trypsin prefers are exposed on its own surface, ready for attack by other trypsin molecules.

The fact that they operate as a team during digestion suggests that these enzymes might be related in some way. Their amino acid sequences make the point even better. The three protein chains are illustrated as strings of beads on the opposite page, beginning with the amino end and continuing to the carboxyl end. Each bead represents one amino acid, and positions where the *same* amino acid is encountered in all three enzymes are colored black. Locations where one of the enzymes omits one or more amino acids in a chain shortcut are marked by dashes. The long connections between nonadjacent amino acids represent covalent connections between two cysteine residues, in what are called *disulfide bridges*. These are important in helping to hold many proteins together, although myoglobin and hemoglobin, discussed in Chapter 22, had none. After the protein chain is polymerized at the ribosomes and folded, the bridge is formed by a removal of hydrogen

Schematic diagram of the amino acid sequence of the three ▶ protein-digesting enzymes. Each circle represents one amino acid. Amino acid positions that are identical in all three proteins are in solid black. Long connections between nonadjacent amino acids represent disulfide bonds. Locations of the three catalytically important side chains are marked.

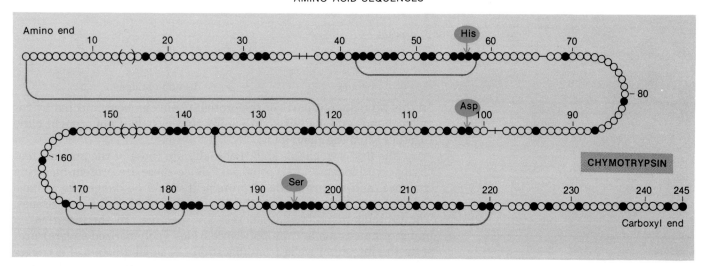

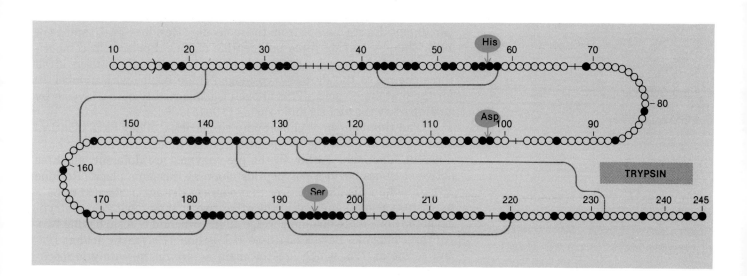

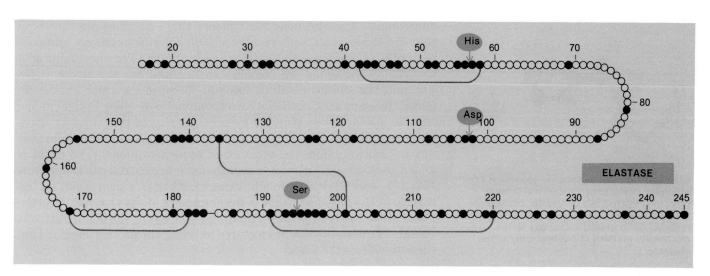

atoms from the cysteines:

$$\overset{H}{\underset{}{\text{C}_\alpha}}\!-\!CH_2\!-\!S\!-\!H \quad H\!-\!S\!-\!CH_2\!-\!\overset{}{\underset{H}{\text{C}_\alpha}} \quad \rightarrow \quad \overset{H}{\underset{}{\text{C}_\alpha}}\!-\!CH_2\!-\!S\!-\!S\!-\!CH_2\!-\!\overset{}{\underset{H}{\text{C}_\alpha}} \quad +\,2H$$

← main chains →

cysteine   cysteine   disulfide bridge

In this way, distant parts of the protein chain can be connected by co-valent bonds and stabilized, providing that cysteines are brought close together when the chain folds.

The first two chains shown actually are those of the pre-enzymes chymotrypsinogen and trypsinogen. Since these are protein-digesting enzymes, and we are made of protein, it would be dangerous to have the enzymes begin operating too soon and attacking our own tissues. The proteins made in the pancreas are inactive. In the intestines, a lining of mucus made from polysaccharides (polymerized sugars) protects the intestinal walls from digestion. A small amount of a trigger enzyme begins the activation of trypsinogen to trypsin in the intestines, and this trypsin then takes over and completes the activation of trypsinogen and chymotrypsinogen. When chymotrypsinogen is activated, two dipeptides are cut out from the molecule (Residues 14–15 and 147–148), thereby leaving three polypeptide chains. For ease in comparisons, the chymotrypsinogen numbering conventionally is used in all three chains, so the shorter trypsinogen chain begins with number 10 for the first amino acid. Trypsinogen is converted to active trypsin by cutting away the first six amino acids (10–15).

The three enzymes show many similarities. They have identical amino acids at 62 of the 257 positions, even though the proteins have different functions. Although the pre-enzymes are different, all three active enzymes begin a polypeptide chain at the same place (Residue 16). The four disulfide bridges that connect distant parts of the chain in elastase also are present in the other two enzymes, with chymotrypsin having one more disulfide bridge all its own, and trypsin having two. All three enzymes have a histidine at Position 57, aspartic acid at 102, and serine at 195, which are the main actors in the catalytic mechanism.

X-ray crystal structure analyses have revealed that these three proteolytic (protein-cutting) enzymes are folded the same way in three dimensions. The backbone skeletons of these enzymes are shown on the next three pages, with numbered balls for alpha carbons, and connecting sticks for the —CO—NH— amide groups. The only amino acid side chains illustrated are His 57, Asp 102, and Ser 195 at the active site, and the various disulfide bridges. Because the three chains are folded the same way, positions corresponding to disulfide bridges in one enzyme also are close together even in an enzyme that does not have that particular bridge. Now you can see another important feature that was not obvious from the amino acid sequences alone. The chain is folded back on itself in such a way that the three catalytic side chains (57, 102, and 195) are brought close together at a depression on the surface of the molecule. This is the *active site* of the enzyme. It is the place where the food protein chain that will be cut during digestion is bound. If these enzymes are pictured as biting the protein chain in two, the active site is the jaws.

ACTIVE SITE OF THE TRYPSIN MOLECULE

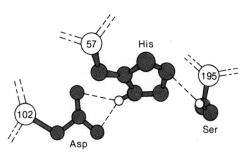

Aspartic acid 102, histidine 57, and serine 195 are found in the same geometrical arrangement at the active site of trypsin, chymotrypsin, and elastase. They are the chemical groups responsible for catalytic cleavage by the mechanism outlined at the beginning of the chapter.

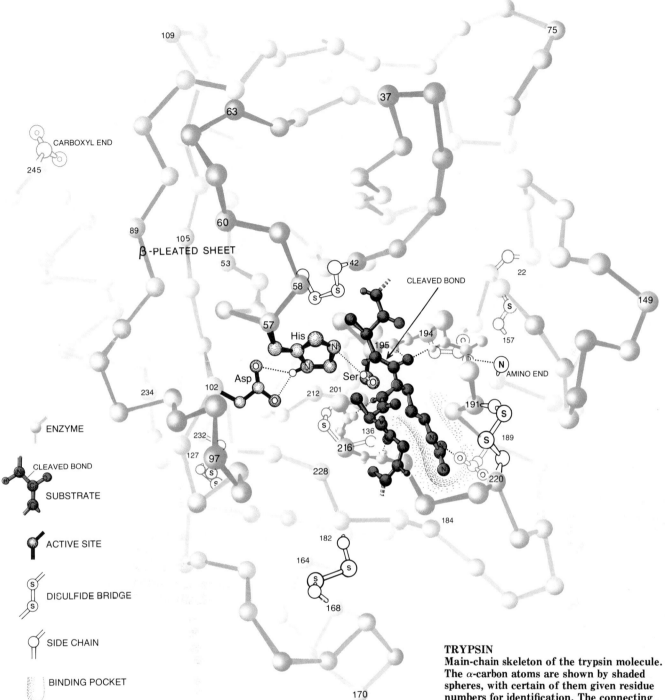

109
75
63
37
CARBOXYL END
245
89 105
60
β-PLEATED SHEET
53
58
57
42
22
CLEAVED BOND
His
N
194
195
157
Asp
Ser
102
AMINO END
234
201
212
191
ENZYME
232
136
189
127 97
216
220
228
CLEAVED BOND
SUBSTRATE
184
ACTIVE SITE
182
164
DISULFIDE BRIDGE
168
SIDE CHAIN
BINDING POCKET
170

TRYPSIN
Main-chain skeleton of the trypsin molecule.
The α-carbon atoms are shown by shaded
spheres, with certain of them given residue
numbers for identification. The connecting
—CO—NH— amide groups are represented by
straight lines. Disulfide bridges are shown in
outline, and a portion of the polypeptide chain
substrate appears in dark color. The specificity
pocket is sketched in shading, with a lysine
side chain from the substrate molecule inserted. The catalytically important Asp, His,
and Ser are poised for cleavage of the peptide
bond marked by an arrow. Drawing by Irving
Geis; from "A Family of Protein-Cutting Proteins," by R. M. Stroud, *Scientific American,*
July 1974. Copyright © 1974 by Stroud, Dickerson, and Geis.

Very little α helix is present in these three proteins, unlike myoglobin and hemoglobin. A short helix is found near Residues 168–170
at the bottom of the molecule, and the chain ends with a helix at Residues 230–245 at the left rear. A more important structural feature is a
silklike twisted β sheet of nearly parallel extended chains. One of these
can be seen at the upper left of trypsin, in the chains that contain Residues 60, 89, 105, and 53. Another twisted sheet in the lower right of the
molecule is harder to see in this view. These two cores of twisted β

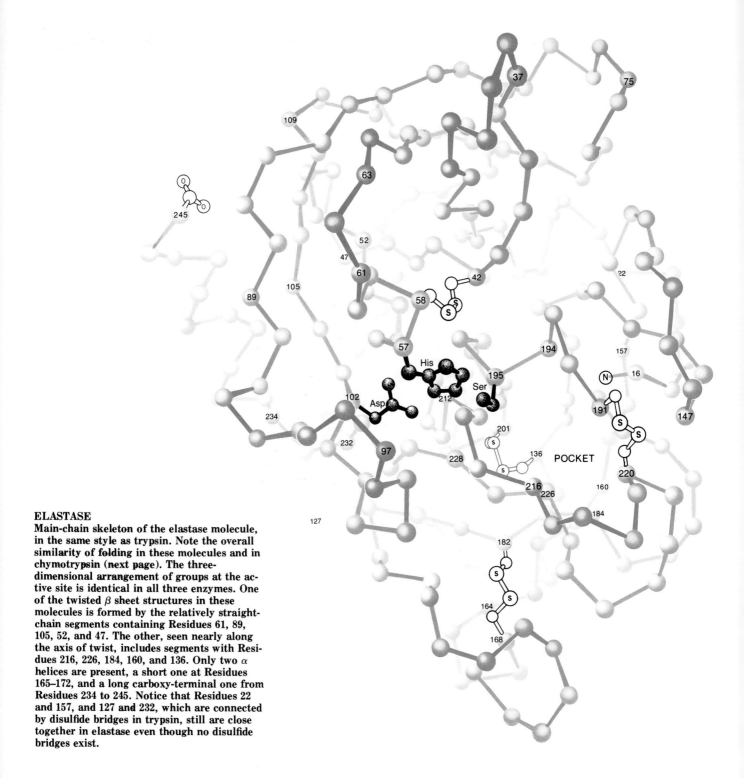

ELASTASE
Main-chain skeleton of the elastase molecule,
in the same style as trypsin. Note the overall
similarity of folding in these molecules and in
chymotrypsin (next page). The three-
dimensional arrangement of groups at the active site is identical in all three enzymes. One
of the twisted β sheet structures in these
molecules is formed by the relatively straight-
chain segments containing Residues 61, 89,
105, 52, and 47. The other, seen nearly along
the axis of twist, includes segments with Residues 216, 226, 184, 160, and 136. Only two α
helices are present, a short one at Residues
165–172, and a long carboxy-terminal one from
Residues 234 to 245. Notice that Residues 22
and 157, and 127 and 232, which are connected
by disulfide bridges in trypsin, still are close
together in elastase even though no disulfide
bridges exist.

sheets define the shape of the molecule, and the active site sits in a
groove between them. As with the globins, the interiors of these enzymes are packed with hydrophobic residues, and charged side chains
lie on the outside. The proper order of different kinds of amino acids
along the sequence tells the polypeptide chain how to fold correctly in
three dimensions.

594

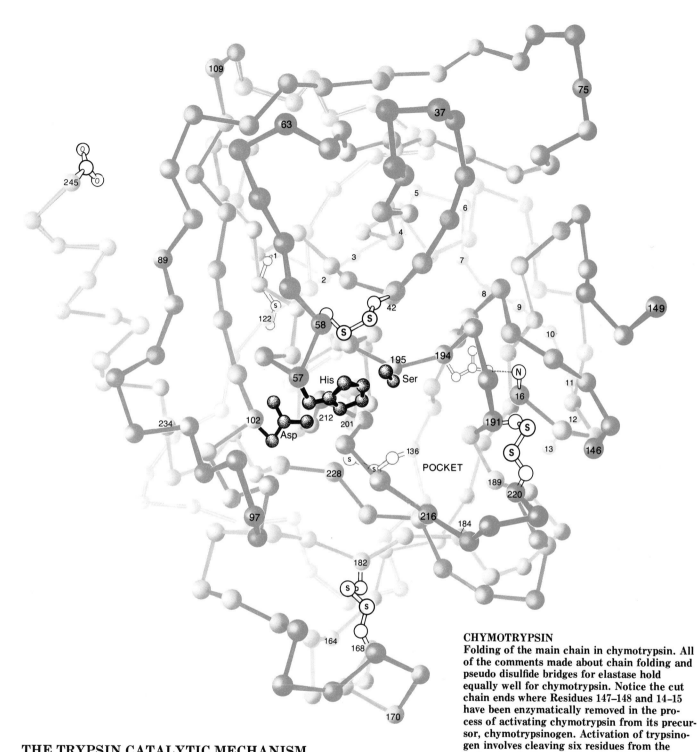

Labels within figure: 109, 75, 63, 37, 245, 5, 6, 89, 4, 3, 1, 2, 42, 58, S, S, S, 122, 57, His, 195, 194, 149, Ser, 8, 9, 10, 11, 16, N, 102, 212, 201, 191, S, S, 12, 146, Asp, 234, 13, 136, POCKET, 189, 220, 228, 216, 184, 97, 182, S, S, 164, 168, 170

THE TRYPSIN CATALYTIC MECHANISM

Trypsin, chymotrypsin, and elastase not only share a common structure, they share a common catalytic mechanism as well. The mechanism, which has been determined from chemical and x-ray studies, is shown at the beginning of the chapter and is repeated in the margins of the next two pages. The protein chain to be cut binds to the molecule with one portion hydrogen-bonded to Residues 215–219 in an anti-

CHYMOTRYPSIN
Folding of the main chain in chymotrypsin. All of the comments made about chain folding and pseudo disulfide bridges for elastase hold equally well for chymotrypsin. Notice the cut chain ends where Residues 147–148 and 14–15 have been enzymatically removed in the process of activating chymotrypsin from its precursor, chymotrypsinogen. Activation of trypsinogen involves cleaving six residues from the amino terminal end of the chain. Drawings on these two pages by Irving Geis; from "A Family of Protein-Cutting Proteins," by R. M. Stroud, *Scientific American,* July 1974. Copyright © 1974 by Stroud, Dickerson, and Geis.

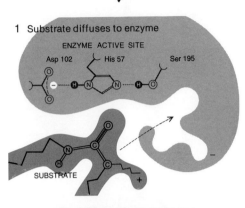

1 Substrate diffuses to enzyme

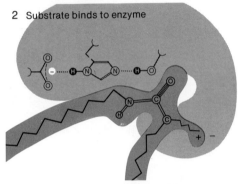

2 Substrate binds to enzyme

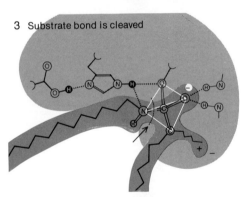

3 Substrate bond is cleaved

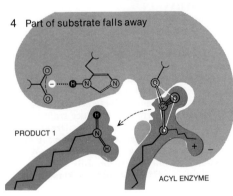

4 Part of substrate falls away

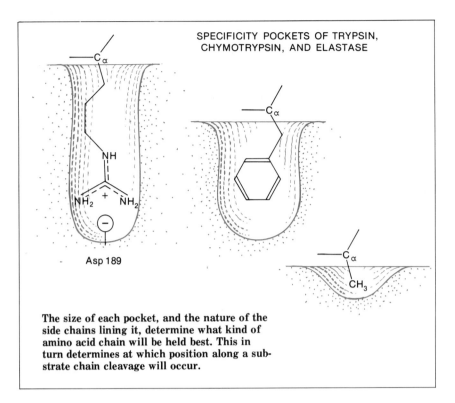

SPECIFICITY POCKETS OF TRYPSIN, CHYMOTRYPSIN, AND ELASTASE

The size of each pocket, and the nature of the side chains lining it, determine what kind of amino acid chain will be held best. This in turn determines at which position along a substrate chain cleavage will occur.

parallel manner, like adjacent chains in silk. This helps to hold the "victim" chain in place. At the bend in the substrate chain, the —NH —CO— bond that will be cut is brought close to His 57 and Ser 195. The side group of the victim chain just prior to this bond is inserted into a pocket in the surface of the enzyme molecule. This pocket, bordered by Chains 214–220, a disulfide bridge, and Chains 191–195, can be seen in the skeletal drawings on the preceding three pages. (The rim of the pocket from 215 to 219 is the silklike antiparallel binding site for the victim chain.) The pocket provides the explanation for the different specificities of the three enzymes for the bonds that they will cut. In trypsin the specificity pocket is deep, and has a negative charge from aspartic acid 189 at the bottom. (See drawings above.) The pocket is designed to accept and hold a long, positively charged basic side chain: lysine or arginine. In chymotrypsin the corresponding pocket is wider and completely lined with hydrophobic side chains, thereby providing an efficient receptacle for a large, bulky aromatic group. In elastase the pocket is blocked by valine and threonine at the positions where the other two enzymes have only glycine, which has no side chain. This closes the pocket in elastase, so any side chain of appreciable size will be unable to bind to the enzyme surface.

The mechanism of catalysis, shown in the margins of these two pages, is essentially that of cyclohexaamylose. Although these enzymes evolved to cut polypeptide chains during digestion, they also will cleave esters because the bonds and the neighboring C=O carbonyl groups are similar. The first four steps, shown downward in the left margin, describe the bonding of protein chain, cleavage, and removal of one half of the substrate chain. The last four steps, arranged to be read *up* the right margin, describe the combination of the other half of the substrate with —OH from a water molecule, and its removal from the enzyme surface. The eight steps are arranged in this way in the margins to emphasize the reversibility of any enzyme reaction. An enzyme catalyzes the reverse reaction as well as the forward reaction. It only hastens the attainment of thermodynamic equilibrium, without affecting the equilibrium conditions. The reverse reaction can be observed by reading the panels down the right margin and up the left. Each panel in one margin describes the same chemical step as the corresponding panel in the other margin, but for a reaction in the opposite direction.

In Steps 1 and 2 of the forward reaction, a polypeptide chain approaches and binds to the active site of the enzyme, with the proper type of side chain inserted into the specificity pocket. The three catalytically active groups on the enzyme, Asp 102, His 57, and Ser 195, are connected by hydrogen bonds in what has been called a "charge relay system."

In Step 3 of the mechanism the histidine nitrogen acts first as a general base, pulling the serine H atom toward itself, and then as a general acid, donating the H to the lone electron pair on the nitrogen atom of the polypeptide bond to be cleaved. The aspartic acid group helps the histidine to attract the H atom by taking its other H atom away from it on the other side of the ring. As the serine H—O bond is broken, a bond is formed between the serine O and the carbonyl carbon on the polypeptide chain. This carbon becomes tetrahedrally bonded, and the negative charge that began on Asp 102 is relayed to the carbonyl oxygen atom of the substrate. This O is held in place by hydrogen bonds to N—H groups on the enzyme backbone. The transition state of Step 3, termed the tetrahedral intermediate because of the bonding around the carbonyl carbon atom, is short-lived and cannot be isolated, but there is chemical evidence for its presence.

The enzyme passes quickly through the tetrahedral intermediate to Step 4. As the polypeptide N accepts the H atom from histidine, the N—C bond is weakened and finally broken. One half of the polypeptide chain falls away as a free amine, R—NH$_2$. The other half remains bound covalently to the enzyme in an acylated intermediate analogous to that formed in the cyclohexaamylose reaction. This acyl enzyme complex is stable enough to be isolated and studied in special cases where further reaction is blocked.

The steps to deacylate the enzyme and restore it to its original state (Steps 5-8) are like the first four steps run in reverse, with H$_2$O playing the role of the missing half chain. A water molecule attacks the carbonyl carbon of the acyl group in Step 5, and donates one H atom to histidine 57 to form another tetrahedral intermediate (Step 6). This intermediate breaks down when the H atom is passed on from histidine to serine (Step 7). The second half of the polypeptide chain falls away (Step 8), aided by charge repulsion between the carboxyl group and the negative charge that now is back on aspartic acid 102. The enzyme is restored to its original state, ready to bind and cleave another polypeptide chain.

Elegant chemical experiments have been carried out to find how choosy chymotrypsin is among its substrates. Most of these have been

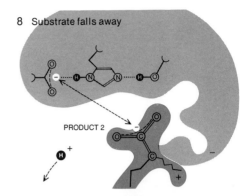

8 Substrate falls away

PRODUCT 2

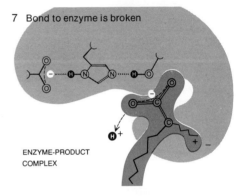

7 Bond to enzyme is broken

ENZYME-PRODUCT
COMPLEX

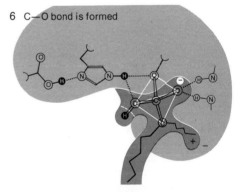

6 C—O bond is formed

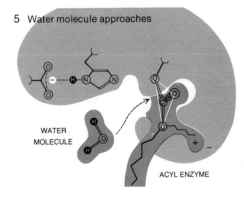

5 Water molecule approaches

WATER
MOLECULE

ACYL ENZYME

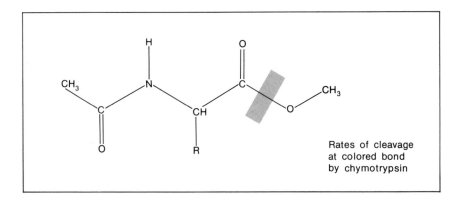

Rates of cleavage
at colored bond
by chymotrypsin

The nature of the side chain, R—, affects the rapidity with which the colored bond is cleaved by chymotrypsin.

Corresponding amino acid	—R	Relative rate of reaction
Gly	—H	1
Glu	—CH₂—CH₂—C (with O, O⁻)	3.5
S-Methyl Met	—CH₂—CH₂—S⁺ (CH₃, CH₃)	21
Leu	—CH₂—CH (CH₃, CH₃)	160,000
Met	—CH₂—CH₂—S—CH₃	230,000
Phe	—CH₂—(benzene ring)	4,200,000
— —	—CH₂—(cyclohexane ring)	8,000,000
Tyr	—CH₂—(benzene ring)—OH	36,500,000
Trp	—CH₂—(indole ring)	42,000,000

done using esters, R—CO—O—R′, instead of polypeptide chains, R—CO—NH—R′, because the smaller molecules are easier to handle. The catalytic mechanism is the same. The type of ester shown at the top of the page, CH₃—CO—NH—CHR—CO—O—CH₃, is particularly informative because the CH₃—CO—NH— portion looks like the continuation of a polypeptide chain, even having a carbonyl group that can hydrogen bond to the enzyme backbone like a polypeptide chain does. The R— side group fits into the specificity pocket, and the CO—O ester bond is cleaved just like the polypeptide bond. How good a substrate the molecule is, and how fast it is cleaved, depend upon how well the R— side chain fits into the chymotrypsin pocket.

Typical results are shown in the left margin. If the hydrogen atom of a glycinelike side chain is taken as the standard, then glutamic acid binds better than glycine and is cleaved 3.5 times faster. Even a negatively charged chain evidently is better at holding the substrate molecule in place than no chain at all. The larger S-methyl methionine chain is better still, in spite of its positive charge. Eliminating the charge (in leucine) makes a dramatic improvement—from 21 to 160,000 in relative reaction rates—even though the side chain is smaller. Methionine is similar to leucine, and the large aromatic phenylalanine ring causes another eighteen-fold improvement in binding and reaction rates. A cyclohexane side chain is twice as good, tyrosine is four times better yet, and tryptophan, which has the largest amino acid side chain of all, leads to a reaction rate 42 million times faster than that for glycine. The specificity, or selectivity, of the chymotrypsin molecule ranges over seven orders of magnitude in reaction rates.

INHIBITORS

Some molecules resemble an enzyme's proper substrate closely enough that they can bind to the active site, but then cannot undergo chemical reaction. They simply sit there, blocking the site and preventing the enzyme from functioning with real substrates. These molecular dogs in the manger are termed *competitive inhibitors* because they compete

598

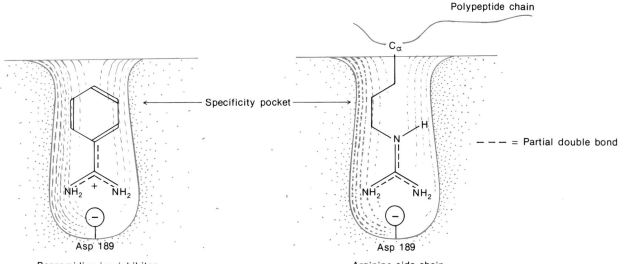

Polypeptide chain

Specificity pocket

---- = Partial double bond

C_α

NH_2 + NH_2

NH_2 NH_2

H
N

Asp 189

Asp 189

Benzamidine ion inhibitor

Arginine side chain

with the true substrates for active sites. The benzamidine ion (above) is one such competitive inhibitor for trypsin. When protonated, the amidine end of the molecule has the same flat, delocalized-electron structure found in protonated arginine side chains. To the specificity pocket of trypsin, a benzamidine ion looks like the outer half of an arginine side chain, and is accepted and bound as such. A molecule inhibited in this way is useless for further catalysis. One might think that a benzamidine-inhibited trypsin thereafter would function as elastase, cutting chains with small side groups. Careful x-ray examination of the inhibited trypsin has shown, however, that the benzamidine ring is just a little too large, and gets in the way of the alpha carbon of any potentially binding polypeptide chain, even if the side chain is only the —H of glycine.

Many competitive inhibitors are known for other enzymes. Succinic dehydrogenase in the citric acid cycle converts succinic acid into fumaric acid:

$$HOOC-CH_2-CH_2-COOH \rightarrow \begin{array}{cc} HOOC & H \\ \diagdown & \diagup \\ C=C & \\ \diagup & \diagdown \\ H & COOH \end{array} + 2H$$

Competitive inhibitors that bind to the succinic dehydrogenase enzyme but then cannot react further include oxalic acid (HOOC—COOH, with no —CH$_2$— spacers between its carboxyl groups), malonic acid (HOOC—CH$_2$—COOH, with one spacer too few), glutaric acid (HOOC—CH$_2$—CH$_2$—CH$_2$—COOH, with one spacer too many), oxaloacetic acid (HOOC—CH$_2$—CO—COOH, with the wrong kind of polar spacer), and even pyrophosphate (^{2}O$_3$P—O—PO$_3^{2-}$). Such competitive inhibitors are reversible, since they can be flushed off the enzyme with a sufficient excess of true substrate.

Other *irreversible inhibitors* ruin an enzyme permanently by chemically modifying part of its active site. Diisopropylfluorophosphate (DFP), shown at the top of the next page, is an irreversible inhibitor of proteases, such as trypsin, which contain an essential serine

Benzamidine is a competitive inhibitor with trypsin because it can fill the specificity pocket and hence block the enzyme from binding its true substrate.

599

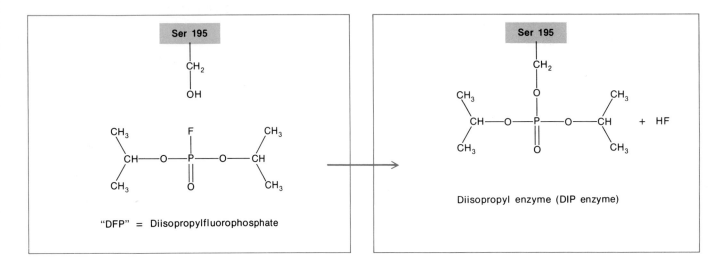

"DFP" = Diisopropylfluorophosphate

Diisopropyl enzyme (DIP enzyme)

DFP is an irreversible inhibitor with trypsin, chymotrypsin, and elastase. It forms a covalent bond with the serine 195 side chain, thereby preventing subsequent catalysis. The DIP enzyme (right) is irrevocably ruined.

at the active site. It binds covalently and reversibly to serine 195 to form diisopropyl-serine-195-trypsin (DIP-trypsin). DFP is a potent and lethal nerve gas because it also irreversibly inhibits the enzyme *acetylcholinesterase*, which is essential for the conduction of nerve impulses. DFP effectively turns off all nerve signals, and the victim suffocates because he stops breathing and his heart stops beating and circulating O_2-containing blood. Many organophosphorus compounds are deadly nerve gases for the same reason, and perhaps a regrettable amount of research has been carried out on these inhibitors in recent years.

Of the four roles of an enzyme outlined at the end of the preceding section, these proteolytic enzymes illustrate three. The three side chains at the active site, Asp 102, His 57, and Ser 195, provide a *mechanism* for catalysis, or an easier way to hydrolyze a polypeptide bond than simply pulling the chain apart in solution and adding a water molecule to the cut ends. The hydrogen bonding between polypeptide chain and enzyme, and other interactions brought about by the shape of the active site, provide the right *orientation* to bring the peptide bond next to His 57 and Ser 195. Finally, the different specificity pockets on the three enzymes provide a *selectivity*, by ensuring that each enzyme will cut the protein chain next to its own kind of amino acid side chains. *Coupling* of two chemical reactions is not illustrated by these digestive enzymes because they have a rather simple degradative function.

THE EVOLUTION OF A FAMILY OF ENZYMES

The similarity of trypsin, chymotrypsin, and elastase is apparent in their amino acid sequences. In the chain diagrams seen on Page 591, 24% of the amino acids are identical in all three proteins, and an additional 44% are the same in two of the three. Only at 32% of the positions does each enzyme have a different amino acid. Four of the disulfide bridges recur in all three molecules. The similarity in three-dimensional folding is even more pronounced. Not only do these en-

600

zymes have an identical active-site structure, they are folded identically on the other sides of the molecule that the polypeptide substrate never sees. From a functional standpoint there is much more similarity than would seem to be called for. As with myoglobin and hemoglobin, the inference is strong that we are seeing three protein molecules that are similar today because they share a common protein ancestor.

Trypsin, chymotrypsin, and elastase act in concert to cut digestible protein chains in different places. They appear to have evolved from a common protein-cutting ancestor that probably was less specific and could do the job of all three of the modern enzymes. Why then would three enzymes develop where one was operating before? The answer is that the more general ancestral enzyme, to be more general, would have to bind a substrate chain less well, thereby making it less efficient than the modern enzymes. Tighter binding brings about faster cleavage, but tighter binding also means a closer fit between substrate and active site. This brings with it a greater "fussiness" about the shapes of molecules that will or will not be accepted. One multipurpose but slow enzyme is more economical in terms of genetic coding; but three specialized, rapid enzymes are so much more advantageous in the digestion of foods that this is why they ultimately evolved.

All three of these enzymes are *serine proteases*, so named because a serine group is the key to their catalytic mechanisms. Other serine proteases, which carry out a variety of roles, are found in vertebrates. *Thrombin* triggers the blood clotting process by converting another protein, fibrinogen, into fibrin, the substance of the clot. The blood clot eventually is dissolved by *plasmin*, another serine protease. The immune response against infection is a chain reaction that involves several trypsinlike enzymes to activate the next step in the chain. Fertilization of an egg by a sperm is aided by an *acrosomal protease*, an enzyme in the sperm head that has a size, specificity, and sensitivity to inhibitors resembling that of trypsin. All of these enzymes are triggers that cause something important to happen at the proper time by taking a bite out of another protein molecule. They are trypsinlike in their specificity, because charged groups are more likely to be found on the outside of a protein molecule than are the hydrophobic groups that chymotrypsin favors. Trypsin, a digestive enzyme, is relatively indifferent to the nature of the amino acids on either side of the lysine or arginine adjacent to the bond being cleaved. In contrast, some of these other trigger enzymes are quite particular about what they will cut. They read the identity of side chains several places to either side of a prospective cleavage point, since they are designed to operate on only certain highly specific places on other proteins.

Serine proteases are not limited to vertebrates. For example, *cocoonase* helps mature moths to break out of their cocoons. The soil bacterium *Bacillus sorangium* has a trypsinlike protease, and *Streptomyces griseus* has a protease so similar that it cannot be described as trypsinlike; it is trypsin. Since all living things are made of protein, the ability to cut protein chains is one of the most necessary and most widespread of talents. Where we have not found serine proteases yet, it probably is only for want of looking.

All of the serine proteases just mentioned seem to be members of the trypsin–chymotrypsin–elastase family, with a common active-site

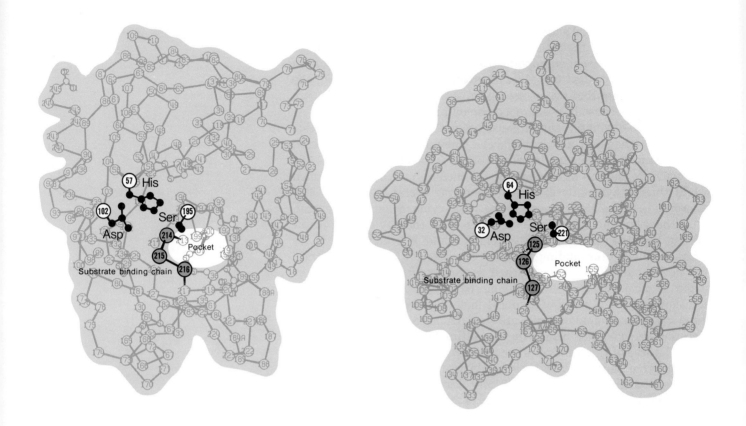

Trypsin and subtilisin have the same three-dimensional structure at their active sites, defined by the side chains Asp, His, and Ser, shown here in black. They also have the same specificity pocket (white hole) into which a critical side chain from the substrate can fit. The chain that binds a substrate is positioned similarly in both molecules. Otherwise, these two molecules are totally different, indicating they are not related in the way that trypsin, elastase, and chymotrypsin are. Trypsin and subtilisin are molecular examples of independent, convergent evolution of a common function, like the wings of birds, bats, and insects.

structure and folding architecture that betray a common ancestry. A second family of serine proteases exists, of which the best known is *subtilisin*, from the soil bacterium *B. subtilis*. Subtilisin and trypsin have completely different amino acid sequences and utterly different three-dimensional folding, yet the structures of their active sites are identical! (See above.) Both enzymes have active sites—with Asp, His, Ser; a specificity pocket; and a rim for hydrogen bonding the polypeptide substrate chain—in the same three-dimensional arrangement, even though the order in which the three catalytic side chains occurs is different in the two enzymes. In trypsin the order is histidine 57 · · · aspartic 102 · · · serine 195, and in subtilisin the order is aspartic 32 · · · histidine 64 · · · serine 221. The structures of trypsin and subtilisin preclude any common ancestry as with trypsin, chymotrypsin, and elastase, yet their active sites are the same. This is the clearest case known of convergent evolution at the molecular level. If a polypeptide chain is to be cut by an acylated serine mechanism, then this seems to be the only arrangement of amino acid side chains that will do the job. It is a remarkable illustration of the strictness of the requirements for an operative active site.

The idea of a family of modern proteins, all descendants of a common ancestral protein, recurs in myoglobin and hemoglobin, in antibody molecules, in the cytochromes of photosynthesis and respiration, in the dehydrogenases that transfer H to NAD$^+$ during glycolysis and the citric acid cycle, and in many other enzyme-controlled systems. The more we learn about protein structures, the more we see evidence that molecules evolve, just like bone structures and other large-scale features of living organisms do.

LARGER ENZYMES

Trypsin, chymotrypsin, and elastase are examples of small and reasonably simple enzymes, which are designed to chop up polypeptide chains. *Ribonuclease* and *deoxyribonuclease* digest nucleic acids in the intestines. *Lysozyme* is found in many external bodily secretions, such as tears and sweat, where it helps protect against invading bacteria by cutting the polysaccharides of their cell walls. All of these are small, single-chain, single-subunit enzymes like trypsin.

Other enzymes, such as those used in glycolysis and the citric acid cycle, are much larger and are built from two or more subunits. *Hexokinase*, the enzyme that adds a phosphate group to glucose to make glucose-6-phosphate at the beginning of glycolysis, has two identical subunits of molecular weight 51,000 each. *Lactate dehydrogenase*, which converts pyruvate to lactate in human muscle when insufficient oxygen is present for complete oxidation, contains four identical subunits of 36,000 molecular weight each, whereas *alcohol dehydrogenase*, which converts pyruvate to alcohol in yeast, has two subunits of 41,000 each. These are fairly typical sizes and subunit structures for enzymes, but larger units are known. *Pyruvate dehydrogenase*, which converts pyruvate to acetyl coenzyme A at the beginning of the citric acid cycle, removing CO_2 in the process and reducing NAD^+ to NADH, really is a complex of three different enzymes, with 10 to 60 molecules of each, and a total molecular weight of around 10,000,000. In this extreme case, three enzymes are linked physically because they must cooperate in a complicated series of chemical reactions, and the product from one step is handed on as the substrate for the next step. For similar reasons, successive enzymes of the respiratory chain are grouped adjacent to one another on the inner membrane of the mitochondrion, so the substances they act on never have to travel far.

There are other, and more elegant, reasons why some enzymes are built up from more than one subunit. If the product of an enzymatic reaction tends to remain bound to the active site and clog the enzyme for later reactions, this is termed *product inhibition*. This process often is useful, since an oversupply of product thus can keep the enzyme from making even more. But if this product is the last of a series of half a dozen synthetic steps, then the intermediate steps are wasteful. It would have been better to turn off the synthesis at the first step rather than the final one.

Allosteric inhibition occurs when an enzyme that produces one molecule can be inhibited by a quite different molecule, binding at a site somewhere different than the active site. ("Allo-stery" means "different structure.") In cases where the molecular structure is known, the allosteric regulatory site and the catalytic site are found to be on different subunits. The best-studied allosteric enzyme, aspartate transcarbamylase (ATCase), combines aspartic acid and carbamyl phosphate (right) in the first of several chemical reactions that eventually will lead to cytidine triphosphate (CTP). ATCase has 12 subunits, 6 identical regulatory units and 6 identical catalytic units. Although CTP bears no resemblance to the direct product of the ATCase reaction, it can bind to the regulatory units and induce a conformational change in the molecule that "turns it off," thereby preventing more carbamyl phosphate and aspartic acid from being used. The engineer refers to this

Cytidine triphosphate, the end product of a long set of synthetic reactions, is an allosteric inhibitor of one of the early stages in its synthesis. This feedback inhibition is efficient because it prevents the buildup of intermediate compounds when the end product is not needed. From R. E. Dickerson and I. Geis, *The Structure and Action of Proteins*, W. A. Benjamin, Inc. Copyright © 1969 by Dickerson and Geis.

603

kind of behavior as *feedback control,* but it was invented by nature billions of years before we copied it.

ATP is an allosteric inhibitor at several steps in glycolysis and the citric acid cycle, shutting the machinery down when too much ATP is present. Citrate is an allosteric inhibitor of the second step in glycolysis, conversion of fructose-6-phosphate to fructose diphosphate, and oxaloacetate is an allosteric inhibitor of the succinate-to-fumarate step, which occurs three steps before oxaloacetate in the citric acid cycle. Allosteric control need not be all negative, and there are many cases known where binding of an allosteric activator or promoter to a regulatory site on an enzyme can *increase* the rate of activity at the catalytic site. An excess of citrate activates one of the enzymes that shunts acetyl coenzyme A off to storage as fatty acids, for use later when needed. The net result is that when the energy-storage metabolism is running too fast and too much citrate is piling up in the citric acid cycle, the glycolysis "burner" is turned down at the early fructose-6-phosphate stage. The end product of glycolysis is shunted off into storage as fatty acids instead of entering the citric acid cycle. This process occurs because citrate is an allosteric inhibitor for one enzyme, and an allosteric activator for another. Other feedback control points involving other molecules and intermediates are known for glycolysis and the citric acid cycle. One of the most interesting unsolved problems in protein structure today is the molecular basis for this type of allosteric control.

QUESTIONS

1. What is the energy of activation for a chemical reaction? How is it related to the rate at which a reaction occurs? How does a catalyst affect the activation energy?

2. How does a catalyst affect the final equilibrium conditions of a reaction? How will a catalyst change the equilibrium position if the reaction is exothermic? If it is endothermic?

3. What is the primary point of attack for ester hydrolysis catalyzed by protons? How does proton catalysis of this reaction differ from general acid catalysis?

4. What is the primary point of attack for ester hydrolysis catalyzed by hydroxide ions? How does hydroxide ion catalysis of this reaction differ from general base catalysis?

5. How do general base catalysis and nucleophilic attack resemble one another, and how do they differ? How can they be distinguished experimentally?

6. How does substrate orientation affect the rate of a chemical reaction? How does an enzyme use this factor to accelerate a reaction?

7. In what way does the cleavage mechanism in cyclohexaamylose resemble that of trypsin or chymotrypsin?

8. How does cyclohexaamylose exhibit substrate specificity? Which proteolytic enzyme does it most resemble in specificity: trypsin, chymotrypsin, or elastase?

9. Why is coupling of reactions often important? How do enzymes bring this coupling about? Illustrate with the glutamine synthetase reaction.

10. How does our body avoid being digested by our own digestive enzymes—trypsin, chymotrypsin, and elastase? Which of these three enzymes would you expect to be more dangerous to body proteins, and why? How is this related to the stability of these three enzymes in solution?

11. What evidence is there to suggest that chymotrypsin and elastase are evolutionarily related to trypsin, but that subtilisin is not? In what ways does subtilisin resemble the other three enzymes?

12. In what ways are the structures of trypsin, chymotrypsin, and elastase related? How do they differ? How do these differences affect their respective chemical behavior?

13. What parts do aspartic acid 102, histidine 57, and serine 195 play in the catalytic mechanism of trypsin? What role does the rim of the specificity pocket play?

14. What is a "tetrahedral intermediate" in trypsin catalysis? Show how it occurs twice during the cleavage and removal of a polypeptide chain.

15. What is the acyl enzyme? Which half of the substrate chain is attached to the protein in the acyl enzyme, and how is it attached? What would be the equivalent of the acyl enzyme in the cleavage of an ester by cyclohexaamylose?

16. How do α helices contribute to the structure of trypsin? What part do structures resembling β sheets play? Where are the β-sheetlike regions? How does the presence, or absence, of disulfide bridges suggest that the three proteolytic enzymes discussed in this chapter are evolutionarily related?

17. What is the difference between a competitive and an irreversible inhibitor for an enzyme? Which type is more likely to resemble the true enzyme substrate?

18. Why is benzamidine an inhibitor for trypsin, and what kind of an inhibitor is it? Why does benzamidine–trypsin not function as an elastaselike enzyme?

19. What is DFP, and how does it inhibit trypsin? Will it also inhibit elastase? What type of an inhibitor is it?

20. Why would you expect that various control enzymes found throughout the body would be more trypsinlike than chymotrypsinlike in their activity? Give three examples.

21. What is allosteric inhibition, and how does it differ from the simpler competitive and irreversible inhibition? From a logical control viewpoint, what is advantageous about allosteric inhibition?

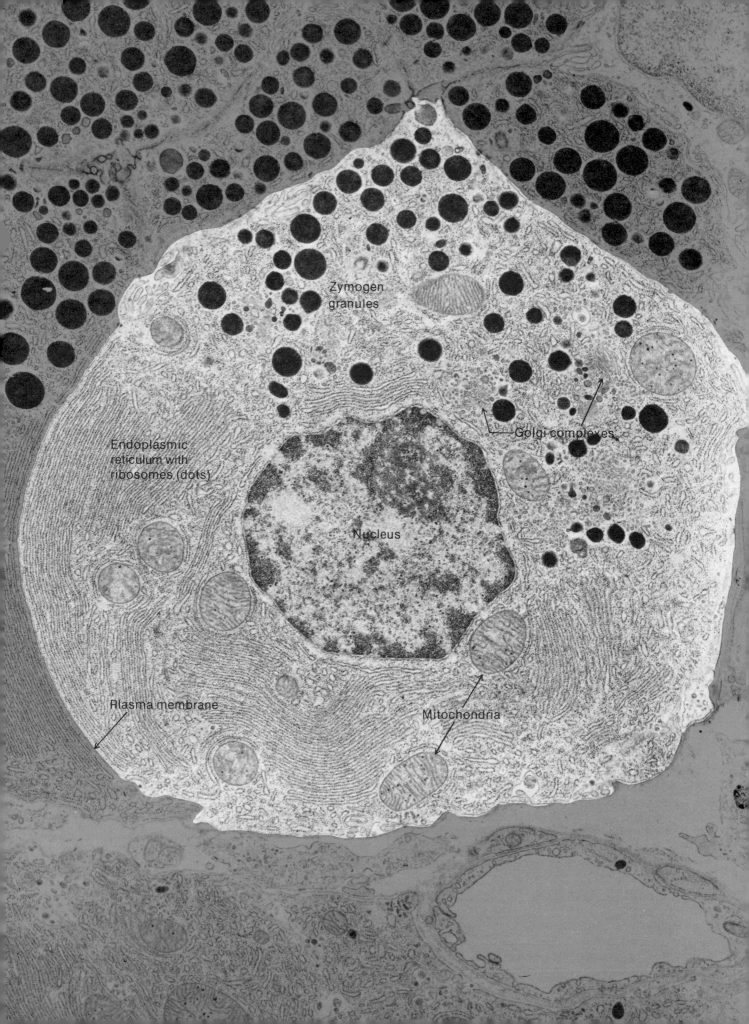

Zymogen granules

Golgi complexes

Endoplasmic reticulum with ribosomes (dots)

Nucleus

Plasma membrane

Mitochondria

CHAPTER 25

Self-Sustaining Chemical Systems: Living Cells

So far we have been looking at the pieces of a living organism. Now it is time to put the pieces together and see where, and how, they fit. This approach often is neglected in chemistry. An electronics expert who analyzed a transistor radio by pounding it to bits and then running an elemental analysis on the wreckage would not get high marks for insight; yet this is not too fanciful a parody of attitudes in what can be called the "Waring blender" school of biochemistry. You can search carefully through one or two well-known biochemistry textbooks and find hardly a hint of the structure of a living cell, or a clue as to where the various biochemical reactions of a cell take place. Yet one of the primary methods of control of reactions in a cell is physical separation. If the elaborate structure of a cell, shown on the opposite page, is destroyed, then the intricate chemical edifice collapses, too. In many ways, a chemist who looks only at the reactions and not at the organization of cells is missing the point. As with the transistor radio fragments, he will see the metal but he will never hear the music.

Living cells have one striking difference from such simple man-made devices as transistor radios: They have a history. Every living cell developed from an earlier cell that was almost, but not quite, like its offspring. The further back one goes, the less alike a modern cell and its ancestor become. As we trace the lineage backward, we see the outlines of the evolution of life and ultimately the beginnings of life from nonliving chemical systems. This will be the ultimate chemical triumph: to understand in detail how this process came about. The present chapter is devoted to the role of structure and organization in a functioning chemical cell, and the final chapter will be addressed to the problem of the origin of life.

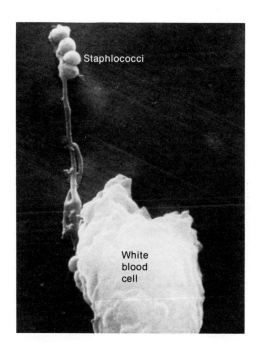

Procaryotic cells (bacteria) and a eucaryotic cell (white blood cell from an animal). In this photomicrograph the white blood cell is about to protect its host by devouring the bacteria. Reprinted from A. S. Klainer and C. J. Betsch (1973), *J. Infectious Diseases* 127: 686; by permission of the University of Chicago Press. Copyright ©1973, University of Chicago.

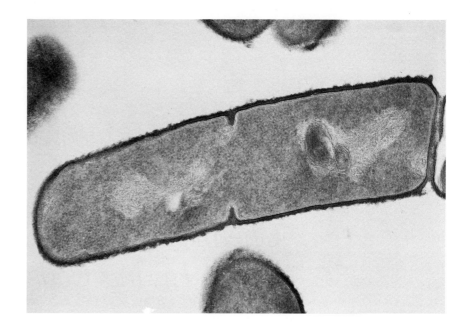

Electron micrograph of a *Bacillus subtilis* bacterium. Notice the dark cell wall outside the bacterial membrane. This is the soil bacterium that secretes subtilisin, a digestive enzyme mentioned in Chapter 24. Reprinted with permission of Dinah Abram. From *Principles of Microbiology and Immunology* by Bernard D. Davis *et al.*, Harper & Row Publishers, Inc.; copyright © 1968.

PROCARYOTIC CELLS

Living cells exist on this planet in two basic patterns: procaryotes and eucaryotes. As we saw in Chapter 23, procaryotes are older and simpler in design, and are represented today only by bacteria and blue-green algae. The eucaryotic pattern is newer and more complex and is found in every other type of living cell: green, red, and other algae, fungi, protozoa, and higher plants and animals. Both kinds of cells carry out the essential functions outlined at the beginning of Chapter 22: They propagate, grow, metabolize at the expense of their surroundings, use and protect themselves from their environment, and evolve in response to slow changes in the environment. They may go about things in different ways, but they all face similar challenges and have similar goals: to meet those challenges well enough to survive.

Bacteria and blue-green algae have the simplest pattern of organization. They may be rod-shaped, as shown above, spherical as shown on the previous page, or helical; they also may occur singly or in clusters. The main features of a bacterial cell are diagrammed at the far right. These features are relatively few: cell membrane, wall and capsule, cytoplasm or cell fluid, photosynthetic vesicles or membranes, DNA, ribosomes for protein synthesis, mesosomal infoldings of the cell membrane, and sometimes flagella or pili on the outside. Bacteria are small; for example, *Escherichia coli (E. coli)* from our intestines is a rounded-end cylinder 10,000 Å across and 20,000 Å long, weighing about 2×10^{-12} gram.

The bacterial *cell membrane* plays the vital role of separating the bacterium from its environment. Without such a barrier, a cell existing as a local concentration of ordered molecules and reactions would be impossible. The membrane is a lipid–protein bilayer 70 Å thick. It is somewhat simpler than that of eucaryotes, and resembles the unit-membrane model seen in Chapter 21. The membrane is freely permeable to water, but not to simple ions or charged molecules, or neutral molecules larger than glycerol.

The membrane controls the contents of the cell. Water and small neutral molecules can enter and leave by free diffusion. Other specific ions and molecules can diffuse across the membrane with the aid of carrier molecules, in the process of *passive transport*. Although carrier molecules are necessary to make the penetration of the membrane possible, passive transport still represents a diffusion along a concentration gradient, from the side of the membrane with an excess of the molecule or ion, to the side where it is in short supply. *Active transport* also exists, in which some ions and molecules can be taken into or out of the cell against the normal concentration gradient, and accumulated on the side of the membrane where they already are in excess. Such backward flow leads to a state of higher free energy, and is thermodynamically nonspontaneous. The energy to drive active transport comes from ATP. We shall see passive and active transport in more detail with eucaryotes.

All but a very few bacteria have a *cell wall*, 100 Å to 800 Å thick. The wall provides rigid mechanical protection, but is not a barrier to molecular diffusion. It is built from glycopeptide, which is a polymer of glucose derivatives that is cross-linked by short polypeptide chains. Lipids also are present in the wall in the form of lipid-peptide combinations, or lipopeptides. The bacterial cell wall often is surrounded by yet another protective coating, the *capsule*. This is a gelatinous outer layer made from short-chain sugar polymers.

The cell membrane is the locus of the respiratory electron-transport system. In respiring bacteria, the flavoproteins, quinones, and cytochromes of the electron-transport chain are found in the inner surface of the bacterial membrane, as are the enzymes necessary for ATP synthesis. In certain electron microscope preparations, the inner surface of the membrane appears covered with tiny spheres on stalks (lower right). These structures resemble the inner membrane spheres seen in mitochondria (Page 617), and like them, they may be the locations at which respiration and ATP synthesis occur. Glycolysis takes place in the cytoplasm, or cell fluid, of the bacterium, as do the reactions of the citric acid cycle in those bacteria that respire. The reduced carrier molecules from glycolysis and the citric acid cycle then diffuse to the outer membrane and enter the respiratory chain.

The photosynthetic pigments in purple bacteria are located on extensive infoldings of the outer membrane that sometimes look like little hollow bags or vesicles, sometimes are interconnected in hollow tubules, and more often appear as dense, stacked layers of unit membrane. These photosynthetic membrane structures have their counterparts in blue-green algae and in the chloroplasts of eucaryotes. Green bacteria carry their photosynthetic pigments in quite different cigar-shaped vesicles, which are just under the outer membrane but are not connected with it. The light reactions of photosynthesis occur in these membrane folds or vesicles, and the dark reactions take place in the cytoplasm.

The outer membrane frequently has larger infoldings called *mesosomes*, which seem to be involved in cell division. These and the photosynthetic apparatus are the nearest things that bacteria have to organs.

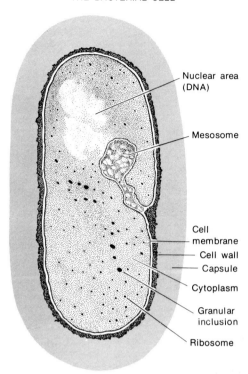

Nuclear area (DNA)

Mesosome

Cell membrane
Cell wall
Capsule
Cytoplasm
Granular inclusion
Ribosome

Diagram of a typical bacterial cell, showing the relatively few structural components that it contains.

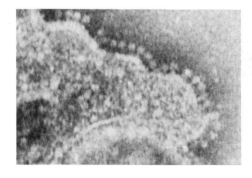

Fragment of the cell membrane of a ruptured *B. stearothermophilus* bacterium. The inner surface of the membrane is the location of the respiratory enzymes. It is studded with small spheres on stalks, similar to those observed on the inside surface of the inner membrane of a mitochondrion. Reprinted with permission of Antoinette Ryter. From *Principles of Microbiology and Immunology* by Bernard D. Davis *et al.,* Harper & Row Publishers, Inc.; copyright © 1968.

The *cytoplasm* (cell fluid) is viscous, and any internal structure that it might have in terms of barriers or compartments is obscured by densely packed ribosomes, although some scientists believe that compartments do exist. The fluid is a 20% protein solution in water, containing ions and small molecules and serving as a pool or reservoir for the small metabolites of the cell. It contains the enzymes for all cell processes other than respiration and the light reactions of photosynthesis. These processes include glycolysis, glucose synthesis, various other syntheses, and DNA replication and transcription.

The cytoplasm is filled with *ribosomes*, as many as 15,000 per *E. coli* cell. These ribosomes are 180-Å-diameter spheres, composed of half protein and half RNA. They are built from two unequal parts, with molecular weights 1,800,000 and 900,000, and are designated "70 S" ribosomes from their sedimentation behavior in the ultracentrifuge. Ribosomes in eucaryotes are 35% larger and are termed "80 S" ribosomes. They have a 200-Å diameter, and are made from two pieces with molecular weights 2,400,000 and 1,200,000. Mitochondria and chloroplasts in eucaryotic cells also have ribosomes of their own for protein synthesis, but these ribosomes are smaller, like those of bacteria. This is one of the many pieces of evidence that suggests an ancient bacterial origin for these eucaryotic organelles.

The cytoplasm also contains storage granules filled with glycogen (or starch), lipids such as poly-β-hydroxybutyric acid, and polymetaphosphate (endless chains of linked phosphate tetrahedra). All of these compounds are means of storing energy in bacteria.

The *chromatin*, or genetic material, in bacteria is not housed in a separate nucleus, but in packed, aggregated bundles of fibers of double-stranded DNA floating in the cytoplasm. In *E. coli* and in many other bacteria, the DNA occurs in one continuous circular loop rather than an open strand. The enzymes for DNA replication, and transcription of information to messenger RNA, also are free-floating in the cytoplasm. This is the most striking difference between procaryotes and eucaryotes. In eucaryotes the DNA is organized into chromosomes and is segregated into a nucleus surrounded by a nuclear membrane. None of this nuclear structure exists in procaryotes.

Bacteria also have special external structures: flagella for motion, and pili (hairs), which are used in sexual conjugation and possibly for other functions. Bacteria are rather simple living machines, but they contain all of the essentials for survival, and in fact have managed to survive on this planet twice as long as eucaryotes. They show a biochemical variety and versatility that far surpasses that of eucaryotes. Part of this variety may reflect the extent to which eucaryotes have "settled down" with the most favorable of the biochemical options, and part may be the result of special chemical adaptations that bacteria made later to survive in competition with eucaryotes.

EUCARYOTIC CELLS

Eucaryotes evolved more recently than procaryotes, and they obviously represent a higher level of organization. More specialization is seen within the cell, and there is more compartmentalization of the cell chemistry. Listed in the table below are eleven major components of a eucaryotic cell, which includes plant as well as animal cells. The photomicrograph on Page 606 shows a typical animal cell—a secretory cell from the pancreas of a bat. In the schematic drawing below, labels indicate major features that are visible in the chapter-opening photomicrograph. The round dark objects, called zymogen granules, contain enzymes packaged for export from the cell.

1. CELL MEMBRANE—similar to bacteria but more elaborate 2. CELL WALL—only in plants 3. CYTOPLASM—cell fluid similar to bacteria 4. NUCLEUS with DNA surrounded by nuclear membrane	5. ENDOPLASMIC RETICULUM—folded and flattened membrane in the cytoplasm with ribosomes attached 6. RIBOSOMES—sites of protein synthesis 7. GOLGI COMPLEXES—centers for packaging molecules	8. MITOCHONDRIA—centers for respiration and ATP synthesis 9. CHLOROPLASTS—photosynthetic apparatus in green plants 10. LYSOSOMES—bags of destructive enzymes 11. PEROXISOMES—vesicles for eliminating peroxides

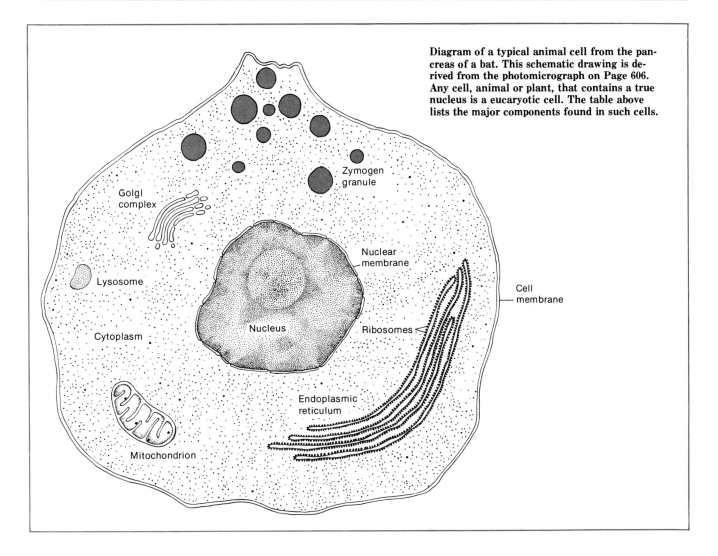

Diagram of a typical animal cell from the pancreas of a bat. This schematic drawing is derived from the photomicrograph on Page 606. Any cell, animal or plant, that contains a true nucleus is a eucaryotic cell. The table above lists the major components found in such cells.

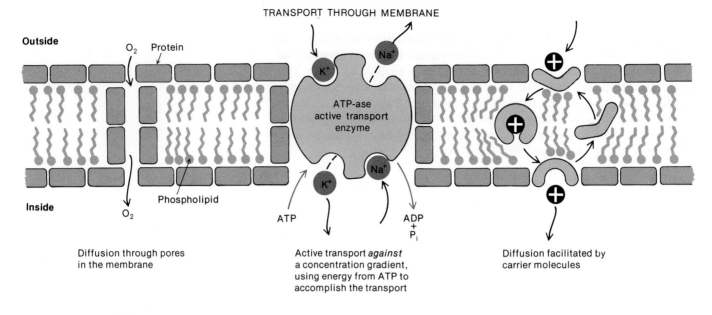

TRANSPORT THROUGH MEMBRANE

Outside

O₂   Protein

ATP-ase
active transport
enzyme

K⁺   Na⁺

Inside

O₂

Phospholipid

ATP   K⁺   Na⁺   ADP + P_i

Diffusion through pores
in the membrane

Active transport *against*
a concentration gradient,
using energy from ATP to
accomplish the transport

Diffusion facilitated by
carrier molecules

Key

= Protein

= Phospholipid

Schematic diagram of active and passive transport through a membrane barrier. Circles with tails are phospholipid molecules; shaded "bricks" are globular protein molecules. *Left and right:* Passive diffusion down a concentration gradient.

In contrast to this structural complexity, there is less diversity in the actual cell chemistry. All eucaryotes respire using O_2, although yeast and some other eucaryotes can get along with glycolysis alone when O_2 is unavailable. All eucaryotes have mitochondria, with obviously homologous enzymes for use in the citric acid cycle and respiration. Photosynthetic eucaryotes all have Photocenters I and II, and obtain reducing equivalents by decomposing water and releasing O_2. (Among procaryotes, only blue-green algae have two-center photosynthesis using H_2O.) The differences between any procaryote and any eucaryote are far greater than between the most diverse of the eucaryotes: fungi and primates, redwood and dragonfly.

EUCARYOTIC CELL MEMBRANE

A eucaryotic cell membrane is thicker than that of bacteria, around 90 Å. To a first approximation the lipid-bilayer unit membrane described in Chapter 21, with a covering of protein on both sides, is a good model (see above). As was mentioned in Chapter 21, some proteins appear to extend all the way through the membrane, and the lipid must be exposed to the surface in places. The cell membrane is a selective barrier that passes some molecules in and out, and excludes others. The free permeability to H_2O, O_2, CO_2, and other small uncharged molecules suggests the existence of pores, as drawn at the left above. From the rates at which molecules of different sizes penetrate the membrane, the pores are thought to be approximately 8 Å in diameter and to occupy one twentieth of a percent of the total surface area. Some cations can pass through the pores but anions cannot, which implies that the rim of a pore might contain negative charges such as carboxyl groups.

Some molecules cannot get through the cell membrane by themselves, but are brought through by carrier molecules in a passive-transport process, such as the one diagrammed at the right above. We can

612

tell that carriers are involved because we can saturate the carriers with "cargo." Up to a point, the rate at which a carried molecule diffuses across the membrane is proportional to its concentration; but when every carrier has all the molecules it can handle, increasing the concentration of cargo molecules has no effect on the diffusion rate. A model for this passive transport is the ability of some small antibiotics to make a natural membrane or an artificial lipid bilayer permeable to alkali metal ions. Most of these antibiotics are closed-ring compounds with many —O— or C=O groups, as in nonactin (right). Nonactin wraps around a potassium ion, with its oxygen atoms coordinated to the ion, and with hydrophobic groups exposed to the exterior. It is the exact opposite of the oil-drop model of a protein, in which the protein has a hydrophobic interior and a polar exterior. The inverted structure of the antibiotic presumably makes it possible for nonactin and a K^+ ion to diffuse through the lipid bilayer of the membrane. Nonactin, in effect, gives the ion a hydrophobic overcoat. Gramicidin can carry all of the alkali metal ions through a membrane, but valinomycin carries only K^+, Rb^+, or Cs^+. Such antibiotics are toxic because they make membranes susceptible to alkali metal ions when they should not be. Cells waste their ATP by pumping K^+ in and Na^+ out, only to find them leaking the wrong way again, with the aid of these carrier molecules.

These particular antibiotics are not involved in the normal passive transport of ions by cells, but they are believed to be models for real carriers. Glycerol is brought into red blood cells, and galactose into *E. coli* bacteria, by carriers known as permeases. These permeases are thought to be enzymes, although little else is known about them.

All such permeases and carrier molecules are still only aids to the movement of molecules "downhill" along a concentration gradient. A more useful talent is the ability to carry ions or molecules from regions where they are scarce to regions where they are already concentrated, and to build up an excess on one side of the membrane. K^+ and Na^+ ions, phosphate, sugars, and some amino acids are concentrated by this active-transport process, which provides a way of gathering nutrients and storing them inside the cell for later use. Energy is required to bring things in or out against a concentration gradient, and this energy is supplied by ATP.

The most familiar active-transport mechanism is the "sodium pump," by which Na^+ is expelled from the cell and K^+ is brought in. One molecule of ATP is used for every three Na^+ ejected and two K^+ brought in. The enzyme that helps to accomplish this is embedded in the cell membrane. It receives ATP from inside the cell and releases ADP back to the inside, so only the ions being transported actually cross the membrane. The diagram at the top of the opposite page shows the transport enzyme picking up ions on one side of the membrane, rotating, and dropping them off at the other side. It is not likely that the enzyme physically rotates, but the net effect is the same.

The cell membrane is a part of the active chemical machinery of the cell, controlling what goes in and out and actively pumping some substances one way or the other. Unlike bacterial membranes, it has no respiratory or photosynthetic roles. In eucaryotes these roles are played by special organelles.

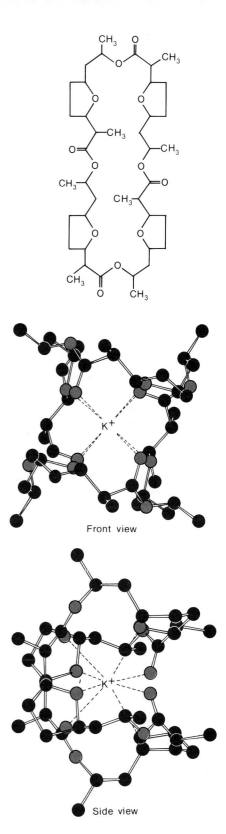

Front view

Side view

Molecular structure of one carrier of potassium ions, the antibiotic *nonactin*. The antibiotic molecule wraps around the ion, coordinating it with oxygen atoms. The outside surface of the complex is oily (hydrophobic), thereby enabling it to slip through the membrane easily. (Courtesy of Prof. J. D. Dunitz.)

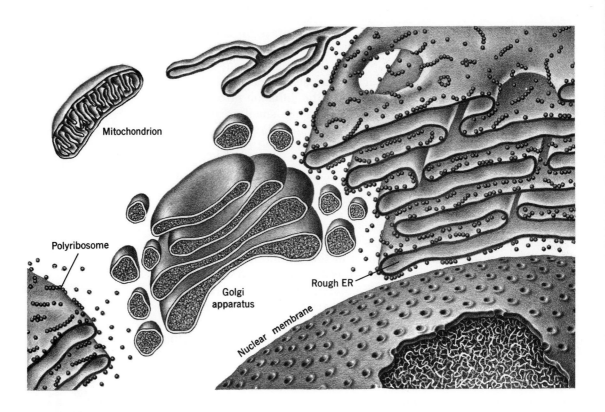

Mitochondrion

Polyribosome

Golgi apparatus

Rough ER

Nuclear membrane

Exploded cutaway view of the organelles found in a typical animal cell. DNA in the nucleus is enclosed in a double-layer nuclear membrane with pores. The rough endoplasmic reticulum is layered and folded, with ribosomes only on one side. Proteins assembled at these ribosomes diffuse to the nearby Golgi complex (apparatus) for collection and packaging into granules for export. Mitochondria provide sources of ATP for driving energy. Reprinted with permission; from A. Nason and R. L. Dehaan, *The Biological World;* copyright © 1973 John Wiley & Sons, Inc.

CYTOPLASM

As in bacteria, the cytoplasm of eucaryotes is a 20% aqueous protein solution, containing dissolved ions, small molecules, and many enzymes. In eucaryotic cells, cytoplasm also is the suspension medium for the nucleus, mitochondria, and other organelles. It is a viscous fluid with some degree of structure. Filaments 40 Å in diameter and 200-Å-diameter microtubules can be seen anchoring various organelles to one another. Many important chemical reactions take place in the cytoplasm, including glycolysis as far as pyruvate, gluconeogenesis from phosphoenolpyruvate back to glucose, fatty-acid synthesis from acetyl coenzyme A, biosynthesis of the amino acids that the cell can make (this varies from one organism to another), synthesis of porphyrin and other organic molecules, and the priming of tRNA with amino acids for protein synthesis.

CELL NUCLEUS

DNA in eucaryotes is confined within a nucleus, which is bounded by a double-layer nuclear membrane or envelope that is pierced by pores. The cutaway drawing of part of a cell (above) gives some impression of the structure of the nucleus and its pores. The DNA is combined with histones, which are basic proteins that probably help to control the use and suppression of information on different parts of the DNA. DNA is further organized into packages known as *chromosomes*. During cell division, DNA goes through a complicated copying process that is beyond this discussion, but the enzymes for both the replication of DNA and the formation of messenger RNA are found inside the nucleus. Other specialized organelles such as the nucleolus and the centrioles, which are outside the nucleus, are essential parts of the reproductive process, but are not of immediate concern to us in a discussion of cells as organized systems of chemical reactions.

ENDOPLASMIC RETICULUM AND RIBOSOMES

The endoplasmic reticulum (ER) is a densely folded stack of unit membranes, often with the appearance of being wrapped in concentric layers around the nucleus. As the drawing on the opposite page shows, the membranes of the ER have an "inside" and an "outside" and enormous surface area. One side of these folded ER membranes—the side facing the cytoplasm—is liberally peppered with ribosomes for protein synthesis. Other ribosomes are found floating loose in the cytoplasm. Although the details are hard to see in any one micrograph, serial sections reveal that the highly folded ER actually is continuous with the outer cell membrane. In reality it is a folded membrane that encloses a labyrinth of deep cavities inside the body of the cell. The side of the ER that lacks ribosomes is topologically connected with the exterior of the cell, and the ribosome-containing side is everywhere in contact with the cytoplasm. The ER also is connected to the nuclear membrane and the Golgi complexes. It provides channels for access from the cell surface to deep within its interior, and an exit route for small molecules produced in the cell.

In addition to protein synthesis, the inner surface of the ER is the place where fatty acids are esterified to fats for storage in fat globules in the cytoplasm, where phospholipids and cholesterol are synthesized for use in membranes, and where sugars are polymerized to mucopolysaccharides for secretion between cells.

GOLGI COMPLEX

The Golgi complex is another set of folded and nested membranes. At times these membranes are continuous with the ER and ultimately with the cell surface. The exact role of the Golgi complex is not clear, but one of its known functions is to collect proteins, fats, polysaccharides, and other molecules that have been synthesized on the ER, and package them into spherical vesicles for storage within the cell or secretion to the outside. The pancreatic secretory cell, illustrated at the beginning of the chapter, synthesizes the precursors of trypsin and chymotrypsin at its ER, and with the aid of its Golgi complex, secretes these pre-enzymes into the pancreatic duct for transfer into the digestive tract and activation into enzymes (see drawing on next page). The Golgi complex is a "loading dock" for synthesized molecules, and may have other functions also.

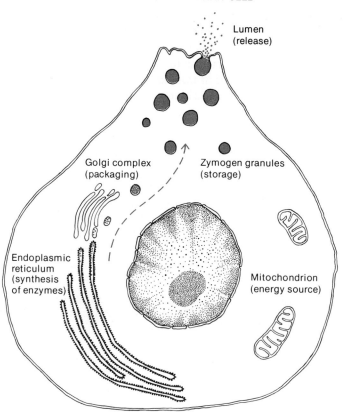

Flow diagram of molecules in a secretory cell such as the pancreatic cell on Page 611. Enzyme precursor molecules are synthesized at the ribosomes on the endoplasmic reticulum, concentrated and packaged in the Golgi complex, and stored in zymogen granules before being secreted from the cell. The precursor molecules are activated to digestive enzymes only in the intestines, where they are needed. A single pancreatic acinar cell is shown at the right, and a column of cells appears below.

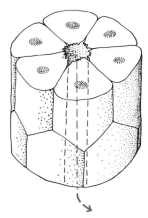

Pancreatic secretory cells as they are stacked in a cylindrical array. The secretory enzymes descend to the intestine down the central lumen.

MITOCHONDRIA

The cell membrane, ER, Golgi complexes, and nuclear membrane together make up a topologically connected set of membranes with a very large surface area. Connections between these organelles are made and broken as their membranes divide, fuse, and pinch off vesicles. Together they form an integrated whole with an inside and an outside. The inner surface of the cell membrane, the ribosome surface of the ER, the outer surface of the Golgi complex and nuclear envelope, and even the inside of the nucleus through the pores, all are topologically inside, and at times are connected. In contrast, the outer cell surface, the side of the ER without ribosomes, the inner region of the Golgi complex, and the space between the two layers of the nuclear envelope all are outside, in the same sense of lacking access to the cytoplasm.

Another important organelle also is topologically outside the cell, although it floats in the cytoplasm. This is the *mitochondrion*, which is illustrated in the electron micrograph at the upper far right. Mitochondria are the sites of the citric acid cycle, respiration, and ATP synthesis. More than a thousand mitochondria are found in a typical rat liver cell. They are highly variable in size and shape in different cells and organisms, but typically measure 5000 Å by 20,000 Å, or about the size of a bacterium. They are "outside" the cell because they are completely surrounded by a smooth outer membrane, which resembles the cell membrane and which completely separates them from the cytoplasm. Within this outer membrane is an inner membrane that is highly convoluted and folded, with deep incursions into the heart of the mitochondrion. If a mitochondrion were the size of an ordinary two-cell flashlight, its inner membrane would have the total surface area of *eight* 6 ft × 6 ft tablecloths—an impressive feat of folding! These deep infoldings of the inner membrane, called *cristae*, resemble the ER of the cell, and may perform similar functions of increasing surface area and access to the interior. The mitochondrion inside the inner membrane is filled with a gelatinous *matrix*, which is a semifluid with 50% protein content.

Approximately 25% of the inner-membrane protein is made up of the flavoproteins, cytochromes, and enzymes of the respiratory chain and ATP synthesis. The other 75% is structural protein, in association with lipids. The inner membrane is more like a bacterial membrane than that of a eucaryotic cell, both in chemical composition and in thickness and structure. Electron micrographs of comparable preparations of bacterial membranes (Page 609) and mitochondrial inner membranes (lower right) show the same spheres on stalks. It has been proposed that the respiratory chain in mitochondria is located at the base of these stalks, and that the spheres contain the coupling factors for ATP synthesis. The enzymes of the citric acid cycle float freely in the matrix, like the enzymes of glycolysis in the cytoplasm.

The reactions of glucose metabolism are shared between the cell and the mitochondria. (This separate-but-equal language is appropriate since a mitochondrion is topologically outside the cell.) Degradation of glucose to pyruvate via the glycolytic pathway is carried out in the cell cytoplasm. In anaerobic metabolism by yeast, pyruvate is reduced to ethanol, no net NADH is produced, and the story ends. In oxygen-starved human muscles, the same process is followed with lactate as the end product.

If enough oxygen is present, then pyruvate diffuses through the two membrane layers into the mitochondrial matrix and enters the citric acid cycle. The enzymes of this cycle all are dissolved in the matrix except for three: succinate, pyruvate, and α-ketoglutarate dehydrogenase. Succinate dehydrogenase is the only enzyme that transfers hydrogen atoms to FAD rather than NAD^+ (see the citric acid cycle diagram on Page 565). The succinate dehydrogenase molecule must be embedded in the inner mitochondrial membrane alongside the respiratory cytochromes and enzymes, because its carrier molecule, $FADH_2$, is permanently bound to the enzyme and cannot diffuse from one place to another as can NADH. Pyruvate and α-ketoglutarate dehydrogenase both are large, multienzyme complexes with molecular weights in the millions, and are similarly embedded in the inner mitochondrial membrane. The other citric acid cycle enzymes float freely in the matrix. NADH produced in the cycle diffuses to the inner membrane surface, where it and $FADH_2$ are reoxidized by the respiratory chain. Oxygen is reduced to H_2O, and ADP is phosphorylated to ATP, both processes occurring at the inner membrane surface.

It is the inner membrane that isolates the mitochondrion chemically from the cell in which it sits. The outer membrane is permeable to most molecules of low molecular weight. The inner membrane will

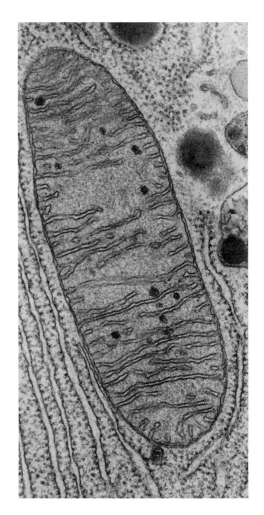

Cross section of a mitochondrion from a pancreatic secretory cell. The inner membrane is folded back and forth in "cristae," which look like fingers in this transverse section. The respiratory enzymes are found on this inner membrane, and most of the enzymes of the citric acid cycle are free in solution inside the mitochondrion. (Courtesy of K. R. Porter.)

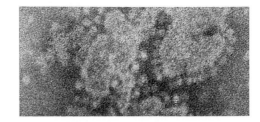

Inner mitochondrial membrane, showing spheres and stalks resembling those seen on the inside of some preparations of bacterial membranes. Such evidence reinforces the hypothesis that mitrochondria may have evolved from respiratory bacteria living symbiotically inside a larger host cell. (Courtesy of Prof. Walther Stoeckenius.)

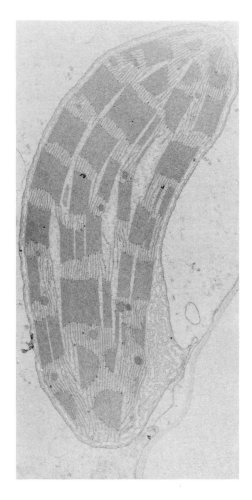

Electron micrograph of a chloroplast from maize. The stacked discs in the grana are visible. (Courtesy of Dr. L. K. Shumway, Genetics Program and Department of Botany, Washington State University.)

allow only water, small neutral molecules, and short-chain fatty acids to pass through. It is impermeable to cations and anions, most amino acids, sucrose and other sugars, coenzyme A and its esters with acetate and succinate, and ADP, ATP, NAD^+, and NADH. Some of these molecules are transported back and forth by carrier molecules, or permeases. One such permease exchanges ADP and ATP across the inner membrane on a one-for-one basis. Other shuttle molecules can transport fatty acid–coenzyme A complexes, phosphate, hydroxide ion, citrate, isocitrate, succinate, and malate, but not oxaloacetate. This impermeability of the inner membrane to oxaloacetate is the reason for the conversion of oxaloacetate to malate and back again during gluconeogenesis, mentioned on Page 570.

If the inner mitochondrial membrane is impermeable to NAD^+ and NADH, it is somewhat of a puzzle how the NADH produced in the cytoplasm during glycolysis ever gets to the site of the respiratory chain where it can be reoxidized and its energy used to make ATP. NADH from glycolysis never enters the mitochondrion at all, but passes its free energy to a shuttle molecule that can penetrate the membrane. What is not clear is the identity of the shuttle. In the most likely mechanism, the shuttle molecule is reduced by NADH outside the mitochondrion, diffuses inside, and then is reoxidized in the process of reducing FAD to $FADH_2$. Since the respiratory chain makes only two ATP per $FADH_2$, this represents a loss or a "toll fee" of one of the three ATP equivalents for every NADH made by glycolysis outside the mitochondrion. If this is the actual mechanism, the net production of ATP per molecule of glucose would be reduced from 38 to 36, but we will continue to use the 38 ATP figure for simplicity. This uncertainty illustrates both the shallowness of our present knowledge about some aspects of cell chemistry, and the remarkable extent to which the mitochondrion is really "outside" the rest of the cell.

Mitochondria also have their own limited genetic apparatus: DNA, polymerase and transcriptase enzymes to make more DNA and to copy the information off as messenger RNA, and ribosomes for protein synthesis. The DNA of mitochondria is small and circular, like that found in bacteria. The polymerases are different from those found in a cell nucleus, and the ribosomes resemble bacterial ribosomes rather than those of cell cytoplasm. The mitochondrion is capable of transcribing information to messenger RNA and synthesizing proteins. A few years ago it was believed that the only proteins coded in mitochondrial DNA were some of the structural proteins of the inner membrane and cristae. Recently other proteins have been found, including some of the polypeptides of enzymes involved in the respiratory chain. However, most of these enzymes, and all other enzymes of the citric acid cycle and ATP synthesis, are synthesized from nuclear DNA in the cytoplasm, and diffuse into the mitochondria afterwards.

Mitochondria have a semi-autonomous life of their own. Their framework, if not their contents, is independent of information in the cell nucleus. During cell division, daughter-cell mitochondria are produced by division of the mitochondria of the parent. During sexual reproduction, the mitochondria come with the egg from the mother, and later divide and increase in number. Mitochondria usually are located in the cell at places where energy is needed (along myofibrils in muscle cells, or in regions of secretory activity requiring ATP), or where stored energy is available (near fat globules in the cytoplasm). In liver cells mitochondria are capable of free motion within the cytoplasm. They are not fixed, static organelles.

There is an old but recently resurrected suggestion that mitochondria in cells are the highly specialized remains of respiring bacteria, which at one time established a symbiotic relationship with larger, nucleated cells that were incapable of respiration. The host cell supplied its own waste product, pyruvate, as food for the guest, which in turn made better use of it and donated some of its excess ATP back to the host. Functionally, the host cell and the guest bacterium would stand in a relationship similar to that of a cow and the cellulose-digesting bacteria in its rumen. In time, host and guest gradually became increasingly interdependent, and many of the genetic functions once possessed by the guest were transferred to the nucleus of the host. With its own bacterialike inner membrane, and wrapped completely in a hostlike outer membrane, a mitochondrion is really outside the eucaryotic cell even though it is physically surrounded by it. This theory was first proposed many years ago on the basis of a general resemblance between mitochondria and bacteria, but was neglected for lack of evidence. Recent new evidence, involving bacterial and mitochondrial membrane structure, DNA, polymerases, ribosomes, and inhibition by antibiotics, has made this old theory not only respectable but probably correct. The same lines of research suggest that chloroplasts in photosynthesis probably are the relics of once-symbiotic blue-green algae.

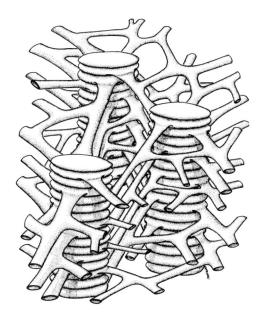

Diagram of stacks of thylakoid discs in grana, with tubular connections. The chlorophyll light reactions take place in the grana membranes, and the enzymes of electron transport also are located in these membranes. The glucose-synthesizing dark reactions take place in solution inside the thylakoid discs. (Courtesy of Dr. T. E. Weier.)

CHLOROPLASTS

Chloroplasts are the sites of photosynthesis in eucaryotes (far left). In purple photosynthetic bacteria the light-trapping pigments are found in folded pockets or vesicles in the outer membrane. In blue-green algae these vesicles are enlarged, flattened, and stacked, with adjacent vesicles sometimes fused or connected. In chloroplasts this development of structure is continued. The individual vesicles, called *thylakoids*, are stacked like pennies into grana, with extensive connections by hollow membrane tubules from one stacked granum to the next (right). Light stimulates the growth and development of grana in the chloroplast, just as it does the photosynthetic vesicles in bacteria.

The light reactions of photosynthesis take place in Type-I and Type-II pigment centers in the thylakoid membranes, and electron-transport chains from Photocenter II to I and from Photocenter I to NAD^+ also are found in the thylakoid membrane surface. The dark reactions of carbohydrate synthesis occur in the chloroplast matrix between grana. The organization resembles that of mitochondria and bacteria: glucose degradation or synthesis in the interior matrix of an organelle, and electron-transport chains—flavoproteins, quinones, cytochromes, and copper proteins—at the inner surface of the surrounding membrane.

Chloroplasts are semi-autonomous in a eucaryotic cell in the way that mitochondria are. They too have DNA, replication enzymes, and small ribosomes, although it is not clear what proteins are coded by chloroplast DNA. Like mitochondria, chloroplasts are not constructed *de novo* by the cell, but reproduce within the cell by dividing. They are topologically outside the cell by virtue of a surrounding outer membrane, and are suspected of having originated initially as symbiotic blue-green algae.

LYSOSOMES AND PEROXISOMES

Lysosomes are small cell vesicles that contain enzymes for degrading proteins, nucleic acids, and polysaccharides. The lysosomes segregate these dangerous enzymes from the body of the cell, thereby permitting them to play a digestive role without damaging their host. A white blood cell, scavenging for foreign bacteria, will absorb an intruder and destroy it with the hydrolytic enzymes in its lysosomes. Upon the death of a cell in a multicelled organism, lysosomes rupture and digest the cell contents. They have been called "suicide vesicles" and compared with the cyanide capsules familiar from spy novels, but this may unfairly neglect the digestive and degradative functions that they carry out during the life of the cell.

Peroxisomes are more of a mystery. They contain the enzyme *catalase*, which is possibly one of the earliest heme proteins and a precursor, or at least a predecessor, of cytochromes and globins. Catalase is one of the largest single-chain enzymes, containing more than 500 amino acids in one polypeptide chain, and a heme group. Its only known function is to destroy hydrogen peroxide, either with or without the release of oxygen:

$$2H_2O_2 \rightarrow 2H_2O + O_2 \qquad \text{or} \qquad H_2O_2 + H_2R \rightarrow 2H_2O + R$$

In the non-oxygen-releasing reaction above, H_2R represents any oxidizable organic compound.

In the face of general bafflement as to the purpose of peroxisomes, an ingenious theory has been proposed, according to which peroxisomes and catalase arose as an early defense mechanism of primitive anaerobic organisms *against* atmospheric oxygen. Many essential reactions in a cell lead to reduced flavoproteins, which then are reoxidized by anaerobic means. Traces of oxygen in the surroundings of an anaerobe could upset things by reoxidizing the flavoproteins directly, and producing hydrogen peroxide:

$$FPH_2 + O_2 \rightarrow FP + H_2O_2$$

Peroxides of all kinds are reactive and dangerous oxidants, and must be removed for the safety of the cell. Catalase may have evolved to meet this need by using some expendable organic molecules (H_2R) as a reducing donor:

$$H_2O_2 + H_2R \xrightarrow{\text{catalase}} 2H_2O + R$$

Catalase is one of the most efficient and rapid enzymes known. One molecule of the enzyme can destroy ten million molecules of H_2O_2 per second. The various kinases of the citric acid cycle have comparable turnover numbers (rates of reaction) of 1000 substrate molecules acted upon per second per enzyme molecule. Chymotrypsin has a turnover number of 300 molecules per second, and a succinate dehydrogenase molecule only dehydrogenates 20 succinic acid molecules per second. As a catalyst for the destruction of H_2O_2, catalase is ten million times as rapid as a simple heme group is, and ten billion times as fast as a ferric ion. It does a small job, but does it supremely well.

By this hypothesis, reactions of organic compounds with O_2 first began, not as a means of extracting energy from organic molecules, but as a way of detoxifying the cell and eliminating the adverse effects of O_2. Harnessing of the energy released by combination with O_2 came later. The theory is plausible. Peroxisomes also contain rudimentary metabolic cycles that reduce flavoproteins, and which may be the vestigial remains of bypassed respiratory mechanisms. The peroxisomes could be the remnants of a primitive respiratory system that was abandoned by the cell when it struck up a symbiotic relationship with the bacterial ancestors of mitochondria. By this theory, these metabolic relics are reduced today to doing the only thing that mitochondria cannot do better: eliminate peroxide.

THE STRATEGY OF A EUCARYOTIC CELL

A eucaryotic cell is an elaborately structured chemical system. We have taken note throughout this chapter of where different chemical reactions occur, and these are summarized in the table on the following page. The individual chemical reactions and reaction networks all are controlled by enzymes, and are regulated by several different factors:

1. the concentrations of reactants and products
2. the availability of enzymes that can speed up one reaction over another, and hence decide which pathways will make the most use of a given starting material
3. the availability of a supply of ATP to make an energetically unfavorable reaction possible
4. direct inhibition of an enzyme by its immediate products
5. indirect or feedback control, positive or negative, of an allosteric enzyme by a molecule produced later in the reaction network
6. physical separation of the enzymes for a given process in one part of the cell or another
7. control by selectively permeable membranes over the circulation of metabolites and ions between various parts of the cell.

The structure of the cell thus has a strong influence on the chemistry that goes on within it.

Procaryotes have simpler structures, but are more diverse in their chemistry than are eucaryotes. Primitive bacteria extract energy by the relatively simple process of glycolysis. To this process some bacteria have added respiration using sulfate, oxygen, or nitrate. Other bacteria have developed photosynthesis with a single photocenter, employing H_2S, H_2, or organic molecules as reductants. From these possibilities blue-green algae have selected O_2 respiration and have developed a two-center photosynthesis, using H_2O as a source of reducing electrons. It

LOCATION OF VITAL CHEMICAL REACTIONS IN THE EUCARYOTIC CELL

Process	Location in cell
Genetic transmission and protein synthesis	
DNA replication	Nucleus
Histone synthesis	Nucleus
Protein synthesis other than histones	
Copying out of messenger RNA	Nucleus
Biosynthesis of nonessential amino acids	Cytoplasm
Activation, attachment of amino acids to tRNA	Cytoplasm
Polymerization of amino acids to protein chain	Ribosomes
Packaging enzymes for storage or export	Golgi complexes
Production of driving energy as ATP	Mitochondria
Energy extraction	
Carbohydrate metabolism	
Glycolysis as far as pyruvate	Cytoplasm
Pyruvate to acetyl coenzyme A	Mitochondrial inner membrane
Citric acid cycle	Mitochondrial matrix
(Except α-ketoglutarate DH and succinate DH)	(Mitochondrial inner membrane)
Respiratory chain and ATP synthesis	Mitochondrial inner membrane
Fatty acid oxidation	
Hydrolysis of fat globules to fatty acids	Cytoplasm
Activation of fatty acids with coenzyme A	Mitochondrial outer membrane
Breakdown of fatty acids to acetyl coenzyme A	Mitochondrial matrix
(Remainder as for carbohydrates)	
Amino acid metabolism	
Hydrolysis of proteins to amino acids	Extracellular
Various conversions of amino acids	Cytoplasm and mitochondria
Energy storage	
Gluconeogenesis	
Early steps prior to phosphoenolpyruvate (PEP)	Mitochondrial matrix
Phosphoenolpyruvate to glucose	Cytoplasm
Fat and lipid synthesis	
Fatty acid synthesis from acetyl coenzyme A	Cytoplasm
Esterification of fatty acids to fats	Endoplasmic reticulum
Photosynthesis	
Light reactions, trapping of energy	Chloroplast grana
Dark reactions, synthesizing glucose	Chloroplast matrix
Isolation and protection	
Biosynthesis of phospholipids and cholesterol	Endoplasmic reticulum
Mucopolysaccharide synthesis	Endoplasmic reticulum
Selective admission and release of molecules	Cell membrane
Destruction of peroxide	Peroxisomes
Acid and enzyme hydrolysis of proteins, nucleic acids, and polysaccharides	Lysosomes
Other processes	
Sulfur metabolism	Endoplasmic reticulum
Biosynthesis of porphyrin for chlorophyll and heme	Cytoplasm

is a reasonable working hypothesis that eucaryotic cells evolved from an initial symbiosis between a large, nucleated, but nonphotosynthetic and possibly nonrespiring host, and small respiring bacteria that became the ancestors of mitochondria. Photosynthesis in eucaryotes probably developed from a symbiotic relationship between early nucleated, mitochondria-containing eucaryotic cells and blue-green algae. The traces of carbohydrate metabolism are preserved in the dark reactions of chloroplasts, and a rudimentary genetic machinery remains in both chloroplasts and mitochondria. With the "invention" of the eucaryotic cell 1.2–1.4 billion years ago, the way was clear for the evolution of large, multicelled organisms.

QUESTIONS

1. What is the difference between the basic cell structure of procaryotes and eucaryotes? What kinds of living organisms are representative of each type?

2. Are bacteria procaryotes, or eucaryotes? How is the DNA stored in a bacterial cell?

3. What is the difference between a bacterial cell wall, capsule, and outer membrane? Which of these is most important in controlling entrance and exit of molecules and ions?

4. What is the distinction between active and passive transport across a membrane? Which of these processes can lead to accumulation of an excess of substance on one side of the membrane? Which of these requires an outside source of energy? Where does this energy come from?

5. Where does glycolysis take place in a bacterial cell? In respiring bacteria, where are the enzymes of the respiratory chain located?

6. Where does glycolysis take place in a eucaryotic cell? Where are the citric acid cycle enzymes located? How do the products of glycolysis reach these enzymes? Where are the respiratory enzymes found?

7. In photosynthetic bacteria, where do the light reactions of photosynthesis take place? Where are the enzymes of the dark reactions located?

8. How do green sulfur bacteria and purple sulfur bacteria differ in the structure of their photosynthetic regions of the cell?

9. What is the biochemical function of ribosomes? How do the ribosomes of bacteria and of eucaryotes differ? Which do mitochondrial ribosomes more nearly resemble?

10. What kinds of eucaryotic cells have cell walls? What is their purpose?

11. How is the DNA of eucaryotic cells packaged or stored?

12. How do some antibiotic molecules assist ions in passage through the cell membrane? Is this an example of active, or passive, transport?

13. What is a sodium pump in cells? Where does it build up an excess of sodium ions? Is this active, or passive, transport?

14. What is the endoplasmic reticulum and how is it associated with ribosomes? What chemical processes of the cell take place at the endoplasmic reticulum?

15. In what sense is the ribosome-free side of the endoplasmic reticulum "outside" the cell? In what sense is a mitochondrion "outside" the cell even though it is physically surrounded by it?

16. What is a Golgi complex? What is its biochemical function?

17. How many membranes does a mitochondrion have? How many mitochondria are found in a typical eucaryotic cell?

18. What energy-related biochemical reactions take place within a mitochondrion?

19. Some of the enzymes for the reactions of Question 18 float freely in the mitochondrial matrix, whereas others are embedded in the inner membrane surface. Which enzymes are found where?

20. In what ways do mitochondria resemble bacteria? How could such a resemblance have come about?

21. Which product of glycolysis diffuses through the mitochondrial membranes to provide the fuel for the citric acid cycle?

22. Can all of the intermediates of glycolysis penetrate through the mitochondrial membranes? Why would this be a disadvantage, if it were so?

23. How does the NADH produced in glycolysis arrive at the site of the respiratory chain inside a mitochondrion, if the mitochondrial membrane is impermeable to NADH?

24. To what extent do mitochondria have their own genetic apparatus, and what proteins do they make?

25. What are thylakoids and grana in green-plant chloroplasts?

26. Where do the light and dark reactions of photosynthesis take place relative to these thylakoids and grana?

27. Are chloroplasts "inside" or "outside" the cell in the sense mentioned previously for mitochondria? What symbiotic origin has been suggested for chloroplasts?

28. What are lysosomes? What types of biochemical reactions occur within them?

29. What are peroxisomes? What very ancient enzyme do they carry? What is the present function of this enzyme? In what sense might the ancestors of peroxisomes have been made obsolete by mitochondria?

CHAPTER 26

The Origin of Life on Earth

Primates are naturally curious, and this curiosity is most highly developed in *Homo sapiens*. The question "Where did we come from?" has been one of the most compelling quandaries for as long as man has been able to frame enquiries. In one guise or another, this question has been at the root of most religions.

As long as animals and the rest of Earth's creatures were considered only automata, as Descartes characterized them, or as subordinate creatures placed here for our express benefit, the question of origins was narrowly confined to man. But as we gradually have come to understand our fellow creatures and to realize our biological and biochemical kinship, the question has broadened to the more comprehensive one: "Where did life come from?"

Two possibilities exist, special creation or spontaneous generation. Special creation has long been the purview of theologians. For many centuries the rational view was considered to be that of spontaneous generation. Every practical observer of the world around him knew that life develops spontaneously from nonliving matter by the action of heat, light, moisture, and (after it was discovered) electricity. Maggots come from decaying meat, and lice from sweat-soaked clothing. Beetles develop from rotting wood, and horseflies from transmuted manure.

It is difficult to put forward so thoroughly eroded an idea as spontaneous generation today without arousing smiles from the listeners. If ever a generally accepted idea was revealed by careful experiments to be nothing but old wives' tales, spontaneous generation was. Francisco Redi demonstrated more than 300 years ago that meat, shielded from egg-laying flies by cloth, never developed maggots. Others following him showed that nutrient broths that are boiled and then kept isolated from airborne contamination never produce microorganisms. Spontaneous generation died hard; its proponents claimed that the life forces were delicate and were destroyed by boiling. The early experiments were crude, and failed just often enough to keep the controversy alive. This reluctance to abandon spontaneous generation was not an example of the obstinacy of the superstitious, but was the stubbornness of those who considered themselves defenders of the rational approach, and the only alternative to divine whimsy.

The defenders were wrong. Louis Pasteur sealed the fate of spontaneous generation in a series of careful experiments, in 1861. He demonstrated clearly that microorganisms are carried in the air, and that they grow in previously sterilized broths only when the broths are contaminated by air or similar sources. "All Life from Life" became one of the fixed and immutable points of biological dogma. This led to a dilemma that has been expressed as the chicken-and-egg paradox. Which came first, the chicken or the egg? If all eggs come only from chickens, and if all chickens come only from eggs, then there must once have been either a first chicken or a first egg. This demanded a Creator, a celestial clockmaker who at least set the entire machinery of life in motion before stepping back to let things take their "natural" course thereafter. The operations of life and the mechanisms of life hence were areas of fruitful research, but the *origin* of life was not a legitimate subject for scientific investigation. Pasteur apparently had disproved the only theory of the origin of life that was subject to scientific testing.

While Pasteur was tamping the last dirt over the grave of spontaneous generation, another extraordinarily important idea was developing in biology—one that would not have its impact on chemistry for nearly a century. This was the theory of *evolution*, as proposed by Charles Darwin, Alfred Wallace, and the very able propagandist, Thomas Huxley. Reproduction in all living creatures is never perfect. Variations show up in the offspring, which give them different efficiencies in meeting the challenges of any given environment. The environment exerts a selective action on the population of offspring: The best adapted survive in the greatest numbers to breed and produce new offspring. Thus the traits that encourage survival in any environment are preserved. As adaptation to a given environment improves, and as environments gradually change on the planet, the organisms themselves change, adapt, and evolve.

This is the key to the chicken-and-egg paradox. If we trace the evolution of chickens and eggs back far enough, we will not find a First Egg. Instead, we will realize slowly that we are not looking at chickens any more, but at feathered reptiles. Tracing the line back further, we will see amphibia, bony fish, cartilaginous fish, and invertebrates. The trail, if pursued long enough, leads back to one-celled life. But where did this one-celled life come from? Is a bacterium-and-spore paradox any less frustrating than the chicken-and-egg? Unless we suffer from mental fatigue or atrophied curiosity along the way, we must eventually ask "Where did the earliest one-celled life come from?" With such simple organisms, the problem becomes as much chemical as biological.

The question of the origin of life was studiously ignored by the scientific community for three quarters of a century after Pasteur, with two isolated exceptions: A. I. Oparin in Russia, and J. B. S. Haldane in England. The very finality of Pasteur's experiments had made chemical inquiry into the development of life from nonliving chemicals not really respectable. This chapter is concerned with the reawakening of the concept of spontaneous generation in a new, restricted, and scientifically verifiable form. We do not claim now that it happens all the time; Pasteur took care of that. What we do believe is that the spontaneous generation of life happened once on this planet, and that it then destroyed the conditions under which it could happen again.

THE COMMON BIOCHEMICAL HERITAGE OF LIFE

We have no fossilized citric acid cycle or glycolytic enzymes for study, and never shall have, so the starting point for understanding chemical evolution must be the reactions that occur in present-day organisms. Eucaryotes all obtain energy by oxygen-using respiration; and those that are photosynthetic obtain reducing power from water and release oxygen. This metabolic uniformity is missing in the older procaryotes. Some bacteria do respire with O_2, but others can use nitrate as an oxidant if O_2 is not available. Since the same enzymes are involved, and O_2 always is their first preference, nitrate respiration probably is a relatively recent special adaptation that is of little interest in tracing the evolution of life.

Desulfovibrio sewage bacteria respire and extract energy from their foods by using sulfate as an oxidizing agent, emitting the H_2S that contributes to sewage stench. Different enzymes are used in the electron-transport chain of sulfate respiration, and this appears to be a genuinely independent solution to the problem of getting more energy from foods by combining them with an oxidizing agent. Sulfate is not as good an oxidant as O_2, but it is acceptable. Sulfate-respiring bacteria are strict anaerobes, which are poisoned by the mere presence of O_2. They are restricted to life in rotting sewage and other microenvironments that are reducing in character. They may be living fossil remains of an era when the planet had little or no free atmospheric oxygen.

Other bacteria such as the *Clostridia*, which produce botulism in foods and gangrene in wounds, do not respire at all. They obtain all of their energy by anaerobic fermentation (glycolysis), giving off as waste products lactate, acetate, ethanol, butyrate, propionate, or other small organic molecules. They all are compulsory or obligate anaerobes, for whom free oxygen gas is lethal. (This is why botulism only develops in sealed but imperfectly sterilized cans of food, and why aerating a wound helps to prevent gangrene.) The ability to respire and oxidize foods is a special talent not possessed by all life, but glycolysis is universal. Glycolysis accompanied by the storage of energy as ATP appears to be the irreducible minimum for life.

Those organisms that go no farther than glycolysis cannot tolerate the presence of gaseous O_2. In contrast, with few exceptions, those bacteria that can live in the presence of O_2 also have learned to use it for respiration. It is too good a source of extra energy to neglect. These facts suggest that life began as fermenting one-celled organisms, at a time when no free oxygen was present in the atmosphere.

The eucaryotic pattern of two-center photosynthesis yielding ATP and NADPH, in which water is broken down and O_2 is released, is followed also by blue-green algae but not by bacteria. Purple nonsulfur bacteria avoid the need for a reducing agent by running the same electrons around again and again in cyclic photophosphorylation, but then must depend on a citric acid cycle for production of reducing power in the form of NADH (not NADPH). They also possess a respiratory chain and, if grown aerobically in the dark, can obtain energy from glycolysis, the citric acid cycle, and O_2 respiration just as we do. They are unique among bacteria in combining photosynthesis with respiration, and appear to be a metabolic halfway house on the road to blue-green algae and eucaryotes.

The purple and green sulfur bacteria are less versatile, and depend on noncyclic photophosphorylation for production of both ATP and NADH. This demands a source of reducing equivalents; lacking Photocenter II, they use H_2S or H_2, both of which are intrinsically stronger reducing agents than H_2O. These sulfur bacteria are compulsory anaerobes that are poisoned by an oxygen atmosphere. Once again the biochemical evidence suggests that early life arose under conditions where free oxygen was absent, but where hydrogen and hydrogen sulfide might be found.

The *chemoautotrophs* are a special class of bacteria that can synthesize carbohydrates like the photosynthetic bacteria do, but which obtain the energy for doing so from inorganic reactions rather than from the sun. Some of them obtain energy by oxidizing ammonia to nitrite or nitrate, others convert H_2S to elemental sulfur, thiosulfate, or sulfate, and still others oxidize Fe(II) to Fe(III). One might think that chemosynthesis, which uses inorganic reactions for energy, is an older mechanism than photosynthesis. This is unlikely, since all chemoautotrophic bacteria have well-developed respiratory chains and use O_2 as an oxidant. It is more likely that these chemoautotrophs are specially adapted forms, which found an alternative means to solar radiation to power their carbohydrate syntheses. They can be neglected in a search for the origin of life.

CONDITIONS FOR THE APPEARANCE OF LIFE

The most important conclusion from a comparison of how bacteria and higher forms of life obtain energy is that all living creatures have a common fermentative metabolism, which suggests a common evolutionary origin. The various types of respiration and photo- or chemosynthesis that have been added to glycolysis, do not obscure this basic unity.

Oxidation with O_2 yields vastly more energy than fermentation alone, and had oxygen been present at the time when life evolved, it surely would have been used. In that case, O_2 respiration would be as common to all life as fermentation is. However, this is not the case, which leads us to a second conclusion: Life arose from less complex, nonliving chemical systems at a time when the atmosphere was reducing in character, not oxidizing. Other evidence points to the same conclusion. The atmospheres of the other planets generally are reducing, as we shall see later in the section on geological evidence. Old mineral beds on this planet suggest that they were laid down in contact with a reducing atmosphere. Organic compounds themselves are unstable in an O_2 atmosphere, and are auto-oxidizable. Organic matter today is constantly produced anew by the action of living organisms. If all life were to end tomorrow, O_2 would begin to reclaim the organic matter on our planet, and the process would stop only when no more free oxygen remained. It is inconceivable that large quantities of organic substances could have remained unoxidized long enough for life to evolve from them, if they were constantly exposed to O_2 in the atmosphere.

If the original atmosphere was reducing, why is it oxidizing today? One source of O_2 is the photodissociation of water vapor by ultraviolet light in the upper atmosphere, followed by the loss of light hydrogen atoms from the Earth's gravitational field. This alone could lead to an oxygen concentration of around 0.1% of the present-day level. The main source of oxygen in the atmosphere today is green-plant photosynthesis, and this probably is what turned the planetary atmosphere from reducing to oxidizing. Life evolved under reducing conditions, where organic molecules would be stable for long periods of time; but this same life was responsible later for changing the original atmosphere to its present-day composition.

THE OPARIN–HALDANE THEORY OF THE ORIGIN OF LIFE

The first scientist after Pasteur to address himself seriously to questions about the origin of life was the Russian biologist A. I. Oparin. He presented his ideas in a paper before the Botanical Society of Moscow in

1922. They were published two years later, not in a scientific journal, but as a monograph. The paper sank into obscurity and had no effect on his contemporaries. It was not translated into English until 1967. Only when Oparin expanded this pioneering article into a full-length book in 1936, and this book was translated from the Russian, did his ideas begin to attract attention outside his homeland. The English biologist J. B. S. Haldane began thinking independently along the same general lines, although he never read Oparin's writings. In an eight-page article in the "Rationalist Annual" for 1929, Haldane published a complete synopsis of a theory of the origin of life.

The ideas of these two men were simple, elegant, and almost identical. According to their theory, life evolved in the oceans during a period when the atmosphere was reducing—containing H_2, H_2O, NH_3, CH_4, and CO_2, but no free O_2. Organic compounds were synthesized nonbiologically by ultraviolet light energy, which in the absence of an ozone shield would penetrate the upper layers of the ocean. Without free O_2 to oxidize them, these organic molecules would be stable, and would accumulate in a warm, dilute broth that has been nicknamed "Haldane soup." The first living organism would be little more than a few chemical reactions wrapped up in a film or membrane to keep them from being diluted and destroyed. These organelles would absorb chemicals, grow, divide, and obtain energy by fermenting the available organic molecules around them. Photosynthesis would arise eventually as an alternative energy source when natural foods ran short. The oxygen released by photosynthesis would have the side effect of screening out the ultraviolet radiation with an ozone layer in the upper atmosphere, and eventually would turn the atmosphere from reducing to oxidizing. Free oxygen would lead to the evolution of respiration and to modern eucaryotic metabolism.

This Oparin–Haldane theory was a remarkably complete blueprint for the ideas still held today. It was especially remarkable because in 1929 virtually none of the biochemical details of the previous chapters were known. None of the chemistry of glycolysis, respiration, or photosynthesis was understood, aside from the overall reactions. Enzymes were a mystery, and were not even thought to be proteins. The nature of the genetic machinery was unknown—scientists were as likely to choose proteins as they were nucleic acids for the carriers of genetic information. The Oparin–Haldane theory was an accurate extrapolation far beyond the limits of chemical knowledge of the time, which undoubtedly contributed to its general neglect. It is to the credit of both men that much of what we have learned since then has been a filling in of the blanks in their proposals.

What hard evidence do we have today for a theory of the origin of life? The first area is comparative biochemistry along the lines we have been following. The more we learn, the more the Oparin–Haldane ideas make sense. In addition, we have geological evidence from the Earth's own history, including evidence for a primitive reducing atmosphere and fossil remains of primitive microorganisms. These fossils allow us to assign dates to the various biochemical steps in the origin of life. Finally, laboratory demonstrations point out the feasibility of the nonbiological synthesis of the molecules of life, and of the formation of simple, organized chemical systems. These considerations cannot prove the theories about what actually happened billions of years ago, but they can give them plausibility.

THE GEOLOGICAL EVIDENCE

What geological evidence is there to suggest that the Earth originally may have had a reducing atmosphere? The elemental composition of the universe, given in Chapter 8, supports this idea with an overwhelming predominance of hydrogen. The atmospheres of other planets, especially the larger ones whose gravitational fields would have prevented loss of their early atmospheres, are composed primarily of H_2, He, CH_4, CO, CO_2, N_2, NH_3, and H_2O, with no free oxygen.

The Earth as a whole is built mainly from metal silicates. These silicates are 90% oxygen by volume, but this oxygen is locked up in the mineral framework. Iron in minerals can serve as a barometer of the state of oxidation of its surroundings. The familiar red and orange of oxidized Fe(III) compounds from sands are only skin deep. A short distance below the surface, these colors give way to the green and black of reduced Fe(II) compounds. The oxidized minerals are a thin surface layer that is exposed to an O_2-containing atmosphere that is anomalous among the planets. Life has "rusted" the surface of our planet, but has had little effect on its interior.

We can learn much from old sedimentary rocks about the conditions under which they were deposited. Rocks that crystallized in the interior and then were thrust to the surface have little to tell us about the atmosphere of the time. In contrast, sedimentary rocks deposited by the weathering away of older minerals during a long contact with the atmosphere preserve a record of that atmosphere. If the atmosphere were oxidizing, then the sediments would be at least partially oxidized; if reducing, then the sediments would remain reduced. Present-day sands are mainly quartz and other forms of SiO_2. Most other minerals in the rocks that weathered to make sand have been oxidized. Their oxidized metal cations have been leached out, ultimately to be redeposited elsewhere as clay minerals. The result is that sedimentary rocks deposited during oxidizing conditions are of three main types: silicate sands, clay minerals, and carbonate deposits of biological origin (from shells of marine life). The sedimentary rocks laid down during the past 500 million years and more are of this type. All indicate that oxidizing conditions existed during their original weathering period.

Weathering proceeds differently under a reducing atmosphere. Quartz is still a major component of sedimentary material. The other minerals that contain metals in lower oxidation states are less soluble and do not leach out completely. Among the reduced iron minerals in such sands one finds pyrite ($Fe^{II}S$), siderite ($Fe^{II}CO_3$), and magnetite (Fe_3O_4, or $Fe^{II}O \cdot Fe_2^{III}O_3$). Other metal oxides and sulfides in low oxidation states are common. Ancient Precambrian sediments containing sands with such reduced minerals have been found in Canada, Brazil, and South Africa. These deposits have been studied intensively because the reduced materials often include elemental gold and uranium ore.

Precambrian animal fossil from the Ediacara Hills deposits in Australia, approximately 800 million to 600 million years old. Although it vaguely resembles a small jellyfish two centimeters in diameter, it has no known living descendants. (Courtesy of M. F. Glaessner, University of Adelaide, South Australia.)

Geologists have concluded that these are the remains of ancient sedimentary beds laid down under reducing atmospheric conditions. Radioisotopic methods have dated these various beds from 1.8 billion to 3.0 billion years old. The Earth is 4.5 billion years old, so for the first 2.5 billion years of its existence, it had a reducing atmosphere like the other planets.

Additional evidence comes from banded iron ore deposits with mixed oxidation states, found in Minnesota, Finland, Russia, South Africa, India, and Australia. These deposits are thought to have been laid down under reducing conditions, although the evidence is not as conclusive. These banded iron beds are 1.8 to 2.5 billion years old. In contrast, "red beds" of fully oxidized hematite ore (Fe_2O_3) are never dated earlier than 1.4 billion years ago.

The conclusion from these iron deposits is that the atmosphere was predominately reducing prior to 1.8 billion years ago, has been oxidizing for the past 1.4 billion years, and underwent a period of gradual transition in the time between. This is not to imply that oxygen suddenly appeared in the atmosphere 1.8 billion years ago, or that water-using photosynthesis was invented only then. Photosynthesis on a small scale probably appeared nearly a billion years earlier. It is difficult to calculate how fast O_2 would accumulate in the atmosphere, or how great the O_2 concentration would have to be before it could begin to influence the oxidation state of iron minerals in sediments. All we can say is that by the time this had begun, the O_2 concentration must have been appreciable.

So the stage was set for an Oparin–Haldane type of evolution of life in a reducing atmosphere. But did the actors really appear on cue? For this, we must turn to the fossil evidence.

PRECAMBRIAN FOSSILS

Only a few years ago, the expression "Precambrian fossils" would have been considered almost a contradiction in terms. At the beginning of the Cambrian era, 600 million years ago, there was a veritable explosion in the fossil record. Every major branch of modern animal life was present at the start of the Cambrian era except vertebrates. Geologists even define and identify the beginning of the Cambrian era by this sudden increase in volume of the fossil record. Prior to 600 million years ago the fossil record quickly shrinks to almost nothing. Jellyfish and other soft-bodied marine life from 900 million to 600 million years ago are known from deposits in Australia and a few other places (top left). Much of the trouble is that these creatures *are* soft-bodied. Jellyfish do not preserve well in the fossil record in comparison with shellfish. Part of the Cambrian explosion is not a sudden burst of life, but a sudden increase in the use of hard, protective materials such as shells and body armor. No matter what the reason, most paleontologists only a few years ago considered that little was to be learned from the fossil record prior to this Cambrian population explosion.

A change came about when we learned how, and where, to look for fossil microorganisms. Elso Barghoorn and his associates have studied polished thin sections of silica-rich cherts from the Gunflint region of northern Minnesota and southern Canada. With the aid of optical and electron microscopes they have found a rich collection of fossil bacteria, blue-green algae, fungi, and other microorganisms with unknown present-day relatives. Two examples are shown below. Their association

Precambrian fossils from the Gunflint deposits on the Minnesota–Ontario border, approximately 1.9 billion years old. Left: Colony of algae resembling the modern blue-green algae *Rivularia,* and therefore named *Paleorivularia ontarica.* The diameter of the colony is 60 microns. Right: Twisted tubular filaments resembling some present-day blue-green algae. (Courtesy of E. S. Barghoorn.)

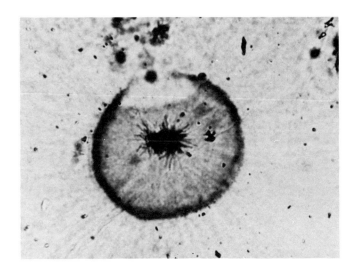
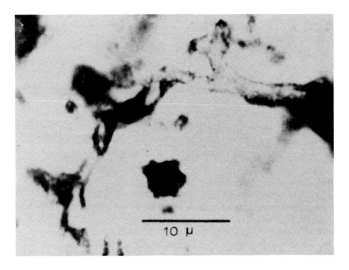

The oldest recognizable fossil organism, a rod-shaped bacterium called *Eobacterium isolatum* ("solitary dawn bacterium"). This specimen was found in the Fig Tree chert formation of South Africa and is 3.1 billion years old. The bacterium was moved during specimen preparation, and is visible at the top, with its negative impression below. The black and white calibration strip at the right indicates one micron. (Courtesy of E. S. Barghoorn and J. W. Schopf.)

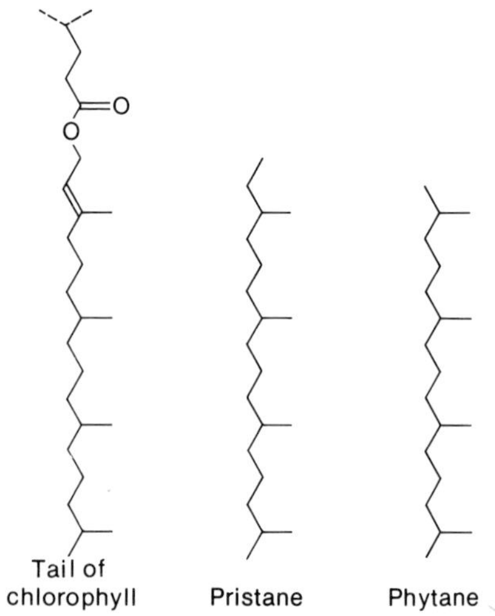

Tail of chlorophyll   Pristane   Phytane

Phytane and pristane are long-chain hydrocarbons with a pattern of branching methyl groups (straight lines to the right), which suggests that the molecules may be degradation products of the phytol tail of the chlorophyll molecule. Hence phytol and pristane in fossil microorganism deposits may be evidence for photosynthesis.

with banded iron ore formations means that these cherts probably were laid down under reducing conditions, and radioisotopic methods date them at 1.8 billion to 2.1 billion years old. The Gunflint cherts also were found to contain pristane and phytane, diagrammed at the left. These are organic compounds that can occur as breakdown products of chlorophyll, and have been regarded as possible evidence for photosynthesis.

Other microfossil deposits around 2.7 billion years old, from Australia, Rhodesia, and South Africa, contain what appear to be fossil remains of bacteria and blue-green algae. The oldest sediments with true microfossils are the Fig Tree cherts from the Transvaal, and the Onverwacht sediments from Swaziland, both in South Africa. The Fig Tree cherts, which are 3.1 billion years old, contain fossil bacteria of the type shown at the left, spheroids resembling blue-green algae, filamentous organic structures, and complex hydrocarbons including pristane and phytane. The Onverwacht sediments are more than 3.2 billion years old, and are carbon-rich cherts containing spheroids and filaments that possibly are of biological origin.

For unambiguous evidence of photosynthesis one must return to no more than 1.6 billion years ago, to limestone deposits identical to those produced today in hot springs by blue-green algae. These deposits, called stromatolites (upper right margin), are scattered widely over the world. Some in Rhodesia are as much as 2.7 billion years old. The 1.6-billion-year-old stromatolites in the western Sahara are unusual in that they contain alternating layers of $CaCO_3$ and $Fe(OH)_3$, as if they were laid down by colonies of photosynthetic blue-green algae and O_2-respiring iron-containing bacteria. The oxygen released by the algae would be used by the bacteria, which would not then be dependent on significant amounts of atmospheric oxygen. It is likely that such mutual aid, or symbiosis, was common in this era, with respirers living next to and using the oxygen from photosynthesizers, just as bacteria live in mixed colonies in sewage and swamps today, with one species being dependent on the waste products of another species for its food or raw materials. It is not necessary to assume that oxygen respiration had to wait for the complete conversion of the atmosphere to oxidizing conditions before it could develop.

It is clear that organisms resembling bacteria and blue-green algae were in existence 3 billion years ago, and is probably true that some of these organisms were photosynthetic and oxygen-liberating. Well over a billion years may have been required for photosynthetic life to pour so much O_2 into the atmosphere that its character was changed. By 1.6 billion years ago, oxygen-emitting photosynthesis and oxygen-using respiration were in full swing. It is encouraging that the date for the Sahara stromatolites falls right in the middle of the atmospheric transition period predicted from the oxidation states of iron deposits. What is remarkable is that the South African rocks from the Transvaal and Swaziland tell us that less than 1.5 billion years elapsed from the condensation of the Earth to the evolution of life at the bacterial level. As an indication of how difficult the next step—the development of eucaryotes—was, this second step required fully as much time as the creation of the planet and evolution of bacteria!

The first fossil evidence of cells with nuclei and internal structure like eucaryotes comes from dolomite rock from Beck Springs, California.

636

These rocks are 1.4 billion to 1.2 billion years old (below). From this time on, the evidence is increasingly solid. The changeover of the atmosphere to oxidizing conditions, the development of enough O_2-respiring procaryotes to show up plentifully in the fragmentary fossil record, and the development of eucaryotic cells, all apparently took place 1.8 to 1.3 billion years ago.

The key dates in the evolution of life, obtained from geological and fossil evidence, can be summarized as follows:

4.5 billion years ago: Planet formed

3.2 billion years ago: Life already at the level of simple bacteria, some probably photosynthetic; reducing atmosphere still

2.0 billion years ago: Rich microfauna of procaryotic life, both bacteria and blue-green algae; photosynthesis occurring

1.8–1.4 billion years ago: Gradual changeover from reducing to oxidizing atmosphere, detectable by effects on sedimentary iron deposits; colonies of oxygen-producing and oxygen-using microorganisms

1.4–1.2 billion years ago: First evidence of the presence of eucaryotic cells

As an interesting sidelight to this chronology, one can compare the amino acid sequences from a protein that is present in many forms of life to obtain a rough measure of how distantly related these forms are, and how long ago their ancestors diverged. The sequences of respiratory cytochrome c from more than 67 eucaryotic species have been compared, including vertebrates of all kinds, insects, microorganisms, and higher plants. Examination of the rates at which the cytochromes change in different lines of descent suggests that plants and animals diverged approximately 1.2 billion years ago, in excellent agreement with the fossil evidence for early eucaryotes.

Stromatolite deposits of alternating calcium carbonate and ferric hydroxide, found in a 1.6-billion-year-old deposit in the western Sahara. By comparison with modern stromatolite deposits, these probably were produced by closely associated colonies of photosynthetic blue-green algae and iron-metabolizing bacteria, at a time when the Sahara was a shallow sea. (Courtesy of N. Menchikoff.)

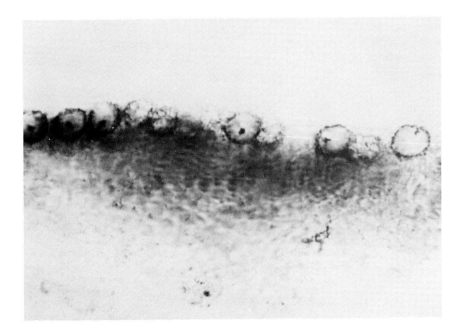

The oldest identified fossil eucaryotes are these globular cells, found in 1.2- to 1.4-billion-year-old stromatolite deposits from Beck Springs, California. The cells are 14–18 microns (1 micron = 10^{-6} meter) in diameter and resemble green algae. The dark spot within each cell is believed to be the nucleus. (Courtesy of Gerald Licari.)

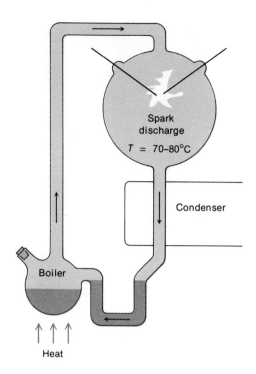

The Miller reflux apparatus for studying the synthesis of organic, and possibly prebiotic molecules, by spark discharge in gas mixtures. The key element in synthesis is the spark. The boiler and condenser are only to set up circulation of gases. After a week of cycling, the original mixture of ammonia, hydrogen, methane, and water was observed to contain simple organic molecules, including some amino acids. (Courtesy of Stanley L. Miller.)

THE LABORATORY EVIDENCE

One aspect of the Oparin–Haldane theory that has been neglected so far is the very beginning of life. Is it reasonable that the organic compounds necessary as the precursors of life would have been synthesized naturally and abiotically in a reducing atmosphere? Where would the energy have come from? This is the type of experiment that can be carried out in the laboratory.

The first such simulation experiments were attempted by Harold Urey and his graduate student, Stanley Miller, in 1953. In 1952, Urey had published, in his book *The Planets*, a survey of the atmospheric chemistry of the planets, and had pointed out the consistently reducing character of their atmospheres. Miller decided to see if biological molecules could be produced in a mixture of such reducing gases by a spark discharge, as an analog of lightning. His experimental setup, shown at the left, consisted of a completely closed system, with gases flowing past a spark discharge; the condensed gases were recirculated by boiling. The gases tried were mixtures of methane, ammonia, water, hydrogen, and other reduced molecules.

The results of a typical run beginning with H_2, H_2O, NH_3, and CH_4 are recorded in the graph below. Ammonia disappeared steadily during the experiment. During the first 25 hours of boiling and refluxing, most of the ammonia and methane was being converted to HCN and aldehydes, with a slow synthesis of amino acids. During the next 100 hours, HCN and aldehydes reached a steady state, being used in further reactions as rapidly as they were made. The main products from these compounds were amino acids. They probably were the result of a Strecker synthesis (bottom next page), in which ammonium cyanide reacts with aldehydes to make amino acid nitriles, and these nitriles hydrolyze in water to amino acids. After 125 hours, as the supplies of ammonia and

Results of a typical experimental run with the Miller apparatus. As the concentration of ammonia decreases, hydrogen cyanide and aldehydes first accumulate and then disappear as they in turn react to form amino acids.

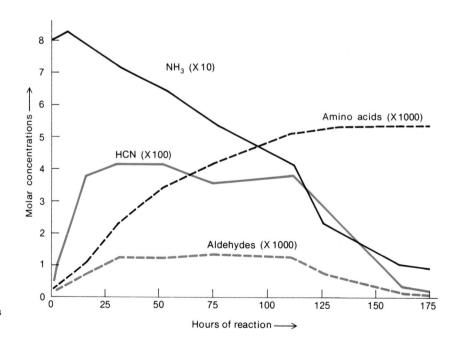

methane were depleted, HCN and aldehyde concentrations began to decrease. The amino acid concentration leveled off as more of the simple amino acids were incorporated into short peptides.

Many similar experiments followed, by Miller and others, using both electrical discharge and ultraviolet light. The compositions of the gas mixtures were varied, and included H_2S, CO, and CO_2. Almost any starting mixture containing compounds of both nitrogen and carbon led to amino acids, *as long as free oxygen was absent*. It seems that the spontaneous formation of amino acids by lightning and ultraviolet radiation would have been virtually inevitable on Earth in a reducing atmosphere, but impossible in an oxidizing atmosphere. The first products in these experiments usually were hydrogen cyanide (HCN), cyanogen (NC—CN), cyanoacetylene (H—C≡C—C≡N), formaldehyde (HCHO), acetaldehyde (CH_3CHO), and propionaldehyde (CH_3CH_2-CHO). These products then reacted to form various nitriles (R—CN), which subsequently hydrolyzed in aqueous solution:

$$CH_3\text{—}CN + 2H_2O \rightarrow CH_3\text{—}COOH + NH_3$$

  acetonitrile   acetic acid

The results were mixtures of formic, acetic, propionic, lactic, succinic, and other organic acids; glycine, alanine, aspartic and glutamic acids, and other biological and nonbiological amino acids; urea, methylurea, and various other small molecules. None of these artificially synthesized molecules showed optical activity; they all were equal mixtures of D and L isomers. As has been mentioned previously, the optical activity that biological molecules exhibit today is a result of choices by enzymes in living organisms.

Even heat was effective in bringing about prebiotic reactions. At elevated temperatures aqueous solutions of formaldehyde (HCHO) and hydroxylamine (HO—NH_2) yielded amino acids and short poly-

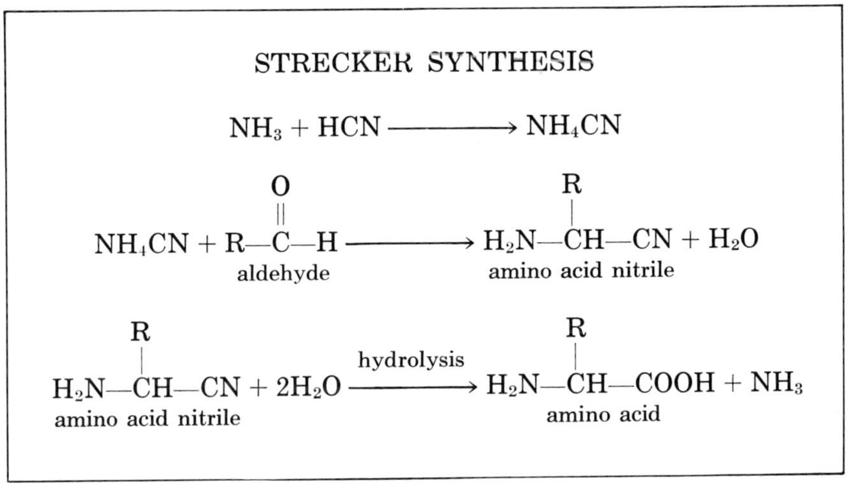

STRECKER SYNTHESIS

$$NH_3 + HCN \longrightarrow NH_4CN$$

$$NH_4CN + R\overset{\overset{\displaystyle O}{\|}}{—C}—H \longrightarrow H_2N—\overset{\overset{\displaystyle R}{|}}{CH}—CN + H_2O$$

                aldehyde   amino acid nitrile

$$H_2N—\overset{\overset{\displaystyle R}{|}}{CH}—CN + 2H_2O \xrightarrow{\text{hydrolysis}} H_2N—\overset{\overset{\displaystyle R}{|}}{CH}—COOH + NH_3$$

amino acid nitrile   amino acid

Strecker synthesis of amino acids from ammonia, hydrogen cyanide, and aldehydes. Ammonium cyanide is produced first and then reacts with aldehydes to form amino acid nitriles. In water the nitriles hydrolyze to yield amino acids, whose side chains depend on the nature of the original aldehydes.

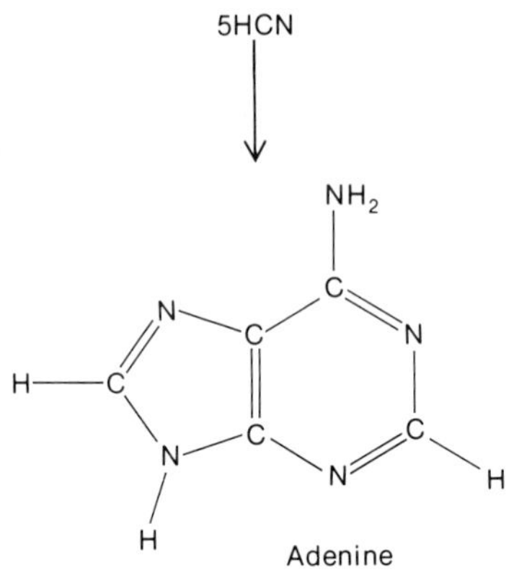

Adenine, $C_5H_5N_5$, can be considered as a pentamer of hydrogen cyanide, HCN.

mers. Solutions of HCN kept at $90°C$ for several days yielded adenine, as shown at the left. Perhaps the fact that adenine is simply a pentamer of HCN and is so easily formed abiotically is the reason it is used in the energy storage ATP molecules, in preference to guanine, cytosine, thymine, or uracil.

Comparable experiments showed possible synthetic pathways for purines, pyrimidines, and carbohydrates. Given ultraviolet radiation, electrical discharge, and other energy sources on the primitive Earth, and a reducing atmosphere, one might expect the inevitable appearance of amino acids, purines, pyrimidines, ribose and deoxyribose, and even nucleosides and nucleotides. At least the building blocks of life would have been available on the primitive Earth. The "Haldane soup" was real.

THE PROBLEMS OF ORGANIZED CELLS

So far we have glibly bypassed a massive problem. How do we get from the Haldane soup to even the simplest fermenting bacterium? A long, long step exists between amino acids, sugars, and nucleosides, and simple cells of the Fig Tree type, and this is the step about which we know least. From the short time span involved from the formation of the planet to the development of these simple photocells, it can be argued that the problem must be simpler than we think. An equal time span occurred from protocells to eucaryotes, and we think we have a good idea as to how this change came about. The difficulty is that we have visible evidence for this latter process, in microfossils and living survivors, but no such evidence has survived for the evolution of protocells.

This is a continual problem in evolutionary history, the erasure of the older record. Survival on this planet is based on efficiency, and there are no museums of unsuccessful types. Even among the bacteria, we do not have samples of all of the ancestral chemistries, only those that enabled their possessors to get along in odd corners where their more "advanced" eucaryotic competitors could not survive. We should not view the present-day bacteria as representative of the ancestors of the main stream of development, but rather as the "oddballs." Nevertheless, we do have this record to study from the protocells of the Fig Tree deposits to the first eucaryotes. For periods earlier than this, we have nothing at all. We know how the planet began, and how this first phase in the evolution of life ended. The gap between must be filled by imagination tempered by the results of laboratory experiments.

The chemical problems to be overcome are many. How were polymers of proteins, nucleic acids, and lipids formed in an aqueous environment, when polymer formation requires the removal of water and is thermodynamically nonspontaneous? How were the first reacting systems isolated from their surroundings to avoid a lethal dilution and cannibalism by other competing systems? How were the chemical reactions of a protocell integrated into a coherent and efficient "metabolism" that would increase its chances for survival? And finally, having achieved all these things, how did the successful protocell find a way of preserving its gains and passing them on? These are the next questions that we must try to answer.

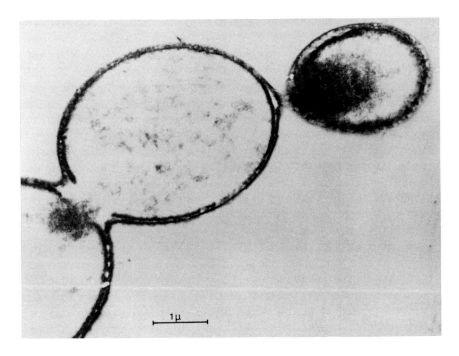

Artificial proteinlike polypeptides in hot water can form microspheres, which have a double-layer boundary similar to the membranes of microorganisms. The horizontal scale bar is one micron (10^{-6} meter) long. These microspheres illustrate the influence that physical forces have on the shapes of simple living organisms. (Courtesy of Sidney Fox.)

POLYMERS AND MICROSPHERES

The first problem beyond the stage of Haldane soup is imagining how protein polymers could form in dilute aqueous solution, when polymerization is a dehydration, or water-removing, process. Equilibrium strongly favors cleavage, not polymerization. Sidney Fox has found that *dry* amino acids, heated to 160–210°C, will form polymers of molecular weights up to 300,000, provided that aspartic and glutamic acids are included in the mixture. The sequences of these "thermal proteinoids" are not completely random, but show some internal order. These polymers display a limited catalytic activity, probably resulting from their charged side chains of acidic and basic amino acids. They catalyze the decomposition of glucose reasonably well. It is important not to read too much into this catalytic activity, since even protons and platinum atoms are catalysts. It would be surprising if a polymer with such a mixture of side chains was *not* catalytic for some reaction. However, some such weakly catalytic polypeptides, with or without metal ions, probably were the ancestors of the much more efficient and selective enzyme catalysts of today.

These thermal proteinoids have another interesting property. If a hot proteinoid mixture is washed with water or salt solution, microspheres of a fairly uniform 20,000-Å diameter are formed, as in the photograph above. These are small globules of proteinoid polymer solution, enclosed by a semipermeable proteinoid film with some of the physical properties of simple cell membranes. Microspheres shrink and swell in salt solutions of different concentrations. They will grow at the expense of dissolved proteinoid material, and have been observed to bud like yeast cells to produce "daughter" microspheres. They can be induced to fission by $MgCl_2$ or by a pH change. The enclosing film is a

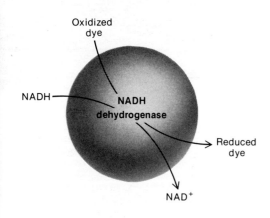

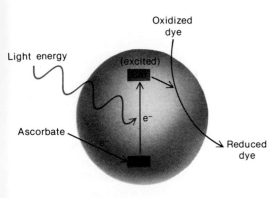

Chemical substances can diffuse in and out of coacervate drops, and enzymes contained within the drops can carry out reactions that mimic those encountered in living organisms. See text for details.

double layer resembling those found in soap films and artificial and natural membranes.

Fox hypothesizes that proteinoid material first polymerized on hot, dry volcanic cinder cones, and then was leached into the oceans by rain to form microspheres, which then could have become the early segregated chemical systems that eventually led to protocells. This cinder cone hypothesis, while ingenious, is not accepted by many scientists as more than an interesting idea. What has been demonstrated is that membrane formation, swelling, budding, and division all can occur by physical chemical forces, and are not necessarily tied in with living organisms. A weakness of the theory is the requirement of dry heat for polymerization. It is hard to imagine such high concentrations of dry amino acids occurring on the early planet. It is difficult to make roast beef out of Haldane soup.

Various mechanisms have been suggested by which amino acids could be induced to polymerize spontaneously, even in an aqueous environment. These mechanisms usually involve making intermediate molecules with high free energy, and using this free energy to bring about the joining of amino acids during the polymerization process. Such mechanisms are analogous to the priming of molecules with phosphate groups or coenzymes, which we have seen in glycolysis and the citric acid cycle. While the problem of natural formation of protein chains by abiotic means has not been solved completely, we tend to think of it as solvable. No matter how an early proteinoid polymer might have been formed, Fox's microsphere experiments, divorced from their volcanic cinder cone hypothesis, remain relevant as a possible way of producing isolated, enclosed regions of aqueous solution for further evolution.

COACERVATE DROPS AND "PROTOBIONTS"

Oparin in Russia has had similar goals to Fox's, namely, to see how isolated and bounded regions of a solution could arise naturally, as potential centers for the development of life. If a concentrated solution of polypeptides, nucleic acids, polysaccharides, or almost any polymer is gently shaken, it will separate into two phases of different polymer concentrations. Concentrated droplets will form in a more dilute solution. These *coacervate drops* are typically 20 μm (200,000 Å) in diameter, and may contain 5% to 50% polymer, depending on how they are formed. They have a skin or membrane around them, which is visible in a microscope. Coacervate drops, like microspheres, are the result of physico-chemical forces and have no direct connection with life.

If materials of smaller molecular weights are added to a solution of coacervate drops, they will distribute themselves unequally between drops and bulk solution, depending on their relative solubilities in the two polymer phases. Coacervates tend to concentrate some molecules in their interior, an ability that the most rudimentary of protocells would need. This behavior of coacervates shows how early protocells could have achieved internal compositions that were different from their surroundings, and could have developed a certain amount of chemical independence.

642

Even more interesting are coacervates prepared with enzymes inside. These can absorb substrate molecules from solution, catalyze chemical reactions, and let the products diffuse out. If coacervates containing the enzyme phosphorylase are prepared, and glucose-1-phosphate is added to the bulk solution, the primed glucose molecules will diffuse into the coacervate droplets and be polymerized there into a starch polymer (top far left). If the coacervates also contain the enzyme amylase, then the starch produced by the first enzyme is chopped back to disaccharide molecules of maltose, which diffuse into the bulk solution again. Coacervates with these two enzymes are miniature factories for turning glucose-1-phosphate into maltose, using the energy of the phosphate bond in the starting molecules.

In another experiment, coacervates were prepared that contained mitochondrial NADH dehydrogenase, the flavoprotein enzyme found at the beginning of the respiratory chain. These droplets could absorb NADH and a reducible dye from the solution, reduce the dye molecules, and release dye and NAD^+ back into solution (center far left).

In the most spectacular model experiment of all, coacervate drops containing chlorophyll were allowed to absorb ascorbic acid and an oxidized dye that could not be reduced spontaneously by ascorbate alone. When the droplets were kept in the dark, nothing happened; but when they were illuminated by light the dye became reduced. In a very close parallel to the single-center photosynthesis of bacteria, chlorophyll molecules absorbed light energy, and used their excited electrons to reduce

Lipid molecules spontaneously form a monolayer at an air–water interface, with hydrophobic tails in the air and polar heads in the water. Wave action can create droplets with lipid bilayer membranes that resemble membranes of simple cells. In these spherical droplets (below), the hydrophobic tails are turned to the center of the bilayer membrane. Top illustration adapted from the "Great Wave," a woodblock print by Katsushika Hokusai (1760–1849).

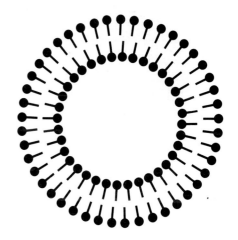

the dye molecules. Ascorbate merely played the role of H_2S in the electron-transfer chain by providing the electrons required to restore the electron deficit in the chlorophyll molecules. Reduction occurred with a net increase in free energy, the increased energy coming from the absorbed light.

All of these, of course, are models and nothing more. They show what could have happened, and what is not impossible. Oparin has suggested an evolutionary scheme for protocells or "protobionts" along the lines suggested by his coacervate experiments. He proposes that in lakes or ponds with appreciable concentrations of polymerized material, coacervate droplets would be formed naturally by wave action, as diagrammed on the preceding page for a lipidlike material. In general, the composition of these droplets would differ from that of the bulk solution. These "microenvironments" in time could develop into enclosed systems of chemical reactions that absorb high-energy compounds from their surroundings (like the glucose-1-phosphate experiment) to perform protective reactions or other necessary syntheses. The absorption of light for synthetic purposes, as in the chlorophyll–ascorbate experiment, might have occurred first at this prebiological stage. In this limited sense, "photosynthesis" might have preceded life.

The experiments of Fox and Oparin with microspheres and coacervates suggest a model for how living organisms might have developed. The first stage along the road to life would have been stable, self-maintaining, enclosed chemical systems such as these—perhaps growing and propagating by simple fission or division into smaller droplets that had the same chemical abilities and growth potential. Control of reactions in these protobionts would be effected by weak natural catalysts, also made by the protobiont and passed along to each daughter fragment during fission.

This would have been the era of chemical evolution, where the criterion for success would be the ability to find or synthesize the chemicals necessary for the continuance of the droplet, and the ability to prevent its own materials from being cannibalized for use in a neighboring system. The development of an efficient outer membrane that could exert control on what came into and left the protobiont would be a strong aid to survival, as would an active-transport system that could concentrate certain substances inside the membrane. The ability to carry out reactions quickly, and to grow to such a size that the protobiont droplet would fall apart into many independent daughter droplets, also would be advantageous to the survival of one particular kind of protobiont. Enzymes or their simpler catalytic precursors therefore would confer a great survival advantage on a droplet.

The second stage in the development of a living cell would be characterized by the ability to transfer to daughter fragments during division, not samples of all catalytic substances, but the *instructions* for making more of these pre-enzymes from simpler molecules. This would mark the beginning of hereditary information storage, and of evolution by genetic variation and natural selection. It is a convenient point at which to draw a boundary between prelife and life. This original information-storage system would have been far simpler than today's DNA–RNA–protein machinery, but all traces of it would have been erased as later improvements took over.

644

THE DRAMA OF LIFE

We can bring together everything that has been said in this chapter about the evolution of life, and some of the earlier remarks about the formation of the planet, into a fourteen-point scenario, a script for one element of the cosmic drama as seen from our planet. Although the scenario format enables us to describe events in simple declarative sentences without a constant repetition of "probably" and "most likely," bear in mind that this is at best a theory, a consistent set of hypotheses to account for what happened. Some of the statements are on very firm ground, but others are outlines for future research, to which chemists will make a major contribution.

1. The universe began roughly 20 billion years ago, and our galaxy, the Milky Way, approximately 13 billion to 15 billion years ago. Our sun is a second-generation star in this galaxy, formed from the heavy-element-rich debris from earlier stars. As the new star formed by gradual accretion of matter from a dust cloud, local nodes of material in the plane of rotation of the flattened dust cloud began to build up into protoplanets, moving around the sun. One of these aggregates became our Earth.

2. The young Earth was too small to retain whatever original atmosphere it may have had, and what remained was an airless ball of rock, made up mainly of elements, such as silicon, oxygen, and metals, that could form nonvolatile compounds. Heat from compression and from natural radioactive decay caused the interior of the planet to become fluid, leading to the stratification by density that exists today: iron–nickel core, olivine mantle, and a crust of lighter silicates and other minerals.

3. Volcanic outgassing from the interior created a new atmosphere for the planet, made up of reduced compounds: H_2, CH_4, N_2, NH_3, H_2O, and H_2S. In the absence of today's high-altitude ozone shield, ultraviolet radiation from the sun penetrated all the way to the surface of the Earth. This radiation, lightning discharges, volcanic heat, and natural radioactivity all provided energy sources for the spontaneous reaction of the atmospheric gases to form more complex molecules: HCN and aldehydes, nitriles, organic acids and bases, simple carbohydrates and amino acids. These were leached into the oceans by rain, where they slowly built up a thin "Haldane soup," which was stable for long periods of time in a reducing atmosphere.

4. Life evolved from this soup, perhaps through intermediate stages of localized but nonreproducing chemical systems, protected by simple barrier membranes. Catalytic proteins, or crude enzymes, developed from random polymers of amino acids, sometimes in association with metal ions and organic molecules. Energy for chemical syntheses was provided by the breakdown of polyphosphates, or later by molecules such as ATP, both formed originally by nonbiological means. As competition depleted the natural supply of many necessary substances in their surroundings, the more successful "protobionts" developed the ability to synthesize these

substances from more plentiful molecules. Those primitive chemical systems that also developed a machinery for duplicating all of this chemistry in daughter systems, crossed the threshold of what we would define as life. The primitive information-transfer system need have borne little resemblance to the elaborate DNA–RNA–ribosome system of today, but the function would have been the same.

5. As the natural supply of polyphosphates and ATP ran short, some protocells evolved glycolysis as a means of degrading organic molecules and saving the energy as homemade ATP. This pattern of metabolism became so advantageous that only those organisms that possessed it survived to the present. Glycolysis and gluconeogenesis developed, with the necessary enzymes floating freely in the cell fluid. The stage of the fermenting bacteria was reached. Even with this metabolic capability, the amount of life on the planet was strictly limited by the available supply of nonbiologically produced organic molecules for use as energy sources.

6. In the face of constant competition for the limited amounts of organic matter, certain bacteria (if we may now call them that) found ways to enhance their survival by using metalloporphyrins and similar delocalized ring molecules to absorb solar energy. Perhaps at first the absorbed energy was used only as heat to accelerate all reactions uniformly. Later, this electronic excitation of chlorophyll molecules was coupled to the production of ATP and NADH. Two of the best reducing agents that were available, H_2 and H_2S, were used to supply reducing equivalents for making NADH. Carbohydrates were synthesized from this ATP, NADH, and atmospheric CO_2 by taking some of the reactions of gluconeogenesis and turning them into the Calvin cycle. The stage of the present-day green and purple sulfur bacteria had been reached.

7. Sulfate, although not a substance that would have been present in quantity on the primitive Earth, was given off as a waste product from bacterial photosynthesis. The ancestors of *Desulfovibrio* developed the ability to squeeze a little more energy out of their foods by oxidizing them with this sulfate. Colonies of green sulfur bacteria and sulfate-respiring bacteria could have existed in close symbiotic association, as they sometimes do today, passing oxidized and reduced sulfur compounds back and forth and drawing their common support from the sun. Respiration had been invented, although not the kind that was to dominate the planet in later years.

8. The slow development of a citric acid cycle as an alternate source of NADH gradually liberated the purple sulfur bacteria from their dependence on H_2S and noncyclic photosynthesis. The ancestors of the purple nonsulfur bacteria arose, which were dependent mainly on cyclic photophosphorylation for ATP energy.

9. Close relatives of these photosynthetic bacteria found a way, via a second chlorophyll photocenter, to absorb two photons of light where one had been absorbed before, and to use the extra energy to make an acceptable reducing agent out of H_2O. Instead of aban-

doning a scarce reducing agent, H_2S, they managed to trade it for a much more plentiful one, H_2O. In these ancestors of the blue-green algae, green-plant photosynthesis was born. This step may have been reached as early as 3 billion years ago.

10. Oxygen began to accumulate locally around these photosynthetic organisms. They and the purple nonsulfur bacteria learned to use O_2 with NADH from their citric acid cycle to obtain much more energy than ever before. The sequence of glycolysis–citric acid cycle–respiration, familiar in eucaryotes today, was complete. As today, blue-green algae and purple nonsulfur bacteria made relatively little use of respiration, depending mainly on photosynthesis for ATP energy, but the facility was there. Oxygen respiration need not have required more than local concentrations of free O_2, just as the earlier sulfate respiration would have required only local concentrations of sulfate around green and purple sulfur bacteria.

11. The great efficiency of water-splitting photosynthesis led to an explosion of life on the planet, and this may be why we see fossil remains for the first time in the Fig Tree cherts. With oxygen respiration still of minor importance, excess O_2 gradually accumulated in the atmosphere, changing it slowly from reducing to oxidizing. This development had three important consequences for the future evolution of life. An ozone shield in the upper atmosphere blocked off the shorter ultraviolet wavelengths, thereby ending one source of nonbiological synthesis of organic molecules as possible foods for living organisms. Free oxygen in the atmosphere hastened the destruction of those organic molecules that already had been synthesized, with the result that for all time to come, organic compounds would be associated almost entirely with living organisms. Lastly, with the lethal ultraviolet radiation screened out, life could come up from the lower depths to inhabit the upper ten meters of the seas and, eventually, the land itself.

12. With the increasing oxygen content of the atmosphere, respiration became more important. Oxygen-respiring bacteria evolved from purple nonsulfur photosynthetic bacteria by the loss of photosynthetic ability. This explanation of the origin of respiration would account for the remarkable similarity of the electron-transport chains of photosynthesis and O_2 respiration, and their great difference from the processes involved in sulfate respiration in *Desulfovibrio*. It also would explain the near identity in molecular structure of cytochrome *c* in respiring eucaryotes and in respiring and photosynthetic bacteria.

13. Eucaryotes developed from procaryotes by a symbiotic relationship between a nonrespiring host, respiring bacteria that were the ancestors of mitochondria, and photosynthesizing blue-green algae that degenerated with time into chloroplasts. This step probably was complete about 1.6 billion years ago, judging from the Beck Springs fossil deposits.

14. In the interval between the development of the first eucaryotes and the beginning of the Cambrian era, plants and animals di-

verged, soft-bodied multicelled organisms developed, and most of the evolutionary lines arose that later would lead to the major classes of living organisms. We move solidly from chemical evolution and prehistory into the known fossil record.

This is the picture of life on Earth that we have been able to develop so far. Whether life on other planets would have the same chemistry is a question we cannot answer. We would assume it to be carbon-based and water-mediated, but whether nucleic acids are inevitable as genetic records, and proteins as structural materials and catalysts, is more than we can predict. The real understanding of the limits of chemical systems and their organization into living creatures has yet to begin.

QUESTIONS

1. In what sense has spontaneous creation been discredited as an explanation for the origin of life on Earth, and in what sense is it still the most acceptable theory?

2. If spontaneous creation is rejected as the origin of life, what other explanation could there be?

3. Why has the evolution of life at one moment on this planet made it unlikely that life ever will evolve independently on Earth again? What was wrong with the medieval picture of spontaneous generation?

4. What portion of the energy-extracting machinery of eucaryotes is a common heritage of all forms of life? Give an example of bacteria that depends solely on this type of energy production.

5. What types of respiration are encountered in bacteria, in addition to respiration with O_2? Which type probably is related to O_2 respiration, and which is quite different in evolutionary history?

6. There is no *a priori* reason why nearly all bacteria that do not make use of molecular O_2 as an oxidant should be poisoned by the presence of O_2, but this state of affairs is at least understandable in terms of how bacterial metabolism evolved. Why is it reasonable that the nonuse of O_2 and the intolerance of its presence should go together?

7. How do bacterial and green-plant photosynthesis differ? Which more closely resembles the photosynthesis of blue-green algae?

8. What suggestions are there from bacterial metabolism that life evolved in an O_2-free, reducing environment?

9. What geological evidence is there for a reducing atmosphere on the early Earth? Approximately when did the transition to oxidizing conditions occur, judging from the geological record?

10. What are chemoautotrophs, and why are they unlikely to be examples of a very primitive and ancient metabolism?

11. How does the presence of atmospheric O_2 interfere with the spontaneous synthesis of organic molecules by the nonbiological process that must have occurred during the evolution of life?

12. How does the presence of atmospheric O_2 make it improbable that organic molecules would evolve into living organisms a second time, if all life on Earth were to be quickly extinguished?

13. What is the main source of organic compounds on the Earth today?

14. How can organic compounds exist in an atmosphere of oxygen, if oxidation of all of these compounds is thermodynamically spontaneous?

15. What is "Haldane soup," and how is it relevant to the problem of the origin of life?

16. How is it now believed that the organic molecules of "Haldane soup" were formed?

17. Why would the fossil record tend to underestimate the proportions of jellyfish to clams living at any one time? How is this relevant to the issue of a shortage of Precambrian fossils?

18. What are pristane and phytane, and why is their presence considered as evidence for photosynthesis?

19. What is the oldest fossil evidence for bacterialike organisms? Where are these fossils found, and how old are they?

20. What is the oldest fossil evidence for eucaryotes? Where were they found, and how old is the deposit?

21. What are stromatolites? What organisms are believed to build them? How does the presence of stromatolites constitute evidence of a tentative sort for photosynthesis? How old are the oldest stromatolite formations?

22. What arguments led Stanley Miller to choose hydrogen, methane, ammonia, and water as components of his trial "primitive atmosphere?" What energy source was used to bring about chemical change? What natural phenomenon would this correspond to? What compounds were formed in the course of the reaction?

23. What is the Strecker synthesis, and how does it lead to the formation of amino acids? What determines the nature of the amino acid side chain, R—?

24. What are microspheres and coacervate drops, and what relevance do they have to the problem of the evolution of life? Why is a relative isolation from the surroundings advantageous to any living organism?

25. How did Oparin's experiments with coacervate drops mimic some of the metabolic activities of living organisms?

26. What advantage does water-decomposing photosynthesis have for the organism that possesses it, in comparison with H_2S-using photosynthesis, if water is such a poor reducing agent compared with H_2S?

27. What radical change in the environment of nonphotosynthetic organisms was brought about by water-decomposing photosynthetic organisms? How did this lead in time to a much more efficient means of extracting free energy from organic molecules?

APPENDIX 1

Useful Physical Constants and Conversion Factors

PHYSICAL CONSTANTS

Atomic mass unit	$1\ \text{amu} = 1.66053 \times 10^{-24}\ \text{g}$
Avogadro's number	$N = 6.022169 \times 10^{23}\ \text{mole}^{-1}$
	($^{12}\text{C} = \text{exactly } 12$)
Bohr radius	$a_0 = 0.52918\ \text{Å}$
Boltzmann's constant	$k = 1.38062 \times 10^{-16}\ \text{erg deg}^{-1}$
	molecule^{-1}
Electron rest mass	$m_e = 0.0005486\ \text{amu} = 9.1095 \times 10^{-28}\ \text{g}$
Electronic charge	$e = 4.80325 \times 10^{-10}\ \text{esu}$
	($\text{cm}^{3/2}\text{g}^{1/2}\text{sec}^{-1}$)
	$e = 1.6021 \times 10^{-19}\ \text{coulomb}$
Faraday's constant	$\mathscr{F} = Ne = 96{,}487\ \text{coulombs equivalent}^{-1}$
	$= 23.056\ \text{kcal volt}^{-1}\ \text{equivalent}^{-1}$
Gas constant	$R = Nk = 8.3143 \times 10^{7}\ \text{ergs deg}^{-1}\ \text{mole}^{-1}$
	$R = 0.082054\ \text{liter atm deg}^{-1}\ \text{mole}^{-1}$
	$R = 1.98726\ \text{cal deg}^{-1}\ \text{mole}^{-1}$
Neutron rest mass	$m_n = 1.008665\ \text{amu} = 1.67492 \times 10^{-24}\ \text{g}$
Planck's constant	$h = 6.6262 \times 10^{-27}\ \text{erg sec}$
Proton plus electron	$m_p + m_e = 1.007862\ \text{amu}$
Proton rest mass	$m_p = 1.007277\ \text{amu} = 1.67261 \times 10^{-24}\ \text{g}$
Velocity of light	$c = 2.9979 \times 10^{10}\ \text{cm sec}^{-1}$

CONVERSION FACTORS

1 electron volt (eV) $= 1.6022 \times 10^{-12}\ \text{erg}$
1 erg $= 6.2420 \times 10^{11}\ \text{eV} = 2.3901 \times 10^{-11}\ \text{kcal} = 1\ \text{g cm}^2\ \text{sec}^{-2}$
1 kcal $= 4.1840 \times 10^{10}\ \text{ergs} = 2.612 \times 10^{22}\ \text{eV}$
1 volt coulomb $= 1\ \text{joule} = 10^7\ \text{ergs} = 0.23901\ \text{cal}$
1 eV molecule$^{-1} = 23.056\ \text{kcal mole}^{-1} = 8065\ \text{cm}^{-1}$
100 kcal mole$^{-1} = 34{,}982\ \text{cm}^{-1}$

1 atomic unit (au) of energy $= 27.21$ eV molecule^{-1}
$$= 4.3592 \times 10^{-11} \text{ erg molecule}^{-1}$$
$$= 219,470 \text{ cm}^{-1} = 627.71 \text{ kcal mole}^{-1}$$
1 amu of mass $= 931.481 \times 10^{6}$ eV of energy $= 931.481$ MeV

$2.303\, RT = 1.346$ kcal mole^{-1} at $298°$K

INTERNATIONAL SYSTEM OF UNITS (SI)

In 1960, the International Bureau of Weights and Measures established the International System of Units (SI) to simplify communication among world scientists. In this text we have not been rigorous about using only SI units, because the traditional units (e.g., angstroms and calories) are still common and you should be familiar with them. However, you should be aware that the trend among scientists is toward the use of strict SI units, and some scientific and engineering journals and textbooks are using them exclusively.

The International System has seven base units: metre (m), kilogram (kg), second (s), ampere (A), kelvin (K), mole (mol), and candela (cd). Supplementary units are radian (rad) for plane angle and steradian (sr) for solid angle. All other SI units are derived from these base and supplementary units. The following table lists examples. For more on the subject, see "The International System of Units (SI)," *National Bureau of Standards Special Publication 330*, 1972, U.S. Government Printing Office, Washington, D. C., and Martin A. Paul, "International System of Units (SI)," *Chemistry* **45**, 14(1972).

Physical quality	SI unit (symbol)	Conversion factors
Length	metre (m)	1 inch (in) $= 0.0254$ m (exactly)
		1 angstrom (Å) $= 10^{-10}$ m
Volume	cubic metre (m^3)	1 in^3 $= 16.4$ cm^3 (approx.)
		1 litre $= 10^{-3}$ m^3
Mass	kilogram (kg)	1 pound (lb) $= 0.45359237$ kg (exactly)
		1 amu $= 1.66053 \times 10^{-27}$ kg (approx.)
		1 gram (g) $= 10^{-3}$ kg
Time	second (s)	1 day (d) $= 86,400$ s
		1 hour (h) $= 3,600$ s
		1 minute (min) $= 60$ s
Frequency	hertz (Hz $=$ s^{-1})	
Force	newton (N $=$ m kg s^{-2})	1 dyne (dyn) $= 10^{-5}$ N (exactly)
Pressure	pascal (Pa $=$ N m^{-2})	1 atm $= 101,325$ Pa (exactly)
		1 torr $= 101,325/760$ Pa (exactly)
Energy	joule (J $=$ N m)	1 erg $= 10^{-7}$ J
		1 cal (thermochemical) $= 4.184$ J (exactly)
		1 electron volt (eV) $= 1.60219 \times 10^{-14}$ J (approx.)

Physical quality	SI unit (symbol)	Conversion factors
Electric current	ampere (A)	
Quantity of electricity	coulomb (C = A s)	$e = 1.60219 \times 10^{-19}$ C (approx.)
Thermo-dynamic temperature (T)	kelvin (K)	replaces °K; Celsius tempera-ture (t) $= T - 273.15$ K in °C
Amount of substance	mole (mol)	
Concentration	mole per cubic metre (mol m^{-3})	1 mole liter^{-1} $= 10^3$ mol m^{-3} (exactly)

Standard Enthalpies and Free Energies of Formation, and Standard Third-Law Entropies, at 298°K

This table gives the standard heat (ΔH^0) and free energies (ΔG^0) of formation of compounds from elements in their standard states and the thermodynamic, or third-law, entropies (S^0) of compounds, all at 298°K. The state of the compound is specified by: (g) = gas; (l) = liquid; (s) = solid; (aq) = aqueous solution. Occasionally the crystal form of the solid also is specified. Compounds are arranged by the group number of a principal element, with metals taking precedence over non-metals and O and H being considered least important.

This table is an abbreviated version of a more complete one in R. E. Dickerson, *Molecular Thermodynamics*, W. A. Benjamin, Menlo Park, Calif., 1969. Other convenient tabulations are found in the *Chemical Rubber Company Handbook of Chemistry and Physics*, and in *Lange's Handbook of Chemistry*.

	Substance	ΔH^0_{298} (kcal mole^{-1})	ΔG^0_{298} (kcal mole^{-1})	S^0_{298} (cal deg^{-1} mole^{-1})
	H(g)	52.089	48.575	27.393
	H$^+(aq)$	0.0	0.0	0.0
	H$_2(g)$	0.0	0.0	31.211
IA	Li(g)	37.07	29.19	33.143
	Li(s)	0.0	0.0	6.70
	Li$^+(aq)$	−66.554	−70.22	3.4
	LiF(s)	−146.3	−139.6	8.57
	LiCl(s)	−97.70	−91.7	(13.2)
	LiBr(s)	−83.72	−81.2	(16.5)
	Na(g)	25.98	18.67	36.715
	Na(s)	0.0	0.0	12.2
	Na$^+(aq)$	−57.279	−62.589	14.4
	Na$_2$O(s)	−99.4	−90.0	17.4

	Substance	ΔH^0_{298} (kcal mole^{-1})	ΔG^0_{298} (kcal mole^{-1})	S^0_{298} (cal deg^{-1} mole^{-1})
	NaOH (aq)	−112.24	−100.18	11.9
	NaF (s)	−136.0	−129.3	14.0
	NaCl (s)	−98.232	−91.785	17.3
	NaBr (s)	−86.030	−83.1	—
	NaI (s)	−68.84	−56.7	—
	Na$_2$CO$_3$ (s)	−270.3	−250.4	32.5
	K (g)	21.51	14.62	38.296
	K (s)	0.0	0.0	15.2
	K$^+$ (aq)	−60.04	−67.46	24.5
	Rb (g)	20.51	13.35	40.628
	Rb (s)	0.0	0.0	16.6
	Rb$^+$ (aq)	−58.9	−67.45	29.7
	Cs (g)	18.83	12.24	41.944
	Cs (s)	0.0	0.0	19.8
	Cs$^+$ (aq)	−59.2	−67.41	31.8
IIA	Be (g)	76.63	67.60	32.545
	Be (s)	0.0	0.0	2.28
	Be^{2+} (aq)	−93	−85.2	—
	Mg (g)	35.9	27.6	35.504
	Mg (s)	0.0	0.0	7.77
	Mg^{2+} (aq)	−110.41	−108.99	−28.2
	MgO (s)	−143.84	−136.13	6.4
	MgCl$_2$ (s)	−153.40	−141.57	21.4
	MgCl$_2$·6H$_2$O (s)	−597.42	−505.65	87.5
	Ca (g)	46.04	37.98	36.99
	Ca (s)	0.0	0.0	9.95
	Ca^{2+} (aq)	−129.77	−132.18	−13.2
	CaCO$_3$ $(s$, calcite$)$	−288.45	−269.78	22.2
	CaCO$_3$ $(s$, aragonite$)$	−288.49	−269.53	21.2
	Sr (g)	39.2	26.3	39.325
	Sr (s)	0.0	0.0	13.0
	Sr^{2+} (aq)	−130.38	−133.2	−9.4
	Ba (g)	41.96	34.60	40.699
	Ba (s)	0.0	0.0	16
	Ba^{2+} (aq)	−128.67	−134.0	3
	BaO (s)	−133.4	−126.3	16.8
	BaCO$_3$ (s)	−291.3	−272.2	26.8
VIIB	Mn (s)	0.0	0.00	7.59
	Mn^{2+} (aq)	−52.3	−53.4	−20.0
	MnO$_2$ (s)	−124.5	−111.4	12.7
VIII	Fe (g)	96.68	85.76	43.11
	Fe (s)	0.0	0.0	6.49
	Fe^{2+} (aq)	−21.0	−20.30	−27.1
	Fe^{3+} (aq)	−11.4	−2.53	−70.1
	Fe$_2$O$_3$ $(s$, hematite$)$	−196.5	−177.1	21.5
	Fe$_3$O$_4$ $(s$, magnetite$)$	−267.9	−242.4	35.0
	Ni (s)	0.0	0.0	7.2
	Ni^{2+} (s)	−15.3	−11.1	−38.1
IB	Cu (g)	81.52	72.04	39.744
	Cu (s)	0.0	0.0	7.96
	Cu$^+$ (aq)	(12.4)	12.0	(−6.3)

Substance	ΔH^0_{298} (kcal mole^{-1})	ΔG^0_{298} (kcal mole^{-1})	S^0_{298} (cal deg^{-1} mole^{-1})
$Cu^{2+}(aq)$	15.39	15.53	−23.6
$CuSO_4(s)$	−184.00	−158.2	27.1
$Ag(g)$	69.12	59.84	41.3221
$Ag(s)$	0.0	0.0	10.206
$AgCl(s)$	−30.362	−26.224	22.97
$AgNO_2(s)$	−10.605	4.744	30.62
$AgNO_3(s)$	−29.43	−7.69	33.68
IIB			
$Zn(s)$	0.0	0.0	9.95
$Zn^{2+}(aq)$	−36.43	−35.18	−25.45
$Hg(g)$	14.54	7.59	41.80
$Hg(l)$	0.0	0.0	18.5
$HgCl_2(s)$	−55.0	−44.4	(34.5)
$Hg_2Cl_2(s)$	−63.32	−50.35	46.8
IIIA			
$B(g)$	97.2	86.7	36.649
$B(s)$	0.0	0.0	1.56
$Al(g)$	75.0	65.3	39.303
$Al(s)$	0.0	0.0	6.769
$Al^{3+}(aq)$	−125.4	−115.0	−74.9
$AlCl_3(s)$	−166.2	−152.2	40
IVA			
$C(g)$	171.698	160.845	37.761
$C(s, \text{diamond})$	0.4532	0.6850	0.5829
$C(s, \text{graphite})$	0.0	0.0	1.3609
$CO(g)$	−26.4157	−32.8079	47.301
$CO_2(g)$	−94.0518	−94.2598	51.061
$CO_2(aq)$	−98.69	−92.31	29.0
$CH_4(g)$	−17.889	−12.140	44.50
$CF_4(g)$	−223.00	−212.34	62.50
$CCl_4(g)$	−24.00	−13.92	74.12
$C_2H_2(g)$	54.194	50.0	47.997
$C_2H_4(g)$	12.496	16.282	52.45
$C_2H_6(g)$	−20.236	−7.860	54.85
$C_3H_6(g)$ cyclopropane	12.74	24.95	56.75
$C_3H_8(g)$	−24.82	−5.61	64.51
$C_4H_8(g)$ cyclobutane	6.37	26.30	63.43
$n\text{-}C_4H_{10}(g)$	−29.81	−3.75	74.10
$i\text{-}C_4H_{10}(g)$	−31.45	−4.30	70.42
$C_5H_{10}(g)$ cyclopentane	−18.46	9.23	70.00
$C_6H_6(g)$	19.820	30.989	64.34
$C_6H_6(l)$	11.718	29.756	41.30
$C_6H_{12}(g)$ cyclohexane	−29.43	7.59	71.28
$n\text{-}C_8H_{18}(g)$	−49.82	3.92	111.55
$n\text{-}C_8H_{18}(l)$	−59.74	1.55	86.23
$HCOOH(g)$	−86.67	−80.24	60.0
$HCOOH(l)$	−97.8	−82.7	30.82
$HCOOH(aq)$	−98.0	−85.1	39.1
$HCOO^-(aq)$	−98.0	−80.0	21.9
$H_2CO_3(aq)$	−167.0	−149.00	45.7

Substance	ΔH^0_{298} (kcal mole^{-1})	ΔG^0_{298} (kcal mole^{-1})	S^0_{298} (cal deg^{-1} mole^{-1})
$HCO_3^-(aq)$	−165.18	−140.31	22.7
$CO_3^{2-}(aq)$	−161.63	−126.22	−12.7
$CH_3COOH(l)$	−116.4	−93.8	38.2
$CH_3COOH(aq)$	−116.743	−95.51	—
$CH_3COO^-(aq)$	−116.843	−89.02	—
$HCHO(g)$	−27.7	−26.2	52.26
$HCHO(aq)$	—	−31.0	—
$CH_3OH(g)$	−48.10	−38.70	56.8
$CH_3OH(l)$	−57.036	−39.75	30.3
$CH_3OH(aq)$	−58.77	−41.88	31.63
$CH_3OCH_3(g)$	−43.99	−26.99	63.83
$C_2H_5OH(g)$	−56.27	−40.30	67.4
$C_2H_5OH(l)$	−66.356	−41.77	38.4
$CH_3CHO(g)$	−39.76	−31.96	63.5
$CH_3CHO(aq)$	−49.88	—	—
$C_6H_{12}O_6(s)$ glucose	−301.2	−219.7	69.04
$C_{18}H_{36}O_2(s)$ stearic acid	−226.8	—	—
$Si(g)$	88.04	77.41	40.120
$Si(s)$	0.0	0.0	4.47
$SiO_2(s, quartz)$	−205.4	−192.4	10.00
$Ge(g)$	78.44	69.50	40.106
$Ge(s)$	0.0	0.0	10.14
$Sn(g)$	72	64	40.245
$Sn(s, gray)$	0.6	1.1	10.7
$Sn(s, white)$	0.0	0.0	12.3
$Pb(g)$	46.34	38.47	41.890
$Pb(s)$	0.0	0.0	15.51
$Pb^{2+}(aq)$	0.39	−5.81	5.1
$PbSO_4(s)$	−219.50	−193.89	35.2
$PbO_2(s)$	−66.12	−52.34	18.3

VA

Substance	ΔH^0_{298} (kcal mole^{-1})	ΔG^0_{298} (kcal mole^{-1})	S^0_{298} (cal deg^{-1} mole^{-1})
$N(g)$	112.965	108.870	36.6145
$N_2(g)$	0.0	0.0	45.767
$NO(g)$	21.600	20.719	50.339
$NO_2(g)$	8.091	12.390	57.47
$NO_2^-(aq)$	−25.4	−8.25	29.9
$NO_3^-(aq)$	−49.372	−26.43	35.0
$N_2O(g)$	19.49	24.76	52.58
$N_2O_4(g)$	2.309	23.491	72.73
$N_2O_5(s)$	−10.0	32	27.1
$HNO_3(l)$	−41.40	−19.10	37.19
$HNO_3(aq)$	−49.37	−26.41	35.0
$NH_3(g)$	−11.04	−3.976	46.01
$NH_3(aq)$	−19.32	−6.36	26.3
$NH_4^+(aq)$	−31.74	−19.00	26.97
$NH_4Cl(s)$	−75.38	−48.73	22.6
$(NH_4)_2SO_4(s)$	−281.86	−215.19	52.65
$(NH_2)_2CO(s)$	−79.63	−47.12	25.00
$(NH_2)_2CO(aq)$	−76.30	−48.72	41.55
$P(g)$	75.18	66.71	38.98
$P(s, white)$	0.0	0.0	10.6

	Substance	ΔH^0_{298} (kcal mole^{-1})	ΔG^0_{298} (kcal mole^{-1})	S^0_{298} (cal deg^{-1} mole^{-1})
	P$(s$, red$)$	−4.4	−3.3	(7.0)
	P$_4(g)$	13.12	5.82	66.90
	PCl$_3(g)$	−73.22	−68.42	74.49
	PCl$_5(g)$	−95.35	−77.57	84.3
	As(g)	60.64	50.74	41.62
	As$(s$, gray metal$)$	0.0	0.0	8.4
	As$_4(g)$	35.7	25.2	69
VIA	O(g)	59.159	54.994	38.469
	O$_2(g)$	0.0	0.0	49.003
	O$_3(g)$	34.0	39.06	56.8
	OH$^-(aq)$	−54.957	−37.595	−2.52
	H$_2$O(g)	−57.798	−54.635	45.106
	H$_2$O(l)	−68.317	−56.690	16.716
	S(g)	53.25	43.57	40.085
	S$(s$, rhombic$)$	0.0	0.0	7.62
	S$(s$, monoclinic$)$	0.071	0.023	7.78
	S$^{2-}(aq)$	10.0	20.0	—
	SO$_4^{2-}(aq)$	−216.90	−177.34	4.1
	H$_2$S(g)	−4.815	−7.892	49.15
	H$_2$S(aq)	−9.4	−6.54	29.2
VIIB	F(g)	18.3	14.2	37.917
	F$^-(aq)$	−78.66	−66.08	−2.3
	F$_2(g)$	0.0	0.0	48.6
	HF(g)	−64.2	−64.7	41.47
	Cl(g)	29.012	25.192	39.457
	Cl$^-(aq)$	−40.023	−31.350	13.2
	Cl$_2(g)$	0.0	0.0	53.286
	HCl(g)	−22.063	−22.769	44.617
	HCl(aq)	−40.023	−31.350	13.2
	Br(g)	26.71	19.69	41.8052
	Br$^-(aq)$	−28.90	−24.574	19.29
	Br$_2(g)$	7.34	0.751	58.639
	Br$_2(l)$	0.0	0.0	36.4
	HBr(g)	−8.66	−12.72	47.437
	I(g)	25.482	16.766	43.184
	I$^-(aq)$	−13.37	−12.35	26.14
	I$_2(g)$	14.876	4.63	62.280
	I$_2(s)$	0.0	0.0	27.9
	I$_2(aq)$	5.0	3.926	—
	HI(g)	6.2	0.31	49.314
	ICl(g)	4.2	−1.32	59.12
	IBr(g)	9.75	0.91	61.8
0	He(g)	0.0	0.0	30.13
	Ne(g)	0.0	0.0	34.45
	Ar(g)	0.0	0.0	36.98
	Kr(g)	0.0	0.0	39.19
	Xe(g)	0.0	0.0	40.53
	Rn(g)	0.0	0.0	42.10

Index

Fluorine, 8, 32, 64, 234
  molecular-orbital structure of F_2, 178
  oxides of, 85
Formaldehyde, 491, 639
Formic acid, 493
Fossils
  Australian, 635
  Beck Springs, 636
  Gunflint, 635
  precambrian, 635
Fox, Sidney, 641
Free energy, 305
  equilibrium constant and, 337
  and escaping tendency, 416
  and living organisms, 308, 313
  and metabolism, 557
Freezing point, 422
Freezing point constants, 424
Freezing point depression, 422
Frequency, 133
Fructose, 516
Fumarate, 566
Functional group, 485
Fusion, 253

Galactose, 516
Gamma (γ) rays, 132
Gas, 3
  noble, 33
  standard state, 273
Gas constant (R), 24
Gasoline, 465
General acid catalysis, 585
General base catalysis, 585
Geometrical isomer, 469
Germanium, 225
Glass, 80, 112
Globular proteins, 534, 540
Gluconeogenesis, 570
Glucose, 271, 509, 516, 556
  metabolism, 557, 559
Glutamic acid, 536, 588
Glutamine, 536, 588
Glutamine synthetase, 589
Glutamyl phosphate, 589
Glutaric acid, 599
Glyceraldehyde-3-phosphate (G3P), 562
Glycine, 502, 536
Glycogen, 522
Glycolysis, 558, 562
Glycopeptide, 609
Golgi complexes, 615
Goodyear, Charles, 474
Gramicidin, 613
Grana, 619
Granite, 112
Graphite, 54, 207, 477
Green sulfur bacteria, 575, 630

Ground state, 152, 156
Groups
  functional, 485
  in periodic table, 98, 203
Guanine, 543
Guanosine, 543
Gunflint fossils, 635
Guttapercha, 475
Gypsum, 212

Haber, Fritz, 228
Hair, 538
Haldane, J. B. S., 629, 632
Haldane soup, 632
Half cell potentials, 434
Half-life, 258, 355
Half-reaction method, 250
Half-reactions, 250, 432–435
  and reduction potentials, 434
Halogenation, 472
Halogens, 234
Heat, 88, 266
  and chemical reactions, 266
Heat of atomization, 277
Heat of combustion, 270
Heat of formation, 272, 274
Heat of reaction, 266
  calculation of, 278
Heat of vaporization, 267
Heisenberg, Werner, 147
Helium
  bonding in He_2^+, 172
  isotopes, 10
Heme, 220, 527, 540
Hemoglobin, 220, 542
Heptane, 464
Hess' law of heat summation, 269
Heterogeneous catalysis, 403
Heterogeneous catalyst, 377
Hexagonal close packing, 207
Hexane, 464
Hexokinase, 603
High-spin complex, 221
Histidine, 536
Homogeneous catalysis, 403
Homogeneous catalyst, 377
Honey, 518
Hormones, 516
Hubble, Edwin, 141
Huxley, Thomas, 629
Hybrid atomic orbital, 183
  sp, 186
  sp^2, 185
  sp^3, 183
Hydrated ion, 377
Hydration, 62, 72
Hydrazine, 85
Hydroacids, 234
Hydrocarbons, 51, 463
  aliphatic, 478

bonding in, 183–191
derivatives of, 472–475, 485–503
reactions of, 470
saturated, 463, 466, 471–472
unsaturated, 469
Hydrochloric acid, 379
Hydrocyanic acid, 380
Hydrofluoric acid, 64
Hydrogen
  absorption spectrum, 140
  atomic structure, 6
  bonding in, 12–13, 172
  energy diagram, 13
  energy levels, 137
  isotopes, 9
Hydrogen bond, 60
  in proteins, 538
  in water, 60
Hydrogen cyanide, 639
Hydrogen fluoride, 379
  molecular-orbital theory for HF, 180
Hydrogen fusion, 4
Hydrogen–iodine reaction, 327
  reaction mechanism, 357
Hydrogen molecule-ion, H_2^+, 172
Hydrogen sulfide, 116
Hydrolysis, 106, 497
Hydroxide catalysis, 585
Hydroxide ion, 63
Hypergolic, 85
Hypertonic environment, 426
Hypochlorous acid, 116
Hypotonic environment, 426

Ice, 60
Ideal gas law, 19, 24–26
Indicator, acid-base, 194, 399
Information-carrying molecules, 532
Infrared radiation, 132
Inhibition
  allosteric, 603
  product, 603
Inhibitors, 598
  competitive, 598
  irreversible, 599
Inner mitochondrial membrane, 617
Inner transition metals, 154
Insulators, 225
Invertase, 518
Ion-product constant of water, 383
Ionic bonds, 40, 47
Ionic radii, 99, 204
Ionization, 137
Ionization energy, 35–38
  first, 36, 180
  second, 36
  third, 36
Ions, 4
  hydrated, 377